Machine Design
Theory and Practice

Aaron D. Deutschman
Walter J. Michels
Charles E. Wilson

Newark College of Engineering
New Jersey Institute of Technology

Machine Design

Theory and Practice

Macmillan Publishing Co., Inc.
NEW YORK

Collier Macmillan Publishers
LONDON

Macmillan Publishing Co., Inc.
866 Third Avenue
New York, New York 10022

Collier-Macmillan Canada, Ltd.

Library of Congress Cataloging in Publication Data

Deutschman, Aaron D
  Machine design; theory and practice.

  Bibliography: p.
  1. Machinery—Design. I. Michels, Walter J.,
joint author. II. Wilson, Charles E., joint author.
III. Title.
TJ230.D45   621.8'15   73-14430
ISBN 0-02-329000-5 (Hardbound)
ISBN 0-02-979720-9 (International Edition)

Printing: 13   Year: 4 5

ISBN   0-02-329000-5

Preface

This book was written for the student interested in beginning a study of the art and science of machine design. Assuming that the reader has already completed basic engineering and mathematic courses, the authors have demonstrated how engineering fundamentals are applied to mechanical engineering design. This course assimilates knowledge from many disciplines, and this book is oriented toward practical engineering principles that demonstrate how functional and economically feasible solutions can be obtained through proper design. Modern analytical concepts, by which essential mechanical theories can be visualized, have also been included and derived.

The first four chapters are devoted not only to a review of important material properties and fabricating techniques but, more significantly, to establishing how these broad disciplines affect design. The authors recognize that many engineering schools still offer formal courses in materials science, engineering metallurgy, and production processes. Nevertheless, it is equally true that many institutions are leaning in the direction of engineering science and, consequently, have reduced emphasis on, or virtually eliminated, these courses from their curricula. Thus, these early chapters represent an introduction to mechanical design as well as a sound, reasonably comprehensive review of previously studied topics, which now must be applied to the development of mechanical systems. Depending upon the background required for this course, this material may be studied rigorously or serve as an overview and review. Where courses in material properties and fabricating techniques are not required or not available, study of the first four chapters should prepare the student to read with reasonable understanding and comprehension the detailed information in later chapters related to specific machine elements.

The remaining chapters deal with the methods of stress and deflection analysis and techniques involved in designing and selecting individual machine parts. In addition, emphasis has been given to the engineer's ability to solve relevant problems concerning mechanical systems. These chapters on specific machine elements, which constitute the bulk of the book, are largely independent of one another. This permits the instructor a great deal of latitude in structuring his course and makes this book sufficiently flexible to be used with a variety of existing course syllabuses without major modifications.

Although the book has been designed primarily for use by mechanical engineering students, the thoroughness of the presentation has been main-

v

tained at such a level that the professional or the industrial designer will find it a valuable reference. Much of design involves more than a single method of solution to a given problem, and an attempt is made to show alternate approaches. Some methods not covered in the text are illustrated by computer problems at the end of the chapter.

Well-defined analytical procedures are used and illustrated via carefully selected example problems. The book also contains illustrative problems that demonstrate modern methods; for example, numerical, graphical, and digital methods are employed. The methods have been selected for generality of application so that the reader may build upon these techniques to solve problems not treated in a textbook.

The authors wish to express their deep indebtedness to Professor Alfred R. Holowenko of Purdue University, Professor Barton L. Jenks of Penn State University, and Professor L. J. Powers of Texas Tech, who read, thoughtfully critized, and made helpful suggestions for improving the original manuscript. Their penetrating commentaries (both pro and con) resulted in a substantially improved book. We greatly appreciate their invaluable assistance. And for the task of organizing the amounts of typed and illustrative material into a printable book, we wish to extend our sincere thanks to Mr. John J. Beck, Technical Editor at Macmillan. Most especially, we are grateful to him for his patient and kind attitude in working with us. The authors would invite students, instructors, and practicing engineers to write them concerning any questions that may arise. All comments and suggestions would be appreciated.

A. D. D.
W. J. M.
C. E. W.

Contents

5

Analysis of Stress and Displacement 235

6

Theories of Failure Used in the Design of Machine Elements 301

7

Shafts, Keys, and Couplings 331

8

Journal Bearings and Lubrication 405

1

Introduction

SYMBOLS

N_u = factor of safety based on ultimate strength

N_y = factor of safety based on yield strength

The object of engineering is to provide society with the requirements of a modern civilization. Thus, engineering becomes the link that connects and converts nature's gifts to man's needs. It is apparent that it has been with us since man first walked the face of this earth and struck flint to start a fire or shaped his first arrowhead. Engineering is not directly concerned with seeking nature's truths. This is primarily the province of the scientist. Instead, it concerns itself with understanding scientific principles and applying them to achieve a designated goal. In this sense, engineering might be considered an applied science.

As an applied science, engineering uses scientific knowledge to achieve a specific objective. The mechanism whereby a requirement is converted to a meaningful and functional plan is called **design.** In other words, design is the formulation of a plan, a scheme, or a method to translate a need into a satisfactorily functioning device that satisfies the original need. For example, the builders of superhighways must follow the plans of design engineers. The manufacturers of plastic extruding machinery likewise must follow the plans of design engineers. In fact, virtually all technical functions depend upon design for their successful operation.

Engineering school curricula tend to strong emphasis on courses in engineering science and mathematics, and the student begins to look upon these courses as ends in themselves. In reality, these courses are only tools in the process of design. The student should be aware that just as "all roads lead to Rome," all engineering disciplines lead to design. Even those students who will spend their working lives in some aspect of engineering other than design must realize that they are in some way involved in design. It is therefore advantageous for the neophyte to become acquainted with design engineering to be a successful professional engineer.

The remainder of the chapter will concentrate on the design process and those aspects contributing to a satisfactory design.

The Design Flow Diagram

Figure 1-1 is a typical form of design flow diagram. Other types may be found in published material [1, 2, 3][1] too numerous to mention here. However, regardless of which reference is reviewed, most flow diagrams will contain some or all aspects of Figure 1-1, depending upon the product to be designed and the particular company procedure.

To understand fully all that must be considered in the design process, we will proceed to explain the characteristics of each box of Figure 1-1.

Recognition of a need

This aspect of design can have its origin in any number of sources. Customer reports on the product function and quality may force a redesign. This source is emphasized by the feedback loop of Figure 1-1 that emanates from the product release box. Business and industrial competition are constantly forcing the need for new equipment, processes, and machinery designs. For example, high-speed "hot-lead" type of printing machinery is being replaced by higher speed photographic type printers that are computer controlled. Another example is that of numerical tape control for machine shop equipment when large quantities of complex parts must be manufactured to exacting dimensions. Development of patents into engineered products or incorporating them in overall designs is still another source of needs.

Among the largest generators of needs are the various agencies of the government. Typical current needs are better mail handling services, which will ultimately lead to automated post offices, development of a variety of early warning defense devices and systems for national security, all kinds of antipollution equipment for environmental improvement and control. This last area in itself will foster a host of secondary and tertiary needs for years to come.

Certainly, the reader can think of many other sources of needs that give rise to engineering design problems. Regardless of the source, the important thing is to recognize that a need exists, to use all of one's senses and background experience to focus on the need, justify its gratification, and gather as much information as possible concerning it.

Specifications and requirements

Once a need has been established, its requirements must be carefully spelled out. This step in the design flow diagram is labelled specifications and requirements. Many engineering organizations label this area design and

[1] All bibliographical material is listed at the end of each chapter.

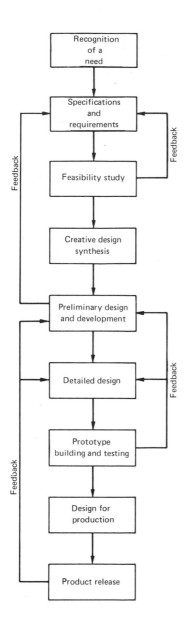

Figure 1-1 Design flow diagram with feedback loops.

performance requirements. Very often the initial phase of a project is stymied at this point because specifications are stated in such general terms as to indicate that the client (for example, sales department, consumer, and so on) has only a vague idea of what he really wants.

On the other hand, various local, state, and federal agencies (particularly the military and the Atomic Energy Commission) and a variety of sophisticated engineering clients (for example, companies that maintain their own engineering staffs) submit specifications that are written in great detail, where both the design and performance requirements are carefully stated. In fact, whenever health, safety, or any other legal or code requirement applies, this requirement becomes part of the original specification. In addition, governmental, commercial, and industrial standards (for example, Unified Standard Thread, National Electrical Manufacturers Association Standards for wiring, motors, and so on, American Iron and Steel Institute Material Standards and many more) are invariably made part of a specification. Quite often, specifications are tailored to satisfy the production competence and capacity of the parent company.

Feasibility study

Once the specifications have been prepared, accepted, and submitted, the next phase of the design flow is to make a feasibility study. The purpose of this study is to verify the possible success or failure of a proposal both from the technical and economic standpoint. Various questions must be answered. (1) Is any natural law being defied? (2) Are some of the specifications beyond what is technically available at present? (3) Is there a dependency on scarce materials? (4) Will the end product cost be so high as to completely eliminate the product from further consideration?

The feasibility study should not be misinterpreted as having the demise of a product as its purpose. However, it is quite likely that the "enthusiasm" of the sales department or members of management will, at times, override potentially severe technical difficulties thereby wasting many man-hours of design time. Many man-hours may also be wasted by overzealous design engineers constantly seeking perfection at the expense of the overall project cost. This does not mean that "anything goes" as long as the project is completed within the allotted time and cost. It merely means that experienced judgement must be exercised to determine that the design objectives have been obtained via good engineering practice and that further effort will be economically wasteful.

It is apparent, then, that the individuals responsible for making a feasibility study are going to be engineers with strong design backgrounds, knowledge of the engineering sciences, and a good grasp of material usage, production methods, and sales department requirements. In fact, it is likely that the men responsible for the feasibility study will be the same engineers who will ultimately inherit the design responsibility for the overall project.

Quite often, as a result of the feasibility study, changes are made in the specifications and requirements in order to provide a greater likelihood of project success. This action is indicated by the feedback loop in Figure 1-1 that goes from the feasibility study back to the specifications and requirements box.

Creative design synthesis

Once the feasibility of the design is established, the design flow diagram continues to the next step in Figure 1-1 labelled creative design synthesis.

This phase is perhaps the most challenging and interesting part of design. Here, unless one is restricted from doing so, the designer can act as engineer, inventor, and artist all in one—for now he is called upon to create.

Creativity can be defined as the synthesis of various new and/or old ideas and concepts in such a way as to produce an overall new idea or concept (at least new to its creator). Psychologists and educators have not, as yet, devised a method for teaching creativity, although methods to stimulate it have been tried. Creativity is an aspect of human behavior that is still being investigated by psychologists, and an in-depth understanding is still lacking. It is generally agreed, however, that all of us have the ability to create at various competence levels. Creating involves thinking, and certainly we all think—to a greater or lesser extent. In this regard, proper educational preparation should enhance creative processes. It must be remembered, nevertheless, that psychological handicaps tend to lessen the capacity for logical thought and creative effort [see references 4 to 10 inclusive].

Preliminary design and development

After the process of creative design synthesis is complete, there will be one or more possible designs that satisfy the given set of specifications and requirements. It then becomes necessary to decide which of the "solutions" to choose for the preliminary design and development stage that is the next step in the design flow diagram. The bases for making decisions are many and varied. Techniques range from the "seat of the pants" approach to complex procedures involving matrix tables, probability theory, and so on. An in-depth analysis of decision making techniques can be found in references [9] through [15].

Once a choice has been made we enter the domain entitled preliminary design and development. At this stage, layout drawings showing machine or system interfaces are made to determine the overall configuration and to establish functional relations between various parts of the machine or system. These layout drawings will contain important dimensions and notations as well as auxiliary and sectional views completely explaining the proposed design. In addition, kinematic studies are made that include complete machine layouts and machine cycle diagrams. Note that this stage is primarily concerned with detailing the results of creative design synthesis on drawing paper in order to validate the functional and overall size requirements of the specifications.

Rarely are all specifications and requirements achieved during this phase. Therefore, referring back to Figure 1-1, we see a feedback loop from the preliminary design and development box to the specifications and requirements box, indicating that it is necessary to reduce the stringency of some specifications (if possible) in order to carry the design to completion.

In addition, while making the preliminary design layout, further development work may be required to prove an idea, to determine some material properties, to evaluate a device, or to determine some unknown quantity based on substantive technical information or experience. Thus, certain areas of the preliminary design might be delayed or halted pending further development data. In fact, the need for development work may also arise during the next step of the flow diagram.

Detailed design

Detailed design is concerned with the actual sizing and dimensioning of all the individual components, both fabricated and purchased, that go into making the total product, device, or system. Here individual orthographic drawings are prepared for each component, showing the necessary views and all the dimensions and tolerances, the material and heat treatment (if any), the quantity of such components per assembly, the name of the components, and perhaps the assembly drawing number where the component part is used. Many companies and government agencies follow a set of drafting standards and procedures that may include more data than is stated above. Nevertheless, the primary criteria are that the information given on the drawing must be such that the shop knows specifically how the part is going to be fabricated. It is apparent that dimensions cannot be in any way redundant, for then the machinist making the part would have a choice of dimensions and the decision he made might be wrong. At the same time, no dimensions or information should be missing that make it impossible to fabricate the component. A short discussion of dimensioning will be found in Chapter 4, Sections 4-6 to 4-14 inclusive.

Usually a draftsman or junior designer makes these drawings under the supervision of the design engineer. The design engineer, in turn, must provide the necessary sketches, data, and back-up information. In order to obtain this information, the design engineer, working with the preliminary layouts, must size the parts, choose the materials, specify the commercial components, and so on, based on the analytical techniques available to him and his storehouse of past experience. This means that he must draw upon his background[2] of mathematics, mechanics, strength of materials, fluid mechanics, kinematics, vibrations, metallurgy, and shop processes. At times, he may have to seek assistance from experts in specialized fields. As stated earlier, the major portion of this text will be devoted to the techniques for selecting the machine elements comprising a design.

Prototype building and testing

After completing all the details, the subassemblies and assembly drawings including the materials and parts list, the completed design is sent to the prototype or model shop for fabrication. According to Figure 1-1, the completed design is now ready for prototype building and testing.

---

[2] Note that the design engineer is not only involved in innovative processes; he is also required to have and to use almost all of his engineering education. It is apparent that design engineering can be considered the zenith of engineering work. The individual at work in this area is expected to be well prepared both in mathematics and engineering science.

At this juncture, the parts are fabricated, commercial components are purchased, and the machine or system, after having been assembled, is ready for evaluation and testing. The output of this test period may or may not yield data that requires changes or modifications in the preliminary design or detailed design area. This possibility is indicated by the feedback loop of Figure 1-1. After the changes and/or modifications are made, when necessary, the new components are incorporated into the prototype assembly for continued testing and evaluation. The procedure of making continuous revisions and improvements to the design is repeated until the design engineer is satisfied that the performance specifications have been met. At this point, all the drawings, parts, and materials lists are sent to the production engineering department where the drawings are modified so that the completed project can be designed for production.

Design for production

Consideration is now given to design changes that would be compatible with the best (often the most economical) methods of production. In modern day nomenclature, this is sometimes called **value analysis** [see references 11 and 12] and is becoming an ever-growing and more important consideration in design. For example, the production engineer may consider a part suitable for manufacture by stamping, casting, or, perhaps, forging. For large quantity manufacturing, any of these processes would be more economical than individual part machining. Of course, in making a decision, consideration must be given to the necessary tooling costs and whether they can be amortized over the quantity produced.

Another example of what the production engineer may look for is the possibility of combining several fabricated parts into one or replacing some parts with commercially available equivalents. Still another consideration of the production engineer is the possibility of replacing some of the materials with equivalently satisfactory but less expensive materials. When the production drawings have been completed, they are sent to the production department for product release.

Product release

Production prototypes are usually made and tested, and any malfunction that cannot be easily corrected is generally referred back to preliminary design and development or to detailed design for alteration. This process is indicated by the feedback loop originating in the product release box of Figure 1-1.

By no means is the previous description complete in all its detail nor is it the only path that is followed in the design of a product, device, or system. However, to appreciate fully the aforementioned description of the design process, it is necessary to be involved with the procedure on a daily basis.

Design Analysis

Once a choice of a design has been made, preliminary and subsequent detailed design takes place as shown in Figure 1-1. At this time it is necessary to draw the layouts, provide the details, perform the tests, make the supporting calculations, and so on, that will ultimately result in prototype design. This is the area where the designer must specify dimensions, select components and materials, and in general consider such things as methods of manufacture, cost, reliability [see references 13 and 14], serviceability, and safety. The designer must rely upon his analytical ability and training in the engineering sciences to accomplish these objectives.

At this point in the discussion it is very necessary to understand that the mathematical model chosen and the subsequent calculations that are made *merely approximate reality*. One must, therefore, be fully aware of the various assumptions and limitations (for example, of linearity, homogeneity, and so on) that were made in deriving the equations used in the study of the engineering sciences. The designer, in his anxiety to apply the appropriate equations to his mathematical model, may have so oversimplified his model that it no longer represents the real case.

Therefore, it is very important to keep in mind that good design is based upon good theory while emphasizing that the numbers that result from applying the theory are merely "ball park" figures, which give the design engineer a rational basis for substantiating his work. Unfortunately, not all topics in design have a firm analytical base from which to work. In those cases, we must depend upon a semirational or empirical approach to solving a problem or selecting a design element.

Factor of Safety

In the light of what has been said in the aforementioned paragraph concerning analytic models, it seems reasonable to provide for the uncertainties associated with any design based upon such models. In addition, a designer may at various times also have to consider the following additional uncertainties:

1. **Variations in material properties.** Because no two furnace melts are exactly alike and some materials may have inclusions, and so on, the strength properties given in materials tables are usually average values. If the value is a stated manufacturer's value, it probably is the minimum value.
2. **Effect of size in stating material strength properties.** Property tables, unless otherwise stated, list strength values based upon a $\frac{1}{2}$-in. test

specimen. Yet larger components generally fail at a lower stress than a similar smaller component made of the same material.

3. **Type of loading.** A simple static load is easy to recognize, but what of those cases that fall between impact and suddenly applied loads? How does one take account of infrequently applied fatigue loading mixed with some shock loads (for example, cams, links, or feeding devices)?

4. **Effect of machining or forming processes.** These production operations may, and usually do, introduce stress concentrations and residual stresses.

5. **Effect of heat treatment upon the physical properties of material.** Improper heat treatment can cause residual stresses and cracks. In addition, the actual yield stress may be quite different from that used in making the design calculations.

6. **Effect of wear upon the functions and life of a machine member.** Constant rubbing without proper lubrication can appreciably reduce the working life and must be considered.

7. **Effect of time and environment in which the device is expected to operate.** Certainly great caution must be taken when components are operating in radioactive regions or corrosive atmospheres. When a material is expected to be subjected to creep (that is, loaded member at an elevated temperature for a long period of time), one must provide for this contingency. Operation at lower than normal temperatures is also a condition that often must be considered.

8. **Specific requirements for life and reliability.** For example, a machine gun must be reliable but usually has a finite life. Certain machines, however, may have an almost infinite life through which they are not wholly reliable but are expected to be periodically repaired.

9. **Overall concern for human safety.** All designs must consider safety of the operator and other persons who may be near or in contact with the machine or device. Unexpected, sudden overloads may cause breakage and considerable bodily harm.

In order to take these listed uncertainties into account in design, engineers have introduced what is familiarly called the factor of safety. (Some engineers think it should be called "the factor of ignorance.")

We are sure that the reader has, in the past, employed or calculated a factor of safety. For example, dividing the yield point stress by the calculated stress results in the factor of safety. This appears to be a simple and straightforward procedure to follow; unfortunately, things are never quite that simple. The designer must be fully aware of what he means when he calculates such a factor or when he bases his design on such a factor. Improper use of a "safety factor" may result, in some cases, in a needless waste of material or, in other cases, in physical or operational failure. Thus, one must define what he means when he uses the factor of safety.

For ductile materials, assumed to have the same ultimate and yield stress in both tension and compression, we say

$$N_u(\text{design}) = \frac{\text{ultimate stress}}{\text{working or design stress}} \qquad (1\text{-}1)$$

$$N_y(\text{design}) = \frac{\text{yield stress}}{\text{working or design stress}} \qquad (1\text{-}2)$$

Most often, equation (1-2) is used because mechanical equipment is frequently considered nonfunctional if some important component has yielded. A typical example of such a failure would be the local permanent yield that might be caused by a cam follower on a cam surface.

If a machine or mechanical component has already been sized (that is, its dimensions are known), then the factor of safety is defined as

$$N_u(\text{actual}) = \frac{\text{ultimate stress}}{\text{calculated stress}} \qquad (1\text{-}3)$$

$$N_y(\text{actual}) = \frac{\text{yield stress}}{\text{calculated stress}} \qquad (1\text{-}4)$$

For nonlinear types of problems, such as columns or rods subject to failure by buckling, the yield or ultimate stress can no longer be used. Instead, the actual failure load is used as the basis for a factor of safety. Thus, we have

$$N(\text{actual}) = \frac{\text{failure load}}{\text{calculated load}} \qquad (1\text{-}5)$$

Mechanical components subject to a continuously varying load have their factor of safety based upon the endurance limit of the material. However, because of the cyclic and static load that may exist, the definition depends upon the Soderberg fatigue analysis, which is covered in Chapter 6, Section 6-5.

Joseph P. Vidosic [15] suggests the following factors of safety as being reasonable. These factors are based on yield strength.

1. $N = 1.25$–1.5 for exceptionally reliable materials used under controllable conditions and subjected to loads and stresses that can be determined with certainty. Used almost invariably where low weight is a particularly important consideration.
2. $N = 1.5$–2 for well-known materials, under reasonably constant environmental conditions, subjected to loads and stresses that can be determined readily.
3. $N = 2$–2.5 for average materials operated in ordinary environments and subjected to loads and stresses that can be determined.
4. $N = 2.5$–3 for less tried or for brittle materials under average conditions of environment, load, and stress.

5. $N = 3$–4 for untried materials used under average conditions of environment, load, and stress.

6. $N = 3$–4 should also be used with better known materials that are to be used in uncertain environments or subjected to uncertain stresses.

7. Repeated loads: the factors established in items 1 to 6 are acceptable but must be applied to the endurance limit rather than the yield strength of the material.

8. Impact forces: the factors given in items 3 to 6 are acceptable, but an impact factor should be included.

9. Brittle materials: where the ultimate strength is used as the theoretical maximum, the factors presented in items 1 to 6 should be approximately doubled.

10. Where higher factors might appear desirable, a more thorough analysis of the problem should be undertaken before deciding upon their use.

In some cases, the selection of the factor of safety is stipulated by code or contract requirements. For example, the ASME[3] Unfired and Fired Pressure Vessel Code, the ASME Pressure Vessel Code for Nuclear Vessels, various building codes and specific values that are stipulated in contracts for both civilian and governmental designs.

It is apparent that the selection of an appropriate factor is rather empirical and very much dependent upon an individual's or industry's accumulated experience. Where a product or device has a long history of use, the factors based upon such a history are reliable. In fact, one may still depend upon such data even though modifications in design and materials have been made.

Statistical methods [16, 17] have also been employed in establishing a factor of safety. Here, account is taken of the variance in both the dimensions and strength of a mechanical component. This approach results in a factor of safety that, in general, is smaller than that based upon pure judgement. However, this method also requires estimation of possible load and strength variations, thereby making the method somewhat less than rational. Nevertheless, the statistical approach should be more than just of passing interest to the modern designers, particularly in those areas where experience data for certain components have been accumulated. Moreover, this method permits the use of a relatively low factor, if a small percentage of failure is acceptable. Unfortunately, space limitations do not permit a detailed discussion, but the reader is urged to investigate the given references.

SECTION 1-4

Reliability

Consumer products, industrial machinery, and military equipment are intently evaluated for reliability of performance and life expectancy. Although the "military" and particular industrial users (for example, power

---

[3] American Society of Mechanical Engineers.

plants—both fossil fuel and nuclear fuel) have always followed some sort of reliability programs, consumer products have of late received the widest attention and publicity. One of the most important foundations for product reliability is its design, and it is apparent that the designer should at least be acquainted with some of the guidelines.

The article entitled "A Manual of Reliability" [13] offers the following definition of reliability: "Reliability is the probability that a device will perform without failure a specific function under given conditions for a given period of time." From this definition, we see that a thorough and in-depth analysis of reliability will involve statistics and probability theory. Because of space limitations, we cannot enter into a detailed study of this subject. We do, however, recommend references [13] and [14].

As a guide to help the design engineer in producing a reliable product, Tangerman [13] suggests the following considerations:

A. Product Requirements
   1. Are all functional, reliability, and other requirements specified?
   2. What are the environmental requirements? Are they reasonable, based on experience? Are they based on measurement or conjecture?
   3. What are the reliability requirements? Are they too severe or too lenient? Consistent?

B. Preliminary Design
   1. What proven design can meet functional requirements?
   2. What standard components and assemblies can be used?
   3. Does this environment differ enough to affect factors 1 and 2?
   4. How much environmental extrapolation is necessary?
   5. Is expert advice available?

C. Design Analysis
   1. How does each component and material behave under these environments?
   2. How dependable are available life data?
   3. Can reliability be calculated from available data? Do gaps exist and, if so, can they be filled?
   4. Can complete units be built for test?
   5. What are the weakest links in the design?
   6. Is reliability high enough or is redesign indicated?

D. Corrective Action
   1. Will expert technical assistance help?
   2. Can manufacturing or quality control give advice?
   3. Is the reliability set by one or two components? If so, can they be redesigned or derated, or is redundancy the answer?
   4. Can the environment be changed—heating, cooling, shock mounting, shielding?
   5. Is redesign indicated?
(Steps C and D may have to be repeated several times)

    E. Final Design
1. Can production, inspection or purchasing help in writing the specifications?
2. Can specifications be written to assure 100% test and inspection?
3. If component characteristics cannot be 100% tested, are there suitable manufacturing and quality control procedures?
4. Which component will be subcontracted or purchased? Is there a list of approved vendors?
5. Can procedures for inspection and test be inserted to reject defective parts early in manufacturing?
6. What minimum number of tests and inspections must be made at each stage? Must all characteristics be tested?
7. Will a "shakedown" test eliminate substandard units more easily?
8. How much testing can be done safely without cutting product life appreciably?

    F. Redesign After Pilot Run
Must be carried back to Step C.

SECTION 1-5

Cost

Without doubt, cost is an extremely important factor in most (if not all) designs. Achievement of an economical design depends on the designer's experience, knowledge, ingenuity, and ability to "trade-off" one design parameter against other design parameters.

In fact, the desire to get one's "moneys worth" has developed into a new engineering methodology called **value analysis.** Its origin is ascribed to L. D. Miles, and the various techniques employed are explained in his book *Techniques of Value Analysis and Engineering* [11]. Briefly, value analysis is the organized procedure of cost reduction covering the phases of design, production, materials, and distribution while maintaining product reliability. Although we cannot here enter into the detailed aspects of value analysis, an illustrative example should serve to convey its objectives and what may be accomplished by the application of its techniques. Figure 1-2 of a bracket shows the before and after results of value analysis and was taken from a paper by R. N. Mooney [12].

    The cast iron bracket, part of a signaling device, was found to be one of the more expensive parts of the assembly. It was being used as part of a drive sprocket sub-assembly. The contributing factor to the high cost was the finishing required for certain internal and external surfaces. In fact, the unfinished casting by itself was only five per cent of the total cost of the part.

    Value Analysis showed that a simpler bracket design could be used if it were relocated at a different point in the assembly.

Figure 1-2 Before and after value analysis. [R. N. Mooney: Savings through use of value analysis techniques in engineering. *ASME Paper No. 68-DE-44,* 1968.]

As a result of using the simpler bracket, a saving of fifty per cent was achieved for the bracket. And, as a result of its relocation to a new drive position, some parts, including a gear, shaft and two bearings were eliminated. A one hundred per cent saving was effected by the elimination of these parts.

The overall saving for the entire project was thirty per cent.

The type of objectivity involved in value analysis should be included in a good designer's "tool box." This means that in achieving a functionally satisfactory design, where possible, the least expensive materials that are consistent with the life and wear of the part as well as its operating environment should be used. In addition, other cost considerations such as method of manufacture, tolerances, use of standard or commercially available components, method of assembly, tooling, quantity to be produced, and, finally, simplicity of maintenance should always be evaluated for every design. Lastly, an attempt should be made to keep to a minimum the number of components that constitute an assembly.

SECTION 1-6

Safety

As in the case of reliability, equipment and machinery must be designed so that they are safe both for the operator and the surrounding community.

For fired and unfired pressure vessels, the ASME code is usually the minimum standard of safety required. In the nuclear power field and related areas, the AEC[4] demands that specific safety requirements be followed both for design and operation. In mining, the Bureau of Mines has rigid safety requirements. These requirements are, at times, loosely enforced for lack of adequate inspection. Recently, the automotive industry has been required to design safer automobiles although specific government standards are still in

[4] Atomic Energy Commission.

a state of flux. Also, we should not forget that the military services require that definite specifications concerning safety be followed in supplying their equipment. The American National Standards Institute in New York, The National Safety Council in Chicago, The Bureau of Mines, The Bureau of Labor Statistics, and The National Bureau of Standards all located in Washington, D.C., are good sources of safety information and statistics.

The vast American industrial complex, however, has, in the past, taken a rather pedestrian view of the general problem of equipment and machinery safety as it relates to the operator and the plant employee. The designer can play an extremely important role in providing adequate safety protection for the worker by providing the necessary safeguards at the earliest possible design stage.

A brief list of items that the designer should consider in designing equipment for operator safety follows.

1. Covers or enclosures should be provided for moving components that are in close proximity to the operator.
2. Parts, which may cause injury to the operator (for example, clothing getting caught and so on), should not project from the equipment.
3. The design should be such that any adjustments, lubrication, or general maintenance can be performed with little difficulty or hazard.
4. The equipment or machine should be inoperative as long as the operator's hands, feet, arms or other parts of his anatomy are in a work zone (for example, the working area of a press).
5. Sharp corners and edges should be avoided.
6. Electrical equipment should be properly enclosed and grounded.
7. Natural or forced ventilation (if required) should be provided where the atmosphere is contaminated with fumes, dust, or other particles.
8. Provision should be made to avoid exposure to various forms of radiation (that is, x rays, ultraviolet rays, radioactive materials, and so on).

This list indicates only a small portion of the number of hazards that a designer must provide against for adequate safety. For each specific design, the engineer must educate himself concerning the singular peculiarities of his problem by referring to the appropriate codes and/or standards.

SECTION 1-7

Closure

In this chapter, we have given a brief description of design methodology and several important associated aspects. As with all endeavors, professionalism and maturity are attained by practice and experience—some of which will be realized in a machine design projects course. Unfortunately, because of space limitations, we cannot here become involved in the broader aspects of design. We can only hope that this introduction and the references cited will aid the student to think more logically about design procedures.

The remainder of this text will therefore concentrate on that phase of machine design that will provide the student with sufficient background to select various machine elements properly as well as enable him to perform design analysis. However, past experience in teaching machine design has indicated that most students welcome a review of engineering materials, methods of manufacture, and strength of materials. Thus, parts of Chapters 2, 3, 4, and 5 are presented with this view in mind.

REFERENCES

[1] M. Asimow: *Introduction to Design.* Prentice-Hall, Inc., Englewood Cliffs, N.J. 1962.

[2] Joseph P. Vidosic: *Elements of Design Engineering.* The Ronald Press Co., New York, 1969.

[3] D. H. Edel, Jr. (ed.): *Introduction to Creative Design.* Prentice-Hall, Inc., Englewood Cliffs, N.J.,1967.

[4] N. L. Munn: *Psychology.* Houghton Mifflin Co., Boston, 1946.

[5] M. S. Allen: *Morphological Creativity.* Prentice-Hall, Inc., Englewood Cliffs, N.J. 1962.

[6] Eugene Raudsepp: Forcing ideas with synetics. *Mach. Des.*, pp 134–139 (October 16, 1969).

[7] John E. Arnold: Useful creative techniques. *Creative Engineering Seminar*, Stanford University, 1959.

[8] A. F. Osborn: *Applied Imagination.* Chas. Scribner's Sons, New York, 1963.

[9] Leo Spector (ed.): Denovate. *Mach. Des.*, pp 20–28 (April 3, 1969).

[10] D. L. Marples: *The Decisions of Engineering Design.* The Institution of Engineering Designers, London, England, July 1960.

[11] L. C. Miles: *Techniques of Value Analysis and Engineering.* McGraw-Hill Book Co., New York, 1961.

[12] R. N. Mooney: Savings through use of value analysis techniques in engineering, *ASME Paper Number 68-DE-44*, 1968.

[13] E. G. Tangerman (ed.): A manual of reliability. *Prod. Eng.*, pp 65–96 (May 16, 1960).

[14] Robert Lusser: A study of methods for achieving reliability of guided missiles. *Technical Report No. 75*, U.S. Naval Air Missile Test Center, July 10, 1950.

[15] Joseph P. Vidosic: *Machine Design Projects.* The Ronald Press, New York, 1957.

[16] Ray C. Johnson: *Optimum Design of Mechanical Elements.* John Wiley and Sons, Inc., New York, 1961.

[17] Hsuan-Loh Su: Design by quantitative factor of safety. *Trans. ASME. J. Eng. Ind.*, p 387 (Nov. 1960).

2

Metallurgical Properties of Engineering Materials

SYMBOLS

S_u = ultimate strength, psi
S'_n = endurance limit for polished specimen, psi
AISI = American Iron and Steel Institute
ASM = American Society for Metals

ASTM = American Society for Testing Materials
BHN = Brinell hardness number
SAE = Society of Automotive Engineers

This chapter will review ferrous materials and nonferrous materials, the fundamentals of heat treatment, and plastics from the designer's point of view. In addition, the reader will be reacquainted with the various properties of materials that are so important in making strength and dimensional calculations for machine elements.

The young designer often favors a more analytical approach to design, often overlooking the significance of selecting a material from both its functional and economic standpoint. Thus, a review of the subject matter presented in this chapter will serve to emphasize how a viable as well as an economic design can be achieved.

SECTION 2-1

Brittle and Ductile Fracture

Metals fracture in one of two ways, (1) brittle fracture and (2) ductile fracture. **Brittle fracture** occurs with virtually no plastic flow or reduction of area. Separation takes place along cleaveage planes and appears as bright granular surfaces. Brittle fracture will show the fracture planes to be perpendicular (or nearly so) to the acting tensile force. Furthermore, the normal stress on the plane of fracture will be higher than any other plane. In addition

17

to the type of material, dynamic loading and low temperatures can also be causes of brittle fracture.

In **ductile fracture,** there is plastic flow with separation taking place in the direction of the highest resolved shearing stress. Tensile testing of such metals produces cup and cone fractures, and the appearance at the point of fracture is silky and smooth. Fractures of this kind are called transcrystalline fractures because slip takes place within the grain.

SECTION 2-2

Improving the Strength of Materials

There are basically five ways in which the strength of metals may be increased: (1) growth of metal whiskers, (2) smaller grain size, (3) strain hardening, (4) alloying, and (5) heat treating.

1. The larger the specimen, the greater the propensity for crystal defects to exist. Thus there is a greater likelihood of failure at a lower strength. Presently much research is being carried out with whisker metals that are made in the laboratory. These **metal whiskers** are needlelike crystal filaments only a few millimeters in length and from 1 to 10 microns (μ) in diameter. Being small in size, they are free of defects and their strength is nearly that of their theoretically calculated values. For example, the tensile strength of commercially produced iron is about 100,000 psi (100 ksi). Laboratory made iron whiskers, however, have been tested to 2,000,000 psi (2000 ksi). The results produced to date in the case of many metals made in laboratories have been quite amazing. The concept, nevertheless, requires much further study and investigation before it will evolve as a commercially feasible method.

2. A **smaller grain size** in a metal improves its strength by providing a longer and more complex path for slip lines to traverse. The most important method for controlling grain size is by controlling the rate at which a metal is cooled. Rapid cooling produces a fine grain. A slow rate of cooling results in a coarse grain. There are a number of ways to control the cooling rate. For example, pouring a melt into a sand mold (sand casting) and allowing it to air cool will produce relatively coarse grains. On the other hand, pouring a melt into a metal mold and allowing it to cool produces a finer grain. Still more rapid cooling can be provided by coolants like water or oil, which are circulated through the mold (die casting). This procedure produces a very fine grain structure.

3. **Strain hardening** (also called work hardening or cold working) is a way of producing a small grain size by mechanical means. Typical of such an operation is the cold rolling of carbon steel bars to a specific diameter in a rolling mill. The material is forced to deform in accordance with its slip system as earlier explained. However, its resistance to slip increases as the process of deformation continues. The result is a smaller grain size, an

increase in hardness and yield strength, but a loss in toughness and ductility. The loss of ductility and toughness due to strain hardening can be recovered by a process called annealing, which is discussed in Section 2-9.

It is possible for hot working to reduce the grain size of a metal and still avoid the ductility and toughness loss attributed to cold working. In this process, a metal is shaped and formed when it is above a certain temperature, known as the recrystallization temperature. A typical example of hot work is the forging of a steel component (for example, axles, shafts, cutlery, horseshoes, and so on). Proper control of the forging loads and temperature produces a metal that is both strong and tough.

4. The intentional addition of small amounts of a metal or metals to a base metal is called **alloying.** These additions are made not only for purposes of increasing the strength of the base metal by heat treatment but also to improve corrosion resistance, electrical properties, ductility, machinability, toughness, and so on. When an alloyed metal is not heat treated, it is called a simple alloy.

There are three forms of alloy compositions. These are mechanical mixtures, solid solutions, and intermetallic compounds. (a) When two constituent metals are not soluble in their solid states, they form a **mechanical mixture.** This type of alloy is one in which each component metal retains its own properties and crystal structure. (b) When two metals are soluble in their solid states, they form an alloy that is a **solid solution.** In forming a solid solution, the alloying atoms may randomly replace lattice atoms of the base metal. This is called a **substitutional solution.** It is also possible for the alloying atoms to randomly locate themselves within the lattic structure of the base metal. This type of solution is called an **interstitial solution.** (c) When the alloying atoms replace the base metal atoms by proportional quantities and are located in a regular manner rather than randomly, the alloy is called an **intermetallic compound.** Alloys of this kind are generally higher in tensile strength, less ductile than their constituents, and tend to be more resistant to deformation than their constituents.

5. The most important way to increase the strength of a metal is by heat treatment. **Heat treatment** is defined as the controlled heating and subsequent cooling of a metal or alloy. It is employed to obtain properties that are desirable and appropriate for a particular application. The subject of heat treatment is so important that we shall devote Sections 2-6 to 2-10 inclusive to its detailed discussion.

SECTION 2-3

The Iron-Carbon Diagram

The iron-carbon equilibrium diagram is the most important representation of an alloy system the designer will encounter. It provides a complete picture of phase relations, microstructure, and temperature for the knowledgeable

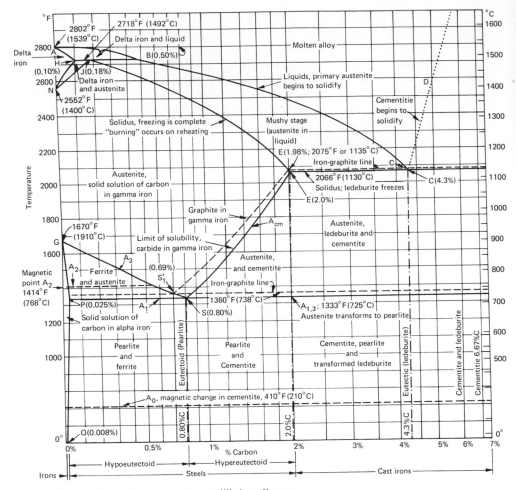

Figure 2-1 The iron-carbon equilibrium diagram.

heat treatment of steel. In addition, it clearly indicates the division between steel and cast iron, depending on carbon content. Figure 2-1 shows an iron-carbon diagram complete with the accepted standard nomenclature and lettering for various points. To be strictly correct, the diagram should be called the iron–iron carbide diagram because the carbon in equilibrium does not appear as free carbon but in the form of iron carbide (Fe_3C) known as **cementite.** Common usage, however, terms it the iron-carbon diagram.

On close inspection of Figure 2-1, we see that pure iron (that is, 0 % carbon) has several allotropic[1] forms. At room temperature, the iron has a body-centered cubic structure that has magnetic properties. This form is called **alpha (α) iron.** As the temperature is increased to 1414°F the crystal structure

[1] The property that certain chemical elements have of existing in two or more different forms.

remains unchanged, but the iron loses its magnetic properties.[2] A further increase of temperature to 1670°F changes iron to a face-centered cubic structure, which remains nonmagnetic. This form is stable to a temperature of 2552°F, at which point another change takes place. The iron again takes on a body-centered cubic structure and is called **delta** (δ) **iron.** Finally, when the temperature is increased to 2802°F, the delta iron melts and becomes liquid.

Pure iron is important because each form has a different capacity for maintaining carbon in solid solutions. These different capacities for retaining carbon are the basis for the heat treatment of steel. Industrially, delta iron is of little importance and, therefore, can be dropped from further consideration.

As the reader will observe from Figure 2-1, carbon is soluble in alpha iron to a maximum of 0.025% at 1333°F (point P) and only to 0.008% at room temperature. The result is an interstitial solid solution with dissolved carbon. Alpha iron is commonly called **ferrite.**[3] It is the softest of all materials in the diagram.

At a temperature of 2066°F, carbon is soluble in gamma (γ) iron to a maximum of about 2.0% (point E, Figure 2-1). The name commonly given to this interstitial solid solution is **austenite.**

Under equilibrium conditions, the carbon is in the form of iron carbide (Fe_3C) called cementite. This material, containing 6.67% carbon, determines the right hand boundary of the equilibrium diagram. It is brittle, weak in tension, strong in compression, and is the hardest of any material in the equilibrium diagram.

Point C, in Figure 2-1 is a **eutectic point**[4] containing 4.3% carbon and consists of a mixture of austenite and cementite known as **ledeburite.** This material is not observable because austenite is unstable at room temperature (except under special conditions) and continues to change on cooling.

Of special significance is point S, at which iron contains 0.8% carbon at 1333°F. This point is called a **eutectoid**[5] and is the lowest point on the diagram at which austenite will disappear when slowly cooled. The material formed at this eutectoid is called **pearlite.** Pearlite is a mechanical mixture of ferrite and cementite. When viewed under a microscope, the mixture appears in

[2] Some metallurgists call this form of iron beta (β) iron, but we shall continue to refer to the region (i.e., OPG in Figure 2-1) as alpha iron.

[3] In reality, the alpha solution should be called alpha ferrite to distinguish it from delta ferrite (i.e., delta iron at 2552°F). However, since delta ferrite has no role in engineering metallurgy, alpha ferrite is simply called ferrite.

[4] A eutectic point is a point on the equilibrium diagram at which two constituent metals solidify simultaneously at the same temperature. Also, it is the point at which the alloy has the lowest freezing (or melting) temperature of any other alloy combination (point S in Figure 2-1).

[5] A eutectoid as defined in Vol. 1 of the *Metals Handbook*, is "an isothermal reversible reaction in which a solid solution is converted into two or more intimately mixed solids on cooling, the number of solids formed being the same as the number of components in the system."

lamellar layers of cementite within a field of white ferrite. The name pearlite has its origin in the fact that the microstructure resembles that of mother-of-pearl.

The iron-carbon diagram is divided into two major sections (see Figure 2-1). Alloys having less than 2% carbon (some of the literature specifies 1.7%) are called **steels**; alloys containing over 2% carbon are called **cast iron**. In addition, the classification for steel is again divided into two sections. Steels having less than 0.8% carbon (some literature specifying 0.83%) are called **hypoeutectoid steels**; those above 0.8% carbon are called **hypereutectoid steels**. Figure 2-2 shows the effect of different carbon contents on the microstructure of slowly cooled steels.

SECTION 2-4

Wrought Iron

Wrought iron is a mixture of pure iron and 1–3% slag. It also contains traces of carbon, manganese, silicon, phosphorus, and sulfur. Wrought iron is made by pouring molten slag from the open-hearth furnace into vessels containing iron. The final mix is then squeezed in a press to remove excess slag and reduced into billets by a rolling mill. The billets can be reheated to form bars, tubing, plate, structural shapes, pipe, forgings, nails, rivets, barbed wire, fittings, and so on. Wrought iron is ductile and soft and is most readily forged and forge welded. In addition to its ductility, it tends to resist corrosion by forming an oxide film quickly when exposed to a corrosive environment. Figure 2-3 is a photomicrograph of a transverse and longitudinal section of wrought iron.

Due to rolling, wrought iron has stronger mechanical properties[6] in the longitudinal direction (that is, the direction of rolling) than in the transverse direction. The strength of wrought iron can be further increased by alloying. Typical of such alloying is the addition of 1.5–3.5% nickel. The ultimate strength of wrought iron can also be increased by cold working[7] and subsequent aging. Properties of unalloyed and $3\frac{1}{4}$% nickel wrought iron are listed as follows:

	Unalloyed Wrought Iron (longitudinal properties)	Nickel Wrought Iron ($3\frac{1}{4}$% Ni)
Tensile strength, psi	42,000–52,000	55,000–60,000
Yield point, psi	26,000–35,000	45,000–50,000
Elongation (8 in.), %	25–40	25–30
Reduction in area, %	40–55	35–45

[6] Various mechanical properties are defined in Chapter 3.

[7] See Section 2.2.

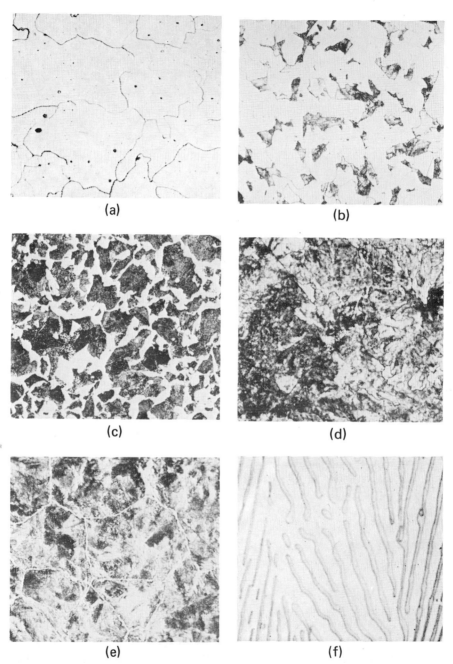

Figure 2-2 Change of microstructure of steel with change in carbon content.
(a) Practically carbon-free iron, × 100. **(b)** Steel with 0.25% carbon. Ferrite (white) and
pearlite (black), × 100. **(c)** Steel with 0.45% carbon. Ferrite (white) and pearlite (black), × 100.
(d) Steel with 0.85% carbon. All pearlite, × 100. **(e)** Steel with 1.10% carbon. Pearlite (dark)
and cementite (white), × 100. **(f)** Pearlite highly magnified showing lamellar structure.
Ferrite (white) and cementite (black), × 2500. [Courtesy of U.S. Steel Corporation.]

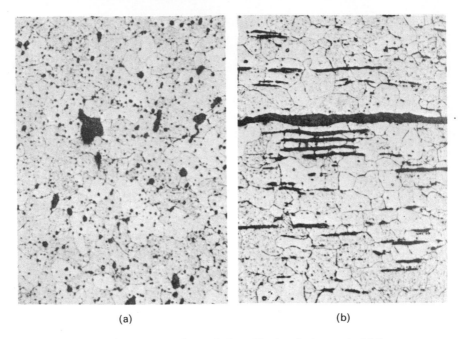

(a)   (b)

Figure 2-3 The microstructure of wrought iron. Slag in a ferrite matrix. **(a)** Traverse section. **(b)** Longitudinal section. Etched in 2 % Nital, × 100. [Courtesy of Buehler Ltd.]

In reversed bending and reversed axial loading, the endurance properties are 19,000–23,000 psi and 11,000–16,000 psi respectively. Impact tests indicate a Charpy value of 5 ft-lb for transverse "granular" sections and 18 ft-lb for longitudinal "granular" sections. At subzero temperatures, nickel wrought iron displays a strong propensity for maintaining its impact strength. At 700°F, wrought iron drops in tensile strength, which is reduced to one half its room temperature value at 900°F.

SECTION 2-5

Cast Iron

As indicated in Figure 2-1, when the carbon content of the iron-carbon system is in the range of 2–6.67% carbon[8] the resultant alloy is cast iron. Most commercial types of cast iron contain between 2.5 and 4% carbon. It is obvious that, with such a high carbon content, the resulting material will be brittle and have a low ductility. Consequently, cast iron cannot be cold worked. Because cast iron flows readily when liquid, it is easily cast into intricate shapes that can be machined after cooling and aging. Although relatively weak in tensile strength, cast iron is very strong in compression.

[8] Some sources consider a carbon content of 1.7% and above to be cast iron.

Furthermore, the properties of cast iron can be varied extensively with the addition of alloying metals and proper heat treatment. Cast iron alloys have been developed for use as crankshafts in engines, gearing, dies, and so on.

There are four primary types of cast iron. These are (1) white cast iron, (2) malleable cast iron, (3) gray cast iron, and (4) nodular cast iron.[9] In addition, one may consider two other forms, which are chilled cast iron and alloy cast iron.

White cast iron

White cast iron consists of pearlite (that is, transformed austenite) in a matrix of white cementite (Figure 2-4a). Such a microstructure has virtually all of its carbon in the form of cementite. White cast iron is difficult, if not impossible, to machine because it is extremely hard and brittle. This cast iron is termed "white" cast iron due to its white appearance when fractured.

The uses of white cast iron are quite limited, although it is employed in such applications as ball mills, extrusion dies, and liners for cement mixers. Machines of this kind need the strong wear resistant properties of white cast iron.

Malleable cast iron

By far the greatest use of white cast iron is in the manufacture of malleable cast iron. If white cast iron is maintained at 1600°F for an extended time period and then cooled slowly,[10] the cementite loses carbon ($Fe_3C \rightleftharpoons 3Fe + C$). The resulting microstructure when this substance is cooled to room temperature consists of free carbon nodules in a sea of ferrite (Figure 2-4b).

Malleable cast iron has mechanical properties that are superior to gray cast iron (discussed next) except for wear. The material is readily machined and is best employed for relatively thin sections (for example, $\frac{1}{2}$–2 in.). Wide use of the material can be found in making equipment for automotive, oil, agricultural, and railroad industries. Specifically, malleable cast iron is used to make gear housings, brake pedals in cars, spring hangers, tractor parts, and so on.

By adding manganese, malleable cast iron can be made to retain more combined carbon and thus form **pearlite malleable** iron when slowly cooled to normal temperatures. Pearlite malleable iron can also be formed by first heating a ferritic malleable cast iron above its lower critical temperature followed by rapid cooling in a quenching medium (for example, air, oil). The resulting microstructure is shown in Figure 2-4b. Tempering of pearlite malleable iron after it has been quenched will spheroidize[11] the pearlite.

---

[9] Also called ductile cast iron.

[10] The procedure of heating to and holding a metal at a designated temperature for a period of time and then cooling it at a controlled rate is called **tempering**. When the process is applied to white cast iron, it is called malleablizing for obvious reasons.

[11] Spheroidizing is heating and cooling to produce a globular form of carbide in a steel or iron.

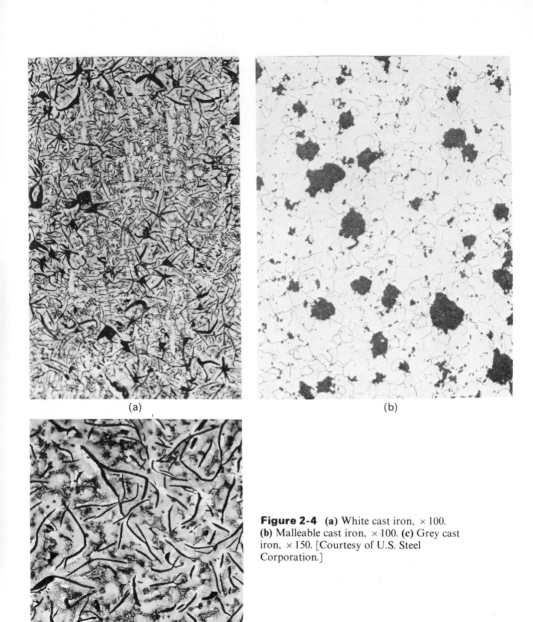

(a)

(b)

(c)

Figure 2-4 **(a)** White cast iron, × 100.
(b) Malleable cast iron, × 100. **(c)** Grey cast
iron, × 150. [Courtesy of U.S. Steel
Corporation.]

It is also possible to add alloying metals to malleable cast iron to influence its mechanical properties. Those alloys most often used are copper or both copper and molybdenum at the same time. The addition of copper improves corrosion resistance, tensile strength, yield strength, and reduces ductility. The combination of copper and molybdenum further improves corrosion resistance and strength. The following table shows a comparison of the mechanical properties of ferrite, pearlitic, and copper-moly malleable iron.

	Tensile Strength, psi	Yield Strength, psi	Elongation (in 2 in.), %	BHN
Ferritic	50,000–60,000	32,000–39,000	10–20	110–156
Pearlitic	65,000–120,000	45,000–100,000	2–16	163–269
Copper-moly alloy	58,000–65,000	40,000–45,000	15–20	135–155

Two popular grades of malleable cast iron are ASTM A47-52 grade 32 510 and A47-52 grade 35 018. The mechanical properties of these two materials are given in Table A-1 of Appendix A.

Gray cast iron

Gray cast iron is the most widely used of all cast irons. In fact, it is common to speak of gray cast iron just as cast iron. It contains between 2.5 and 4.00% carbon and usually somewhat more than 2% silicon. Upon solidification, the cementite, being unstable, breaks up into austenite and graphite called graphitic carbon. The silicon acts as a graphitizer. The graphite shows up as irregularly shaped graphite flakes, which give the gray cast iron its gray appearance when fractured.

The structure of the resulting alloy at room temperature is greatly affected by the amount of graphite in the matrix. If, on the one hand, the proeutectoid cementite[12] and eutectic cementite separate, the resulting matrix will consist of pearlite and graphite. On the other hand, a large quantity of silicon will cause the cementite to separate from the pearlite, reducing the strength of the resulting material. The strength of gray cast iron is determined by varying the composition of its matrix from pearlite to different mixtures of pearlite and ferrite to virtually pure ferrite. The strongest and hardest form is pearlitic gray iron. The weakest and softest is the graphite-ferrite mixture of gray iron having the lowest carbon content. Strength and hardness increase with increasing carbon content. Figure 2-4c shows a photomicrograph of gray cast iron.

The ASTM specification A48-46 classifies gray cast iron into seven classes: Numbers 20, 25, 30, 35, 40, 50, and 60. Each class number indicates the minimum tensile strength. For example, class 20 gray iron has a minimum

[12] The cementite was formed prior to the formation of the eutectoid and therefore is termed proeutectoid cementite. It is the cementite formed in the region between lines A_{cm} and $A_{3.1}$. See Figure 2-1.

tensile strength of 20,000 psi, class 25 gray iron has a minimum tensile strength of 25,000 psi, and so on. A complete listing of the mechanical properties for gray cast iron can be found in Table A-1 of Appendix A.

Gray cast iron is often used for foundation supports for machinery and structures due to its high compressive strength and good damping characteristics. Also, because of its capacity for damping, high torsional shear strength and low notch sensitivity, gray cast iron has been used in the manufacture of engine crankshafts. The ease with which it may be cast and excellent wear properties allow it to be used extensively (in some cases exclusively) in the manufacture of engine blocks, brake drums, sliding surfaces of machines, gearing, gear housings, and so on.

In those instances where the use of gray iron may be appropriate yet not considered because of significantly higher tensile stresses, the higher classes of gray iron may be used. For example, in fabricating valves, fittings, or piping and their connections, one might specify a class 40, 50, or 60 gray iron. However, as the cost of class 60 iron is about 2.5–3 times that of class 30 iron, the designer must consider his selection with attention to this cost factor.

The designer should be careful when making stress calculations before selecting a value of E (the modulus of elasticity). Because the stress-strain curve for cast irons is not linear, the modulus of elasticity is not constant. Thus, an arbitrary value is established by drawing a line from the origin of the stress-strain curve to a point corresponding to one quarter of the tensile strength. The slope of this line is taken as the value for E.

Cast irons (all kinds) are not easily welded. By proper preparation, however (that is, preheating, surface preparation, choice of welding method and welding rod) successful welds are possible. Care must be exercised to make certain that the heating and subsequent cooling of nonuniform sections do not cause the casting to crack.

Nodular cast iron

Nodular cast iron (also called **ductile iron**) consists of spheroidal shaped graphite within a steel matrix. The spheroidal shaped graphite is due to the addition of small quantities of magnesium (for example, in the form of nickel-magnesium alloy) or cesium to a desulfurized iron melt just before casting. In contrast with malleable iron, nodular cast iron is formed on solidification and requires no tempering.

The matrix can be predominantly ferritic or mixtures of ferrite and pearlite iron. Nodular cast iron containing no more than 10% pearlite is called a **ferritic iron.** It is a tough, ductile iron with good machinability. Those matrix structures that are predominantly pearlitic are called **pearlitic nodular iron** and can be obtained by casting or by heat treatment.[13] It is also

---

[13] The heat treatment used here is called **normalizing.** This procedure consists of heating to above the $A_{1.3}$ line and then cooling in air. (See Figure 2-1.)

possible to produce a matrix that is martensitic[14] by heating and then quenching (that is, rapid cooling) in oil or water. Martensitic structures are stronger and harder than either the pearlitic iron or ferritic iron. However, the pearlitic iron, although not as ductile as ferritic iron, is much stronger.

With the addition of certain alloying elements, an austenitic matrix may be produced. Such structures display good resistance to corrosion and creep at high temperatures.

Nodular cast iron is stronger, more ductile, tougher, and less porous than gray cast iron. It is used in the fabrication of crankshafts, pistons, cylinder heads, forming rolls, pulleys, forming dies, and so on. Figure 2-5 shows the microstructure of a ferritic nodular iron and a pearlitic nodular iron. The mechanical properties of nodular cast iron can be found in Table A-1 of Appendix A.

Chilled cast iron

Chilled cast iron is made by placing metal "chill bars" inside the mold but near its surface. As the molten metal is poured, that part of the melt coming in contact with the chill bars is cooled more rapidly. This produces a surface of white cast iron which is predominantly cementite and therefore very hard. Below this surface the material is gray cast iron. Chilled cast iron can only be machined by grinding and is used in making stamping dies, mill and crushing rolls, railway wheels, and so on.

Alloy cast iron

In addition to the aforementioned common types of cast irons, there are various kinds of alloy cast irons. These cast irons contain different alloying elements.[15] By controlling the rate of graphitization, these elements develop special capabilities, such as better mechanical properties, improved resistance to heat, corrosion, wear, or brittle fractures. Also, alloying can improve both the castability and machinability properties of castings. Common alloying elements are nickel, copper, chromium, molybdenum, and vanadium. Many alloy cast irons are proprietary materials of different companies. For example, Ni-Resist, an alloy of nickel, chromium, and manganese, is an International Nickel Company product. Meehanite cast iron, produced under patent protection, is made with the addition of a calcium-silicon alloy. Various grades of Meehanite are produced. See Table A-1 in Appendix A for the properties of some alloy cast irons.

---

[14] Randomly arranged needlelike crystals that are hard and strong. Such a matrix is a supersaturated (with carbon) solution of cementite in a body-centered tetragonal iron.

[15] The reader should not mistake impurities such as manganese, phosphorus, silicon, and sulfur for alloying elements. The processes for mass producing steel, cast iron, nonferrous materials, and so on, are not designed for complete deletion of all impurities.

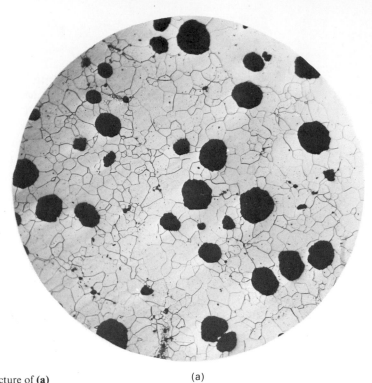

Figure 2-5 Microstructure of **(a)** ferritic nodular iron, × 125 and **(b)** pearlitic nodular iron, × 500. [Courtesy of The International Nickel Company, Inc.]

(a)

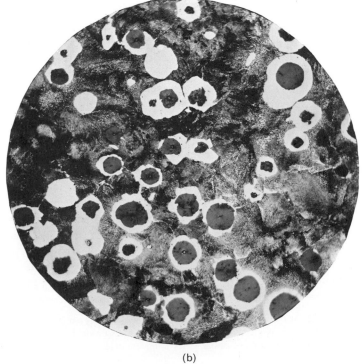

(b)

SECTION 2-6

Heat Treatment of Steels

Heat treatment is defined as the heating and cooling of a metal alloy to alter its mechanical properties. These alterations are varied and have different purposes. For example, an intended heat treatment may be for the purposes of strengthening and hardening a metal, relieving its internal stresses, hardening its surface only, annealing a cold-worked piece, or improving its machinability by spheroidizing.

The most important part of the iron-carbon diagram in the heat treatment of steel is that portion involving the transformation from austenite to the region below the lower critical temperature (see Figure 2-1). Transformation of austenite, upon slow cooling, begins at the upper critical temperature line A_3 or A_{cm} (actual transformation probably begins at a somewhat lower temperature as earlier indicated in Section 2-3). At this line the gamma iron is transformed to alpha with a small quantity of interstitial carbon (that is, ferrite). As the temperature continues to fall through the transformation region, more carbon is precipitated out of solution forming cementite (Fe_3C) because alpha iron cannot hold as much carbon as gamma iron. Further cooling past the lower critical line produces a hypoeutectoid steel (pearlite and ferrite), a hypereutectoid steel (pearlite and cementite), or a eutectoid steel (pearlite). Which of the three steels is eventually formed depends solely on the carbon content.

However, if the cooling rate is such that the transformation temperature (Ar_1 or $Ar_{1,3}$) is much lower than that for equilibrium transformation, the time available for the carbon to diffuse out of solution is greatly reduced. As a result, the gamma iron cannot readily transform to alpha iron because the carbon is still in solution. Consequently, a supersaturated solid solution of carbon in iron is formed. This structure is called **martensite** (also known as **fresh martensite**) and is shown in Figure 2-6. A martensite structure has a white needlelike random arrangement that is very hard and unstable. It is important to note that the change from austenite to martensite involves an increase in volume.[16]

It is obvious that the rate at which the transformation from austenite to martensite takes place is significant in preventing the formation of softer constituents. Thus, for a steel of a fixed chemical composition and known austenite grain size (that is, temperature of the austenite), there is a cooling rate that will transform all of the austenite to martensite. This is called the **critical cooling rate.** If for some reason cooling during transformation is stopped, then transformation cannot continue. The temperature at which martensite first begins to form is designated by M_s. The temperature at which martensite is completely formed is designated by M_f. However, for

---

[16] This is so because the atoms of austenite are more densely packed than the atoms of martensite.

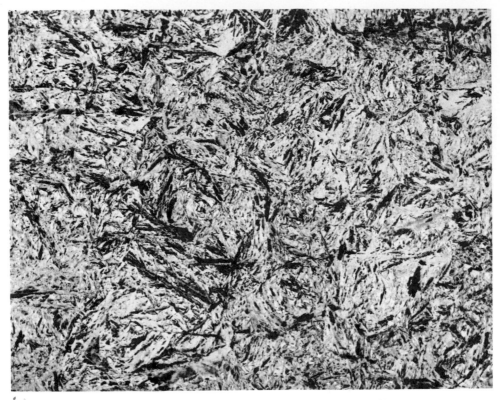

Figure 2-6 The structure called martensite, × 500. [Courtesy of Buechler, Ltd.]

any one alloy, the cooling rate has no effect on temperature M_s or in preventing the formation of martensite.

Martensite is the agent that contributes to the hardness to steel. It is apparent that sufficient carbon must be present to produce enough martensite. Thus, the extent to which a steel may be hardened depends solely on its carbon content. Steels with less than 0.35% carbon are not considered commercially hardenable.[17] Steels with a carbon content of 0.35–0.70% (these are called medium carbon steels) display the greatest percentage increase in hardness. As a result, the medium carbon steels are usually considered for machine elements because they can be hardened while retaining their ductility.

Higher carbon steels are also readily hardenable but, due to distortion, warping, or cracking as a result of rapid cooling, are considered for use in special cases only.

The process of cooling is called **quenching** and the rapidity with which heat is removed depends upon the quenching medium. A good quenching

---

[17] It should not be overlooked that alpha martensite will nevertheless be formed with a very high cooling rate.

medium should initially permit very rapid cooling and then reduce the cooling rate at lower temperatures to minimize distortion. In order of decreasing severity of distortion and cracking, the following quenching media are most often used: (1) a 10% salt solution in water, (2) plain tap water, (3) liquid salts, (4) soluble oil and water, (5) oil, and (6) air.

After quenching, the martensite is so hard and brittle that it is of little practical use. To relieve the internal stresses brought on by quenching, reduce the hardness, and improve both the toughness and ductility, steel is subjected to a process called **tempering.** The tempering process involves reheating the unstable martensite to any temperature below Ac_1, holding it at this temperature for a fixed time period (for example, $\frac{1}{2}$ hr) and then cooling the steel in air to room temperature. Reheating to 150–400°F, for example, will relieve internal stresses but will reduce the hardness only by a small amount.[18] Further increases in tempering temperature produce more strain free steel with lower hardness and greater ductility.

Figure 2-7 shows schematically the various micrographic structural changes possible for tempering at different range levels of temperature. Figure 2-7 also shows that, if a hardened steel is tempered to a point just below Ac_1 and held there for an extended time, the cementite forms globular or spheroidal shapes. Such a structure is known as **spheroidite.** It is produced not only as a sequence in the hardening-tempering cycle described above but is also an established method of annealing (still to be discussed). For illustrations of the effect of tempering a steel, refer to Table A-4 of Appendix A. From Table A-4, we can readily see that, as the tempering temperature increases, the tensile strength, yield strength, and hardness decrease while the reduction of area, elongation, and Izod impact values increase.

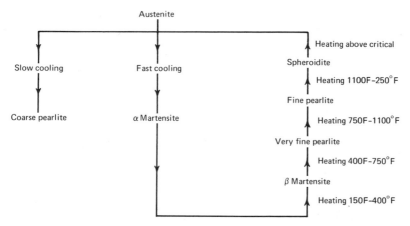

Figure 2-7 Schematic flow diagram for hardening and tempering steel. Alpha (α) martensite is unstable and beta (β) martensite is stable.

[18] At 200°F, the unstable martensite (that is, fresh martensite) becomes stable martensite. This is sometimes referred to as tempered martensite.

SECTION 2-7

Isothermal Transformation Diagrams

The discussion in Section 2-6 briefly reviewed the phase change that takes place when austenite is transformed to martensite by very rapid quenching under equilibrium conditions. However, the time-temperature combination at which the austenite is transformed can markedly affect the structure resulting from this temperature. Thus, the main objective of heat treating (to develop desirable mechanical properties) may not be achieved. In other words, we may ask, "What will the final structure and its mechanical properties be if we allow transformation to begin at temperatures lower than those at equilibrium (that is, at subcritical temperatures) and then quench the metal?"

This question is best answered by the use of the isothermal transformation (I-T) diagrams (also referred to as the TTT or S diagrams).[19] Figure 2-8 is typical of an I-T diagram. These diagrams are obtained by cutting small specimens from a bar of steel with a specific carbon and/or alloying content. The first S curve from the left is where transformation begins and the extreme right curve is where the transformation ends. The form of all diagrams is very much alike, except for a eutectoid carbon steel from which the middle heavy line in the upper portion of the diagram is missing.

With few exceptions the diagrams shift to the right (that is, increased time) with increasing alloy content or grain size of austenite at temperatures higher than about 900°F. This is the point where the curve bends back on itself and is called the "knee" or the "nose" of the beginning curve. The dotted portion of the curves indicates some uncertainty as to the exact curvature. M_s, M_{50} and M_{90} respectively signify the beginning of the formation of martensite, the 50% formation of martensite, and the 90% formation of martensite. Note that not all I-T diagrams have calculated values for the per cent of martensite formed. Many diagrams have values for M based upon actual experiment.

Starting from the top of Figure 2-8 we see that, as the subcritical temperature falls, the time at which transformation begins is also reduced along with the time of transformation. The shortest time of initiating and completing transformation is at the "knee" of the curve. With a further reduction of the subcritical temperature, both the start of transformation and time for transformation increase. The right hand side of Figure 2-8 shows the structure to which the austenite has changed and the temperature range at which these changes occurred. This information does not normally appear on I-T diagrams but was put here for clarification purposes only. Actually, the diagrams indicate each phase constituent by an appropriate letter and

---

[19] TTT stands for time-temperature-transformation diagrams. S diagrams is a term also used because the shape of the curves resembles the letter S. A most excellent and complete set of such curves may be obtained from the U.S. Steel Corporation.

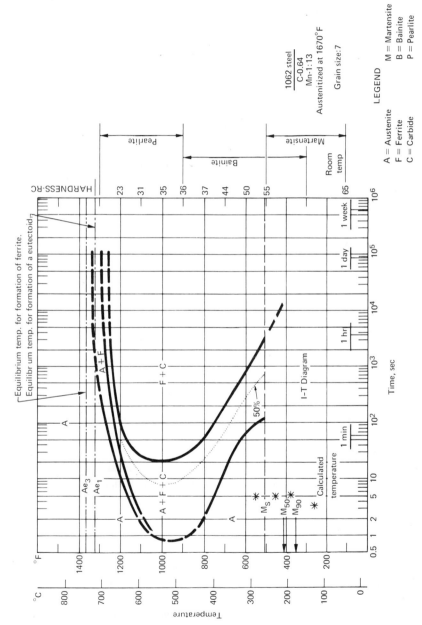

Figure 2-8 Isothermal transformation diagram for 1062 steel. [Courtesy of U.S. Steel Corporation.]

35

legend as can be seen in Figure 2-8. Notice that the I-T curves are asymptotic to the 1333°F line. This implies that it would require an infinite time to convert austenite to pearlite. Such a concept is in full agreement with the transformation criteria of established transformations in the iron-carbon diagram, namely, that equilibrium conditions exist.

Keep in mind that austenite, once completely transformed at a particular temperature, will not form another phase when cooled to a lower temperature. If we wish, for example, to form bainite[20] or martensite with the 1062 steel in Figure 2-8, it is obvious that the austenite must be rapidly cooled to about 500°F within 0.75 sec and held at this temperature for about 1 hr to make certain of complete transformation. Any time less than 1 hr would end the transformation in the $A + F + C$ region. Cooling, then, to room temperature would change a percentage (depending on time in $A + F + C$ region) of austenite to complete martensite, with the remainder being lower bainite.

Two questions become apparent in this example. (1) "How can cooling from, let us say, 1500 to 500°F be accomplished within 0.75 sec?" (2) "Is 1 hr too long a period of time to wait for complete transformation?" The answer to these questions is primarily a design decision. If the material is very thin (for example, needles of a needle bearing) and a very rapid quenching medium such as ice water or iced brine is used, it might be possible to quench to 500°F in 0.75 sec. Such rapid quenching (for 1062 steel) is necessary to avoid touching the "knee" or entering the I-T curve at 950°F. Should the cooling curve touch the "knee" (or enter the $A + F + C$ region), some pearlite would be formed. This is what we do not want if we wish to form only lower bainite and martensite.

If a large component is to be hardened to the bainite-martensite range, it is therefore unlikely that it can be accomplished without the formation of some pearlite. Whether the resulting mechanical properties are satisfactory to the designer is a decision only he can make after the consideration of many factors.[21] The answer to the question of maintaining 500°F for 1 hr depends upon the equipment available and whether the time will affect the rate of production. One aspect the designer can investigate to mitigate such problems is to seek out another carbon steel or, if necessary, an alloy steel where the "knee" of the I-T diagram would be further to the right on the time scale. Thus, the I-T diagrams provide the designer with a vast choice of steels having both the strength and toughness to satisfy the requirements of his design.

Because we can readily measure the temperature-time coordinates of a steel specimen as it is being cooled (regardless of the quenching medium),

---

[20] Bainite (formerly called troosite) is formed between 900 and 700°F and resembles pearlite. In this region it is called upper or feathery bainite. At a lower range of 700 to 500°F, the transformation is called lower or acicular bainite and begins to resemble martensite.

[21] Strength, cost, application, environment, quantity produced, and so on.

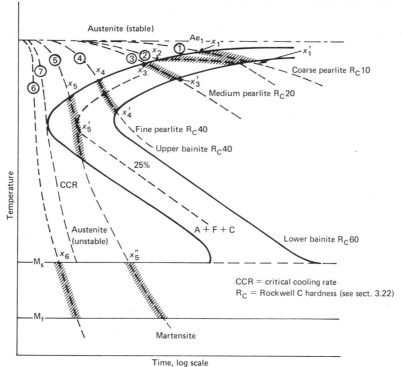

Figure 2-9 A hypothetical I-T diagram of a eutectoid steel with superimposed cooling curves. The circled numbers distinguish the different rates of cooling and the cross-hatching indicates the transformation. [S. H. Avner: *Introduction to Physics Metallurgy.* McGraw-Hill Book Co., Inc., New York, 1964.]

a more meaningful and descriptive I-T diagram is possible. All that is necessary is to superimpose the temperature-time cooling values on the I-T diagram. Figure 2-9 shows such a superimposition on a hypothetical I-T diagram. The cooling curves are numbered 1 to 7 and each represents an increased rate of cooling.

Curve 1 has the slowest cooling rate, beginning its transformation at x_1 and completing it at x_1'. Although the temperature change during transformation was small, the time of transformation was relatively long. The transformed material structure is coarse pearlite (a soft and ductile material) and it will retain this structure as it is cooled to room temperature from x_1' regardless of the cooling rate. Curve 1 is typical of conventional annealing. Curve 2 is also an annealing process. However, the material is first cooled more rapidly to a selected temperature, x_2, and held within the transformation area with little temperature change. The result is a uniformly distributed and somewhat finer pearlite structure.

Curve 3 is typical of what is termed normalizing[22] and is performed at a somewhat faster cooling rate than annealing (curve 1). The resulting structure

[22] This term is explained in Section 2-9.

is a medium pearlite. Curve 4, having a faster cooling rate than curve 3, produces a fine pearlite structure.

Curve 5 is one of great interest since it results in a mixed microstructure and is tangent to a 25 % $A + F + C$ line within the transformation region. At x_5, the fine pearlite begins to form and completes its transformation at x'_5. At this point, only 25 % of the unstable austenite has been transformed to fine pearlite. This leaves 75 % yet to be transformed. Inspection of the cross hatching below point x'_5 indicates that the cooling curve is cutting lines (not shown in Figure 2-9) with less than 25 % pearlite. Thus, no further transformation will take place below point x'_5 until the cooling reaches x''_5 at which point the 75 % austenite begins to convert to martensite completing its change at line M_f. The resulting structure consists of 25 % pearlite within a 75 % martensite matrix.

Curve 6 represents an extremely rapid quenching which, upon completion, shows the whole microstructure to be martensitic. Curve 7, which is tangent to the "knee" of the transformation curve, is the limiting cooling rate for producing a completely martensitic structure. This limiting cooling rate is the critical cooling rate mentioned earlier in this section. A well-explained and detailed discussion of I-T diagrams, cooling rates, and so on, can be obtained from reference [2]. It is also of importance to mention that cooling curves 4, 5, 6, and 7 are usually followed by tempering to relieve internal stresses.

Martempering and austempering

With the advent of I-T diagrams, it has become possible to "map out" new heat treating paths. Two such paths are known as martempering and austempering. These processes are shown schematically in Figures 2-10 and 2-11.

In **martempering,** the steel is quenched (usually in a molten salt bath) to a temperature slightly above M_s. It is held in the bath until all of the steel's cross section is at the bath temperature. The steel is then taken from the bath, allowed to cool in air to form martensite, and is subsequently tempered as shown in Figure 2-10. The purpose of martempering is to prevent distortion and any tendency towards quench cracking. Large steel components that must be quenched to a high hardness are very prone to these undesirable characteristics. If the quenching rate is not fast enough, the cooling curve may not miss the "knee" completely, resulting in some bainite in the final structure. Nevertheless, distortion and the tendency towards cracking will have been greatly minimized.

Austempering is a hardening process where the resulting microstructure is both hard and tough (bainite) and is accomplished without the need of tempering. Referring to Figure 2-11, we see that the steel is again cooled from above the Ae_3 line by means of a rapid quench in a molten salt bath to a temperature just above M_s. While still in the bath, the steel is isothermally transformed into bainite, after which it is allowed to air cool. The resulting

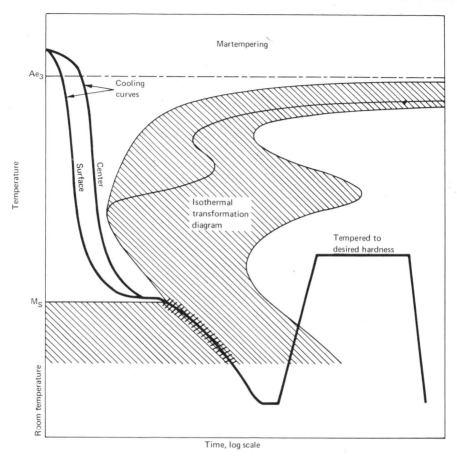

Figure 2-10 Schematic chart illustrating relationship of martempering to a typical I-T diagram. [Courtesy U.S. Steel Corporation.]

bainite is, of course, hard but tougher than martensite. By selecting the isothermal temperature, it is possible to achieve a variety of hardness-toughness combinations without tempering. The process is usually limited to small diameter parts because the temperature of the bath retards the cooling rate.

SECTION 2-8

Hardenability

Hardenability can be defined as the characteristic of a steel that determines its depth and uniformity of hardness resulting from quenching. As we learned in the previous section, isothermal transformation can be retarded (that is, there is a tendency to move the I-T curves to the right) by the addition

Chapter 2: Metallurgical Properties of Engineering Materials

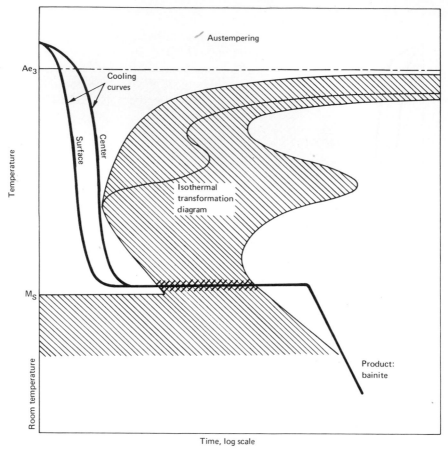

Figure 2-11 Schematic chart illustrating relationship of austempering to a typical I-T diagram. [Courtesy U.S. Steel Corporation.]

of an alloying agent(s) or by increasing the grain size of the austenite. Thus, even relatively slow cooling rates can produce a completely martensitic structure at room temperature. Large grain size is generally not recommended because the hardened steel looses toughness upon subsequent quenching. Also, large grains are prone to cracking or distortion when quenched.

To this point, hardenability has been discussed (including prior sections) in terms of the various transformations required to achieve different levels of hardness. But what of the depth of hardness in a steel specimen? All things being equal, can we expect the same hardness throughout the cross section of two steel bars of different diameters when both are similarly heat treated? The answer, as expected, is no! In fact, because each grade of carbon or alloy steel can range within a specified chemical composition, many steel bars with the same diameters and subjected to like heat treatments will have different hardness values both for their surfaces and interiors.

Other factors affecting hardenability are the size-shape relationship of the component and its surface condition. Quenching operations are, in reality, heat transfer phenomena; therefore, the rate at which the heat is extracted depends upon mass, surface area, metal conductivity, surface heat transfer coefficient, and temperature difference between the metal, and quenching medium. Obviously, heat will be more rapidly extracted from those components having high surface to mass ratios and no scale to act as an insulator.

Jominy test [3]

For a designer, the task of specifying a hardness is problematical, considering the complex shapes and variety of steels he encounters. He has, at least, to be reasonably sure that his requirements will be met. Therefore, various tests for measuring hardenability have been devised. One test, among many, has emerged with the widest acceptance. It is called the Jominy test [3] (also referred to as the end-quench hardenability test) and has been standardized by the ASTM (for example, A255–48T), the SAE and the AISI. In the test, all parameters affecting the depth of hardening are constant from specimen to specimen. Because the only variation in the specimens is the chemical composition, hardenability can be indicated solely by the depth of hardening.

The test specimen is a 1-in. diameter bar, 4 in. in length, having a larger diameter shoulder at one end in order that it may be hung vertically in a test fixture.[23] The bar is heated to a proper austenizing temperature in an inert atmosphere (to avoid scaling), removed from the furnace, and hung vertically in the test fixture. A stream of water at $75 \pm 5°$F is then impinged on the lower end of the hanging test specimen. The nozzle diameter is $\frac{1}{2}$ in. and the pressure head is such that the water column is $2\frac{1}{2}$ in. with the nozzle in a vertical position. When the apparatus is assembled, the end of the specimen is $\frac{1}{2}$ in. above the nozzle opening. As a result, upon hitting the end of the specimen, the effluent water forms a spherical surface. Figure 2-12 shows a test bar in its fixture as it is being quenched.

After a 10-min quenching, the bar is removed and two parallel longitudinal flats are ground on opposite sides. The grinding operation is performed to a depth of 0.015 in. per side; Rockwell hardness measurements (see Section 3-22) are made on these flats in $\frac{1}{16}$-in. spacing from the quenched end. The hardness readings versus the distance from the end of the bar are then plotted. Representative curves for several steels are shown in Figure 2-13.

A steel with good hardenability is one in which the hardness does not fall too rapidly with the distance from the quenched end. Such steel is called a "deep-hardening" steel. Figure 2-13 shows 4340 to be a deep-hardening steel, whereas 4620 obviously cannot be so classified. Thus, 4620 is called a "shallow-hardening" steel. Because the test specimen has experienced a gradation of cooling rates along the bar from rapid quenching at the water

[23] Notice that all specimens have fixed surface to mass ratios since every specimen has the same dimensions.

Figure 2-12 End-quench hardenability test bar in quenching fixture. [Courtesy U.S. Steel Corporation.]

end to air cooling at the other end and because the cooling rate is also independent of the type (that is, the composition) of the steel, it is possible to convert the distance and hardness from the quenched end to the same hardness at the center of an equivalent diameter steel bar subjected to different quenching media.[24] As a result of the Jominy test data,[25] we can confidently specify the hardness of a large component or make a choice in selecting an economical steel.

Because Jominy testing has proved reliable, it has become possible to select a steel by hardenability with parameters like chemical composition, grain size, and so on, being of lesser importance. The AISI and the SAE jointly have established hardenability bands for most alloy steels. These bands are minimum and maximum Jominy hardenability curves and have been determined from hundreds of heats of each grade of steel. Steels that are specified and purchased on this basis are designated by the suffix letter H. Figure 2-13 shows 4140 H to be a steel that may be purchased on the basis of a hardenability band. The H steels are guaranteed to meet minimum and maximum hardenability. These steels should not be confused with the minimum-maximum hardenability ranges possible with steels that are defined by chemical composition limits. Figure 2-14 shows this distinction for 4140 steel.

To use the curves in Figure 2-14, it is necessary to know the hardness at some interior point of a particular bar of steel. Such curves may also be used to find the carbon content (by using the relationship between carbon and hardness) of a satisfactorily quenched and tempered steel. There are

[24] The method of conversion is discussed in reference [3].

[25] See *U.S.S. Carilloy Steels*, The United States Steel Corporation, Pittsburg, Pa.

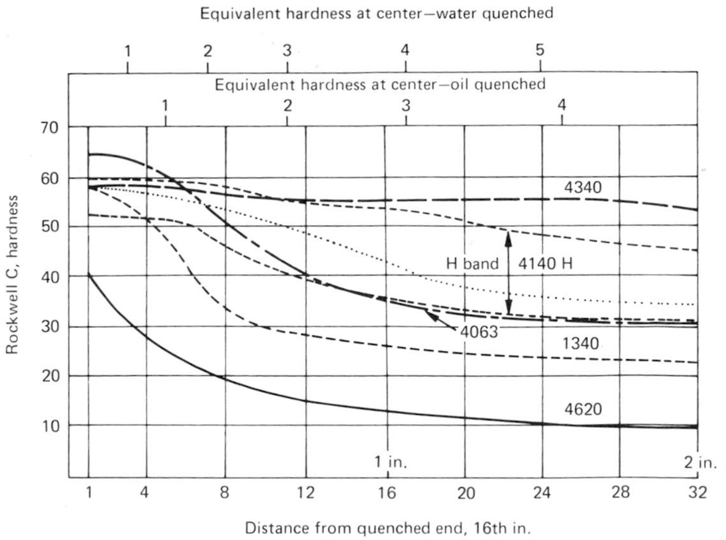

Figure 2-13 Hardenability curves. The materials shown were selected to show differences. Notice that the hardness of AISI 4340 holds up well with depth, that the higher carbon 4063 has the hardest surface, that the same carbon steels, 4340 and 1340, have practically the same surface hardness (at $\frac{1}{16}$ in.), and that the low carbon 4620 (actual 0.17% C) has lower hardness all the way. The individual lines are typical actual test values. The H band shown for 4140 is suitable for specifications. The top coordinates are defined by this example: a 2-in., oil-quenched piece of 4063 has a hardness at its center of $R_c = 42$. [Courtesy Bethlehem Steel Corporation.]

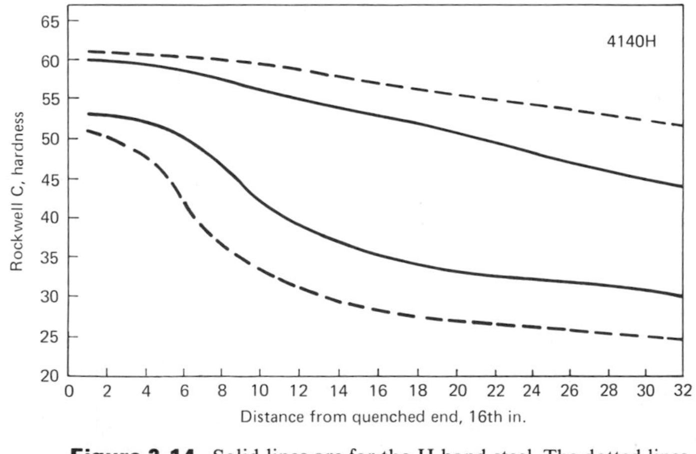

Figure 2-14 Solid lines are for the H band steel. The dotted lines are 4340 steel based on the limits of chemical composition. [*Metals Handbook*, 8th ed., Vol. 1. American Society of Metals, Metals Park, Ohio, 1961.]

Chapter 2: Metallurgical Properties of Engineering Materials

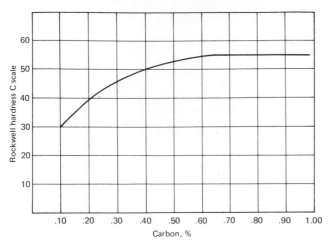

Figure 2-15 Minimum as-quenched hardness for obtaining best properties after tempering as a function of carbon content. [Courtesy U.S. Steel Corporation.]

available a whole series of curves[26] for materials other than those shown in Figure 2-14. Also, there are curves of Rockwell hardness versus carbon content for different percentages of martensite formations. Figure 2-15 is representative of these curves and is perhaps the most helpful. It can be used by the inexperienced designer in the selection of a steel that will be of sufficient hardness after quenching and tempering to yield optimum properties. To see how one might employ these curves, we refer to Example 2-1.

Example 2-1. Because all the other round bar stock in a metal wire straightening and cutting machine is already 1340, the material of the main drive shaft is to be changed to 1340 steel. A saving could be realized if the shaft were made of the same material. The shaft is subjected to a bending load that varies continuously from 0 to 50,000 psi.
Specify: the maximum diameter of a through hardened shaft and its hardness.

Solution: In order to find a solution, we must anticipate some of the equations and data of Sections 3.22 and 3.24. We therefore have

$$S_u \approx 500 \times \text{Brinell hardness number (BHN)} \qquad (3\text{-}12)$$

$$S_n' = 0.5S_u \qquad (3\text{-}13)$$

therefore

$$S_n' = (250)(\text{BHN})$$

where S_n' = the endurance limit in psi, and S_u = the ultimate strength in psi. Since it is anticipated that the shaft size will exceed $\frac{1}{2}$ in. in diameter, a size correction factor of 0.85 will be used (see Section 3-26). Thus we now have

$$S_n' = (0.85)(250)(\text{BHN}) = 215\,\text{BHN}$$

[26] *U.S.S. Carilloy Steels*, United States Steel Corporation, Pittsburg, Pa.

If we assume a factor of safety of 50% (see Section 1-3), the endurance limit becomes

$$1.5S'_n = 215\,\text{BHN}$$

We can now solve for the BHN value

$$\text{BHN} = \frac{1.5 \times (50{,}000)}{215} = 349$$

From Figure 3-17, we get a Rockwell C hardness number of about 38 for a BHN = 349. Turning now to Figure 2-15, we note that a steel with a carbon content of no less than 0.18% carbon would produce the desired hardness after it has been quenched and tempered. From Figure 2-13, it can be seen that, if we use the 1340 steel, it exceeds our minimum requirement of 0.18% carbon. Also, an oil-quenched shaft $1\frac{1}{4}$ in. in diameter or a water-quenched shaft $1\frac{3}{4}$ in. in diameter can be through-hardened to a Rockwell C of 38. ●[27]

It is important to state at this point that the problems of shaft diameter and stress have in no way been treated in Example 2-1. All that was demonstrated was the feasibility of achieving a through-hardness of Rockwell C = 38 for two possible diameter shafts made of 1340 steel. Interestingly, according to Figure 2-13, the alloy steel 4620 would not have satisfied the requirements of the problem.

SECTION 2-9

Heat Treatment Definitions[28]

For the purpose of continuity, the following heat treating terms have been assembled in this one section. Some of the terms have already been mentioned, but are presented once again for completeness of definition. Other terms are defined and explained here for the first time.

Aging. The change in a metal by which its structure recovers from an unstable condition produced by quenching (quench aging) or by cold working (strain aging). The change in structure is due to the precipitation of one of the constituents from a saturated solid solution and results in a material that is stronger and harder but usually less ductile. This type of aging takes place slowly at room temperature; it may be accelerated by a slight increase in temperature. The process is then called precipitation hardening. (Also see stress relieving.)

Age hardening. The same as aging.

Annealing. A process involving heating and cooling applied usually to induce softening. The term is also used to cover treatments intended to

---

[27] The symbol ● designates end of Solution.

[28] Some of the definitions and descriptions are based on material in the *Machinery's Handbook*, 15th ed., The Industrial Press, New York. All of these terms have been adopted by the American Foundrymen's Association (AFA), the American Society for Metals (ASM), the American Society for Testing Materials (ASTM), and the Society of Automotive Engineers (SAE).

remove stresses, alter mechanical or physical properties, produce a definite microstructure, and remove gases. Certain specific heat treatments of iron-base alloys covered by the term annealing are black annealing, blue annealing, box annealing, bright annealing, full annealing, graphitizing, malleablizing, and process annealing.

Annealing, black. A process of box annealing iron-base alloy sheets after hot rolling, shearing, and pickling.[29] The process does not impart a black color to the product if properly done. The name originated in the appearance of the hot-rolled material before pickling and annealing.

Annealing, blue. A process of softening iron-base alloys in the form of hot-rolled sheet, in which the sheet is heated in the open furnace to a temperature within the transformation range and cooled in air. The formation of a bluish oxide on the surface is incidental.

Annealing, box. A process of annealing that, to prevent oxidation, is carried out in a suitable closed metal container with or without packing material. The charge is usually heated slowly to a temperature below, but sometimes above or within, the transformation temperature range and cooled slowly. It is also called **close annealing** or **pot annealing.**

Annealing, bright. A process of annealing that is usually carried out in a controlled furnace atmosphere so that surface oxidation is reduced to a minimum and the surface remains relatively bright.

Annealing, flame. A process in which the surface of an iron-base alloy is softened by localized heat applied by a high temperature flame.

Annealing, full. A softening process in which an iron-base alloy is heated to a temperature slightly above Ac_3 and, after being held for the proper time at this temperature, slowly cooled below the transformation range. The parts are ordinarily allowed to cool slowly in the furnace, although they may be removed from the furnace and cooled in some medium that assures a slow rate of cooling.

Annealing, inverse. A heat treatment, analogous to precipitation hardening, usually applied to cast iron to increase its hardness and strength.

Annealing, process. A heat treatment that is applied for the purpose of softening the component for further cold working in those cases where previous cold work has caused severe stresses and brittleness. The iron-base alloy is heated to a temperature close to, but below, the lower limit of the transformation range and is subsequently cooled. This process produces less scaling than full annealing.

Austempering. This is a hardening process consisting of quenching an iron-base alloy from above the transformation range in an isothermal salt bath ranging in temperature from 300 to 1100°F. The bath temperature depends upon the material and is maintained slightly above the M_s temperature forming bainite. The process is generally reserved for small components.

---

[29] Pickling is the removal of oxides from metal surfaces by dipping in chemically reactive solutions or by electrochemical methods.

Bluing. A treatment of the surface of iron-base alloys, usually in the form of sheet or strip, on which, by the action of air or steam at a suitable temperature, a thin blue oxide film is formed on the initially scale-free surface as a means of improving appearance and resistance to corrosion. This term is also used to denote a heat treatment of springs after fabrication in order to reduce the internal stress created by coiling and forming.

Burnt steel. A term applied to a permanently damaged metal by heating close to its melting point or by intergranular oxidation. This damage is sometimes caused by incorrect grinding, which results in the discoloration of the workpiece due to the heat.

Carbonitriding. A surface hardening process (see case hardening).

Case hardening. A process where the surface layer (or **case**) of an iron-base alloy is made substantially harder than the metal's interior core. Case hardening can be separated into two classifications. The first, which includes carburizing, nitriding, carbonitriding, and cyaniding, is based upon the diffusion of carbon or ammonia gas to some depth of the steel surface. The second class consists of flame hardening or induction hardening. Here the change of surface temperature as compared to the core, without the addition of other materials and the subsequent cooling, hardens the case and not the core of the steel. Figure 2-16 compares the range of case depths possible by the methods of diffusion.

Carburizing. A process where carbon is added to a solid iron-base alloy by heating it to about the 1600–1700°F range while it is in contact with carbonaceous material, which may be a solid, liquid, or gas. The depth of case depends on the time of exposure to the carbon atmosphere. After a sufficient time period, the metal is quenched and then tempered (for example, 300–450°F) to produce the desired case hardness and core

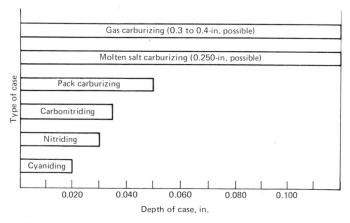

Figure 2-16 General ranges in case depth possible by different methods of case hardening. [R. W. Bolz: *Production Processes, Their Influence on Design.* The Penton Publishing Co., Cleveland, Ohio, 1956.]

toughness. Not all steels can be carburized. Steels with no higher than 0.20% carbon (there are one or two with about 0.30–0.32% C) are so treated. Such steels are known as carburizing grades. (See Table A-3 in Appendix A for a partial list of carburizing grade steels. The table also indicates the case and core properties.) The case structure is hypereutectoid, whereas the core changes from a eutectoid steel to a hypo-eutectoid steel as the depth increases.

Solid pack (or box) carburizing places the steel part in contact with carbonaceous materials such as charcoal, burned bone, burned peach pits, coke, coal, and so on.

Gas carburizing takes place when the part is heated in a gaseous atmosphere like methane (natural gas), propane, ethane, or butane. The process, which takes place in a horizontal rotary oven, is usually used for quantity production. The method is well adapted to small parts such as ball and roller bearings, chain links, small axles, bolts, and so on.

Liquid carburizing requires that the part be placed in a molten salt bath (for example, sodium cyanide) where the steel absorbs carbon in its surface; the depth of absorption again depends upon the time of immersion. The advantages of liquid baths include rapid action, uniform carburization, minimum distortion, and elimination of the packing and unpacking required when carbonaceous mixtures are used. In selective carburizing, the portions of the part not to be carburized are copper plated.

Carburization is generally used on those parts, such as gears, cams, gages, and so on, that are subject to wear. The biggest disadvantage resulting from carburizing is that the part usually tends to warp. However, the endurance limit is usually positively affected (see Section 3-30, Carburizing).

Nitriding. A process in which the machined and heat treated part is placed in a nitrogen atmosphere (ammonia gas) in an air tight box and heated to about 950–1000°F. After a period of exposure to the ammonia, the steel is slowly cooled. The case is hardened by iron nitride, which is formed by the released nitrogen combining with the iron. As a result, quenching is not necessary and therefore nitrided steels are not prone to warping.

Nitriding is mostly applied to certain alloy steels that contain elements such as aluminum, chromium, molybdenum, or vanadium. These alloy steels nitride better than carbon steels. Nitralloy steel is the name given to a special group of such steels (for example, Nitralloy N, a product of the Nitralloy Corporation). However, some carbon steels can also be treated (for example, 4340). The core properties of the part can be imparted by previous heat treatment and are not affected by drawing temperatures up to 950°F. The Nitralloy steels are readily machinable in both the heat treated and annealed state. Prior to nitriding, the part must be annealed to relieve stress due to rolling, forging, or machining. Those components not requiring heat treatment should be machined to the dimensions required.

Nitriding produces an extremely hard surface (for example, Nitralloy N nitrided at 970°F has a hardness of 780 on the Brinell scale) and is excellent in resisting wear. The process also has beneficial effects on the endurance limit of the component (see Section 3-30, Nitriding) and improves corrosion resistance and the tendency to gall (that is, seize).

Nitriding does have some disadvantages: the higher cost of material, the procedure is more critical than others, the annealing of parts necessary before nitriding, and the limitation of machining to grinding only (a procedure not recommended unless very carefully performed).

Typical applications for nitriding are cams, camshafts, cylinder liners, gears, king pins, piston pins, pistons, pump sleeves, pump shafts, valve seats, splines, wear plates, wire forming rollers, and so on.

Carbonitriding. A process of case hardening an iron-base alloy in which both carbon and nitrogen are simultaneously absorbed by heating in a gaseous atmosphere of suitable composition (for example, hydrocarbons and nitrogen or molten salt mixtures containing carbonaceous materials and nitrides). This is usually followed by either quenching or slow cooling as required. For example, an atmosphere containing about 15% ammonia in the carburizing gas can be hardened without quenching. With small amounts of ammonia (for example, 1%), quenching is required.

Cyaniding. A process of case hardening a *machined* steel part by the simultaneous absorption of carbon and nitrogen by heating in a cyanide bath. The bath temperature is between 1450 and 1650°F and the bath consists of sodium cyanide (NaCN) in liquid salt mixture. The percentage of cyanide varies over a wide range, depending upon the steel used and the properties required. However, the most frequently used composition consists of 30% sodium cyanide, 40% sodium carbonate (Na_2CO_3) and 30% sodium chloride (NaCl). This mixture is most stable and is used for continuous operations. After immersion in the cyaniding bath for the proper time period, the part is quenched in a suitable medium. The process is intended to produce a thin but very hard outer surface on low carbon steels. The hardness is known as superficial hardness and, because the surface becomes quite brittle, it does not have high shock resisting qualities. Although a thin layer is produced, the surface is quite wear resistant.

Flame hardening. A process of surface hardening a steel by heating to above the transformation temperature range by means of a high temperature flame and then quenching in caustic, brine, water, oil, or air. The quenching medium is usually sprayed on the surface but, in some cases, the part is immersed in the medium. This hardening method is especially used for large parts (for example, steel forgings and castings, which must be finish machined prior to heat treatment) or for parts that are irregular in size or shape and cannot be readily placed in a furnace or bath. The source of heat is an oxyacetylene torch, which rapidly heats the steel surface. The torch may have multiple flame tips and also be equipped with holes for spraying the quenching medium.

This method is not case hardening in its truest sense, since no diffusion takes place. Medium carbon and many low alloy steels as well can be hardened in this manner. Steels with a carbon content of between 0.40 and 0.45% have excellent core properties after such treatment. Higher carbon steels (for example greater than 0.60%) can also be flame hardened, but great care must be taken upon quenching to avoid cracking. For large quantity production such as the hardening of gears, splines, shafts, and so on, special machines are used.

Induction hardening. This process of hardening involves placing the part in a high frequency electrical field that can vary between 500 and 15,000,000 cycles per second (cps) and that causes the surface of the component to be heated above the transformation range to a fixed depth. The part is subsequently quenched in oil or water, but caustic brine or air are also used. Induction hardening is particularly suitable to parts that require localized hardening or controlled depth of hardening and is also suitable to irregularly shaped parts such as cams, gear teeth, or shafts that require uniform surface hardening around their contours. The method is principally applied to 0.35–0.55% carbon steels. Cast irons and malleable irons can also be surface hardened by this method.

Advantages of induction hardening are (1) a short heating and quenching cycle, (2) absence of the tendency to produce oxidation or decarburization, (3) control of hardening depth and area, (4) close regulation of the degree of hardness, (5) minimization of warping and distortion, and (6) the possibility of replacing higher cost alloy steels with carbon steels. Figure 2-17 shows how the depth of hardness of a gear tooth may be controlled by induction hardening.

Controlled cooling. A term used to describe a process by which a steel part is cooled from an elevated temperature. Cooling is usually from the final hot-forming operation and is performed in a predetermined manner to avoid hardening or cracking externally or internally.

Cores. (1) The interior portion of a steel which, after case hardening, is substantially softer than the surface layer or case (see case hardening). (2) The term core is also used to designate the relatively soft central portion of certain hardened tool steels.

Cyaniding. See case hardening.

Decarburization. The loss of carbon from the surface of a steel because of heating in an atmosphere (for example, hydrogen, oxygen) that reacts with carbon. This loss can occur during heat treatment, hot rolling, or forging. Decarburization can be deleterious in two ways. The first is that a maximum hardness cannot be achieved in heat treatment. The second, and of greater importance, is that a steel with a decarburized surface has poor fatigue resistant properties and is likely to develop cracks on its surface.

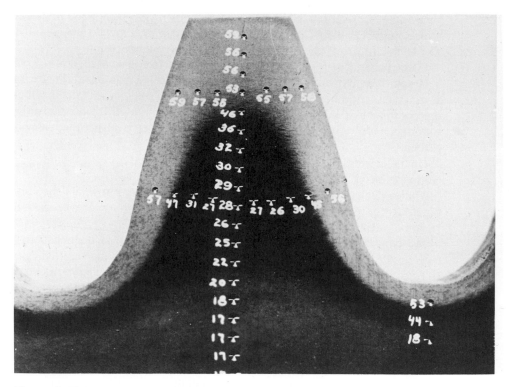

Figure 2-17 Hardness of a gear tooth, induction hardened. Observe the hardness close to the surface and near the middle of the base of the tooth (where the lower hardness indicates a tough core). Hardness readings are Rockwell C. [Courtesy Tocco Div., Park-Ohio Industries.]

The biggest source of decarburized steel is that processed at the mill during fabrication. To correct for this deficiency, many steel mills will supply carburized bars in which the surface carbon is restored as part of the final processing. This remedy can also be instituted by the end user. Sometimes, the mill "bark" is removed by grinding, but subsequent heat treatment may again cause decarburization unless the treatment is performed in a controlled nonoxidizing atmosphere. In addition, the effects of grinding may be equally damaging to steels subjected to fatigue. Nevertheless, some improvements have been cited. For example, automotive leaf springs that retained decarburized surface failed when subjected to repeated loading between 50,000 and 75,000 psi, depending upon the surface finish. On the other hand, springs that had been ground down below the decarburized surface and then carefully polished withstood a repeated stress of 125,000 psi indefinitely [6]. This same reference cited 30,000 psi as the endurance limit for decarburized springs in torsion and 115,000 psi when the decarburized layer had been removed.

Drawing. Drawing is synonymous with tempering, which is the preferred terminology. Drawing can be confused with drawing a metal through a die. The term tempering, therefore, is preferred to avoid confusion.

Flame hardening. A surface hardening process (see case hardening).

Graphitizing. An annealing process applied to some iron-base alloys, such as cast iron, and some steels with high carbon and silicon contents, in which the combined carbon is wholly or partially precipitated from solution in rounded nodules as free or graphitic carbon. This is also called **temper carbon.**

Homogenizing. A high temperature heat treating process intended to eliminate or decrease chemical segregation by diffusion.

Malleabilizing. A process of annealing white cast iron in which the combined carbon is wholly or partially transformed to graphite or free carbon. In some cases, the carbon is completely removed.

Martempering. A hardening process where the steel is quenched in a molten salt bath to a temperature just above that at which martensite begins to form. It is held at this temperature until temperature equalization occurs throughout the part, and then is followed by air cooling.

Nitriding. A surface hardening process (see case hardening).

Normalizing. A softening process in which a steel is heated to about 100°F above the upper critical temperature and then is allowed to cool in still air at room temperature. The procedure is intended to produce steel in a uniform, unstressed condition of small grain size and refinement that permits proper response to further heat treatments. Normalizing is particularly important for steel forgings that are to be subsequently heat treated. Depending upon the material composition, normalizing may or may not leave the steel sufficiently soft for machining with the tools available. Sometimes, annealing for machinability is preceded by normalizing. This combined treatment, frequently called a double anneal, produces a result superior to a simple anneal.

Overheated. A metal is overheated if it has been exposed to an unduly high temperature and develops an undesirable coarse grain but is not damaged. The grain structure can be corrected by suitable heat treatment, by mechanical work, or by a combination of the two. In this respect, it is different from a burnt metal.

Preheating. (1) A general term used to describe a heating preliminary to some further thermal (for example, welding) or mechanical treatment. (2) As applied to tool steel, the term preheating describes a process in which the steel is heated slowly and uniformly below the hardening temperature and is then transferred to a furnace where the temperature is substantially above the preheating temperature.

Precipitation hardening. A process of hardening an alloy in which a constituent precipitates from a supersaturated solution. Also see aging.

Quenching. The rapid cooling of a metal from an elevated temperature by injecting or spraying the metal with a suitable quenching medium for the purpose of increasing hardness. (Also see austempering and martempering.) If only certain portions of a component are to be hardened, then a **differential quenching** is used.

Spheroidizing. Any process of heating or cooling that produces a rounded or globular form of carbide. Spheroidizing of low carbon steels is performed to meet certain strength requirements before subsequent heat treatment. High carbon steels are spheroidized to improve machinability, especially in continuous cutting operations, such as with lathes and screw machines. Tool steels may also be spheroidized. This is done by heating them to slightly above the critical temperature, holding them at this temperature for a period of time, and then letting them cool in the furnace. Spheroidizing also tends to improve abrasion resistance and is desirable when the material is to be severely cold worked (for example, extruding, bending, drawing, or cold upsetting).

Stress relieving. A heat treatment designed to relieve internal residual stresses induced by cold working, machining, welding, casting, normalizing, or quenching. Stress relieving is a subcritical anneal, where the steel is heated to a temperature below Ac_1 and held at this temperature from 1 to 3 hr. The part is then allowed to cool slowly in air. To obviate distortion, it is particularly effective after machining operations.

Tempering. A process of reheating hardened or normalized steel to a temperature below the transformation temperature range followed by any desired rate of cooling.

Transformation range. For ferrous alloys, the transformation range within which austenite forms on heating or disappears upon cooling.

SECTION 2-10

Supplementary Metallurgical Terms

The following terminology, some of which has been previously mentioned in the text, is listed separately from Section 2-9, which defines heat treating terms, because the terms to be listed cannot be strictly classed as heat treating nomenclature.

Alloy. A material with metallic properties consisting of two or more elements, one of which is a basic metal.

Alloying elements. An element(s) deliberately added to a metal for the expressed purpose of altering the mechanical or physical properties of the metal.

Anistropy. That characteristic of a material which exhibits different property values in different directions with respect to a set of reference axes. For example, property values "with the grain" as compared to the value of the same properties "transverse to the grain."

Cold shortness. The brittleness that exists in some metals at temperatures below their recrystallization temperature.

Damping capacity. The ability of a metal to dissipate the energy of vibratory or cyclical stresses by means of internal friction. Some materials such as lead have a high damping capacity; cast iron also has good damping characteristics. Steel, however, has poor damping characteristics.

Embrittlement. Embrittlement is the loss of ductility of a metal. This loss may be caused by physical or chemical changes.

Flaking. After hot working steel, stresses caused by local transformation and reduced hydrogen solubility while cooling produce internal microcracks and "flakelike" fractures. This adverse phenomenon is known as flaking and can be corrected by cycle cooling to at least 600°F before air cooling.

Homogeneity. A material is said to be homogeneous when it has the same properties throughout. For example, steel, with its various size crystals and different material in the grain boundaries, is *not* a homogeneous material.

Hydrogen embrittlement. The low ductility of a metal caused by the absorption of hydrogen.

Isotropic. A material having the same properties in all directions is said to be isotropic.

Killed steel. A steel that has been deoxidized with a strong deoxidizing agent such as silicon or aluminum. Such oxidation reduces the free oxygen content to a point where the carbon cannot oxidize as the steel solidifies. Killed steel contains few gas holes; this characteristic contributes towards better forgings and rolled sections.

Red shortness. A brittleness of the steel and tendency towards cracking at high temperatures caused by the formation of iron sulfide.

Rimmed steel. A low carbon steel that has not been completely deoxidized. The ingot solidifies with a sound surface (that is, rim), but the core contains blowholes that are eliminated in the subsequent rolling of sheet and strip steel.

Semikilled steel. A steel that has been partially deoxidized but still contains enough oxygen to reduce shrinkage in the ingot by forming carbon monoxide.

Temper brittleness. A brittleness resulting from holding certain steels within a particular temperature below the transformation range or by cooling slowly through this range. The brittleness appears at or below room temperature.

SECTION 2-11

Alloying Elements in Steel and Their Functions

An alloying element is deliberately added to a metal to alter its physical or mechanical properties. Plain carbon steel contains small quantities of manganese, phosphorus, sulfur, and silicon, but the amounts are not sufficient to alter the basic effect of the carbon. Thus, various alloying elements are added to carbon steel in smaller or larger quantities to produce one or more of the following effects: (1) increase strength, (2) improve hardenability,[30] (3) improve low or high temperature properties, (4) increase resistance to corrosion, (5) improve machinability, and (6) improve resistance to wear.

Table 2-1, adopted from the 1948 edition of the *Metals Handbook* [reference 4] is a summary of the effects of the major alloying elements in steel. In addition to the elements listed in the table, five other elements are added to some alloys to promote particular properties. These are copper, boron, lead, tellurium, and sulfur.

Copper. An element used as an alloying agent primarily to improve the corrosion resistance of steel when exposed to the atmosphere. The addition of copper also improves the fluidity of steel when poured. It is usually added in quantities from 0.10 to 0.40%. When more than 0.75% copper is added, steel can be precipitation hardened.

Boron. A nonmetallic element that, when added to steel in quantities not exceeding 0.003%, is very effective in increasing the hardenability of low and medium carbon steels. Boron has no effect upon the steel's tensile strength.

Lead. Additions of lead to steel do not form alloys. Other than improving the machinability, lead has no effect upon the steel's mechanical properties. The self-lubricating properties of lead, which reduce the cutting tool friction, are said to improve machinability. The amount of lead depends upon the particular steel considered and varies from 0.15 to 0.35%.

Tellurium. When this element is added to a leaded steel, it will further improve the machinability of the steel. The amount of tellurium depends upon the lead content and varies from 0.03 to 0.05%.

Sulfur. A nonmetal, sulfur is considered to be an undesirable impurity in a steel because of the formation or iron sulfide, which can result in cracking. However, in the presence of the proper amount of manganese, it forms manganese sulfide, which improves the machinability of steel. The sulfur content can vary between 0.06 and 0.30%.

SECTION 2-12

Classification of Steels

Steels are categorized as (1) plain carbon steel, (2) high-strength, low alloy steel, (3) low alloy structural steel, (4) cast steel, (5) stainless steel, (6) tool steel, and (7) special purpose steel.

Plain carbon steel

Plain carbon steel is divided into three groups. (1) Low carbon steel has a carbon content between 0.05 and 0.30%. (2) Medium carbon steel has a carbon content between 0.30 and 0.50%. (3) High carbon steel has a carbon content over 0.50%.

---

[30] This term is not to be confused with hardness (see Section 2.8).

Table 2-1 Alloying Elements in Steel and Their Effects

Element	Solid Solubility, %		Influence on Ferrite	Influence on Austenite (Hardenability)	Influence Exerted Through Carbide		Principal Functions
	In Gamma Iron	In Alpha Iron			Carbide-Forming Tendency	Action During Tempering	
Aluminum	1.1 (increased by C)	36	Hardens considerably by solid solution	Increases hardenability mildly, if dissolved in austenite	Negative (graphitizes)	. . .	1. Deoxides efficiently 2. Restricts grain growth (by forming dispersed oxides or nitrides) 3. Alloying element in nitriding steel
Chromium	12.8 (20 with 0.5C)	Unlimited	Hardens slightly; increases corrosion resistance	Increases hardenability moderately	Greater than Mn; less than W	Mildly resists softening	1. Increases resistance to corrosion and oxidation 2. Increases hardenability 3. Adds some strength at high temperatures 4. Resists abrasion and wear (with high carbon)
Cobalt	Unlimited	75	Hardens considerably by solid solution	Decreases hardenability as dissolved	Similar to Fe	Sustains hardness by solid solution	1. Contributes to red hardness by hardening ferrite
Manganese	Unlimited	3	Hardens markedly; reduces plasticity somewhat	Increases hardenability moderately	Greater than Fe; less than Cr	Very little, in usual percentages	1. Counteracts brittleness from the sulfur 2. Increases hardenability inexpensively
Molybdenum	3 ± (8 with .3 C)	37.5 (less with lowered temperature)	Provides age-hardening system in high Mo-Fe alloys	Increases hardenability strongly (Mo > Cr)	Strong; greater than Cr	Opposes softening, by secondary hardening	1. Raises grain-coarsening temperature of austenite 2. Deepens hardening 3. Counteracts tendency toward temper brittleness 4. Raises hot and creep strength, red hardness 5. Enhances corrosion resistance in stainless steel 6. Forms abrasion-resisting particles

Element	Solubility in gamma iron (%)	Solubility in alpha iron (%)	Influence on ferrite	Influence on hardenability	Tendency to form carbides	Influence exerted during tempering	Principal functions
Nickel	Unlimited	10 (irrespective of carbon content)	Strengthens and toughens by solid solution	Increases hardenability mildly, but tends to retain austenite with higher carbon	Negative (graphitizes)	Very little in small percentages	1. Strengthens unquenched or annealed steels 2. Toughens pearlitic-ferritic steels (especially at low temperature) 3. Renders high-chromium iron alloys austenitic
Phosphorus	0.5	2.8 (irrespective of carbon content)	Hardens strongly by solid solution	Increases hardenability	Nil	...	1. Strengthens low-carbon steel 2. Increases resistance to corrosion 3. Improves machinability in free-cutting steels
Silicon	2± (9 with 0.35)	18.5 (not much changed by carbon)	Hardens with loss in plasticity (Mn < Si < P)	Increases hardenability moderately	Negative (graphitizes)	Sustains hardness by solid solution	1. Used as general-purpose deoxidizer 2. Alloying element for electrical and magnetic sheet 3. Improves oxidation resistance 4. Increases hardenability of steels carrying nongraphitizing elements 5. Strengthens low-alloy steels

Titanium	0.75 (1± with 0.20 C)	6± (less with lowered temperature)	Provides age-hardening system in high Ti-Fe alloys	Probably increases hardenability very strongly as dissolved. The carbide effects reduce hardenability	Greatest carbides (2% Ti renders 0.50% carbon steel unhardenable)	Persistent carbides probably unaffected. Some secondary hardening	1. Fixes carbon in inert particles
							  a. Reduces martensitic hardness and hardenability in medium-chromium steels
							  b. Prevents formation of austenite in high-chromium steels
							  c. Prevents localized depletion of chromium in stainless steel during long heating

Tungsten	6 (11 with 0.25 C)	33 (less with lowered temperature)	Provides age-hardening system in high W-Fe alloys	Increases hardenability strongly in small amounts	Strong	Opposes softening by secondary hardening	1. Forms hard, abrasion-resistant particles in tool steels 2. Promotes hardness and strength at elevated temperature
Vanadium	1 (4 with 0.20 C)	Unlimited	Hardens moderately by solid solution	Increases hardenability very strongly, as dissolved	Very strong (V < Ti or Cb)	Maximum for secondary hardening	1. Elevates coarsening temperature of austenite (promotes fine grain) 2. Increases hardenability (when dissolved) 3. Resists tempering and causes marked secondary hardening

SOURCE: *Metals Handbook*, Vol. I, 8th ed. American Society of Metals, Metals Park, Ohio. 1961.

Low carbon steel is used in a wide variety of industrial products and also in the construction industry. Typical uses are for pipes and tubes, buildings, storage tanks, railroad cars, automobile frames, nuts, bolts, automobile bodies, and galvanized sheet steel. When this steel has a high sulfur content, it is known as **free-cutting steel** and is used extensively in automatic screw machines. Many industrial applications use this steel directly in hot- or cold-rolled form. Cold rolling improves the steel's strength, machinability, and stock dimensions. Where a wear resistant surface is required, this steel can be case hardened.

Medium carbon steel can be quenched and tempered by conventional heat treatment methods. Thus it can be used for applications requiring greater strength and wear. Typical products made from medium carbon steel are forgings, castings, axles, shafts, crankshafts, connecting rods, and any machined part that requires a strength above that which can be supplied by a low carbon steel.

High carbon steel is used extensively where a product must have high strength, hardness, and good resistance to wear. It is obvious that this steel must be heat treated to achieve the desired properties. It is often purchased in an annealed condition, and the finished product is then heat treated to its proper hardness. High carbon steel is used in making forgings and a wide variety of tools, such as drills, taps, reamers, dies, and hand tools. It is also used for making products requiring cutting edges (for example, cutlery, chisels, shear blades, planer tools, and so on) for spring wire, and for cable and wire rope.

The use of high carbon steel must be carefully considered due to its loss of strength and hardness at high temperatures. These are undesirable characteristics for certain cutting tools and for hot-forming operations. Also, this steel, when quenched, is prone to distortion, warping, and even cracking. Lastly, high carbon steel has the disadvantage of being shallow-hardening unless the part is relatively thin. To this extent, the full benefit of heat treatment may not be attained from high carbon steel.

High strength, low alloy steel

High strength, low alloy steel is used in the "as is" condition (other than annealing or normalizing) or heat treated to develop and improve its mechanical properties. For use "as is," the alloying elements are added mainly to strengthen the ferrite, in which the mechanical properties are not fully developed. When subjected to various heat treatments, high strength, low alloy steel improves in such properties as strength, through-hardness, ductility, toughness, and so on.

Low alloy structural steel

Low alloy structural steel was developed mainly for use in the transportation and construction fields. This steel is not heat treated and, consequently, to a large extent the desired properties depend on a proper blending of alloying elements and carbon content. A typical low alloy structural steel has a yield strength of about 50,000 psi and an ultimate tensile strength of about 70,000 psi. This steel is easily welded and does not harden in air. To attain a higher strength steel, the carbon content is increased to about 0.30%. However, the higher strength is obtained at the expense of ductility, formability, and weldability.

Cast steel

Cast steel has a chemical composition similar to wrought steel except for the addition of larger quantities of silicon and manganese as deoxidizing and degassing agents. These additions are made as the steel is being molded. Steel castings offer a means of fabricating complex components with mechanical properties approximating those of wrought steel at a cost lower than other methods of manufacture. Although cast steels have mechanical properties superior to the cast irons, they are inferior to equivalent wrought steel compositions. However, standard heat treating procedures can be employed to adjust the mechanical properties to satisfy specific requirements.

Since the mechanical properties of cast steel are similar to those of wrought steel, cast steel can, with few exceptions, be used for the same applications. Thus, one will find steel castings used in railroad equipment, rolling mills, mining machinery, electrical machinery, automotive equipment, marine equipment, machine tools, and so on.

There are five classes of commercial steel castings. These are (1) low carbon steel, where the carbon content is below 0.2%; (2) medium carbon steel, containing from 0.20 to 0.50% carbon; (3) high carbon steel, with a carbon content above 0.50%; (4) low alloy steel, with a total alloy content below 8%; and (5) high alloy steel, with a total alloy content over 8%. Those high alloy steel castings with compositions similar to wrought stainless steel constitute a group that is of the heat resistant or corrosion resistant type. By far the greatest number of steel castings produced are of medium carbon steel. The low and high carbon steel classifications are considered special because the compositions of many are formulated for particular products and applications.

Most steel castings are purchased on the basis of ASTM specifications, which cover virtually all classes and types of steel castings. Table A-1 of Appendix A lists the mechanical properties of plain carbon steel castings. The lower strength grades, such as class 60000 and 70000, are specified by ASTM A27-58. The high strength cast steels, such as class 80000, 85000, and so on, are specified by ASTM A148-58.

Stainless steel

Stainless steel consists of three types: (1) austenitic, (2) ferritic, and (3) martensitic. All of these steels possess corrosion resistant properties to various degrees, depending mainly on the chromium content. Stainless steel, particularly the austenitic type, polishes to a high luster and finish. As a result, it also has many decorative uses in, for example, architecture. In addition stainless steels are also used for heat resisting applications.

The type of stainless steel is specified by an AISI numbering system. The SAE employs the same system except for the addition of two prefix numbers. The AISI numbering system employs three digits: the first identifies the particular series of stainless steel and the last two serve as identification of the steel. Any suffix letters that follow the three digits represent a modification in that series. The series designations are shown in the following table.

AISI	SAE	General Group Classifications
2XX	203XX	Wrought chromium-nickel-manganese austenitic steel, non magnetic and not hardenable by thermal treatment
3XX	303XX	Wrought chromium-nickel austenitic steel, non magnetic and not hardenable by thermal treatment
4XX	514XX	Wrought chromium-iron martensitic stainless steel, magnetic and hardenable by thermal treatment
4XX	514XX	Wrought chromium-iron ferritic stainless steel, magnetic and not hardenable by thermal treatment

Austenitic stainless steel is the chromium-nickel group and is known as the 300 series. The chromium-nickel-manganese group, consisting of types 201 and 202, was developed during World War II as a result of the shortage of nickel. Manganese was used as a substitute for some of the nickel. The outcome produced stainless steel comparable to types 301 and 302 except for a slightly reduced ability to resist chemical corrosion. Due to continued use, types 201 and 202 were added to the "regular" list of AISI designations.

The 300 series generally is superior to the martensitic and ferritic types of stainless steel in resisting corrosion. Of all the stainless steels, it possesses the highest resistance to scaling and has superior high temperature strength characteristics. Type 302 is the basic type in this series and is often called 18-8[31] stainless steel. It is the "work horse" of the 300 series and is used extensively in food processing and handling machinery, kitchen equipment, architectural trim, dairy plants, some textile machinery, and so on.

A most important field of application for the stainless steels is nuclear engineering. Stainless steels are used as cladding for fuel elements, reactor vessels, piping systems, valves, fittings, and so on. They are used *extensively* in the nuclear field because they sustain minimum damage from nuclear

[31] Some other types of 300 stainless steels are also known as 18-8, but these are followed by suffix letters. For example, type 305 is also known as 18-8FS. Effort is being made to use only the type numbers in order to avoid confusion.

radiation, have high corrosion resistance, reasonably good fabricating characteristics, good cold and hot ductility properties (that is, are thermally shock resistant), low neutron capture cross section,[32] and are readily available at a reasonable cost. The most common types of stainless steels used are 304, 316, 346, and 347.

The austenitic stainless steels are *not* hardenable by quenching but respond readily to cold working, followed by a quick annealing for severe cold working. Austenitic stainless steels are difficult to machine due to work hardening, and they have machinability ratings of about 50 % of the reference steel B1112. The 300 series is very ductile, but due to its propensity towards work hardening, it does not possess the most desirable formability properties.

Austenitic stainless steels are readily forgeable and weldable by all fusion methods. The best welds are made when the joint to be welded is protected from the atmosphere during welding. Also, chromium-nickel steels have low coefficients of thermal conductivity and high coefficients of thermal expansion, which results in distortion while cooling. Thus, proper jig design and use of cooling bars may be required to avoid distortion and warping. Annealing after welding is required for grades other than the 300 series.

Ferritic stainless steel (part of the 400 series) is not hardenable by thermal treatment and does not therefore work harden to an appreciable degree. Being ductile, this steel can readily be drawn, formed, coined, or bent. Cold working will increase its yield strength about 30 % with a lesser increase in ultimate strength. Ferritic stainless steel is readily forged or rolled but its machinability is poor and requires that the cutting tools always be kept sharp.

This steel can be arc or resistance welded but must be annealed in order to avoid embrittlement and to improve toughness. The strongest types of welds are obtained with austenitic welding rods. At elevated temperatures, ferritic steel has low notch toughness properties, poor creep properties, and poor rupture strength.

Martensitic is the third type of stainless steel. Like the ferritic type, martensitic steel belongs to the chromium-iron group and is part of the 400 series. The basic martensitic stainless steel is type 410 and it is the most expensive of this type. Martensitic type stainless steel has good impact properties and is hardenable by quenching in oil from 1800°F, followed by tempering.

The applications for the type 400 martensitic steels are wide and varied. For example, 410 is used for valves, screens, pump shafts, cutlery, bolts, nuts, and various parts in the chemical and petroleum industries. Type 403 is used to make steam turbine blades, jet engine compressor blades, and, in general, parts that are highly stressed. Type 416 is used in the manufacture of car-buretor parts, instrument parts, valve trim, shafts, fishing reels, and golf clubs. Type 420, as a result of heat treatment, has a high hardness and is used

---

[32] A term used to indicate the probability of a nuclear reaction taking place.

in manufacturing cutlery, surgical instruments, and so on. Type 440C, because of its good wear resistance, is used in the manufacture of ball bearings, bushings, valve parts, valve seats, and more expensive cutlery.

With high carbon grades, machining can only be performed at slower cutting speeds and feeds. Types of these steels suitable for cold forming are limited mainly to 403 and 410. All of the martensitic types are readily hot forged or rolled at temperatures between 1900 and 2250°F.

Both arc and resistance welding of martensitic stainless steel are restricted mostly to types 403, 410, and 416. For satisfactory welds (that is, without resulting embrittlement or cracking), the parts should be preheated to between 150 and 300°F and air cooled to between 1200 and 1350°F after welding.

Martensitic stainless steel exhibits excellent creep and rupture strengths up to 1000°F.

All three types of stainless steel can be soft and hard soldered. Soft soldering (that is, using filler materials of tin-lead mixtures) presents no problem since it is performed at a relatively low temperature and does not produce unwanted carbides. Hard soldering, more properly called silver soldering and/or silver brazing, is performed at higher temperatures (1145°F being the lowest). It may produce unwanted carbides in the austenitic types of stainless steel. It is, therefore, preferable to use low carbon or stabilized grades of steel when hard soldering is required. It is possible, also, to copper braze stainless steel, but this method requires high purity copper and a protective atmosphere while brazing. Temperatures of about 2000°F are required, and the effect upon any previous heat treatment must be carefully considered. This method of joining is restricted to relatively small parts.

There is a class of stainless steel called **precipitation hardening stainless steel,** that is a modification of the 18-8 type austenitic steel. This steel possesses corrosion resistant properties much like austenitic stainless steel, but it can be hardened by relatively low temperatures to a high yield strength without any distortion or scaling. It possesses high strength to weight ratios, much like aluminum, magnesium, and titanium.

Hardening of this steel is accomplished (1) by the transformation of austenite to martensite by thermal treatment or cold working, and (2) by precipitation of carbon and low temperature aging, which tempers the martensite. The types that respond to direct thermal treatment are the martensitic grades. These include 17-4PH, 15-5PH, and Ph13-8Mo, which are products of Armco Steel Corporation; AM362, which is made by Allegheny Ludlum Steel Corporation; and Custom 455, which is a product of the Carpenter Steel Corporation. The second type is classed as semi-austenitic grade and includes 17-7PH, PH15-7Mo, Ph14-8Mo (Armco products) and Am350 and Am355 (Allegheny Ludlum products). These types are austenitic when solution treated, and the resulting ductility permits them to be worked much like the ordinary 18-8 stainless steel. For parts that do not require good ductility, the austenite can be transformed to martensite by cold working and low temperature aging which is performed after fabrication. Such treatment can result in an ultimate strength of about 300,000 psi.

The semiaustenitic grades are best for cold forming, whereas the martensitic grades are best for forging. All grades machine with the same difficulty as ordinary stainless steel, so speeds and feeds are relatively low and cutting tools must be sharp. Because the steels are precipitation hardened, welding poses no problem as in other stainless steels.

Table A-6 in Appendix A contains properties of some representative wrought stainless steels. Also see Table A-1 in Appendix A for properties of some cast stainless steels.

Tool steel

The chemical compositions of tool steel make it possible through heat treatment to produce characteristics essential for cutting tools, shearing tools, forming dies, drills, punches, gages, and so on. This steel is not intended for the manufacture of hand tools but is sometimes used for making machine components which may profit from its special mechanical properties.

In the broadest sense, tool steel should satisfy the following requirements: (1) The ability to retain its hardness and strength at the elevated temperatures caused by machining (that is, "hot hardness"). (2) The ability to withstand shock and suddenly applied loads without chipping or breaking (that is, toughness). (3) The ability to withstand the wear and abrasion of continuous use in order to minimize resharpening or changing tools.

No one tool material can completely satisfy all the above requirements. Thus, some are sacrificed or modified, as the situation warrants, in order to obtain desired objectives. Tool steel has been classified[33] in accordance with AISI specifications (also used by the SAE), which include quenching methods, applications, special properties, and steels used in particular industries. There are six major groups some of which have subgroups. Table 2-2 lists these groups. A tool steel is identified by the group letter and a suffix number (for example, W3, D3, and so on). The AISI has completely tabulated the chemical compositions of each type and number. To discuss the detailed properties of each group is beyond the scope of this text. The interested reader is directed to reference [7] and the *Tool Engineers Handbook* of the American Society of Tool Manufacturing Engineers, published by McGraw-Hill Book Company, Inc.

It should be noted, however, that the water hardening group is the least expensive and will satisfy most requirements. Its major fault is that it is subject to red hardness and warping due to quenching. The oil hardening steels, although more expensive, are not as subject to red hardness or warping after being quenched.

[33] Many users persist in keeping the various manufacturer's names and designations for tool steel even though most are identifiable by the AISI classification.

Table 2-2 AISI Tool Steel Designation

Group and Symbol		Type
Water hardening	(W)	
Shock resisting	(S)	
Cold work	(O)	Oil hardening
	(A)	Medium alloy air hardening
	(D)	High-Carbon high-chromium
Hot work	(H)	H1–H19 inclusive, chromium base H20–H39 inclusive, tungsten base H40–H59 inclusive, molybdenum base
High speed	(T)	Tungsten base
	(M)	Molybdenum base
Special purpose	(L)	Low-alloy
	(F)	Carbon-tungsten
	(P)	Mold steels (P1 to P19, low-carbon, P20 to P39 inclusive, other types)

Special steel

Special steel may be needed when design requirements call for special material properties. Special steel is sometimes necessary for high or low temperature applications, unusually high strength requirements, and so on.

High temperature service. Power plant equipment, gas turbines, jet engines, petroleum refineries, chemical plants, and so on, all have components requiring steels that will resist oxidation and have good creep properties (see Section 3-31) for high temperature service. Also, such steel will not change its crystal structure or suffer embrittlement under long exposure to high temperatures. Some austenitic stainless steels (for example, 302, 309, 310, 316, 321, and 327) are used for continuous service for temperatures between 1700 and 2000°F, but their creep strengths drop sharply above 1100°F. Some martensitic and ferritic stainless steels (for example, 405, 410, 418, 430, and 446) can also be used for continuous temperature exposure between 1300 and 2000°F. Their creep strengths, however, are relatively poor even at 1000°F, and are almost nil at higher temperatures. Thus, they cannot be used where strength is an important design factor. Stainless steel has good resistance to scaling. For example, type 440 can resist scaling in continuous service up to a temperature of 1400°F. All of the other types can withstand scaling at temperatures higher than 1400°F.

Table 2-3   Typical Tensile Strengths of
Ultrahigh-Strength Steel

Type of Steel	Yield Strength, ksi	Ultimate Strength, ksi
Medium carbon alloy steels	250	300
Modified hot work tool steels	240	290
Martensitic stainless	235	245
Cold rolled austenitic stainless	180	200
Semiaustenitic stainless	220	235
18% Ni Maraging steel	350	355
High-strength, low-carbon hardenable steels	245	285
High-alloy Q and T steels	290	350
High-carbon steel wire	580	600

The mechanical properties listed are approximate and represent typical maximum strength levels used in current applications. In many applications, higher strength levels are possible, but mill practice or manufacturing technology does not allow these levels to be considered commercially feasible at this time.

SOURCE: *1970 Metals Reference Issue, Machine Design.* Penton Publishing Co., Cleveland, Ohio.

In addition to stainless steel, alloy steel has been developed expressly for high temperature service. A representative listing of such alloys is given in Table A-13 in Appendix A.

Low temperature environments. Special properties for steels subjected to low temperature environments have become increasingly important. Food processing, dewaxing of petroleum, liquefaction of gases, synthetic rubber manufacture, hydrocarbon polymerization, high altitude aircraft, military requirements, and so on, are but a few of the industrial areas that require low temperature steels.

The largest classification of steels possessing properties suitable for low temperature applications is the austenitic stainless steel group. (Also see Section 2-18.) Since the components of a low temperature system are likely to be welded, the welded joint should also show both ductility and good notch sensitivity. Generally, welds made with austenite stainless steel welding rods meet these requirements.

Ultrahigh strength steel. There is also a group of steels known as ultrahigh strength steel. It can develop very high yield strength and ultimate strength values. Table 2-3 provides a list of the nine broad categories that are classified as ultrahigh strength steel.

SECTION 2-13

AISI-SAE Designations for Wrought Steel

The most widely accepted method of specifying a steel is based on the SAE four- and five-digit system developed in the earlier part of this century. With passing time and the creation of new alloys, the SAE and the AISI worked out a system known as the AISI-SAE, which retains the basic concept originated by the SAE. The system is structured as follows: The first digit indicates the type of steel (that is, the principal alloying element), the second specifies the *approximate* percentage of the predominant alloying element, and the last two (or three) digits indicate the average points of carbon

Table 2-4 AISI–SAE Designation Numbers for Wrought Steel

SAE Designation	Type	SAE Designation	Type
10XX	Plain carbon (nonsulfurized and nonphosphorized)	48XX	Nickel 3.50%, molybdenum 0.25%
		51XX	Chromium 0.80%
11XX	Free cutting (resulfurized, e.g., screw stock)		
12XX	Free cutting (resulfurized and rephosphorized)	514XX	Corrosion and heat resisting steels
13XX	Manganese 1.60–1.90%	515XX	Corrosion and heat resisting steels
23XX	Nickel 3.50%	52XX	Chromium 1.50%
25XX	Nickel 5.00%	61XX	Chromium 0.78%, vanadium 0.13%
31XX	Nickel 1.25%, chromium 0.60%	86XX	Nickel 0.55%, chromium 0.50% molybdenum 0.20%
32XX	Nickel 1.75%, chromium 1.00%	87XX	Nickel 0.55%, chromium 0.50%, molybdenum 0.25%
33XX	Nickel 3.50%, chromium 1.50%	88XX	Nickel 0.55%, chromium 0.50% molybdenum 0.35%
34XX	Nickel 3.00%, chromium 0.80%	92XX	Manganese 0.80%, silicon 2.00%
303XX	Corrosion and heat resisting steels	93XX	Nickel 3.25%, chromium 1.20% molybdenum 0.12%
40XX	Molybdenum 0.25%	94XX	Manganese 0.95%–1.25%, nickel 0.45%, chromium 0.40%, molybdenum 0.12%
41XX	Chromium 1.00%, molybdenum 0.20%	97XX	Nickel 0.55%, chromium 0.17% molybdenum 0.20%
43XX	Nickel 1.83%, chromium 0.80% molybdenum 0.25%	98XX	Nickel 1.00%, chromium 0.80%, molybdenum 0.25%
46XX	Nickel 1.75%, molybdenum 0.25%		

NOTES: 1. The percentages of the alloying elements are average
2. In the AISI system, the prefix letters have the following meaning: A = basic open-hearth alloy steel, B = acid bessemer carbon steel, C = basic open-hearth carbon steel (no prefix also means basic open- hearth carbon steel), D = acid open-hearth carbon steel, and E = electric furnace steel (usually an alloy).
3. When the letters B or L appear in the middle of a number, it means that boron or lead have been added. For example, 94B40 and 11L41.
4. Suffix letters added to the end of the numbers indicate certain guarantees, restrictions and conformities as follows (a partial list only): A = restricted chemical composition, C = guaranteed segregation limits, H = guaranteed hardenability (see section 2.8), and I = guaranteed conformity to nonmetallic inclusions.

in the steel where one point is equivalent to 0.01%. When using the AISI criteria, the four- and five-digit numbers are the same as for SAE designations except for prefix and suffix letters. Table 2-4 lists the various designations and associated types of steel.

As an example of how the system works, an AISI C1040 (SAE 1040) steel is a plain carbon steel made by the basic open-hearth process containing 40 points or 0.40% carbon. As another example, AISI 4340 (SAE 4340) steel is a "nickel, chrome, moly" steel with 1.83% average nickel, 0.80% average chromium, 0.25% average molybdenum, and 40 points or 0.40% carbon.

Tables A-2 and A-3 in Appendix A list the mechanical properties of various plain carbon and alloy steels in the "as drawn," "as rolled," and heat treated conditions. Also, Tables A-4 and A-5 in Appendix A show, respectively, the effects of various tempering temperatures and masses on the properties of some heat treated plain carbon and alloy steels.

SECTION 2-14

Wrought Aluminum Alloys

Second to steel, aluminum is the most widely used metal and its applications are manifold. It is available in all forms, such as wire, bars, extrusions (including structural shapes), powder, sheets, plates, forgings, and castings. Aluminum possesses a high resistance to most corrosive atmospheres because it readily forms a passive oxide surface coating. Different alloying elements affect the corrosion resistance of aluminum to varying degrees; however, all alloys are essentially corrosion resistant. Halogen acids and strong alkalies are two of the few types of solutions that will attack aluminum because these substances can remove the oxide coating and expose fresh aluminum.

Aluminum has good electrical and thermal conductivity as well as high light reflectivity. It is easily formed, drawn, stamped, spun, machined (with the exception of "O" temper), welded, or brazed, depending upon the temper of the particular alloy.

As a structural material, it can develop strengths comparable to steel. Because the modulus of elasticity of aluminum is about one third that of steel, it is not as stiff and will deflect more than steel when subjected to a comparable load. This characteristic can also affect dimensional accuracy during machining if too heavy a cut is taken without proper clamping or support of the work piece. However, aluminum has a high strength-to-weight ratio, which can be a very important consideration in design of, for example, aircraft, missiles, trains, and so on. Due to its elastic modulus, cold forming operations require that the aluminum be bent or shaped much further than the final required shape (as compared to using steel) because of metal spring-back. In fact, to assure proper forming, aluminum should be deformed beyond its yield point.

The wear resistance of aluminum is not very good, and it should not be used where this characteristic is a major design parameter. In addition, the fatigue strength of aluminum is not very high, and careful thought must be given to those situations where varying loads are an important consideration before a decision can be made regarding its use.

The coefficient of thermal expansion of aluminum is about 1.5 times that of steel, and the coefficient of thermal conductivity of aluminum is about 5 times that of steel. These two factors require that both machining and welding be performed very carefully. When machining aluminum, the energy of cutting will cause the work piece to expand due to its high thermal expansion. This results in dimensional inaccuracies. To minimize this problem, cutting tools should be kept sharp, feeds and speeds should be moderate, and a good coolant should be used.

A four digit system is used to designate and identify wrought aluminum alloys (see Table 2-5). The first digit identifies the alloy group. The second digit indicates modifications of the original alloy or an impurity limit. The last two digits identify the alloy or indicate the aluminum impurity.

Some clarification of this system seems to be appropriate at this juncture. The last two digits of the 1XXX group are the same as the two digits to the right of the decimal point in the minimum aluminum percentage to the nearest 0.01%. The second digit indicates the modification, if any, in the impurity limits. These can be any number from 0 to 9, where zero indicates that there is no special control of individual impurities, and the numbers 1 to 9 inclusive indicate a special control of one or more of the impurities. For example, the aluminum alloy 1060 indicates a minimum of 99.60% aluminum, which requires no impurity control. Aluminum alloy 1100,

Table 2-5   Wrought Aluminum Alloy
Designations

Alloy	Group Number
Aluminum, 99.00% min. and greater	1XXX
Copper	2XXX
Manganese	3XXX
Silicon	4XXX
Magnesium	5XXX
Magnesium and silicon	6XXX
Zinc	7XXX
Other elements	8XXX
Unused series	9XXX

however, indicates a minimum of 99.00 % aluminum, which requires some control of one or more of the impurities.

For the remaining alloy groups (that is, 2XXX to 8XXX inclusive), the last two digits *only* identify the different aluminum alloys within the group. For example, aluminum alloy 2017 is in the copper alloy group and nominally contains 4.0 % copper, 0.5 % manganese, and 0.5 % magnesium. Aluminum alloy 2024 is also in the copper alloy group but nominally contains 4.5 % copper, 0.6 % manganese, and 1.5 % magnesium. The second digit of the 2XXX to 8XXX groups serves *only* to indicate alloy modifications. The assigned numbers can be 0 to 9 inclusive, where zero signifies the original alloy and the numbers 1 to 9 (consecutively assigned) indicate alloy modifications.

The temper designation system indicates the strength, hardness, and ductility for wrought and cast aluminum and aluminum alloys with the exception of ingots. The system is based on letters that represent the primary temper designations. Numbers following these letters indicate temper subdivisions. Table 2-6 is a list of the temper designations.

Aluminum alloys harden and achieve a high strength by heat treatment in a manner different from that of steels. The aluminum alloy is first solution heat treated,[34] then quenched, and finally age hardened. In contrast to steel, which hardens upon quenching, aluminum alloys become soft and ductile. They harden and increase in strength by age hardening. This process precipitates some of the hardening elements (mainly copper assisted by magnesium, manganese, and sometimes silicon and nickel) throughout the alloy structure. Some alloys age harden at room temperature; others age harden more quickly with the application of heat. The process of heat application to aluminum alloys is called **artificial aging.** Alloys that have been treated by this process are listed under the "T" temper designation. Another method of hardening aluminum alloys, known as **strain hardening,** places the alloy in the "H" temper designation (see Table 2-6). For design conditions requiring a high degree of corrosion resistance, a wrought aluminum alloy called alclad is available. Alclad aluminum is manufactured by cladding a thin layer of pure aluminum to the alloy surface while it is being rolled. Such a layer may be applied to one or both sides of the alloy sheet or plate.

Table A-7 in Appendix A lists the mechanical properties and manufacturing characteristics of some wrought aluminum alloys. This table also indicates a variety of applications for these alloys.

---

[34] As defined in the *Metals Handbook*, solution heat treatment is "the heating of an alloy to a suitable temperature, holding it at that temperature long enough to allow one or more constituents to enter into solid solution and then cooling rapidly enough to hold the constituents in solution. The alloy is left in a supersaturated, unstable state and may subsequently exhibit quench aging."

Table 2-6 Temper Designations* and Subdivisions for Aluminum Alloys

−F   **As fabricated:** Applies to products that acquire some temper from shaping or forming processes (wrought products).

−O   **Annealed, recrystallized:** Safest temper of the wrought alloys.

−H   **Strain hardened:** Applies to products that have their strength increased by cold working only. The −H is always followed by two or more digits. The first digit indicates the specific combinations of basic operations or as follows:

   −H1   *Strain hardened only:* The second digit following this designation indicates the extent to which the alloy has been hardened by cold working. The numeral 8 designates the "full-hard" temper, the numeral 4 designates the "half-hard" temper, etc. Thus, −H18 is "full-hard", −H17 is "seven eights-hard", −H16 is "three quarters-hard", etc. Although 8 is "full-hard", 9 is used to indicate an "extra-hard" temper. When a third digit is used, it indicates the degree of control of temper or slightly different mechanical properties than those for the two-digit −H temper.

   −H2   *Strain hardened and then partially annealed:* Products are strain hardened more than desired and then reduced in strength to the desired level by partial annealing. The number following the designation indicates the degree of strain hardening remaining after annealing, and uses the same numerical coding as −H1.

   −H3   *Strain hardened and then stabilized:* Products are strain hardened and then stabilized by low temperature heating to lower their strength and increase ductility. This designation applies only to alloys containing magnesium. The second digit indicating the degree of strain hardening after stabilization, follows the same coding as −H1.

−W   **Solution heat treated (wrought products):** An unstable temper applicable only to those alloys that spontaneously age at room temperature after solution heat treatment. This designation is specific only when the period of natural aging is indicated (e.g., −W $\frac{1}{2}$ hr).

−T   **Solution heat treated to produce stable tempers** (other than −F, −O, or −H with or without supplementary strain hardening). The −T is always followed by numerals 2 through 10 inclusive, each of which indicates a sequence of basic operations as shown below. Deliberate variations of the conditions resulting in different product characteristics are indicated by adding one or more digits to the basic designations listed.

   −T2   Annealed to improve ductility and to increase dimensional stability (cast products only).

   −T3   Solution heat treated and then cold worked for the primary purpose of improving strength (wrought products).

   −T4   Solution heat treated and naturally aged to a substantially stable condition. Applies when the products is not cold worked after heat treatment (wrought or cast products).

   −T5   Artificially aged after cooling from being formed at an elevated temperature (wrought or cast products).

   −T6   Solution heat treated and then artificially aged (wrought or cast products).

   −T7   Solution heat treated and then stabilized (wrought or cast products).

   −T8   Solution heat treated, cold worked and then artificially aged (wrought products only).

   −T9   Solution heat treated, artificially aged and then cold worked (wrought products only).

   −T10 Artificially aged and then cold worked (wrought products only).

*Based on material from *The Aluminum Data Book,* Reynolds Metals Co., 1959.

SECTION 2-15

Aluminum Casting Alloys

Aluminum casting alloys are versatile engineering materials and are fast becoming more popular with the development of new alloy combinations. Depending upon the particular alloy, aluminum casting alloys are usually readily diecast, permanent mold cast, sand cast, plaster mold cast, premium quality cast, investment cast, and centrifugally cast. They can be treated to a variety of surface finishing processes (for example, shot peened, etched, sandblasted, and so on), are machinable and with proper casting design (that is, wall thickness, section thickness), and can be welded with ease. Brazing is limited to a few alloys such as the sand casting alloy A712.0, the permanent mold casting alloy C712.0, and alloy 443.0, which can be both sand cast and permanent mold cast.

The disadvantages associated with aluminum alloy castings result from their large shrinkage (for example, from 3.5 to 8.5% by volume), possible hot shortness, and gas absorption. The effects of shrinkage can be minimized by careful design of the casting, providing for gradual change in sections, and observing the standards established for minimum wall thickness depending upon the type of casting (for example, $\frac{3}{16}$ in. minimum thickness for sand castings). Proper pouring rate, temperature, and so on, can reduce or eliminate the effect of hot shortness and/or gas absorption.

It is apparent from the variety of casting processes that aluminum alloys can be produced in singular units, small lots, or in large quantities.

Table A-8 in Appendix A lists the mechanical properties of some typical aluminum casting alloys that can be used in different casting processes.

SECTION 2-16

Copper and Copper Alloys

Copper

Due to its high electrical and thermal conductivities, pure copper is used almost exclusively in the electrical and electronics industries (although some inroads into these industries have been made by aluminum wire and cable), and in the petroleum, chemical, and power generating industries (for example, in heat transfer equipment). Copper used for electrical conductors is either tough-pitch copper, which has been electrolytically refined, or oxygen-free copper, which has a high conductivity. Tough-pitch copper is subject to embrittlement, whereas oxygen-free copper is not. Both tough-pitch copper and oxygen-free copper contain 99.90 + % copper.

Copper as well as most copper alloys cannot be heat treated. The mechanical properties are altered and strengthened by cold working. However, beryllium copper is an exception because it is hardenable.

Copper alloys

There are approximately 250 copper alloys. Due to the various numbering designations (ASTM, SAE, Federal Specifications, Navy Specifications, and so on) and the continued use of alloy names by industry, identification of the various copper alloys is rather confusing. Recently, the Copper Development Association has classified copper alloys by number and type, but these designations have been slow in "taking hold."

Copper alloys are divided into brasses and bronzes. Brass is principally an alloy of copper and zinc. The basic brass alloys are alpha brasses (for example, red and yellow brass) and alpha-beta brasses. It is also possible for basic brass to contain, separately, small quantities of lead or tin. These alloys are called, respectively, leaded brass and tin brass (for example, admiralty, naval, and tobin brass). When a brass contains a relatively large percentage of nickel (no more than 20%), it is known as nickel silver. When a brass contains no more than 2.75% lead and no more than 12.00% nickel, it is known as leaded nickel silver. There is also a "brass" called cupronickel that contains no zinc at all; instead it is an alloy of copper and nickel (30% cupronickel also contains a small quantity of iron).

Bronze is principally an alloy of copper and tin. However, there are some alloys classified as bronzes that contain little or no tin. Many of these alloys are classified as bronze because they have a color similar to that of bronze. The principal bronze alloys are phosphor bronze, silicon bronze, aluminum bronze, and manganese bronze. Table A-9 in Appendix A is a selected list of some copper alloys and their pertinent mechanical and manufacturing properties. Table A-10 in Appendix A lists the properties of some cast copper base alloys.

SECTION 2-17

Magnesium Alloys

Magnesium is the lightest metal (specific gravity $= 1.74$) known that is used for engineering purposes. Alloying is necessary, however, to develop its maximum usefulness and strength.[35] The alloying elements used are aluminum, zinc, zirconium, manganese, thorium, and the rare earths. The ASTM classifies magnesium alloys according to the alloying elements as follows: aluminum is indicated by the letter A, zinc by the letter Z, zirconium by the letter K, manganese by the letter M, thorium by the letter H, and the rare earth metals by the letter E. The addition of thorium and rare earths radically improves the elevated temperature properties of magnesium alloys.

The ASTM type designation is quite simple and is best explained by an example. ASTM type AZ61A-T4 contains 6% aluminum and 1% zinc. The

---

[35] For forging extrusions, plate, sheet, and strips, the yield strength in tension is greater than the yield strength in compression. Both strengths are the same for castings.

letter A signifies that this alloy was the first one of this composition (that is, of aluminum and zinc) to become standard. The T4 is a temper designation and is the same system that is used for aluminum. Thus, this alloy has been solution heat treated as indicated by T4.

Magnesium alloys have a high strength-to-weight ratio and are ideal for intermediate stage aircraft and missile components (for example, frame and skin stiffeners, fairings, bulkheads, engine parts, wheels, and so on), trucks and ordnance vehicles (for example, crankcases, transmission housings, fuel pumps, roof rails, and so on), materials handling equipment (for example, dockboards, hand trucks, gravity conveyors, platform trucks, and so on), hand tools, optical equipment, office equipment, and die cast components.

These alloys are readily machinable (for example, machinability index = 500 based on 100 for B1112 free cutting carbon steel) and are virtually adaptable to all forms of metal working and joining such as casting, forging, extruding, inert gas-arc welding, resistance welding, and riveting. Caution is advised when machining magnesium alloys because finely divided particles are easily ignited. Large pieces of magnesium are difficult to ignite because heat transfer is so efficient that the material cannot reach its melting point. The usual practice is to moisten the areas where fine magnesium dust collects and frequently sweep it into a container.

Magnesium alloys show good resistance to atmospheric exposure, although salt water will attack them unless they are protected by surface finishing. They also have good resistance to attack by chromic and hydrofluoric acids, alkalies, solvents, and most organic compounds such as hydrocarbons, aldehydes, alcohols, phenols, amines, esters and oils.

Table A-11 in Appendix A lists the properties of three popular magnesium alloys.

SECTION 2-18

Nickel and Nickel Alloys

Nickel is used in a variety of applications, particularly those where corrosion resistance and oxidation resistance is an important requirement. In addition, some nickel alloys are extremely tough (that is, 200 ft-lb Charpy V-notch test) so that they can be used at temperatures as high as 2000°F as ultrahigh strength and superalloy structural materials. Other nickel alloys are excellent for cryogenic applications and are strong, tough, and ductile even at temperatures as low as −400°F.

Wrought nickel alloys have good manufacturing characteristics; they are readily machinable, cut, sheared, punched, cold worked, hot worked, and weldable. The casting alloys can be machined, ground, welded, and brazed.

Although more costly than either steel or aluminum, nickel alloys are less costly than the refractory metals for solving severe temperature-strength problems. Also, they display magnetic, magnetostrictive, electrical, and thermal properties that are important for particular applications.

There are some nickel and nickel alloy specifications based on ASTM, ASME, AMS, and governmental standards, but, to date, the customary practice is to refer to these alloys by their trade names with the exception of a few high nickels (that is, 94% or more nickel—for example, Nickel 200, Nickel 201, Nickel 210, Duranickel 301, and Berylco Nickel 440). Table A-13 in Appendix A lists the mechanical properties of some nickel and nickel alloys at room temperature. Table A-14 in Appendix A lists the mechanical properties of some nickel and nickel alloys at low temperatures. One need only compare the corresponding mechanical properties in these tables to see why a nickel alloy is considered a tough material, capable of satisfying the severe requirements of high and low temperature environments.

SECTION 2-19

Plastics

The name plastics, used to describe a very large number of synthetic[36] organic compounds, is misleading in that such materials are only truly plastic during a particular stage of processing. However, plastics represent a vast and growing field of synthetic materials. These substances have such diverse properties that there are few areas of modern civilization where they are not in use. A design engineer's interest in plastics concerns their use as structural materials as well as their use for special applications.

The basic building blocks of plastics are carbon, hydrogen, and oxygen. These are linked together in saturated[37] or unsaturated[38] organic compounds. Methane and ethane are typical saturated compounds. Ethylene and acetylene are typical unsaturated compounds (see Figure 2-18). When heat, pressure, and suitable catalysts are used, the unsaturated bonds of a molecule

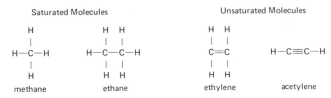

Figure 2-18 Typical saturated and unsaturated molecules.

[36] There are natural plastics such as resins (for example, copal, rosin, pitch, ambers, and shellac).

[37] Saturated means that the four valence bonds of carbon in a compound are satisfied (e.g., methane, CH_4).

[38] Unsaturated means that the four valence bonds of carbon in a compound are not satisfied. This situation arises when there are not enough hydrogen or oxygen atoms to link with the carbon atoms present. In this case, the unsatisfied carbon valence bonds link with each other. These are represented by double or triple lines (e.g., ethylene and acetylene).

allow additional similar molecules to join and form a long chain. This process is called polymerization. The resulting long chain molecule is called a polymer, and the component smaller molecule is called a monomer. Figure 2-19 shows a long chain polymer made up of ethylene monomers. A large number of other polymers can be produced by replacing the hydrogen with oxygen or linking two or more different monomers, each with different properties. New structural arrangements of the same elements of a molecule, which form what are known as isomers, are also possible. This is similar to the existence of allotropic forms of an element (for example, sulfur).

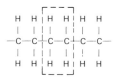

Figure 2-19   Long chain molecule of ethylene units.

When two or more polymers are crosslinked, the process is called copolymerization. It results in a class of plastics known as **thermosetting plastics.** Thermosetting plastics experience a chemical change upon the application of heat and pressure, and once formed *cannot* be resoftened. Polymers that are not crosslinked result in a class of plastics known as **thermoplastic plastics.** These materials soften with increasing temperatures, and harden with decreasing temperatures. This cycle of heating and cooling can be repeated as often as one wishes without destroying the material's properties.

Thermosetting and thermoplastic resins may be mixed. This results in a compound having some of the properties of each type. These compounds can be resoftened, but not to the same degree as the thermoplastic constituent. The addition of different fillers, such as paper, cotton, linen, asbestos, or glass, results in two groups of plastic materials known as reinforced plastics and laminates. These plastics possess special characteristics (that is, high toughness, wear resistance, low dielectric losses, and so on), depending upon the particular laminate. Mention should also be made of the recently developed filament wound composite, which is formed with an epoxy base (for example, diglycidyl ethers of bisphenol A). It is being used for rocket motor cases, chemical tanks, pressure containers, high strength tubing, shotgun barrels, and missile bodies.

Table A-15 in Appendix A lists the properties of plastic materials for applications that are of primary interest to the designer. The plastics are identified in this table by their generic names. A particular plastic material taken from this table is likely to be produced by several manufacturers, each of whom labels it with his own trade name. Such a list would be extraordinarily lengthy and, therefore, cannot be given here.

SECTION 2-20

Elastomers

Elastomers is a term used to describe materials that are resilient and possess rubberlike qualities. They include natural rubber and many synthetically compounded materials that have special properties. Elastomers are used to

Table 2-7   ASTM Designations and General Properties of Elastomers

ASTM D 1418 Designation	Common Name or Representative Trade Name	Chemical Designation	General Properties
NR	Natural	Natural polyisoprene	Excellent physical properties; good resistance to cutting, gouging, and abrasion; low heat, ozone, and oil resistance; poor resistance to petroleum-base fluids
IR	Polyisophrene	Synthetic polyisoprene	Same properties as natural rubber; requires less mastication than natural rubber
CR	Neoprene	Chloroprene	Excellent ozone, heat, and weathering resistance; good oil resistance; excellent flame resistance
SBR	SBR	Styrene-butadiene	Good physical properties; excellent abrasion resistance; not oil, ozone, or weather resistant
NBR	Buna N	Acrylonitrile-butadiene	Excellent resistance to vegetable, animal, and petroleum oils; poor low-temperature resistance
IIR	Butyl	Isobutylene-isoprene	Excellent weathering resistance; low permeability to gases; good resistance to ozone and aging, low tensile strength and resilience
IIR	Chloro-butyl	Chloro-isobutylene-isoprene	Same general properties as butyl
BR	Butadiene	Polybutadiene	Excellent abrasion resistance and high resilience; used principally as a blend in other rubbers
T	Thiokol	Polysulfide	Outstanding solvent resistance; other properties poor
EPM	EPR	Ethylene propylene	Good aging, abrasion, and heat resistance; not oil resistant
EPDM	EPT	Ethyl propylene terpolymer	Good aging, abrasion, and heat resistance; not oil resistant
CSM	Hypalon	Chlorosulfonated polyethylene	Excellent ozone, weathering, and acid resistance; fair oil resistance; poor low-temperature resistance
VMQ PVMQ FMQ	Silicone Silicone Fluorosilicone	Methyl-vinyl siloxane Phenyl-methyl-vinyl siloxane Trifluoropropyl siloxane	Excellent high and low temperature resistance; good mechanical properties at high temperature; low compression set; fair oil resistance Fluorosilicone rubber has excellent oil resistance
AU	Urethane	Polyurethane diisocyanate	Exceptional abrasion, cut and tear resistance; high modulus and hardness; poor moist-heat resistance
FPM	Viton	Fluorinated hydrocarbon	Excellent high-temperature resistance, particularly in air and oil
ACM	Acrylic	Polyacrylate	Excellent heat, oil and ozone resistance; poor water resistance

SOURCE: *1971 Plastics/Elastomers Reference Issue, Machine Design.* The Penton Publishing Co., Cleveland, Ohio

make products for commercial and industrial application. Tires, soles and heels, footwear, floor covering, gloves, wearing apparel, electricians' tape, household utensils, and so on, are some examples of their commercial application. Industrial applications, however, are of greater interest to the design engineer. Examples of some industrial applications are V belts, hoses for steam, chemicals, water, and oil, tubing for experimental and medical purposes, gaskets, oil shaft seals, bearing seals, rubber springs, machinery mounts, and vibration dampers. Table 2-7 lists the ASTM designations and general properties of various elastomers.

Important properties of elastomers are evaluated by standard ASTM tests. Tests have been standardized for hardness, tensile strength, elongation, elastic modulus, tensile and compression set,[39] abrasion resistance, resilience, oil resistance, low temperature characteristics, and deterioration resistance from exposure to oxygen, ozone, light, and heat. Table 2-8 indicates some quantitative strength values for some general purpose elastomers. Reference [8] includes an excellent elastomer selection guide and extensive information about the properties of elastomers.

Table 2-8   Properties of General Purpose Elastomers

Hardness, Shore	Elastomer*	Tensile Strength, psi	Elongation %
	Soft		
20	EPR, NR, §	500–1000	400–700
30	CR	500–2000	400–800
	Medium		
40	EPR, SBR,	500–3000	400–600
50	NR, §	500–4000	250–500
60	IIR, CR,	500–4000	250–500
70	NBR	500–4000	150–300
	Medium Hard		
80	SBR,	500–3000	100–200
90	NR, §	500–2000	75–125
50†	CR,	1000–2000	50–100
60†	NBR	1000–3000	25–50
	Hard		
70†	SBR,	3000–6000	2–20
80†	NR, §	3000–6000	2–10
90†	NBR	3000–7000	2–5
100†		3000–8000	2–5

*Elastomers in each group are listed in order of increasing cost.
† Shore D scale. (Hardness ratings are always A scale unless otherwise indicated.)
§Recommendations for natural rubber, in general, include synthetic natural (IR). The current trend is to replace the tree-grown varieties with the synthetic isoprene types.

SOURCE: *1971 Plastics/Elastomers Reference Issue, Machine Design.* The Penton Publishing Co., Cleveland, Ohio.

[39] Tension set is the amount of deformation remaining after removal of the tensile load. Compression set is the same as tension, except the load is compressive. The tests are performed at different fixed temperatures and for different fixed periods of time.

PROBLEMS

1. What methods are available for improving the strength of metals? Which of these methods are most commonly employed?

2. What effect does cold working have upon steel?

3. Explain why a smaller grain metal is stronger than the same metal with a larger grain. How does ductility and toughness vary with grain size?

4. What is the foremost reason for adding an alloying material to a steel? Are there any other reasons?

5. What is the difference between wrought steel and cast iron?

6. Name the four types of cast irons and indicate the advantages and disadvantages of each as a structural material.

7. Define the following: (a) hypoeutectoid steel, (b) hypereutectoid steel, (c) eutectoid steel.

8. What are the constituents of the following: (a) austenite, (b) ferrite, (c) cementite, (d) pearlite, (e) martensite.

9. List in proper order the procedure involved in hardening a plain carbon steel by heat treatment. Name the metallurgical phase that exists at each step.

10. Why isn't low carbon steel hardened by heat treatment? Explain your answer. How is low carbon steel generally hardened?

11. What is meant by tempering a steel, and why is this process employed?

12. Distinguish between annealing and normalizing. What is the purpose of these processes?

13. From the heat transfer aspect, what is the difference between using oil or water as a quenching medium? How do they affect the material being hardened?

14. Explain how an isothermal transformation diagram is used for heat treating.

15. In general, what effect does an alloying metal have on isothermal transformation diagrams?

16. Distinguish between hardness and hardenability.

17. Name the seven different steel categories.

18. Plain carbon steels are divided into three groups. Name these groups and indicate some typical applications for each.

19. Identify the major alloying agent and per cent carbon content of the following steels: (a) 1020, (b) 1095, (c) 1112, (d) 2330, (e) 3140, (f) 4340, (g) 5120, (h) 8740, (i) 9255.

20. Which of the steels in Problem 19 is known as a "free machining steel"? Which is often called "drill rod"?

21. How does case hardening (also called surface hardening) differ from through-hardening? What is its purpose? Name the various case hardening methods.

22. What are the advantages of nitriding over carburizing and cyaniding? What are the disadvantages of nitriding over cyaniding?

23. What are the causes of decarburization and why is it deleterious?

24. What advantages can be had with high strength, low alloy steels?

25. Describe martempering and austempering.

26. Differentiate between age hardening and precipitation hardening. What is artificial aging?

27. Name the three grades of stainless steel. What constituent in stainless steel makes it particularly resistant to corrosion? List some typical applications for each grade.

28. Which of the three grades of stainless steel is hardenable by heat treatment? How are the other two grades hardened?

29. What requirements must a tool steel satisfy?

30. What two methods are used to harden aluminum alloys?

31. For most atmospheres aluminum is known to resist corrosion. Explain why.

32. How are wrought aluminum alloys designated?

33. What is the difference between brass and bronze?

34. How are wrought copper alloys hardened? (See Table A-9 of Appendix A.)

35. List some advantages and disadvantages of wrought magnesium alloys as a structural material.

36. What group of metal alloys are particularly well suited for high and low temperature applications?

37. Name the two general classifications of plastic material. Explain their significance.

38. List some applications for each classification mentioned in Problem 37.

REFERENCES

[1] E. P. De Garmo: *Materials and Processes in Manufacturing*, 2nd ed. The Macmillan Co., New York, 1962.

[2] S. H. Avner: *Introduction to Physical Metallurgy*. McGraw-Hill Book Co., Inc., New York, 1964.

[3] W. E. Jominy and A. L. Boegehold: Hardenability tests for carburizing steel. *Amer. Soc. Metals Trans.*, **26**, (June 1938).

[4] *Metals Handbook*, Vol. 1, 8th ed. American Society for Metals, Metals Park, Ohio, 1961.

[5] R. W. Bolz: *Production Processes*, Their Influence on Design. The Penton Publishing Co., Cleveland, Ohio, 1956.

[6] H. W. Gillet: *The Behavior of Engineering Material*. John Wiley & Sons, Inc., New York, 1951.

[7] *1970 Metals Reference Issue, Machine Design*. The Penton Publishing Co., Cleveland, Ohio.

[8] *1971 Plastics/Elastomers Reference Issue, Machine Design*. The Penton Publishing Co., Cleveland, Ohio.

3

Mechanical Properties of Engineering Materials

SYMBOLS

BHN = Brinell hardness number

C_F = fatigue strength reduction factor due to surface finish

C_R = fatigue strength reduction factor based on reliability

C_S = fatigue strength reduction factor due to size

C_W = fatigue strength reduction factor due to welding

D.M.F. = deviation multiplication factor

E = elastic modulus in tension, psi

G = elastic modulus in shear, psi

K_f = fatigue stress concentration factor

K_t = theoretical stress concentration factor

K_{ts} = theoretical stress concentration factor for shear

q = notch sensitivity factor

R = Rockwell hardness number

S_e = working endurance limit, psi

S_F = fracture strength, psi

S_n = endurance strength for a fixed number of cycles, psi

S'_n = endurance limit, psi

S_u = ultimate tensile strength, psi

S_{uc} = ultimate compressive strength, psi

S_{us} = ultimate shear strength, psi

S_{yp} = yield point, psi

U_p = modulus of resilience, in.-lb/in.^{3}

U_T = modulus of toughness, in.-lb/in.^{3}

VHN = Vickers hardness number

γ = angular strain, rad

ε = linear strain, in./in.

ε_f = strain at fracture, in./in.

θ = angular deformation, radians

τ_{max} = maximum shearing stress, psi

τ_0 = nominal shearing stress, psi

v = Poisson's ratio

σ_c = compressive stress, psi

σ_t = tensile stress, psi

The primary purpose of this chapter is to review those mechanical properties that the reader may have studied in more specialized courses dealing with engineering materials. In addition, we wish to highlight and supplement those material aspects that have a decided affect upon the design and manufacture of an engineering device or structure.

SECTION 3-1

Mechanical Properties of Materials

Mechanical properties are those that indicate how the material is expected to behave when subjected to various loads or combinations of loads. These mechanical properties are determined by standardized test methods that are outlined by The American Society of Testing Materials (ASTM). Knowledge of these properties permits the designer to determine the size, shape, and method of fabricating structural and machine elements. Since no two test specimens, even from the same "melts" are exactly alike, the results given in the tables of materials are often minimum values, average values, or minimum-maximum values. Thus, one must consider the assigned table value of a particular material carefully before making a decision. This is particularly true where high strength-to-weight ratios are being sought. Often, it is wise to verify the values of interest with a particular supplier before proceeding further with a material selection.

One of the most complete compendiums of ferrous and non-ferrous materials is the *Metals Handbook*, Volume 1 published by The American Society for Metals (ASM). Volume 1 deals with the properties and selections of metals and is periodically up-dated to reflect the latest data. Of particular importance is the emphasis placed upon the statistical distribution obtained for metal properties. Thorough understanding of the definitions and meanings of the various mechanical properties is of paramount importance to the intelligent selection of a material. Much of the discussion that follows is concerned with the definition of some of these properties.

SECTION 3-2

Homogeneity

A material that exhibits the same properties throughout is said to be homogeneous. Homogeneity is an ideal state that is not achieved by real materials, particularly metals. However, the variation in properties is so small that calculations for stress and deflection assume that a material is homogeneous throughout.

SECTION 3-3

Elasticity

Elasticity is defined as the ability of a body, when subjected to an external load, to return to its original size and shape when the external load is removed.

SECTION 3-4

Isotropy

A material that displays the same elastic properties in all loading directions is said to be isotropic. The equations of elasticity and strength of materials are based upon this assumption. However, in more recent times, great interest is being displayed in those materials that are not isotropic (for example, filament wound plastic and other fibrous materials).

SECTION 3-5

Plasticity

When a material is subjected to an external load of such magnitude that deformation continues with no apparent further increase in load, the material is said to have become plastic. Once in this region, the material will have experienced a permanent set (that is, deformation) and will not return to its original size and shape when the load is removed. Thus, plasticity can be considered as the opposite of elasticity. This definition is for a theoretically perfect material. Actually, a material such as metal (except for a very low carbon steel) will continue to deform with only a very small further increase of load (see Figure 3-1).

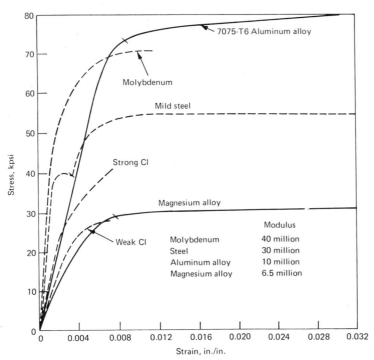

Figure 3-1 Stress-strain diagrams of some metals.

SECTION 3-6

Tensile Strength

Tensile strength, S_u, given in pounds per square inch and also called ultimate strength, is the highest point plotted for a material on a stress-strain curve when the material is subjected to a tensile test (see Figure 3-2). Non-brittle materials display the same stress-strain curve for both tension and compression, whereas brittle materials do not have this characteristic.

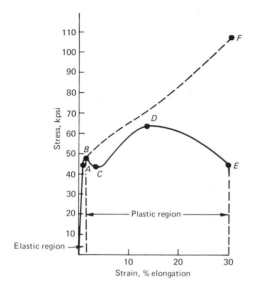

Figure 3-2 Stress-strain curve for a mild (low-carbon) steel, showing the stress variation based on the original cross-sectional area of the specimen and the true variation of stress based on a reduced cross-section area. Point A is the proportional limit, B is the upper yield point, C is the lower yield point, D is the tensile strength (ultimate strength), and E is the fracture strength. Point F is the true fracture strength.

SECTION 3-7

Stress

Stress, S, is also given in pounds per square inch. There are three kinds of simple stresses. These are tensile stress, compressive stress, and shearing stress (this includes torsional stress). The numerical value of these stresses is determined by dividing the load by the original area of the member. Although it is common practice, a stress calculated in this way is really a nominal or engineering stress as contrasted to the true stress. The true stress would be that stress obtained by dividing the load by the reduced cross-sectional area. This area must be that measured area associated with the measured load. As a result, the true stress is much higher than the stress based upon the original area. Figure 3-2 illustrates this point.

SECTION 3-8

Strain

In tensile testing, strain (ε, linear measured in inches per inch, and γ, angular measured in radians) is defined as the change of the specimen length divided by the original gage length. This strain is sometimes called the nominal strain, engineering strain, or conventional strain. There is also a term called true strain, which is defined as the logarithm of the ratio between the specimen length at the time of measurement and the original gage length. For shearing stress there is an associated shearing strain. This value, a dimensionless quantity, measures the angular change in radians between two lines that were originally at right angles on the test specimen.

SECTION 3-9

Fracture Strength

Fracture strength, S_F, given in pounds per square inch and also called the breaking strength, is that value at which a test specimen actually separates. To obtain this value, the load at separation is divided by the original cross-sectional areas. Again we must recognize that the value so obtained is not the true value. To obtain the true strength, the load at separation should be divided by the cross-sectional area at separation (see Figure 3-2).

SECTION 3-10

Proportional Limit

The proportional limit, given in pounds per square inch, is defined as that point on a stress-strain curve beyond which the stress is no longer proportional to strain (see Figure 3-3). The actual value of the proportional limit is quite difficult to establish because it depends greatly upon the sensitivity and quality of the measuring instruments used. Except where it is absolutely necessary to know this value, it is generally not used in engineering calculations.

SECTION 3-11

Elastic Limit

Elastic limit, given in pounds per square inch, is that point on the stress-strain curve where the material being tested begins to display a slight deviation from a straight line. Most elastic materials, when strained to their elastic limits, will return to their original size and shape when the applied load is removed. Very often the elastic limit and proportional limit are taken to have the same values.

SECTION 3-12

Proof Stress

Since the proportional limit and the elastic limit are such undeterminable parameters, a term called proof stress, also given in pounds per square inch, is employed. Thus proof stress is that stress which will cause a small but permanent strain in a material. This permanent strain is specified as 0.01 %

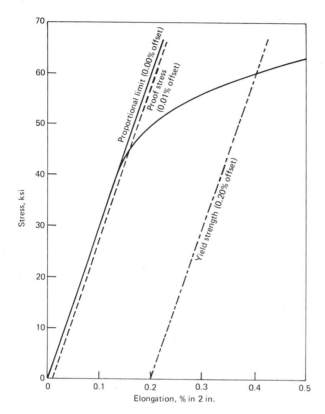

Figure 3-3 Stress-strain curve defining proportional limit, proof stress, and yield strength. [*Technical Editor Speaks.* The International Nickel Co., Inc., New York, 1943.]

in 2 in. or called the 0.01 % offset. One can readily see that this type of stress specification can become the basis for assuring a user that the supplier is delivering a material with a consistent and reliable "yield property" (see Figure 3-3).

SECTION 3-13

Yield Point

Also called yield strength, the yield point (S_{yp}, pounds per square inch) is that point on the stress-strain curve where the test specimen experiences a relatively large increase in deformation with no increase in load. This is an ideal statement based upon what is considered a perfectly elastic and perfectly plastic material. Actually, the location of the yield point depends very much on the material being tested.

Figure 3-4 demonstrates this inconsistency. The curve for metal A is typical of that for a mild steel (that is, low carbon). Note that this curve

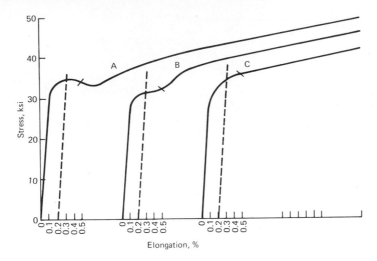

Figure 3-4 Stress-strain curve showing clearly defined yield points for metal A and metal B, as displayed by the dip in those curves. Metal C shows no such dip. [*Technical Editor Speaks.* The International Nickel Co., Inc., New York, 1943.]

shows a dip, indicating that the stress is actually reduced while the strain continues. After straining to a certain point, the material recovers and continues to increase in stress (at a much reduced rate) with increasing strain. In fact, curve A is said to display an "upper yield point" and a "lower yield point." The curve for metal B is typical for hard steels (for example, medium carbon) and some nonferrous metals. Here we see that the curve no longer has a distinct dip but does display a break in what otherwise would be a smooth curve. High carbon steels, alloy steels, and most nonferrous metals have a stress-strain curve similar to that shown by the curve for metal C. In this case, there is no dip, no break, but only a smooth curve and therefore a distinct yield point is nowhere indicated.

Because of the possible confusion that might result in specifying the yield point, it has been agreed to use a 0.2% offset line to establish the yield point. Thus, if we draw a line parallel to the elastic part of the stress-strain curve but offset 0.2% in elongation, the point on the curve cut by this line is taken to be the yield point. This is clearly shown on Figure 3-4. For copper base alloys, the offset is usually taken as 0.5%. Other factors such as stress relieving[1] and cold drawing[2] can also have an appreciable effect upon the yield point value. Figure 3-5 for a mild steel bar indicates these variations.

[1] See Section 3-30 (that part dealing with heat treatment).

[2] See Section 3-30 (that part dealing with mechanical surface treatment).

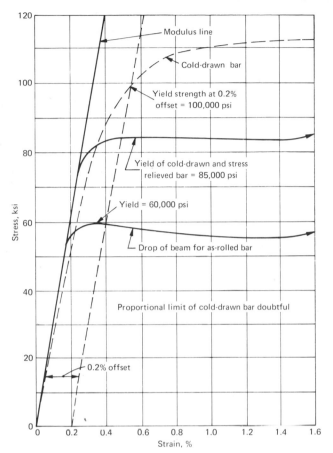

Figure 3-5 Effect of cold working and/or stress relieving on a steel Bar. [Batelle Memorial Institute: *Prevention of the Failure of Metals Under Repeated Stress.* John Wiley & Sons, Inc., New York, March 1949.]

SECTION 3-14

Modulus of Elasticity

The modulus of elasticity (*E* for tension and *G* for shear, pounds per square inch) is the ratio of stress to strain measured within the proportional limit of the material. Thus, the modulus is really a measure of the stiffness (for tension or compression) or rigidity for shear of a material. For ductile material, the modulus of elasticity is the same for both tension and compression. In particular, it is called "Young's modulus" and is represented by the letter *E*. For brittle materials such as cast iron, certain magnesium alloys, and so on, this modulus is not the same for both tension and compression.

For the case of shear (or torsion), the modulus analogous to that for tension is called the shear modulus or modulus of rigidity. (It is also known as the transverse modulus.) The symbol used to signify this modulus is G. The modulus of rigidity and Young's modulus are related by the equation

$$G = \frac{E}{2(1 + v)} \tag{3-1}$$

where v is Poisson's ratio and is defined as the absolute value of the ratio of the transverse strain to the axial strain when an axial load is being applied to a body.

Hooke's Law

Hooke's law is really implicit in the aforementioned definition of the moduli of elasticity. Directly stated it says that stress is proportional to strain up to the proportional limit of the material. Thus, for tension (or compression) we have

$$S = E\varepsilon \tag{3-2}$$

For shear (and torsional stress) we have

$$S_s = G\gamma \tag{3-3}$$

Direct Shear Strength

Shear strength values are obtained by simple tests as shown in Figure 3-6 for single shear and Figure 3-7 for double shear. The specimen to be tested is sheared between the hardened edges of the supporting block and the block to which the load is applied. The shearing strength is the load at separation divided by the cross-sectional area being sheared. Thus, if the separation load is P and the specimen has a thickness t in. and is l in. long, the direct shearing strength (in single shear) is $S_{su} = P/tl$. Similarly for direct double shearing strength we have $S_{su} = P/2tl$.

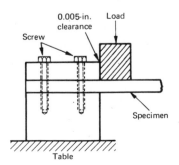

Figure 3-6 Fixture for direct single shear. [*Technical Editor Speaks.* The International Nickel Co., Inc., New York, 1943.]

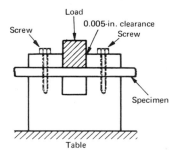

Figure 3-7 Fixture for direct double shear. [*Technical Editor Speaks.* The International Nickel Co., Inc., New York, 1943.]

Note that the phrase shear strength was prefixed by the word direct, implying that this is the only stress placed upon the test specimen. However, inspection of the test fixtures as illustrated by Figures 3-6 and 3-7 indicates that bending stresses do exist and the stress cannot be considered as pure shear. Therefore, the shearing stress as calculated above is an average stress. This type of calculation is justified in analyzing bolts, rivets, welded parts, of any other mechanical member where the bending moments are considered negligible. Also, because strain measurements are difficult, if not impossible to measure, few values of yield strength are determined by testing. It is of interest to note that tests of bolts and rivets have shown that the strength in double shear can at times be as much as 20% below that for single shear. In those cases where the ultimate shear stress for a material is not easily available, the following rule of thumb relations may be employed.

$$\left.\begin{array}{rl} \text{Wrought steel:} & S_{su} = 0.82S_u \\ \text{Malleable iron:} & S_{su} = 0.90S_u \\ \text{Cast iron:} & S_{su} = 1.30S_u \\ \text{Copper and copper alloys:} & S_{su} = 0.90S_u \\ \text{Aluminum and aluminum alloys:} & S_{su} = 0.65S_u \end{array}\right\} \quad (3\text{-}4)$$

SECTION 3-17

Shear Yield Point

As stated above, values for the yield point in shear (S_{yp}, pounds per square inch) are generally not available. However, those values that are listed are usually obtained by torsional testing of round test specimens. The equation used for plotting the stress-strain curve for shear (that is, torsion) is

$$S_s = \frac{Gr\theta}{L} \tag{3-5}$$

where r is the radius of the test specimen in inches, L the length of the test specimen in inches, and θ the angular deformation (that is, twist) of the shaft in radians. The yield point can then be determined from the plotted curve as discussed earlier. Where information concerning shear yield values is not readily available, one may use the following approximations:

$$\left.\begin{array}{l} \text{Aluminum and alluminum alloys:} \quad S_{syp} = 0.55S_{yp} \\ \text{Wrought steel:} \quad S_{syp} = 0.58S_{yp} \end{array}\right\} \quad (3\text{-}6)$$

SECTION 3-18

Ductility

Ductility is defined as that property that permits a material to be deformed without fracture. Ductility is usually expressed as a per cent elongation in a 2-in. gage length. A ductile material has a value greater than 5% and a brittle material less than 5%. Since the per cent elongation is not a measure of the actual strain of the specimen, another method of measuring ductility is also used. This method is based on a per cent reduction of cross-sectional area between a specimen fractured in tension and the original area of the test specimen.

Ductility, an often overlooked material property, can play a very important role in deciding which material one should select for a particular design. For example, it is possible to have two materials of approximately equal tensile strengths and hardnesses, yet the one with greater ductility would be able to withstand a greater overload than the material with lesser ductility. Indeed, this conclusion would be obvious should one of these materials be

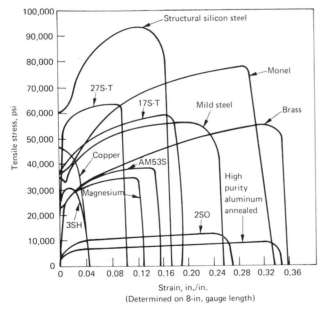

Figure 3-8 Ductility curve (in tension) for some metals and alloys. [*Technical Editor Speaks.* The International Nickel Co., Inc., New York, 1943.]

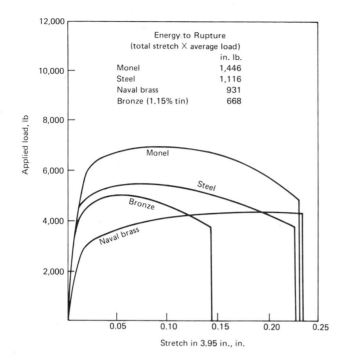

Figure 3-9 Ductility curves (in tension) for $\frac{3}{8}$-in. diameter bolt made of various materials. [*Technical Editor Speaks.* The International Nickel Co., Inc., New York, 1943.]

brittle and the other ductile. Material used for making bolts would be an application for a highly ductile material because bolt material is often subjected to prestressing in addition to its normal loads. Still another circumstance where good ductility is a highly desirable property is when material must be cold worked, such as in deep drawing, spinning, cold heading, bending, and so on. Unfortunately, materials that are both hard and of high tensile strength usually are not as ductile as those with lower hardness values and tensile strengths.

Figure 3-8 shows ductility curves for some metals and alloys based on an 8-in. gage length rather than a 2-in. gage length. Figure 3-9 shows the results of some strength-ductility tests on $\frac{3}{8}$-in. diameter bolts performed at Columbia University.

SECTION 3-19

Malleability

Malleability can be defined as the same as ductility, except that it is applied to compression. Thus, one can say that malleable materials permit high plastic deformation in compression without fracture. A malleable material is one that can easily be flattened or rolled without preheating. Gold, aluminum, copper, and lead are representative of materials that are highly malleable.

Modulus of Resilience

The modulus of resilience (U_p, inch-pounds per cubic inch) is defined as the ability of a material to absorb energy within its proportional limit. Thus, the area of the triangle formed by the elastic part of the stress-strain curve and the line dropped from the proportional limit perpendicular to the strain axis determines the numerical value of the modulus of resilience. Any area under the elastic curve less than that which determines the modulus is called the **strain energy** of the material. A detailed discussion of strain energy and its applications will be found in Chapter 6. For the present, we will merely note that, for a uniform member subjected to a tensile stress σ_t[3] the strain energy stored in the member is

$$U = \tfrac{1}{2}\sigma_t \varepsilon \qquad (3\text{-}7)$$

Since Hooke's law applies (that is, $\sigma_t = E\varepsilon$), equation (3-7) becomes

$$U = \frac{\sigma_t^2}{2E} \qquad (3\text{-}8)$$

If σ_t is the proportional strength S_p, then equation (3-8) becomes

$$U_p = \frac{S_p^2}{2E} \qquad (3\text{-}9)$$

where U_p is the modulus of resilience in inch-pounds per cubic inch of volume. In a similar manner, we can express the moduli of resilience for other types of loading, such as torsion, bending, and direct shear.

Modulus of Toughness

Toughness (U_T, inch-pounds per cubic inch) is the ability of a material to absorb energy and plastically deform before it fractures. Thus, as in the case for resilience, toughness can be calculated by evaluating the area under the stress-strain curve. The maximum toughness of a material is then

$$U_T = \int_0^{\varepsilon_f} \sigma \, d\varepsilon$$

To integrate this equation, one would have to know the explicit relation of σ as a function of ε. Because this is not generally known (at least in the plastic

---

[3] The English alphabet will be used for strength, and the Greek alphabet for stress.

region) other "schemes" are used to express a modulus of toughness. One of these is simply

$$U_T = S_u \varepsilon_f \tag{3-10}$$

where ε_f is the strain at fracture. Still another method is to multiply the strain at fracture by the arithmetic average of S_{yp} and S_u. Thus

$$U_T = \left(\frac{S_{yp} + S_u}{2}\right)\varepsilon_f \tag{3-11}$$

Toughness is usually associated with the ability of a material to withstand an impact or shock load. Two popular tests have been devised to determine the impact strength of materials. One such test is called the Izod impact test and the other is called the Charpy impact test.

The modulus of toughness is obtained by recording the difference between the potential energy of the pendulum weight before free fall and after the specimen is struck.[4] The values are indicated on a dial shown in Figure 3-10.

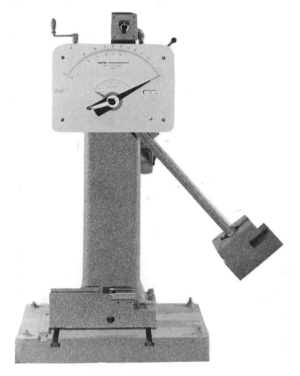

Figure 3-10   Izod impact testing machine. [Courtesy of Ametek, Inc.]

This difference in potential energy of the pendulum weight is the impact energy absorbed by the test specimen. A brittle material will generally break, whereas a tough material will only bend. To assure fracture, the specimens are notched to introduce a stress concentration.

[4] Variations of the Izod and Charpy tests are also used for torsional impact and tensile impact.

Although the data obtained by testing do not agree with calculated values based on the area under the stress-strain curve, it does permit the comparison of materials on a relative basis. Such information can help a designer select the tougher of two or more materials.

SECTION 3-22

Hardness

Selecting a material that has good resistance to wear and erosion is very much dependent upon the hardness and surface condition. For example, a material that must withstand both dynamic loading and wear should have both toughness and hardness. Such a material might be used for gears, cams, mechanical slides, and so on. The most generally accepted definition of hardness is the ability of a material to resist plastic indentation. Other measures of hardness are determined by the scratch test, the file test, and the Durometer test.

Several types of hardness testers are available for accurately measuring the hardness of all shapes of wrought materials. These are the Brinell, Rockwell, Vickers, and Shore Scleroscope hardness testers (see Figures 3-11, 3-12, 3-13, and 3-14, respectively).

Figure 3-11   Air-O-Brinell hardness testing machine. [Courtesy Tinius Olsen Testing Machine Co.]

Figure 3-12 Rockwell hardness testing machine. [Courtesy Wilson Instrument Division of ACCO, Bridgeport, Conn.]

Figure 3-13 Vickers pyramid hardness testing machine.

Figure 3-14 Scleroscope hardness testing machine. [Courtesy Shore Instrument and Manufacturing Co., Inc.]

The Brinell test is mainly used for materials whose thickness is $\frac{1}{4}$ in. or greater. The testing technique is to impress a 10-mm diameter hardened steel ball into the surface of the material under 3000-kg load for 15–60 sec. A smaller load is used when testing softer metals and alloys. The diameter, in millimeters, of the dent made by the ball is measured by a microscope, and the area is calculated. The Brinell hardness number is then found by dividing the load by the calculated area of the indentation. Representative values might be 250 BHN (3000 kg) or 100 BHN (500 kg).

One of the most popular types of testers is the Rockwell hardness tester. Since no measurements are made (as compared with the microscope measurements for the Brinell tester) and hardness can conveniently be read from an indicating dial, the device lends itself to production or shop use. Normally, materials of no less than $\frac{1}{16}$ in. in thickness are tested. The procedure is to indent the material with an initial load of 10 kg thus making a small penetration. The dial indicator is then set back to zero and a final heavier load is applied (see Figure 3-12). After the dial indicator has come to rest, showing that penetration has ended, the load is removed and the hardness is read directly from a scale on the dial indicator. Depending upon the material being tested, the penetrators can be a $\frac{1}{16}$-in. or $\frac{1}{8}$-in. diameter hardened steel ball or a diamond cone called a Brale. The following table shows a list of dial scales, indenters, indenting loads, and the associated materials to be tested.

Rockwell Scale	Indentor	Load, kg	Material
R_A	Brale	60	Very hard metals (e.g., tungsten carbide)
R_B	$\frac{1}{16}$-in. dia. ball	100	Soft metals (e.g., soft steel, copper alloys)
R_C	Brale	150	Hard metals (e.g., hardened steel, heat treated alloy steel)
R_D	Brale	100	Very hard metals
R_E	$\frac{1}{8}$-in. dia. ball	100	Soft metals (e.g., bearing materials, magnesium, aluminum)

R_F ($\frac{1}{16}$-in. dia. ball), R_H, R_K, R_L, R_M, R_R, R_S, (all with different size ball indentors) are used for soft materials (e.g., plastics, very soft metals, etc.)

R_G uses a $\frac{1}{16}$-in. ball indentor and is used for metals such as phosphor bronze

The Vickers hardness test is similar in principle to the Brinell test, as hardness is determined by the ratio of the impressed load to the indented area. However, rather than being a hardened steel ball as is the case in Brinell testing, the indenter is shaped like a square pyramidal point and is made of diamond. The diagonal lines formed by the diamond on the material surface are measured by a micrometer and are converted to an area. This area, divided into the applied load, is a measure of the material hardness. Of all the methods used to measure hardness, the Vickers is considered to be the most reliable. Hardness values are designated as follows: 250 $VHN_{10\text{-}p}$ or 150 $VHN_{120\text{-}b}$. The first designation says that a 10 kg load using a diamond pyramid reported a hardness of 250. The latter designation says that a 120 kg load using a 2-mm diameter ball reported a hardness of 150.

The last of the more common hardness measuring devices to be described is the Shore Scleroscope. This device measures the rebounding height of a freely falling diamond hammer that is dropped from a fixed height. The rebound is measured on a graduated dial scale that indicates the hardness. For example, a typical hardness is reported as 18 Shore. An arbitrary scale of 100 represents the highest hardness value. This number is based on the hardest tool steel. The material tested should have a relatively smooth surface for good results. The method is popular because it is easy and rapid to use. However, the results obtained are the least reliable of all machine methods.

For certain materials such as acrylics, phenolics, acetates, polyvinyl chlorides, fluorocarbons, and other "high-impact" molded or extruded plastics, the Rockwell hardness tester can be used. The hardness of softer plastics and wool felts is measured by the Shore Scleroscope.

Chapter 3: Mechanical Properties of Engineering Materials

Figure 3-15 Durometer hardness tester. [Courtesy The Shore Instrument and Manufacturing Co., Inc.]

Synthetic rubber, natural rubber, foam plastics, synthetic fiber felts, and similar materials are types that employ a Durometer hardness tester (see Figure 3-15). This instrument measures the hardness of a material by noting its resistance to elastic deformation and so no permanent indentation remains. The hardness readings are given in Durometer hardness numbers based on an arbitrary scale of 100.

Commonly used hardness numbers are not simply convertible each into the other. Figure 3-16 shows a conversion plot between Brinell, Rockwell, and Vickers hardness numbers. Also, Figure 3-17 shows the conversion

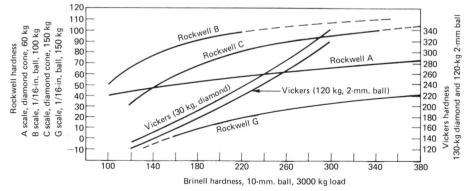

Figure 3-16 Conversion chart showing the approximate relation between Brinell, Rockwell, and Vickers hardness numbers. [*Technical Editor Speaks*. The International Nickel Co., Inc., New York, 1943.]

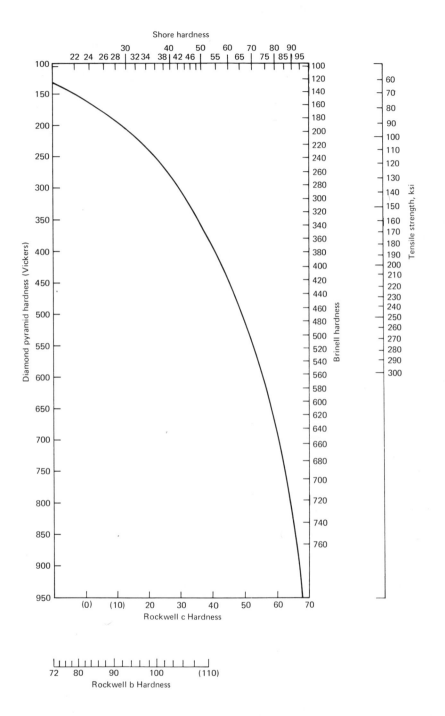

Figure 3-17 Hardness conversion and relationship to the ultimate tensile stress of steel. [Courtesy of The International Nickel Co., Inc.]

plot between Brinell, Rockwell C, Vickers and Shore hardness numbers, and the ultimate tensile strength of steel. Note that these curves are nonlinear and that the related values are only approximate. However, tests have shown a relationship between the Brinell hardness number and the ultimate tensile strength of carbon and alloy steels. This relationship (equation 3-12) is approximate and should only be employed when more definitive data are lacking,

$$S_u \cong 500 \, (BHN) \, psi \qquad (3\text{-}12)$$

Note that equation (3-12) should only be applied for steels with a Brinell hardness between 200 and 350 BHN.

SECTION 3-23

Endurance Strength (S_n, psi)

The endurance strength (also called **fatigue strength**) is the maximum, completely reversed stress under which a material will fail after it has

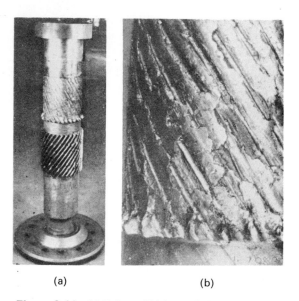

(a)   (b)

Figure 3-18 (a) Failure of high speed pinion by fatigue cracking of gear teeth. High tooth pressures produced pitting and "shelling-out," but the final fatigue failures, cracking, and fracture at the base of the teeth, were caused by repeated bending stresses on the weakened tooth sections. Torsional vibration of the shaft was probably a contributory cause. The teeth were initially too soft to resist wear. Thus this is a complex cause of failure. (b) At the right is shown an enlarged view of part of the pinion. [Batelle Memorial Institute: *Prevention of the Failure of Metals Under Repeated Stress.* John Wiley & Sons, Inc., New York, March 1949.]

experienced the stress for a specified number of cycles. Thus, when a value for the endurance strength of a material is stated, it *must* be accompanied by the number of stress cycles. Fatigue failures are quite damaging because such failures occur with no warning and at a stress much lower than the ultimate stress.

A fatigue failure usually has its origin in some surface imperfections (sometimes an imperfection below the surface can be the cause). These imperfections are manifold and can be due to manufacturing methods, heat treatment, environment, handling, raw material production, size effects, residual stresses, and surface coatings. Failure begins with the development of a small surface crack, transverse to the direction of the tensile stress (for example, rotating beam test). Because the load is alternating, the crack is continually "opened and closed"; this motion causes the adjacent faces to rub against one another, making these surfaces both smooth and polished in appearance. The remaining material finally is reduced to such a small area that it can no longer withstand the load and so breaks suddenly. The final area appears as a gray, granular structure, conveying the *false* argument that a brittle fracture has taken place. This misconception continues to persist. The fact that there are two distinct regions in a fatigue fracture is often useful in helping to find just how a structural or machine member failed because it is known that the material first started to separate at the point where the parted surfaces are shiny.

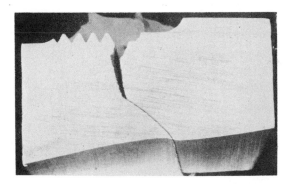

Figure 3-19 (× 3) Design error. The drawing failed to call for an undercut just beyond the threads to reduce the cross section below that at the base of the threads, and to decrease the stress concentration arising at the base of the last thread. This was in hard steel, 285 Brinell. The fracture was by fatigue down to the base of the open V, without deformation: from there down, by a sudden deformation failure. The broken parts were photographed together. This error caused failure in flight and resulted in a crash, killing the pilot. [Batelle Memorial Institute: *Prevention of the Failure of Metals Under Repeated Stress.* John Wiley & Sons, Inc., New York, March 1949.]

Figure 3-20 (× ¾) Propeller shaft that failed in flight after 150 hours. [Batelle Memorial Institute: *Prevention of the Failure of Metals Under Repeated Stress*. John Wiley & Sons, Inc., New York, March 1949.]

Figures 3-18, 3-19, 3-20, 3-21, and 3-22 are photographs of actual fatigue failures.

Endurance Limit

The endurance limit (S'_n, in pounds per square inch and also called **fatigue limit**) is the maximum, completely reversed stress for which it is assumed a material will "never" fail regardless of the number of stress cycles. Thus, the endurance limit is stated *without* an associated number of cycles to failure. It is generally accepted as being standard that ferrous materials that survive at least 10,000,000 cycles of stress reversals will have an infinite life. Non-ferrous materials such as brass, copper and copper alloys, aluminum, and

Figure 3-21 (× ⅕) Fatigue failure of aircraft engine crankshaft starting from keyway. [Batelle Memorial Institute: *Prevention of the Failure of Metals Under Repeated Stress*. John Wiley & Sons, Inc., New York, March 1949.]

Figure 3-22 Fatigue failure of a shaft. Failure started at the keyway where the transverse cracks grew to be so large that the remaining material could no longer sustain the load and the shaft finally broke. Note the shiny surface from the keyway to the break, which is granular in appearance. [Courtesy of Joseph T. Ryerson and Sons, Chicago, Ill.]

magnesium do not have an endurance limit; therefore only an endurance strength can be established for these materials.

Three types of endurance tests are performed. These are tension, torsion, bending, and combinations of these. The most common test is that of reversed bending and is performed by an R. R. Moore rotating beam test. Figure 3-23 shows such a machine and a standard test specimen. To perform a test, the specimen is loaded with a selected weight. Turning on the motor rotates the specimen, but not the weight. The longitudinal fibers of the specimen alternately feel a tensile and compressive stress for each rotation. Rotation is continued until rupture takes place, at which time the number of cycles (revolutions) to rupture is noted. ASTM *Special Technical Publication No. 91-A* entitled "Tentative guide for fatigue testing and the statistical analysis of fatigue data" clearly specifies the procedure that is to be followed and how the data are to be evaluated. The results of the tests are plotted on log-log or semilog paper where the rupture stress is the ordinate and the number of cycles to failure the abscissa.

Figure 3-24 is a typical plot of what the scatter of test points would look like. More in accord with the ASTM fatigue test, Figure 3-25 shows not only the scatter but the upper and lower survival levels. This figure demonstrates that an 84% survival rate represents about 1.4 times the standard deviation from the mean with a confidence level of 50%. This implies that the mean of future groups, from the same test batch, would have a survival rate greater than 84%, 84% of the time. A greater spread from the mean (for example, 2.8 times the standard deviation) would result in a survival rate of 99.5%.

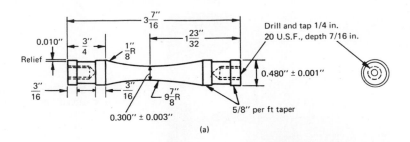

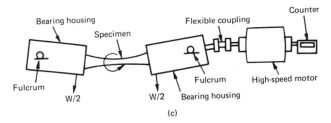

Figure 3-23 (a) Rotating beam test specimen. (b) The R. R. Moore rotating beam fatigue testing machine. (c) Schematic of the R. R. Moore testing machine. [Courtesy of Satec Systems, Inc.]

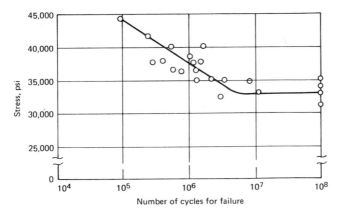

Figure 3-24 Endurance diagram for 0.37% carbon steel annealed. [From *Elements of Strength of Materials*, 2nd ed., by S. Timoshenko and Gleason H. MacCullough © 1940 by Litton Educational Publishing, Inc. Reprinted by permission of Van Nostrand Reinhold Company.]

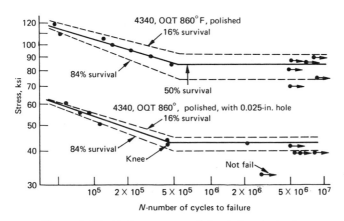

Figure 3-25 Endurance strength bands for rotating beam test. Notice for ductile steel that the upper and lower bands tend to converge at 10^3 cycles for ductile steel. [From V. M. Faires: *Design of Machine Elements*, 4th ed., The Macmillan Co., New York, 1965, p. 102.]

ASTM *Special Technical Publication No. 91-A* discusses in greater detail the important ramifications to be considered in various statistical aspects of fatigue testing. Most often, fatigue curves as well as tabulated values of endurance strengths and endurance limits are based upon a 50% probability curve. As a result, designers do not resort to using scatter-band curves like Figure 3-25 unless they are concerned with a design that involves a statistical approach. When the designer requires information of the highest order of reliability, he should *always* contact the manufacturer and/or run tests.

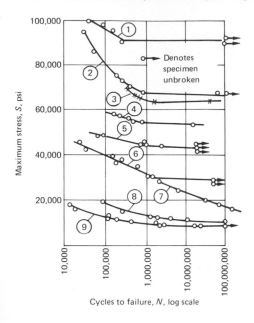

Figure 3-26 *S-N* diagrams from endurance tests. ① 1.20% carbon steel, quenched and drawn 860°F. ② SAE 3420, quenched and drawn 1200°F. ③ Alloy structural steel. ④ SAE 1050, quenched and drawn 1200°F. ⑤ SAE 4130, normalized and annealed. ⑥ Ordinary structural steel. ⑦ Duralumin. ⑧ Copper, alternately annealed. ⑨ Cast iron. [From Oscar J. Horger (ed.): *ASME Handbook, Metals Engineering Design*, 2nd ed. McGraw-Hill Book Co., New York, 1965.]

Figure 3-26 is a *S-N* plot showing the results of tests for several different materials. Notice that the curves for steel display a decided break (or "knee"), and many of these knees occur before or near 10×10^6 cycles. This establishes the reason for using this value as the basis of the endurance limit for steel, although many steels have values between 2×10^6 and 10×10^6 cycles. Using 10×10^6 cycles as the criteria for infinite life design, then, is rather conservative.

It is of interest to note that nonferrous materials do not show a break in their *S-N* curves and, as a result, a distinct endurance limit cannot truly be specified. Instead a stress value for a particular number of cycles will be given for various nonferrous materials. However, it has become customary to use the endurance strength at 100×10^6 or 500×10^6 cycles as the endurance limit for nonferrous materials.

Experiments have shown little correlation between the endurance limit and such mechanical properties as yield strength, ductility, and so on. However, some relationship between the endurance limit and tensile strength for *unnotched* and *polished* specimens tested by the rotating beam method is indicated experimentally. For steels not exceeding a tensile strength of approximately 200,000 psi, an endurance limit ratio (also called fatigue ratio) of 0.50 can be used when no specific endurance information is available. Thus we have (for 50% survival)

$$S'_n = 0.5S_u \qquad \text{for wrought steel where } S_u < 200,000 \text{ psi}$$
$$\text{and BHN} < 400 \tag{3-13}$$
$$S'_n = 100,000 \text{ psi} \qquad \text{for wrought steel where } S_u > 200,000 \text{ psi}$$

$S'_n = 0.4S_u$ for cast steel and cast iron   (3-14)

$S'_n = 0.38S_u$ for magnesium casting alloys and magnesium wrought alloys (based on 10^6 cycle life)   (3-15)

$S'_n = 0.45S_u$ for nickel-based alloys and for copper based alloys   (3-16)

$S'_n = 0.38S_u$ for wrought aluminum alloys up to a tensile strength of 40,000 psi[5] (based on 5×10^8 cycle life)   (3-17)

$S'_n = 0.16S_u$ for cast aluminum alloys up to a tensile strength of 50,000 psi (based on 5×10^8 cycle life)   (3-18)

where all of the relations are based on a 50% survival rate.

The endurance limit for reversed axial loading of a polished, unnotched specimen seems to have a 15% lower value than that for reversed bending. As a guide to design (since the results are based on widely scattered data) we can use relation (3-19) for reversed axial loading of steel specimens.

$S'_n = 0.85 \times$ endurance limit in reversed bending $= 0.43S_u$ (steel only) (3-19)

On first thought, one would expect the axial fatigue values to agree "exactly" with the bending fatigue values because in bending the longitudinal fibers are alternately stressed in tension and compression. The discrepancy is attributed to the great difficulty in applying a purely axial load without introducing a bending component. Also, in axially stressing the test specimen, all of the longitudinal fibers are subjected to the same average stress. In bending, however, the stress varies linearly from the neutral axis to the outer fibers.

For reversed torsional testing of polished, unnotched steel, specimens, the endurance limit is approximately 58% of that in bending. Therefore, we have relation (3-20) for the torsional endurance limit.

$$S'_{sn} = 0.58 \times \text{endurance limit in reversed bending}$$
$$= 0.29S_u \quad \text{(steel only)} \tag{3-20}$$

For cast iron and copper respectively, relations (3-21) and (3-22) can be used.

$$S'_{sn} \leqq 0.8 \times \text{endurance limit in reversed bending}$$
$$\leqq 0.32S_u \quad \text{(for cast iron)} \tag{3-21}$$

$$S'_{sn} \leqq 0.48 \times \text{endurance limit in reversed bending}$$
$$\leqq 0.22S_u \quad \text{(for copper)} \tag{3-22}$$

---

[5] For higher values of tensile strength, the endurance limit peaks out at about 16,000 psi (at 55,000 psi tensile strength) and then dips somewhat at still higher values of tensile strength.

All of the previous discussion relating to the endurance (that is, fatigue) strength is based on testing a polished laboratory specimen of a fixed size and geometric shape. As a result, the designer must modify these data by those factors that adversely affect results determined under laboratory conditions. The factors are a direct result of manufacturing, heat treating, geometry, environment, and so on. In fact, F. B. Stulen, H. N. Cummings, and W. C. Schulte [8] suggest that "the fatigue strength of a part based on the actual alternating stress seldom exceeds 70 per cent of the handbook value." J. Marin [9] suggests that the list of factors given in Table 3-1 be considered when determining an endurance strength or limit value to be used for design purposes.

Table 3-1 Factors Influencing Fatigue Strength

Material Effects	Environmental Effects
1. Chemical composition	1. Corrosion
2. Failure condition	2. Rest periods
3. Material variation	3. Superimposed static stress
4. Size and shape	4. Temperature
5. Speed	5. Varying amplitudes
6. Understressing & overstressing	6. Exposure to nuclear radiation
Manufacturing Effects	**Miscellaneous Effects**
1. Fretting fatigue and fretting corrosion	1. Surface fatigue
2. Heat treatment	2. Combined stresses
3. Method of manufacture	
4. Stress concentration	
5. Surface treatments	

Table 3-1 contains many factors that influence fatigue. These factors must be used in design applications with great care because much of the available information is based on specific specimens and tests. Literature pertaining to the effect of these factors on fatigue properties is quite scattered. Thus, the reader should make use of a few source references which, in turn, will lead him to specific documents having much greater detail. Of course, it goes without saying that one must always be "on top of" current work in order to take advantage of the latest information. Among the many excellent references available, (1) *Metal Fatigue* by G. Sines and J. L. Waisman, McGraw-Hill Book Co., New York 1959; (2) *Residual Stresses and Fatigue in Metals* by J. O. Almen and P. H. Black, McGraw-Hill Book Co., New York 1963; and (3) references [4], [10] and [11] cited at the end of this chapter, have been found most useful.

A full discussion of all the factors listed in Table 3-1 is beyond the scope of this text. Here we shall consider only those factors for which quantitative data are available. This information will be used to adjust the endurance limit S'_n to a value S_e—a working endurance limit. However, for completeness, some brief comments will be made in Section 3-30 on some of the more significant nonquantitative factors in Table 3-1 that can affect the value of S_n or S'_n.

SECTION 3-25

Effects of Material Variation— Reliability Factor

Material variation is one very important factor often overlooked by a designer or analyst when evaluating a mechanical component. Figures 3-24 and 3-25 show typical scatter values and scatter bands obtained in fatigue testing of metals. As mentioned earlier, most plots and tabulated data of endurance values are mean values and thereby imply a 50% survival rate. Since fatigue analysis is, at best, an estimate, it becomes desirable to design for some level of reliability that will acount for material variations in reported S-N data.

Lacking specific reliability information, it is suggested [8] that "8 per cent of the long-life strength may be assumed as a standard deviation provided the material is of good quality." Fatigue tests on various alloys have generally displayed a statistically normal curve distribution, so that the fatigue limit for fixed percentages of survivals can be obtained by sub-tracting a specified (that is, desired) number of standard deviations from the mean fatigue strength. Viewed from the standpoint of a fatigue strength reduction factor, we can write equation (3-23).

$$C_R = 1 - 0.08\,(\text{D.M.F.}) \tag{3-23}$$

where C_R = fatigue strength reduction factor based on reliability and D.M.F. = deviation multiplication factor from Table 3-2.

Table 3-2 Reliability Levels

Survival Rate, %	Deviation multiplication factor (D.M.F.)
90.00	1.28
95.00	1.64
98.00	2.05
99.00	2.33
99.90	3.08
99.99	3.62

SECTION 3-26

Influence of Size—Size Factor

The influence of size upon fatigue strength values can be a significant factor. It would seem to be obvious that there must be some effect due to size as a rotating beam test specimen is 0.3 in. in diameter at the smallest section. Although little quantitative data are available, due to the unlimited testing that would be required, endurance limits of the same material and hardness have been found to tend to decrease with increasing size for specimens subjected to bending and torsional loading (see Figure 3-27). The rationale for this decrease of endurance strength with increasing size is that a larger specimen is more apt to have internal defects (for example, inclusions, nonuniform cooling, and so on).

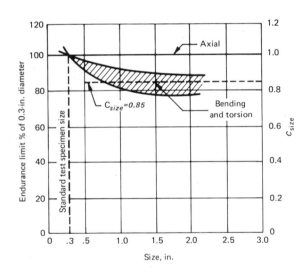

Figure 3-27 Size effect—bending, axial, and torsional loads. [From C. Lipson and R. C. Juvinall: *Handbook of Stress and Strength*. The Macmillan Co., New York, 1963.]

For bending and torsion of specimens greater than 0.3-in. diameter, the endurance strength is reduced by 15% up to specimens of 0.5-in. diameter. For specimens larger than 0.5-in. diameter, the reduction remains relatively constant up to approximately 2-in. diameter after which it begins to increase. One cannot generalize about the reduction required for larger specimens, but it can be as high as 25–30%. Prudent design would suggest using a factor $C_s = 0.70$, lacking other information. For critical designs, testing of component specimens must be performed for more accurate values. However, lacking specific information, relation (3-24) may be used as a fatigue strength reduction factor[6] due to size.

$$C_s = 0.85 \quad \text{(for bending and torsion of specimens from } \tfrac{1}{2} \text{ in. dia to 2 in. dia)} \quad (3\text{-}24)$$

[6] For varying loads of 1000 cycles or less, it is assumed that the loading is "static" and so $C_s = 1.0$.

For specimens in axial loading, tests have indicated that no size correction is necessary. The hypothesis for this is that, regardless of specimen size, there is a zero stress gradient.

SECTION 3-27

Effects of Methods of Manufacture— Surface Finish Factor

The method of manufacture has a most important effect on the endurance properties of metals. Different manufacturing techniques, such as casting, hot forging, cold forming, turning, grinding, polishing, welding, riveting, bolting, and so on, all contribute to altering the endurance strength of the material. One of the more obvious effects is that of the surface finish or condition of a machine or structural component.

Machining

A great deal of work has been done to elucidate the effect of surface finish on fatigue properties and the results are so diffuse that they cannot be adequately covered. However, Chapter 7.5 of reference [11] cites many references that contain more detailed information for the interested reader. We will merely review those aspects that are of immediate use and concern to the designer.

Noll and Lipson [12] collected the data concerning surface finish from various sources and plotted average curves of endurance limit versus tensile strength for each type of surface encountered. Figure 3-28 is the result of this task. The data used for Figure 3-28 were further employed to plot a series of curves that relate the tensile strength of each type of surface finish as a function of per cent of the endurance limit. These curves can be used as surface correction factors for the endurance limit of a steel. The curves and factors are shown in Figure B-3 of Appendix B.

The surface finish reduction factor C_F is used as a multiplying coefficient in modifying the endurance limit of a material in the same way that C_R and C_S are used. Also, as in the case of C_R and C_S, for loading cycles of 1000 or less, C_F can be taken as unity because the load application is assumed to be static.

The "hot-rolled curve" in Figure B-3, Appendix B, included data from specimens having slight surface irregularities, oxide, and scale defects as well as some decarburization.[7] The "as-forged" curve included specimens with larger surface irregularities as well as contained oxides and scale defects in addition to having had a total surface decarburization. This combination of surface defects and decarburization contributes greatly to reducing the endurance limit.

---

[7] Decarburization (see Section 2-9) not only reduces the static strength properties but also lowers the endurance strength and leaves a residual surface tensile stress.

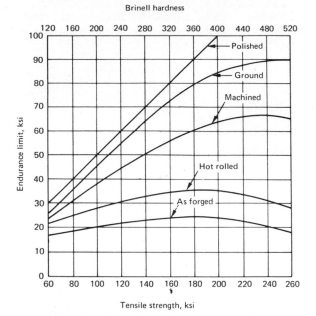

Figure 3-28 Endurance limit versus tensile strength for
various surface finishes of ferrous metals and alloys. The
results are based on unnotched test specimens subjected to
reversed bending. [From C. Lipson and R. C. Juvinall:
Handbook of Stress and Strain. The Macmillan Co., New
York, 1963.]

All the curves plotted are conservative; thus, any improvement in machining, scale removal, reduction of surface irregularities, or elimination of decarburization will increase the value of C_F. To obtain a more refined value of C_F, one can interpolate between the polished, ground, and machine curves using values from Figure 4 - 57 for different machining operations.

With non-ferrous metals and alloys such as aluminum, magnesium, copper, brass, and so on the surface finish reduction factor need not be considered when making fatigue calculation because the suppliers of these materials have accounted for the surface finish in stating endurance strengths.

Welding

Welding, which has become a popular method of manufacture particularly since the advent of automatic welding machines, can cause greatly reduced endurance properties of materials. The basic reason for this is that a weld produces a geometric change of shape at the joint and thus acts as a geometrical stress concentration factor. Figure 3-29 shows both a single and double butt weld. Load F causes stress lines to flow as shown, thereby causing stress increases at points 1, 2, 3, and 4. In addition, poor welding techniques, which prevent full penetration at such points as 1–2 and 5 and permit porosity and slag inclusions, contribute to stress intensity increases,

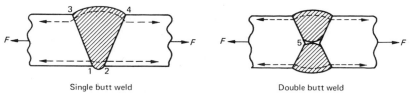

Single butt weld   Double butt weld

Figure 3-29 Points of stress concentration on typical butt welds.

causing a reduction of the weld's endurance strength. Grinding off the reinforcing weld material (that is, that part of the weld above the material surface) improves fatigue strengths by as much as 10–20 % [21]. This improvement was obtained for both longitudinal and transverse butt welds.

Reinforcing straps placed over a butt weld reduced its fatigue strength. Generally welding is confined to hot-rolled, annealed, or normalized materials because their strength is based on their composition rather than their heat treatment or cold working. Only certain alloy steels, austenitic stainless or heat treated aluminum are welded, and then mainly by spot or plug welding. Welded joints that are air cooled rapidly as compared to the base metal should be annealed after welding to reduce residual tensile stresses and possible cracking. Some weld materials, however, become brittle with annealing. Heavy sections should be preheated to a proper temperature before welding to avoid severe tensile stresses in the weld on cooling.

More detail and methods of analysis will be found in Chapter 17. Also, the *Welding Handbook* of the American Welding Society has a brief but excellent discussion concerning fatigue in welding. Until more extensive and reliable information is available, we may use the strength reduction factors as listed in Table 3-3.

Table 3-3 Endurance strength reduction factor C_w for welds

Type and Location of Weld	C_w
Reinforced butt weld	0.833
Toe of transverse fillet weld	0.667
End of parallel fillet weld	0.370
T butt joint with sharp corners	0.500

SOURCE: C. H. Jennings, *Welding Design*. Trans. ASME, Vol. 58, pp. 497–509, 1936.

SECTION 3-28

Effect of Stress Concentration

The causes of stress concentrations (also called stress raisers) are varied and numerous. Some causes, namely, surface finish, nonmetallic inclusions, and so on have already been discussed.

A stress concentration (or stress raiser) is any material condition that causes the local stress to be greater than the nominal stress. For some conditions, it is possible to introduce a fatigue strength reduction factor (that is, C_F for surface finish) and for others (for example, fretting) it is possible only to rely on qualitative data and direct experience. Geometry or shape of the specimen, one of the important stress concentration contributors, does have (at least for simple cases) a rational basis. In those instances which do not yield to analytical techniques, experimental methods (that is, photoelasticity, brittle coating, membrane analysis, strain gage) or testing of the actual component to be used have provided large quantities of useful data for design. In fact, much work is still proceeding to determine these factors for combined stresses.

The definition of the stress concentration factor is

$$\left.\begin{array}{c} K_t = \dfrac{\text{maximum stress at the section of interest}}{\text{nominal stress at the section of interest}} = \dfrac{\sigma_{max}}{\sigma_0} \\[2em] K_{ts} = \dfrac{\tau_{max}}{\tau_0} \end{array}\right\} \quad (3\text{-}25)$$

where K_t is considered as the theoretical (that is, geometric) stress concentration factor as it is a function solely of the specimen geometry. K_{ts} is the theoretical factor for shear.

Consider the flat plate in Figure 3-30a. Observe that the force flow lines are uniformly spaced at each end of the plate. At the notch, however, the outside force lines must change direction and are no longer uniformly spaced. Thus, within the vicinity of the notch, more force lines are flowing through a unit area. The local stress is thereby increased. The force flow line that is caused to bend the most represents the highest stress. As the lines move away from the notch, becoming straight again, the stress is reduced to its nominal value.

Figure 3-30b shows a stepped shaft that has been divided into four hollow tubes and a solid center shaft. The concentric tubes of the larger and smaller diameter sections are joined by smooth lines as indicated. The thickness of the outer tube at the point where the sections join is relatively thin. This

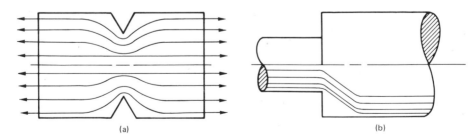

(a)   (b)

Figure 3-30 (a) Tensile stress flow lines. (b) Equitorque stress tubes for a circular stepped shaft.

means that the outer tube experiences a high stress. Note that the wall thickness increases with decreasing radius because the thickness is chosen so that the angle of twist per unit length is the same for each tube. This requirement is necessary because the concentric tube model must not experience any angular slip if it is to be equivalent to a solid shaft. As with a flat plate, the force lines are "crowded together" as they flow past a point of changing (that is, restrictive) geometry.

An additional example illustrating the influence of geometric change is that of a semi-infinite plate in tension with a small hole in the middle as shown in Figure 3-31. Theoretical analysis indicates a stress distribution such that the stress line tangent to the hole σ_{max} is 3 times as large as the nominal stress σ_0. Thus, the theoretical stress concentration factor K_t is 3.

The many geometric combinations subjected to different loadings are charted or tabulated in Appendix B. This appendix is by no means complete, and the reader is advised to investigate the references cited and other sources for those geometric combinations not included in this text.

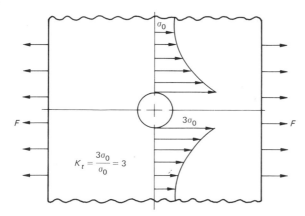

Figure 3-31   Stress distribution for a semi-infinite plate with a hole. Plate is in tension.

Look once again at Figure 3-30a. If the force lines are considered as fibers, they tend to straighten out at those points where they pass a discontinuity. In this case, it is the V notch. As a result, the distance between the notches is prone to increase slightly. This is called the biaxial effect due to geometric stress raisers. It results in a slight reduction of the theoretical stress concentration factor K_t. However, the reduction is small (of the order of 10%) and is generally ignored as a modifying factor in most design applications.

Theoretical stress concentration factors K_t are dependent solely upon the geometry of the specimen concerned. If all materials were uniformly homogeneous and free of surface marks or scratches, one would be justified in using K_t "as is" for fatigue stress calculation. However, materials are not homogeneous or free of surface defects. They can crack just as readily at a tool mark or scratch as they can at a fillet, keyway, or edge of a hole. Fatigue tests have shown that the theoretical stress concentration factor is rarely obtained (except for some high strength steels). Instead, a value smaller than K_t is indicated. It therefore becomes necessary to define a fatigue stress concentration factor K_f.

$$K_f = \frac{\text{endurance limit of a specimen free of notches}}{\text{endurance limit of a notched specimen}} \quad (3\text{-}26)$$

Since unlimited testing would be required to produce values of K_f, it is desirable to relate the theoretical K_t to the fatigue K_f for various notch sizes, materials and heat treatments. R. E. Peterson [14] suggests the ratio in (3-27) called the notch sensitivity factor q

$$q = \frac{K_f - 1}{K_t - 1} \quad (3\text{-}27)$$

or for torsion (or shear)

$$q = \frac{K_{fs} - 1}{K_{ts} - 1} \quad (3\text{-}28)$$

Solving equations (3-27) and (3-28) for K_f gives

$$K_f = 1 + q(K_t - 1) \quad (3\text{-}29)$$

$$K_{fs} = 1 + q(K_{ts} - 1) \quad (3\text{-}30)$$

Equations (3-29) and (3-30) can now be used to find a value of K_f, provided one knows what to assign for q.

Although little information exists concerning q for a large number of materials, Figure B-2 in Appendix B provides data for ferrous material of different hardness and an aluminum alloy. In those instances where one lacks specific data concerning q, it is not unreasonable to choose q to be $0 \leqslant q \leqslant 0.2$ for materials that are prone to be insensitive to notching (for example, low strength cast irons). For a cast iron ASTM No. 50, T. E. Eagan [15] states that one may use $K_f = 1.25$. On the other hand, if one is uncertain of a value for q, it would be conservative to let $q = 1$ and therefore $K_f \equiv K_t$.

The reader should note that K_t is not only the theoretical (or geometric) stress concentration factor but is based on static loading conditions. Consequently, brittle materials such as cast iron and concrete, which do not display a yield point, will suddenly fail when stressed to their ultimate value. Therefore, in all cases of *static* loading involving brittle materials, K_t must be used to account for any stress raiser. One may write for the static loading of brittle materials

$$N = \frac{S_{ut}}{K_t \sigma_t} \quad \text{(for tension)} \qquad N = \frac{S_{uc}}{K_t \sigma_c} \quad \text{(for compression)} \quad (3\text{-}31)$$

where S_{ut} and S_{uc} are the ultimate strengths for tension and compression, respectively, N is the factor of safety, and σ_t and σ_c are the nominal calculated stresses for tension and compression.

Brittle materials are rarely considered for fatigue stress applications because most such materials have low fatigue strength properties, and their use would require a large factor of safety. However, certain cast irons (for example, nodular) do have "acceptable" values for endurance limits and can be analyzed rationally by using the Goodman line of failure (see Chapter 6).

Considerable effort has been expended on explaining the theoretical stress concentration factor; therefore, the reader may be surprised to learn that its use is normally restricted to ductile materials subjected to varying (that is, fatigue) loads (note its inclusion in this section on fatigue). The explanation for the restriction is quite simple. It results from the fact that a ductile material will not fracture immediately past the yield point but will "give" instead, becoming plastic. This relieves the stress concentration at the discontinuity. Consequently, the stress concentration factor is usually ignored in static loading of ductile materials. However, when the load is continuously varying, fatigue cracks can develop so that plastic yielding at a point of stress concentration is of no value in delaying possible failure. Thus, $1/K_f$ is used as a multiplying coefficient for correcting the endurance limit. This is discussed in Section 3.29.

The problems encountered in "real life" situations are, as one might expect, much more complex than those ordinarily encountered in an "ideal" classroom situation. For example, it is most likely that a machine component, such as a drive shaft, will have portions of different diameters—a keyway, oil holes, press-fitted surfaces, and possibly other areas that act as stress raisers. The novice very often will consider the point of the shaft that has the highest stress concentration factor K_t. This may be a grave mistake because the mechanics of the problem and the location of the stress raiser are the deciding factors for finding the "worst" spot for analysis. Admittedly, such a location may sometimes be chosen by observation, but it is strongly suggested that all locations be considered before one is decided upon as the "worst of the lot". Chapter 7, dealing with shaft design, clarifies this point.

Quite often two stress concentration factors must be considered for the same location. For example, an oil hole at the fillet of a stepped shaft is representative of such a case. The meager information available indicates that the cumulative results of two such factors are greater than the individual factors but less than the product of both factors. However, Lipson and Juvinall suggest using the product of both theoretical stress concentration factors in the notch sensitivity equation (3-29) or (3-30) to obtain K_f or K_{fs}.

A good designer must do his best to reduce or eliminate areas with severe stress concentrations. Inspection of Figure 3-30 suggests that the intensity of the stress concentration factor would be much reduced if the paths of the force flow lines did not cause sharp changes or crowding of lines. Figure 3-32 illustrates various ways in which geometric changes can contribute to

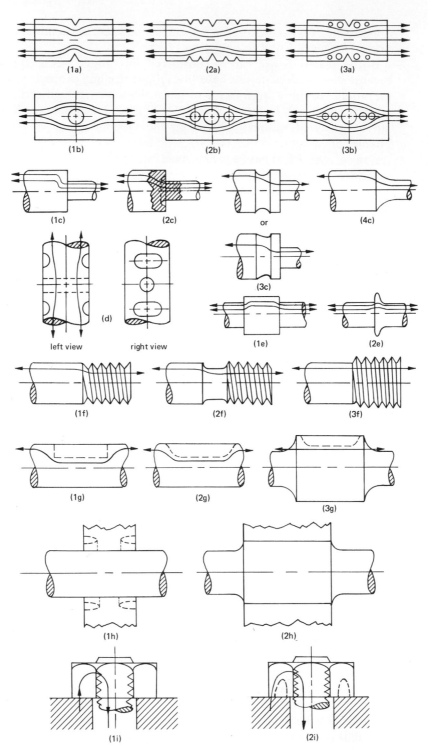

(1a) (2a) (3a)

(1b) (2b) (3b)

(1c) (2c) or (4c)

(3c)

(d)

left view right view

(1e) (2e)

(1f) (2f) (3f)

(1g) (2g) (3g)

(1h) (2h)

(1i) (2i)

118

Figure 3-32 *Opposite*: Different ways to mitigate stress concentrations. The recommendations are obvious except perhaps for case (*i*). In this case, by cutting away part of the nut bearing surface, the stress has been transferred from the bolt to the nut preventing it (that is, the bearing stress) from being concentrated at the bolt threads.

reducing stress concentrations. Notice that the modifications shown in Figure 3-32 allow the force flow lines to pass through the specimen more smoothly than if there were no modifications. In other words, it is desirable to reduce or eliminate abrupt changes in the direction of these lines. Figures 3-33b, d, and f are also ways of reducing stress concentrations due to force fits.

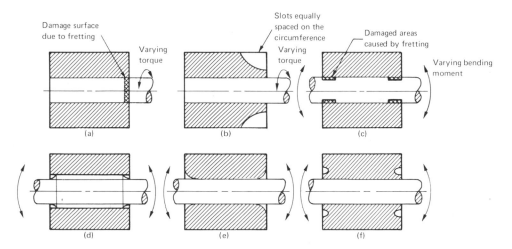

Figure 3-33 (a) Press-fitted shaft in torsion. (b) Relief of fretting problem due to torsion by permitting greater movement of the housing and thereby reducing slip. (c) Press-fitted shaft in bending. (d), (e), and (f) Alternate ways to relieve fretting caused by bending. Further improvement can be obtained by prestressing (that is, surface compression) that part of the shaft that has not benefited from the increased flexibility of the housing.

SECTION 3-29

A Working Equation for the Endurance Limit

The various endurance limit reduction factors are used to establish a modified (that is, working) endurance limit S_e.

$$S_e = C_R C_S C_F C_W (1/K_f) S'_n \tag{3-32a}$$

$$S_{es} = C_R C_S C_F C_W (1/K_{fs}) S'_{ns} \tag{3-32b}$$

where

C_R = reliability factor (from equation 3-23)

C_S = size correction factor (from equation 3-24)

C_F = surface finish correction factor (from Figure B-3, Appendix B)

C_W = weld correction factor (from Table 3-3)

S_n' = endurance limit of the material

K_f = fatigue stress concentration factor (from Appendix B)

K_{fs} = fatigue stress concentration factor for shear

The coefficients in equations (3-32a and b) are used as required. Equation (3-32) is extremely important in fatigue problems. The designer may further decide to reduce the value of S_e calculated by equation (3-32a) by factors due to tensile surface stress, nonmetallic inclusions, effect of heat treatment, grain flow and size, and so on. Unfortunately, these factors have no quantitative values. The values assigned (that is, smaller than 1 if the effects are deleterious and greater than 1 if the effects are beneficial) will depend on the designer's experience, judgement, and job observation. These and other nonquantitative factors affecting S_n' and S_{ns}' are discussed in Section 3-30.

SECTION 3-30

Effect of Some Important Nonquantitative Factors

Fretting fatigue

Fretting fatigue takes place in those instances when two mating parts, which are in close contact, rub against each other because of vibrations or repeating loads. The rubbing is usually confined to local areas and contributes to the deterioration of the contact surfaces. Deterioration may be so severe that the damaged surfaces actually begin to crack. This must ultimately lead to a reduced fatigue strength, and possibly to eventual fracture. Applications in which fretting fatigue and fretting corrosion problems must be considered are press or shrink fits of various elements onto shafts or pins, keyed shafts and joints, bolted or riveted connections, spring connections, splined connections, balls and ball races of bearings, bearing race and shaft, bearing race and housing, crankpins, wrist pins, gear teeth, leaf springs, clamps, and so on. Note that the examples given represent cases such as interference fits, bolted and riveted connections, and ball and roller bearings, which have little if any pressure but develop high contact pressures due to repeated loading that leads to fretting failures.

Fretting corrosion

Fretting corrosion is often classified as a part of fretting fatigue but is actually quite distinct and has a nature of its own. In fretting corrosion, the repeated loads are too weak to cause fracture by fatigue and any damage to the material (cracking or corrosion) takes place at the edge of the contacting parts or within the local contact area. In fact, we may think of fretting corrosion as a type of damage that is associated with wear, surface damage, and accumulated debris. On the other hand, in fretting fatigue, we may think of the damage in terms of direct fracture.

Factors such as atmosphere, materials, temperature, humidity, load, load frequency, number of cycles, relative motion between parts (that is, slip), lubrication, surface finish, and closeness of fit all play a part in governing the rate of fretting corrosion. Few of these factors can be controlled; but the designer still wishes to know how to eliminate or reduce fretting corrosion and fatigue. He may consider (1) changing the combination of mating materials [see reference 16], (2) using a lubricant such as MoS_2 (molybdenum disulfide) in combination with corn syrup, grease, or petroleum jelly, (3) insertion of plastic (for example, teflon, nylon) or rubber shims between the contacting surfaces, (4) electroplating with cadmium, nickel, or zinc, (5) introducing surface compressive stresses by mechanical means (for example, shot peening, rolling) or by a heat treating method (method 5 is particularly effective with interference fits) or (6) increasing the contact load so that relative motion is eliminated. (Of course, if the relative motion is not completely eliminated by increasing the contact load, the fretting damage will worsen, and the designer must make design adjustments to relieve the harmful effects of fretting.) Figure 3-33 shows some ways of reducing fretting in press-fitted shafts subject to torsion or bending.

Heat treatment

Proper heat treatment of metals can be extremely beneficial in improving the fatigue properties of a metal. In particular, it is one of several ways **residual stresses** may be introduced which, if properly used in design, have beneficial effects in reducing fatigue damage. Residual stresses are classified into two categories. These are macrostresses and microstresses. Macrostresses are stresses that can be determined quantitatively and are based on elastic-plastic analysis. Microstresses are those stresses concerned with the granular structure, its loading and deformation or slip. These stresses are, therefore, described by qualitative means. Before proceeding further, it would be helpful to describe how a residual stress might be introduced into a metal.

For purposes of illustration, assume that a stress-free rectangular mild steel bar is subjected to a pure bending moment M, large enough to cause the bar to become completely plastic. Looking at Figure 3-34a we see that the path OAB on the stress-strain curve has been traversed. The stress distribution on the bar appears as shown in Figure 3-34b. The bending moment is now slowly but completely removed. Removing M allows the material to spring back and the stress-strain curve follows Hooke's law. It proceeds along BC, parallel to OA as shown in Figure 3-34a. Note that there is now a permanent strain OC. The unloading stress distribution is

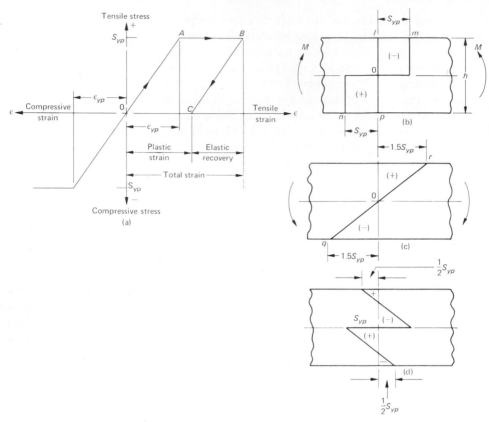

Figure 3-34 Ideal elastic-plastic model for obtaining a residual stress in the outer fibers of a bar (or beam). The magnitude of the stress in part (a) is obtained by noting that, because of equilibrium, the moment of the triangular stress distribution taken about the neutral axis is equal to the moment of the rectangular stress distribution taken about the same axis. The magnitude of the residual stress is obtained by algebraically adding the stress values of parts (b) and (c) to obtain part (d).

shown in Figure 3-34c. Superimposing the elastic unloading curve in Figure 3-34c on to the perfectly plastic loading curve in Figure 3-34b results in the final stress distribution as shown in Figure 3-34d. Part d shows the residual stress distribution throughout the bar caused by plastic flow. Close observation of this part d indicates that the top fibers, which were originally loaded in compression, now have a residual tensile stress, and the bottom fibers, which were originally loaded in tension, now have a residual stress of compression.

The quenching process used in the course of heat treating a steel can also introduce residual surface stresses that are either tensile or compressive. Which of the two stresses finally appears depends on whether the quench was thermal or was both thermal and metallurgical. For example, consider

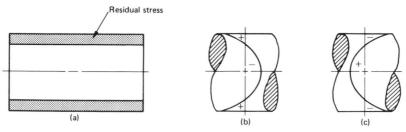

Figure 3-35 Resulting residual stress pattern caused by quenching.

a round bar of steel, as shown in Figure 3-35, that has been heated above its upper critical temperature (for example, 1500°F) so that the steel is basically all austenitic. The specimen is then quenched (for example, in oil, water, or brine) quickly and forms a metallurgical structure (that is, pearlite, bainite, or martensite) depending on the quenching temperature and the time.

Analyzing this rather rapid process sequentially, we find that, due to cooling, the surface of the bar (shown by the gray area in Figure 3-35) tends to contract. Since it is, however, part of the hotter core, it is prevented from doing so. The surface layer, then, is momentarily in tension while the core is in compression.[8] Next, as the outside layers harden and form crystals (for example, martensite), the tensile stress is somewhat reduced because the transformation to martensite causes a slight expansion in volume. By now, the surface is rather cool; the core, however, still being hot, continues to cool and therefore contracts. This contraction of the core causes the outside to contract again and again be placed in compression or reduced tension while the core is in tension. Finally, as the core reaches the temperature to form martensite, it expands. This expansion now acts on the outer layer, which is quite hard and will not readily move with the core. As a result, the stress in the outside layer of the bar is changed to tension or reduced compression. The resulting stress distribution would have a profile as shown in Figure 3-35b.

On the other hand, if the bar had been heated to 1200°F, a temperature too low to form austenite, it would not have experienced a phase transformation with its associated volume increase on cooling. The outer layer of the bar shown in Figure 3-35 would cool and tend to contract before the core. However, it is prevented from doing so readily by the core. The outer layer is subjected to tension whereas the core is in compression. As the core cools further, it tends to contract and place the outer layer in compression, because this layer has already cooled to about room temperature. Consequently, the core is in tension. The final stress distribution is that shown in Figure 3-35c.

Note that the procedure for heat treatment involved both thermal contraction and phase-change volume expansion, whereas the latter process

---

[8] Surface cracks may develop in brittle material due to high temperature gradients and subsequent heating or cooling. This cracking is called spalling.

involved only thermal contraction. Quenching in general, regardless of the initial temperature, must be performed carefully, otherwise warping or surface cracks may develop that would be injurious to the material when subjected to fatigue loads.

Since fatigue failures are always due to tension, a residual compressive surface stress would help to counteract the effect of fatigue stressing.

In completing a heat treating process, tempering is often specified to relieve unwanted residual stresses. Care must be exercised, however, in order that a desired surface compression is not removed and perhaps even changed to tension.

The method described above (that is, quenching and subsequent tempering) will not only produce a compressive stress on the surface of a steel part but will also result in hardening the section throughout. The gradations of hardness as we move from the surface towards the middle portions will vary according to rate of quench, quenching medium, and component size and shape (see Section 2-8).

It is sometimes desirable to heat treat only the surface of a part in order that its surface be hard while its middle remains tough. Two popular methods used to attain this objective are flame hardening and induction hardening (see Section 2-9). Both methods heat the surface of the steel, after which it is rapidly quenched. This produces a residual surface stress as well as a hardened surface. If the steel is of high enough carbon or alloying content, the heated surface will undergo a volume increase due to the formation of martensite. The surface, then, will be left with a residual compressive stress. For induction hardening, the depth of hardened case is about 0.100–0.200 in. depending on the carbon content, alloying constituents, and quenching medium. For flame hardening, the case varies between $\frac{1}{8}$ and $\frac{1}{4}$ in. thickness. It is also of interest to note that flame or induction hardened parts that are press-fitted (therefore subject to fretting erosion) show greater resistance to fatigue failure due to the residual surface compressive stress.

Any form of heat treatment in addition to the ones mentioned will produce a residual stress in the component part. The kind of stress and whether it is beneficial or injurious depends on many factors, and the size and shape of the part are of paramount importance. Some of the other factors are carbon content, heating temperature, type and temperature of cooling medium, and cooling rate. If little thought is given to a heat treating operation and no account is taken of the physical shape of the part, not only can unfavorable residual stresses occur but actual failure due to what is called "quench cracking" [1] takes place. Temperature of the heated surface, final surface hardness, and the depth of hardness all in combination determine the affinity of a part towards cracking. In turn, the size of the component and carbon content of the material have to be compatible with the hardness and depth to avoid cracking.

Grain size, which varies with heat treatment, is considered to be of little significance in fatigue [4]. Apparently, the only significant effect of grain size is that both strength and hardness (that is, notch sensitivity) increase with decreasing grain size.

Grinding

There is much evidence [17, 18] to show that grinding produces unfavorable tensile residual stresses in the surface of steels that decreases the endurance strength. However, other investigators [13, 19] have found that careful grinding in the longitudinal direction of round and flat components did not adversely affect the endurance properties of the material (for example, AISI 521000 steel with 20% vanadium, which was quenched and tempered to Rockwell C 45 and 59). For cases where the grinding was not carefully performed, the endurance limit was reduced about 25%. Shot peening and tumbling did, nevertheless, help to bring the material back to its original endurance strength.

Polishing

Hand polishing in a direction parallel to loading (with fine grade emery cloth) produces a greater fatigue strength than that produced by electro-polishing [16]. The reason for this phenomenon is suggested by Cina [19] as being due to a slight cold-working of the surface caused by mechanical polishing. Electrolytic polishing, however, has little affect or can even remove the benefit of cold working. The modern technique of electrolytic grinding causes no residual stresses while producing surface finishes of 5–10 μ.

Mechanical surface treatment

Surface treatment of mechanical or machine elements can have a very marked effect on both the endurance and static strength properties of the material used. These effects can be either negative or positive, depending on the particular process involved. As indicated earlier, most grinding operations are not beneficial because they result in an unwanted residual tensile stress in the material surface. On the other hand, careful grinding and subsequent polishing can produce a desirable residual compressive surface stress. Flame or induction hardening followed by quenching can produce beneficial surface compression or adverse tensile stresses—even cracking, depending on the rate of quench, quenching medium, and so on.

There are several **cold working** processes that are used to introduce residual surface compressive stresses. These methods are shot peening, surface rolling, air hammering, stretching and drawing. Of these methods, shot peening and surface rolling are the more frequently used operations. All of the methods cause the metal surface fibers to stretch past the yield point and into the plastic region. The material layers underneath the surface, having also been stretched by the outer fibers, remain elastic and return to their original length when the cold working operation is completed. This gives the outer surface fibers a compressive stress—the layers of material below the surface (that is, the core) remain in tension.

Chapter 3: Mechanical Properties of Engineering Materials

Shot peening is performed by one of two types of machines. One machine ejects pellets at a high velocity from a centrifugal wheel and is capable of raining a large volume of shot onto the surface being treated. For volume production the centrifugal type is preferred. The other machine uses compressed air to "shoot" the pellets out at a high velocity. This method is often employed in shot peening difficult spots, such as holes, recesses, and so on. Shot peening results in a metal surface finish having a roughness of about 65–200 microinches (μin.)

The positive effect of shot peening can be quite significant and, at times, even remarkable. Figures 3-36, 3-37, 3-38, and 3-39 as well as Table 3-4 attest to this improvement. Figures 3-36, 3-37, and 3-39 are obvious and need no comment. Figure 3-38 clearly demonstrates the depth of compressive stress caused by shot of different diameters. It is desirable that the depth of the residual stress be deep enough to offset any tendency of surface failure due to repeated loads. Table 3-4 indicates that markedly improved fatigue strengths are to be obtained by shot peening. The amount of improvement, however, depends on the surface condition of the material. It appears that the manufacturing process having the "roughest" surface finish realizes the greatest improvement in fatigue strength.

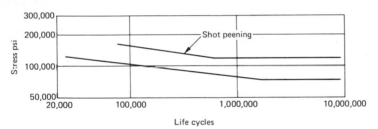

Figure 3-36   Effect of shot peening on the endurance strength of spring steel [Courtesy Wheelabrator-Frye, Inc.]

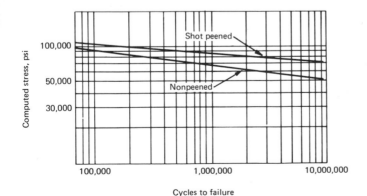

Figure 3-37   Effect of shot peening on carburized spur and helical automotive gears. [Courtesy Wheelabrator-Frye, Inc.]

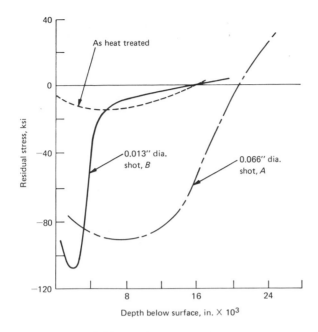

Figure 3-38 Profile of residual stress due to shot peening. The material is SAE 5147 alloy steel with a hardness of Rockwell C scale of 48. [From R. L. Mattson: *Proc. Int. Conf. Fatigue Metal.* Institute of Mechanical Engineering, London, 1956.]

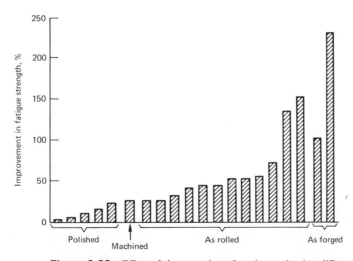

Figure 3-39 Effect of shot peening of steel parts having different surface finishes. [From C. Lipson: More realistic measure of shot-peening effectiveness. *Steel*: (Aug. 6, 1951).]

Table 3-4 Effect of Shot Peening on Endurance Limit with Different Metals having Prior Surface Treatment

Mateiral	Specimen	Treatment Prior to Shot Peening	Surface Prior to Shot Peening	Increase in Endurance Limit, %
SAE 1020 steel	Plate	As rolled	Polished	9
SAE 1045 steel	Plate	Normalized	Polished	11
SAE 1050 steel	Plate	As rolled	Polished	22
SAE S4340 steel	Standard	Quenched and drawn	Polished	18
Ni-Cr-Mo steel	Standard	Carburized	Polished	4
Alloy steel	Bar	Hardened	Polished	2
Alloy steel	Bar	Hardened	Machined	23
SAE 1020 steel	Plate	As rolled	Hot rolled	34
SAE 1045 steel	Plate	Induction hardened	Hot rolled	50
Rail steel	Rail	As rolled	Hot rolled	32
0.65 steel	Wire	As drawn	Hot rolled	42
SAE 1095 steel	Wire	As drawn	Hot rolled	50
Ni-Cr-Mo steel	Standard	Carburized	Hot rolled	23
NE 9470 steel	Standard	Carburized	Hot rolled	50
NE 9240 steel	Standard	Carburized	Hot rolled	53
NE 8650 steel	Axle	Quenched and tempered	As forged	100
NE 8650 steel	Axle	{ Normalized and tempered	As forged	54
NE 8650 steel	Flat bar	{ Quenched and tempered	Severely ground	90
4340 steel	Shaft	{ Quenched and tempered	Chrome plating*	90
Phosphor bronze	Coil spring			40
Beryllium copper	Coil spring			80
S-816 (Co-Cr-Ni base)	Coil spring			80
18-8 stainless	Coil spring			70
13-2 stainless	Coil spring			50

SOURCE: C. Lipson, G. C. Noll, L. S. Clock: *Stress and Strength of Manufactured Parts*. McGraw-Hill Book Co., Inc., New York, 1950.

*Shot peening performed before chrome plating.

Surface rolling[9] improves the fatigue properties, as does shot peening, by causing the metal surface to sustain a residual surface compressive stress. However, with surface rolling, it is easier to obtain greater depths of compressive stress. These depths can be calculated [24, 25, 26], giving this method a more rational basis than shot peening.

The method uses sets of hardened rollers that press against the surface to be worked with a high pressure. The procedure is not as universal in application as shot peening and is reserved mainly for cold working round surfaces at significant locations of stress concentration such as fillets,

[9] Do not confuse this term with cold rolled steel, which is a method of manufacturing a standard steel warehousing item. The item is continuously reduced in size by means of a rolling mill.

Table 3-5   Surface Rolling Effects on the Endurance Limits of Specific Materials

Material	Specimen	Treatment Prior to Cold Working	Surface Prior to Cold Working	Increase in Endurance Limit, %
		Cold rolling		
SAE 1045	Bar	Normalized	Polished	6
SAE 1045	Bored	Quenched and tempered	Polished	52
SAE 1045	Bored	Quenched and tempered	Polished	33
SAE 1045	Bar	Normalized	Machined	27
SAE 1045		Notched	Machined	120
SAE 1045		Notched	Machined	52
SAE 1050	Press fit	Normalized	Machined	150
3.1 Ni	Press fit	Normalized	Machined	33
0.35 C	Thread	Quenched and tempered	Machined	33
0.20 C	Bars	Hot rolled	Hot rolled	67
Alloy steel	Shaft with fillet	Normalized and tempered	Polished	68
Alloy steel	Shaft with fillet	Normalized and tempered	Polished	56
Alloy steel	Shaft with fillet	Quenched and tempered	Polished	30

SOURCE: C. Lipson, G. C. Noll, L. S. Clock: *Stress and Strength of Manufactured Parts*, McGraw-Hill Book Co., Inc., New York, 1950.

grooves, diameters subject to interference fits, and so on. Surface rolling is also used in thread rolling, on splined surfaces, and on welded joints called planishing. Table 3-5 indicates that much benefit is to be gained in improving endurance limits by surface rolling.

Carburizing

Carburizing (see Section 2.9) is a surface hardening process primarily intended to resist wear or abrasion and is produced on a low carbon steel. Tests, however, have shown that fatigue properties also benefit greatly from carburizing. For example, in tests [27] by the rotating beam method, a $\frac{5}{16}$-in. AISI 2317 normalized steel has an endurance limit of 48,000 psi. This same steel was then carburized (0.05-in. case), water quenched, and tempered. The rotating beam test for the treated specimen showed an endurance limit of 120,000 psi—a clear increase of 150%. The same test for a AISI 2513 normalized, resulted in an endurance strength of 54,000 psi before carburizing and an endurance strength of 123,000 psi after carburizing—an increase of 123%.

Other tests [28] on a 0.2% carbon steel, 0.3-in. diameter bar resulted in an endurance limit of 33,000 psi. After carburizing with a 0.03-in. thick case, the endurance limit rose to 45,000 psi. This test produced an increase of only 36.4%, but nevertheless an increase. The same steel with a radial hole had an endurance limit of 48,000 psi when tested before carburizing and 62,300 psi after carburizing. This shows how carburization can overcome the drawbacks of stress raisers.[10] The same material when tested [27] in reversed torsional fatigue showed an improvement of 159% (17,000 psi to 41,000 psi) in its endurance limit.

Carburized and hardened gears are more desirable than through-hardened gears when fatigue is a serious factor. Tests [29] have shown that carburized and hardened gears improved fatigue strengths from 20 to 90% over 'that of oil- or air-hardened gears.

A summary compiled by E. R. Gadd [30] indicates that carburizing and hardening produce improvements of 32–105% for unnotched specimens and 82–230% for notched specimens. In particular, the advantage of carburizing is greatly enhanced when the depth of case (that is, the thickness of the hardened surface) is deeper than some surface defect or stress raiser. This is due to the fact that the case is in compression.

Carburizing produces an outer case on the material with a hardness range of 58–63 Rockwell C obtained by tempering at 300–400°F after hardening. The thickness of the case and its hardness are of primary concern in design. Both of these parameters are a function of time and temperature [11]. Case thicknesses vary from a few thousands of an inch to as much as $\frac{1}{4}$ in. or more. Commercial practice specifies a "light case" as being from 0.02 up to 0.04-in. thick, a "medium heavy case" as being from 0.04 up to 0.06 in. thick, and a "heavy case" as being over 0.06-in. thick. Figure 3-40 shows a representative hardness versus depth profile for a carburized specimen.

The problem facing the designer in specifying the case depth and hardness is whether the case hardened layer or the core will be most likely to fail when subjected to a specified loading. Lipson and Juvinall [10] present an analytical model that can help the designer resolve this dilemma. Although, as shown in Figure 3-40, the hardness varies inversely with the depth of case, the model assumed by Lipson and Juvinall is one in which there are two distinct hardness levels. The first is the outer layer, which is uniformly hard throughout its thickness. The second is the core, which is also uniformly through-hardened but is not as hard as the outer case. For a detailed explanation of this concept, the reader should refer to reference [10].

Nitriding

Nitriding (see Section 2.9) produces somewhat similar results to those of carburizing but does not produce the distortion caused by severe quenching of carburization because no heat treatment is required after the steel is heated to just below the critical temperature. However, nitriding does induce higher residual stresses along with a sharp increase of strength and

---

[10] Any machine operation (e.g., drilling, grooving, etc.) must be performed before carburizing.

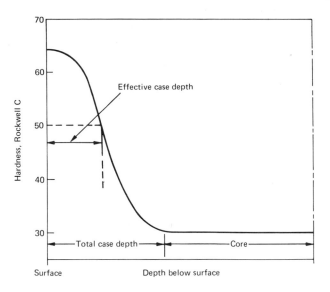

Figure 3-40 A representative hardness profile of a carburized
part. Total case depth means the *total* depth of carbon
penetration. Effective case depth is that depth below the surface
of the specimen at which a hardness of 50 Rockwell C is
exceeded. The case depth and effective depth are design
parameters and should be carefully considered and specified.
[From Oscar J. Horger (ed.): *ASME Handbook, Metals
Engineering Design*, 2nd ed. McGraw-Hill Book Co., New York,
1965.]

is more expensive than carburizing. Not all steels can be nitrided, and the
process is reserved for certain alloy steels.

The needed depth of case depends on the wear that the part will experience,
the distortion of the part due to machining, the size and shape of the part,
and the endurance limits required for both the core and the case. Case
depth varies with the time of nitriding and is carried out between 925 and
1000°F, depending on the material. Case thicknesses can be obtained from
as little as a few thousandths of an inch to as much as 0.030–0.040 in.
Attaining the latter depth takes about 60–100 hr, although nitriding is
primarily a light case process.

Certain nitriding steels have been developed that produce excellent case
and core properties. These steels are Nitralloy[11] 135 (modified), Nitralloy 135,
Nitralloy N, and Nitralloy Ez. Other steels that can be nitrided are certain
grades of stainless steel, alloy steels such as AISI 4140 and 4350, and various
high speed tool steels.

[11] A product of the Nitralloy Corporation.

Among the many advantages to be obtained by nitriding, the one of primary interest to us is its affect on the fatigue strength of steels. Typical results [1] showing improved fatigue limits are listed as follows:

Specimen Condition	Endurance Limit Before Nitriding, psi	Endurance Limit After Nitriding, psi
Without a notch	45,000	40,000
With a semicircular notch	25,000	87,000
With a V notch	24,000	80,000

Other surface hardening methods are cyaniding, carbonitriding, induction and flame hardening (the latter method discussed earlier under heat treatment).

Corrosion

Corrosion of a metal surface has a very damaging effect on the static strength properties of metals because, ultimately, it causes a reduced cross-section and can lead to eventual failure. The effect of both corrosion and stress on strength characteristics is called **stress corrosion**. When the load is variable, the combination of corrosion and varying stress is called **corrosion fatigue**. It is obvious, in the light of what we have already said about fatigue, that the probability for fatigue failure is very much increased by the rough surface and pit marks caused by corrosion.

Corrosion can be controlled in several ways: (1) selecting the right material for the associated environment, such as stainless steel, copper alloys, titanium, and so on; (2) using nonmetallic coating, such as organic film, plastic film paints, and lacquers; (3) ceramic coating, such as porcelain; (4) electrochemical surface treatment, such as anodic coating for aluminum or magnesium; (5) sacrificial metallic coatings, such as zinc; (6) hot dipping of the base metal in zinc, lead, or tin; (7) cathodic protection; and (8) electro-deposition[12] of chromium, nickel, cadmium, copper, zinc, tin, or lead on the base metal.

Plating causes a reduction in fatigue strength. It is generally postulated that the primary cause is residual tensile stresses in the deposited material. Baking at specified temperatures (for example, 600–800°F) has improved fatigue strengths of some plates. Shot peening and then plating seems to produce a much greater improvement. However, shot peening, plating, and then baking can bring the fatigue limit to a point that is even higher than that of the base metal [11].

---

[12] Electrodeposited metals are also used to enhance appearance, to reduce friction, to provide a wear resistant surface, and to rebuild parts that have been worn.

Temperature

Large temperature deviations have a marked affect on the fatigue strength of metals and must be of concern when designing power plants (fossil and nuclear), oil refineries, chemical processing plants, supersonic aircraft, and so on. As can be observed from Figure 3-41, both carbon and alloy steels exhibit a higher fatigue limit at lower temperatures. However, the carbon steels first show an improved fatigue limit with increasing temperature then "drop off" as the temperature continues to increase. The alloy steels show no comparable improvement; they immediately display lower fatigue values as the temperature is increased.

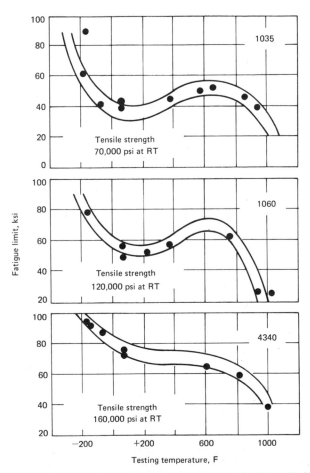

Figure 3-41 Effect of temperature on the fatigue limit of 1035, 1060 carbon steel, and 4340 alloy steel. [From *Metals Handbook*, 8th ed., Vol. I. The American Society for Metals, Metals Park, Ohio.]

If a mechanical component is subjected to both a steady and a varying load at a relatively high temperature, the likely mode of failure becomes time dependent (see Section 3-31). Thus, at high temperature and for long periods of time, it is the creep-rupture strength of the material that will determine failure, and variable loading will have little effect. One might then conclude that failure (at elevated temperatures) due to fatigue will most likely occur at an early time in the life of the material.

SECTION 3-31

Creep

Materials under a steady load at high temperatures for a long time period begin to deform plastically. This deformation is called creep and is time dependent because deformation increases with time until rupture takes place. As was stated in the previous section, fatigue failure would most likely take place early in the life of a material. However, because steam or gas turbines, power plant piping, chemical process and refinery piping, food processing equipment, and so on, are designed to operate at elevated temperatures for long periods of time, there is great interest in the phenomenon of creep. This interest is not confined to possible failure by rupture but includes failure by large deformations that can make equipment inoperative.

Unfortunately, there is no relation between creep and the mechanical properties of a material at normal temperatures but there are many inter-related factors concerning creep, including metallurgical changes. Consequently, this complex phenomenon has not been well-examined experimentally or thoroughly explained by theory. Thus, if a designer is faced with decisions concerning creep, his most reliable source of information is a test program under simulated or actual conditions. But, the expected operating life of most equipment designed to withstand creep is usually 10–20 years. It is apparent that actual long time testing is not likely to be undertaken, although some sparse test data are available from suppliers of alloy steels and nonferrous metals.

So-called long-time tests are undertaken for 1000 hr. This is the recommended time specified in the ASTM *Standards*, Part I, Metals, 1958. The tests are performed under carefully controlled stress (load), temperature, time, and creep (elongation) conditions. To conserve time, tests for different constant loads are performed simultaneously on different specimens of the same material. The usual procedure is to plot the creep versus time curve, but other combinations are possible. A theoretically shaped creep curve is shown in Figure 3-42. The **initial strain** takes place almost immediately and consists of the elastic strain plus plastic strain if the deformation extends beyond the yield point. The **first stage** shows a decreasing rate of elongation due to strain hardening. The **second stage** begins at a minimum strain rate and remains constant because of the balancing effects of strain hardening and annealing. The **third stage** shows a rapid increase of the creep rate accompanied by severe necking and ultimate rupture.

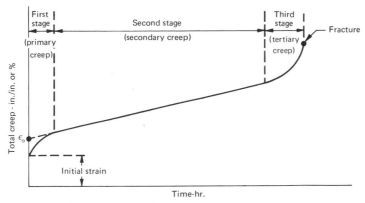

Figure 3-42 Ideal long time creep versus time curve.

When there are large deformations, the cross-sectional area change is large enough to alter the concept of fixed stress at a fixed load. When warranted, some adjustments can be made to maintain a constant stress. However, most interest usually concerns the second stage because no designer is going to permit the material to enter the third stage. Thus the creep versus time data of 1000-hr test is plotted, and the second stage is extrapolated to the number of hours of equipment life. This is done for each of the creep curves plotted. In making this extrapolation, it is assumed that the 1000 hr test allowed the material to enter the second stage, and the material behaved in a manner similar to Figure 3-42.

The problem may also be treated algebraically if the second stage is extended to cut the ordinate at ε_0 (see Figure 3-42). Thus ε_0 can be taken as the initial creep and the equation of a straight line would then represent the first and second stages of creep. The slope of the line, $d\varepsilon/dt$, is obtained from testing at a particular stress. Other creep curves for the same material at different stresses are then known by merely calculating a new slope from an empirical relationship. Those who are interested in pursuing this subject further are directed to references [1] and [9] which, in turn, contain additional references.

SECTION 3-32

Other Temperature Sensitive Properties of Materials

Modern civilization is widening the scope and range of materials being used in extreme temperature environments. At the low temperature end of the spectrum, there is the military with demands for equipment that operates at $-60°F$ and lower. The petroleum industry requires $-150°F$ for its dewaxing process. Food packaging and freezing require some temperatures as low as $-100°F$. Piping or shipping oil from Alaska will require materials to withstand the same low temperatures as the military. The field of cryogenic studies has grown vastly in recent years.

At the high end of the spectrum, there is the ever rising demand of the power generating field for materials to operate in a temperature environment of 1000°F and above. Similarly, industries such as chemical processing, petroleum refining, high speed aircraft, and so on are demanding materials to withstand the severity of high temperature operation.

Low temperature effects

As the temperature is lowered, there is an increase in yield strength, tensile strength, elastic modulus, and hardness and a decrease in ductility for metals such as aluminum and aluminum alloys, nickel alloys, austenitic steels, lead, and copper. Carbon and low alloy steels tend to become embrittled at much higher temperatures than the aforementioned metals. Embrittlement is measured by loss of toughness over a small temperature range (for example, see Section 3.21) when tested by the Charpy or Izod machines. The transition temperature is taken to be that for which the impact energy is reduced by 50% of its ductile value. Figure 3-43 shows some average value curves of toughness (energy in foot-pounds) versus temperature for a variety

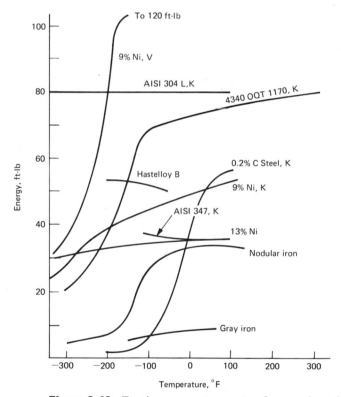

Figure 3-43 Toughness versus temperature for several metals. Note the sharp drop in toughness that takes place within a narrow temperature range. [From V. M. Faires: *Design of Machine Elements*, 4th ed. The Macmillan Company, New York, 1965.]

of metals and alloys. It is apparent from this figure that the range of temperature that causes embrittlement is relatively narrow.

High temperature effects

For short time static testing of metals at elevated temperatures, it is generally
found that the ultimate strength, yield strength, and elastic modulus are
lowered with increasing temperature whereas the ductile properties increase
with temperature. Figures 3-44 and 3-45 show these variations graphically.

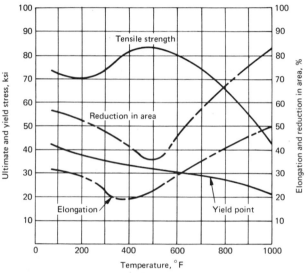

Figure 3-44 Effect of temperature on the strength and
ductility of a mild carbon steel, ASTM A 212B.

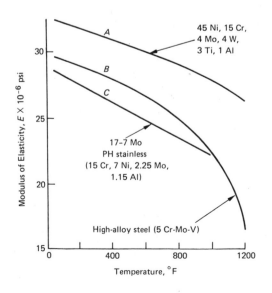

Figure 3-45 Change of elastic modulus
with temperature. These steels are for high
temperature service. [From V. M. Faires:
Design of Machine Elements, 4th ed. The
Macmillan Company, New York, 1965.]

The variations in directions of the curves in Figure 3-45 are caused by metallurgical changes that take place as the temperature increases. This is particularly true for steel.

The problem of designing for extreme temperatures is a special one in which information concerning material properties is not overly abundant. It would be wise for a designer to work closely with the supplier and test department before making a final materials decision in this area.

SECTION 3-33

Wear

Wear can be defined as the surface damage caused by the environment and the effect of one or more surfaces moving past each other while in contact.

Lipson [31] classifies wear into the following catagories:

Galling (also called scuffing, scoring, and seizing)

This type of wear is considered to be caused by the adhesion[13] between two contacting asperities that are welded together and then sheared by the relative motion between the sliding parts. A "strong" weld will transfer material from one surface to the other. A "weak" weld will produce a loose particle. Severe galling will ultimately cause surface failure and seizure of the moving parts. Careful selection of material with different hardnesses and proper lubrication helps to prevent galling.

Abrasion

The loose particles (as indicated by the previously mentioned adhesion theory), asperities of the harder surface, and any hard foreign matter finding their way in between the rubbing surfaces can cause abrasive wear. These particles embed themselves in the softer surface and tend to scratch and score the harder surface. Abrasion, although not eliminated, can be controlled by heat treatment, plating, anodizing, spraying, hard facing, or surface hardening.

Pitting (also known as pitting corrosion or spalling)

This kind of wear is caused by repetitive contact stress and is a form of surface fatigue.

Frettage (also known as fretting corrosion or false brinelling)

Frettage is a surface damage caused by small movements between mating surfaces, as in press fits. The constant oscillation removes any oxide film that may form, which finally acts as an abrasive and causes more serious

[13] This theory is also the basis for fretting corrosion as explained in Section 3.30.

damage. This form of surface failure and its control was discussed earlier in Section 3.30.

Cavitation erosion

Cavitation erosion is caused by a high relative motion between a fluid and a mechanical surface. If the fluid velocity is high enough, the local static pressure at some point along the surface will drop below the liquid's vapor pressure. Local boiling begins, and small vapor bubbles are formed. As equilibrium is restored, the static pressure rises and the bubbles collapse, producing liquid particles with a high velocity. These high energy particles impinge on the metal surface, causing cavitation pits. Repeated action of this phenomenon will ultimately cause fatigue failure of the metal.

Propeller, turbine, and pump blades are usually subject to this kind of damage and show pit marks at the blade edges. The most immediate and straightforward way to fight cavitation is to use hardened materials or a plate of chromium or chrome-nickel compounds. Other cures are to reduce the vapor pressure with additives, reducing turbulence, changing the liquid temperature, or adding air to the system to act as a cushion for the collapsing bubbles.

Galvanic corrosion

Galvanic corrosion is a form of electrochemical attack where two dissimilar metals, connected electrically, are within an electroyte. This model is called a galvanic cell, and damage is caused by the dissolution of the anode (that is, the metal that is higher in the electromotive series). The rate of attack depends on the metals involved, the area of each metal, the type of electrolyte, the current density, polarization of the cathode, temperature, and so on.

Another form of galvanic corrosion takes place when two like metals (or two different points on the same metal part) are surrounded by an electrolyte with different concentration pockets or different concentrations of dissolved oxygen. These conditions form what is commonly known as a **concentration cell**. Specifically, the cell formed by different electrolyte concentrations is called a **metal-ion concentration cell** and that formed by the dissolved oxygen is called an **oxygen concentration cell.**

SECTION 3-34

Radiation Effects

With the advent of nuclear reactors and nuclear handling equipment, the designer should be aware of the problems and/or changes generated by exposure of various materials to strong radiation fields. Fortunately, the metals generally used for fabricating components are little affected by exposure. In fact, in some cases, exposure may bring about some beneficial effects. However, organic compounds can be severely damaged and even destroyed by a little exposure to radiation.

Properties such as the elastic moduli, electrical resistivity, thermal conductance, and density are insensitive to radiation exposure. However some alloys have experienced a threefold increase in yield strength. This is accompanied by a smaller increase in tensile strength and a sharply decreased ductility. It has also been observed that the rate at which work hardening takes place is less for exposed materials.

The sharpest change takes place in the notch-impact transition temperature. This means that exposure to strong radiation (that is, neutron bombardment) will make most steels and steel alloys subject to ductile fracture due to their reduced ability to absorb energy. Figure 3-46 clearly shows this

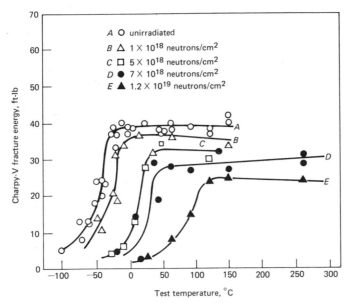

Figure 3-46 Charpy V-notch impact energy curves for ASTM A 212 grade B steel irradiated to various fast neutron (>1 mev) doses at 175°F. [From Oscar J. Horger (ed.): *ASME Handbook, Metals Engineering Design*, 2nd ed. McGraw-Hill Book Company, New York, 1965.]

reduction in impact energy. However, the austenitic stainless steels do not seem to be at all affected by radiation with respect to their notch sensitivity. This is fortunate as most of the equipment (for example, pumps, vessels, condensers, and so on) and piping used in nuclear energy and testing are made of stainless steel.

PROBLEMS

1. In designing a part, the engineer will necessarily be referring to material property tables similar to those of Appendix A. What should he keep in mind in using the data from such tables?

2. When is the stress of a structural member no longer linearly proportional to its strain?

3. What is meant by true stress? Engineering (or nominal) stress?

4. A camshaft on a knitting machine is made from AISI 1040 carburized steel and is found to have too great a deflection when in operation. The maintenance engineer has suggested replacing the shaft with one made of heat treated alloy steel (for example, AISI 4340) in order to reduce its deflection. Will his suggestion solve the problem? State the reason for your answer.

5. A particular type of alloy steel is to be used for a shaft. Its modulus of elasticity in tension is given as 29×10^6 psi, and the Poisson ratio is known to be 0.27. Since the shaft will be subjected to torsion, you will also need to know its shear modulus. Can you obtain this value with the given information? If so, what is it?

6. A bar 0.75 in. in diameter by 10 ft long is subjected to a tensile load of 26,500 lb. Measurements under load indicate that the bar increased 0.24 in. in length and decreased in diameter by 0.0005 in. Find (a) modulus of elasticity in tension; (b) Poisson's ratio; (c) shear modulus; (d) the general class of materials in which this bar can be found.

7. In tensile testing a 0.875-in. diameter plain carbon steel bar, the following data were obtained: at 20,000 lb, the test specimen elongated 0.0087 in. in 8 in.; at 36,000 lb, it elongated 0.022 in. in 8 in.; yielding was first observed at 33,000 lb, and fracture occurred at 60,000 lb. Find (a) the yield point strength; (b) the ultimate strength; (c) the elastic modulus in tension; (d) the AISI number identifying this steel.

8. A $\frac{1}{4}$-in. thick plate is being fed to a 150-ton mechanical press. How many holes of 1 in. diameter can be punched if the material is AISI 1020 steel, cold drawn? How many holes if the material is AISI 1020, annealed? How many holes if the material is AISI 3140, annealed?

9. A round bar of AISI 1020, annealed steel is 30 in. long. It is subjected to a tensile load of 25,000 lb. If the factor of safety is to be no greater than 3, find the diameter of the bar for the limiting yield stress.

10. Find the maximum strain energy at impact of the 50 lb weight for (a) a bar made of steel, (b) brass, (c) aluminum. Assume that 80% of the energy of the falling weight is elastically absorbed.

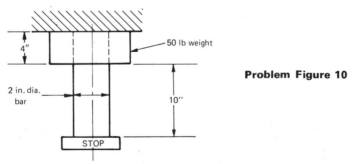

Problem Figure 10

50 lb weight

4"

2 in. dia. bar

10"

STOP

11. For each of the following materials, calculate the modulus of resilience: (a) AISI 1020 annealed steel; (b) AISI 4340 normalized steel; (c) AISI Type 302 stainless steel, cold worked; (d) 2024-T4 aluminum; (e) manganese bronze A, half-hard; (f) ASTM Type ZK60A-T5 magnesium alloy; (g) inconel X-750.

12. Find the strain energy relation for the two systems shown. The bars are round.

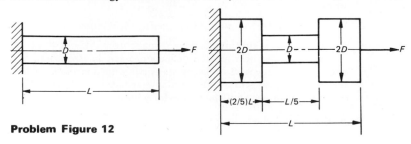

Problem Figure 12

13. After the weight W strikes the "stop" on the bottom of the bar, the tensile stress should not be greater than 20,000 psi. Assuming that all of the energy of the falling weight is elastically absorbed, determine **(a)** the weight W and **(b)** the weight W if all of the bar were 1 in. in diameter. The bar is made of steel.

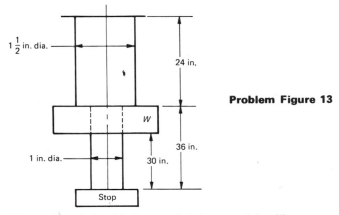

Problem Figure 13

14. Discuss the relationship between brittleness and ductility.

15. What circumstances would make toughness an important property?

16. In selecting a material for the base of a machine which is periodically transmitting dynamic loads, what important property would a designer wish to have? Name such a material.

17. Using Table A-2 of Appendix A, calculate the modulus of toughness of any six different materials. For each of the six materials chosen, calculate the modulus for three conditions of the same material. (You will have 18 separate calculations.)

18. (a) Calculate the ultimate strength of the following AISI steels by means of equation (3-12).

1. 1040 HR	4. 4140 CDA	7. 6150 N	10. 9255 HRA
2. 1040 CD	5. 4140 N	8. 8640 CD	11. 9440 N
3. 1095 N	6. 4640 CDA	9. 8740 N	

(b) Calculate the per cent difference between the results of part (a) and the values found in Table A-2 of Appendix A.

(c) Make the same comparison as in part (b), but this time compare your calculated results with the values obtained from Figure 3-17.

19. Describe the mechanism of fatigue failure.

20. (a) For the steels listed in Problem 18a, calculate the endurance limits S'_n.

(b) Using equation (3-14), compare (that is, calculate per cent difference) the endurance limit of class 20, 30, and 50 cast irons with values found in Table A-1 of Appendix A.

(c) Repeat part (b) for class 65000, 105000 and 200000 cast steels found in Table A-1 Appendix A.

21. List six conditions that tend to make a metal more prone to fatigue failure.

22. A flat plate $\frac{1}{4}$ in. thick and 3 in. wide contains two $\frac{1}{4}$-in. semicircular notches that are cut out opposite each other. What is the theoretical stress concentration factor K_t if the plate is loaded in **(a)** tension, and **(b)** bending in the plane of the plate?

23. A drive shaft at some point along its length has a change of diameter from 2 in. to $1\frac{1}{2}$ in. with an $\frac{1}{8}$-in. fillet radius at the discontinuity. Determine the theoretical stress concentration factor K_t if the shaft is subjected to **(a)** bending, **(b)** tension, **(c)** torsion.

24. In Problem 23, what would one use as the theoretical stress concentration factor if a $\frac{3}{32}$-in. diameter oil hole were drilled radially to the $1\frac{1}{2}$-in. diameter part of the shaft and located *very close* to the $\frac{1}{8}$-in. fillet? Determine proper values of K_t for **(a)** bending, **(b)** tension, **(c)** torsion.

25. The figure shows a class 25 cast iron bar subjected to a steady tensile load. What is its factor of safety? What is the factor of safety if the steady load is compressive and of the same magnitude?

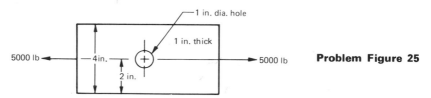

Problem Figure 25

26. In Problem 25, what would the factor of safety be if the center of the 1-in. diameter hole were located $\frac{3}{4}$ in. from the longer edge of the plate? (Consider the tensile case only.)

27. Repeat Problem 25 for the case where the hole is **(a)** $\frac{1}{2}$-in. diameter, **(b)** $\frac{1}{8}$-in. diameter.

28. The socket wrench shown in the figure is made of class 50 cast iron. What is the maximum torque that can be applied if the factor of safety is not to exceed 2? (Consider only the change of section at the fillet radius.)

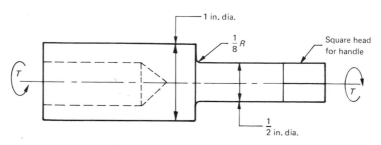

Problem Figure 28

29. *This figure shows a cantilever beam machined from AISI 1040, annealed steel. The load F is unsteady and it is necessary therefore to base the design of this beam on its endurance strength (for a finite life) or its endurance limit (for an infinite life). For a 95% survival rate, establish the value to be used for S_e. In solving this problem use equation (3-13) and compare your final answer with the one that would have been obtained by using **(a)** equations (3-12) and (3-13), and **(b)** by only using Figure 3-28.

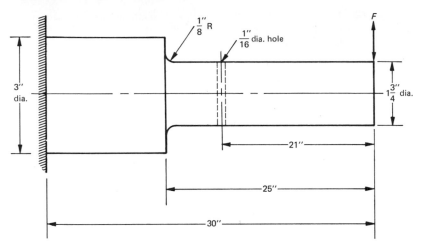

Problem Figure 29

30. *Work Problem 29 for the case where the drilled hole is located at the $\frac{1}{8}$-in radius fillet.

31. *Work Problem 29 for the case of an unsteady torsional load.

32. *The shaft is made of AISI 4340 HRA steel, and is machined to the dimensions shown. It is then quenched in oil and tempered at 1475°F. If an unsteady bending moment is applied, determine a working endurance limit S_e for each stress concentration.

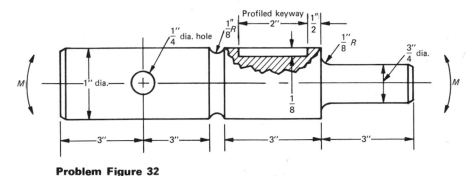

Problem Figure 32

* These problems are presented here only as a means of familiarizing the student with the procedure followed in obtaining a working endurance limit S_e. The application of this term to a complete problem is carried out in Chapter 7 only.

33.*Repeat Problem 32 for an unsteady torsional load.

34.*Repeat Problem 32 for an unsteady axial load. Assume there is no keyway for this problem.

35.*(a) In Problem 32, what would be the expected improvement in the endurance limit at both the groove and fillet if each were formed by surface rolling? What is the reason for this improvement?
  (b) Would the same improvement be achieved if the shaft were shot peened?
  (c) What other ways can you think of that would improve the endurance limit of the shaft?

REFERENCES

[1] *Metals Handbook*, Vol. I, 8th ed. The American Society for Metals, Metals Park, Ohio, 1961.

[2] *Technical Editor Speaks*. The International Nickel Co., Inc., New York, 1943.

[3] J. H. Frye: Selection of bar steel used as rolled or drawn. *Metal Progr.*, **47**: 497–504 (March 1945).

[4] Batelle Memorial Institute: *Prevention of the Failure of Metals Under Repeated Stress*. John Wiley & Sons, Inc., New York, March 1949.

[5] S. Timoshenko and G. H. MacCullough: *Elements of Strength of Materials*, 2nd ed. D. Van Nostrand Co., Inc., New York, 1940, p. 318.

[6] V. M. Faires: *Design of Machine Elements*, 4th ed. The Macmillan Co., New York, 1965, p. 102.

[7] Lionel S. Marks (ed.): *Mechanical Engineers' Handbook*, 5th ed. McGraw-Hill Book Co., Inc., New York, 1951.

[8] F. B. Stulen, H. N. Cummings, and W. C. Schulte: Preventing fatigue failures, Part 5, *Mach. Des.*, **33**, (June 22, 1961).

[9] Joseph Marin: *Mechanical Behavior of Engineering Material*. Prentice-Hall, Inc., Englewood Cliffs, N.J., 1962.

[10] C. Lipson and R. C. Juvinall: *Handbook of Stress and Strength*. The Macmillan Co., New York, 1963.

[11] Oscar J. Horger (ed.): *ASME Handbook, Metals Engineering Design*, 2nd ed. McGraw-Hill Book Co., New York, 1965.

[12] G. C. Noll and C. Lipson: Allowable working stresses. *Proc. Soc. Exp. Stress Anal.*, **3**(2): 89–101 (1946).

[13] C. H. Jennings: Welding design. *Trans. ASME*, **58**: 497–509 (1936).

[14] R. E. Peterson: Relation between stress analysis and fatigue of metals. *Proc. SESA*, **11**(2): 199–206 (1954).

[15] T. E. Eagan: Cast ferrous metals, Part 3, *Steel*, **135**(22), (1954); **135**(29), 80–82 (1954).

[16] R. B. Heywood: *Designing Against the Fatigue of Metals*. Reinhold Publishing Corp., New York, 1962, p. 158.

[17] H. E. Boyer: Effects of grinding on physical properties of hardened steel parts. *Trans. ASME*, **40**: 491–503.

[18] J. Frisch and E. G. Thomsen: Residual grinding stresses in mild steel. *Trans. ASME*, **73**: 337–342 (April 1951).

[19] B. Cina: Effect of surface finish on fatigue. *Metallurgia*, **55**: 11–19 (Jan. 1957).

[20] *Shot Peening*. Wheelabrator-Frye Inc., Mishawaks, Ind., 1962.

[21] R. L. Mattson: *Proceedings, International Conference on Fatigue of Metals*. The Institute of Mechanical Engineering, 1956, London.

[22] C. Lipson: More realistic measure of shot-peening effectiveness. *Steel*, (Aug. 6, 1951).

[23] C. Lipson, C. G. Noll, and L. S. Clock: *Stress and Strength of Manufactured Parts*. McGraw-Hill Book Co., Inc., New York, 1950.

[24] H. R. Thomas and V. A. Hoersch: Stresses due to the pressure of one elastic solid upon another. *University of Illinois Engineering Experimental Station Bull. No. 212.*

[25] S. Way: *J. Appl. Mech.*, **57**: A69–A71 (June 1935). Discussion with reference to articles by O. J. Horger entitled "Fatigue strength of members as influenced by surface conditions" which appeared in *Prod. Eng.*, Nov., Dec., 1940, and Jan., 1941.

[26] R. E. Peterson and A. M. Wahl: *J. Appl. Mech.*, **58**: A74–A75 (June 1936). Discussion of a report by H. F. Moore entitled "A study of fatigue cracks in car axles," *University of Illinois Engineering Experimental Station Bull. No. 165*, June 14, 1927.

[27] J. M. Lessells: *Strength and Resistance of Metals*. John Wiley and Sons, New York, 1954.

[28] H. F. Moore and J. B. Kommers: An investigation of the fatigue of metals. *University of Illinois Engineering Experimental Station Bull. No. 124*, 1921.

[29] R. A. C. Fosberry and H. D. Mansion: Bending fatigue of gear teeth. *Motor Industry Research Association Report*, 1950–1957.

[30] E. R. Gadd: Fatigue from the metallurgists viewpoint. *J. Roy. Aeronaut. Soc.*, **57**: 565 (Sept. 1953).

[31] Charles Lipson: *Wear Considerations in Design*. Prentice-Hall, Inc., Englewood Cliffs, N.J., 1967.

Manufacturing Processes and Design

SYMBOLS

rms = root mean square surface roughness, microinches (μin.)

T = total tolerance accumulation, in.

T_n = tolerance of the nth assembled part, in.

σ = standard deviation of the sum of assembled parts, $\pm$ in.

σ_n = standard deviation of the nth assembled part, $\pm$ in.

The development of a device or a machine that is functional on paper is only part of the overall task of design. If the designer's creation is to leave the drawing board and become a physical piece of hardware, it must be manufacturable. Manufacturable means that all of the component parts can be fabricated and assembled at a competitive cost. To meet this objective, the designer must have more than just a "passing acquaintance" with manufacturing processes. In particular, he must be familiar with those manufacturing and production facilities within his own company.

The designer is not expected to be a tool maker, a machinist, and so on. Rather, the implication here is that he must know the capabilities of basic manufacturing and shop process equipment. Only by knowing these can he properly design component parts, select materials, specify tolerances, consider assembly procedures, and so on.

Different production methods, materials, tolerances, and procedures are likely to be employed when a part is to be fabricated in millions, or in thousands, or only as a single unit. As stated in Chapter 1, designing involves compromise, and method of manufacturing merely adds yet another facet to the overall decision making process concerning design.

In the present chapter, we will briefly summarize the basic methods of manufacturing and indicate the function and limitation of each method. We shall also review dimensioning and finally close the chapter with comments on good design practice.

Introduction

Manufacturing processes can be classified[1] into two general groups known as primary and secondary processes. The **primary processes** (see Figure 4-1), namely, casting, powder metallurgy, forging, cold heading, cold extruding, stamping, deep drawing, spinning, roll forming, hot extruding, brake forming, and so on, are those that convert raw material into shapes. These forming methods include both hot and cold working processes and, in general, will still require further finishing operations in order to obtain an end product.

The **secondary processes** are those that bring the part to the dimensions and surface finish specified. One may also include in the secondary processes such operations as heat treating and surface treatments for corrosion resistance, hardness, and appearance. Secondary processes are planing, shaping, turning, milling, drilling, boring, reaming, broaching, grinding, honing, lapping, polishing, and special methods of metal removal such as electrodischarge machining and electrochemical machining. Operations like screw cutting, tapping, thread milling, gear cutting, and so on, are secondary processes that are merely adaptations of one of the aforementioned processes.

Primary Processes

Figure 4-1 illustrates schematically some of the primary manufacturing processes. A complete discussion of these procedures is beyond the scope of this text. Therefore, we will confine ourselves to succinct descriptions of the most prominent techniques.

Castings

Castings are identified by the type of mold or the force required to fill the mold. Molds are either permanent or expendable. The pattern of sand, shell, and plaster molds, however, can be used repeatedly for making new molds. Castings are made by pouring molten metal into a mold or die. As the metal cools, it takes the shape of the cavity. Tables A-1, A-8, A-10, A-11, and A-12 in Appendix A indicate the wide variety of metals that can be used in the cast processes. The basic casting methods are described below.

Sand Castings. 1. The *green sand* process is one in which moist, bonded sand is packed around a wood or metal pattern. The pattern is then removed and molten metal is poured into the cavity. When the metal solidifies, the mold is broken and the casting is removed. Almost any metal can be used,

---

[1] There is no clearly defined method of classifying manufacturing processes. Upon investigation, one will find that some references base manufacturing classifications on hot and cold working methods, others on casting, forming and machining, and still others on the type of stress created, etc.

Number	Process	Schematic Diagram	
1	Rolling		
2	Forging		
3	Extruding		
4	Shear spinning		
5	Tube spinning		
6	Swaging or kneading		
7	Deep drawing		
8	Wire & tube drawing	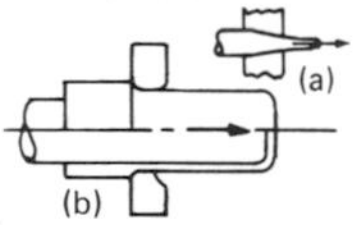 (a) (b)	
9	Stretching		
10	Straight bending		
11	Contoured flanging	(a) Convex	
		(b) Concave	

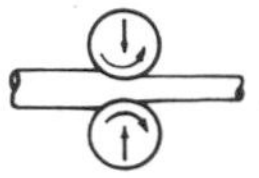

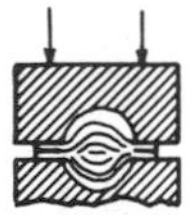

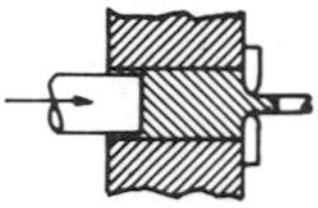

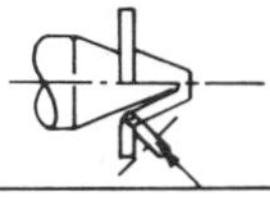

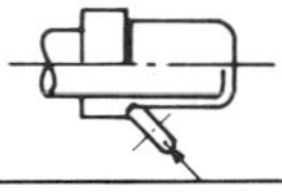

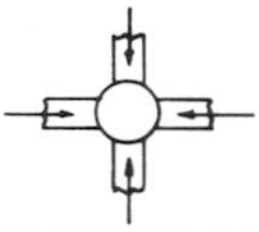

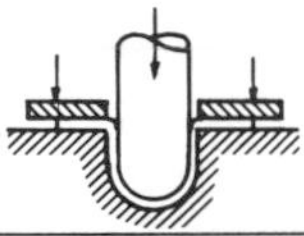

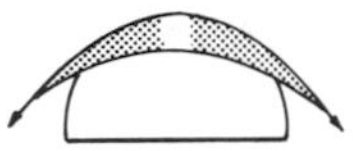

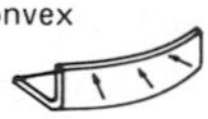

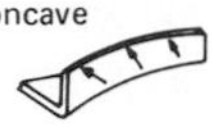

Coining

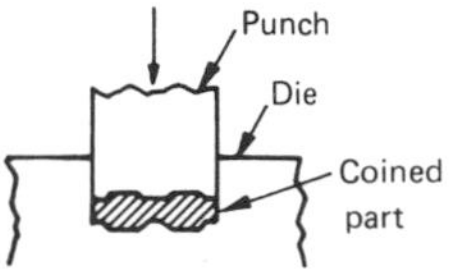

Punch
Die
Coined part

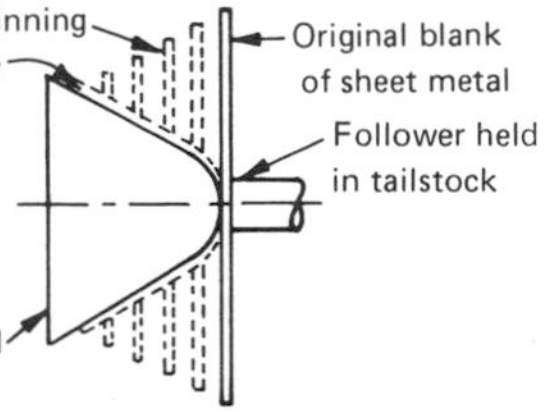

Steps in spinning
Final shape
Spinning
Original blank of sheet metal
Follower held in tailstock
Form attached to headstock spindle

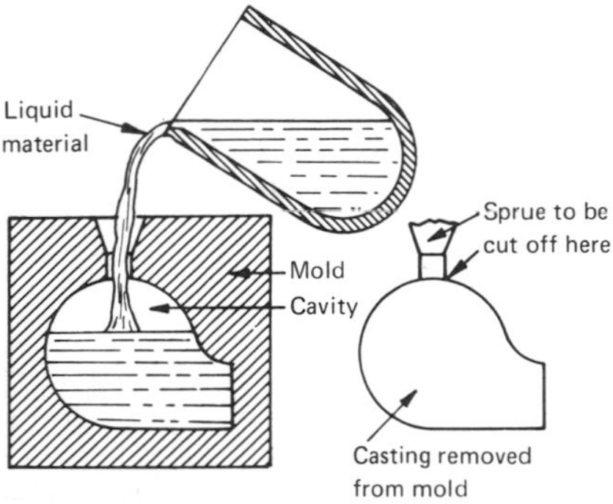

Liquid material
Sprue to be cut off here
Mold
Cavity
Casting removed from mold
CASTING

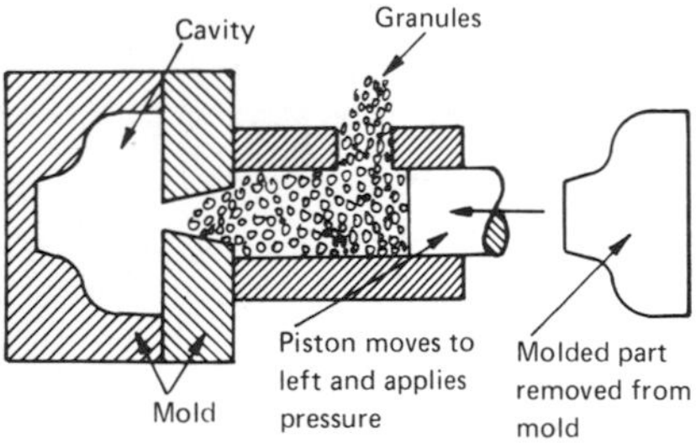

Cavity
Granules
Piston moves to left and applies pressure
Mold
Molded part removed from mold
MOLDING

Figure 4-1 Schematic drawings of primary processes.,

with virtually no limit as to the size or shape of the part. The method permits casting complex components at a low tooling cost and is the most direct route from pattern to casting.

Some machining is always necessary with the green sand process, and large castings have a rough surface finish. Close tolerances are difficult to achieve, and long, thin projections should not be cast. It is possible, however, to design for bosses, undercuts, and inserts. The minimum core hole diameter advisable is $\frac{3}{16}-\frac{1}{4}$ in., and the minimum section thicknesses advisable are aluminum, $\frac{3}{16}$ in.; copper, $\frac{3}{32}$ in.; iron, $\frac{3}{32}$ in.; magnesium, $\frac{5}{32}$ in.; and steel, $\frac{1}{4}-\frac{1}{2}$ in.

2. The *dry sand* process is similar to the green sand process except that core boxes are used in place of patterns. This method is usually limited to smaller parts than method 1. The sand is bonded with a setting binder, and the core is then oven baked at 300–400°F to remove the moisture.

3. The *carbon dioxide sand* process is one in which the sand molds are bonded with sodium silicate solutions and set by forcing carbon dioxide gas through the sand. This type of mold is strong and permits the production of better dimensionally controlled castings than either methods 1 or 2.

4. The *core-sand* mold process is one where the molds are put together completely from oven baked cores set with organic binders such as oil or dextrines.

Figure 4-2 shows the construction of a typical sand mold.

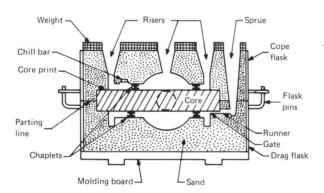

Figure 4-2 Typical sand molds for ferrous and nonferrous metals. [From *1970 Metals Reference Issue, Machine Design,* Penton Publishing Co., Cleveland, Ohio.]

Shell Mold Casting. This is a process where the molds are made by coating the sand with a thermosetting plastic (see Figure 4-3). The mold is then supported on the outside by sand or shot, and molten metal is poured. When the metal has solidified, the mold is broken away from the finished casting.

Shell molding produces castings with smooth surfaces, uniform grain structure, high dimensional accuracy, rapid production rate and minimal amount of finishing operations. The minimum section thickness castable is

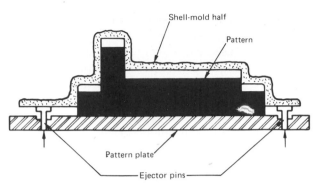

Figure 4-3 Shell mold being stripped from pattern. [From *1970 Metals Reference Issue, Machine Design*, Penton Publishing Co., Cleveland, Ohio.]

$\frac{1}{16}$–$\frac{1}{4}$ in., but section differences where the maximum-minimum ratio is greater than 5 to 1 should be avoided. Bosses, undercuts and inserts are easily cast, and the minimum cored hole diameter is $\frac{1}{8}$–$\frac{1}{4}$ in. The method is relatively costly and is limited to few metals.

Full-Mold Casting. A process in which a green sand or cold-setting resin bonded sand is packed around a foamed plastic pattern (for example, polystyrene). The plastic pattern is vaporized with the pouring of the molten metal into the mold. An improved casting surface can be obtained by putting a refractory type of coating on the pattern surface before sand packing. The pattern can be one piece or several pieces, depending upon the complexity of the part to be cast.

The plastic patterns are handled easily. They do not require any draft, and produce no flash on the casting. For small quantity production this method can be expensive, depending upon the size and complexity of the casting. The minimum recommended section thickness is 0.1 in., and the maximum section thickness is unlimited. Bosses, undercuts, and inserts present no problem in this type of casting. The minimum cored hole diameter is $\frac{1}{4}$ in.

Permanent Mold Castings. These are formed by a mold that can be used repeatedly. Some applications have reported as many as 25,000 castings being made from the same mold. Usually, the mold requires some redressing after about 3000 uses. The molds are machined of metal (for example, gray iron) for casting nonferrous metals and cast irons. Machined graphite molds are used to cast steel.

This method produces castings that have a good surface finish as well as a good grain structure, low porosity, and high dimensional accuracy. The initial mold cost is relatively expensive, but castings weighing as little as several ounces to castings weighing about 500 lb can be produced. Permanent mold castings are limited to relatively simple shapes and forms. The maximum recommended section thickness is about 2.0 in. The minimum thickness, however, depends upon the material being cast as follows: $\frac{3}{16}$ in. for iron,

$\frac{3}{32}$–$\frac{1}{8}$ in. for aluminum, $\frac{5}{32}$ in. for magnesium, and $\frac{3}{32}$–$\frac{5}{16}$ in. for copper. The minimum castable holes are $\frac{3}{16}$–$\frac{1}{4}$ in. in diameter.

Die Casting. A process used extensively in the quantity production of intricately shaped zinc, aluminum, lead, and magnesium alloys. The method is limited in use with tin and copper alloys.

Castings are formed by forcing molten metal under pressures of 1500–25,000 psi into an accurately machined steel die. The steel die, which is water cooled, is held together by a hydraulic press until the metal casting(s) solidifies. To ease the ejection of the cast parts, a lubricant is sprayed on the die forming surface and the ejection pins. For small diecast components, multiple cavity dies are used.

The surface finish of the resulting castings is quite smooth and has excellent dimensional accuracy. Although the cost of production is relatively cheap, the initial die cost is high. Diecasting is limited to nonferrous metals and by the size of the part that can be cast. The maximum wall section thickness is usually restricted to $\frac{3}{16}$ in. but certainly to no greater than 0.50 in.

Figures 4-4a and b show the two basic types of die casting machines.

Plaster Mold Castings. These are made by pouring a nonferrous alloy (for example, aluminum, copper, or zinc alloy) into a plaster mold, which is then broken to remove the solidified casting. The castings produced by this process are smooth, have high dimensional accuracy, low porosity, and can be made in many intricate shapes. The method, however, has disadvantages in that it is limited to nonferrous metals, small castings, and also requires a relatively long time to make the molds. The minimum wall section thickness is 0.040–0.060 in. for a cast area that is less than 2 sq. in. For larger cast areas, the minimum wall thickness increases accordingly.

The Shaw process, developed within the last decade, is a most promising method. It employs the use of plaster molds. This procedure produces castings with fine detail and excellent dimensional accuracy and surface finish.

Ceramic Mold Casting. This process uses a mold made of a ceramic powder, binder, and gelling agent. The mold can also be made of a ceramic facing reinforced with a sand backing. The method is restricted to casting intricate parts requiring fine detail, close tolerances, and smooth finishes. The minimum wall thickness recommended is 0.025–0.050 in. There is, however, no limit to the maximum wall thickness.

Investment Castings. These are made when parts are desired that are intricate in shape, have excellent surface finish, and require a high degree of dimensional accuracy (for example, 0.003–0.007 in. the first dimensional inch, and 0.002 in. for each additional inch). In addition, this method of casting permits the use of a variety of metal alloys (see Table A-12 in Appendix A) and does not have any metal flashing to be removed from the finished casting.

The technique of investment casting requires careful workmanship and expensive patterns and molds. The minimum castable wall thickness is

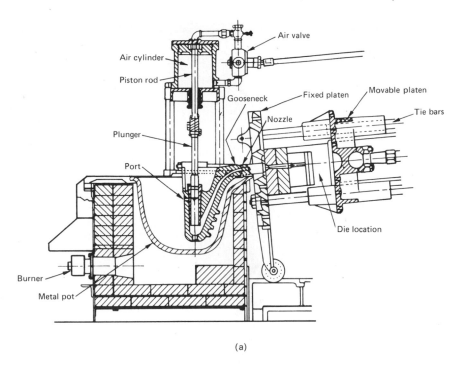

(a)

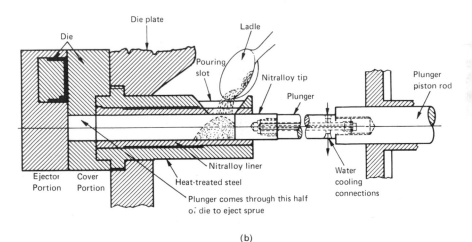

(b)

Figure 4-4 (a) The hot-chamber die casting machine where the molten metal in the metal pot is pushed through the gooseneck and the nozzle into the forming die by the plunger. (b) The cold-chamber of the die casting machine where a predetermined quantity of molten metal is poured into the machine by a ladle, after which a plunger forces the material into the die. The rate of production is higher for the hot-chamber machine except for high melting temperature materials (for example, brass, bronze). [Courtesy of the New Jersey Zinc Company.]

Figure 4-5 Gas turbine blades and vanes made by the method of investment casting. The materials used were cobalt and nickel base alloys for their temperature and strength properties. [Courtesy of Howmet Corporation, Pechiney Ugine Kuhlmann Group.]

about 0.025–0.050 in., and the maximum thickness should not exceed 3 in. Figure 4-5 illustrates the complexity of products that may be investment cast.

Centrifugal Casting. This is a method of casting a shape by pouring the molten metal into a rotating flask containing the mold. The molds are made of sand, metal, or graphite (depending on the metal cast) and are rotated about their axial centers either in a horizontal or vertical position.

Relatively large diameter and bulky components are made by centrifugal casting. Typical products produced by this method are pipe, gun barrels, hollow shafts, machinery drive rolls, long sleeves, tubing, and so on. Where the diameter to length ratio is rather large, the rotational axis can be vertical. Parts cast in this manner are ring gears, gear blanks, engine cylinder liners, bearings, rings, and so on. Figure 4-6 shows a horizontal casting machine.

When cores are used in vertically mounted molds, the method is called **semicentrifugal casting,** and it is used to make parts such as wheels, turbo-supercharger diaphragms, disks, flywheels, and so on. Figure 4-7 shows a schematic section of a semicentrifugal casting of a cored flywheel.

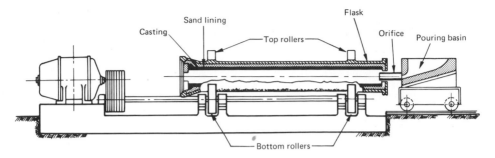

Figure 4-6 True horizontal type centrifugal casting machine. The sand is packed progressively when the flask is in the vertical position before it is placed on the rollers. [Courtesy of American Cast Iron Pipe Company.]

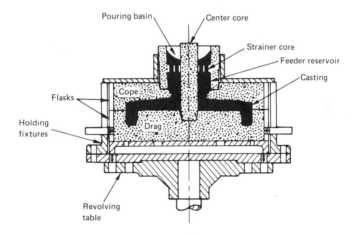

"Semicentrifugal" casting of fly wheels and gear blanks.

Figure 4-7 Section through the flask of a semicentrifugal mold and casting. [Courtesy of American Cast Iron Pipe Company.]

Generally, the method of centrifugal casting is expensive and is also limited in the shapes which can be cast. However, the castings made by this method are very sound and have good dimensional accuracy. It should also be noted that this method is the only way to obtain a large cylindrical part.

Continuous Casting. This is a method whereby a molten metal is continuously gravity fed from a ladle into an ingot mold of a desired shape which is open at both ends. As the metal "falls" through the mold, it takes its shape, and is rapidly cooled by a water spray. It is then cut to specific lengths.

The continuous casting process has the advantage of being low in cost and having a high rate of production. In addition, this method permits casting materials that cannot be extruded. However, continuous casting is restricted to shapes of uniform cross section (that is, in the direction of casting), and cast holes must be in the direction of the casting. The minimum wall thickness recommended is $\frac{1}{8}$ in., and the maximum thickness depends on the shape being cast. The minimum size of casting is $\frac{1}{2}$ in., and the maximum size is about 9 in.

Powder metallurgy

Powder metallurgy, P/M, is an old art. Historically, it was employed as far back as 3000 B.C. in ancient Egypt. Porous metal bearings first appeared in quantity just after World War I and came into their own during World War II.

The material employed in making P/M parts consists of pure metal powders or mixtures thereof with some additive metal powder (for example 95% copper and 5% tin, a low tin bronze). The particle size used can be from 1–100 microns (μ). The method of manufacture involves placing the powder (or mix) into a forming die for compacting. After the part is formed by the die, it is presintered (that is, heated at a low temperature) for the purposes of increasing the component strength, removing lubricants, and so on. Following this step, the part can be machined and subsequently sintered (heated to a higher temperature in a controlled atmosphere) in order to obtain the desired mechanical and physical properties. In the manufacture of sintered bearings (for example, Oilite), the part is impregnated with a lubricating oil that fills the pores of the component. This operation is performed by dipping in oil or by spraying with oil during the sintering

Figure 4-8 A wide representation of parts made by powder metallurgy. [Courtesy of the Amplex Corporation, Division of the Chrysler Corporation.]

process. The final component can be coined, heat treated, machined, and so on.

Typical parts made by P/M techniques are gears, ratchets, pawls, levers, cams, clutch friction facings, rollers, guides, splines, bushings, turbine blades, spacers, permanent magnets, and so on (see Figure 4-8). This method of manufacture has the advantage of controlling the mechanical and physical properties of a finished part at a rapid rate of production with little scrap loss. In addition, it is possible by means of compacting and sintering to alloy metals that cannot be alloyed by conventional methods. Finally, powder metal parts can be made with fairly close tolerances and smooth surfaces. Often they eliminate the need for secondary operations.

On the debit side, P/M parts are somewhat limited as to the size and shape which can readily be fabricated. This method is uneconomical for short runs unless the part is large and has a high unit value.

Forging

Forging dates back to ancient times and, before the advent of modern production methods, was associated with the "village blacksmith shop." Forging is a production method whereby heated metal stock is shaped to a desired form by compressive forces or by sharp hammerlike blows. Virtually all ductile materials may be forged by first preheating the work piece (that is, a billet, a wrought bar, a cast or sintered ingot, or a powder metal form) to a forging temperature. However, there are some materials, such as stainless steel, that are forged at room temperature or slightly above.

Figure 4-9 Forging of a six cylinder crankshaft of a diesel engine. The upper photo is that of the forged crankshaft "as is." The lower photo is an etched longitudinal section through the crankshaft. Note how the fiberlike flow lines follow the contour of the forging, and how they are closely spaced (that is, densely). [Courtesy of the Wyman-Gordon Company.]

Figure 4-10 *Opposite:* A 50,000-ton hydraulic press. [Courtesy of Wean B-L-H, Inc.]

Forging has a marked beneficial effect on metals. Their strength and toughness are improved because the "kneading" of the dies results in a beneficial orientation of their grain structure. The constant hot working performed by the forming or shaping dies causes the material to become more dense and the grain "flow lines" to follow the contour of the final component shape. An illustration of this phenomenon is shown in Figure 4-9.

There are several forms of forging, but there is some disparity identifying processes with names in different references. However, the following classification and description of each may be considered as basic.

Open Die Forging. Open die forgings, also known as hand or smith forgings, are made by using hammers or presses in conjunction with blacksmith tools or flat type dies. There is little, if any, lateral confinement of the work piece, and the desired shape is obtained by manipulating the forging in between blows.

This procedure, which employs low cost tooling, is relatively simple, but it has less control in determining grain flow, mechanical properties and dimensions than do other forging methods. The technique is applicable to a wide range of forging sizes and is restricted to short run production. Also, the final cost of production can be higher than other forging methods because finished machining is often required. Open die forging has some other disadvantages, namely, relatively poor material utilization, restriction to simple shapes, difficulty of maintaining moderately close tolerances, and absolute need for skilled labor.

Closed Die Forgings. These are produced by hammering the work piece into a desired shape by means of closing dies. The hammering or pressing is performed, respectively, by a mechanical or hydraulic press. Small and medium size forgings are generally made in presses ranging in capacity from 500–10,000 tons. Figure 4-10 is a photograph of a 50,000-ton press used to make large integral forgings.

Closed die forging, as compared to open die forging, makes good utilization of the work piece material and has excellent reproducibility with good dimensional accuracy. The resulting mechanical properties are also better than those developed in open die forging. Furthermore, this method is suited for rapid production rate. But, because of the initially high cost of tooling, it should not be considered for short-run production.

Upset Forging. This is a method of forging intended for large quantity and rapid production of symmetrical parts such as gears, gear clusters, worm gears, shafts, axles, and so on. In the past, rivets, nails, bolts, and the like were also produced by upset forging, but the method has largely been replaced by cold heading.

Upset forging is performed in a horizontal forming machine which is rated by the diameter of the largest billet or form it will accept. Figure 4-11 shows an automatic upset forging machine for producing rear axles with flanges.

Figure 4-11 An automatic upset forging machine capable of accepting work pieces 6 in. in diameter. This machine produced the axles shown in Figure 4-12. [Courtesy of the Ajax Manufacturing Company.]

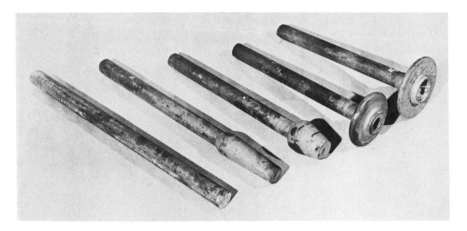

Figure 4-12 Axles made on an automated 6-in. forging machine. The sequential steps required to form an axle by upset forging are shown from left to right. [Courtesy of the Ajax Manufacturing Company.]

Usually where the upsetting of a large amount of metal is required, the process is completed by a series of steps in several machines rather than by one automatic machine (see Figure 4-12).

The final product manufactured by upset forming lends itself to reasonably intricate forms with good dimensional accuracy as well as rapid production rates. However, the size of the product is limited, and it does not have a finish equal to that of other forgings. Also, tooling can be quite expensive.

Other processes

Other important primary processes for forming and shaping metal products are (1) cold heading, (2) cold extruding (also known as impact extruding), (3) stamping, (4) deep drawing, (5) spinning, (6) roll forming, (7) hot extruding, (8) press-brake forming, (9) section contour forming, (10) rotary swaging, (11) wire and metal ribbon forming, (12) thread and roll forming, (13) hobbing, (14) rubber forming, (15) hydraulic forming, (16) explosive forming, (17) electrohydraulic forming, (18) electromagnetic forming, (19) pneumatic-mechanical forming and (20) electroforming.

The use of a particular method depends upon a variety of factors: the type of item to be fabricated, the quality and accuracy required, the quantity to be produced, the material to be formed, the limiting cost of the item, the size of the item, and so on.

The processes are too numerous to describe in this text. However, the reader can find many fine books (for example, reference[2]) that give detailed descriptions of these methods. In particular, reference [3] is especially recommended because it discusses production processes and their influence on design.

Figures 4-13 to 4-21 inclusive show respectively the production processes of stamping, drawing, spinning, form rolling, hot extruding, and press-brake forming.

Figure 4-13 Sixty-ton high speed reproduction type stamping press. [Courtesy Niagra Machine & Tool Works.]

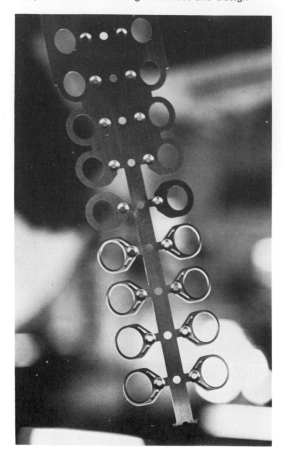

Figure 4-14 Different stages of a typical stamping produced by a multiple-die high speed stamping press. The photo shows the forming of the "pull-tab" for a soft drink (or similar) can. [Courtesy Niagra Machine & Tool Works.]

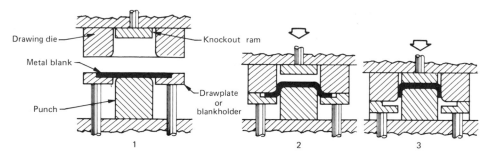

Figure 4-15 Drawing sequence for cylindrical cup. Punch is shaped to produce desired configuration on interior of cup. Drawplate, or blankholder, and drawing die hold the metal blank. Drawing begins in step 2 as blankholder and drawing die move downward and stretch the blank over the punch. Completed part in step 3 is ejected from the drawing die by the knockout ram after the tooling has returned to the starting position. [From *1970 Metals Reference Issue, Metals Design,* Penton Publishing Co., Cleveland, Ohio.]

Figure 4-16 Left tube was drawn to $1\frac{1}{2}$-in. diameter, $9\frac{1}{2}$ in. long with a 0.035-in. wall. This tube was formed from a hot-rolled steel plate $4\frac{3}{8}$-in. in diameter by 0.140 in. thick. The tube was formed by five draws. The right tube is made of aluminum and was also made in five draws. The original stock was $2\frac{7}{8}$ in. in diameter by $\frac{3}{8}$ in. thick. [Courtesy of McCauley Metal Products, Inc.]

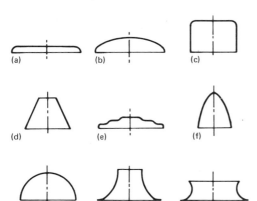

Figure 4-17 Shapes that are readily formed by spinning. [From *1970 Metals Reference Issue, Machine Design.* Penton Publishing Co., Cleveland, Ohio.]

Figure 4-18   Yoder M-2 roll forming machine with flying cutoff, used in the manufacture of building siding. This unit is capable of making siding of prepainted aluminum or stainless steel. [Courtesy Yoder Company.]

Figure 4-19 Typical aluminum shapes formed by hot extrusion. [Courtesy of the Reynolds Metal Company.]

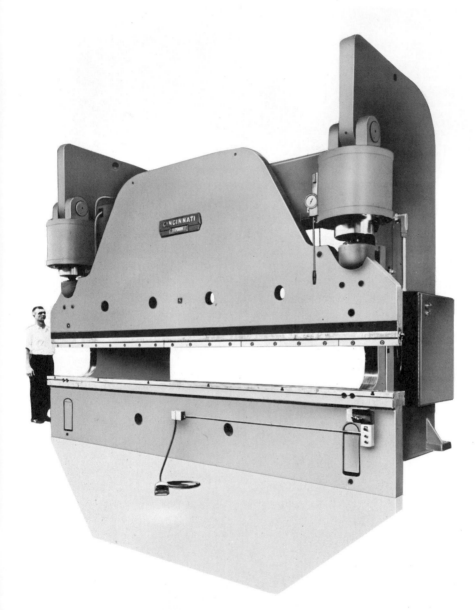

Figure 4-20   A 900-ton press brake bending a machine base. [Courtesy of Cincinnati Incorporated.]

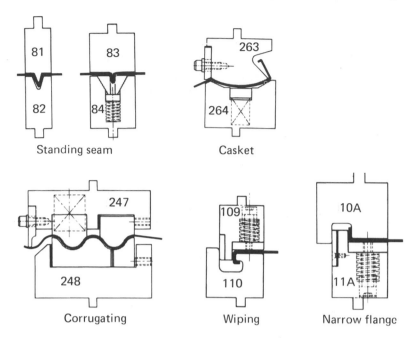

Figure 4-21 Representative shapes that can be formed by press brake die sets. [Courtesy of Cincinnati Incorporated.]

SECTION 4-3

Forming of Plastics

There are about 15 different methods of forming products made of plastic material (see Table A-15 in Appendix A for properties of some plastics). However, the primary methods are hot compression molding, injection molding, transfer molding, extrusion forming, laminating, cold molding, and casting.

Hot Compression Molding. A press operation in which a molding powder (or preform) is placed inside a heated mold and melted. The male portion of the mold is then lowered into the open cavity forcing the melting plastic to assume the shape of the mold. Figure 4-22 shows a typical set of molding dies used for hot compression molding.

Injection Molding. (See Figure 4-23.) A forming process that is very similar to die casting. In this process, granular thermoplastic material is fed from a hopper into a heated chamber by means of a plunger. The granules melt, and the semiliquid material is formed through a nozzle into a mold cavity by an arrangement of sprues and runners. Because the dies are cooled, the melted plastic solidifies rapidly while assuming the mold cavity shape.

Injection molding is a high production rate process that produces a product having a good surface finish as well as dimensional control. Many parts can be produced with little finishing work required.

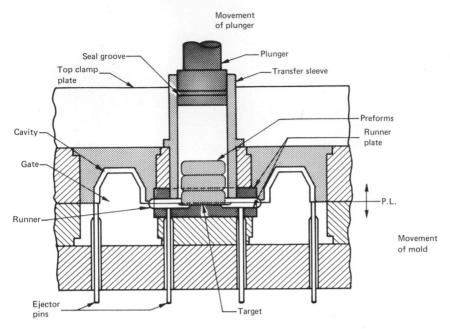

Figure 4-22 Schematic of hot compression forming process. [Courtesy Hooker Durez Division, Hooker Chemical Corp.]

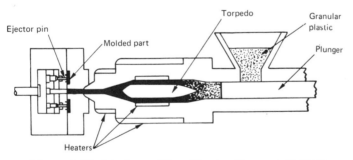

Figure 4-23 Injection molding. [Courtesy Tennessee Eastman Corporation.]

Transfer Molding. This process is similar to injection molding and avoids some of the disadvantages of hot compression molding (for example, uneven flow). In transfer molding, a thermosetting powder or preform is placed into a heated transfer chamber. When the material charge is melted, it is forced into the cavity of a closed mold where polymerization takes place (Figure 4-24). In comparison with hot compression molding, the dies are initially closed and the product is formed not so much by pressure as by the free flow of the melted plastic.

POT TRANSFER

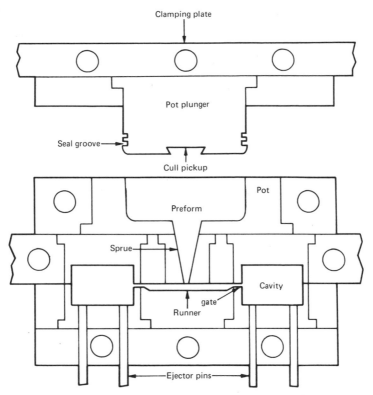

Figure 4-24 Transfer molding process. [Courtesy Hooker Durez Division, Hooker Chemical Corp.]

The molds are kept hot, and the formed part is ejected from the mold without any cooling other than that which is due to the ambient temperature. Transfer molding permits the fabrication of thin-sectioned components in addition to being capable of "molding in" metal inserts.

Extrusion Forming. This process is illustrated in Figure 4-25. Thermoplastic resin in granular or powder form is placed in a feed hopper. The

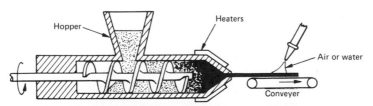

Figure 4-25 Schematic of the extrusion process. [From E. Paul De Garmo: *Materials and Processes in Manufacturing*, 3rd ed. The Macmillan Company, New York, 1971.]

material then enters a heated cylinder within which a feed screw forces the plasticized material through a hot die having the desired extrusion shape. The extruded form passes from the die onto a conveyer or set of rollers and is solidified by air or water.

Laminating. A fabricating method whereby materials such as paper, cloth, wood, asbestos, and so on are immersed in a liquid thermosetting resin and cut to some appropriate length. A sufficient number of sheets to produce a desired thickness are then stacked in a hydraulic press and compressed at an elevated temperature to produce a laminated sheet. It is possible to produce shapes other than flat sheets by using shaped molding dies between the forming press platens.

If directional properties of the final product are of importance, it is possible to produce a relatively homogeneous material by using a shredded or ground filler (that is, paper, wood, fabric, and so on) in the resin, and then follow the normal molding procedure. Figure 4-26 emphasizes the directional differences of the mechanical properties of two gears.

Cold-molded parts are made by compressing a powdered resin in a non-heated die by means of a plunger type press. The compacted parts are then oven baked at an elevated temperature (that is, 225–500°F, depending on the resin) for 12–14 hr.

Figure 4-26 The left gear was cut from laminated blanks. The right gear was cut from a material blank containing a ground fabric. [Courtesy of The Formica Corporation.]

The powdered materials are either the nonrefractory type having a phenolic resin base or the refractory type containing an inorganic binder (for example, asbestos). Thus, any components formed by this method are effective in withstanding heat and also have good electrical resistivity.

Casting. An inexpensive way of forming parts for a "short run" production or for use as a prototype. Molds can be made of wood, plaster, metal, or lead. Molds made of these materials only permit the casting of simple shapes (that is, no undercuts, reentrant curves, and so on). More complicated shapes are molded by means of split molds or molds made of rubber.

The materials commonly used in casting are acrylics, styrenes, polyesters, epoxies, silicones, and nylons. Frequently, these materials are mixed with reinforcing fillers such as glass cloth, glass mat, flock, wood, and Fuller's earth.

Plastic castings are used in making jewelry, ornaments, novelties, and so on, but are also used in the fabrication of drill jigs, punches, dies, and a variety of other tools.

Miscellaneous methods of molding or shaping are blow molding, vacuum forming, slush molding, and filament winding.

SECTION 4-4

Welding[2]

The American Welding Society defines welding as "a localized coalescence of metals wherein coalescence is produced by heating to suitable temperatures with or without the application of pressure and with or without the use of filler metal. The filler metal either has a melting point approximately the same as the base metals or has a melting point below that of the base metals but above 800°F."

There are 34 different welding processes. Figure 4-27 is a master chart of these processes and shows their connection to a major welding method. The proper choice of a particular method of weld must be carefully considered by the designer. And, before making a final selection, the designer will have to consider, evaluate, and weigh such factors as the metals to be joined, the joint design, the thicknesses (or bulk) of metals, the type of load, the equipment available, the production rate, and the environment to which the weld will be subjected. It is apparent that there are no "hard and fast" rules that one can use in making a decision with the exception, perhaps, of a particular case where one requirement or condition is of overall importance.

Because of space restrictions, it is not possible to discuss in detail each of the processes in Figure 4-27. We shall confine ourselves to describing briefly the most widely used welding methods.[3]

Gas welding

Gas welding is "a group of welding processes wherein coalescence is produced by heating with a gas flame or flames with or without the application of pressure and with or without the use of filler material."

---

[2] For the analysis of welded joints, refer to Chapter 17.

[3] The definitions quoted are those found in the American Welding Society's booklet No. AWS A3.0-69 entitled *Terms and definitions*. For an in-depth analysis of welding, the reader is advised to study the American Society of Welding *Handbook(s)*, Vols. 1 through 5.

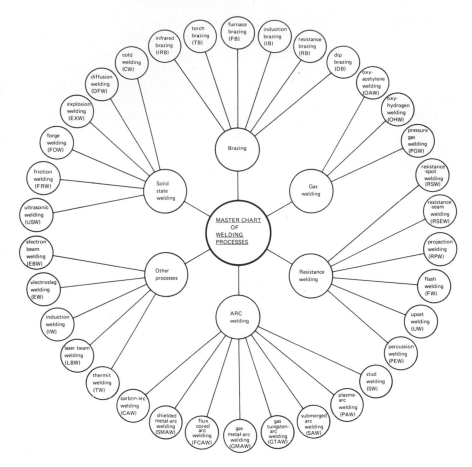

Figure 4-27 Master chart of welding processes. [Courtesy of The American Welding Society.]

Of the three types of gas welding, **oxyacetylene welding (OAW)** is the one most frequently employed. This method uses a mixture of oxygen and acetylene to produce heating. Fluxes may be used to reduce oxidation and to promote a better weld joint. This type of welding is suitable for both ferrous (including cast iron) and nonferrous metals and is capable of welding thick metal sections.

Oxyhydrogen welding (OHW) is used for low melting point metals such as aluminum, magnesium, and lead.

Pressure gas welding (PGW) uses an oxyacetylene flame for a heat source but does not require a filler rod. Instead, fusion is obtained by applying pressure to the heated parts, either while being heated or after the parts are heated. This form of welding can be used for joining both ferrous and nonferrous metals.

Arc welding

Arc welding is "a welding process wherein coalescence is produced by heating with an arc or arcs with or without the application of pressure and with or without the use of filler metals." As indicated in Figure 4-27, there are eight different arc welding processes. These are (1) carbon-arc welding, (2) shielded metal-arc welding, (3) flux cored arc welding, (4) gas metal-arc welding, (5) gas tungsten-arc welding, (6) submerged arc welding, (7) plasma-arc welding, and (8) stud welding.

The most widely used of these methods is the **shielded metal-arc welding** (**SMAW**) process. It is defined as "an arc welding process wherein coalescence is produced by heating with an arc between a covered metal electrode and the work. Shielding is obtained from decomposition of the electrode covering. Pressure is not used and filler metal is obtained from the electrode." Figure 4-28 shows the nomenclature associated with arc welding.

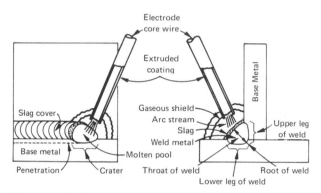

Figure 4-28 Elements of the arc welding process.

The shielded metal-arc process is employed in both manual and automated production setups. Electrodes are available that permit the welding of ferrous metals (including cast iron), all grades of carbon steels, low-alloy high-strength steels, stainless steels, copper bearing steels, copper alloys, aluminum, nickel, nickel alloys, and bronze. This welding technique is used in many fields, particularly in the manufacture of machinery, transportation equipment, piping systems and in various structures (for example, buildings, trusses, machine bases, and so on).

The next two most widely used arc welding methods are the submerged arc welding (SAW) process and the plasma-arc welding (PAW) process.

Submerged arc welding (**SAW**) is "an arc welding process wherein coalescence is produced by heating with an arc or arcs between a bare metal electrode or electrodes at work. The arc is shielded by a blanket of granular, fusible material on the work. Pressure is not used and filler metal is obtained from the electrode and sometimes from a supplementary welding rod."

This method can be used in fully automated equipment where the feeds of both the electrode and granular flux are controlled. The method is also adaptable for semiautomatic equipment where the feed of the electrode and granular flux are controlled manually. Since the granular flux must cover the joint to be welded, this method is restricted to parts in a horizontal position and is particularly suited for welding long straight joints. Also, fewer passes are needed to weld thick metal sections than are usually required by shielded metal-arc welding.

Submerged arc welding can be used to weld low carbon steels, high-strength low-alloy steels, chromium steels and austenitic chromium-nickel steels. With special methods, it is also possible to weld high-alloy air-hardening steels. Figure 4-29 shows the arrangement and nomenclature of the submerged arc welding process.

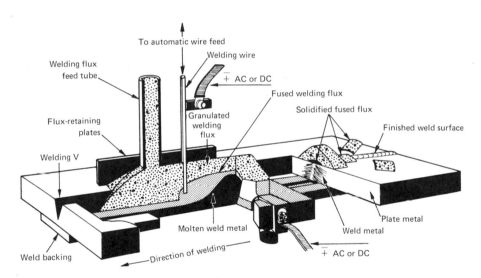

Figure 4-29 Submerged arc welding. [Courtesy Union Carbide Corp., Linde Division.]

Plasma-arc welding (PAW) is "an arc welding process wherein coalescence is produced by heating with a constricted arc between an electrode and the workpiece (transferred arc) or the electrode and the constricting nozzle (nontransferred arc). Shielding is obtained from the hot, ionized gas issuing from the orifice, which may be supplemented by an auxiliary source of shielding gas. Shielding gas may be an inert gas or a mixture of gases. Pressure may or may not be used, and filler may or may not be supplied."

Plasma-arc welding is used for quality welding and can easily weld 5-in. thick aluminum sections or stainless steel sections up to 4 in. thick. Since there are no products of combustion, the welded joints have no porosity and display a strong resistance to high stresses and impact loading.

The plasma torch is constructed with an electrode centrally within a metal cup that guides an inert streaming gas past the electrode. In the plasma-arc torch, the discharge end of the cup is smaller in diameter than the upper diameter so that a discharge nozzle is created. In addition, the inner wall of the nozzle is lined with a ceramic material.

Although a plasma stream can be created with any gas, a gas that is nonoxidizing should be used. Another important requirement is the thermal conductivity of the gas rather than the temperature it may attain. Thus, gases of higher conductivity can transfer more heat, making it possible to weld "bulky" sections more easily. Argon, helium, and hydrogen are the gases most frequently used. Hydrogen has the higher thermal conductivity and produces hotter arcs than those produced by argon or helium.

Other forms of arc welding, namely, carbon-arc (CAW), flux cored arc (FCAW), gas metal-arc (GMAW), gas tungsten-arc (GTAW) and stud welding (SW) are used for joining particular metals or for mass production. For example, carbon-arc welding is used to join galvanized sheet steel, brass, bronze, and aluminum, whereas flux cored arc welding uses a flux cored electrode, continuously fed from a spool for quantity production.

Stud welding is accomplished by means of a stud-welding gun, which welds a stud to the surface of a workpiece. The method is extensively employed in the automotive, shipbuilding, railroad, and building construction industries.

Resistance welding

Resistance welding is "a group of welding processes wherein coalescence is produced by the heat obtained from resistance of the work to electric current in a circuit of which the work is a part, and by the application of pressure." Figure 4-27 indicates that there are six types of resistance welding processes. These are (1) resistance spot welding, (2) resistance seam welding, (3) projection welding, (4) flash welding, (5) upset welding, and (6) percussion welding. Resistance welding is widely used for quantity production. By means of proper controls and tooling, it is readily adaptable to automation, including any required preheating or heat treatment after welding. The most widely used types of resistance welding are the spot, seam, and projection forms of welding.

Resistance Spot Welding (RSW). "A resistance welding process wherein coalescence at the faying surfaces[4] is produced in one spot by the heat obtained from the resistance to electric current through the work parts held together under pressure by electrodes. The size and shape of the individually formed welds are limited primarily by the size and contour of the electrodes" (see Figure 4-30).

Spot welding is primarily restricted to thin metals (for example, 0.001-in. thick to $\frac{1}{8}$-in. thick for steel and magnesium, $\frac{5}{32}$-in. thick for aluminum),

---

[4] Faying surface is "that surface of a member which is in contact or in close proximity with another member to which it is to be joined."

Chapter 4: Manufacturing Processes and Design

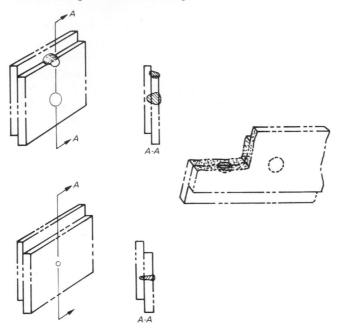

Figure 4-30 Schematic of a spot weld. [Courtesy of the American Welding Society.]

namely, steels, stainless steels, aluminum, magnesium, nickel, nickel alloys, bronze, and brass. Some dissimilar metals can be spot welded, but with difficulty.

Resistance Seam Welding (RSEW). "A resistance welding process wherein coalescence at the faying surfaces is produced by the heat obtained from resistance to electric current through the work parts held together under pressure by the electrodes. The resulting weld is a series of overlapping resistance-spot welds made progressively along a joint by rotating the electrodes." In principle, seam welding is similar to spot welding except that the weld is continuous by virtue of the rollers rather than discontinuous as in spot welding (see Figure 4-31).

Seam welding is primarily used for quantity production but is restricted to joining metal gages that are thinner than those which can be joined by spot welding. The "normal" range of thicknesses compatible with seam welding is $0.100-\frac{1}{8}$ in.

Projection Welding (RPW). "A resistance welding process wherein coalescence is produced by the heat obtained from resistance to electric current through the work parts held together under pressure by electrodes. The resulting welds are localized at predetermined points by projections, embossments, and intersections."

Projection welding is a process similar to spot welding except that the projections tend to localize the heat, permitting thicker materials to be

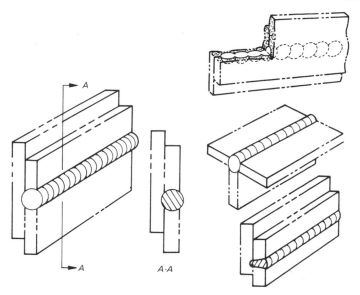

Figure 4-31 Schematic of a seam weld. [Courtesy of the American Welding Society.]

weldcd. Simultaneous welds are readily made by this method, and result in a stronger welded structure than that obtained with spot welding.

Flash Welding (FW). In this process abutting surfaces to be welded are clamped in fixtures and brought within close proximity (or light contact) of each other so that an electric arc is produced between the surfaces causing them to heat to a fusible temperature. At this point, the two surfaces are forced together, completing the weld. Forcing the two surfaces together causes the metal to be displaced (that is, bulge) outward from the welded joint. This "upset" metal is usually removed after welding. Preheating (for large bulk parts) and postheating (that is, heat treatment) can readily be made part of the overall welding cycle.

Materials that are easily weldable by spot welding are also weldable by flash welding, although the method is used mostly with ferrous metals. Copper, copper alloys, and some aluminums cannot be relied upon to produce satisfactorily welded joints. However, dissimilar metals can readily be welded by this method, including even refractory metals such as tungsten, molybdenum, and tantalum.

Upset Welding (UW). A process similar to flash welding except the parts to be welded are held in close contact with each other before the electric circuit is closed. Thus, there is no flashing in this method. Upset welding is extensively used in the fabrication of tubular sections, pipe, and heavy steel rings; it is also used for joining small ferrous and nonferrous strips.

Percussion Welding (PEW). "A resistance welding process wherein coalescence is produced simultaneously over the entire abutting surfaces by heat obtained from an arc produced by a rapid discharge of electrical energy with pressure percussively applied during or immediately following the electrical discharge."

Percussion welding is used for special joining situations (for example, joining dissimilar metals that cannot be welded economically by flash welding). This welding method is also used to weld pins, studs, bolts, and so on, to other components as well as to join sections of pipe, rod, or tube to each other or to flat sections.

Brazing

Brazing[5] is "a welding process wherein coalescence is produced by heating to suitable temperatures and by using a filler metal having a liquidus above 800°F (427°C) and below the solidus of the base metals. The filler metal is distributed between the closely fitted surfaces of the joint by capillary attraction." As indicated by Figure 4-27, there are six brazing methods, namely, (1) infrared brazing (IRB), (2) torch brazing (TB), (3) furnace brazing (FB), (4) induction brazing (IB), (5) resistance brazing (RB), and (6) dip brazing (DB). Among these methods, the primary difference is the manner in which the metals to be joined are heated. Also, only four of the six methods are of industrial importance, torch brazing, furnace brazing, induction brazing, and dip brazing. These methods are defined and briefly described in the following paragraphs.

Torch Brazing. A joining process that may employ acetylene, natural gas, butane, or propane in combination with air or oxygen to supply the heat required to melt the filler rod and diffuse it into the surface of the base metal. This technique is not extensively used for continuous mass production.

Furnace Brazing. A high production fabrication method where the heat is supplied by gas or electric heating coils. The furnaces are of the box type or the continuous type, which employ a wire mesh belt to transport the parts to be brazed. Furnace brazing requires that preformed shapes of filler metal be placed on the parts to be joined prior to entering the furnace. This method of brazing is well suited to high production and can avoid the use of fluxing by maintaining an inert atmosphere in the furnace.

Induction Brazing. Like furnace brazing, induction brazing requires the use of preformed shapes of filler metal. Heat is produced by placing the parts to be brazed within the field of a high frequency induction coil. The work pieces are heated by eddy currents because the parts to be joined offer electric-magnetic resistance to the changing induction field. Heating is very rapid, and by properly shaping the induction coils, the heat can be applied in the local area of the joint to be brazed. Induction brazing can be used for mechanized production when properly designed tooling and feeding devices are incorporated into the production setup.

---

[5] Brazing includes the joining method called silver soldering. This term is erroneously used to denote brazing by employing silver-base filler rods.

Dip Brazing. Parts can be dip brazed by one of two methods. In chemical dip brazing, the parts to be joined are prepared with preformed filler metal, after which they are placed into a molten bath of brazing flux. In the molten metal bath process, the assembled parts are first prefluxed and then immersed into a molten bath of filler metal. This latter method of brazing is restricted to small parts, whereas the former method is more adaptable for joining large parts.

Other welding processes

The master chart of welding processes (Figure 4-27) shows, in addition to the aforementioned methods, a series of solid state welding techniques and some other processes. These methods are defined by the American Welding Society as follows:

Ultrasonic Welding (USW). "A solid state welding process wherein coalescence is produced by the local application of high frequency vibratory energy as the work parts are held together under pressure."

Friction Welding (FRW). "A solid state welding process wherein coalescence is produced by heat obtained from mechanically induced sliding motion between rubbing surfaces. The parts are held together under pressure."

Forge Welding (FOW). "A solid state welding process wherein coalescence is produced by heating and by applying pressure or blows sufficient to cause permanent deformation at the interface."

Explosion Welding (EXW). "A solid state welding process wherein coalescence is effected by high velocity movements produced by a controlled detonation."

Diffusion Welding (DFW). "A solid state welding process wherein coalescence of the faying surfaces is produced by the application of pressure and elevated temperatures. The process does not involve macroscopic deformation or relative motion of parts. A solid filler metal may or may not be inserted."

Cold Welding (CW). "A solid state welding process wherein coalescence is produced by the external application of mechanical force alone."

Thermit Welding (TW). "A group of welding processes wherein coalescence is produced by heating with superheated liquid metal and slag resulting from a chemical reaction between a metal oxide and aluminum with or without the application of pressure. Filler metal, when used, is obtained from the liquid metal."

Laser Beam Welding (LBW). "A welding process wherein coalescence is produced by the heat obtained from the application of a concentrated coherent light beam impinging upon the surfaces to be joined."

Induction Welding (IW). "A welding process wherein coalescence is produced by the heat obtained from resistance of the work to induced electric current with or without the application of pressure."

Chapter 4: Manufacturing Processes and Design

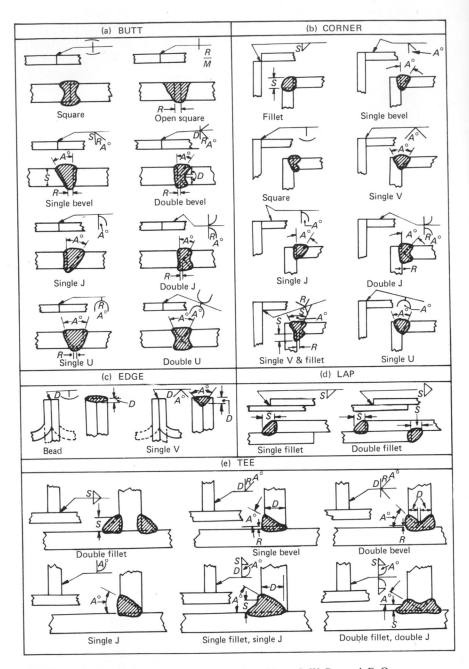

Figure 4-32 Fundamental types of welded joints. [From S. W. Bernard, E. O. Waters, and C. W. Phelps: *Principles of Machine Design*. The Ronald Press Company, New York, 1955.]

Electroslag Welding (EW). "A welding process wherein coalescence is produced by molten slag which melts the filler metal and the surfaces of the work to be welded. The weld pool is shielded by this slag which moves along the full cross section of the joint as welding progresses. The conductive slag is maintained molten by its resistance to electric current passing between the electrode and the work."

Electron Beam Welding (EBW). "A welding process wherein coalescence is produced by the heat obtained from a concentrated beam composed primarily of high velocity electrons impinging upon the surfaces to be joined."

Figure 4-32 shows schematically the basic types of welded joints and the plate edge preparation (that is, single U, double U, single J, and so on) required to insure a full depth weld when joining thick plates. Also shown in the figure, are the standard symbols denoting each type of weld. Figure C-1 in Appendix C summarizes the American Welding Society's nomenclature of standard welding symbols used for specifying welds.

SECTION 4-5

Secondary Production Processes

Secondary production processes, in contrast with primary production processes, remove metal from a workpiece in order to achieve a specified shape or configuration. The methods of metal removal may be classified into three categories, namely, chip removal, chipless removal, and metal removal by heat. The most widely used of these methods is chip removal. It employs a hardened cutting tool to form (and remove) the chip. The most commonly used forms[6] of chipless machining are electrochemical machining, chemical milling, electrical discharge machining, electrolytic grinding, and photoforming. The third form of metal removal by heat employs a hot flame, which is capable of melting the work piece material (for example, oxyacetylene, plasma, and so on).

Figures 4-33, 4-34, and 4-35 show schematically the various ways in which machines are used for chip removal. The designer is not expected to be a machinist, but he is expected to be able to design various parts for a machine, structure, system, and so on, and, therefore, be knowledgeable about the capabilities, type of cutting, and dimensional limitations of machine shop equipment. Because it is not possible, due to space limitations, to study or review the various secondary production processes, the reader is advised to refer to the many fine texts (for example, reference [2]) and handbooks available on this subject matter.

Figures 4-33, 4-34, and 4-35 are basic representations because, in almost every type of operation, special or high-production rate machines exist that

---

[6] New developments in chipless machining employ laser beam and ultrasonics. However, these methods have, as yet, not come into wide use due to various limitations.

Figure 4-33 Schematic of machine tool operations for machining flat surfaces. [From E. Paul De Garmo: *Materials and Processes in Manufacturing*, 3rd ed. The Macmillan Company, New York, 1971.]

Operation	Diagram of Work and Tool Motion	Most Commonly Used Machines	Machines Less Frequently Used	Machines Seldom Used
Shaping	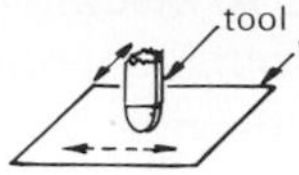	Horizontal shaper	Vertical shaper	
Planing	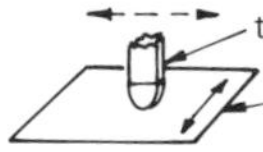	Planer		
Milling	Slab milling 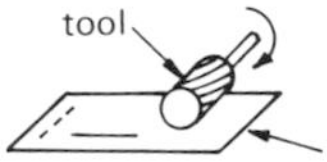 / Face milling	Milling machine		Lathe (with special attachment)
Facing	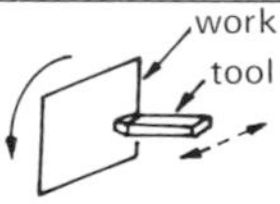	Lathe	Boring mill	
Broaching		Broaching machine		
Grinding		Surface grinder		Lathe (with special attachment)
Sawing	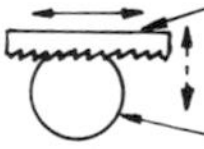	Cutoff saw	Contour saw	
	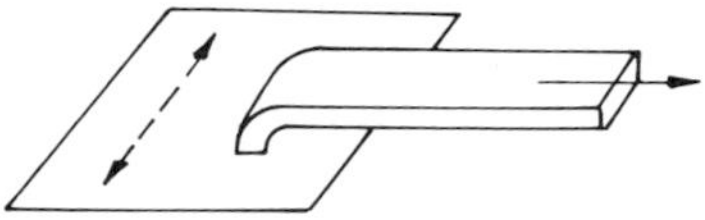	Vertical shaper		
——— Tool and work motion – – – Feed only				

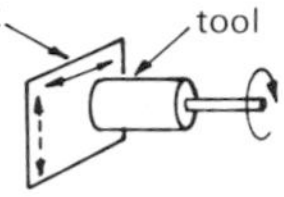

182

Figure 4-34 Schematic of machine tool operations for machining internal cylindrical surfaces. [From E. Paul De Garmo: *Materials and Processes in Manufacturing*, 3rd ed. The Macmillan Company, New York, 1971.]

Operation	Diagram of Work and Tool Motion	Most Commonly Used Machines	Machines Less Frequently Used	Machines Seldom Used
Drilling	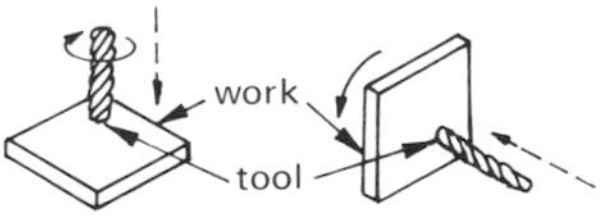	Drill press	Lathe	Milling machine Boring mill Horizontal boring machine
Boring	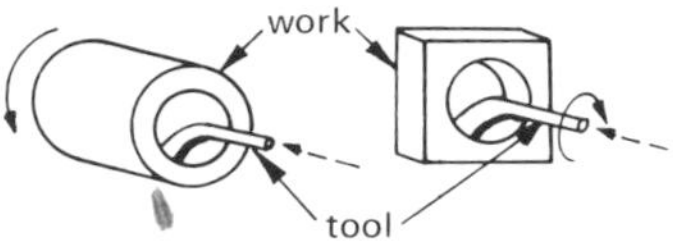	Lathe Boring mill Horizontal boring machine		Milling machine Drill press
Reaming	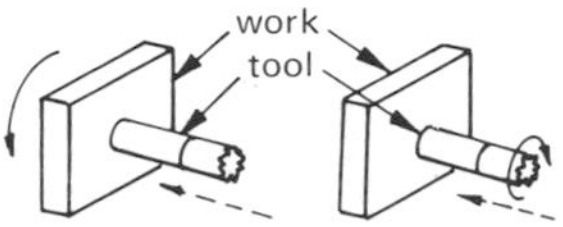	Lathe Drill press Boring mill Horizontal boring machine	Milling machine	
Grinding	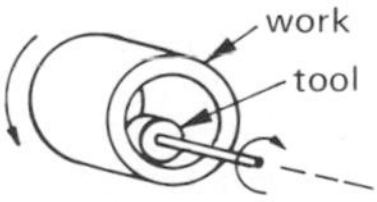	Cylindrical grinder		Lathe (with special attachment)
Sawing	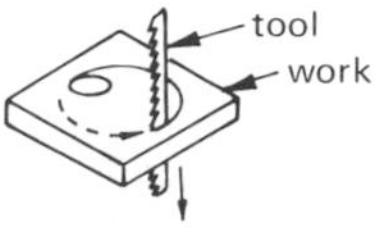	Contour saw		
Broaching	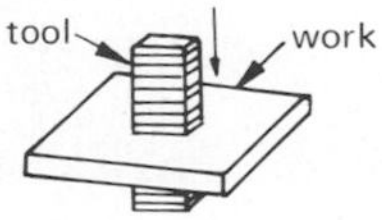	Broaching machine		

Chapter 4: Manufacturing Processes and Design

Figure 4-35 Schematic of machine tool operations for machining external cylindrical surfaces. [From E. Paul De Garmo: *Materials and Processes in Manufacturing*, 3rd ed. The Macmillan Company, New York, 1971.]

Operation	Diagram of Work and Tool Motion	Most Commonly Used Machines	Machines Less Frequently Used	Machines Seldom Used
Turning	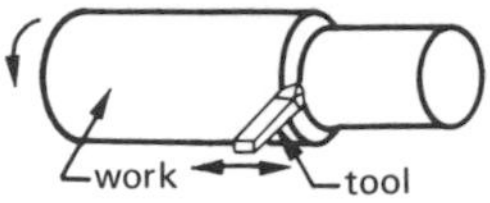 work — tool	Lathe	Boring mill	Vertical shaper Milling machine
Grinding	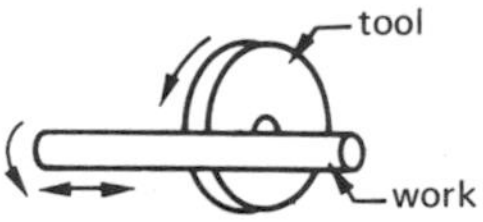 tool — work	Cylindrical grinder		Lathe (with special attachment)
Sawing	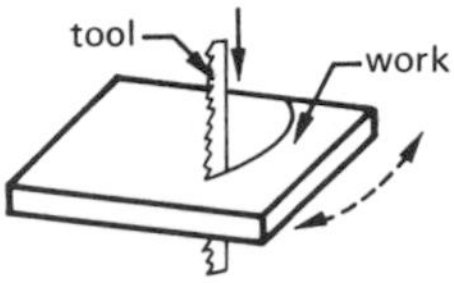 tool — work	Contour saw		

Figure 4-36 Electrochemical machining of burs (electrochemical deburring) on an automobile engine connecting rod. [Courtesy of the Ex-Cell-O Corporation.]

Figure 4-37 Parts made by chemical milling. [Courtesy of the Chemcut Corporation.]

employ the same basic method of metal removal (for example, drill press and radial drill, engine lathe and turret lathe, and so on).

Electrochemical Machining (EMC). In this process the metal work piece is shaped by the removal of metal from its surface as a result of electrochemical action. The tool (cathode) moves towards the work piece (anode), completing the electrolytic circuit through the electrolyte. The feed rate of the tool, electrolyte, and current density, depends upon the material being removed and the final shape desired. Figure 4-36 shows a typical electrochemical operation.

Chemical Milling (CHM). Also called chemical blanking and chemical machining, chemical milling is a controlled etching process. The process does not use electricity but depends on the etching action of an acid or alkali (depending on the material) that uniformly attacks all exposed areas of the work piece. Thus, in order to obtain a desired configuration or shape, it is necessary to use a mask or a protective coating on those surfaces which are not to be etched. Figure 4-37 shows some typical parts produced by this method.

Electrodischarge Machining (EDM). This process, also known as electro-spark machining, is intended to machine "difficult" materials (for example, carbides, tool and die steels, heat resistant alloys, and so on). The work piece is brought to the desired shape by electric sparks which remove the metal being worked by vaporization. The tool is shaped to produce the desired configuration. Sparking is initiated when the forming tool is brought into close proximity to the work piece. Electrodischarge machining is a slow process and is not intended for production purposes. Figure 4-38 is a photograph of a typical part produced by the EDM process.

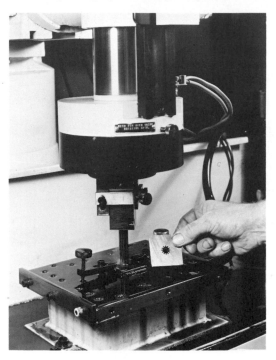

Figure 4-38 A splined hole machined by the electrodischarge method. [Courtesy of the Ex-Cell-O Corporation.]

Electrolytic Grinding (EGG). Also called electrochemical grinding, this is a process similar to electrochemical machining. In this machining method, the grinding wheel is the cathode, and the work piece is the anode. Although this method was originally developed for sharpening carbide cutting tools (which normally causes rapid wearing of diamond grinding wheels used in normal sharpening), electrolytic grinding can also be used for grinding other hard materials. The results produced by this method are of high quality (for example, a surface finish of 5–10 μin. can be obtained, and dimensions can be held within 0.005 in.), and are also obtained more rapidly than from ordinary grinding methods. Figure 4-39 shows a schematic setup for the electrolytic grinding of a cutting tool.

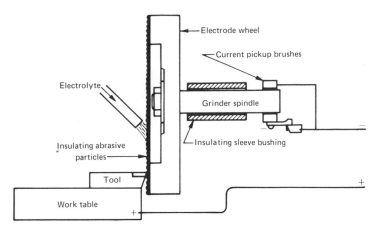

Figure 4-39 Schematic setup for electrolytic grinding. [From E. Paul De Garmo: *Materials and Processes in Manufacturing*, 3rd ed. The Macmillan Company, New York, 1971.]

Photoforming. A method akin to chemical milling in that metal is removed by chemical etching. However, it is different than chemical milling in that the areas not to be etched are masked by shapes that are photographically produced to very close dimensions. In addition, photoforming removes all the metal from an exposed area, whereas chemical milling merely removes enough material to produce cavities in the work piece surface. Photoforming is usually intended for relatively thin material and is used for making masks for the manufacture of transistors, printed circuits, strain gages, and so on. Figure 4-40 shows the sequential process of machining a part by photoforming.

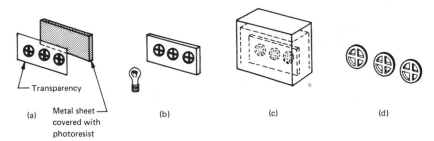

Figure 4-40 Photoforming. (a) A transparency containing an image of the desired shape is applied to a metal sheet containing a photoresistive coating. (b) The sheet is exposed to light, and a subsequent bath removes all resist material except that shaded by the image. (c) The remaining resist then serves as a mask in a chemical etching operation, which (d) removes all unmasked metal to produce a part having a profile identical to the initial image. [*1970 Metals Reference Issue, Machine Design.* Penton Publishing Co., Cleveland, Ohio.]

Ultrasonic Machining. An important unconventional machining method intended for work on hard and/or brittle materials. This method employs a

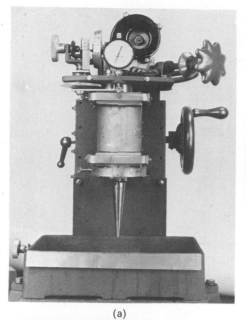

(a)

(b)

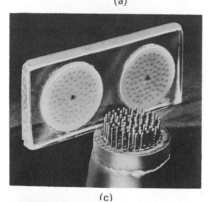

(c)

Figure 4-41 Ultrasonic machining (impact grinding). (a) The head unit of the machine. (b), (c), and (d) Representative *difficult* types of products that can be produced by this method of fabrication. (b) Long-life heading and stamping dies cut from tungsten, carbide steel. (c) A ceramic spacer with multiple drilled holes. (d) Holes and slots cut in a ceramic spacer for an electronic tube. [Courtesy Raytheon Manufacturing Company.]

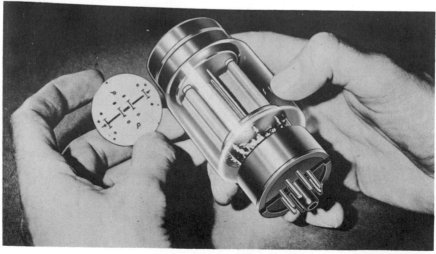

(d)

tool of a softer material (cold rolled steel, brass, or copper) than the work piece which has the contour of the shape to be cut. This tool is mounted on a high frequency, low amplitude (for example ± 0.002 in.) transducer, and oscillates as shown in Figure 4-41 at approximately 25,000 cycles per second (cps). While this motion is taking place, a slurry containing abrasive particles, such as silicon carbide, boron carbide or aluminum oxide, is directed at the tool and the work piece, cutting the shape of the tool into the work surface. The tool is subject to some wear, but is inexpensive to replace.

SECTION 4-6

Engineering Drawings and Dimensions

The result of a designer's efforts must be translated into a set of instructions to the shop in order that the part or parts can be fabricated and assembled. Thus, a set of engineering drawings are prepared showing the sizes (that is, to scale), shapes, and dimensions to which parts are to be made. Unfortunately, many designers consider this phase of engineering design to be trivial. Realistically speaking, however, it may be of greater importance than the design solution itself.

Consider, for the moment, what an engineering drawing represents. It is a detailed set of instructions (that is, orders) that tells the machinist, molder, die caster, and so on, "make this part in accordance with the information indicated and to the dimensions specified—any unauthorized deviations or errors made in fabrication are your responsibility." This statement is, of course, exaggerated. Nevertheless, it is meant to convey the importance of the complete and proper dimensioning of engineering drawings—the responsibility for which rests with the designer. Careless dimensioning can lead to increased production costs and/or outright waste as a result of errors.

Due to the fact that no part can be manufactured to an "exact" dimension, shop drawings are prepared in accordance with a system of tolerances and allowances. Many companies, by reason of their shop facilities and experience, rely on their own standards for dimensioning drawings. We will base our discussion on the widely used ANSI[7] (American National Standards Institute) "Preferred limits and fits for cylindrical parts" (Standard B4.1–1967) published by the American Society of Mechanical Engineers (see Tables C-1, C-2, C-3, C-4, and C-5 in Appendix C). These tables indicate the limits imposed on different sized components that will result in a particular class of fit between two mating parts. The tables provide a common basis for dimensioning components for interchangeable manufacture.

When closer fits than those indicated by the tables are required, the designer may reduce the tolerance of the mating parts. However, taking such action could result in increased fabrication costs. In order to avoid any increased

---

[7] ANSI was formerly known as the United States of America Standards Institute (USASI), and prior to that was known as the American Standards Association (ASA).

cost, the designer would of necessity have to resort to selective assembly. The idea behind selective assembly is to specify large tolerances for the mating parts, and then grade them by gaging in small, medium, and large fits. Thus, a small shaft mating with a small hole, a medium shaft mating with a medium hole, and a large shaft mating with a large hole will all possess the same fit allowance. One should, nevertheless, keep in mind that the additional cost of purchasing the gages as well as the labor required for gaging may offset any saving achieved by selective assembly.

SECTION 4-7

Definitions of Dimensioning Terms

For a thorough understanding of fits and tolerances, the following terms[8] must be clearly understood.

Allowance. The allowance is the tightest fit between mating parts. For interference fits, the allowance is negative.

Nominal Size. The nominal size is the designation used for the purpose of general identification. For example, a $2\frac{1}{2}$-in. diameter nominal pipe is actually 2.875 in. in diameter.

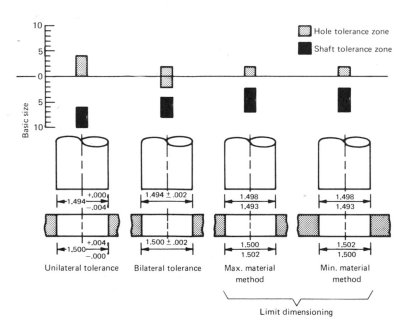

Figure 4-42 Examples of the three systems of dimensioning. The trend is to adopt limit dimensioning as the preferred system.

[8] This list does not include all of the ANSI terms but only those that are pertinent to the understanding of specifying fits and tolerances.

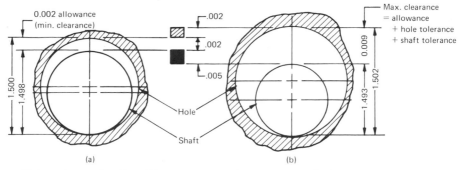

(a)

Minimum clearance (i.e. tightest fit)
is equal to the smallest hole dia.
minus the largest shaft dia. The
minimum clearance is the allowance

(b)

Maximum clearance (i.e. loosest fit)
is equal to the largest hole dia. minus
the smallest shaft dia. The max. clearance
is determined as indicated in the above figure

Clearance Fit

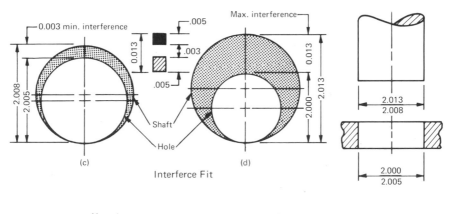

(c)

(d)

Interferce Fit

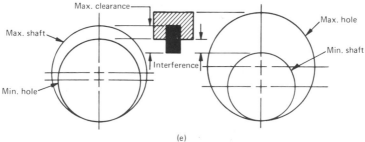

(e)

Transition Fit

Figure 4-43 The representations shown are in accordance with the basic hole system. **(a)** and **(b)** A clearance fit using the limit dimensions of Figure 4-42. **(c)** and **(d)** Maximum and minimum interference fit based on the dimensions as shown. For interchangeability, there must be clearance between parts when they are at maximum material condition (MMC), as in (a). Interference between parts is dimensioned on the basis of the least material condition (LMC), as in (c).

Tolerance. A tolerance is the total permissible variation in the size of a part.

Basic Size. The basic size is that size from which limits of size are derived by the application of allowances and tolerances.

Unilateral Tolerancing. Unilateral tolerancing is a system of dimensioning where the tolerance (that is, variation) is shown in only one direction from the nominal size. Unilateral tolerancing allows the changing of tolerance on a hole or shaft without seriously affecting the fit (see Figure 4-42).

Bilateral Tolerancing. Bilateral tolerancing is a system of dimensioning where the tolerance (that is, variation) is split and is shown on either side of the nominal size (see Figure 4-42).

Limit Dimensioning. Limit dimensioning is a system of dimensioning where only the maximum and minimum dimensions are shown. Thus, the tolerance is the difference between these two dimensions. Two methods of designating limit dimensions are considered as standard. One method is the maximum material method in which the large dimension is placed above the smaller dimension for male parts, and the reverse is true for female parts. This method is well suited for small lot quantities because it is likely that the machinist himself may check the dimensions of the parts. In so doing, he will be verifying initially the larger dimension of the male part and the smaller dimension of the female part. The other method is the maximum number method and is preferred by production and quality control departments. In this method of designating a dimension, the larger number is always placed above the smaller number, regardless of whether the part is male or female.

Clearance Fit. A clearance fit is one having limits of size so prescribed that a clearance always results when mating parts are assembled (see Figure 4-43a and b).

Interference Fit. An interference fit is one having limits of size so prescribed that an interference always results when mating parts are assembled (see Figure 4-43c and d).

Transition Fit. A transition fit is one having limits of size so prescribed that either a clearance or an interference may result when mating parts are assembled (see Figure 4-43e).

Basic Hole System. A basic hole system is a system of fits in which the design size of the hole is the basic size from which the allowance is subtracted to obtain the diameter of the shaft. The basic hole is the preferred system because standard drills, reamers, broaches, plug gages, and so on can be used and shafts can then easily be machined to fit.

Basic Shaft System. A basic shaft system is a system of fits in which the design size of the shaft is the basic size to which the allowance is added to obtain the diameter of the hole. (Normally most design offices adhere to the basic hole system because of standard tooling and the fact that tolerance tables are based on the basic hole system. However the use of the basic hole system has the great advantage in that it is possible to use a standard size shaft.)

SECTION 4-8

Classes of Fits

As indicated in Section 4-6, the ANSI Standard B4.1–1967, "Preferred limits and fits for cylindrical parts," is widely used for establishing tolerances for various classes of fits. The letter symbols appearing in this standard (Tables C-1, C-2, C-3, C-4, and C-5 in Appendix C) represent the following classes:[9] RC (running or sliding fit), LC (locational clearance fit), LT (transition fit), LN (locational interference fit), and FN (force or shrink fit).

Running or sliding fits

Running or sliding fits (Table C-1, Appendix C) provide a similar running performance with suitable lubrication allowance throughout the range of sizes. The clearance for the first two classes, used chiefly as slide fits, increases more slowly with diameter than the other classes, in order that accurate location is maintained even at the expense of free relative motion. There are nine types of RC fits which are defined as follows.

RC1. Close sliding fits are intended to locate accurately parts that must assemble without perceptible play.

RC2. Sliding fits are intended for accurate location, but with greater maximum clearance than class RC1. Parts made to this fit move and turn easily but are not intended to run freely and, in the larger sizes, may seize with small temperature changes.

RC3. Precision running fits are the closest fits that can be expected to run freely and are intended for precision work at slow speeds and light journal pressures. However, they are not suitable where appreciable temperature changes are likely to be encountered.

RC4. Close running fits are intended chiefly for running fits on accurate machinery with moderate surface speeds and journal pressures where accurate location and minimum play is desired.

RC5 and RC6. Medium running fits are intended for higher running speeds or heavy journal pressures or both.

RC7. Free running fits are intended for use where accuracy is not essential or where large temperature variations are likely to be encountered, or under both of these conditions.

RC8 and RC9. Loose running fits are intended for use where materials such as cold-rolled shafting and tubing made to commercial tolerances are involved.

A graphical representation of RC fits is shown in Figure 4-44.

---

[9] These letter symbols (i.e., RC, LC, etc.) are not used on manufacturing drawings but are intended to guide the designer to select tolerances consistent with his design requirements. Other symbols such as H5, g4 (H5g4), H6h5, etc., are in accordance with the American, British, Canadian (ABC) system.

Chapter 4: Manufacturing Processes and Design

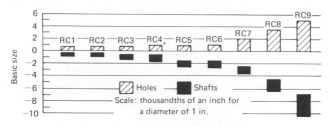

Figure 4-44 Graphic representation of running and sliding fits.

Location clearance fits

Location clearance fits (Tables C-2, C-3, and C-4 in Appendix C) are intended to determine only the location of the mating parts; they may provide rigid or accurate location, as with interference fits, or some freedom of location, as with clearance fits. Accordingly, they are divided into three groups: clearance fits, transition fits, and interference fits. These fits are more fully described as follows:

LC. **Locational clearance fits** (Table C-2, Appendix C) are intended for parts that are normally stationary but can be freely assembled or disassembled. They run from snug fits for parts requiring accuracy of location, through the medium clearance fits for parts such as spigots, to the looser fastener fits where freedom of assembly is of prime importance.

LT. **Transition fits** (Table C-3, Appendix C) are a compromise between clearance and interference fits for application where accuracy of location is important, but either a small amount of clearance or interference is permissible.

LN. **Locational interference fits** (Table C-4, Appendix C) are used where accuracy of location is of prime importance and for parts requiring an alignment with special requirements for bore pressure. Such fits are not intended for parts designed to transmit frictional loads from one part to another by virtue of the tightness of fit, as these conditions are covered by force fits.

A graphical representation of clearance locational fits, transition location fits, and interference locational fits is shown in Figure 4-45a, b, and c respectively.

Force fits

Force fits (Figure C-5, Appendix C) or shrink fits constitute a special type of interference fit, normally characterized by maintenance of constant bore pressures through the range of sizes. The interference, therefore, varies almost directly with diameter, and the difference between its minimum and maximum values is small to maintain the resulting pressures within reasonable

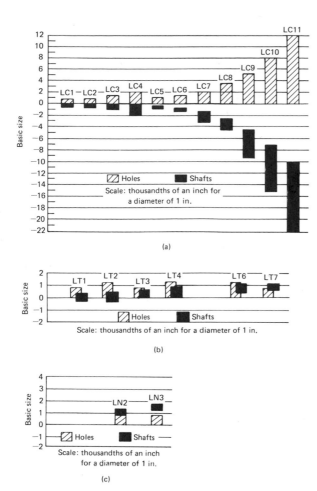

Figure 4-45 Graphic representation of (a) clearance locational fits, (b) transitional locational fits, and (c) interference locational fits.

limits. There are five types of force fits, which are described as follows:

FN1. Light drive fits are those requiring light assembly pressures and produce more or less permanent assemblies. They are suitable for thin sections or long fits or in cast iron external members.

FN2. Medium drive fits are suitable for ordinary steel parts or for shrink fits on light sections. They are about the tightest that can be used with high grade, cast iron external members.

FN3. Heavy drive fits are suitable for heavier steel parts or for shrink fits in medium sections.

FN4 and FN5. Force fits are suitable for parts that can be highly stressed or for shrink fits where the heavy pressing forces are impractical.

A graphical representation of force fits or shrink fits is shown in Figure 4-46.

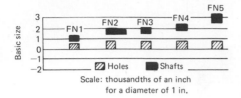

Figure 4-46 Graphic representation of force or shrink fits.

SECTION 4-9

Selecting Tolerances

Selecting tolerances is not a random process. It requires careful judgement based upon design calculations, production facilities, and cost. As a rule, tolerances should be as large as possible because they generally will determine the method of manufacture and, thus, markedly affect the cost of production. This aspect is clearly indicated by Figure 4-47 where it is readily observed that, as the tolerances decrease, the relative cost of production rises (quite rapidly for small tolerance values).

It is essential that in selecting a tolerance the designer be aware of the accuracies attainable from various machine shop operations and other

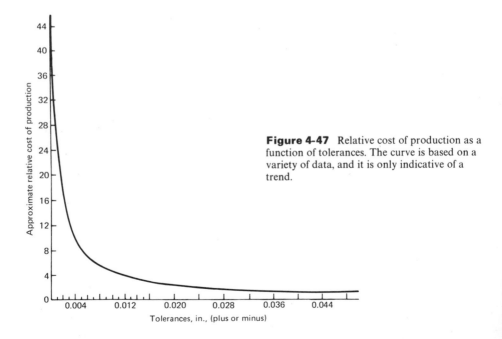

Figure 4-47 Relative cost of production as a function of tolerances. The curve is based on a variety of data, and it is only indicative of a trend.

manufacturing processes such as casting, molding, forging, and so on (see Sections 4-2, 4-5, and Figure 4-48). To assist him in making a wise decision, the designer may refer to Table 4-1 and Figure 4-48. A tolerance selected from Table 4-1 determines the grade of machine work required. Knowing the

Figure 4-48 Machining processes expected to produce work within a given tolerance. [Courtesy of the ASME, ANSI Standard B4.1–1967.]

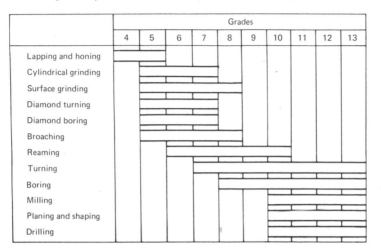

Table 4-1 Standard Tolerances Arranged According to Size of Part and Grade of Machine Work (value in thousandths of an inch)

Nominal Size Range Inches Over — To	Grade 4	Grade 5	Grade 6	Grade 7	Grade 8	Grade 9	Grade 10	Grade 11	Grade 12	Grade 13
0.04– 0.12	0.15	0.20	0.25	0.4	0.6	1.0	1.6	2.5	4	6
0.12– 0.24	0.15	0.20	0.3	0.5	0.7	1.2	1.8	3.0	5	7
0.24– 0.40	0.15	0.25	0.4	0.6	0.9	1.4	2.2	3.5	6	9
0.40– 0.71	0.2	0.3	0.4	0.7	1.0	1.6	2.8	4.0	7	10
0.71– 1.19	0.25	0.4	0.5	0.8	1.2	2.0	3.5	5.0	8	12
1.19– 1.97	0.3	0.4	0.6	1.0	1.6	2.5	4.0	6	10	16
1.97– 3.15	0.3	0.5	0.7	1.2	1.8	3.0	4.5	7	12	18
3.15– 4.73	0.4	0.6	0.9	1.4	2.2	3.5	5	9	14	22
4.73– 7.09	0.5	0.7	1.0	1.6	2.5	4.0	6	10	16	25
7.09– 9.85	0.6	0.8	1.2	1.8	2.8	4.5	7	12	18	28
9.85– 12.41	0.6	0.9	1.2	2.0	3.0	5.0	8	12	20	30
12.41– 15.75	0.7	1.0	1.4	2.2	3.5	6	9	14	22	35
15.75– 19.69	0.8	1.0	1.6	2.5	4	6	10.	16	25	40
19.69– 30.09	0.9	1.2	2.0	3	5	8	12	20	30	50
30.09– 41.49	1.0	1.6	2.5	4	6	10	16	25	40	60
41.49– 56.19	1.2	2.0	3	5	8	12	20	30	50	80
56.19– 76.39	1.6	2.5	4	6	10	16	25	40	60	100
76.39–100.9	2.0	3	5	8	12	20	30	50	80	125
100.9– 131.9	2.5	4	6	10	16	25	40	60	100	160
131.9– 171.9	3	5	8	12	20	30	50	80	125	200
171.9– 200	4	6	10	16	25	40	60	100	160	250

SOURCE: ASME: ANSI Standard B4.1–1967.

grade, the designer can then determine the likely machining operation. Table 4-1 has been prepared so that it also indicates the level of tolerance achievable in any one machining operation for all of the nominal size ranges listed.

As an illustration, we see from Table 4-1 that a grade 10 milling operation (Figure 4-48) can be expected to produce a tolerance of 0.004 in. for a work piece within the 1.19–1.97 in. range. On the other hand, the expected tolerance for a larger work piece, for example the 4.73–7.09 in. range, is 0.006 in. Thus, it becomes apparent that it is easier to achieve a smaller tolerance with smaller work pieces for the same machining operation. Of course, one must also note that any machining operation is capable of yielding a range of grades as indicated by Figure 4-48. The smaller tolerances (that is, lower grades) are most likely to be obtained from machines that are in excellent condition and from careful workmanship. The larger tolerances can be expected from machines that are in somewhat less than average condition or from poor workmanship.

To further illustrate the use of the tolerance tables and Figure 4-48 consider Example 4-1.

Example 4-1. Figure 4-49 is a drawing of a drive shaft that is used to drive a small centrifugal fan by means of a V-belt drive. The power input is through a gear keyed to the shaft. The shaft is free to rotate in self-lubricated flanged bearings, which are held in the machine frame. Fit requirements are as follows: The flanged bearings are to have a locational interference fit (LN2) with the frame, the shaft is to have a free running fit (RC4) with the inner diameter (I.D.) of the bearing, the V-belt pulley is to have a force fit (FN5) with the shaft, and the gear is to have a free running fit (RC7) with the shaft.

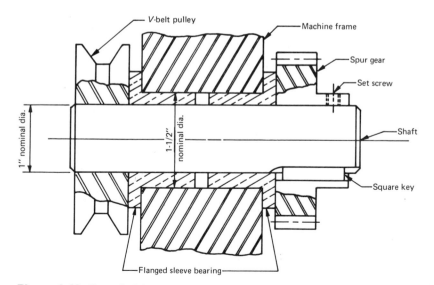

Figure 4-49 Example 4-1.

Determine the limit dimensions for the flanged bearings, the pulley mounting hole, the gear mounting hole, and the shaft.

Solution: First we establish the locational interference fit LN2 between the frame and the flanged bearings. Using the basic hole system, and referring to Table C-4 in Appendix C, we establish the following:

Hole diameter in the frame: 1.5000/1.5010 in.
O.D. for the bearings: 1.5016/1.5010 in.

Thus, we see that the loosest fit between the bearings and the housing is 0.0000 in. (that is, "line-to-line" fit) and the tightest fit is a negative allowance or interference fit of 0.0016 in.

Now we proceed to establish the limit dimensions for the pulley, I.D. of the bearing, and the mounting hole for the gear. From Figure 4-49, the nominal size to be used for the basic hole system is 1-in. diameter. Referring respectively to Tables C-1 and C-5 in Appendix C we obtain the following tabulated data.

Nominal Size Range in.		RC4				RC7				FN5	
	Limit Clearance	Standard Limits		Limit Clearance	Standard Limits		Limit Clearance	Standard Limits	
		Hole H8	Shaft *f*7		Hole H9	Shaft *d*8		Hole H8	Shaft *x*7
Over To										
0.71–1.19	0.8 2.8	+1.2 0	−0.8 −1.6	2.5 5.7	+2.0 0	−2.5 −3.7			
0.95–1.19							1.3 3.3	+1.2 −0	+3.3 +2.5

Thus we obtain the following for

The gear
  The tolerance for the hole in the gear is 0.0020 in.
  The tolerance for the shaft for the gear is 0.0012 in.
  The allowance between the shaft and gear is 0.0025 in.
The flange bearing
  The tolerance for the hole in the flange bearing is 0.0012 in.
  The tolerance for the shaft for the flange bearing is 0.008 in.
  The allowance between the shaft and flanged bearings is 0.0008 in.
The V-belt pulley
  The tolerance for the hole in the V-belt pulley is 0.0012 in.
  The tolerance for the shaft for the V-belt pulley is 0.008 in.
  The allowance between the shaft and the V-belt pulley is −0.0033 in.

Figure 4-50 shows the limit dimensions for the shaft. The limit dimensions for the mounting hole of the gear are 1.0000/1.0020 in. diameter. The limit dimensions for the I.D. of the flange bearing are 1.0000/1.0012 in. diameter. The limit dimensions for the mounting hole of the V-belt pulley are 1.0000/1.0012 in. diameter.

Chapter 4: Manufacturing Processes and Design

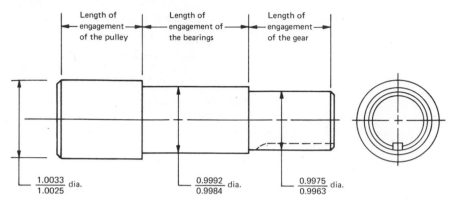

Figure 4-50 Limit dimensions for the shaft of Example 4-1 (not to scale).

From Table 4-1 the grade of machine work for the shaft is as follows:

For the part which mounts the gear: grade 8
For the part which mounts the bearing: grade 7
For the part which mounts the pulley: grade 7

From Figure 4-48, it may be seen that the shaft can be turned (with care) by a lathe operation. Similarly, we may note from Table 4-1 the grade of machine work required to make the holes in the gear, bearings, and pulley. Thus, the gear hole requires grade 9 machine work, the bearing hole requires grade 8 machine work, and the hole in the pulley requires grade 8 machine work. Referring to Figure 4-48, we find that it is possible to bore or ream the holes in the gear, pulley, and bearings. ●

Example 4-1 requires the fabrication of a shaft having three different diameters. Such a shaft is more costly to make than one that has only one diameter. The primary reasons for the increased cost are that the lathe must be stopped, axial measurements made, the cutting tool readjusted, and additional measurements are required for checking. In addition, the transition corner between diameters of the V-belt pulley and the flange bearing requires the corner radius to be such that the bearing flange is in contact with the shaft shoulder. This requirement also adds to the cost. Thus, we see that the fabrication cost of the shaft can be reduced by using a uniform diameter along all of its length. (The reader should realize that in practice a uniform diameter shaft is not always feasible; the material presented here is for illustrative purposes.) To attain our objective, we will use the basic shaft system.

From Example 4-1, we note that the smallest shaft tolerance is 0.0008 in. for both the flange bearings and pulley. Because in the basic shaft system the largest diameter shaft is the basic size, the limit dimensions for the shaft become 1.0000/0.9992 in. diameter. To establish the hole diameter for the gear, flange bearings, and the pulley, it is necessary to know the allowance and maximum limit for each of these parts. The minimum diameter is established by adding the allowance to the basic size (that is, 1.000 in. in this example). The maximum diameter is established by adding the tolerance to the minimum diameter.

	Gear	Flange Bearings	Pulley
Minimum	$1.0000 + 0.0025 = 1.0025$	$1.0000 + 0.0008 = 1.0008$	$1.0000 + (-0.0033) = 0.9967$
Maximum	$1.0025 + 0.0020 = 1.0045$	$1.0008 + 0.0012 = 1.0020$	$0.9967 + 0.0013 = 0.9980$

Referring to Table 4-1 and Figure 4-48, we find that all of the shaft must now be machined by the same methods and to the same grade required by the dimensions determined from the basic hole system. The reader should verify the conclusions.

To minimize the necessity for maintaining an inventory of all sizes of bar stock and to limit the number of tools and gages used, the designer should try to select basic sizes from Table 4-2 and tolerances and allowances from Table 4-3. For example, if the diameter of a bar is determined to be $\frac{15}{16}$ in. use 1 in. if possible. Along this same line of reasoning, select, if possible, a tolerance or allowance from Table 4-3 that can be gaged with tools stocked in the shop rather than selecting a dimension that would require new gages or tooling.

Table 4-2 Preferred Basic Sizes (fractional and decimal) (*continued next page*)

–	0.0100	–	$2\frac{1}{4}$	2.2500	2.25
–	0.0125	–	$2\frac{3}{8}$	2.3750	–
$\frac{1}{64}$	0.015625	–	$2\frac{1}{2}$	2.5000	2.5
–	0.0200	–	$2\frac{5}{8}$	2.6250	–
–	0.0250	–	$2\frac{3}{4}$	2.7500	2.75
$\frac{1}{32}$	0.03125	–	$2\frac{7}{8}$	2.8750	–
–	0.0400	0.04	3	3.0000	3.0
–	0.0500	–	$3\frac{1}{4}$	3.2500	3.25
–	–	0.06	$3\frac{1}{2}$	3.5000	3.5
$\frac{1}{16}$	0.0625	–	$3\frac{3}{4}$	3.7500	3.75
–	0.0800	–	4	4.0000	4.0
$\frac{3}{32}$	0.09375	–	$4\frac{1}{4}$	4.2500	4.25
–	0.1000	0.10	$4\frac{1}{2}$	4.5000	4.5
$\frac{1}{8}$	0.1250	–	$4\frac{3}{4}$	4.7500	4.75
–	–	0.15	5	5.0000	5.0

Table 4-2   (continued)

$\frac{5}{32}$	0.15625	—	$5\frac{1}{4}$	5.2500	5.25
$\frac{3}{16}$	0.1875	—	$5\frac{1}{2}$	5.5000	5.5
—	—	0.20	$5\frac{3}{4}$	5.7500	5.75
$\frac{1}{4}$	0.2500	0.25	6	6.0000	6.0
—	—	0.30	$6\frac{1}{2}$	6.5000	6.5
$\frac{5}{16}$	0.3125	—	7	7.0000	7.0
—	—	0.35	$7\frac{1}{2}$	7.5000	7.5
$\frac{3}{8}$	0.3750	—	8	8.0000	8.0
—	—	0.40	$8\frac{1}{2}$	8.5000	8.5
$\frac{7}{16}$	0.4375	—	9	9.0000	9.0
$\frac{1}{2}$	0.5000	0.50	$9\frac{1}{2}$	9.5000	9.5
$\frac{9}{16}$	0.5625	—	10	10.0000	10.0
—	—	0.60	$10\frac{1}{2}$	10.5000	10.5
$\frac{5}{8}$	0.6250	—	11	11.0000	11.0
$\frac{11}{16}$	0.6875	—	$11\frac{1}{2}$	11.5000	11.5
—	—	0.70	12	12.0000	12.0
$\frac{3}{4}$	0.7500	0.75	$12\frac{1}{2}$	12.5000	12.5
—	—	0.80	13	13.0000	13.0
$\frac{7}{8}$	0.8750	—	$13\frac{1}{2}$	13.5000	13.5
—	—	0.90	14	14.0000	14.0
1	1.0000	1.0	$14\frac{1}{2}$	14.5000	14.5
—	—	1.1	15	15.0000	15.0
$1\frac{1}{8}$	1.1250	—	$15\frac{1}{2}$	15.5000	15.5
—	—	—	16	16.0000	16.0
$1\frac{1}{4}$	1.2500	1.25	$16\frac{1}{2}$	16.5000	16.5
$1\frac{3}{8}$	1.3750	—	17	17.0000	17.0
—	—	1.40	$17\frac{1}{2}$	17.5000	17.5
$1\frac{1}{2}$	1.5000	1.50	18	18.0000	18.0
$1\frac{5}{8}$	1.6250	—	$18\frac{1}{2}$	18.5000	18.5
$1\frac{3}{4}$	1.7500	1.75	19	19.0000	19.0
$1\frac{7}{8}$	1.8750	—	$19\frac{1}{2}$	19.5000	19.5
2	2.0000	2.0	20	20.0000	20.0
$2\frac{1}{8}$	2.1250	—	$20\frac{1}{2}$	20.5000	—
			21	21.0000	—

SOURCE: ASME: ANSI Standard B4.1–1967.

Table 4-3 Preferred Series for
Tolerances and Allowances
of All Shafts and Holes
(dimensions in thousandths
of an inch)

0.1	1	10	100
–	1.2	12	125
0.15	1.4	14	–
–	1.6	16	160
–	1.8	18	–
0.2	2	20	200
–	2.2	22	–
0.25	2.5	25	250
–	2.8	28	–
0.3	3	30	–
–	3.5	35	–
0.4	4	40	–
–	4.5	45	–
0.5	5	50	–
0.6	6	60	–
0.7	7	70	–
0.8	8	80	–
0.9	9	–	–

SOURCE: ASME: ANSI Standard B4.1–1967.

SECTION 4-10

Vague and Superfluous Dimensions

As indicated earlier in this chapter, an engineering drawing is a document
that provides the shop with the information necessary for the fabrication of a
part or parts. A drawing, therefore, should not contain any vague or superfluous data. Vague or superfluous data prevent the shop from making the
component because information is either unclear or lacking, but too much
information can cause difficulty because it provides the shop with a choice. In
fact, lack of information is not as damaging as too much information. With
too little information, the part cannot be made. With too much information,
the part can be made and wasted because of the choice given the shop.

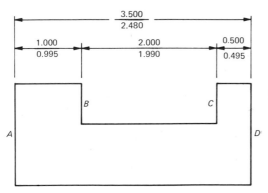

Figure 4-51 Superfluous dimensioning.

Figure 4-51 provides an example of superfluous dimensioning. Assume that the shop chooses to make the part so that length AD is 3.500 in., length AB is 0.995 in., and length BC is 1.990 in. The result is that length CD is 0.515 in. and exceeds the required limit. Similarly, if the choice was to make AD 3.500 in., AB 0.995 in., and CD 0.495 in., the length of BC would be 2.010 in. and would exceed the allowable limit. The solution to this dilemma is to leave out one of the dimensions. The selection of the dimension to be omitted depends upon the functional importance of each of the dimensions. If for a particular reason (for example, information or clarity), all the dimensions are to remain as in Figure 4-51, then one dimension should be marked "Ref."[10] and the tolerance removed.

SECTION 4-11

Accumulation and Nonaccumulation of Tolerances

Again referring to Figure 4-51, we see surface C can be displaced from surface A by a dimension that can vary between 2.985 and 3.000 in. If it is important that C be held to a smaller variational distance from A, the method of dimensioning must be changed. Figure 4-51 represents a system called chain dimensioning where the tolerances accumulate (that is, cumulative tolerances). It is an acceptable method if, for example, length BC is important because of assembly requirements. However, if there is no valid reason for chain dimensioning, this system should be avoided. Instead, a nonaccumulative method (that is, noncumulative tolerances) should be employed. This point is illustrated in Figure 4-52.

Notice in Figure 4-52 that the location of surface C varies less from datum surface A than it does in Figure 4-51 where chain dimensioning is used.

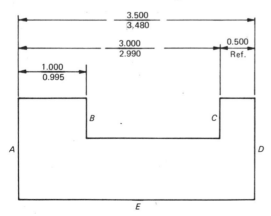

Figure 4-52 Nonaccumulating tolerances.

10 Ref. means "reference only" and that the dimension so marked is not be be used for manufacturing purposes.

Datum surfaces such as A and E (that is, for vertical dimensions) are also very convenient for shop work because many machines are set up for cartesian coordinate locations. It is also convenient to use the center lines of a hole as the origin of a cartesian coordinate dimensioning system. In this instance, because the center of the hole does not exist physically, actual shop measurements are made by putting a small tolerance, ground pin in the hole and measuring from the pin diameter to the points of interest.

SECTION 4-12

Tolerance Stackup

It is possible for an accumulation (that is, stackup) of tolerances to cause an inoperable or malfunctioning assembly. As a simple illustration of this point, consider Figure 4-53. This figure shows a bolted flanged joint connection. This particular bolted joint uses a shoulder screw rather than the conventional stud or bolt in order to limit the gasket compression. Figure 4-53a shows the connection with the limit dimensions for each part. Figure 4-53b shows the bolted joint with all the parts at a maximum and the length of the shoulder bolt at a minimum. Figure 4-53c shows the bolted joint with all of the parts at a minimum and the length of the shoulder bolt at a maximum. Note, in Figure 4-53c, that the result of the "stacked-up" tolerances of the assembly will allow leakage from the vessel past the gasket seal.

SECTION 4-13

Statistical Determination of Tolerances

In designing for quantity production, the cost of the final product will be strongly influenced by the amount of inspection required. Obviously, the greatest savings are realized where there is little or no inspection.

Considering the less than perfect condition of production equipment that is frequently used, some component parts are bound to be larger and some smaller than specified. Consequently, as described in the previous section, some parts and/or assemblies cannot be functionally assembled.[11]

The method used in the previous section illustrating tolerance stackup if applied to a production run would be expressed as

$$T = T_1 + T_2 + T_3 + \ldots T_n \qquad (4\text{-}1)$$

where T is the total tolerance accumulation at assembly, and $T_1, T_2, \ldots T_n$ are the tolerances of each of the assembled parts.

Equation (4-1) is useful when one or two (or very few) assemblies are to be made. However, for quantity production (without complete inspection)

---

[11] In some production shops, parts that are greater than and less than dimensionally specified are used to complete some additional assemblies, thereby reducing waste.

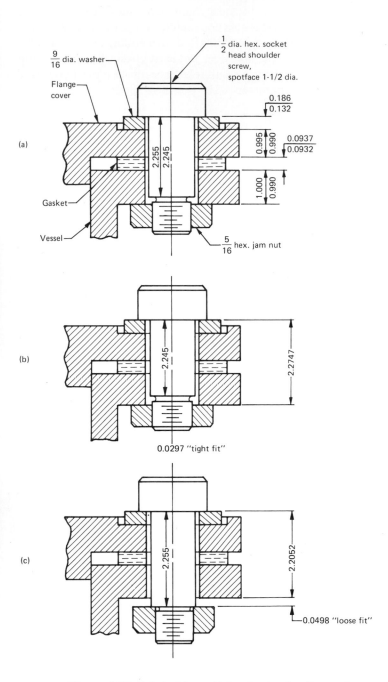

Figure 4-53 A bolted flanged joint showing the effect on the assembly of stacking the tolerances.

Equation (4-1) is not useful because it implies that the largest or the smallest assembly is just as likely to be attained as the intermediate size assembly. Statistical analysis does not bear this out. Instead, results show the dimensions of the components will follow a normal distribution curve. Consequently, the frequency distribution curve of the dimensions of the final assembly will also be a normal curve. Assembly dimensions, thus, can fall on either side of the same mean value.

Since it is not likely that the extreme bounds of this curve will be satisfied, designers have agreed to define a bilateral tolerance (natural spread) as being equal to 3 times the standard deviation (3σ) on either side of the mean.

It can be shown that the standard deviation σ of the sum of parts assembled externally is expressed as

$$\sigma = \sqrt{\sigma_1^2 + \sigma_2^2 + \sigma_3^2 + \cdots + \sigma_n^2} \qquad (4\text{-}2)$$

where σ_n = the standard deviation of the nth part.

Also, from statistics, it can be shown that the expression for the total tolerance accumulation at assembly is

$$T = \sqrt{T_1^2 + T_2^2 + T_3^2 + \cdots + T_n^2} \qquad (4\text{-}3)$$

where T = total tolerance accumulated at assembly in inches and T_n = tolerance of the nth part in inches.

SECTION 4-14

Geometric Dimensioning and Tolerancing

On paper, the designer or draftsman draws geometrically perfect shapes, which are never achieved in actual production. Thus, a part can be made that satisfies the drawing dimensions and yet is not functional due to geometric variations. The characteristics of form or shape such as straightness, flatness, parallelism, squareness, angular displacement, symmetry, concentricity, roundness, and eccentricity can have an adverse effect on the assembly and function of component parts. These characteristic features are concerned with the tolerances of form and position, and are covered by the ANSI Standard Y14.5–1966[12] entitled "Dimensioning and tolerances for engineering drawing."

Space limitations prevent further discussion of geometric dimensioning. The reader is directed to refer to the aforementioned ANSI standard. Also, commercial and governmental standards generally contain a complete description of the rules and symbolisms used in geometric dimensioning.

---

[12] Parts of this standard have also been approved or adopted by the International Standards Organization (ISO R129 and R406) and by Military Standard 8C.

SECTION 4-15

Surface Quality

Most manufactured parts do not require any special quality of surface finish other than that obtained by the method of fabrication. However, there are other component parts (such as bearings, pistons, cylinders, gears, machine feed rolls, and so on) and certain fit requirements (for example, running and sliding fits, interference fits, and so on) that make it necessary to specify the quality of surface finish required. Furthermore, because there is a close relationship between surface quality (that is, roughness) and the endurance limit of metals (see Figure 3-28), it becomes imperative that a designer carefully consider the surface finish required and the manner in which it is to be achieved.

The definitions and symbols used for specifying surface quality are stated and detailed in the ANSI Standard B46.1–1962 entitled "Surface texture." Figure 4-54 shows the meaning of the surface finish terms and the related

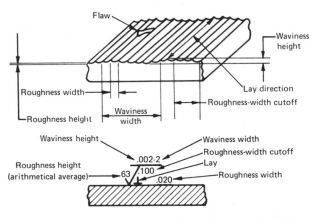

Figure 4-54 Surface texture definitions. [Courtesy of ASME, ANSI Standard B46.1–1962.]

symbol terminology used on engineering drawings. The terms used in this figure are defined as follows:

Roughness. The finely spaced surface irregularities that are caused by cutting edges and machine tool feeds. These surface irregularities are indicated by the height, width and direction of the overall surface pattern. The **height** of the irregularities is expressed in microinches (that is, 1 μin. = 0.000001 in.) sometimes called mu inch. The **width** of the irregularity is the maximum permissible spacing between repetitive units of the surface pattern and is stated in microinches. The roughness width is also used to establish the roughness width cutoff value, and is always greater than the roughness width unless otherwise specified.

Roughness Width Cutoff. The maximum width of surface irregularities that is included in the measurement of roughness height, measured in inches.

Waviness. Irregularities of the nominal surface that are of greater spacing than roughness. The height is given in inches as the distance from peak to valley between waves. The width is given in inches between adjacent waves. Waviness may result from machine deflection, work deflection, vibration, chatter, heat treatment, or warping. Roughness may be considered as superimposed on a wavy surface. The ANSI Standard B46.1–1962 lists commonly used waviness height values.

Lay. The direction of the predominant surface pattern produced by tool marks or grains of the surface determined, ordinarily, by the production method used. Symbols used to indicate the direction of lay are shown in Figure 4-55. The ANSI Standard B46.1–1962 specifies commonly used values for roughness height and lay, depending upon the type of machined surface.

Roughness (in microinches) values should be based upon an arithmetic average that is the average deviation of the surface from the mean. However,

Figure 4-55 Lay notations with surface texture symbols. [Courtesy of ASME, ANSI Standard B46.1–1962.]

LAY SYMBOLS

Lay Symbol	Designation	Example
II	Lay parallel to the line representing the surface to which the symbol is applied.	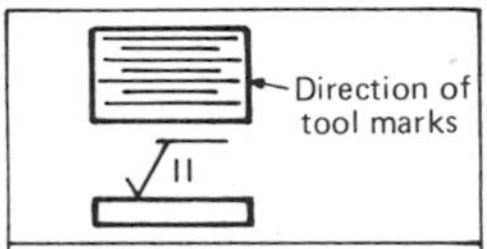 Direction of tool marks
⊥	Lay perpendicular to the line representing the surface to which symbol is applied.	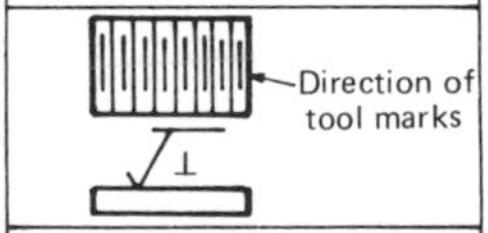 Direction of tool marks
X	Lay angular in both directions to line representing the surface to which symbol is applied.	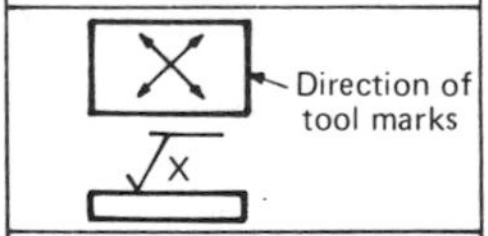 Direction of tool marks
M	Lay multidirectional	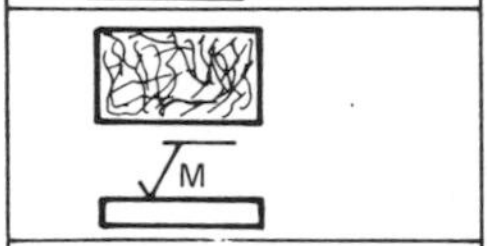
C	Lay approximately circular relative to the center of the surface to which the symbol is applied.	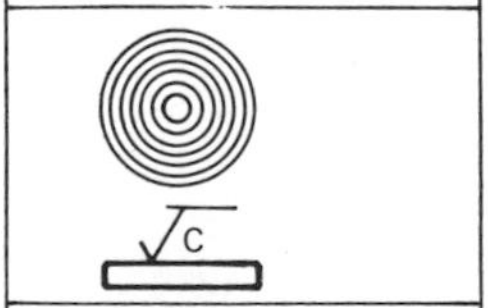
R	Lay approximately radial relative to the center of the surface to which the symbol is applied.	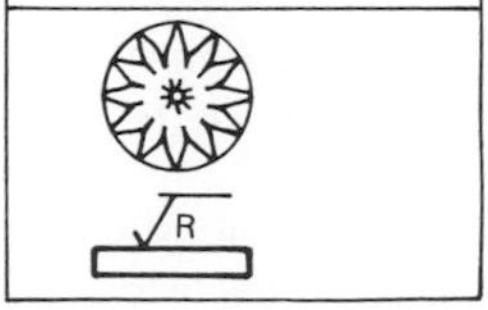

because of earlier types of instrumentation,[13] roughness was specified by the root mean square (rms) average height.

As indicated in the ANSI Standard B46.1–1962, the root mean square average is theoretically 11% higher than the measurements obtained for the arithmetical average. Since readings from point to point on the same machined surface would most likely vary more than 11%, industry has adopted arithmetical average ratings without changing the ratings on older and previous drawings. In fact, surface roughness versus machining charts (and other literature) still specify roughness ratings in terms of rms. However, the designer should adopt the latest standard, which uses the arithmetic average.

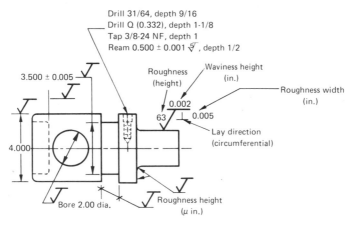

Figure 4-56 Typical applications of the surface roughness. [From *Kent's Mechanical Engineer's Handbook*, 12th ed., John Wiley & Sons, Inc., New York, 1950.]

The symbol used to specify roughness and the manner of its application is shown in Figures 4-54 and 4-56.

The quality of surface finish of a material is directly related to its method of manufacture and the tolerance demanded by the designer. It is apparent that smaller tolerances require finer finishes (hence higher costs) and that the design of a part should be such that its method of manufacture is compatible with the surface finish required.

By means of Table 4-1, Figure 4-48, and Figure 4-57, the designer can relate a production process with an expected tolerance and surface finish. However, the characteristic values determined from Table 4-1 and Figures 4-48 and 4-57 should be used only as a guide. The designer should consider each case on its own merit. For example, from Table 4-1, a 1.5-in. nominal diameter shaft with a standard diameter tolerance of 0.004 in. indicates that

[13] Measuring instruments that read directly the arithmetic average on a face dial are now readily available and in use (e.g., Profilometer and Brush Analyzer).

Figure 4-57 Surface roughness produced by common production methods. [Courtesy of ASME, ANSI Standard B46.1–1961.]

a grade 10 machining operation is required. Reference to Figure 4-48 indicates that the shaft diameter can readily meet the tolerance requirements by turning on a lathe. However, Figure 4-57 shows that for average applications, turning can produce a range of surface finishes as fine as 16 rms or as rough as 250 rms. What finish shall the designer specify? A quick glance at Figure 4-58 shows that a 16 rms finish will cost about 2.65 times the production cost of a 250 rms finish. Thus, the designer must consider the particular application before assigning a surface finish if he is not to increase costs unnecessarily.

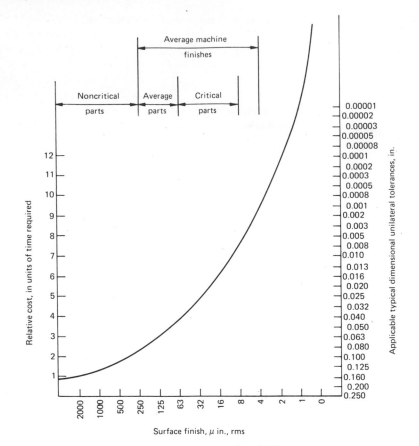

Figure 4-58   Relative cost versus surface finish.

As a guide to what surface finish should be specified for certain applications, the designer can refer to information such as that given in Figure 4-59, industrial or governmental standards, or his own accumulated knowledge of an industry and its requirements.

SECTION 4-16

Design Hints

Without any doubt, cost is virtually the single most important factor in determining the ultimate success or failure of a product. No one (except, perhaps, the obstinate designer) will argue the fact that "the best mousetrap in the world" is unsaleable when it is too expensive. There are, however, a few exceptions to this viewpoint (for example, times of national emergency, the moon shots, and so on). Nevertheless, even in these instances, the cost

Figure 4-59 Characteristic maximum surface roughness finishes for some typical machine components. [From Roger W. Bolz: *Production Processes—Their Influence on Design.* The Industrial Press, New York, 1956.]

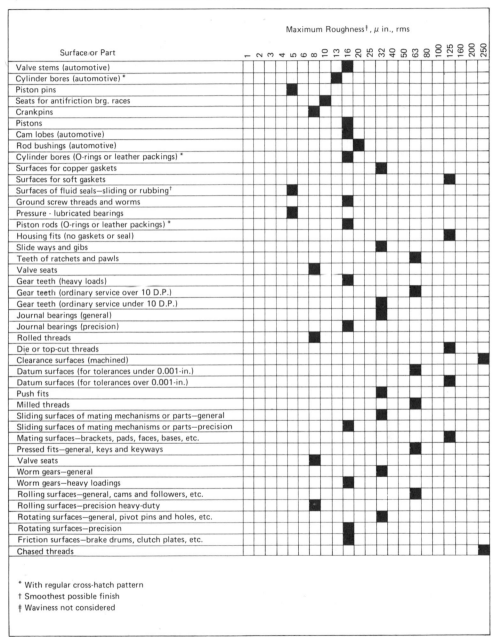

Maximum Roughness†, μ in., rms

Surface or Part	1	2	3	4	5	6	8	10	13	16	20	25	32	40	50	63	80	100	125	160	200	250
Valve stems (automotive)										■												
Cylinder bores (automotive) *										■												
Piston pins				■																		
Seats for antifriction brg. races							■															
Crankpins								■														
Pistons										■												
Cam lobes (automotive)										■												
Rod bushings (automotive)											■											
Cylinder bores (O-rings or leather packings) *													■									
Surfaces for copper gaskets													■									
Surfaces for soft gaskets																			■			
Surfaces of fluid seals—sliding or rubbing†				■																		
Ground screw threads and worms										■												
Pressure - lubricated bearings				■																		
Piston rods (O-rings or leather packings) *										■												
Housing fits (no gaskets or seal)																			■			
Slide ways and gibs													■									
Teeth of ratchets and pawls																■						
Valve seats				■																		
Gear teeth (heavy loads)									■													
Gear teeth (ordinary service over 10 D.P.)																■						
Gear teeth (ordinary service under 10 D.P.)													■									
Journal bearings (general)													■									
Journal bearings (precision)									■													
Rolled threads								■														
Die or top-cut threads																			■			
Clearance surfaces (machined)																						■
Datum surfaces (for tolerances under 0.001-in.)																■						
Datum surfaces (for tolerances over 0.001-in.)																			■			
Push fits													■									
Milled threads																■						
Sliding surfaces of mating mechanisms or parts—general													■									
Sliding surfaces of mating mechanisms or parts—precision										■												
Mating surfaces—brackets, pads, faces, bases, etc.																			■			
Pressed fits—general, keys and keyways																■						
Valve seats				■																		
Worm gears—general													■									
Worm gears—heavy loadings									■													
Rolling surfaces—general, cams and followers, etc.																■						
Rolling surfaces—precision heavy-duty				■																		
Rotating surfaces—general, pivot pins and holes, etc.													■									
Rotating surfaces—precision										■												
Friction surfaces—brake drums, clutch plates, etc.										■												
Chased threads																						■

* With regular cross-hatch pattern
† Smoothest possible finish
‡ Waviness not considered

factor is not wholly ignored. Thus, without intending to be facetious, a good designer is one who practices the art of "penny pinching" as part of his overall design thinking.

Penny pinching must be tempered, naturally, in accordance with the objectives of a particular application. It does establish the basis upon which a designer may satisfy functional requirements while being cognizant of tolerances, finishes, manufacturing methods, quantity required, material choice, availability, and so on, and the effect of these factors upon costs.

In this one section, it is not possible to discuss and detail an extensive number of design hints and their effect on function and cost. However, the following suggestions are offered for the reader's consideration. It is the authors' hope that they will be of assistance in establishing the proper "design attitude." These recommendations and suggestions are not presented in order of importance, but are classified as general and specific. The general recommendations primarily deal with factors that overtly affect cost. The specific recommendations are mainly concerned with improving strength and/or rigidity.

General recommendations

1. "If you can buy it, don't make it!" It seems obvious that, if one could purchase standard components which could be assembled in "erector set" fashion and satisfied design objectives, a device or machine of minimum cost would be achieved. The reader will certainly agree that it would not be sensible to design his own ball bearing or chain and sprocket when they are readily available in a wide variety of sizes and capacities. Yet many designers will design a gear, clutch, brake, and so on, because they claim no supplier has exactly what they need. This is an expensive attitude; it would be a great deal more practical for the designer to consider design changes which would allow him to use commercially available components. A thorough investigation on the part of the designer into the vast number of standard components, parts, and so on, that are available would often eliminate the necessity of his becoming his own supplier. In those situations where a standard component of the required size or capacity is not available and design change is not possible, a design modification or rework of the commercial component or part should be considered before embarking on an individual design.

2. Always consider the ease with which the final product can be assembled, disassembled, and maintained. For example, items such as wrench clearance, bolt location, lubrication points, and so on, can be the source of endless difficulty and criticism once the product "hits the market place." As a further illustration of this point, consider the embarrassment of having designed and built a sophisticated machine, which is ready for delivery to the customer, only to find that there are no lifting lugs or openings in the base for rigging equipment. Thus, the machine must remain just where it is—right on the shop assembly floor.

3. One should design parts that are simple in shape. Whether a component is to be made by a primary or secondary manufacturing process, the cost can rise rapidly with design complexity. Often, it is possible to design a much less expensive and simpler part(s) (or redesign an existing part) by making the more complicated part into an assembly of two or more parts. This idea is aptly illustrated in Figure 4-60.

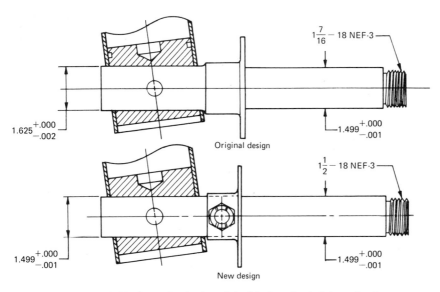

Figure 4-60 Note that in the original design, the shaft is made of one piece of metal having three diameters (exclusive of the threads). The flange is welded directly to the shaft. This not only can lead to the shaft warping but it takes 0.77 man-hr to make. The new design requires only 0.44 man-hr to make. However, the shaft is subject to the effect of welding heat and can be centerless ground since there is only one diameter. [From Roger W. Bolz: *Production Processes—Their Influence on Design.* The Industrial Press, New York, 1956.]

4. The designer should carefully consider the method of manufacture to be used for the most economical production. This requires careful consideration of shop facilities, the quantity to be produced, and the material to be used. Of course, with limited shop facilities and small production, the designer may not have too much choice. On the other hand, for quantity production but limited shop facilities, it is worthwhile for the designer to consider having the part(s) made in outside facilities. A serious consideration affecting choice of manufacturing method is how rapidly the tooling costs can be amortized over the quantity produced.

Proper selection of a production method will usually result in less scrap and fewer rejects. It is also wise for the designer to consider a fabricating operation in which several operations can be performed by one machine or setup, thereby reducing setup and production time (for example, turret

Figure 4-61 An aluminum valve stem body machined from extruded rod (**A**) used 460 lb of material to make 1000 bodies. By changing to an aluminum forging (**B**), the amount of material used to produce 1000 bodies (**C**) was reduced to 220 lb. [Courtesy of Scovill Manufacturing Company.]

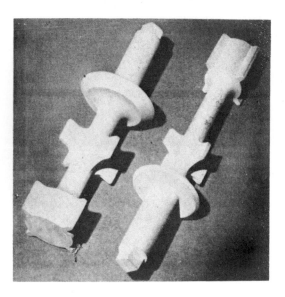

Figure 4-62 A valve stem for a railroad car tank was originally machined from a Monel sand casting at a cost of $18.75 each for quantities of 2000. The valve stem was then redesigned as an investment casting, reducing the cost to $9.00 each per 2000 produced. [Courtesy of International Nickel Company.]

lathes, screw machines, and so on). Figures 4-61 and 4-62 show typical examples of the savings that can be obtained by using proper production methods.

5. The observation that the cost of different materials varies is a trivial one but, from the viewpoint of machinability or formability, material selection becomes important. For example, Figure 4-63 shows the relative machining time for several different metals. Although the lighter alloys are more expensive than the ferrous metals, the obvious savings in machining time (that is, labor savings) can be of such significance as to offset the higher material cost.

When one has little choice in material selection (for example, with high temperature problems), cost reductions must be sought in the area of manufacturing methods.

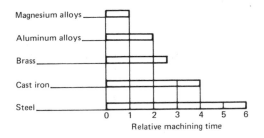

Figure 4-63 Chart comparing the relative machining time of several different metals.

6. Try to design simple parts. Obviously, simple parts will require fewer manufacturing operations which, in turn, will result in lower costs. In addition, savings will be realized as a result of simpler and fewer production tools being needed. The importance of minimizing manufacturing operations by virtue of simple design is emphasized by reference [3], which states, "the greatest saving which can be obtained in designing for production usually results from reducing the number of separate processing operations required to complete a part."[14] An example of this principle is exemplified in Figure 4-64, in which the number of operations to produce the different parts is reduced from 45 to 21. Also, the number of parts was reduced from 14 to 10 while the cylinder was made 40% lighter. The final cost of production was reduced by approximately 600%.

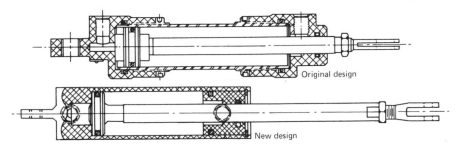

Figure 4-64 Original and new design of hydraulic actuating cylinder for the extension or retraction of an airplane tail wheel. Note the greater simplicity of the new design. [Courtesy of Electrol Inc.]

7. Do not overlook the manner in which a part to be processed is to be held in order that it may be "worked on" by some machine or cutting tool. The designer should consider providing shoulders, centers for turning, bosses, flats, holes, lugs, and so on, which may be needed for properly holding a work piece in a jig, fixture, clamp, or machine. Magnetic chucks and holding devices should be considered for magnetic materials that are awkwardly shaped or otherwise difficult to hold in place.

[14] "Next in importance is reduction in the number of parts used and following that comes savings effected through the use of stock parts or interchangeable parts."

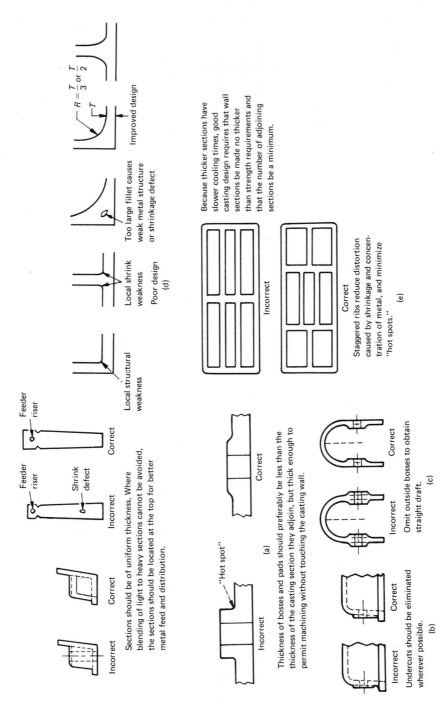

Incorrect   Correct

Sections should be of uniform thickness. Where blending of light to heavy sections cannot be avoided, the sections should be located at the top for better metal feed and distribution.

Feeder riser   Feeder riser

Shrink defect

Incorrect   Correct

Local structural weakness   Local shrink weakness   Too large fillet causes weak metal structure or shrinkage defect

Poor design

(d)

$R = \frac{T}{3}$ or $\frac{T}{2}$

T

Improved design

"Hot spot"

Incorrect   Correct

(a)

Thickness of bosses and pads should preferably be less than the thickness of the casting section they adjoin, but thick enough to permit machining without touching the casting wall.

Incorrect   Correct

Undercuts should be eliminated wherever possible.

(b)

Incorrect   Correct

Omit outside bosses to obtain straight draft.

(c)

Incorrect

Correct

Staggered ribs reduce distortion caused by shrinkage and concentration of metal, and minimize "hot spots."

Because thicker sections have slower cooling times, good casting design requires that wall sections be made no thicker than strength requirements and that the number of adjoining sections be a minimum.

(e)

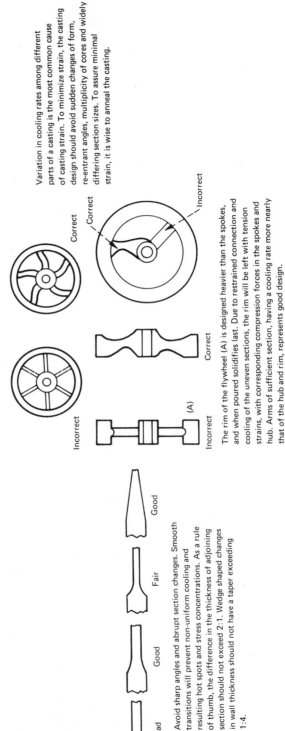

Variation in cooling rates among different parts of a casting is the most common cause of casting strain. To minimize strain, the casting design should avoid sudden changes of form, re-entrant angles, multiplicity of cores and widely differing section sizes. To assure minimal strain, it is wise to anneal the casting.

Correct

Correct

Incorrect

Incorrect

Correct

(A)

Incorrect

(f)

The rim of the flywheel (A) is designed heavier than the spokes, and when poured solidifies last. Due to restrained connection and cooling of the uneven sections, the rim will be left with tension strains, with corresponding compression forces in the spokes and hub. Arms of sufficient section, having a cooling rate more nearly that of the hub and rim, represents good design.

Bad   Good   Fair   Good

Avoid sharp angles and abrupt section changes. Smooth transitions will prevent non-uniform cooling and resulting hot spots and stress concentrations. As a rule of thumb, the difference in the thickness of adjoining section should not exceed 2:1. Wedge shaped changes in wall thickness should not have a taper exceeding 1:4.

Figure 4-65 Hints for good casting design. [From Oliver Smalley: How design is affected by foundry practice. *Prod. Eng.*, 117–121 (Feb. 1950).]

8. Do not specify tolerances and/or surface qualities more restrictive than those minimally required for the part to perform functionally. Indeed, the attitude of the designer should be one of constant questioning of the need for narrow tolerances or superfine finishes. This attitude is justified in the light of Figure 4-47 and by the further savings that may be realized from reduced assembly time, greater interchangeability, and less scrap and waste.

Specific recommendations

Correct design procedure requires constant awareness on the part of the designer of the fabricating methods associated with making a part or component. This awareness contributes greatly to the ease with which a part can be fabricated as well as aiding in the reduction of the fabricating costs and avoiding factors that may contribute to a reduction of strength or stiffness.

1. Casting design is as much an art as a science and is so specialized that the average designer cannot be expected to be an expert. In many cases, it would be wise to consult with a foundry man or patternmaker before proceeding with a particularly complex design. However, if the designer observes a few simple guidelines, he will usually produce a sound casting. Figure 4-65 illustrates some basic considerations for fabricating good castings.

For greater detail, the reader is directed to the *Steel Castings Handbook* published by the Steel Founders' Society of America, to the publications of the Gray Iron Founders' Society, and to reference [2].

2. Forging design, as in the case of castings, requires specialized knowledge, and expert advice should be sought before releasing the design to the die shop. However, by adhering to some fundamental requirements, the designer can contribute much toward the production of a sound forging. Some of the important conditions he must consider are (1) the draft angle, (2) the location of the parting line and forging plane, (3) the fillet and corner radii, (4) the rib heights and rib section thicknesses, and (5) the metal grain flow.

The normal draft angle for ferrous metals is 7 deg for outside surfaces and 10 deg for inside surfaces. Aluminum and magnesium can be forged with draft angles of 5 deg or less, depending upon the shape of the part to be forged (see Figure 4-66).

If possible, a straight parting line should be used so that one-half of the die has all the impressions of the part to be shaped. On the other hand, if other than a straight parting line is required, the forging should be inclined with respect to the forging plane (see Figure 4-66).

Fillets and radii should be as large as possible, whereas rib heights should be as small as possible. However, rib widths should be generous. Recommended sizes for fillets, radii, rib heights, and widths can be found in reference [7], or in the *Tool Engineers' Handbook* of The American Society of Tool Engineers.

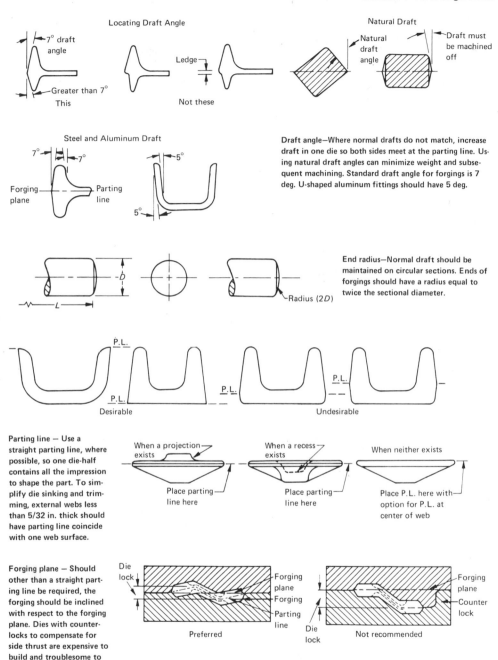

Figure 4-66 Limitations for product and die design to insure strong and sound forgings. [From Checkpoints for practical forging design. *Annual Handbook of Product Design, Product Engineering,* 1954.]

Chapter 4: Manufacturing Processes and Design

Figure 4-67 Design tips which lead to easier machining and lower costs. [From Ernest Geiger: The rights and wrongs of details. *Prod. Eng.*, **12** : 72, 122, 148 (1941).]

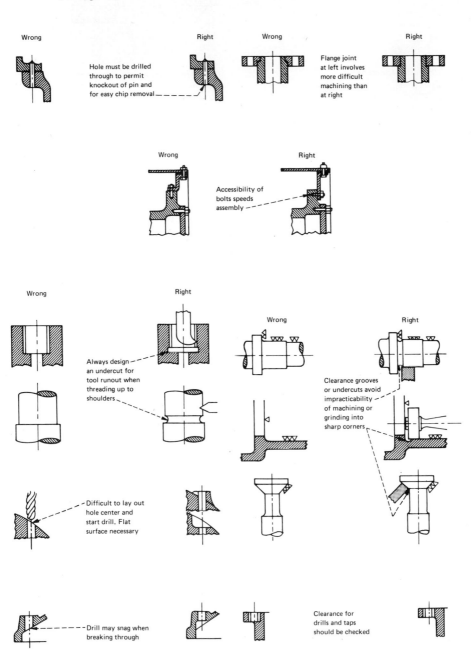

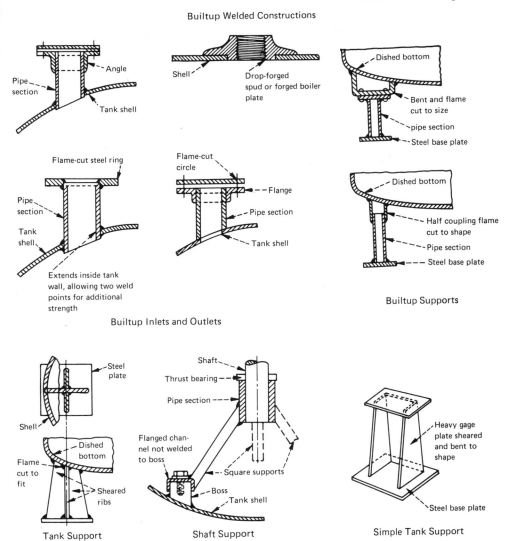

Figure 4-68 Typical welded joint designs for unfired pressure vessels. [From
G. F. Nordenhold, J. Kerr, and J. Sasso: *Handbook of Mechanical Design*.
McGraw-Hill Book Company, New York, 1942.]

One of the most important factors in fabricating a sound forging is to
design the die so that the grain (that is, fiber) flow of the metal to be forged
is maintained (see Figure 4-9).

For a detailed and in-depth study of forging design, the reader is directed
to the publications of the Drop Forging Association and the *Metals Handbook*
of the American Society for Metals.

3. Some planning and forethought by the designer can contribute greatly
to the reduction of both the cost and any fabricating difficulties associated

Chapter 4: Manufacturing Processes and Design

Welding Fittings

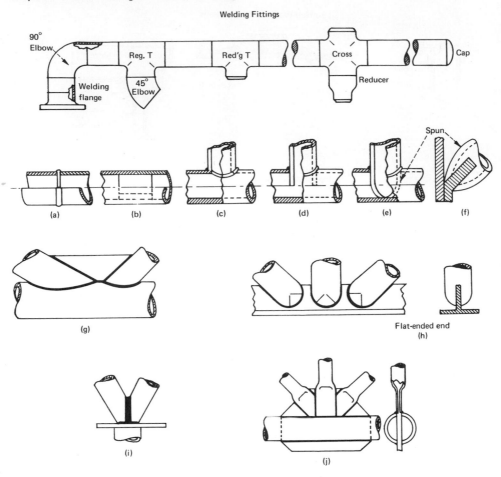

Figure 4-69 Typical weld tube and welded fitting connections. [From W. J. Van Nattan: How service requirements govern design of brazed joints, Sect. G. *Annual Handbook of Product Design, Product Engineering,* 1954.]

with producing a component part in the *machine shop*. Careful consideration of how a part will be machined should be of primary importance. Calling for machining operations or tool room equipment that is beyond the scope and capabilities of the available facilities will lead to having to "farm out" the work. Naturally, this will lead to higher costs. Such obvious faults as calling for drilling excessively long holes, machining after heat treatment (unless required), machining unnecessary surfaces, not specifying grinding or thread "runouts," and so on, can readily be avoided. As the designer acquires more skill and experience, spends more time at the drafting board and has greater contact with the shop, his expertise will grow along with his knowledge of good design practice.

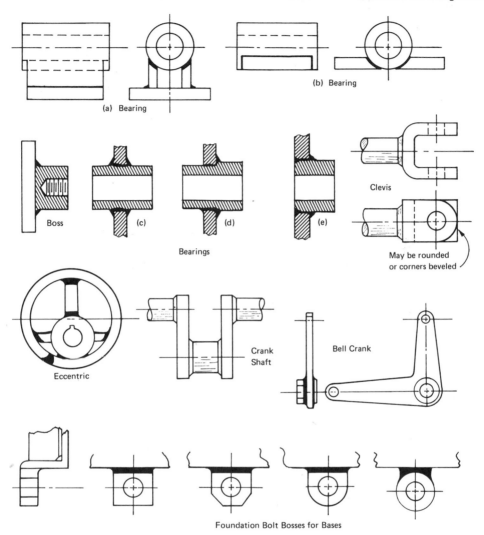

Figure 4-70 Several applications of welding for machinery. [From W. J. Van Nattan: How service requirements govern design of brazed joints, Sect. G. *Annual Handbook of Product Design, Product Engineering,* 1954.]

Figure 4-67 illustrates some of the design mistakes that *can* be avoided.

4. In keeping with the previous discussion, Figures 4-68, 4-69, and 4-70, respectively, suggest ideas and hints of good practice in welding pressure vessel joints and supports, tubes, and machine parts.

Figures 4-71, 4-72, and 4-73, respectively, offer design suggestions for producing good brazing joints, techniques for reducing corrosion, and heat treating considerations that will contribute to the avoidance of cracking and warping.

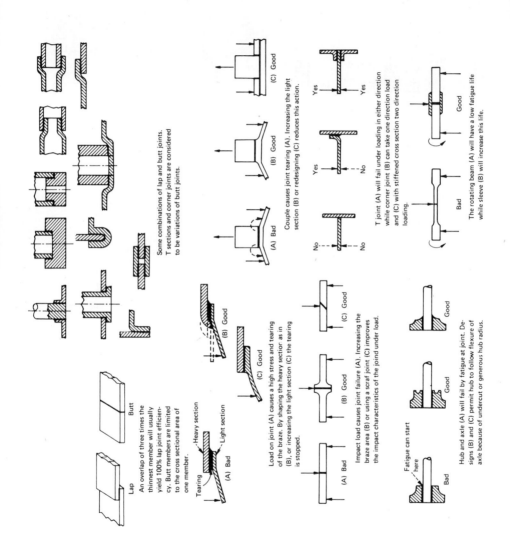

Some combinations of lap and butt joints. T sections and corner joints are considered to be variations of butt joints.

Lap   Butt

An overlap of three times the thinnest member will usually yield 100% lap joint efficiency. Butt members are limited to the cross sectional area of one member.

(A) Bad   (B) Good
Tearing — Heavy section — Light section

Load on joint (A) causes a high stress and tearing of the braze. By shaping the heavy section as in (B), or increasing the light section (C) the tearing is stopped.

(A) Bad   (B) Good   (C) Good

Impact load causes joint failure (A). Increasing the braze area (B) or using a scarf joint (C) improves the impact characteristics of the joind under load.

(A) Bad   (B) Good   (C) Good

Couple causes joint tearing (A). Increasing the light section (B) or redesigning (C) reduces this action.

No   Yes   Yes
No   No   Yes

T joint (A) will fail under loading in either direction while corner joint (B) can take one direction load and (C) with stiffened cross section two direction loading.

Fatigue can start here

Bad   Good   Good

Hub and axle (A) will fail by fatigue at joint. Designs (B) and (C) permit hub to follow flexure of axle because of undercut or generous hub radius.

Bad   Good

The rotating beam (A) will have a low fatigue life while sleeve (B) will increase this life.

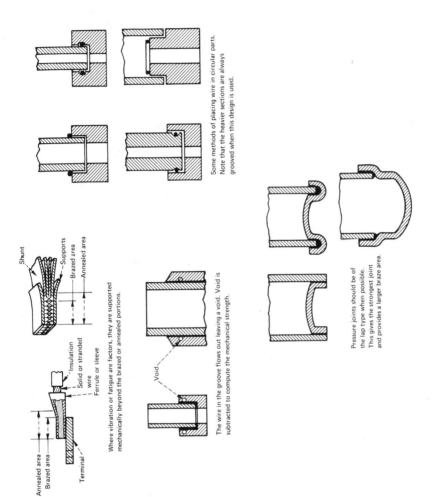

Figure 4-71 Design considerations for brazed joints (see also next page). [From W. J. Van Nattan: How service requirements govern design of brazed joints, Sect. G. *Annual Handbook of Product Design, Product Engineering*, 1954.]

Chapter 4: Manufacturing Processes and Design

Atmospheric Corrosion

Rounded Corners and smooth contours should be used whenever possible to prevent the accumulation of moisture, liquids and
solid matter. Using corrosion resistant materials is often found to
be more economical due to greater service life.

Concentration Cell Corrosion

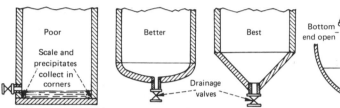

All Liquid Containers should be designed with smooth and rounded corners.
Sharp corners, stagnant areas and other such conditions are favorable to the
accumulation of precipitates, solids and scale which promote concentration-
cell attack. Sloping bottoms should be used with valves arranged for complete drainage.

All Baffles and internal stiffeners
in tanks should have openings arranged to avoid liquid pockets and
permit the free drainage of fluids.

Galvanic Corrosion

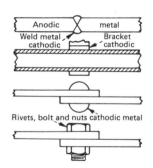

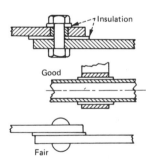

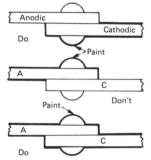

In Joints and connections, the proportions of dissimilar metals should be
chosen so the anodic or less noble metal
has the greater exposed area. If fasten-
ings such as bolts and rivets are required, they should be made of the more
noble or cathodic type material.

When Possible the connection of
dissimilar metals should be separated
by an insulating material to reduce or
prevent the current flow in the galvanic
circuit. Paint or plastic coatings serve to
reduce the galvanic current by increasing the circuit resistance.

Painted Coatings should be applied with caution. Do not paint the less
noble material, otherwise greatly accelerated corrosion will occur at imperfections in the coating. If possible, exposed
surfaces should be painted. Commercial
protectives are now available.

Figure 4-72 Detail design considerations to reduce corrosion (see also next
page). [From F. M. Reinhart: Recommended design details to reduce corrosion,
Sect. G. *Annual Handbook of Product Design, Product Engineering,* 1953.]

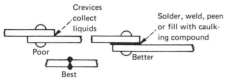

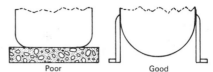

Butt Welded Joints are less likely to corrode and should be used. If lap joints are required, all crevices should be filled with a non-absorbing caulking compound or welded to prevent retention of liquids in crevices.

Storage Tanks and other containers should be supported on legs to allow a free circulation of air underneath. This prevents the possibility of any condensation and collection of moisture under the tank.

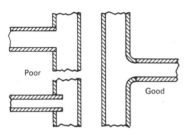

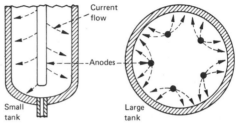

In The Design of liquid passages, all pipes and connections should be constructed to insure uniform flow, with a minimum turbulence and air entrainment. This also reduces settling of solids.

Cathodic Protection of containers with corrosive liquids can be done by immersing a rod of a more anodic material inside. This reverses the galvanic current and the container becomes cathodic and is less likely to corrode. Magnesium and zinc rods are often used.

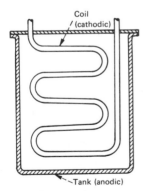

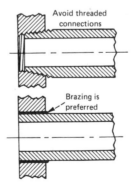

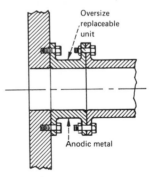

In Designing Equipment, keep different metals far apart in the solution; this increases the resistance of the electrolytic path. Chemical inhibitors are often added to corrosive solutions. Some bare zinc, magnesium or steel in the liquid will counteract corrosion.

In Joining Dissimilar Materials, well apart in the galvanic series, avoid threaded connections since the threads deteriorate rapidly. Brazed joints are preferred using a brazing alloy more noble than at least one of the metals that are being joined together.

At Connections of dissimilar materials, consider using small replaceable sections made of the less noble metal. These expendable parts should be easy to replace and made oversize to increase their corrosive life. Nonmetallic gaskets increases the circuit resistance.

Figure 4-72 (continued)

Chapter 4: Manufacturing Processes and Design

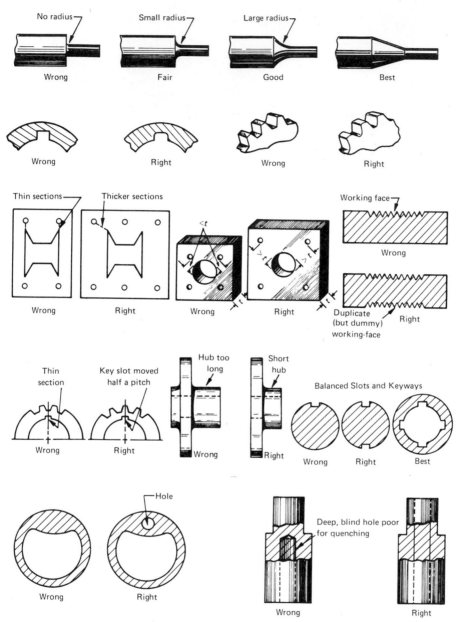

Figure 4-73 The ideal shape for a part to be heat treated is a shape in which every point of any section or surface receives and gives back the same amount of heat with the same speed. Such a shape, of course, does not exist, but it is the designer's task to come as near to it as possible. To do this, keep the workpiece body simple, uniform, and symmetrical. For example, the first figure at the top shows how changes in cross section must be made gradually to minimize stress concentrations during heat treatment. The other figures show further specific ways to keep out of trouble when subjecting parts to heat treatment. Holes, for example, should be correctly located. [Courtesy *Product Engineering*.]

PROBLEMS

1. Into what general categories can manufacturing be classified?

2. List ten ways of making castings. Which of these methods (a) would you recommend for producing large parts in quantity, (b) requires the least amount of finish machining, (c) produces smoother surface finishes, and (d) produces the narrower tolerances?

3. What is draft and why is it required on casting patterns?

4. What are the principal types of metal alloys used to make investment castings?

5. What are some of the advantages to be gained in making parts of powdered metals? What are some of the disadvantages?

6. Explain how the mechanical properties are improved by forging.

7. Compare the advantages and disadvantages of open die forging, closed die forging, and upset forging.

8. List the different methods used in forming plastic products. Which of these are most suitable for quantity production?

9. Name the three types of gas welding. Which of these types is used primarily to join nonferrous metals?

10. Name the eight methods of arc welding. Of these eight methods, which is the most widely used?

11. What metals can be joined by shielded arc welding?

12. What method of arc welding is used for automatic production? Name the metals that can be joined by this method of welding.

13. How is atmospheric shielding obtained in shielded arc welding? What are some of the most important advantages gained in using this type of welding?

14. Name six types of resistance welding methods. For what kind of production is resistance welding mainly employed?

15. What metals may be spot welded? Can dissimilar metals be spot welded?

16. How does spot welding differ from seam welding?

17. What is the difference between flash and upset welding?

18. Which method of resistance welding is used to join dissimilar metals?

19. What are the differences between welding and brazing?

20. What are the differences between brazing and silver soldering?

21. Name the three secondary production processes. Which of these is the most widely used?

22. Define the following: (a) nominal size, (b) basic dimension, (c) tolerance, (d) clearance, (e) allowance, (f) unilateral tolerance, (g) bilateral tolerance, and (h) limit dimensioning.

23. (a) Describe the basic hole system for assigning tolerances. (b) Name the eight classes of fits categorized in this system. (c) What are some of the objections to this system?

24. Explain the differences between selective and interchangeable assembly.

25. What must the designer guard against in assigning tolerances to component parts that are to be assembled in one unit?

26. What is the primary purpose in using preferred basic sizes and preferred series for tolerances and allowances?

27. What is geometric dimensioning and tolerancing? Why is it employed?

28. A shaft has a $2\frac{1}{2}$-in. diameter. Determine the shaft and hole dimensions, allowance and maximum clearance for each of the listed conditions (use the basic hole system): **(a)** a close sliding fit, **(b)** a precision running fit, **(c)** a medium running fit, and **(d)** a loose running fit.

29. Solve Problem 28 using the basic shaft system.

30. A number 306^{15} ball bearing with ABEC 1^{15} tolerances is to be used for a revolving shaft. The housing for the bearing's outer ring is stationary. A bearing catalog specifies the following dimensions: The maximum bearing bore is 1.1811 in.; the minimum bearing bore is 1.1807 in.; the shaft diameter is to be no greater than 1.1816 in., or smaller than 1.1812 in. Determine **(a)** the bore and shaft tolerances, **(b)** the allowance, **(c)** the maximum and minimum metal interference, and **(d)** the class of fit.

31. The same catalog as used for Problem 30 gives the following dimensions for mounting the outer ring in the stationary housing: maximum and minimum bearing outer diameter, respectively, is 2.8346 and 2.8341 in.; maximum and minimum housing bore diameter, respectively, is 2.8353 and 2.8346 in. Determine **(a)** the outer diameter bearing and housing bore tolerances, **(b)** the allowance, **(c)** the maximum and minimum metal interference, and **(d)** the class fit.

32. Specify the dimensions, allowance, and maximum clearance for each of the following conditions (use the basic hole system): **(a)** a $\frac{1}{2}$-in. diameter sleeve bearing and journal for a vacuum cleaner, **(b)** a 2-in. diameter sleeve bearing and journal for a bakery dough mixer, **(c)** a $1\frac{1}{2}$-in. diameter sleeve bearing and journal for a motor generator shaft, **(d)** a $\frac{7}{8}$-in. diameter shaft assembled into a hub by means of an arbor press, **(e)** a $\frac{5}{8}$-in. diameter dowel pin in a hole in die plate, **(f)** an 8-in. diameter rim for a railroad car wheel, **(g)** a $4\frac{1}{2}$ in. diameter crankpin and bearing of a diesel engine, and **(h)** a 4-in. diameter shaft and sleeve bearing of a 1200 rpm gas turbine.

33. A shaft and hole have a nominal diameter of 2 in. The shaft has a tolerance of 0.003 in., the hole has a tolerance of 0.004 in., and the allowance is set at 0.001 in. The dimensions are based on the basic hole system. The parts are made in quantity by screw machines which give a bilateral tolerance of 0.001 in. for the pin and 0.002 in. for the hole. Determine **(a)** the most likely (that is, average) clearance, and **(b)** the expected maximum and minimum clearance.

34. A 3-in. diameter journal and bearing are made to a close running fit. If it is expected that the method of manufacture will produce a natural spread equal to 80% of the tolerance, determine the likely maximum and minimum clearances. Compare your answer with the allowance.

35. The piston wrist pin shown is one of the assembled components of a model airplane engine produced in quantity. The method of manufacturing can maintain the linear dimensions shown. **(a)** What is the tolerance on the overall length? **(b)** What

---

[15] Chapter 9 explains these terms. However, their exact meaning is not needed here to solve the problem: they are used to introduce the reader to their usage.

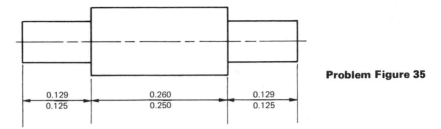

Problem Figure 35

are the maximum and minimum lengths (that is, limit dimensions) of the pin?
(c) If only ten such pins were made, what would be your answer?

36. For each of the tolerances required on various parts, specify a secondary production process.

Final Size Required	Tolerance, in.
(a) 2-in. O.D.	0.007
(b) 2-in. O.D.	0.0005
(c) 1/2-in. diameter hole	0.005
(d) 1/2-in. diameter hole	0.0005
(e) 3-in. thick flat plate	0.014
(f) 3-in. thick flat plate	0.0007

37. For each of the pairs (that is, a,b; c,d; e,f) of Problem 36, determine the expected surface finish in microinches (rms) and compare the relative cost for each pair. (*Note: Do not* use Figure 4-47 to solve this problem because it is included herein for illustrative purposes only.)

38. Make an engineering sketch of a shaft showing all dimensions, tolerances, and surface finishes. The specifications are as follows: The overall length of the shaft is 15.750 ± 0.005 in. Each end of the shaft is nominally $2\frac{1}{2}$ in. in diameter. One of these ends must be turned to a free running fit 5.250 ± 0.002 in. long. This same end contains a $\frac{5}{8}$ by $1\frac{1}{2}$ in. long square sled-runner keyway. The other $2\frac{1}{2}$-in. diameter end is 3.000 ± 0.005 in. long and is to be turned to a free running fit. The middle portion of the shaft is $2\frac{7}{8}$ in. in diameter and contains a $\frac{3}{4}$ by 3 in. long square profiled keyway. This keyway is centered in the middle portion of the shaft. The transition planes between the middle larger diameter and the smaller diameters act as location shoulders for helical gears.

39. At times many of us have exclaimed "What a terrible design. I could have done better than that!" In this regard, select some simple item or device with which you are familiar. Indicate what, in your opinion, are its bad features. Proceed to show how these negative features can be improved or eliminated. Keep in mind that safety, materials, ease of use and/or maintenance, function, and overall cost are but some of the parameters that should influence your thinking and final decision.

REFERENCES

[1] *1970 Metals Reference Issue, Machine Design*. Penton Publishing Co., Cleveland, Ohio.

[2] E. Paul De Garmo: *Materials and Processes in Manufacturing*, 3rd ed. The Macmillan Company, New York, 1971.

[3] Roger W. Bolz: Production Processes—Their Influence on Design. The Industrial Press, New York, 1956.

[4] S. W. Bernard, E. O. Waters, and C. W. Phelps: *Principles of Machine Design*. The Ronald Press Company, New York, 1955.

[5] Oliver Smalley: How design is affected by foundry practice. *Prod. Eng.*, 117–121 (Feb., 1950).

[6] Checkpoints for practical forging design, Sect. D. *Annual Handbook of Product Design, Product Engineering* . McGraw-Hill Publishing Co., New York. 1954.

[7] Ernest Geiger: The rights and wrongs of details. *Prod. Eng.*, **12**: 72, 122, 148 (1941).

[8] G. F. Nordenholt, J. Kerr, and J. Sasso: *Handbook of Mechanical Design*. McGraw-Hill Book Co., New York, 1942.

[9] W. J. Van Nattan: How service requirements govern design of brazed joints, Sect. G. *Annual Handbook of Product Design, Product Engineering*. McGraw-Hill Publishing Company, New York, 1954.

[10] F. M. Reinhart: Recommended design details to reduce corrosion, Sect. G. *Annual Handbook of Product Design, Product Engineering*. McGraw-Hill Publishing Company, New York, 1953.

5

Analysis of Stress
and Displacement

SYMBOLS

c = outer fiber distance, in.

dw/dx = slope, rad.

E = Young's modulus, psi

F = load, lb

G = shear modulus, psi

I = moment of intertia, in.^{4}

J = a geometric constant; the polar moment of inertia for a circular section, in.^{4}

k_t = torsional spring constant, in.-lb/rad

M = moment, in.-lb

N = factor of safety

P = load, lb

P_{cr} = critical load, lb

R = reaction force, lb

S_{yp} = yield point, psi

T = torque, in.-lb

U = strain energy, lb-in.

V = shear force, lb

w = deflection, in.

α = coefficient of thermal expansion, (in./in.)/F°

γ = shear strain, rad.

δ = displacement, in.

ε = strain, in./in.

θ = slope, rad

σ = normal stress, psi

τ = shear stress, psi

v = Poisson's ratio

The most important criteria in machine design are that the machine or machine element must function properly and that it be safe. In most cases, the dimensions of machine elements are based on the strength of the material and predicted maximum stresses. Some design dimensions are based on maximum permissible deflections. In either case, a major difficulty arises in selecting an analytical model to represent the actual proposed design and the predicted system of loading. This step requires considerable engineering judgement, since, if the model is not representative of actual conditions, any further analysis would be meaningless.

SECTION 5-1

The Analytical Model

The analytical model is a compromise, attempting to idealize the system of loading and the load-time relationship as well as the design geometry and the materials used so that a reasonably simple solution is possible. Most engineering materials may be considered homogeneous, continuous, isotropic, and linearly elastic, although no actual material truly meets these specifications. Continuity assumes a lack of structure in a material, but a crystalline substance may be treated as continuous, homogeneous, and isotropic if (1) the part dimensions are large in comparison with the individual crystals and (2) the individual crystals are distributed at random so that the properties at a given section in the part are essentially the same as at any other section in the part, regardless of orientation.

Steel and some other metals have a nearly constant elastic modulus for stresses up to the proportional limit. Beyond this stress level, however, we do not observe linear elasticity. The behavior of a ductile material becomes plastic or elastoplastic beyond its elastic limit. Some materials, particularly nonmetals, fail to exhibit a linear stress-strain relationship. Nevertheless, design is based on linear relationships in almost every case. An average value of elastic modulus for the expected load range may be used. These assumptions are discussed in reference [1].

Most machine parts include discontinuities in section due to fasteners, bearings, or other design considerations. For calculation of stress and deflection, however, the geometry of the part is often simplified; for example, a constant cross section may be assumed, and the results corrected by using stress concentration factors.

SECTION 5-2

The Relationship between "Exact Theory" and the "Strength of Materials" Approach

There is no fine line separating the "theory of elasticity" (see, for example, reference [1]) from the topics and methods of "strength of materials" (references [2], [3], and [4]), and the value of one approach over the other depends on the particular application. In most engineering problems, both methods assume a homogeneous, isotropic, linearly elastic material. Both methods require that equilibrium of force be satisfied. To determine a three-dimensional stress distribution using the theory of elasticity, six stress-strain equations and six strain displacement equations are used in addition to the three equilibrium equations. The unknowns, six stress components, six strain components, and three displacements may then be found for given loading and boundary conditions. If the problem is formulated in such a way that the displacements are not explicitly included, it is necessary to establish compatibility of strains, that is, we must show the material to be continuous in the stressed as well as the unstressed state.

An alternative problem formulation assumes a state of stress that satisfies equilibrium of forces and corresponds to the loading and boundary conditions. Compatibility of strains is not necessarily satisfied. This method, the strength of materials approach, permits the solution of problems that would be very unwieldy by elasticity methods. Because the stress distribution is assumed beforehand, it is apparent that this approach would be meaningless if we were required to find the stress concentration due to a hole in a tension member or for any problem where we have no rational basis for assuming a certain stress distribution.

Where the theory of elasticity results in a tractable formulation, the solution is accurate to the degree of accuracy of description of loading and boundary conditions and to the degree to which the material approaches the ideal assumed homogeneous, isotropic solid. These conditions being met to a reasonable degree, we would expect the elasticity solution to be superior to the strength of materials solution. On the other hand, an assumed stress distribution may accurately portray the system due to factors such as local yielding and, in such cases, the strength of materials method may be favored.

SECTION 5-3

The Nature of Stress and Strain

Consider a finite plane area on the surface of a body or within the body. Average stress is defined as the force on that area divided by the area. If the force is normal to the plane, the stress is called a normal or tensile stress; if the force is parallel to the plane, the resulting stress is a shear stress. The word **stress** will not be used to refer to total force in this work, although that usage is common in structural analysis.

The nature of most engineering materials is such that a small fracture anywhere in a load-carrying machine element may be expected to result in a total failure. Therefore, **average stress** is of little value; we are most concerned with **maximum stress.** Thus, we define stress over an infinitesimal area: the limiting value of force divided by the area over which it acts where the area approaches zero

$$\text{stress} = \underset{\Delta A \to 0}{\text{limit}} \frac{\Delta P}{\Delta A} \tag{5-1}$$

Stress concentration

Following the strength of materials method, relatively simple stress distributions are assumed in machine members (for example, uniform stress in tension members; a linear stress distribution for bending). However, holes, fillets, and other section changes cause high local stresses which may be accounted for by using a **stress concentration factor.** Stress concentration factors and methods of reducing stress concentration are discussed in Chapter 3.

Combined stress

When finding the effect of a combination of loads on a machine member, we must combine stress. In so doing, it is necessary to note the direction of each stress and the plane on which it acts. Failure due to combined stress is discussed in Chapter 6.

Strain

Tensile or normal strain represents the extensional change in length of an element per unit length. In theoretical studies, strain, like stress, ordinarily refers to an infinitesimal element. However, in experimental work, strain may be measured over a finite distance. Shear strain is the change in angle (radians) from a right angle.

Limitations and effect of assumptions

As noted above, we assume that a homogeneous, isotropic, linearly elastic solid will be an appropriate model, applicable to the design of most machine elements. However, as a result of rolling and other processes, there may be preferential grain orientation in some materials so that isotropy does not strictly hold. The linearity and even the elasticity may be in doubt as the loading of a part approaches the ultimate strength of the part; thus, we will ordinarily design for stresses well below the yield strength. One of the most serious questions is whether the mathematical model, which is the basis of our stress analysis, is actually representative of the part that we are attempting to design and of the expected loading. For example, we must design an elevator on the basis of the greatest load that it could reasonably be expected to carry, but we cannot control its use after it is manufactured.

There are many additional assumptions necessary to provide a simple basis for analysis. In the bending of beams (including shafting and other machine elements) the elementary theory is based on the assumption that the slope of the deflected beam is small compared with unity; and in plate theory, accurate results require a stricter limit on deflections: the deflection should be small compared to plate thickness.

If our design is to be based on the yielding or fracture of a material, we must have reliable data on the strength of the material. Yield and tensile strength, however, can only be obtained through destructive testing, and test results vary considerably from sample to sample—even among samples produced from the same heat. Thus, we may approach the problem statistically, accepting strength values corresponding to a satisfactory degree of reliability.

The time history of the loading is critical as well as the (maximum) magnitude of the loading. Even in this respect, however, the actual condition is idealized. That is, we assume that the static value of loading is increased by a factor of 2 or 3 if shock loading is anticipated; or, if some repeated loading is known to occur, we may assume a harmonic component of loading superposed on a constant value of loading.

After we have accounted for all the loading effects that we could reasonably anticipate, it would still be imprudent to allow maximum predicted stresses in a part to approach the failure level closely. For this reason, it is customary to design on the basis of maximum stresses that do not exceed a working stress. Working stress is given by the failure strength (for example, yield point or ultimate strength) divided by a factor of safety. The factor of safety, a number exceeding unity, represents our degree of uncertainty or ignorance concerning loading, material properties, and so on. Its value is influenced by the probable hazard to life and limb and the monetary cost in the event of a part failure.

Measurement of stress and strain

For some machine members, stress can be calculated directly if the loads are given. Experimental stress analysis is used when loading and part geometry are complicated.

The most common method of verifying analytical design methods involves the use of **strain gages.** Thin wire or foil may be bonded to paper or plastic backing, as in Figure 5-1a, forming a resistance strain gage. The gage is

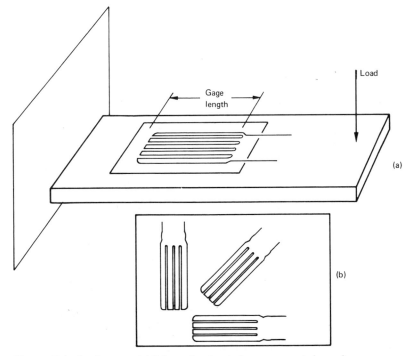

Figure 5-1 Strain gages. (a) Schematic of a strain gage mounted on a beam. (b) A rosette gage.

Figure 5-2 A rosette gage mounted at the clamped end of a cantilever beam. [Courtesy Vishay Research & Education, Romulus, Mich., Division of Vishay Intertechnology, Inc.]

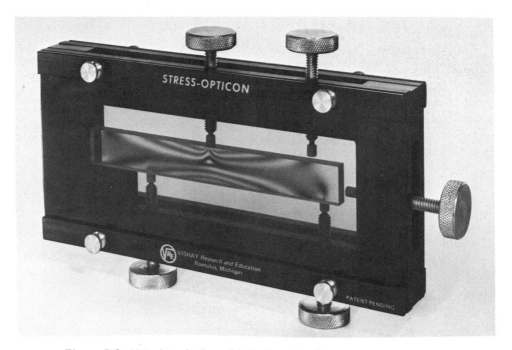

Figure 5-3 (a) A photoelastic model of a beam (see also next page). [Courtesy Vishay Research & Education, Romulus, Mich., Division of Vishay Intertechnology, Inc.]

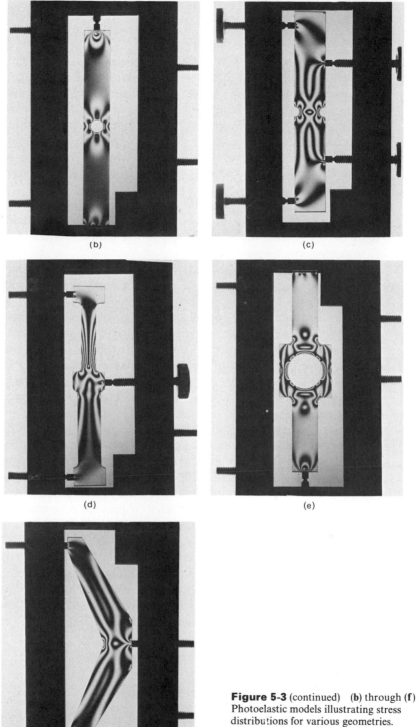

(b)

(c)

(d)

(e)

(f)

Figure 5-3 (continued)   (**b**) through (**f**)
Photoelastic models illustrating stress
distributions for various geometries.
[Courtesy Vishay Research & Education,
Romulus, Mich., Division of Vishay
Intertechnology Inc.]

bonded to the part that is to be tested so that the gage is strained when the part is loaded. Strain in the part is determined from the resistance change in the strain gage and the known gage characteristics. Both static and dynamic loads may be measured. Strain is given by the unit change in resistance divided by the **gage factor** (supplied by the strain gage manufacturer). Since resistance change is small, a bridge circuit is usually required. A strain gage measures average strain over its gage length (usually between $\frac{1}{64}$ and $\frac{3}{4}$ in.). If strain changes rapidly with location, a strain gage with a small gage length should be used.

When the principal directions of strain on a part are unknown, a rosette gage is used (Figure 5-1b). It consists of gages at different orientations. Figure 5-2 (page 240) shows a demonstration model of a cantilever beam instrumented with a rosette gage.

Photoelasticity is a method of experimental stress analysis in which a stress sensitive transparent plastic model is used to represent a machine part (Figure 5-3a, page 240). Loads applied to the model are proportional to loads encountered by the actual part. Using special optical instrumentation (a polariscope), observed patterns can be interpreted to indicate stress in the part. Stress concentration can be examined at holes, notches, and fillets under various types of loading (Figures 5-3b, c, and d, page 241). In addition, shapes that would be difficult to treat analytically may be studied by photoelasticity methods (Figures 5-3e and f). Tests of this type sometimes lead to redesign of a part to reduced stresses.

Vibrating members and other dynamic problems may be studied by observing a photoelastic pattern using stroboscopic light. Three-dimensional stress patterns may be examined by slicing a "frozen" stress pattern or by using special lateral illumination of the model. Instead of using a model, it is also possible to bond a photoelastic coating directly to a machine part.

Brittle lacquer techniques are also used to provide experimental data. A brittle coating is sprayed on a machine part. Then, as the part is loaded in proportion to loads that would be encountered in service, cracks begin to appear in the coating. The extent of the cracks is noted for each increment of load. The coating is "calibrated" by spraying it on a simple beam and observing the strain at which cracks appear. Brittle lacquer techniques alone may be used to obtain quantitative results. Frequently, however, the results are used to aid in placing strain gages for further measurements.

SECTION 5-4

Bending Stresses in Machine Members

In the design of machine members, bending stresses are frequently the major criterion. Let us consider a machine member with one dimension much larger than the others and let there be a vertical plane of symmetry through the longitudinal axis (see Figure 5-4). In that figure, the xz plane is

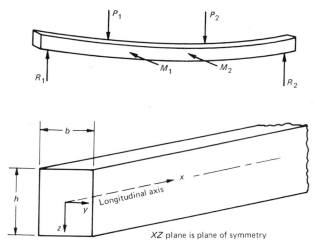

Figure 5-4 Bending loads in machine members.

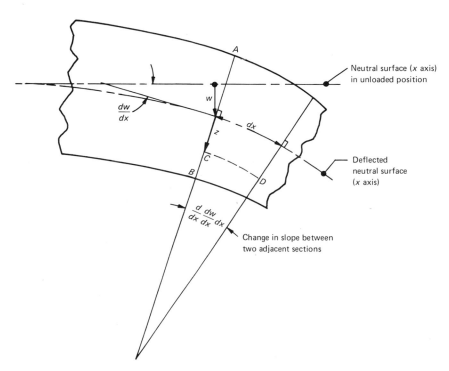

Figure 5-5 Deformation due to bending. The axial strain in element CD is

$$\varepsilon_x = -z \frac{d^2 w}{dx^2}$$

and the tensile stress is

$$\sigma_x = -Ez \frac{d^2 w}{dx^2}$$

the plane of symmetry and the xy plane is the **neutral surface** before deflection. If there is to be no twisting about the longitudinal axis, forces may be applied in the plane of symmetry and moment vectors may be applied perpendicular to the plane of symmetry. Then the (originally straight) longitudinal axis will deflect within the plane of symmetry. Bending effects will predominate and the usual assumptions of beam theory apply.

Let us consider a plane section perpendicular to the longitudinal axis of a member. If that section remains plane and perpendicular to the (deformed) longitudinal axis, then the stress field in the member is readily determined. In Figure 5-5 (page 243) bending stress σ_x is related to the second derivative of deflection w, whereas in Figure 5-6, bending moment M is related to the same quantity. Combining the results, we obtain

$$\sigma_x = \frac{Mz}{I} \tag{5-2}$$

which reaches a maximum at the surface $z = c$ where

$$\sigma_{x(\max)} = \frac{Mc}{I} \tag{5-3}$$

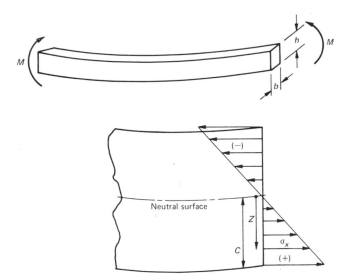

Figure 5-6 Stress due to bending.
Resultant moment

$$M = \int_{\substack{\text{cross} \\ \text{section}}} \sigma_x z \, dA = -EI \frac{d^2w}{dx^2}$$

where

$$I = \int_{\substack{\text{cross} \\ \text{section}}} z^2 \, dA$$

In this sketch, bending is produced by a positive moment, whereas in the preceding sketch the value of d^2w/dx^2 was positive.

This value of stress may be a basis for design when bending moment is computed from the loading. The determination of bending moment due to various forms of lateral loading is illustrated in Section 5.5.

For a rectangular cross section, $c = h/2$ and $I = bh^3/12$. Thus

$$\sigma_{x(max)} = \frac{6M}{bh^2} \tag{5-3a}$$

For a circular cross section, $I = \pi D^4/64$ and

$$\sigma_{x(max)} = \frac{32M}{\pi D^3} \tag{5-3b}$$

The above results assume linear elasticity, that is, σ_x does not exceed the proportional limit. Furthermore, they are based on the assumption that stress is independent of the y coordinate and that y direction stress, $\sigma_y = 0$. These conditions are generally met if the loads are applied in the axial plane of symmetry, if the dimension b is small compared with the length of the member, and if computed stresses are well below the yield point of the material. Analysis of beams having considerable initial curvature is illustrated in Chapter 18.

Composite sections—center of gravity

Some machine members are made in the form of T or I or channel cross sections. In some cases, the center of gravity of the cross section cannot be located by inspection. Consider, for example, the T section, Figure 5-7a, with loads in the plane of symmetry (the vertical plane). In general, the distance from some arbitrary reference to the center of gravity for any cross section is given by

$$\bar{z} = \frac{\int z'\, dA}{\int dA} \tag{5-4}$$

Integration is carried out over the entire area A. Both z' and $\bar{z}$ are measured from the arbitrary reference, which could be, for example, the top of the section.

When it is convenient to separate a cross section into two or more parts, the expression for the location of the center of gravity may be given in terms of the individual cross section areas and the distances from the arbitrary reference to their centers of gravity: For example, the center of gravity of the T section in Figure 5-7b is located by the equation

$$\bar{z} = \frac{z'_1 A_1 + z'_2 A_2}{A_1 + A_2}$$

Using the dimensions in the Figure 5-7a, we obtain $\bar{z} = 0.72$ in.

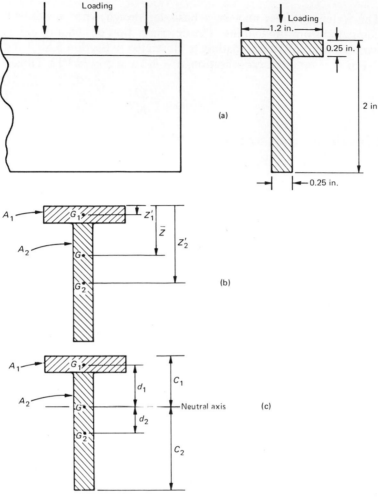

Figure 5-7 Bending of a composite section. (**a**) T section loaded in plane of symmetry. (**b**) Location of center of gravity. (**c**) Moment of inertia.

Moment of inertia for composite sections

In general, the moment of inertia of a cross section is given by

$$I = \int_{\text{cross section}} z^2 \, dA$$

For machine members in bending, we are interested in the moment of inertia about the **neutral axis**—for example, the horizontal axis through the center of gravity G in Figure 5-7c. The moment of inertia of a composite section about its neutral axis may be expressed as the sum of the moments of inertia of its components about that axis. Furthermore, the moment of inertia of each component area may be expressed as the sum of the moment of inertia I_0 of that area about an axis through its center of gravity parallel to the neutral axis plus the transfer effect Ad^2, where A is the individual area and d is the distance from the neutral axis to the center of gravity of that area. Thus, the total moment of inertia about the neutral axis is given by

$$I = \Sigma\,(I_0 + Ad^2) \tag{5-5}$$

summed over all area components. For the T section shown in Figure 5-7, we find $I = 0.291 \text{ in}^4$.

In this example, the bending stresses at the extreme (top and bottom) fibers are not equal. Normal stress (bending stress) at the top is

$$\sigma_x = \frac{Mc_1}{I}$$

where $c_1 = 0.72$ in. and at the bottom,

$$\sigma_x = \frac{Mc_2}{I}$$

where $c_2 = 1.28$ in. One stress will be tensile, the other compressive, depending on loading and support.

When a member is loaded in a vertical plane of symmetry and has a horizontal plane of symmetry as well, the horizontal plane of symmetry forms the neutral surface (the neutral axis on a cross section) and can be located by inspection. In many cases, we may take advantage of the symmetry when determining the moment of inertia. In Figure 5-8, for example, we note that the moment of inertia of the I section with equal flanges is the

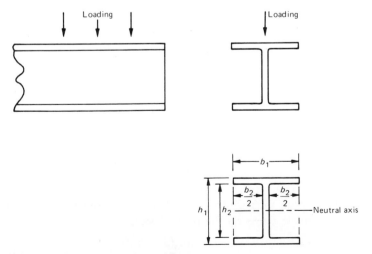

Figure 5-8 I section with equal flanges.

moment of inertia of the outer rectangle less that of the void

$$I = \frac{b_1 h_1^3}{12} - \frac{b_2 h_2^3}{12}$$

Because standard rolled steel sections are not actually made up of rectangular shapes, more accurate values of I can be obtained from tables supplied by the manufacturer.

St. Venant's principle

In effect, St. Venant's principle states that the stress and deflection of a member at points sufficiently distant from points of load application may be determined on the basis of a statically equivalent loading system. We are thereby enabled to solve many problems without undue rigor. For example, by treating gear loads and bearing reactions which are distributed over a small area as their resultant point loads, we may analyze stress and deflection of shafting. Obviously, we must use caution in applying this simplifying device, particularly when we are interested in determining stresses. As an extreme example of *improper* application, consider a slender rod subjected to a tensile force P at each end. If the forces are reversed at each end, it could be argued that the force system is statically equivalent to the first case, but we note that the stress situation is not the same and, even if the first case represented a safe part, the second case could be unsafe on the basis of elastic stability.

An elementary design problem

Consider the design of a handle for a ratchet wrench (Figure 5-9). There are many design decisions, and many different acceptable designs are possible. The length of the handle is based on the torque required for tightening. We set the required torque equal to Pe, where e is the distance from the center of the socket to the line of action of the approximate resultant force P applied by a user. The cross section of the wrench handle would be based on a higher load, however. In removing rusted bolts, it is not unusual to extend the wrench handle by putting a piece of pipe over it, thereby increasing the moment arm, or to hit the handle with a hammer. Although we cannot design an "unbreakable" wrench, we must base our design on the worst loading that could reasonably be expected.

Let us specify an I section for the wrench handle and assume that the critical (most highly stressed) point lies on section A. The moment there is $M_A = Pa$, where a larger value of P is used than required for tightening. A first approximation of moment of inertia about the neutral axis in bending may be made by neglecting the contribution of the web and the contribution of the flanges about their central axes. Then, we have simply $I = 2bhd^2$, and a maximum tensile stress on the outer fiber at section A of

$$\sigma_x = \frac{M_A(d + h/2)}{2bhd^2} \tag{5-6}$$

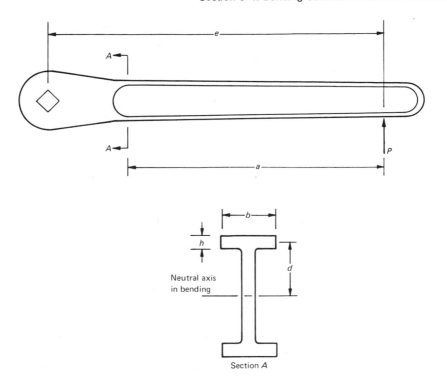

Figure 5-9 Ratchet wrench handle.

We may set σ_x equal to a working strength $\sigma_x = S_{yp}/N$, where S_{yp} is the yield point of the material selected and N is the factor of safety. We would probably select a ductile steel for the design, in which case the first evidence of failure would be yielding. Since this presents no danger to the user, a low factor of safety would be adequate.

In order to complete the problem of designing the section, we may reduce the number of unknowns by arbitrarily relating the section dimensions to one another. Then, we will have a single equation with one unknown dimension to solve for. The handle may be tapered to a smaller section near the end where the force P is applied, provided that the working stress is nowhere exceeded.

As an example, let the overall length of the wrench handle be about 11 in. and let the distance from the applied force to the critical section be 7 in. The applied force would actually be distributed over the part of the handle near the end. However, we would, according to St. Venant's principle, assume a point load near the center of the actual distributed load because the critical section is some distance from the applied load.

Let us arbitrarily specify the proportions of section A (Figure 5-9) by the relationships $b = 4h$ and $d = 4h$. Assuming that a user could apply a maximum force of 100–150 lb to the wrench handle, we might design for an applied force $P = 300$ lb to account for shock or misuse. Let the part be made of steel with a yield point $S_{yp} = 75,000$ psi and, because part failure would not have serious consequences, use a factor of safety $N = 1.5$.

Then, using equation (5-6) we have

$$\sigma_x = \frac{75,000 \text{ psi}}{1.5} = \frac{(300 \text{ lb})(7 \text{ in.})(4.5h \text{ in.})}{2(4h \text{ in.})(h \text{ in.})(4h \text{ in.})^2}$$

from which $h = 0.114$ in. In round numbers, we might use $\frac{1}{8}$ in. thick web and flanges making the I section $\frac{1}{2}$ in. wide by $1\frac{1}{8}$ in. deep. At this point, we could recheck the design, computing an "exact" moment of inertia based on final dimensions. This is unnecessary, however, since the approximate calculation was conservative (that is, on the safe side).

SECTION 5-5

Deflection of Machine Members Due to Bending

Machine members are usually subjected to loads that can be represented by concentrated forces and moments. Distributed loads, especially those arising from the mass of a member, are seldom important in the design of machines. Inertia loading is an exception and, of course, large structures are subjected to significant distributed loads.

The relationship between loading of a machine member and its bending deflection is treated in detail in strength of materials texts (references [2], [3] and [4]). Some of the results are summarized in Figure 5-10 along with the usual sign conventions.

As an application of the expressions in Figure 5-10, let us determine bending deflection in the horizontal part of the machine member shown in Figure 5-11. Let a load of 707 lb be applied at point E as shown. The member is simply supported at points B and C; the support at B resists the horizontal component of load P.

In addition, load P causes a bending moment of 1500 lb-in. and a vertical force of 500 lb at point A. The solution to this problem is illustrated in Figure 5-12. Ignoring the weight of the member itself, reaction R_1 is determined by equating the sum of the moments to zero at the simple support C. Then equilibrium of vertical forces yields R_2 and the shear and moment diagrams may be constructed. Curvature is given by

$$\frac{d^2w}{dx^2} = -\frac{M}{EI} \tag{5-7}$$

but it is not necessary to make an additional plot if E and I are constant. If we have not yet specified the section dimensions, the deflection variable EIw may be determined by integrating twice with respect to x. Constants

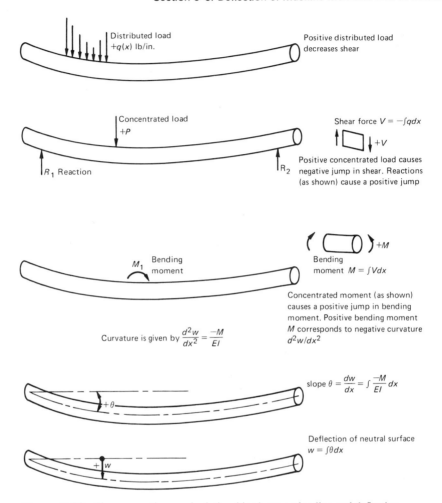

Figure 5-10 Sign conventions and relationships between loading and deflection.

of integration are determined by maintaining continuity of slope and deflection and by setting the deflection equal to zero at *B* and *C*.

Although the slope variable curve was determined analytically in Figure 5-12, graphic integration would produce identical results. If the results are to be the basis for an actual design, it is recommended that the problem be solved both graphically and analytically and the solutions compared.

If we wish to complete the solution graphically, beginning with slope, we may temporarily set $\theta_A = 0$. Then integrate graphically, using the trapezoidal rule. In this problem, $\frac{1}{2}$ in. increments in *x* will produce results within "engineering accuracy." The resulting plot is shown in Figure 5-13. Since the neglected part, θ_A, is a constant, its integral $\theta_A x$ is a straight line. Thus, to obtain the $w = 0$ line, we draw a straight line intersecting the *EIw*

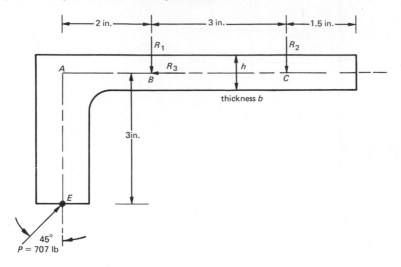

Figure 5-11 Machine member subject to bending loads.

curve at the bearing locations, B and C. The true displacement variable is given by the vertical distance from the $w = 0$ line to the EIw curve.

The value of slope θ_A may now be found by locating the point where $dw/dx = 0$ on the EIw curve. A line is drawn parallel to the $w = 0$ line and tangent to the EIw curve. The point of tangency is the point of zero slope. Projecting that location upward to the $EI\theta$ curve, we may now dimension the slope.

Superposition

Most problems in the bending of machine members may be considered linear problems. Because reactions and shear force are proportional to loading, we see from Figure 5-10 that moment, slope, and deflection are linear functions of the applied load (provided, of course, that the usual assumptions—linear elasticity, small slopes, and so on—are valid). Then, the combined effect of two or more loads acting simultaneously is given by the sum of the effects of each load acting separately. The last sentence is a statement of the principle of superposition. Superposition is a valuable technique for handling statically indeterminate problems and statically determinate problems where two or more loads act on a member.

For convenience in solving such problems, we will begin by collecting a set of solutions to basic statically determinate problems (Figure 5-14). These problems are straightforward in that reactions can be determined by statics (that is, equilibrium relationships) alone. Since dimensions will be expressed in general terms, solutions of this type are obtained analytically.

As an example of superposition, consider a machine member represented by Figure 5-15. The elastic modulus and moment of inertia of region AB

Figure 5-12 Loading and deflection of a machine member

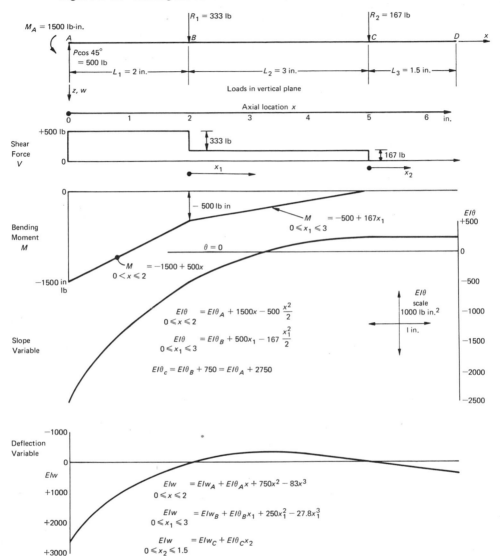

are given by E_1 and I_1 and those of region BC by E_2 and I_2. The applied force F lies in plane ABC and moments of inertia are to be calculated based on bending in the plane ABC. The connection at B is rigid so that moment M and slope θ are continuous there.

For convenience in solving this example, force F is replaced by its horizontal and vertical components. The problem is solved by superposing the slopes and deflection given in Figure 5-14a and b. To avoid ambiguity, subscripts and coordinate axes are changed where necessary.

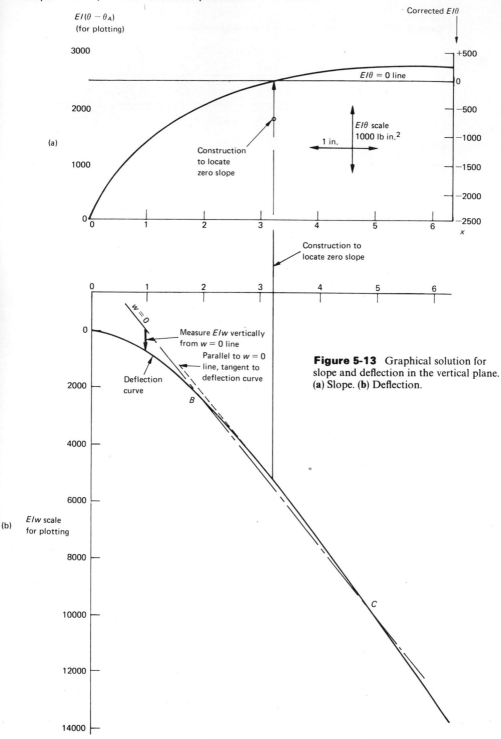

Figure 5-13 Graphical solution for slope and deflection in the vertical plane. (a) Slope. (b) Deflection.

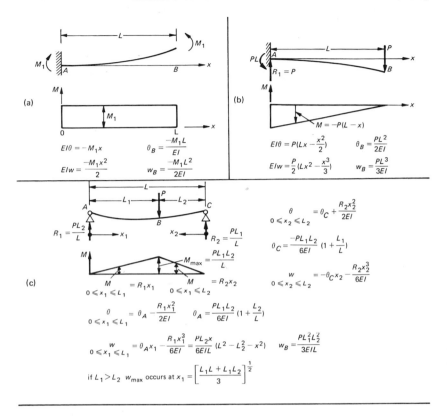

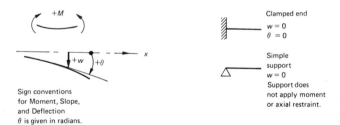

Sign conventions for Moment, Slope, and Deflection
θ is given in radians.

Figure 5-14 Bending of members with constant cross section (*see also next page*).

Bending stress reaches its maximum value Mc/I at the outer fiber of a given cross section. To this, we add direct tensile stress. In region AB, bending moment magnitude may be maximum at A or B depending on the direction of F. Maximum tensile stress is given by the sum of bending stress and direct tension

$$\sigma_{x1(\text{max})} = \frac{|M|_{(\text{max})}c}{I_1} + \frac{F_2}{A_1}$$

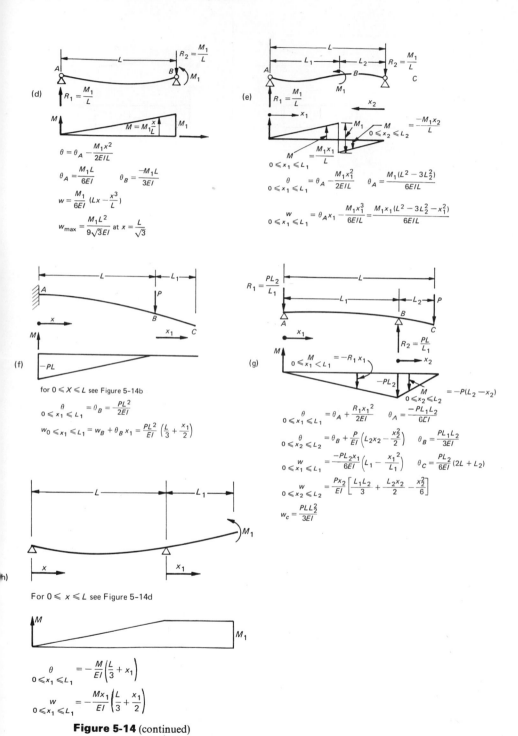

Figure 5-14 (continued)

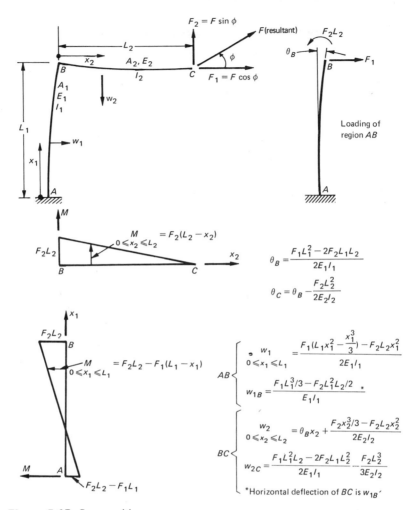

Figure 5-15 Superposition.

In region BC, $M_B = F_2 L_2$ is obviously the maximum value and the corresponding tensile stress is

$$\sigma_{x2(\text{max})} = \frac{M_B c}{I_2} + \frac{F_1}{A_2}$$

The results are based on the assumption that slope θ is everywhere small compared to 1 rad. If this condition is not met, the loading then depends upon the deflection. In the example just described, the axial loading was tensile. When compressive loading occurs, we must also examine the problem of elastic stability to insure that buckling failure will not occur.

Statically indeterminate problems in bending

In the preceding examples, the support reactions were found by using the equations of equilibrium. A machine member clamped at one end and simply supported elsewhere (Figure 5-16a) is **statically indeterminate** in that the equilibrium equations are not sufficient to yield the support reactions.

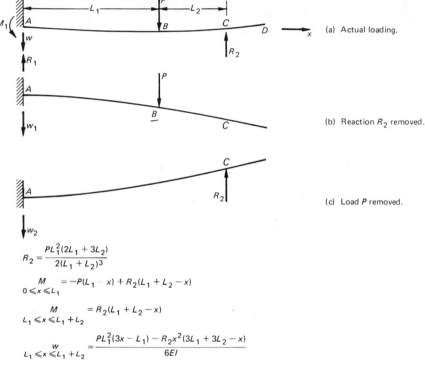

$$R_2 = \frac{PL_1^2(2L_1 + 3L_2)}{2(L_1 + L_2)^3}$$

$$\underset{0 \leqslant x \leqslant L_1}{M} = -P(L_1 - x) + R_2(L_1 + L_2 - x)$$

$$\underset{L_1 \leqslant x \leqslant L_1 + L_2}{M} = R_2(L_1 + L_2 - x)$$

$$\underset{L_1 \leqslant x \leqslant L_1 + L_2}{w} = \frac{PL_1^2(3x - L_1) - R_2 x^2(3L_1 + 3L_2 - x)}{6EI}$$

Figure 5-16 Statically indeterminate member (redundant end support).

This problem is solved by superposing the effects of load P alone (without reaction R_2) upon the effects of R_2 alone (without load P).

The deflection at C due to load P (Figure 5-16b) is

$$w_{c1} = \frac{PL_1^2}{EI}\left(\frac{L_1}{3} + \frac{L_2}{2}\right)$$

calculated from the equations in Figure 5-14f with the necessary changes in symbols. Similarly, for the same point when reaction R_2 is applied (Figure 5-16c), we have

$$w_{c2} = \frac{-R_2(L_1 + L_2)^3}{3EI}.$$

Superposing the two effects, we use the condition

$$w_c = w_{c1} + w_{c2} = 0$$

to obtain support reaction R_2. Using this value of R_2 and the equations in Figure 5-14f, we obtain deflection and slope at any point.

The location of the point of maximum deflection is found by differentiating the deflection equation with respect to x and setting the result equal to

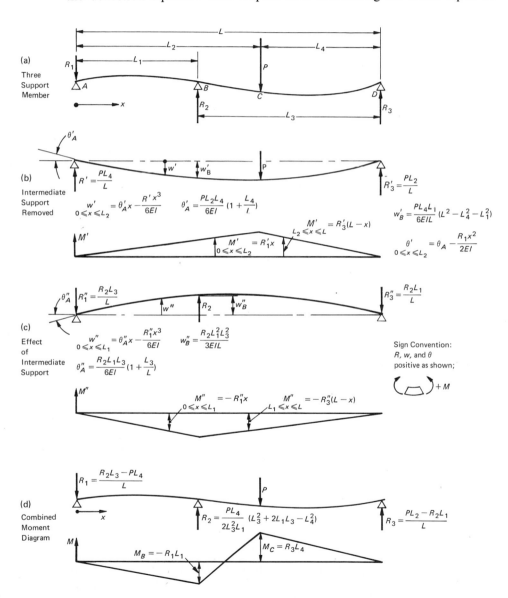

Figure 5-17 Statically indeterminate member (three supports).

zero. In the region from B to C (Figure 5-16a) maximum deflection occurs at

$$x = L_1 + L_2 - \sqrt{(L_1 + L_2)^2 - \frac{PL_1^2}{R_2}}$$

If, for example, load P is equidistant from A and C, then $R_2 = \frac{5}{16}P$ and the greatest bending stress occurs at A where moment is given by $M_A = -\frac{3}{8}PL_1$. For that case, the maximum deflection occurs at $x = 1.106L_1$. In general, we should check each region of a given problem. Solutions that fall outside of the region being checked are rejected, and deflections are examined at end points of the region.

The solution to the three-support member, Figure 5-17 (page 259), is similar. In this case, we superpose the effects of load P (without the intermediate reaction) on the effects of the intermediate reaction alone, treated as a load. These values may be obtained from Figure 5-14c. The magnitude of the reaction is found by setting the displacement at the reaction equal to zero. Parts b and c of Figure 5-17 illustrate the superposition. Because the true deflection $w_B = w_B' - w_B'' = 0$, we have

$$R_2 = \frac{PL_4(L^2 - L_1^2 - L_4^2)}{2L_1L_3^2}$$

For the special case of two equal spans with load P at the midpoint of one span, the center reaction is simply $R_2 = \frac{11}{16}P$. In that case, the maximum bending moment, $M = \frac{13}{128}PL$, occurs at load P.

SECTION 5-6

Shear Stress and Shear Deflection Due to Lateral Load—Shear Center

Bending stresses and bending deflection are usually of primary interest in the design of laterally loaded machine members. However, shear stress and shear deflection due to transverse shear forces are sometimes important as well.

Consider a machine member subjected to lateral loads that lie in a plane of symmetry of the member (Figure 5-18). At some location x, the bending moment has a value M, and there is a linear distribution of axial stress given by

$$\sigma_x = \frac{Mz}{I} \tag{5-8}$$

where z is measured from the neutral axis. Moving to the right a distance dx, the moment increases by $(dM/dx)\,dx$ or $V\,dx$ and axial stresses increase by $[(V\,dx)z]/I$ where V is the shear force.

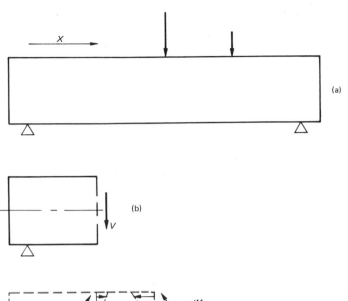

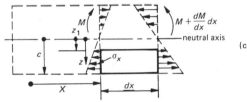

Figure 5-18 Shear stress due to lateral loads. (**a**) Machine member with lateral loads. (**b**) Shear force on cross section. (**c**) Moment and stress distribution. (**d**) Equilibrium of axial force.

Now, consider the element that lies below $z = z_1$ (Figure 5-18c and d). Transverse shear stress τ_{xz} on the top of the element produces shear force $\tau_{xz} b \, dx$ which is balanced by the net tensile force

$$\frac{V \, dx}{I} \int_{z=z_1}^{z=c} z \, dA$$

Solving for transverse shear stress, we get

$$\tau_{xz} = \frac{V}{bI} \int_{z=z_1}^{z=c} z \, dA \tag{5-9}$$

where dA is an element of cross section area and b is the width of the section normal to the page at $z = z_1$ where we wish to find τ_{xz}. Shear stress $\tau_{xz} = 0$ at $z = \pm c$, the outer fibers. The maximum value occurs at the neutral axis

$$\tau_{xz(max)} = \frac{V}{bI} \int_{z=0}^{z=c} z \, dA \tag{5-10}$$

For a *rectangular cross section* of area A, $dA = b \, dz$ and the equation for shear stress becomes

$$\tau_{xz} = \frac{1.5V}{A} \left[1 - \left(\frac{z_1}{c} \right)^2 \right]$$

the maximum value being $1.5V/A$. For a *solid circular shaft*, the maximum transverse shear stress is $\frac{4}{3}V/A$, and for an *I section* loaded in the usual fashion (that is, with load resultants through the plane of the web), transverse shear stress anywhere in the web may be approximated by shear force V divided by web area.

We note that for a member subjected to vertical forces in its plane of symmetry, maximum transverse shear stress occurs at the neutral axis where tensile stress due to bending is zero. Transverse shear stress is zero at the extreme (top and bottom) fibers where tensile stress is a maximum. Bending stress at the extreme fiber is of greatest importance in most solid members of rectangular or circular cross section subject to lateral load. In very short members, transverse shear may govern the design. In shafting, shear stress due to torsion is of prime importance. The effect of combined shear and tensile stress will be considered in Chapter 6. In I-type sections, the combined stress may be critical where the flanges join the web (see Section 6-3, The Maximum Shear Theory).

Shear deflection

Shear deflection arises from shear strain and, in the case of most laterally loaded machine members, shear deflection is small compared with bending effects. The additional slope due to shear is the *shear strain at the neutral axis*

$$\gamma_0 = \frac{\tau_{xz(max)}}{G} \tag{5-11}$$

where G is the shear modulus. Thus, for a *rectangular section*, $\gamma_0 = 1.5V/(AG)$; and for a *circular section*, $\gamma_0 = \frac{4}{3}V/(AG)$ where A is cross sectional area. For an *I section* $\gamma_0 = V/(GA_{web})$ (approximately), which may be 2 or more times $V/(AG)$.

The deflection change between two points on a member is given by the integral of the shear strain between those points. For example, in the case of a *simply supported rectangular member* of length L with central load P, the shear deflection at the center is

$$w_s \left(x = \frac{L}{2} \right) = \int_0^{L/2} \gamma_0 \, dx = \frac{3}{8} \frac{PL}{AG}$$

Total deflection is given by the sum of the shear deflection and the bending deflection. At the center, the bending deflection is $PL^3/(48EI)$, which in the case of most rectangular members is much larger than the shear deflection so that the latter can be ignored. However, shear deflection in short I sections and honeycomb and other sandwich sections may be of the same order of magnitude as bending deflection.

Shear center

In the laterally loaded machine members considered previously, we have assumed that load resultants lie in a plane of symmetry through the longitudinal axis of the member. Thus, we assumed that load resultants go through the center of gravity in the case of a symmetric cross section. Under these conditions, the member should deflect in the plane of symmetry without twisting. This arrangement, however, is not always feasible.

As an example, consider the channel section in Figure 5-19a subject to vertical loads. It is not symmetric about a vertical plane and will tend to twist unless load resultants lie in a certain plane defined by the shear center. Let the shear center lie an unknown distance e from the center of the vertical wall of the channel and assume load resultants do go through the shear center. In the case of a cantilever with load P between the free end and the cut section shown, there is a vertical shear $V = P$ in the vertical wall of the channel. The vertical wall is assumed to take the entire vertical shear force V, whereas the horizontal walls are assumed to have only horizontal shear resultants. The actual shear stress distribution may be very complicated, but we will treat thin sections in a simplified manner, neglecting any variation in stress across the thickness t. Equation (5-9) may be applied to this problem if we integrate along the centerline of the web and then along the centerline of the flange to the free edge of the flange. We may assume continuity of shear stresses where the web joins the flange.

Thus, our approximate shear stress distribution has the parabolic form

$$\tau_{xz} = \frac{V}{I}\left(\int_{z_1}^{h/2} z\, dz + \frac{h}{2}\int_0^d dy' \right)$$

$$= \frac{V}{I}\left(\frac{h^2}{4} + \frac{hd}{2} - z_1^2 \right) \tag{5-12}$$

for location $z = z_1$ in the web. For location $y' = y_1'$ in the flange, shear stress distribution has the linear form

$$\tau_{xy} = \frac{Vh}{2I}\int_{y_1'}^d dy'$$

$$= \frac{Vh}{2I}(d - y_1') \tag{5-13}$$

For this example, shear stress direction is sketched in Figure 5-19b.

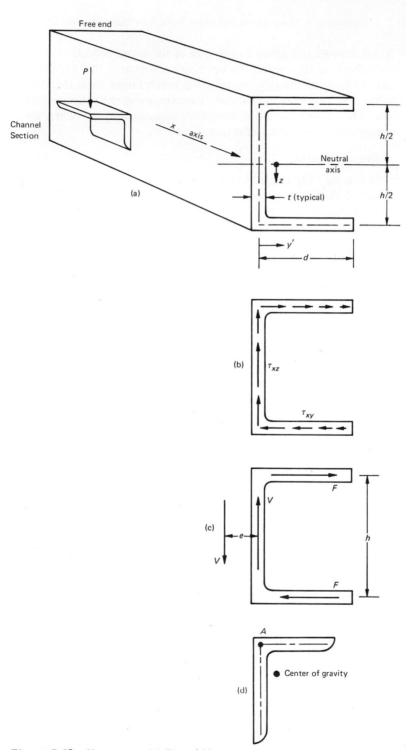

Figure 5-19 Shear center. (a), (b), and (c)
Channel section. (d) Angle section.

If we integrate equation (5-13) over the entire flange, we obtain the shear resultant in the lower flange (on a cut perpendicular to the beam axis) $F = Vhtd^2/(4I)$. An equal and opposite force appears in the upper flange. The moment Fh due to the shear resultants in the flanges is balanced by the moment Ve due to vertical load and vertical shear, provided resultant loads and reactions are applied at the shear center. Equating moments, we may solve for the location of the shear center

$$e = \frac{h^2 t d^2}{4I} \tag{5-14}$$

The value of e found from equation (5-14) locates the plane of loading if the channel is to be free of twisting. This location could seldom be realized in an actual design; therefore, we can expect torsion effects, particularly in nonsymmetric sections.

For the case of thin sections that join at a single point (for example, point A in the angle section, Figure 5-19d), the shear center is that point. For vertical loads on the angle section, there will be no twisting if the loads go through the centerline of the vertical leg. As noted previously, if a section has a vertical plane of symmetry, vertical loads in that plane will not cause twisting.

SECTION 5-7

Torsion

A moment that tends to twist a bar about its own axis is called a torsional moment, or simply a torque. The same force system may cause bending in one member of a machine and torque in another.

Shear stress due to torque in a circular shaft

When a solid circular shaft is subjected to torque T, we assume a linear shear stress distribution within the shaft. On any plane perpendicular to the shaft axis, shear stress τ is assumed to be proportional to the distance from the shaft center r (Figure 5-20). A more rigorous analysis of the problem shows this assumption to be valid for *solid and hollow circular shafts*, but not valid for other shapes.

We write the linear shear stress–torque relationship in the form

$$\tau = \frac{Tr}{J} \tag{5-15}$$

Observing that the shear stress on each element of the cross section contributes to the torque according to the integral

$$T = \int_{\text{cross section}} \tau r \, dA$$

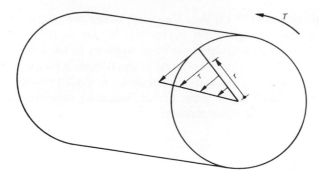

Figure 5-20 Torsion of a circular shaft.

and substituting equation 5-15 we obtain

$$J = \frac{\pi D^4}{32}$$

for the solid circular section of diameter D. The constant J is, of course, the **polar moment of inertia** of the cross section. For the shaft with a central hole of diameter D_i

$$J = \frac{\pi(D^4 - D_i^4)}{32}$$

Maximum shear stress occurs at maximum radius in solid and hollow circular shafts. Thus, from equation 5-15, we have

$$\tau_{max} = \frac{TD}{2J}$$

For the *solid circular shaft*, this becomes

$$\tau_{max} = \frac{16T}{\pi D^3} \tag{5-16}$$

We will see later, however, that for noncircular sections, stiffness is not proportional to the polar moment of inertia and that shear stress is not proportional to radius.

Deflection due to torque

The modulus of elasticity in shear, or simply **shear modulus** is defined by

$$G = \frac{\tau}{\gamma} \tag{5-17}$$

where shear strain γ is dimensionless. Consider an element of shaft of diameter D (Figure 5-21). Let one face rotate through an angle $d\phi$ with respect to the other face. For small strain, the arc of the circumference

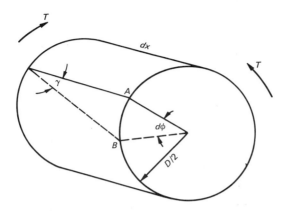

Figure 5-21 Shear strain and deflection.

$(D/2)\,d\phi$ is approximated by $\gamma\,dx$. Equating the two and using equations (5-15) and (5-17), the result is the angular deflection per unit axial length $\theta = d\phi/dx = T/(GJ)$. For constant torque T, relative rotation between two faces at a distance L is given by

$$\phi\ (\text{rad}) = \frac{TL}{GJ} \tag{5-18}$$

It is sometimes convenient to define a **torsional spring constant** k_t for a finite length of shaft as the torque per unit rotation. Thus, from equation (5-18) we have

$$k_t = \frac{T}{\phi} = \frac{GJ}{L} \quad (\text{lb-in./rad}) \tag{5-19}$$

In the case of a stepped shaft, we may subscript k_t, L, and J for each section. If the torque is constant over the entire length, the equivalent spring constant is given by the reciprocal of the sum of the reciprocals of the constants for each diameter

$$k_t = \frac{1}{\dfrac{1}{k_{t1}} + \dfrac{1}{k_{t2}} + \dfrac{1}{k_{t3}} + \dfrac{1}{k_{t4}} + \cdots}$$

Noncircular sections in torsion

Due to the symmetry of a circular shaft, it is quite logical to assume that there is no warping of cross sections (planes perpendicular to the shaft axis). However, a plane cross section of a noncircular shaft will warp to a non-planar shape when subject to torsion.

Consider a noncircular cylindrical section (that is, a shaft or other member of constant but noncircular cross section) subject to a constant torque over

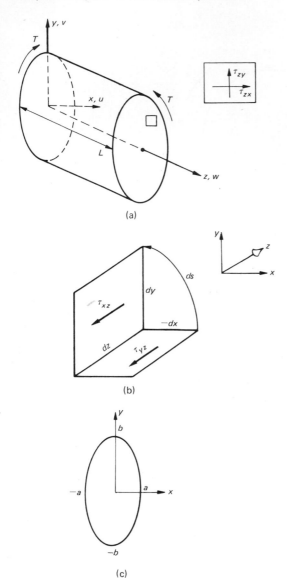

Figure 5-22 (a) Torsion of a non-circular section. (b) Shear on a lateral surface element. (c) Elliptical cross section. Maximum shear stress occurs at $x = \pm a$, $y = 0$.

its length (Figure 5-22a). Because the section does not change, we would have a constant rate of twist (in radians per unit length), which we will designate θ. Let u, v, and w represent displacements of a point in the x, y, and z directions, respectively. Then, for a small total rotation θz, we have

$$u = -\theta z y$$

$$v = \theta z x \qquad (5\text{-}20)$$

$$w = \theta \psi$$

where $\psi = \psi(x, y)$ is, as yet, unknown and represents the warping of cross section planes.

In order to describe the general problem of noncircular sections, we now turn to the shear strains and stresses on a face perpendicular to the shaft axis. The shear strain-displacement relationships are given by

$$\gamma_{zx} = \frac{\partial u}{\partial z} + \frac{\partial w}{\partial x}$$

$$\gamma_{zy} = \frac{\partial v}{\partial z} + \frac{\partial w}{\partial y} \qquad (5\text{-}21)$$

Substituting equations (5-20) into equation (5-21) and using the stress-strain relationships

$$\tau_{zx} = G\gamma_{zx} \quad \text{and} \quad \tau_{zy} = G\gamma_{zy}$$

we obtain

$$\tau_{zx} = G\theta\left(-y + \frac{\partial \psi}{\partial x}\right)$$

$$\tau_{zy} = G\theta\left(x + \frac{\partial \psi}{\partial y}\right) \qquad (5\text{-}22)$$

The sum of the contributions of the shear stresses on each element of the cross section times the moment arm of the element makes up the total torque. Measuring the x and y coordinates from the center of gravity of the cross section, we have the torque

$$T = \int_A (\tau_{zy}x - \tau_{zx}y)\, dA \qquad (5\text{-}23)$$

where A is the entire area of the cross section. Substituting equations (5-22) into (5-23), we obtain $T = GJ\theta$ where

$$J = \int_A \left(x^2 + y^2 + x\frac{\partial \psi}{\partial y} - y\frac{\partial \psi}{\partial x}\right) dx\, dy \qquad (5\text{-}24)$$

An inverse or semiinverse method is sometimes useful in problems of this type. That is, we assume the form of the solution and then find what problem we have solved. The assumption must satisfy the equilibrium equations. For example, we may assume displacement w to be proportional to the product of x and y, that is,

$$\psi = cxy$$

where c is constant. We now examine the boundary conditions to find the nature of the boundary for which this assumption could be valid. With no normal stress in the z direction, the net force is zero on an element of the lateral surface. Balancing axial shear forces on a surface element (Figure 5-22b) the result is

$$\tau_{xz}(dy\,dz) + \tau_{yz}(-dx\,dz) = 0$$

The negative sign preceding the differential dx does not imply negative area, but accounts for the negative change in the x coordinate as sketched in the figure. Noting that $\tau_{xz} = \tau_{zx}$, and so on, and substituting equations (5-22), we obtain the boundary condition

$$\left(-y + \frac{\partial\psi}{\partial x}\right)dy - \left(x + \frac{\partial\psi}{\partial y}\right)dx = 0 \tag{5-25}$$

for a general cylindrical boundary. If we substitute $\psi = cxy$ for this example, equation (5-25) becomes $(c - 1)y\,dy + (c + 1)x\,dx = 0$. Integrating and rearranging terms, we obtain

$$\left(\frac{x}{a}\right)^2 + \left(\frac{y}{b}\right)^2 = 1,$$

the equation of an ellipse. That is, we have solved the problem of *torsion of an elliptical shaft* with semiaxes a and b, where

$$\left(\frac{a}{b}\right)^2 = \frac{1-c}{1+c} \quad \text{or} \quad c = \frac{b^2 - a^2}{b^2 + a^2}$$

(See Figure 5-22c.) Thus,

$$\psi = \frac{b^2 - a^2}{b^2 + a^2}xy \tag{5-26}$$

Evaluating equation (5-24), we obtain

$$J = (1 + c)\int_A x^2\,dx\,dy + (1 - c)\int_A y^2\,dx\,dy \tag{5-27}$$

where the integrals are moments of inertia I_y and I_x, respectively. Substituting for c and using $I_y = \pi a^3 b/4$ and $I_x = \pi ab^3/4$, we obtain

$$J = \frac{\pi a^3 b^3}{a^2 + b^2} \tag{5-28}$$

for the elliptical shaft. Using this value of J, we obtain total rotation

$$\phi = \frac{(a^2 + b^2)LT}{\pi a^3 b^3 G} \tag{5-29}$$

We see from equation (5-27) that the constant J represents the polar moment of inertia *only* when $c = 0$; that is, when the section is circular.

Shear stress is given by

$$\tau_{zx} = \frac{-2Ty}{\pi ab^3} \quad \text{and} \quad \tau_{zy} = \frac{2Tx}{\pi a^3 b}$$

The maximum value of shear stress occurs on the surface at the least radius. It is

$$\tau_{max} = \tau_{zy}(a, 0) = \frac{2T}{\pi a^2 b} \tag{5-30}$$

where $b > a$ for the elliptical shaft oriented as in Figure 5-22c.

The preceding analysis follows the work of St. Venant. The work of Prandtl is also of importance in the study of torsion. The work of both investigators is described by Timoshenko and Goodier [1].

Example 5-1. Compare the torsional stiffness and strength of a solid circular section with a solid elliptical section having a semimajor axis twice the semiminor axis. Let both torsion members be made of the same material and have the same length and the same cross-sectional area.

Solution: Torsional stiffness of the two members can be compared by examining the torsional spring constants of each member (the torque divided by the angular deflection) where

$$k_t = \frac{JG}{L}$$

as given by equation (5-19).

For two members of the same material and equal length, stiffness is simply proportional to the J's. Using equation (5-28) for the *ellipse* where $b = 2a$,

$$J = \frac{\pi a^3 b^3}{a^2 + b^2} = \frac{8}{5}\pi a^4$$

The area of an ellipse is πab, and thus a circle of the same area has a diameter

$$D = 2\sqrt{ab} = 2a\sqrt{2}$$

The stiffness of the *circular section* is proportional to

$$J = \frac{\pi D^4}{32} = 2\pi a^4$$

that is, 25% greater than the elliptical section.

If we let maximum shear stress equal a working stress in shear, we may define torsional strength as T/τ_{max}. From equation (5-30), for an *elliptical section*, we have

$$\frac{T}{\tau_{max}} = \frac{\pi a^2 b}{2} = \pi a^3$$

where $b = 2a$.

For the *circular section* of the same cross-sectional area,

$$\frac{T}{\tau_{max}} = \frac{\pi D^3}{16} = \sqrt{2}\pi a^3$$

representing 41% greater strength. ●

St. Venant showed that a solid member of circular cross section is stronger and stiffer in torsion than any other simply connected cross-sectional shape having the same area. The situation with regard to bending is entirely different. A properly loaded I section, for example, is much stronger and stiffer in bending than a solid circular section of equal cross-sectional area. Hollow circular sections are, for a given cross-sectional area, stronger and stiffer in torsion than solid circular sections.

Thin rectangular cross sections

For the case of torsion of a bar of length L with a thin rectangular cross section $2a$ by $2b$ (where $a \ll b$ as in Figurē 5-23a), the total angle of twist is approximated by

$$\phi = \frac{3LT}{16a^3bG}$$

and the maximum shear stress occurs on the surface at the center of the

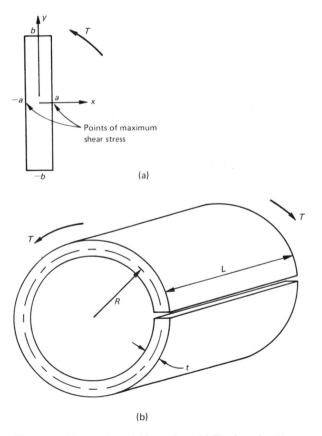

(a)

(b)

Figure 5-23 Torsion of thin sections. (a) Torsion of a thin strip with cross section dimensions $2a \times 2b$. (b) Torsion of a thin open section.

long edges. It is approximately

$$\tau_{max} = \frac{3T}{8a^2b}$$

at $x = \pm a$, $y = 0$. (See Timoshenko and Goodier [1].)

The same approximation may be used for other thin open sections subject to torque (such as angles, channel sections, and tubes that have a seam which is not securely joined). In such cases, a is replaced by half the wall thickness and b is replaced by half the length of the cross section measured along the middle surface.

For the *slotted tube* of Figure 5-23b we have an approximate angle of twist

$$\phi = \frac{3LT}{2\pi GRt^3}$$

and approximate maximum shear stress

$$\tau_{max} = \frac{3T}{2\pi Rt^2}$$

Example 5-2. Compare the torsional strength and stiffness of a hollow shaft with that of a hollow slotted shaft of the same length and material. Both have a 2-in. O.D. and a 1.75-in. I.D.

Solution: As in Example 5-1, for the same material and length, torsional stiffness of the sections is simply proportional to the values of J, and we will again define torsional strength as the ratio of torque to maximum shear stress.

For the *closed section,*

$$\tau_{max} = \frac{TD}{2J} = \frac{16TD}{\pi(D^4 - D_i^4)}$$

For torsional strength

$$\frac{T}{\tau_{max}} = \frac{\pi(D^4 - D_i^4)}{16D} = 0.65\frac{\text{lb-in.}}{\text{lb/in.}^2}$$

and torsional rigidity

$$\frac{TL}{G\phi} = J = \frac{\pi(D^4 - D_i^4)}{32} = 0.65 \text{ in.}^4$$

The *slotted shaft* cross section has the same polar moment of inertia, but, due to warping, a much lower stiffness and strength. For the open section, approximate values are

$$\frac{T}{\tau_{max}} = \frac{2\pi Rt^2}{3} = 0.0307\frac{\text{lb-in.}}{\text{lb/in.}^2}$$

and

$$J = \frac{2\pi Rt^3}{3} = 0.00383 \text{ in.}^4$$

It is obvious that open sections of this type should be avoided when members are designed to resist torsional loads. ●

SECTION 5-8

Thermal Stress

When a machine member is heated to above room temperature, it will tend to expand. If the temperature change is uniform, if the member is made of a single material, and if there are no external restraints, then the unit dimension change (**true strain**) will be constant throughout the member. When these conditions obtain, there will be no stress due to the temperature change. Expansion joints are commonly employed in piping carrying hot fluids and in other structures subject to temperature changes for this reason. On the other hand, stresses may be induced when temperature varies with location within a member or by a temperature change in a member made of dissimilar materials, or by a temperature change in a member with external restraints. Since welding and other manufacturing processes involve non-uniform heating and cooling, **residual stresses** often exist in machine members at room temperatures. Residual stresses are sometimes relieved by annealing. In some cases, residual stresses are desirable. One example is that of a shrink fit of a hub on a shaft.

The **coefficient of thermal expansion** α expresses a rate of thermal strain per unit temperature rise where a material expands freely. Thus, for a temperature rise T, the **free strain** is given by

$$\varepsilon_f = \alpha T \tag{5-31}$$

and the change in a dimension L by

$$\Delta_f = \alpha T L \tag{5-32}$$

if the part is unrestrained. The dimension L may be replaced by an inside or outside diameter if we wish to find the change in that dimension. Since dimension changes are small compared with the original dimension, volume change per unit volume per unit temperature rise is approximately 3α.

Tables of values for the coefficient of thermal expansion are given in references [7], [8] and [9]. A few average values are shown in the following table.

Material	Temperature Range, °F	α, (in./in.)/°F
Structural steel (0.25% carbon)	68–572	7.22×10^{-6}
Machine steel (0.40% carbon)	68–572	6.7×10^{-6}
Machine steel (0.40% carbon)	68–1112	7.94×10^{-6}
High strength cast iron (3% carbon)	68–572	5.8×10^{-6}
Aluminum alloy (2024-T4)	68–212	13×10^{-6}
Magnesium alloy (AZ80A-T5)	68–212	14.4×10^{-6}

Values in metric units are obtained by multiplying by 1.8 Fahrenheit degrees per centigrade degree. For example, the coefficient of thermal expansion for structural steel is $\alpha = 13 \times 10^{-6}$ (cm/cm)/C° in the temperature range of 20–300°C.

Although α may be considered a constant for most engineering work, careful measurements have shown a nonlinear rate of expansion in most metals with increasing temperature. For example, reference [8] gives the free strain in aluminum from 0°C to some temperature t°C as

$$\varepsilon = (22.21t + 0.0114t^2) \times 10^{-6}$$

in the range $10°C \leqslant t \leqslant 90°C$. This will result in a final dimension

$$L = L_0(1 + 22.21 \times 10^{-6}t + 0.0114 \times 10^{-6}t^2)$$

where L_0 is the dimension at 0°C. To convert from Fahrenheit temperature t_F to Centigrade temperature t, we use

$$t = \frac{t_F - 32}{1.8}$$

Thermal stress in a restrained member

A temperature rise T in a member of length L will cause a free strain $\varepsilon_f = \alpha T$ and a length change $\Delta_f = \alpha TL$ if the member is *free to expand* (Figure 5-24a). Other dimensions increase proportionately. If the member is

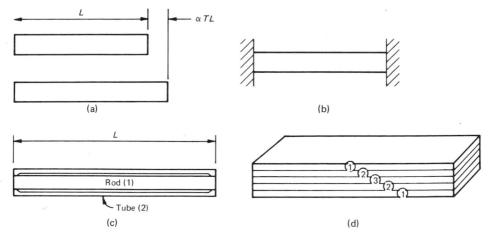

Figure 5-24 Thermal stress. (a) Free expansion due to temperature rise T. (b) Restrained member. (c) Rod and tube subject to temperature rise T. (d) Several elements at different temperatures or several elements of different materials.

subsequently forced back to its original length (Figure 5-24b) while the elevated temperature is maintained, we have the equivalent of an elastic strain $-\varepsilon_f = -\alpha T$. The total effect is a net strain of zero and therefore no change in length. There is also a resulting stress $\sigma_T = -E\alpha T$. Thus, in the case of an **ideally restrained member** subject to temperature rise T, the true strain and length change are zero and the **thermal stress** (the true stress)

$$\sigma_T = -E\alpha T \tag{5-33}$$

provided the member does not buckle.

Symmetric members of two or more materials

Many thermal stress problems arise in members that are neither ideally restrained nor free to expand. When we join members with different coefficients of thermal expansion or have varying temperatures within a body, significant stresses sometimes develop. Consider a rod and tube combination, joined at the ends (Figure 5-24c). If the two are subject to different temperatures or if they are made of different materials and subject to a temperature rise, thermal stresses will, in general, occur. The combination expands freely but as a unit, having the same total expansion over length L. The true strain is, therefore, the same for both

$$\varepsilon = \varepsilon_1 = \varepsilon_2 \tag{5-34}$$

and in each, the true strain depends on the free strain αT and the true stress

$$\varepsilon_1 = \alpha_1 T_1 + \frac{\sigma_1}{E_1}$$
$$\tag{5-35}$$
$$\varepsilon_2 = \alpha_2 T_2 + \frac{\sigma_2}{E_2}$$

In addition, equilibrium of forces yields

$$\sigma_1 A_1 + \sigma_2 A_2 = 0 \tag{5-36}$$

From equations (5-34) and (5-35), we have the true stress

$$\sigma_1 = E_1(\varepsilon - \alpha_1 T_1)$$
$$\tag{5-37}$$
$$\sigma_2 = E_2(\varepsilon - \alpha_2 T_2)$$

where the true strain is given by substituting equations (5-37) into equation (5-36) and rearranging.

$$\varepsilon = \frac{A_1 E_1 \alpha_1 T_1 + A_2 E_2 \alpha_2 T_2}{A_1 E_1 + A_2 E_2} \tag{5-38}$$

If we have n elements joined so that there is no tendency toward bending (for example, Figure 5-24d), then stress is still given in the form of equations (5-37)

$$\sigma_i = E_i(\varepsilon - \alpha_i T_i) \tag{5-39}$$

and strain is given by

$$\varepsilon = \frac{\sum_{i=1}^{n} (AE\alpha T)_i}{\sum_{i=1}^{n}(AE)_i} \tag{5-40}$$

The extension to a symmetric variation in temperature throughout the thickness is illustrated in Example 5-3.

Example 5-3. Let temperature elevation vary through a uniform machine element (Figure 5-25) according to the expression

$$T = T_0\left(1 - \frac{|y|}{2a}\right)$$

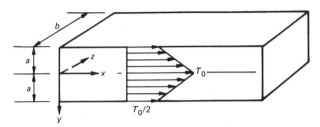

Figure 5-25 A continuous temperature distribution.

(independent of x and z). Find axial tensile stress, assuming zero tensile stress in the y and z directions.

Solution: Extending equation (5-40) to integral form, the true strain is

$$\varepsilon = \frac{\int E\alpha T \, dA}{\int E \, dA}$$

where we integrate over the cross section. Substituting $dA = b \, dy$ and noting that E and α are constant, we obtain

$$\varepsilon = \frac{bE\alpha \int_{-a}^{a} T \, dy}{bE \int_{-a}^{a} dy}$$

Substituting the temperature distribution,

$$\varepsilon = \frac{\alpha T_0}{2a} \int_{-a}^{a} \left(1 - \frac{|y|}{2a}\right) dy$$

$$= \frac{\alpha T_0}{2a}\left[\left(y - \frac{y^2}{4a}\right)_0^a + \left(y + \frac{y^2}{4a}\right)_{-a}^0\right]$$

$$= \tfrac{3}{4}\alpha T_0$$

Local stress (from equation 5-37) is $\sigma = E(\varepsilon - \alpha T)$. Again, substituting the temperature distribution

$$\sigma = E\alpha T_0\left(\frac{|y|}{2a} - \frac{1}{4}\right)$$

which results in a variation from

$$\sigma = -\tfrac{1}{4}E\alpha T_0 \qquad \text{at the center}$$

to

$$\sigma = \tfrac{1}{4}E\alpha T_0 \qquad \text{at the surface} \quad \bullet$$

SECTION 5-9

Energy Methods—Castigliano's Theorem

Certain types of problems, including those involving the deflection of frames and curved beams, are conveniently treated by energy methods. Before applying energy methods to solve design problems, we will examine the concept of strain energy. Consider a slender bar subject to a tensile force P. If the force is increased to produce an infinitesimal change in displacement $d\delta$, then, for an elastic system, the work done on the bar represents an increase in strain energy: $dU = P\, d\delta$. The total strain energy given by the area below the P-δ curve of Figure 5-26a is $U = \int P\, d\delta$.

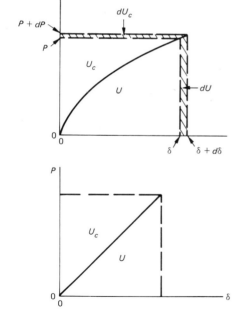

Figure 5-26 Strain energy. (a) Strain energy in tension. (b) Strain energy for a linearly elastic material.

The area to the left of the P-δ curve will be called the complementary energy: $U_c = \int \delta\, dP$. An infinitesimal increase in complementary energy is given by $dU_c = \delta\, dP$ from which we may write $\delta = dU_c/dP$, which is applicable to nonlinear as well as linear problems. For most engineering work, we would assume a linear force-displacement relationship, Figure 5-26b. Then, strain energy is equal to complementary energy; $U = U_c$ and deflection due to a tensile load P is given by

$$\delta = \frac{dU}{dP} \tag{5-41}$$

Equation (5-41), called Castigliano's theorem, is far more general in application than indicated by the above discussion. Consider, for example, strain energy in bending for a beam subjected to uniform moment M. The relative rotation of the ends is given by $\theta = ML/(EI)$ resulting in internal energy $U = \frac{1}{2}M^2L/(EI)$ due to bending for the linear case. If M varies with location, the corresponding energy expression is $U = \frac{1}{2}\int (M^2/EI)\, ds$, where integration proceeds over the entire member or structure. If a structure is subject to bending and direct tension as well, we have

$$U = \frac{1}{2}\int \left(\frac{M^2}{EI} + \frac{F^2}{EA}\right) ds \tag{5-42}$$

where M and F are local bending moment and tensile force, respectively. Now, strain energy U may result from a complicated system of loads and reactions, but if no work is done by the reactions and if the force system is otherwise unchanged by the application of a given load, then equation (5-41) becomes

$$\delta = \frac{\partial U}{\partial P} \tag{5-43}$$

Equation (5-43) gives the deflection at a given load P in the direction of P. Applying this equation to equation (5-42), the result is

$$\delta = \int \left(\frac{MM^*}{EI} + \frac{FF^*}{EA}\right) ds \tag{5-44}$$

where integration is carried out over the entire structure, $M^* = \partial M/\partial P$ and $F^* = \partial F/\partial P$. We see that M^* and F^* are, respectively, moment and force in members of the structure due to a unit load ($P = 1$ lb) applied at the same location and in the same direction as the desired deflection δ. The actual loads on the structure may be elsewhere; thus, the unit load, on which M^* and F^* are based, may be called a "dummy load". Castigliano's theorem and other energy methods are treated in detail by Seely and Smith [10].

Example 5-4. *Given:* Load P_1 acts at point D as shown in Figure 5-27a. The moment of inertia I about the neutral axis of each member in bending is the same and all are made of the same material.
Find: Horizontal deflection δ at point D.

Solution: We employ equation (5-44), integrating over the three members of the frame. Moment M is given by Figure 5-27b. $F = P_1$ in BC; $F = 0$ in the other members.

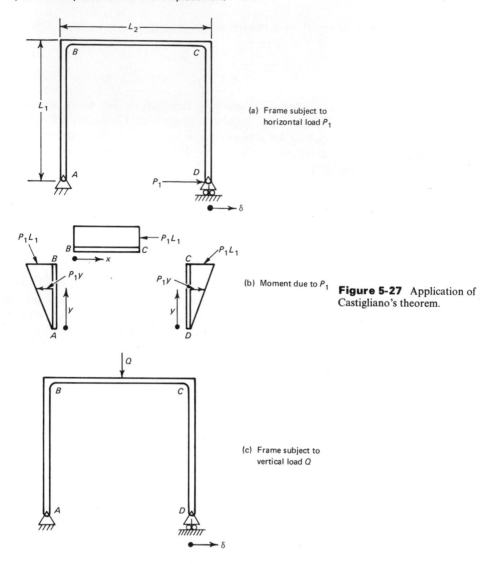

(a) Frame subject to horizontal load P_1

(b) Moment due to P_1

Figure 5-27 Application of Castigliano's theorem.

(c) Frame subject to vertical load Q

For a unit load in the direction of δ applied at D, the moment and force distributions are similar: $M^* = y$ in AB and DC; $M^* = L_1$ in BC. $F^* = 1$ in BC

$$\delta = 2 \int_0^{L_1} \frac{P_1 y^2}{EI} dy + \int_0^{L_2} \frac{P_1 L_1^2}{EI} dx + \int_0^{L_2} \frac{P_1}{EA} dx = \frac{P_1 L_1^2}{EI}\left(\frac{2}{3}L_1 + L_2\right) + \frac{P_1 L_2}{EA}$$

Note that we have assumed small deflections, that is, the moments and forces may be computed on the basis of the undeflected structure. ●

Example 5-5. *Given:* The same frame as in Example 5-4, except that a load Q is applied at the center of the top member as in Figure 5-27c. *Find:* δ, the deflection of point D.

Solution: Moment due to Q is given by

$$M_{0 \leqslant x \leqslant L_2/2} = \frac{Qx}{2} \qquad M_{L_2/2 \leqslant x < L_2} = \frac{Q(L_2 - x)}{2}$$

in member BC. $M = 0$ in AB and CD. The force in AB and CD is $F = -Q/2$; $F = 0$ in BC. The effect of a unit load in the direction of δ, applied at D, is the same as in Example 5-4: $M^* = y$ in AB and CD; $M^* = L_1$ in BC. Thus

$$\delta = \int_0^{L_2/2} \frac{QxL_1 \, dx}{2EI} + \int_{L_2/2}^{L_2} \frac{Q(L_2 - x)L_1}{2EI} \, dx = \frac{QL_1 L_2^2}{8EI}$$

The compressive force in AB and CD does not affect δ in this case. Stability must be examined separately. ●

Example 5-6. *Given:* A frame loaded as in Example 5-5 except that point D is a fixed pin. *Find:* The horizontal reaction at D.

Solution: This problem is statically indeterminate to the first degree. Since $\delta = 0$, we may equate the deflection δ of Example 5-4 plus that of Example 5-5 to zero, from which we obtain the reaction

$$P_1 = \frac{-QL_1 L_2^2}{8[\frac{2}{3}L_1^3 + L_1^2 L_2 + (L_2 I/A)]}$$

There is an equal and opposite reaction at A.

Instead of the above superposition method, however, we may determine the reaction directly from equation (5-44) by setting $\delta = 0$. ●

The above examples illustrate the effectiveness of Castigliano's theorem if we are to find deflection at a single point on a complex frame or machine part. The penalty associated with this method, however, is that we find deflection at only one point, whereas the classical method of successive integrations yields slope and deflection at all points.

In order to find angular deflection (slope) we proceed as in the Examples but differentiate strain energy with respect to moment, obtaining

$$\theta = \int \left(\frac{MM'}{EI} + \frac{FF'}{EA} \right) ds$$

Quantities M and F are moment and force due to actual loading as before, but M' and F' are moment and force due to a unit moment applied at the location where we must find θ.

SECTION 5-10

Elastic Stability

Elastic stability concerns buckling of machine elements due to compressive load.

Slender columns

Most analysis of machine elements is based on a linear relationship between loading and deflection and on a linear relationship between loading and stress. Thus, in most design problems, we do not expect a rapid increase in deflection with small changes in load, providing we do not exceed the yield point of the material. Buckling of slender columns is an important exception to this usually valid relationship. **Stability,** in the sense of this discussion, implies that a load increase will result in a redistribution of stress so that internal stresses balance external forces and moments. When deflections cause an increase in the effect of external forces, thereby increasing moments so that equilibrium cannot be reestablished, we have **instability.** The load at which instability occurs will be called the **critical load** P_{cr}. Critical load is sensitive to support conditions as well as to the geometry and elasticity of the member.

Consider a member having constant cross section A and subject to a compressive load P (Figure 5-28a). The member is **simply supported** (pinned)

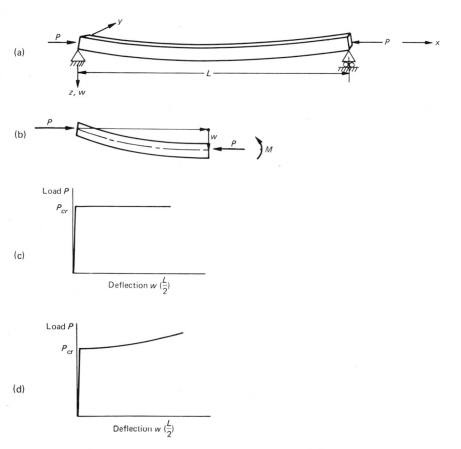

Figure 5-28   Elastic stability. (a) Simply supported compression member. (b) Momentum equilibrium. (c) Load-deflection relationship (small deflection theory). (d) Load-deflection relationship (large deflection theory).

at both ends, but axial motion of one end is unrestrained. Let the moment of inertia about the y axis

$$I = \int_A z^2 \, dA \qquad (5\text{-}45)$$

be the least moment of inertia. Then, buckling will tend to occur in the xz plane. Let us assume that the load P has caused a deflection w of the neutral axis of the member at a distance x from the left end (Figure 5-28b). The part of the member to the left of this point will be in equilibrium if internal stresses at x result in a moment

$$M = Pw \qquad (5\text{-}46)$$

on that section. If we utilize the moment-curvature relationship,

$$M = -EI\frac{d^2w}{dx^2} \qquad (5\text{-}47)$$

and rearrange terms, the stability equation is obtained.

$$\frac{d^2w}{dx^2} + \frac{Pw}{EI} = 0 \qquad (5\text{-}48)$$

The general solution to equation (5-48) is

$$w = C_1 \cos\sqrt{\frac{P}{EI}}x + C_2 \sin\sqrt{\frac{P}{EI}}x \qquad (5\text{-}49)$$

where C_1 and C_2 are arbitrary constants. The boundary conditions that have not already been used are $w(0) = 0$ and $w(L) = 0$. The first yields $C_1 = 0$ and the second yields

$$0 = C_2 \sin\sqrt{\frac{P}{EI}}L$$

The solution $C_2 = 0$ would be trivial, so we have

$$\sin\sqrt{\frac{P}{EI}}L = 0$$

from which we obtain the critical load, the lowest value of P that will cause the simply supported column to fail by buckling

$$P_{cr} = \frac{\pi^2 EI}{L^2} \qquad (5\text{-}50)$$

for the simply supported member. This is also called the **Euler load.**

For an ideal, initially straight member, there is no deflection until the critical load is reached. Using $C_1 = 0$ and $P = P_{cr}$ (equation 5-50) in equation (5-49) we obtain

$$w = C_2 \sin\sqrt{\frac{\pi^2 EI}{L^2 EI}} \, x$$

or
$$w = C_2 \sin\frac{\pi x}{L}$$

that is, the member bends in the shape of half a sine wave at the critical load. The amplitude $C_2 = w$ (at $x = L/2$) can theoretically assume any value (Figure 5-28c).

The results obtained in the preceding discussion are based on "small deflection" theory, that is, the assumption that the slope of the deflected neutral axis is small compared to unity. A more rigorous (though not necessarily better) load-deflection relationship is obtained by admitting the effects of large deflections (Figure 5-28d). Deflection begins at the same load, P_{cr}, but large deflections are obtained only by an increase in load. Loads at or near P_{cr}, however, cause large enough deflections to result in failure of machine parts in most cases. Thus, the results of small deflection theory are usually adequate, and we may allow loads up to

$$P = \frac{P_{cr}}{N}$$

for a slender column where N is an appropriate factor of safety.

For cross section area A, the Euler load P_{cr} as determined above is certainly not valid when P_{cr}/A exceeds S_{yp}, the yield point of the material. Experimental data have suggested that its use be limited to the range

$$\frac{P_{cr}}{A} \leqslant \frac{S_{yp}}{2} \tag{5-51}$$

Slenderness ratio

The ratio of unsupported column length L to least radius of gyration r_n is called the slenderness ratio. Radius of gyration is given by $r_n = \sqrt{I/A}$, where I is the least moment of inertia. Using inequality 5-51 and equation (5-50), we limit the range of validity of the Euler load to *slender columns* for which

$$\frac{L}{r_n} \geqslant \sqrt{\frac{2\pi^2 E}{S_{yp}}} \tag{5-52}$$

Short columns

Simply supported compression members for which

$$\frac{L}{r_n} < \sqrt{\frac{2\pi^2 E}{S_{yp}}} \tag{5-53}$$

may be called short columns. Tests of short columns suggest the relationship

$$\frac{P_{cr}}{A} = S_{yp} - \frac{1}{E}\left(\frac{S_{yp}L}{2\pi r_n}\right)^2 \tag{5-54}$$

called the **Johnson formula.**

Hollow sections and I sections have a greater moment of inertia than solid circular or rectangular rods of the same area and a correspondingly greater critical load. However, we must guard against local buckling or crippling of thin sections.

The results obtained thus far in this section are based on the simply supported member, which is an idealization based on the condition of no resistance to bending moment at the ends. This idealization may be used in cases where each end of a compression member is fastened with one or more bolts or rivets. If several fasteners are used, the joint will be somewhat more rigid than the assumed simple support, but not rigid enough to be considered clamped. Thus, we err on the safe side.

Example 5-7. Find the axial load that may be safely carried by a 1-in. × 1-in. × $\frac{1}{8}$-in. thick steel angle, 50 in. long, used as a brace as in Figure 5-29. The yield point is 50,000 psi and a factor of safety of 2 will be used.

Solution: We will ignore the moment resistance of the end supports and approximate the actual brace by a simply supported member of unsupported

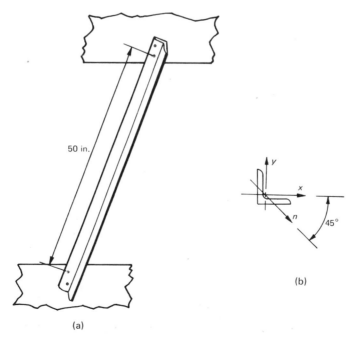

(a)

(b)

Figure 5-29 Angle brace compression member. **(a)** Angle brace. **(b)** The moment of inertia about the *n* axis is a minimum.

length $L = 50$ in. Using a table of properties for steel sections (for example, U.S. Steel Corporation, Hot Rolled Steel Shapes and Plates [5]), we obtain the cross sectional area of the angle: $A = 0.23$ in.^{2} and the radius of gyration about the x, y, and n axes: $r_x = r_y = 0.31$ in. and $r_n = 0.19$ in., the minimum radius of gyration. Buckling will tend to occur about the n axis corresponding to the least moment of inertia

$$I = I_n = Ar_n^2 = 0.0083 \text{ in.}^4$$

Using the modulus $E = 30 \times 10^6$, the inequality for slender columns

$$\frac{L}{r_n} \geqslant \sqrt{\frac{2\pi^2 E}{S_{yp}}}$$

is satisfied.

The critical load is given by equation 5-50

$$P_{cr} = \frac{\pi^2 EI}{L^2} = 980 \text{ lb}$$

and using the factor of safety, we have a safe compressive load

$$P = \frac{P_{cr}}{N} = 490 \text{ lb}$$

For this long, slender member, the buckling strength will undoubtedly govern if compressive loads are anticipated. In general, however, we must check to see that the working stress of the member is not exceeded at the least section (at the holes); we must be sure the fasteners do not shear; and we must check our design for failure of the fasteners or the member in bearing. ●

Eccentrically loaded columns

The load on the column in Figure 5-30 has an initial eccentricity e and the column design may be based on the **secant formula**

$$S_{yp} = \frac{NP}{A}\left(1 + \frac{ce}{r_n^2}\sec\frac{L}{r_n}\sqrt{\frac{NP}{4AE}}\right) \qquad (5\text{-}55)$$

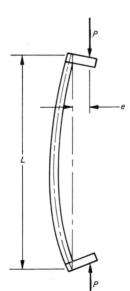

Figure 5-30 Eccentrically loaded column.

where P is the allowable load with factor of safety N; A is cross-sectional area and radius of gyration $r_n = \sqrt{I/A}$. If the loading eccentricity would tend to cause failure in one plane and the minimum moment of inertia would tend to cause failure in another plane, it is necessary to check both possibilities. Equation (5-55) may be applied to short as well as long columns, but it is necessary to determine (or to assume) the initial eccentricity in

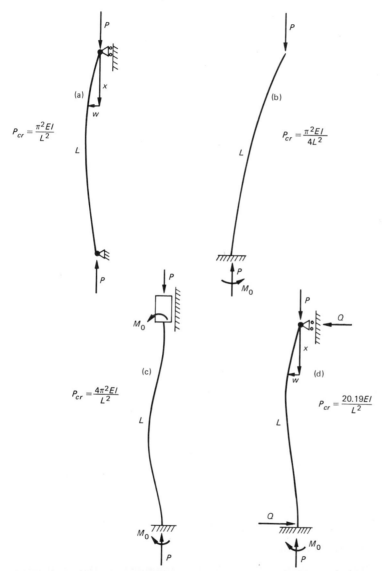

Figure 5-31 Slender columns with various boundary conditions. (a) Simple supports (pinned-pinned). (b) Clamped-free. (c) Clamped-clamped (axial motion only). (d) Clamped-pinned. (e) Clamped-clamped (lateral motion at one end, but no rotation). (f) Pinned-pinned with intermediate, moment-free support.

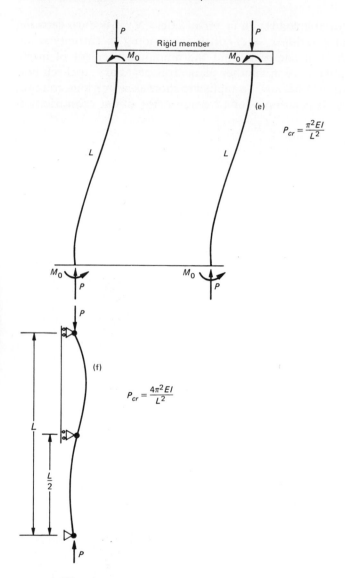

Rigid member

$$P_{cr} = \frac{\pi^2 EI}{L^2}$$

(e)

$$P_{cr} = \frac{4\pi^2 EI}{L^2}$$

(f)

Figure 5-31 (continued)

every case. Because of its unwieldy form, column design by this formula might best be programmed on a computer.

Other boundary conditions

Some compression members cannot be represented by the idealization of simple supports. Increased restraint results in greater load carrying capability when elastic stability governs the design. Slender compression members with other boundary conditions are compared with the simply supported compression member in Figure 5-31 (page 287). In each case, the moment of inertia I represents the minimum moment of inertia. In solving problems of this type, it is important that all forces and reactions be considered.

The **simply supported compression member** (Figure 5-31a) could have no lateral reaction component; if such a force were present at one end, it would require a compensating moment at the other end. For the slender **clamped-pinned member** (Figure 5-31d), a lateral reaction is possible and we must consider its effect on moment equilibrium. We proceed as with the simply supported member, measuring the coordinate x from the pinned end. The governing equation for the **clamped-pinned** member is

$$EI\frac{d^2w}{dx^2} + Pw = Qx \qquad (5\text{-}56)$$

The complementary solution to equation (5-56) is the same as the solution for simple supports, and the particular solution is

$$w_p = \frac{Qx}{P}$$

Thus, deflection of the **clamped-pinned member** is given by

$$w = A\cos\sqrt{\frac{P}{EI}}x + B\sin\sqrt{\frac{P}{EI}}x + \frac{Qx}{P} \qquad (5\text{-}57)$$

In deriving the governing equation, we used the condition of zero moment at $x = 0$, the pinned end. The remaining boundary conditions are

$$w(0) = 0$$

$$\frac{dw}{dx}(L) = 0$$

$$w(L) = 0$$

which lead to the transcendental equation

$$\tan X = X \qquad (5\text{-}58)$$

where

$$X = L\sqrt{\frac{P}{EI}}$$

Equation (5-58) can be solved by plotting values of $\tan X$ and X (in radians) as in Figure 5-32. The lowest nontrivial solution, $X = 4.4934$ leads to the critical load

$$P_{cr} = \frac{20.19EI}{L^2}$$

for the slender **clamped-pinned** compression member. The roots of $\tan X - X = 0$ are also given by Jahnke and Emde [6].

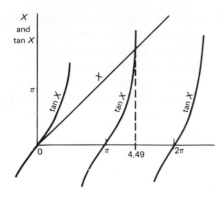

Figure 5-32 Solution to $X = \tan X$ where $X = L\sqrt{P/(EI)}$.

SECTION 5-11

Numerical Methods

This section deals with numerical methods, using digital computer programs. Problems in the design of machines do not always lead to simple analytical solutions. Two numerical methods for obtaining roots of equations will be considered at this point. Both methods are effective for digital computer use and applicable to many different types of problems. The clamped-pinned compression member described in the previous section will be used as an example.

Newton's method

This numerical method, also called the Newton-Raphson method, is a common technique for finding a root of an equation. Suppose we require a root of the equation

$$F(X) = 0$$

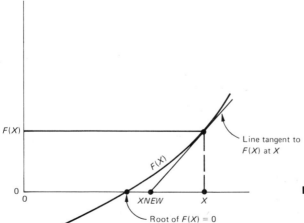

Figure 5-33 Newton's method.

where $F(X)$ is plotted in Figure 5-33. (Of course, we do not have the actual plot; if we did the solution would be obvious.) Selecting a value X for the first approximation of the root, we calculate $F(X)$, which happens to be unequal to zero. A tangent to the curve, however, intercepts the X axis at $XNEW$, a better approximation of the root. The new approximation is given by

$$XNEW = X - \frac{F(X)}{G(X)}$$

where

$$G(X) = \frac{dF}{dX}(X)$$

the slope of the curve at X. If the new approximation $XNEW$ is not good enough, we replace the old value of X by $XNEW$ and repeat the process.

Figure 5-34a shows a computer flowchart for Newton's method. Our input includes X, the first approximation of the root; ERROR, the difference between two successive solutions at which we will terminate the program; and N, the maximum number of trials. For the function sketched in Figure 5-33 we would expect rapid convergence toward the root of $F(X) = 0$. Unfortunately, Newton's method fails us in certain circumstances. These circumstances include the presence of local extremes (maxima or minima) or the presence of inflection points in the region of interest. Furthermore, we must obtain the derivative of the function, and it should not be zero in the region of interest if Newton's method is to be applied. Newton's method tends to be particularly troublesome with transcendental functions. When a function has multiple roots there is always the hazard of failing to obtain the desired root by numerical methods, particularly by machine methods.

Figure 5-34b is a computer program that was used to find the root of $\tan X - X = 0$ (that is, $F(X) = 0$) within ± 0.00001 by Newton's method. For a first approximation of $X = 4.6$, the program computed successive values of X until the solution $X = 4.493409$ was reached. This is the solution to $\tan X = X$ of the preceding section where

$$X = L\sqrt{\frac{P}{EI}}$$

and P is the critical load for the slender clamped-pinned compression member. This solution is more precise than necessary for the physical problem.

We see from Figure 5-32 that a first approximation which is not near the desired root will not lead to the correct solution. For this equation, use of a poor first approximation with Newton's method led to wide oscillations. This is due to the nature of the derivative of $F(X) = \tan X - X$ and due to the fact that $\tan X$ has an infinite number of branches.

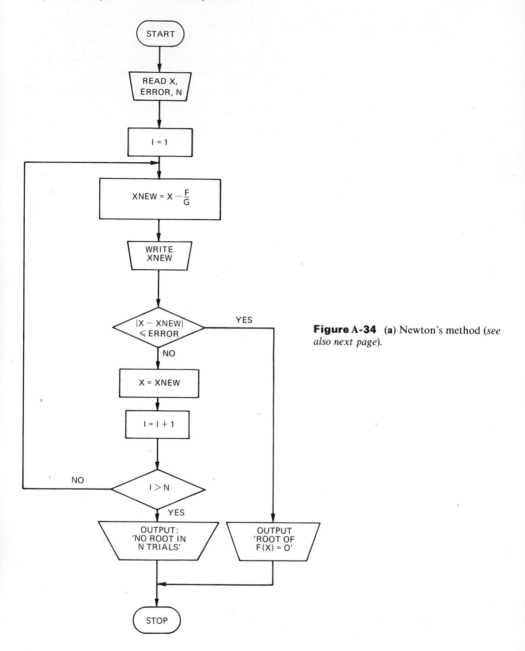

Figure A-34 (a) Newton's method (*see also next page*).

The secant method

While similar to Newton's method, the secant method utilizes a difference quotient instead of a differential. We use a secant line, Figure 5-35 instead of a tangent line. As with the previous example, the figure is used to illustrate a numerical method; in general, we would not plot $F(X)$. It is not necessary

```
            X=4.6
            ERR=1.0E-5
            N=40
            I=1
    4       FX=(SIN(X)/COS(X))-X
            DX=(1./((COS(X))**2))-1.
            XN=X-(FX/DX)
            IF(ABS(FX)-ERR)2,2,1
    2       PRINT,I,FX,X
            GOTO6
    1       I=I+1
            IF(I-N)3,3,5
    3       X=XN
            GOTO4
    5       PRINT,I
    6       CONTINUE
            STOP
            END
```

Figure 5-34 (continued) **(b)** Newton's method, computer program listing.

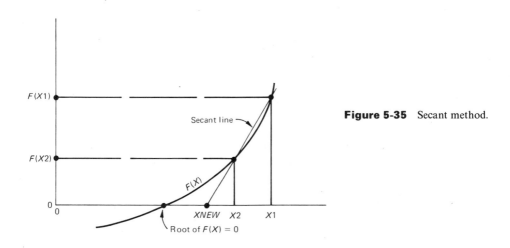

Figure 5-35 Secant method.

to code a derivative when using the secant method, but two initial approximations of the root of $F(X) = 0$ are required. Let $X1$ and $X2$ be the initial approximations. We will take the secant line intercept with the X axis to be a better approximation of the root. The new approximate root is

$$XNEW = X2 - \frac{F(X2)}{G(X2)}$$

where

$$G(X2) = \frac{F(X2) - F(X1)}{X2 - X1}$$

the difference quotient. If $XNEW$ is not a satisfactory approximation, we replace the old value of $X2$ by $XNEW$ and the old value of $X1$ by $X2$ and then repeat the procedure.

For problems of this type the desired root should be obtained rapidly if the initial approximations of X bracket the expected solution. For the solution of $\tan X - X = 0$, both initial approximations of X should be on the same branch of $\tan X$.

PROBLEMS

1. The steel I section shown in Problem Figure 1 has a yield strength of 45,000 psi. Find the factor of safety based on normal stress at the outer fiber.

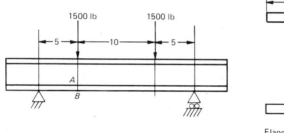

Flanges are $\frac{1}{4}$ inch thick
Web is $\frac{1}{8}$ inch thick

Problem Figure 1

2. (a) Find the neutral axis and moment of inertia of the T section of Problem Figure 2 in terms of thickness t. **(b)** Find required thickness t for a yield point of 60,000 psi, maximum moment of 4000 in.-lb, and a factor of safety of 4.

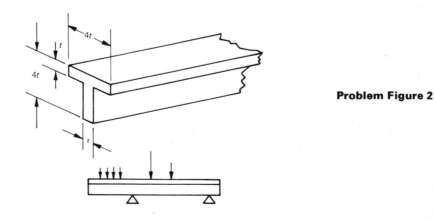

Problem Figure 2

3. Repeat Problem 1 for the case where only the 1500 lb load 5 in. from the left support is applied.

4. Repeat Problem 2 for the case where the horizontal part of the T section has a width of 6*t*.

5. (**a**) Find tensile stress at point *A* in Problem Figure 5. (**b**) Find tensile stress and transverse shear stress at point *B*.

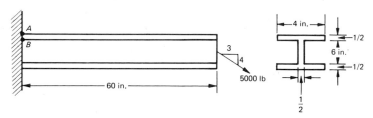

Problem Figure 5

6. Repeat Problem 5 for a similar I section with $\frac{1}{4}$-in. thick web and flanges.

7. A 20-in. long steel bar is pinned (simply supported) at the ends. A 5000 lb load is applied 10 in. from the left end and a 6000 lb load 12 in. from the left end. Both loads are applied vertically downward. If we use a square bar with a yield point of 80,000 psi and a safety factor of 2, find the sectional dimension of the bar.

8. If a round bar is to be used in Problem 7, find the required diameter.

9. A nylon machine element is subject to a maximum moment of 45 in.-lb. (**a**) Using a safety factor of 3 and a tensile strength of 7100 psi, find the sectional dimension if the member is to be square. (**b**) Find the required diameter if a round member is used.

10. (**a**) Find the maximum deflection due to bending in the steel I section shown in Problem Figure 1. (**b**) Find bending deflection 5 in. from the left support.

11. A steel machine member is subject to a 1000-lb load as shown in Problem Figure 11.

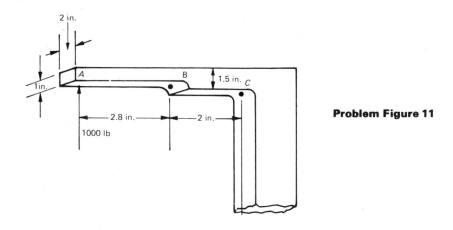

Problem Figure 11

The vertical part may be considered rigid. (a) Draw and dimension shear and moment diagrams. Find bending stress σ_x at B and C. Neglect stress concentration. (b) Draw the curvature diagram. Dimension it. (c) Assume zero slope at point C. Plot θ versus x showing values at A and B. What is the maximum slope in radians?

12. Repeat Problem 10 for the case where only the 1500-lb load 5 in. from the left support is applied.

13. Repeat Problem 11 except that the 1000-lb load at point A points upward and to the left at 45 deg. Find σ_x at B and C due to both direct tension and bending.

14. A steel band 0.032-in. thick and 0.75-in. wide is bent around two pulleys, each of radius $R = 8$ in. The band is subject to a maximum direct tensile load of 200 lb. (a) Find maximum tensile stress. Note that curvature $d^2w/dx^2 = 1/R$. (b) Plot stress across the thickness of the band where it bends to go around the pulley.

15. In Problem 14, find the optimum band thickness based on maximum stress, that is, find thickness for which maximum stress will be least.

16. A 6-in. long machine member is simply supported at the ends. Stiffness $EI_1 = 2000$ lb-in.^{2} for the left half and $EI_2 = 1000$ lb-in.^{2} for the right half. A 60-lb vertical load is applied 2 in. from the left end and a 40-lb vertical load is applied at the center. Find shear, moment, curvature, slope, and deflection. Evaluate slope at the ends and maximum deflection.

17. The rigidity of a 6-in. long machine member is $EI_1 = 10,000$ lb-in.^{2} from $x = 0$ (the left end) to $x = 4$. The rigidity is $EI_2 = 5000$ to the right of $x = 4$. The member is simply supported at $x = 1$ and $x = 3$. A 10-lb overhung load is applied at $x = 5$. Find shear, moment, curvature, slope, and deflection.

18. A 14-in. long circular shaft is simply supported at the ends. At $x = 4$ (measured from the left end) there is a 3000-lb vertical load and a 1000-lb horizontal load. At $x = 10$, there is a 2000-lb vertical load and a 3000-lb horizontal load. Both vertical loads are downward and both horizontal loads are outward. Sketch shear and moment in the vertical and horizontal planes. Evaluate maximum resultant moment at $x = 4$, 7, and 10.

19. A steel bar has dimensions $\frac{1}{2} \times \frac{1}{2} \times 12$ in. It is simply supported at $x = 1$, 6, and 11, (measuring from the left end). A 100-lb vertical load is applied at $x = 3.5$ and another at $x = 8.5$. (a) Find the reactions. (b) Find maximum bending moment.

20. A 5-in. long bar of polycarbonate is clamped at one end and has a 20 lb load at the other perpendicular to its axis. (a) Find the required bar diameter based on a safety factor of 1.8. Use average properties. (b) Find deflection at the loaded end.

21. Repeat Problem 20 for a hollow polycarbonate bar with inner diameter $= 80\%$ of outer diameter.

22. (a) Find shear deflection and total deflection at the center of the I section shown in Problem Figure 1. (b) Repeat for a point 5 in. from the left support.

23. Repeat Problem 22 for the case where only the 1500-lb load 5 in. from the left support is applied.

24. A solid rectangular cantilever beam has a width h and a depth $2h$. A vertical force is applied at the free end. The beam is made of steel with a shear strength of one-half its tensile strength. (a) For what beam length is tensile failure most likely? (b) For what length is failure in transverse shear likely?

25. A $4 \times 2\frac{1}{2}$ channel section is oriented as in Figure 5-19 and subject to vertical loads. Total depth $= 4$ in., total flange width $= 2.5$ in., and average flange and web thickness = 0.5 in. The moment of inertia about the neutral axis is 8.8 in.[4] Find the shear center.

26. (a) Draw shear and moment diagrams for the 1-in. bar in Problem Figure 26. (b) Find bending and shear stress at points B and C on the 1-in. bar.

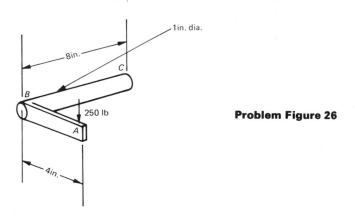

1in. dia.

8in.

C

B

250 lb

A

4in.

Problem Figure 26

27. Find the angular rotation and vertical displacement at point B on the 1-in. steel bar in Problem Figure 26.

28. Repeat Problem 26 with dimension $AB = 8$ in. and dimension $BC = 4$ in.

29. Repeat Problem 27 with dimension $AB = 8$ in. and dimension $BC = 4$ in.

30. An elliptical aluminum bar has a 1-in. major diameter and a $\frac{3}{4}$-in. minor diameter. The bar is 14 in. long and subject to a torque of 125 in.-lb. (a) Find maximum shear stress and its location. (b) Find angular deformation.

31. (a) Find the torsional rigidity of a 9-in. long open steel section similar to Figure 5-23b with an outside diameter of 2 in. and 0.10-in. wall thickness. (b) Find maximum shear stress if 100 in.-lb torque is applied.

32. Find the approximate torsional spring constant and maximum allowable torque for a 60-in. long steel channel section with a 4-in. web and 2-in. legs, having $\frac{1}{4}$-in. section thickness throughout. Allow a working stress of 20,000 psi in shear and use $G = 11.5 \times 10^6$ psi. Find the diameter of a solid steel rod 60 in. long (a) with the same stiffness; (b) with the same strength.

33. Find the torsional spring constant of a solid stepped steel shaft. Its diameter is 1 in. for 8 in. of its length; 1.25 in. for 5 in. of its length; 0.875 in. for 6 in. of its length.

34. A $\frac{1}{2}$-in. diameter steel bolt is tightened snug in a 10-in. long aluminum sleeve with 1 in.[2] cross section. Find the force in each part after a temperature rise of 100F°. Use temperature coefficients of 6.5×10^{-6} for steel and 13×10^{-6} for aluminum.

35. Consider a solid unconstrained aluminum alloy bar with dimensions and co-ordinates as in Figure 5-25. Find the thermal stress after a temperature change of

$$T = T_0 \left(\frac{|y|}{2a} - 1 \right)$$

where $a = \frac{1}{2}$ in. and $T_0 = 190F°$.

36. Consider a composite bar similar to Figure 5-24d which is subject to a 210F° temperature rise. Let layers 1 be 40% carbon machine steel, 0.10-in. thick, layers 2 magnesium alloy, 0.20-in. thick, and layer 3 40% carbon machine steel, 0.25-in. thick. The bar is 1.5-in. wide and 8-in. long. Find elongation and stresses.

37. Find the deflection at the center of the stepped shaft in Problem Figure 37 where $I_1 = I_3$. Use Castigliano's theorem.

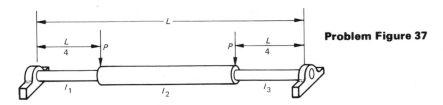

Problem Figure 37

38. Find deflection at the load and at the center of the stepped shaft in Problem Figure 37 if $I_1 = I_3$ and only one load is applied. Use Castigliano's theorem.

39. Using Castigliano's theorem, find deflection at point A in Problem Figure 39.

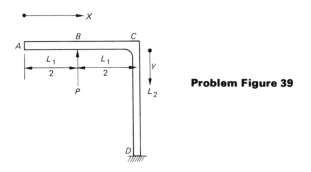

Problem Figure 39

40. Using Castigliano's theorem, find deflection at point B in Problem Figure 39.

41. Let load P be applied vertically upward at point A in Problem Figure 39. Find deflection at A if the section is constant throughout the member.

42. A 3-in. I beam (Problem Figure 42) is loaded in compression. $A = 1.64$ in.^{2}; $I_{11} = 2.5$ in.^{4}; $I_{22} = 0.46$ in.^{4} There is a 72-in. unsupported length between ends that may be considered pinned. Find the safe load based on a factor of safety of 3. Use steel with $S_{yp} = 42,000$ psi.

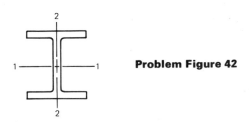

Problem Figure 42

43. Repeat Problem 42 for an unsupported length of 100 in.

44. A 3-in. steel I beam (Problem Figure 42) with 36-in. unsupported length may be considered to have pinned ends. $A = 1.64$ in.^{2}; $I_{11} = 2.5$ in.^{4}; $I_{22} = 0.46$ in.^{4} Find the safe load based on a safety factor of 3. Use $S_{yp} = 42{,}000$ psi.

45. Brace A in Problem Figure 45 is subjected to an axial compressive load F. The angles do not twist, but the brace may rotate about its fasteners at both ends. Find allowable load F for a factor of safety N.

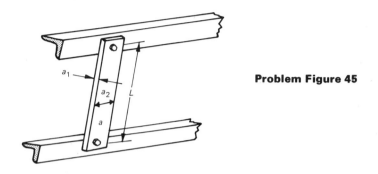

Problem Figure 45

46. Find the second buckling mode of the pinned-clamped compression member using Newton's method. Does this value have any physical significance?

47. Find the second nonzero root of tan $X = X$ using the secant method. Sketch a flowchart for the numerical procedure.

REFERENCES

[1] S. Timoshenko and J. N. Goodier: *Theory of Elasticity*, 2nd ed. McGraw-Hill Book Co., New York, 1951.

[2] S. Timoshenko: *Strength of Materials*, 3rd ed., 2 vols. D. Van Nostrand Co., New York, 1955.

[3] F. E. Miller and H. A. Doeringsfeld: *Mechanics of Materials*, 2nd ed. International Textbook Co., Scranton, Pa., 1962.

[4] E. P. Popov: *Mechanics of Materials*. Prentice-Hall, Inc., Englewood Cliffs, N.J., 1952.

[5] *Hot Rolled Steel Shapes and Plates*. U.S. Steel Corporation, Pittsburg, Pa., 1955.

[6] E. Jahnke and F. Emde: *Tables of Functions*, 4th ed. Dover Publications, Inc., 1945.

[7] V. M. Faires: *Design of Machine Elements*, 4th ed. The Macmillan Company, New York, 1965.

[8] C. D. Hodgman, et al.: *Handbook of Chemistry and Physics*, 37th ed. Chemical Rubber Publishing Co., Cleveland, Ohio, 1955.

[9] O. W. Eshbach, et al.: *Handbook of Engineering Fundamentals*, 2nd ed. John Wiley & Sons, Inc., New York, 1952.

[10] F. B. Seely and J. O. Smith: *Advanced Mechanics of Materials*, 2nd ed. John Wiley & Sons, Inc., New York, 1952.

[11] D. D. McCracken: *A Guide to FORTRAN IV Programming*. John Wiley & Sons, Inc., New York, 1965.

[12] B. A. Boley and J. H. Weiner: *Theory of Thermal Stresses*, John Wiley & Sons, Inc., New York, 1960.

[13] R. W. Hamming: *Calculus and the Computer Revolution*. Houghton-Mifflin Co., Boston, 1968.

[14] H. M. Priest: *Design Manual for High Strength Steels*. U.S. Steel Corporation, Pittsburgh, Pa., 1954.

[15] S. Timoshenko and J. M. Gere: *Elastic Stability*. The McGraw-Hill Book Co., New York, 1961.

6

Theories of Failure
Used in the Design of
Machine Elements

SYMBOLS

N = factor of safety

S_e = endurance limit (modified for actual specimen), psi

S_n = fatigue strength for n cycles, psi

S'_n = endurance limit (for polished test specimen), psi

S_u = ultimate strength in tension, psi

$S_{u(c)}$ = ultimate strength in compression, psi

S_{yp} = tensile yield strength, psi

$S_{yp(c)}$ = compressive yield strength, psi

$\sigma_1, \sigma_2, \sigma_3$ = principal stresses, psi

σ_{eq} = equivalent stress, psi

σ_m = mean stress amplitude, psi

σ_r = range stress amplitude, psi

τ_{max} = maximum shear stress, psi

In many cases, a machine part fails when the material begins to yield plastically. In a few cases, we may tolerate a small dimensional change and permit a static load that exceeds the yield point. Actual fracture at the ultimate strength of the material would then constitute failure. The criterion for failure may be based on normal or shear stress in either case. Fatigure failure is probably the most common mode of failure in machine elements. Other modes of failure include excessive elastic deflection of some part, thereby rendering the machine useless, or failure of a part by buckling. The actual failure mechanism in a real machine element may be quite complicated; each failure theory is only an attempt to model that mechanism for a given class of materials. In each case, a factor of safety is employed. The magnitude of the safety factor depends on the probable accuracy of our assumptions, the danger and cost of a failure, and other design conditions.

SECTION 6-1

Stress at a Point and Combined Stress

Figure 6-1 shows the convention for designating stresses on an element with faces perpendicular to the coordinate axes. Every machine element is, of course, three-dimensional. It is unusual, however, to have stresses of significant magnitude in all three directions. A two-dimensional stress field adequately describes all but a few engineering problems.

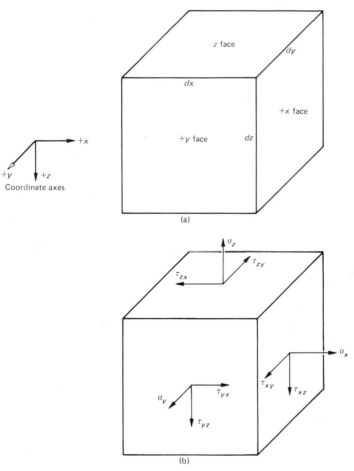

Figure 6-1 Stress at a point. (**a**) An infinitesimal element in a machine member. (**b**) Designation of normal and shear stresses (positive as shown; not all stresses shown).

Combined stress in a two-dimensional stress field

Consider an element within a two-dimensional stress field such that the only nonzero stresses are σ_x, σ_y, and τ_{xy} (Figure 6-2). From equilibrium of

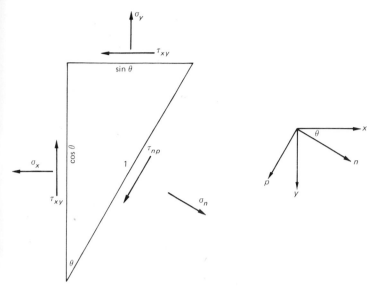

Figure 6-2 Stress at a point in a two-dimensional stress field.

forces, the normal stress on the skew face is given by

$$\sigma_n = \sigma_x \cos^2 \theta + 2\tau_{xy} \sin \theta \cos \theta + \sigma_y \sin^2 \theta \qquad (6\text{-}1)$$

and the shear stress by

$$\tau_{np} = (\sigma_y - \sigma_x) \sin \theta \cos \theta + \tau_{xy}(\cos^2 \theta - \sin^2 \theta) \qquad (6\text{-}2)$$

If the expression for normal stress is differentiated with respect to θ and the result set equal to zero, we obtain the values of θ (the principal directions) corresponding to maximum and minimum normal stress in the xy plane. These are the principal stresses

$$\sigma_1 \text{ and } \sigma_2 = \frac{\sigma_x + \sigma_y}{2} \pm \left[\left(\frac{\sigma_x - \sigma_y}{2} \right)^2 + \tau_{xy}^2 \right]^{1/2} \qquad (6\text{-}3)$$

The third principal direction is the z direction and the corresponding stress $\sigma_z = \sigma_3$ was assumed to be zero. The principal directions (1, 2, and 3) are mutually perpendicular. The planes perpendicular to the principal direction axes are the **principal planes.** Shear stress is zero on the principal planes. Transformation of stresses is discussed in detail in books on mechanics of materials including Douglas [1] and references [1] to [4] of Chapter 5.

The expressions for normal and shear stress, equations (6-1) and (6-2), can be written in terms of the double angle 2θ and expressed graphically. This plot of stress at a point is called the **Mohr circle.** For a *two-dimensional stress field*, the Mohr circle is constructed as follows (see Figure 6-3).

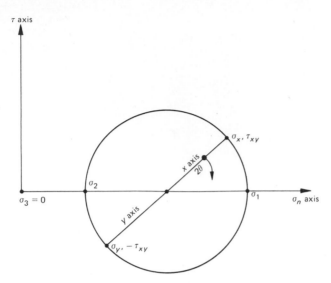

Figure 6-3 State of stress at a point (Mohr circle representation of stresses in the XY plane for a two-dimensional stress field).

1. Plot σ_x, τ_{xy} and σ_y, $-\tau_{xy}$ on σ_n, τ coordinates.
2. Connect the two points to form the diameter of the Mohr circle. Draw the circle.
3. The line from the first point to the center of the circle represents the x axis; the line from the second point to the center represents the y axis. An angle 2θ on the Mohr circle (measured from the x axis) corresponds to an angle θ measured on the actual element as in Figure 6-2. Points on the circle represent stresses in the xy plane.
4. Identify principal stresses σ_1 and σ_2.
5. Identify the coordinate origin as σ_3 (where $\sigma_3 = 0$). See Figure 6-4. Draw another circle with the line between σ_1 and σ_3 as its diameter; draw another with the line between σ_2 and σ_3 as its diameter. The region between the circles represents all possible states of stress at a point in the two-dimensional stress field. Maximum shear stress is given by the radius of the largest circle, that is

$$\tau_{max} = \text{the largest of} \begin{cases} \dfrac{|\sigma_1 - \sigma_2|}{2} \\[2mm] \dfrac{|\sigma_1|}{2} \\[2mm] \dfrac{|\sigma_2|}{2} \end{cases} \qquad (6\text{-}4)$$

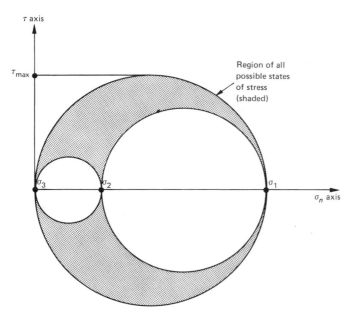

τ axis

τ_{max}

Region of all
possible states
of stress
(shaded)

σ_3 σ_2 σ_1

σ_n axis

Figure 6-4 Completed construction showing maximum shear stress (case where σ_1 and σ_2 have same sign; $\sigma_3 = 0$).

The three-dimensional case

In the general three-dimensional case, we have nonzero values of σ_z, τ_{xz}, and τ_{yz}. It can be shown that the three roots of the determinate

$$\begin{vmatrix} \sigma_x - \sigma & \tau_{xy} & \tau_{xz} \\ \tau_{xy} & \sigma_y - \sigma & \tau_{yz} \\ \tau_{xz} & \tau_{yz} & \sigma_z - \sigma \end{vmatrix} = 0 \qquad (6\text{-}5)$$

which we label σ_1, σ_2, and σ_3 are the principal stresses in the general three-dimensional case [Boresi, 2]. Shear stress is zero on the three corresponding planes, the principal planes. Figure 6-5 shows a Mohr circle representation for the general three-dimensional case, where circle diameters are distances $\overline{\sigma_1 \sigma_2}$, $\overline{\sigma_2 \sigma_3}$, and $\overline{\sigma_1 \sigma_3}$.

Maximum shear stress is given by the greatest circle radius. In general, we have

$$\tau_{max} = \text{the largest of} \begin{cases} \dfrac{|\sigma_1 - \sigma_2|}{2} \\[2mm] \dfrac{|\sigma_2 - \sigma_3|}{2} \\[2mm] \dfrac{|\sigma_1 - \sigma_3|}{2} \end{cases} \qquad (6\text{-}6)$$

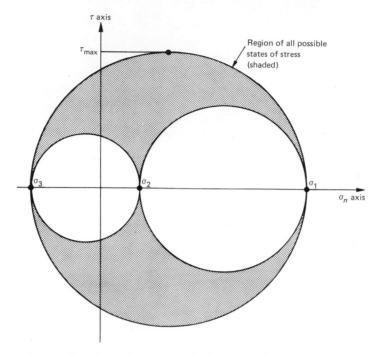

Figure 6-5 State of stress at a point for general three-dimensional stress field.

Principal stresses σ_1 and σ_2 will not, in general, be in the xy plane. Thus, the construction procedure of Figures 6-3 and 6-4 may not be used in the general three-dimensional case.

The Maximum Normal Stress Theory

The maximum normal stress theory is based on failure in tension or compression. It may be applied to materials that are relatively strong in shear but weak in tension or compression.

For problems of static loading, we designate the largest of the positive principal stresses by $\sigma_{\max}$, and the magnitude of the most negative principal stress by $\sigma_{(c)\max}$. For a design based on yielding, with tensile and compressive yield points S_{yp} and $S_{yp(c)}$, respectively, we have

$$\sigma_{\max} \leqslant \frac{S_{yp}}{N} \quad \text{and} \quad \sigma_{(c)\max} \leqslant \frac{S_{yp(c)}}{N} \tag{6-7}$$

for safety factor N. If we have a static load problem where yielding is of no consequence, or design for a material with no distinct yield point, ultimate strengths in tension and compression, S_u and $S_{u(c)}$, may be used. The design criterion then becomes

$$\sigma_{max} \leqslant \frac{S_u}{N} \quad \text{and} \quad \sigma_{(c)max} \leqslant \frac{S_{u(c)}}{N} \tag{6-8}$$

The maximum normal stress theory is often applied to the design of *cast iron* machine elements. Cast iron has no distinct yield point, and the ultimate compressive strength is considerably greater than the ultimate tensile strength. The stress-strain relationship is nonlinear. Bending stresses are not given exactly by the equation

$$\sigma_x = \frac{Mz}{I} \tag{6-9}$$

and the ultimate strength based on

$$\sigma_{x(max)} = \frac{Mc}{I} \tag{6-10}$$

will not equal the ultimate strength based on direct tension. For simplicity, however, equations (6-9) and (6-10) are generally used.

Example 6-1: The Maximum Normal Stress Theory. The cast iron section shown in Figure 6-6 has an ultimate strength in tension $S_u = 30,000$ psi and an ultimate strength in compression $S_{u(c)} = 109,000$ psi. A factor of safety $N = 2$ will be used. Plot stress distribution across the section and find allowable load P.

Solution: The solution will be based on stress on section A-A. The distance to the neutral axis in bending is given by

$$\bar{z} = \frac{\Sigma z'A}{\Sigma A}$$

summed over the two parts of the T section, where z' is used to represent distance from the left edge of the T section to the center of a given part of the T section. We find

$$\bar{z} = \frac{(1.75)(0.25)(1.125) + (1.2)(0.25)(0.125)}{(1.75)(0.25) + (1.2)(0.25)} = 0.72 \text{ in.}$$

as shown in Figure 6-6.

The moment of inertia about the neutral axis in bending is given by

$$I = \Sigma(I_0 + Ad^2)$$

summed over the two parts of the section. The term I_0 is the moment of inertia of a part of the T section about an axis parallel to the neutral axis in bending, but through its own center of gravity. Distance d is measured from that axis to the neutral axis in bending. Thus, we have

$$I = (0.25)(1.75)^3/12 + (1.2)(0.25)^3/12 + (1.75)(0.25)(1.125 - 0.72)^2$$
$$+ (1.2)(0.25)(0.72 - 0.125)^2 = 0.288 \text{ in.}^4$$

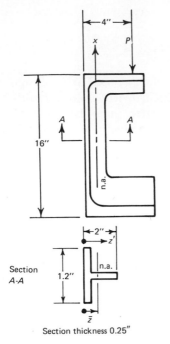

(a) T section
machine
member

Figure 6-6 Design of a cast iron section (n.a. is the neutral axis in bending).

Section A-A

Section thickness 0.25"

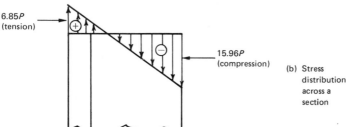

6.85P
(tension)

15.96P
(compression)

(b) Stress
distribution
across a
section

In this problem we have a combination of pure bending and direct compression on section A-A. Total section area is

$$A = (1.75)(0.25) + (1.2)(0.25) = 0.739 \text{ in.}^2$$

The moment arm of the load P is $4 - \bar{z} = 3.28$ and moment on the section is $M = 3.28P$. Distance from the neutral axis in bending to the extreme fiber is $c_1 = \bar{z} = 0.72$ in. on the left (tension) side and $c_2 = 2 - \bar{z} = 1.28$ in. on the right (compression) side. The maximum normal stress is simply the sum of the direct stress and the bending stress. On the left side

$$\sigma_{n(max)} = \sigma_x(c_1) = \frac{-P}{A} + \frac{Mc_1}{I} = 6.85P$$

On the right side:

$$\sigma_{n(min)} = \sigma_x(c_2) = \frac{-P}{A} - \frac{Mc_2}{I} = -15.96P$$

The stress distribution across the section is linear as shown in Figure 6-6b.

Equating maximum tensile and compressive stress to the working strengths we obtain allowable load. On the tension side

$$\sigma_{n(max)} = \frac{S_u}{N}$$

from which

$$P = 2190 \, \text{lb}$$

On the compression side

$$|\sigma_{n(min)}| = \frac{S_{u(c)}}{N}$$

from which

$$P = 3410 \, \text{lb}$$

Tension governs and the allowable load $P = 2190 \, \text{lb}$ ●

SECTION 6-3

The Maximum Shear Theory

The maximum shear theory is particularly useful for the design of ductile steel machine members. It is conservative (safe) and easy to apply. It is based on the assumption that failure occurs when the maximum shear stress reaches a certain value. That value is the shear stress at the instant of failure in the tensile test. We will designate yielding as failure. Referring to Figure

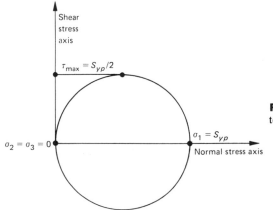

Figure 6-7 Mohr circle representation of the tension test at yielding.

6-7, we see that the shear stress at yielding is half the yield point. Thus, the maximum shear theory is given by

$$\frac{S_{yp}}{2N} = \tau_{max} \tag{6-11}$$

In ductile steels, shear failure sometimes occurs in the standard tension test. If the shear strength of a material exceeds $S_{yp}/2$, however, we still limit the maximum shear stress to $S_{yp}/(2N)$ in order to avoid tensile failure when applying the maximum shear theory. Thus, in a *three-dimensional stress field* we use equation (6-6) to obtain

$$\frac{S_{yp}}{N} \geqslant \text{the largest of}\begin{cases} |\sigma_1 - \sigma_2| \\ |\sigma_2 - \sigma_3| \\ |\sigma_1 - \sigma_3| \end{cases} \quad (6\text{-}12)$$

Consequently, for a two-dimensional stress field where $\sigma_3 = 0$, we have

$$\frac{S_{yp}}{N} \geqslant \text{the largest of}\begin{cases} |\sigma_1| \\ |\sigma_2| \\ |\sigma_1 - \sigma_2| \end{cases} \quad (6\text{-}13)$$

Principal stresses are given by equation (6-3) for the two-dimensional case and equation (6-5) for the three-dimensional case. For the two-dimensional case, if the principal stresses in the xy plane (σ_1 and σ_2) are of *opposite sign*, then maximum shear stress will lie in that plane, and we have the value of maximum shear stress given by

$$\tau_{max} = \left[\left(\frac{\sigma_x - \sigma_y}{2}\right)^2 + \tau_{xy}^2\right]^{1/2} \quad (6\text{-}14)$$

If principal stresses σ_1 and σ_2 have the *same sign*, then maximum shear stress will not lie in the xy plane, and the value computed in equation (6-14) will be only of academic interest because we cannot specify the plane in which a material is to fail. For σ_1 and σ_2 of the same sign and $\sigma_3 = 0$, maximum shear stress is given by

$$\tau_{max} = \frac{|\sigma_1|}{2} \quad \text{or} \quad \frac{|\sigma_2|}{2} \quad (6\text{-}15)$$

For the important special case in which

$$\sigma_y = \sigma_z = \tau_{yz} = \tau_{xz} = 0$$

maximum shear stress lies in the xy plane. Setting $\tau_{max} = S_{yp}/2N$ in equation (6-14), we obtain

$$\frac{S_{yp}}{N} = (\sigma_x^2 + 4\tau_{xy}^2)^{1/2} \quad (6\text{-}16)$$

Example 6-2: Design of an I-Section Machine Member. Let us design a member as shown in Figure 6-8 to support a static load $P = 1000$ lb. A factor of safety $N = 3$ will be used, based on the uncertainty of some values and the danger in case of failure.

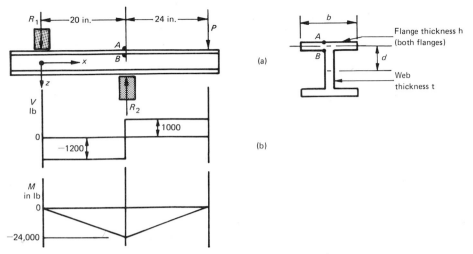

Figure 6-8 (a) Design of an I-section machine member. (b) Shear and moment diagrams.

Solution: There are many possibilities, and we must make a number of design decisions. Let us specify some dimensions and calculate web and flange thickness. If the result is unreasonable, we review the original design decisions. We will specify a ductile steel with a yield point $S_{yp} = 60,000$ psi and let $b = 2$ in. and $d = 1.5$ in.

Assuming the reactions to be equivalent to simple supports and setting the sum of the moments about the left reaction equal to zero, we obtain $R_2 = 2200$ lb. Then $R_1 = 1200$ lb as shown, and we may draw shear and moment diagrams (Figure 6-8b).

The greatest contribution to the moment of inertia of the I section is made by the flanges. Neglecting the moment of inertia of the web and the moment of inertia of the flanges about their own central axes, we obtain an approximation of the moment of inertia of the section

$$I = 2bhd^2 = 9h$$

for flange thickness h.

In problems of this type, we assume $\sigma_y = \sigma_z = \tau_{xy} = \tau_{yz} = 0$, noting that bending occurs in the xz-plane. Maximum tensile stress occurs at the top surface of the flange where moment is greatest (point A). The distance from the neutral axis to point A is $c = d + (h/2)$. The tensile stress at A is given by

$$\sigma_{x(A)} = \frac{Mc}{I} = \frac{4000}{h} + 1333$$

At point A, the shear stress $\tau_{xz} = 0$ and we have the case similar to direct tension. The maximum shear theory reduces to setting $\sigma_{x(A)}$ equal to the working strength S_{yp}/N. We then obtain the required flange thickness: $h = 0.214$ in.

At point B in the web where it joins the flange just to the left of reaction R_2, we have the worst combination of bending and shear. Again using the approximate value of I, and $z = 1.5 - (h/2)$

$$\sigma_{x(B)} = \frac{Mz}{I} = 17,367 \text{ psi}$$

Transverse shear stress may be roughly approximated by

$$\tau_{xz(B)} = \frac{V}{A_{(web)}} = \frac{431}{t}$$

for web thickness t.

Using equation (6-14) with the above values for point B, we obtain the required value of web thickness: $t = 0.089$ (say $t = 0.1$ in.). The results are reasonable, but the reader may wish to compute more exact values of σ_x and τ_{xz} using the values of h and t that we have just found and the equations of Chapter 5. ●

SECTION 6-4

Strain Energy and the Distortion Energy Theory

Strain energy

In the search for a rational criterion for the prediction of failure in machine elements, strain energy has been given considerable attention. For the one-dimensional case (Figure 6-9) the strain energy per unit volume is given by

$$U_{(1 \text{ dimensional})} = \tfrac{1}{2}\sigma_x\varepsilon_x \tag{6-17}$$

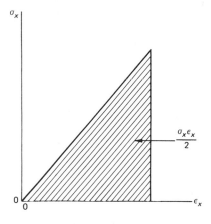

Figure 6-9 Strain energy for the one-dimensional case.

In terms of the principal axes, 1, 2, and 3, equation (6-17) may be extended to total strain energy per unit volume

$$U = \tfrac{1}{2}(\sigma_1\varepsilon_1 + \sigma_2\varepsilon_2 + \sigma_3\varepsilon_3) \tag{6-18}$$

because the principal planes are free of shear stress.

Using the stress-strain relationships

$$\varepsilon_1 = \frac{1}{E}(\sigma_1 - v\sigma_2 - v\sigma_3) \tag{6-19}$$

and so on, we obtain the *three-dimensional expression* for strain energy in terms of the principal stresses alone.

$$U = \frac{1}{2E}[\sigma_1^2 + \sigma_2^2 + \sigma_3^2 - 2v(\sigma_1\sigma_2 + \sigma_2\sigma_3 + \sigma_1\sigma_3)] \qquad (6\text{-}20)$$

Total strain energy, however, is not considered a good criterion for failure prediction because it is believed that uniform stress in three directions, $\sigma_1 = \sigma_2 = \sigma_3$, is unlikely to cause failure. In order to eliminate the contribution due to uniform stress, we define an average stress

$$\sigma_{av} = \frac{\sigma_1 + \sigma_2 + \sigma_3}{3} \qquad (6\text{-}21)$$

Its contribution to strain energy is given by replacing each principal stress in equation (6-20) by σ_{av}. The resulting energy component is

$$U_{\sigma(av)} = \frac{3(1 - 2v)}{2E}\sigma_{av}^2 \qquad (6\text{-}22)$$

or, using the definition of σ_{av},

$$U_{\sigma(av)} = \frac{1 - 2v}{6E}[\sigma_1^2 + \sigma_2^2 + \sigma_3^2 + 2(\sigma_1\sigma_2 + \sigma_2\sigma_3 + \sigma_1\sigma_3)] \qquad (6\text{-}23)$$

Distortion energy

The difference between the strain energy and the contribution due to uniform stress will be identified as the distortion energy. It is given by

$$U_d = U - U_{\sigma(av)} = \frac{1 + v}{3E}(\sigma_1^2 + \sigma_2^2 + \sigma_3^2 - \sigma_1\sigma_2 - \sigma_2\sigma_3 - \sigma_1\sigma_3) \qquad (6\text{-}24)$$

The *failure criterion based on distortion energy* is obtained by comparing distortion energy per unit volume at a point in a machine member with the distortion energy per unit volume at failure in the tension test. In the tensile test

$$\sigma_1 = \sigma_x = S_{yp} \qquad \sigma_2 = \sigma_3 = 0$$

Replacing the yield point by the working strength, we set $\sigma_1 = S_{yp}/N$ in equation (6-24) to obtain the distortion energy for simple tension. Equating the result to the right hand side of equation (6-24), we obtain the **distortion energy theory** for the three-dimensional case.

$$\left(\frac{S_{yp}}{N}\right)^2 = \sigma_1^2 + \sigma_2^2 + \sigma_3^2 - \sigma_1\sigma_2 - \sigma_2\sigma_3 - \sigma_1\sigma_3 \qquad (6\text{-}25)$$

or, in *two dimensions*, where $\sigma_3 = 0$,

$$\left(\frac{S_{yp}}{N}\right)^2 = \sigma_1^2 + \sigma_2^2 - \sigma_1\sigma_2 \qquad (6\text{-}26)$$

Combined bending and torsion or bending and transverse shear

As an example, consider the special case where

$$\sigma_z = \sigma_y = \tau_{xz} = \tau_{yz} = 0$$

The principal stresses are given by

$$\sigma_{1,2} = \frac{\sigma_x}{2} \pm \tau_{max} \tag{6-27}$$

where

$$\tau_{max} = [(\tfrac{1}{2}\sigma_x)^2 + \tau_{xy}^2]^{1/2} \tag{6-28}$$

Substituting in equation (6-26) we obtain

$$\frac{S_{yp}}{N} = (\sigma_x^2 + 3\tau_{xy}^2)^{1/2} \tag{6-29}$$

based on the distortion energy theory for this special case.

If we write the **maximum shear theory** in similar form for comparison, we obtain

$$\frac{S_{yp}}{N} = (\sigma_x^2 + 4\tau_{xy}^2)^{1/2} \tag{6-30}$$

The distortion energy theory has been shown to be quite accurate for predicting failure in steel specimens subject to tensile and shear loading. For cases of fatigue loading in torsion and bending, investigators found that the distortion energy theory predicted average failure values with precision, whereas the maximum shear theory predicted the approximate lower limit of failure values [3].

For the case of combined bending and torsion (equations 6-29 and 6-30), we see that the maximum shear theory is more conservative than the distortion energy theory. This is generally the case. The difference in results is not very great, however, and both theories are widely used in the design of machine elements.

SECTION 6-5

Fatigue Failure and the Soderberg Criterion

In most engineering materials, a stress that fluctuates between two given values, σ_{min} and σ_{max}, is more likely to cause failure than a steady stress equal to σ_{max}. Since fatigue tests are expensive and time consuming, most available data are based on reversed bending in a rotating member. For an element on the surface of a rotating shaft subject to bending loads, the stress-time history is given by Figure 6-10a. The test setup may be similar to the one illustrated in Chapter 3, using a polished test specimen. The stress

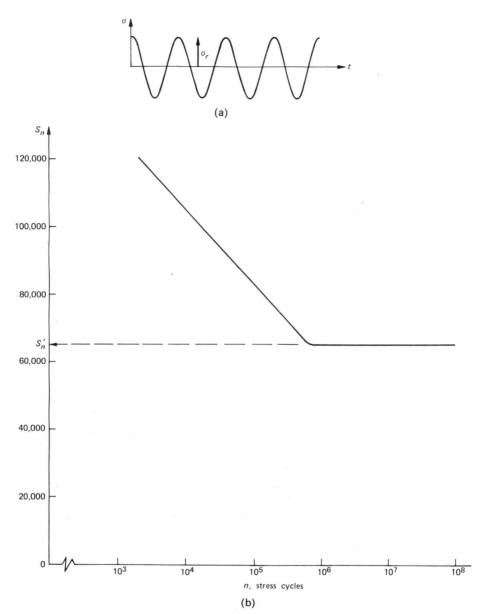

Figure 6-10 Fatigue. (a) Stress-time history for reversed bending. (b) Cycles to failure at various stresses for a typical high strength alloy steel.

amplitude at which the member fails after a given number of stress cycles (n cycles) is designated as S_n, the **fatigue strength of the test specimen.** As $n \to \infty$, S_n may approach a lower limit S_n', the **endurance limit of the test specimen.** Figure 6-10b shows results typical for a high strength alloy steel. More extensive data are given in Chapter 3. An endurance limit has been observed for most steels. The surface imperfections of a typical machine part affect the endurance limit and, in most cases, a value lower than S'_n applies. If we include the effects of surface finish, reliability, size and welding as given in Chapter 3, the modified value of **endurance limit** is given by

$$S_e = C_F C_R C_S C_W S'_n$$

In this chapter, the term *endurance limit* will refer to the modified value S_e as given above. For tensile stress range (amplitude) σ_r and safety factor N, a design for infinite life is described by

$$\sigma_r \leqslant \frac{S_e}{N} \tag{6-31}$$

if mean stress is zero.

An alternative fatigue testing device is shown in Figure 6-11. A flat cantilever beam specimen may be tested in reversed bending, or the vise

Figure 6-11 A flexural fatigue testing machine. [Courtesy Fatigue Dynamics Inc.]

holding the specimen may be adjusted so that stress varies about some nonzero mean value. Crank eccentricity may be changed to provide various ratios of maximum to minimum stress.

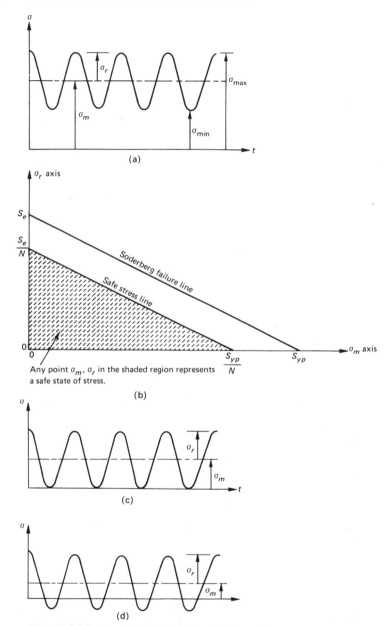

Any point σ_m, σ_r in the shaded region represents a safe state of stress.

Figure 6-12 The Soderberg criterion. (a) Stress-time history for fluctuating stress with nonzero mean stress. (b) The Soderberg plot. (c) Stress-time history for $\sigma_{min} = 0$. (d) Stress-time history for negative σ_{min}.

The Soderberg criterion

If tensile stress at a point is given by a range stress σ_r and a mean stress σ_m as shown in Figure 6-12a, then both of these stresses contribute to failure. The Soderberg failure line (Figure 6-12b) is an approximate representation of this effect. It is a line drawn between the yield point and the endurance limit on mean stress–range stress coordinates. It was observed that most failures of test specimens due to combinations of mean and range loading could be represented as points on or above this line. If we apply a safety factor N to the yield point and endurance limit, we obtain the **safe stress line,** a line parallel to the failure line. A plotted point σ_m, σ_r on or below the safe stress line represents safe loading. A combination of mean and range loading may be checked graphically in this manner. The Soderberg criterion may also be applied to design problems when minimum stress is zero (Figure 6-12c) and when minimum stress is negative (Figure 6-12d), but it is not generally applicable to cases where mean stress is negative. When stress varies randomly between limits σ_{min} and σ_{max}, we simply define

$$\sigma_m = \frac{\sigma_{max} + \sigma_{min}}{2}$$

$$\sigma_r = \frac{\sigma_{max} - \sigma_{min}}{2}$$

If we consider a point on a body where stress concentration is present, we multiply range stress by the stress concentration factor. Then, the state of stress is given by a point $\sigma_m, K_f \sigma_r$, which should fall on or below the safe stress line. When a ductile material is used, a stress concentration factor is not usually applied to mean stress.

Suppose we load a material up to its safe limit with a combination of mean and range stress. The state of stress could be represented by the point $\sigma_m, K_f \sigma_r$ on the safe stress line as in Figure 6-13. Noting that triangles AOB

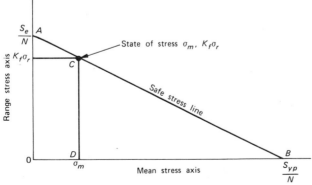

Figure 6-13 Soderberg representation of a material loaded to its safe limit of mean and range stress.

and *CDB* are similar, we obtain the relationship

$$\frac{(S_{yp}/N) - \sigma_m}{K_f \sigma_r} = \frac{S_{yp}}{S_e}$$

which may be rearranged in the form

$$\frac{S_{yp}}{N} = \sigma_m + K_f \sigma_r \frac{S_{yp}}{S_e} \tag{6-32}$$

The right hand side of equation (6-32) may be considered the static equivalent of the state of stress. Thus, we define **equivalent stress**

$$\sigma_{eq} = \sigma_m + K_f \sigma_r \frac{S_{yp}}{S_e} \tag{6-33}$$

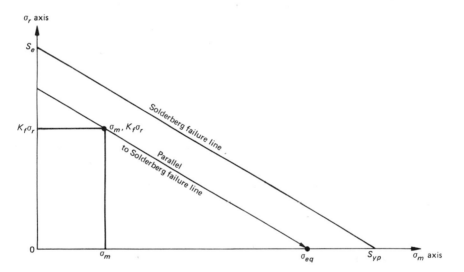

Figure 6-14 Equivalent stress.

Figure 6-14 is a graphic representation of equivalent stress. If we have tentatively dimensioned a part, the "actual" factor of safety at any point is given by

$$N = \frac{S_{yp}}{\sigma_{eq}} \tag{6-34}$$

If that value of N is less than the overall design factor of safety that we have selected, we must redesign the part.

In some problems, we are called upon to design a member to withstand a given ratio of range load to mean load. A straightforward solution may be obtained if the ratio of range stress to mean stress can be determined from some known stress-load relationship. In such cases, it is convenient to rearrange equation (6-32) into the form

$$\sigma_m = \frac{S_{yp}/N}{K_f \dfrac{\sigma_r}{\sigma_m} \dfrac{S_{yp}}{S_e} + 1} \qquad (6\text{-}35)$$

If there is no stress concentration in the part at the point in question, K_f is, of course, replaced by unity. Once mean stress σ_m is found, the stress-load relationship is used to obtain the required part dimension.

Example 6-3: The Soderberg Criterion Applied to Design of a Pressure Vessel.
A thin-wall cylindrical pressure vessel is subject to an internal pressure p, which varies from 100 to 500 psi continuously. Mean radius $R = 30$ in. Find the required thickness t of the cylindrical wall, based on a yield point of 70,000 psi, an endurance limit of 30,000 psi, and a safety factor of 2.

Solution: We will define **mean pressure,** $p_m = (p_{max} + p_{min})/2 = 300$ psi and **range pressure,** $p_r = (p_{max} - p_{min})/2 = 200$ psi. The Soderberg failure line and the safe stress line are shown in Figure 6-15. Tangential, axial, and radial stress,

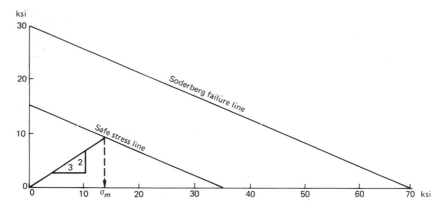

Figure 6-15 The Soderberg criterion applied to design of a pressure vessel.

are respectively, $\sigma_x = pR/t$; $\sigma_y = pR/(2t)$; and $\sigma_z = 0$ (approximately). The Soderberg plot will be based on maximum normal stress, $\sigma_1 = \sigma_x$ with mean value σ_m and range amplitude σ_r. Since σ_x is proportional to p, we know that the ratio σ_r/σ_m is equal to the ratio of range pressure to mean pressure, $p_r/p_m = 2/3$. In this problem, there is no stress concentration, that is, we set $K_f = 1$.

We sketch the locus of points representing σ_m, σ_r for any thickness t. The locus is a line through the origin with a slope of $2/3$. Its intersection with the safe stress line gives the state of stress σ_m, σ_r for the minimum safe value of thickness t. The corresponding value of mean stress is

$$\sigma_m = 13{,}700 \text{ psi}$$

as given by the construction on Figure 6-15 or as given by equation (6-35). Using $\sigma_m = p_m R/t$, we obtain the minimum safe thickness for the pressure vessel: $t = 0.657$ in.

When there is a change in section, a hole, or other cause of stress concentration in a part, the fatigue stress concentration factor K_f is used in the analysis. As noted above, for ductile materials it is usual to apply the stress concentration factor when determining the range stress but not to apply the stress concentration factor to the mean stress. If stress concentration was present in this problem, we would use a line of slope $K_f \sigma_r / \sigma_m$ through the origin to intercept the safe stress line. Otherwise the procedure would be the same. ●

The Soderberg criterion is particularly applicable to ductile steel. However, it may be used safely with almost any material for which an endurance limit and a yield point are known. For a finite life (a given number of cycles) the corresponding fatigue strength may be substituted for the endurance limit. If there is no apparent yield point for a given material, the yield strength based on the offset method may be substituted. If neither of the above are available, the ultimate strength may be used in place of the yield point. If the ultimate strength is used, it would be prudent to increase the factor of safety.

If we have nonzero principal stresses in two or more directions the maximum shear theory or the distortion energy theory might also be considered. In the above example, the maximum shear theory gives identical results. In a one-dimensional stress field, a negative (compressive) mean stress is generally considered less damaging than a positive mean stress. A reasonable design procedure would be as follows:

1. Insure that the magnitude of the maximum compressive stress does not exceed the ultimate compressive strength or the yield point in compression divided by the safety factor

$$|\sigma_c|_{max} \leqslant S_{u(c)}/N \text{ or } S_{yp(c)}/N$$

2. Insure that the range stress amplitude does not exceed the endurance limit divided by the safety factor

$$\sigma_r \leqslant S_e/N.$$

The maximum shear theory applied to fatigue loading

In equation (6-6) τ_{max} refers to the maximum shear stress for all planes in an element. Time dependence was not considered. For repeated torsional loading, we may compute the mean value of τ_{max} and label it τ_m and then the range amplitude of τ_{max} and label it τ_r. The Soderberg criterion may be applied as it was with tensile loading except that the safe stress line lies between the working strengths in shear: $S_{yp}/2N$ and $S_e/2N$.

Applying a stress concentration factor for torsion K_{ft}, a plotted point τ_m, $K_{ft}\tau_r$ that falls on or below the safe stress line indicates a satisfactory design. An analytical solution may be obtained in a manner similar to that used for tensile loading.

For combined stress, we treat the fatigue effect first, and then use the maximum shear criterion. Using equation (6-32) as a model, we simply multiply the varying components of stress by the factor (S_{yp}/S_e) to account for fatigue effects. For the special case in which

$$\sigma_y = \sigma_z = \tau_{yz} = \tau_{xz} = 0$$

we have, from equation (6-16)

$$\frac{S_{yp}}{N} = \left[\left(\sigma_{xm} + K_f \frac{S_{yp}}{S_e}\sigma_{xr}\right)^2 + 4\left(\tau_{xym} + K_f \frac{S_{yp}}{S_e}\tau_{xyr}\right)^2\right]^{1/2} \tag{6-36}$$

When equation (6-36) is applied to shaft design, we may simplify it further. For a point on the surface of a rotating shaft, a constant bending moment M causes tensile stress σ_x which is completely reversed with each rotation. The effect of a steady torque T is a shear stress on the surface that does not vary in time. Thus, for a *rotating shaft* transmitting power at a steady rate, we may write

$$\frac{S_{yp}}{N} = \left[\left(K_f \frac{S_{yp}}{S_e}\sigma_x\right)^2 + 4\tau_{xy}^2\right]^{1/2} \tag{6-37}$$

Tensile stress amplitude

$$\sigma_x = K_s\frac{Mc}{I}$$

and shear stress

$$\tau_{xy} = K_s\frac{Tr}{J}$$

on the shaft surface where K_s is a shock factor based on the nature of the applied load and K_f represents the stress concentration factor. There may be one pair of values for moment and another for torsion. For a solid circular shaft of diameter D, we have

$$c = r = \frac{D}{2}$$

$$I = \frac{\pi D^4}{64} \quad \text{and} \quad J = \frac{\pi D^4}{32}$$

Substituting in equation (6-37), we obtain a shaft design equation based on the maximum shear theory

$$\frac{S_{yp}}{N} = \frac{32}{\pi D^3}\left[\left(\frac{S_{yp}}{S_e}M^*\right)^2 + T^{*2}\right]^{1/2} \tag{6-38}$$

where $M^* = K_s K_f M$ and $T^* = K_s K_f T$.

In the case of a shaft with varying diameters or other causes of stress concentration, the worst combination of moment and torque may not be obvious. It might be necessary to use equation (6-38) at several locations. For a ductile material subject to steady load the stress concentration factor for torsion may be taken as unity because it applies to the steady stress component. The stress concentration factor for moment on a rotating member must be applied at any change of diameter or other stress concentration location. Shock factors and other design details for steady and varying torque are treated in a later chapter.

Fatigue analysis should be considered whenever fluctuating load is present. Springs, for example, frequently fail in fatigue. Section 2 of Chapter 14 treats construction of the Soderberg diagram for spring design.

Distortion energy theory applied to fatigue loading

The effect of a time-varying load may be approximated by defining equivalent values for each principal stress. Representing the component of σ_1 due to steady loading by σ_{1m} and the component due to reversed load by σ_{1r}, we obtain

$$\sigma_{1\,eq} = \sigma_{1m} + K_f \sigma_{1r} \frac{S_{yp}}{S_e} \qquad (6\text{-}39)$$

The other principal stresses are also treated in this way. When stress concentration exists in the presence of alternating bending and alternating torsional loads, the appropriate stress concentration factors should be applied directly to the range components of moment and torque. Using the equivalent values of the principal stresses in equation (6-25), we obtain an expression for the distortion energy theory for fatigue loading

$$\frac{S_{yp}}{N} = \sqrt{(\sigma_1^2 + \sigma_2^2 + \sigma_3^2 - \sigma_1\sigma_2 - \sigma_2\sigma_3 - \sigma_1\sigma_3)_{eq}} \qquad (6\text{-}40)$$

The two-dimensional equivalent (where $\sigma_3 = 0$) is given by

$$\frac{S_{yp}}{N} = \sqrt{(\sigma_1^2 + \sigma_2^2 - \sigma_1\sigma_2)_{eq}} \qquad (6\text{-}41)$$

For the special case where $\sigma_y = \sigma_z = \tau_{xz} = \tau_{yz} = 0$, we have from equation (6-29),

$$\frac{S_{yp}}{N} = \sqrt{(\sigma_x^2 + 3\tau_{xy}^2)_{eq}} \qquad (6\text{-}42)$$

or

$$\frac{S_{yp}}{N} = [(\sigma_{xm} + K_f\sigma_{xr}S_{yp}/S_e)^2 + 3(\tau_{xym} + K_f\tau_{xyr}S_{yp}/S_{e2})]^{1/2} \qquad (6\text{-}43)$$

For the special case of a rotating shaft with constant moment and torque, the distortion energy theory yields

$$\frac{S_{yp}}{N} = \frac{32}{\pi D^3}\left[\left(\frac{S_{yp}}{S_e}M^*\right)^2 + \frac{3}{4}T^{*2}\right]^{1/2} \qquad (6\text{-}44)$$

where the terms are defined in conjunction with equation (6-38). For identical combined moment and torque loading, design by the distortion energy theory would result in a slightly smaller shaft diameter than design by the maximum shear theory.

Modified Goodman criterion for fatigue failure

The modified Goodman criterion resembles the Soderberg except that the former is slightly less conservative. A line is drawn from the endurance limit S_e on the range stress axis to the ultimate strength S_u on the mean stress axis (Figure 6-16). Another line is drawn from the yield point S_{yp} on the mean stress axis, sloping upward and to the left at 45 deg. This pair of line segments

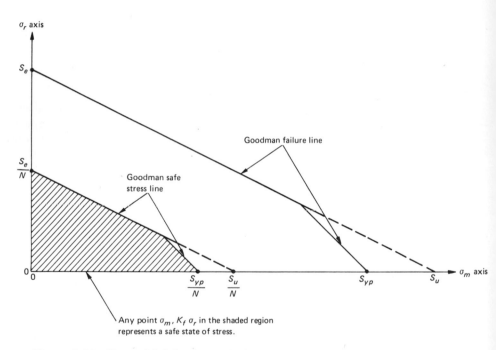

Figure 6-16 The modified Goodman criterion.

form the Goodman failure line as shown in the figure. Note that the 45 deg line segment implies failure when maximum stress exceeds the yield point. The Goodman safe stress line is constructed similarly, using the factor of safety N. As with the Soderberg criterion, a point σ_m, $K_f\sigma_r$ failing on or below the safe stress line constitutes an acceptable state of stress. For simplicity, the Soderberg criterion will be used in preference to the modified Goodman criterion for most problems in this text.

SECTION 6-6

Cumulative Damage

Extensive fatigue data are not generally available for most materials. Usually, the best and safest recourse is to base design stresses on the Soderberg criterion, using the (modified) **endurance limit** S_e. If we have a plot of S_n versus n for a given material (for example, Figure 6-17) we may allow higher

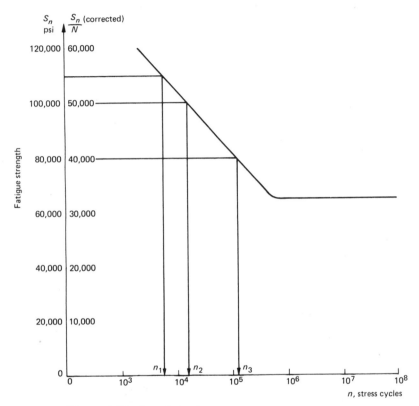

Figure 6-17 Cumulative damage.

stresses for a finite number of cycles. In that case, S_n replaces S_n' in equation (3-32) and design may be based on one of the equations in Section 5 of this chapter.

If a machine part is to operate for a finite time at stress levels exceeding the endurance limit, then we must examine the cumulative damage. **Miner's rule** is the simplest and probably the best criterion for general use. It is applied as follows. Suppose the part is subject to n_{r1} reversed stress cycles at a range stress level S_{n1}; n_{r2} reversed stress cycles at a range stress level S_{n2}, and so on. Now, suppose we select a material described by Figure 6-17. Referring to that figure, let the number of cycles to failure at stress level S_{n1} be n_1 cycles; let the number of cycles to failure at stress level S_{n2} be n_2 cycles, and so on. Then, by Miner's rule,

$$\frac{n_{r1}}{n_1} + \frac{n_{r2}}{n_2} + \cdots \geqslant 1 \tag{6-45}$$

constitutes *failure*.

Of course, an actual machine part is unlikely to correspond exactly to the fatigue test specimen. Thus, we may apply the appropriate correction factors described in Chapter 3 to obtain the corrected fatigue strength of the part, $S_{n(corrected)}$. Furthermore, we may wish to use a factor of safety N. Then, values n_1, n_2, and so on, may be obtained from a plot of $S_{n(corrected)}/N$ versus n. Using these values, inequality (6-45) becomes the criterion for *safe design*.

Example 6-4. Suppose we select a material corresponding to the S_n versus n plot in Figure 6-17. Furthermore, suppose the actual part size and surface finish and the required reliability are determined and that a safety factor is selected. Using equation (3-32) and the safety factor N, we may simply rescale the ordinate as in Figure 6-17. For purposes of illustration, it is assumed that the total effect of all these factors results in values of $S_{n(corrected)}/N$ which are half the S_n values. Let the load on the part produce reversed stresses of 55,000 psi for $n_{r1} = 2000$ cycles; 50,000 psi for $n_{r2} = 5000$ cycles and 40,000 psi for $n_{r3} = 40,000$ cycles.

Solution: The limiting number of cycles corresponding, respectively, to the above stress values are $n_1 = 6000$, $n_2 = 16,700$, and $n_3 = 130,000$ cycles. Using inequality (6-45) the result is

$$\frac{n_{r1}}{n_1} + \frac{n_{r2}}{n_2} + \frac{n_{r3}}{n_3} = 0.940$$

and the part is safe. ●

PROBLEMS

1. (a) Using Problem Figure 26 of Chapter 5, find the principal stresses and the maximum shear stress at point B on the 1" dia. bar. Show a Mohr circle representation. (b) Repeat for point C.

2. Repeat Problem 1 with dimension $AB = 8$ in. and dimension $BC = 4$ in.

3. Find the allowable load for the cast iron machine element in the Example 6-1 if ASTM class 20 cast iron is used.

4. (a) Find the maximum shear stress at point A of the I section in Problem Figure 1 of Chapter 5. (b) Find the overall factor of safety based on a yield point of 45,000 psi.

5. Repeat Problem 4 for the case where only the 1500-lb load 5 in. from the left support is applied.

6. (a) Find bending and transverse shear stress at points A and B in Problem Figure 6. (b) Find maximum normal stress and maximum shear stress at both points. (c) For a yield point of 50,000 psi, find the factor of safety based on the maximum normal stress theory and the maximum shear theory.

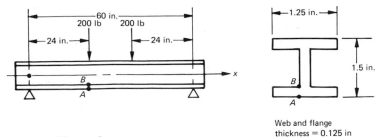

Problem Figure 6

7. Based on a factor of safety of 2, find minimum web thickness and minimum flange thickness for the member in Problem Figure 6.

8. The I section in Example 6-2 was designed on the basis of approximations of moment of inertia and shear stress. (a) Using these results, obtain more accurate values of moment of inertia and shear stress. (b) Find the factor of safety based on failure at *A*. (c) Find the factor of safety based on failure at *B*. Use the maximum shear theory. Draw a Mohr circle representation of stress at *B*. (d) Is there a difference in results if the maximum normal stress theory is used?

9. A machine part utilizes a symmetric I section as shown in Problem Figure 9. Find maximum normal stress and maximum shear stress at points *B* and *C* at section *A-A* in terms of load *F*. Predict failure location based on the maximum normal stress theory and the maximum shear theory.

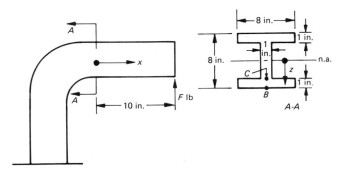

Problem Figure 9

10. A 13-in. long rod is to be subjected to a constant tensile load of 8000 lb and a constant torque of 700 lb-in. The rod is to be made of steel with a yield point of 100,000 psi. Design this rod, using the distortion energy theory and a safety factor of 1.5.

11. Design a nylon rod for the same application as the steel rod in Problem 10.

12. A thin wall cylindrical pressure vessel has an internal pressure $p = 500$ psi and diameter 24 in. Find the required thickness for a material yield point of 60,000 psi and a safety factor of 3. (a) Base design on maximum normal stress. (b) Base design on maximum shear stress.

13. Repeat part (a) of Problem 12 if internal pressure varies from 0 to 500 psi and the material has a corrected endurance limit of 33,000 psi. Use the Soderberg criterion.

14. Repeat Problem 12 using the distortion energy theory if internal pressure varies from 0 to 500 psi and the material has a corrected endurance limit of 33,000 psi.

15. A thin cylindrical pressure vessel of diameter D and thickness t is subject to internal pressure p. **(a)** Find $\sigma_1, \sigma_2, \sigma_3, \tau_{max}$ in terms of p, D, and t. **(b)** Draw *and label* Mohr circles. **(c)** For 20,000 psi allowable shear stress, internal pressure 100 psi, and 25-in. diameter, find the required value of thickness.

16. Based on a safety factor of 2, an endurance limit of 20,000 psi, a yield point of 50,000, find the required diameter of a rotating shaft. Shaft length 10 in. between single row ball bearings. The shaft has a vertical load of 1000 lb at the center and zero torque.

17. A small leaf spring 0.25 in. wide by 3 in. long by t in. thick is subject to a load that varies continuously from 0 to 3 lb (at the center). The leaf spring is supported at the ends. $S_{yp} = 150,000$ psi and $S_e = 70,000$ corrected for size, surface, and so on. **(a)** Draw the Soderberg safe stress line for a safety factor of 2.5. **(b)** Plot state of stress line with slope σ_r/σ_m and find safe limit of σ_m. **(c)** Find required thickness t.

18. Repeat Problem 17 for a load that varies from 3 to 6 lb.

19. Force F varies from 0 to F_{max} continuously 50 times per minute on the part in Problem Figure 19. Assume failure would occur due to bending stress at the fillet. $S_{yp} = 100,000$ and $S_e = 40,000$ psi corrected for size, surface, and so on. **(a)** Show the Soderberg safe stress line using a safety factor of 3. **(b)** Plot state of stress line with slope $K_f\sigma_r/\sigma_m$. Find the safe limit of σ_m. **(c)** Find F_{mean}. **(d)** Find F_{max} (greatest allowable value).

(*Note*: Apply stress concentration factor to alternating stress only.)

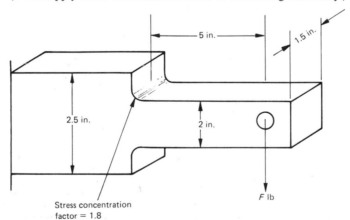

Problem Figure 19

20. Repeat Problem 19 for a load that varies from $\frac{1}{2}F_{max}$ upward to F_{max} downward.

21. Apply the distortion energy theory to the pressure vessel described in Example 6-3.

22. The rotating stepped shaft in Problem Figure 22 is mounted between single-row ball bearings and loaded by two 10-in. pitch diameter pulleys. Use a yield point $S_{yp} = 85,000$ psi, an endurance limit $S_e = 50,000$ psi, and a safety factor of $N = 2$. Use a shock factor $K_s = 1.5$ applied to torque and moment. Apply a stress concentration factor of $K_{fM} = 1.3$ at the step. Find the minimum safe values for diameters D_1 and D_2, using the maximum shear theory.

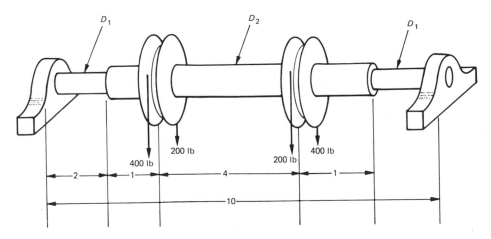

Problem Figure 22

23. Repeat Problem 22 using the distortion energy theory.

24. A solid steel conveyor belt shaft is subject to a maximum moment of 20,000 in.-lb and negligible torque. Find the required shaft diameter based on an endurance limit of 40,000 psi (corrected) and a safety factor of 4. Ignore stress concentration.

25. Design a hollow shaft for the same application as Problem 24. Let the inside diameter be 75% of the outside diameter.

26. A 30-in. diameter cylindrical pressure vessel has a 0.1-in. wall thickness. It is made of steel with a corrected endurance limit of 36,000 psi and a yield point of 90,000 psi. A safety factor of 1.5 is to be used. Pressure fluctuates through a 160-psi range. **(a)** Is a mean pressure of 267 psi safe? **(b)** Find the maximum safe mean pressure.

27. A thin wall cylindrical pressure vessel is subject to an internal pressure p, which varies from 100 to 500 psi continuously. Mean radius is 30 in. Design for a yield point of 70,000 psi and an endurance limit of 30,000 psi, with a safety factor of 3. Base results on the maximum normal stress theory.

28. Find the required thickness of the pressure vessel in Problem 27 based on the distortion energy theory.

29. A solid circular bar is subject to a reversed bending moment of 1200 in.-lb for 2000 cycles; 1000 in.-lb for 100,000 cycles and 900 in.-lb for 10,000 cycles. Find the required bar diameter based on the corrected properties $(S_{n(\text{corrected})}/N)$ given in Figure 6-17.

REFERENCES

[1] R. A. Douglas: *Introduction to Solid Mechanics.* Wadsworth Publishing Co., Belmont, Calif., 1963.

[2] A. P. Boresi: *Elasticity in Engineering Mechanics.* Prentice-Hall, Inc., Englewood Cliffs, N.J., 1965.

[3] O. J. Horger (Ed.): *ASME Handbook of Metals Engineering Design,* 2nd ed. McGraw-Hill, New York, 1965.

[4] G. Sines: *Elasticity and Strength*. Allyn and Bacon, Inc., Boston, 1969.

[5] P. C. Chou and N. J. Pagano: *Elasticity*. D. Van Nostrand Co., New York, 1967.

[6] J. O. Almen and P. H. Black: *Residual Stresses and Fatigue in Metals*. McGraw-Hill Book Co., New York, 1963.

[7] P. G. Forrest, *Fatigue of Metals*. Pergamon Press, Elmsford, N.Y., 1962.

Shafts, Keys and Couplings

SYMBOLS

A = shear area of shaft key, in.

D = diameter of solid shaft, in.

D_i = internal diameter of a hollow shaft, in.

D_i = inside flange diameter, in.

D_o = outside diameter of a hollow shaft, in.

D_o = outside flange diameter, in.

E = elastic modulus in tension, psi

F = load on a shaft key, lb

F = load on a gear, worm, or pulley, lb

F = reaction at bearing supports, lb

F_0 = bolt tension, lb

h = depth of spline tooth, in.

hp = horsepower

I = area moment of inertia, in.^{4}

J = area polar moment of inertia, in.^{4}

K_f = fatigue stress concentration factor due to bending, tension, or compression

K_{fs} = fatigue stress concentration factor due to torsion or shear

K_{sb} = shock factor for bending, tension, or compression

K_{st} = shock factor for torsion

L = length of shaft key, in.

L = length of spline tooth in contact, in.

L_e = effective spline length, in.

M = bending moment, lb-in.

M_m = mean applied bending moment, lb-in.

M_r = range of applied bending moment, lb-in.

N = factor of safety

N = normal load on a key, lb

n_t = number of spline teeth

n = number of bolts

n = number of splines

n_c = critical shaft speed, rpm

P = diametral pitch, in.

r = shaft radius, in.

r_m = mean spline radius, in.

rpm = revolutions per minute

S_c = compressive strength, psi

S_e = corrected endurance limit, psi

S_{es} = corrected endurance limit for shear, psi

S_{syp} = yield strength in shear, psi

S_{yp} = yield strength in tension, psi

T = torque, lb-in.

T_m = mean applied torque, lb-in.

T_r = range of applied torque, lb-in.

V = shear load, lb

w = load per unit length, lb per in. or ft

W = width of shaft key, in.

W_m = weight of the mth rotating mass, lb

x = distance measured in the x direction, in.

y = deflection, in.

y_m = static shaft deflection due to the mth mass, in.

δ = resultant deflection, in.

θ = slope, deg

θ = torsional deflection, deg

μ = coefficient of friction

σ_m = mean bending stress, psi

σ_r = range of stress due to bending, psi

σ_x = bending stress, psi

τ = shearing stress, psi

τ_{max} = maximum shearing stress, psi

τ_{ms} = mean shearing or torsional stress, psi

τ_{rs} = range of stress due to torsion, psi

ω = angular velocity, rad/sec

This chapter deals with the design of shafts, the use of keys to connect other machine elements (for example, gears, pulleys, and so on) to shafts, and the use of various couplings in connecting shafts.

Shafts are used in a variety of ways in all kinds of mechanical equipment. Typical uses are power shafts, cam shafts, line shafts, and so on. As a result of industrial application, particular definitions are associated with shafts used for a definite purpose. These definitions are as follows:

Shaft. A rotating member used for the purpose of transmitting power.

Axle. A stationary member used as a support for rotating elements such as wheels, idler gears, and so on.

Spindle. A short shaft or axle (for example, head-stock spindle of a lathe).

Stub Shaft. (Also called head shaft.) A shaft that is integral with an engine, motor, or prime mover, and is of such size, shape, and projection as to permit its easy connection to other shafts.

Line Shaft. (Also called power transmission shaft.) A shaft that is directly connected to a prime mover and is essentially used to transmit power to a machine(s).

Jackshaft. (Also called countershaft.) A short shaft that connects a prime mover with a line shaft or a machine.

Flexible Shaft. Permits the transmission of motion between two points (for example, motor and machine) where the rotational axes are at an angle with each other. The amount of power transmitted is of relatively low level.

Depending on the loading, shafts are subjected to constant bending and/or torsional stress or a combination of these stresses caused by fluctuating loads. To design a shaft subjected to a fixed loading, the reader should also refer to the analytical methods discussed in Chapter 5, namely, Section 5-7 (for torsion of round sections), Section 5-5 (for simply supported beams with different loading), and so on.

In this chapter, we will consider a shaft as a machine element subjected to fluctuating loads. The associated considerations of stress concentration and endurance, therefore, will play a significant role in its design. A shaft designed from the viewpoint of these considerations will possess adequate strength. However, of equal importance (sometimes of greater importance) is the consideration of shaft rigidity or stiffness. A shaft having too large a lateral deflection can cause excessive bearing wear or failure. A large lateral deflection is also responsible for lowering the critical speed, which may cause the shaft to vibrate violently if its revolutions per minute are at or near this speed.

Keyways are a source of stress raisers as are other geometrical discontinuities, and care must be exercised in their selection and location in order to minimize the resulting stress concentration.

Two shafts can be connected by shaft couplings of which there are many varieties. The angle between two shafts, transmitted power, torsional and lateral vibrations, shock loads, and so on, are all parameters that must be considered in selecting a coupling to connect the shafts.

SECTION 7-1

Shaft Materials

Generally, shafting of $3-3\frac{1}{2}$ in. diameter is made of cold-drawn, carbon steel round bars. Where toughness, shock resistance, and greater strength are needed, alloy steel bars (for example, 1347, 3140, 4150, 4340, 5145, 8650) are commercially available. These bars can be heat treated to produce the desired properties. Where surface wear resistance is the dominant factor, a carburizing grade steel (for example, 1020, 1117, 2315, 4320, 4820, 8620, and so on) can be used. However, to avoid increased cost, the designer should try to use a plain carbon steel if it is at all possible. Other case hardening methods such as nitriding, cyaniding, flame and induction hardening can also be used as a means of producing a wear resistant surface.

Cold-drawn steel bars exhibit higher physical properties than hot-rolled bars of similar steel. They have greater yield values and greater ultimate and endurance strengths. However, the higher endurance values are somewhat offset by the residual surface tensile stresses caused by the cold drawing. Since fatigue (or endurance) failures of shafts are tensile failures (torsional failure is also possible), these residual surface stresses can contribute to higher fatigue stresses. Also, cutting keyways, slots, and so on, relieves the surface stress of the machined areas, causing the shaft to warp. The required straightening adds to the cost, but can be beneficial if hammer peening is used to straighten the shaft. As the reader may recall, peening and similar processes produce a compressive surface stress that counteracts the effect of fatigue stress. Where warping is a serious consideration, and cannot be easily rectified by straightening, an oil-hardening alloy steel (for example 3140, 8640, and others) can be considered. Where closer tolerances on the diameter are needed, warehouses can supply turned, ground, and polished rounds or cold-drawn, ground, and polished rounds.

Shafts larger than $3\frac{1}{2}$ in. diameter are machined from hot-rolled carbon steel. The machining must be deep enough to remove all of the decarburized scale caused by hot rolling. Large diameter shafts, such as railroad axles, press cranks, and so on (for example, a steel of 0.45% carbon) are usually forged and then machined to the required size. Shafts of steel or nodular iron are also made by casting (for example, automotive engine crankshafts).

SECTION 7-2

Bending Moments and Torque Acting on a Shaft

Gears, pulleys, flywheels, friction wheels, cams, and ratchets are mounted on shafting in various combinations and locations. It is obvious from the science of mechanics that, to determine the diameter of the shaft, it is necessary to know the bending moment and torque distribution along the full length of the shaft. With this information the designer can specify the required diameters for different parts of the shaft.

The diameter of the shaft, or the diameter of each section, will depend upon the combined stresses due to the bending moment and torsion. Depending upon the particular problem, the exact location along a shaft where the maximum stress will occur is sometimes obvious. Lacking such obvious information, it is helpful to draw the shear and moment diagrams to locate the points along the shaft where the moments are maximum. The following example is an illustration of the above ideas.

Example 7-1. A 24-in. diameter pulley weighing 100 lb receives 30 hp at 360 rpm from a shaft located at 45 deg below the pulley. An 18-in. pitch diameter gear C weighing 50 lb delivers 40% of the power horizontally to the right. Finally, a 12-in. pitch diameter gear E weighing 25 lb delivers the remaining power to another gear downward to the left at an angle of 30 deg below the horizontal. Both gears have 20 deg pressure angles. The system is to be used in a chemical plant and corrosion can have a long term affect.

Determine the torques transmitted by the pulley and gears and the resultant moment distribution.

Solution: Referring to Figure 7-1, the transmitted torques are computed as follows:

Torque acting on the shaft between B and C

$$T_B = \frac{63{,}000 \text{ hp}}{\text{rpm}} = \frac{63{,}000(30)}{360} = 5250 \text{ lb-in.}$$

The horsepower delivered by gear C is 40% of the 30 hp. Thus, the torque delivered by gear C is

$$T_C = \frac{63{,}000(12)}{360} = 2100 \text{ lb-in.}$$

The remaining 18 hp is delivered by gear E. Thus, the torque between gears C and E is

$$T_E = \frac{63{,}000(18)}{360} = 3150 \text{ lb-in.}$$

The torque on the pulley is

$$(F_1 - F_2)\frac{D_B}{2} = 5250 \text{ lb-in.}$$

or

$$F_1 - F_2 = \frac{5250}{12} = 437.5 \text{ lb.}$$

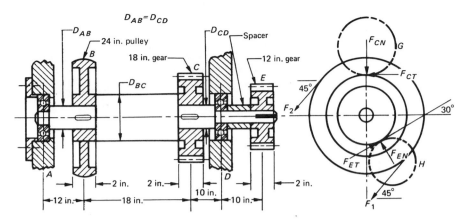

Figure 7-1 Gear C is in mesh with gear G and gear E is in mesh with gear H. The right side view shows the reactive forces of G on C and H on E, respectively.

For a properly mounted flat belt not subject to large overloads and having an appropriate initial tension, we may assume a belt tension ratio[1]

$$F_1/F_2 = 3$$

From the above two equations, we determine that

$$F_1 = 656.25 \text{ lb}$$

$$F_2 = 218.75 \text{ lb}$$

Thus, the total force causing bending at the pulley B is

$$F_B = F_1 + F_2 = 656.25 + 218.75 = 875 \text{ lb}$$

The tangential reactive forces acting on the gears C and E are computed as follows (r_C, r_E are the pitch radii of gears C and E, respectively)

$$F_{CT} = \frac{T_C}{r_C} = \frac{2100}{9} = 233.33 \text{ lb}; \qquad F_{ET} = \frac{T_E}{r_E} = \frac{3150}{6} = 525.00 \text{ lb}$$

The normal force tending to separate the gear teeth in contact is equal to the product of the turning force F times the tangent of the tooth pressure angle (see Chapter 10). Thus, the normal forces tending to separate gears C and G and gears E and H are

$$F_{CN} = F_{CT} \tan 20° = (233.33)(0.364) = 84.93 \text{ lb}$$

$$F_{EN} = (525)(0.364) = 191.10 \text{ lb}$$

The forces acting on the system in Figure 7-1 are shown for clarity on Figure 7-2.
Using Figure 7-2, we take moments about the bearing A in the horizontal plane.

$$(F_B \sin 45°)12 + F_{CT}(30) + D_H(40) + F_{EN} \sin 30°(50) - F_{ET} \sin 60°(50) = 0$$

[1] Actually this ratio depends upon the active arc of belt contact, the coefficient of friction between the belt and pulley, the density of the belt material, and the surface speed of the pulley (see Chapter 12).

Thus

$$D_H = 88.29 \, \text{lb}$$

Since D_H is positive, our choice of its direction as shown in Figure 7-2 is correct. Now we sum the forces in the horizontal plane.

$$A_H - F_B \sin 45° - F_{CT} - D_H - F_{EN} \sin 30° + F_{ET} \sin 60° = 0$$

Thus

$$A_H = 581.15 \, \text{lb}$$

Proceeding in the same manner, we take moments about bearing A in the vertical plane.

$$(F_B \cos 45°)12 + 100(12) + F_{CN}(30) + 50(30) + D_V(40) - (F_{EN} \cos 30°)50$$

$$-(F_{ET} \cos 60°)50 + 25(50) = 0$$

Thus

$$D_V = 186.95 \, \text{lb}$$

Since D_V is positive, our choice of its direction as shown in Figure 7-2 is correct.

Summing the forces acting in the vertical plane.

$$A_V - F_B \cos 45° - 100 - F_{CN} - 50 - D_V + F_{EN} \cos 30° + F_{ET} \cos 60°$$

$$- 25 = 0$$

Thus,

$$A_V = 637.52 \, \text{lb} \quad \bullet$$

We can now proceed to draw (or sketch) the shear and bending moment diagrams for the horizontal plane and for the vertical plane (Figure 7-3).

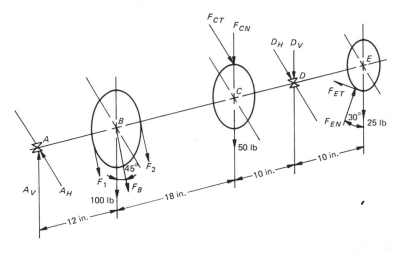

Figure 7-2 Schematic of force system for Example 7-1. The directions of the forces at bearings A and D are arbitrary.

Recall from your mechanics course, if you will, that a maximum bending moment occurs at that point along the shaft length where the shear diagram crosses the zero axis.[2] This statement is verified by inspection of Figure 7-3 from which we can indeed see that the maximum bending moment does occur at the point of zero shear in both the horizontal and vertical planes. For the case shown in Figure 7-3 (that is, for Example 7-1), the maximum moment in both planes is found at the pulley support point *B*. However, the reader should note that this need not always be the case. Thus, the maximum bending moment in both the horizontal and vertical planes need not (and in most cases will not) be found at the same point along the length of the shaft.

Another possibility is the case where the shear diagram crosses the zero shear line at more than one point. This would then indicate that there are one or more "maximum" bending moments, namely, one at each point of zero shear. In such cases, the designer may have to establish the resultant bending moment for the horizontal and vertical planes at each maximum. If the

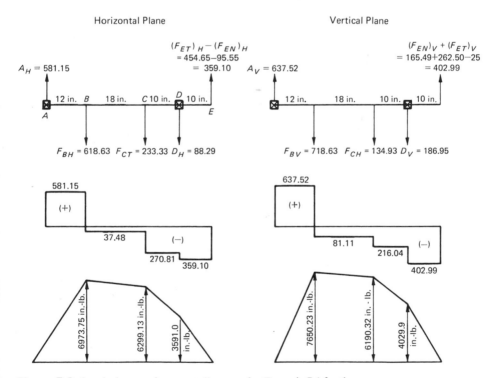

Figure 7-3 Load, shear, and moment diagrams for Example 7-1 for the horizontal and vertical planes.

[2] This conclusion could be invalidated by a couple or moment acting in the longitudinal plane of the shaft. In such cases, the maximum may be at a point other than that where the shear diagram is zero.

shaft is one of constant diameter, it will then be designed for the "maximum," maximum resultant bending moment and the value of the torque at that shaft location. If the torque at *that point* on the shaft is not a maximum, the shaft diameter must also be checked at the point of maximum torque while also accounting for the resultant bending moment at such a point.

If a stepped shaft is being considered (for example, Example 7-1), then the resultant bending moment and torque that will determine each diameter must be considered.

In the preceding discussion, the shaft diameter(s) and corresponding stresses are determined by the combined stress equations.

For Example 7-1, the maximum bending moment in each plane occurs at the pulley (that is, B). The bending moment at B is then the vector sum of the moment in each plane. Thus

$$M_B = [(6973.75)^2 + (7650.23)^2]^{1/2} = 10,351.77 \text{ lb-in.}$$

and we also note again that the maximum torque is also at B,

$$T_B = 5250 \text{ lb-in.}$$

SECTION 7-3

Shaft Design Subjected to Fluctuating Loads Based on the Maximum Shear Theory of Failure

In Chapter 6 we established that the maximum shearing stress of a solid round bar subjected to steady combined static bending and torsion (equation 6-14, if $\sigma_y = 0$) is

$$\tau_{max} = \sqrt{\left(\frac{\sigma_x}{2}\right)^2 + \tau^2}$$

where

$$\sigma_x = \frac{32M}{\pi D^3} \quad \text{and} \quad \tau = \frac{16T}{\pi D^3} \tag{7-1}$$

For a hollow shaft

$$\sigma_x = \frac{32M}{\pi D_o^3[1 - (D_i/D_o)^4]} \quad \text{and} \quad \tau = \frac{16T}{\pi D_o^3[1 - (D_i/D_o)^4]} \tag{7-2}$$

Thus, using the maximum shear failure theory and replacing σ_x and τ, the values from equations (7-1), we get

$$\tau_{max} = \frac{0.5S_{yp}}{N} = \frac{16}{\pi D_o^3[1 - (D_i/D_o)^4]}\sqrt{M^2 + T^2} \tag{7-3}$$

where

τ_{max} = maximum shearing stress, psi (from Mohr's circle)
S_{yp} = tensile yield of material, psi
N = factor of safety
D_o = outer diameter of shaft, in.
D_i = inner diameter of shaft, in.
M = applied bending moment, lb-in.
T = applied torque, lb-in.

Equation (7-3) can also be used for a solid round shaft by making $D_i \equiv 0$.

An equation similar to equation (7-3) for fluctuating loads can be obtained by substituting the Soderberg equation (6-33) for σ_x and its equivalent for τ. Thus we obtain

$$\tau_{max} = \frac{0.5S_{yp}}{N} = \sqrt{\frac{1}{4}\left(\sigma_m + \frac{S_{yp}}{S_e}\sigma_r\right)^2 + \left(\tau_{ms} + \frac{S_{syp}}{S_{es}}\tau_{rs}\right)^2} \qquad (7\text{-}4)$$

As above, we can replace σ_m, σ_r, τ_{ms}, and τ_{rs} by equations (7-2) (using the appropriate subscripts on σ, τ, M and T) to obtain equation (7-4) in terms of bending moment and torque.

$$\tau_{max} = \frac{0.5S_{yp}}{N} = \frac{16}{\pi D_o^3[1 - (D_i/D_o)^4]}\sqrt{\left(M_m + \frac{S_{yp}}{S_e}M_r\right)^2 + \left(T_m + \frac{S_{syp}}{S_{es}}T_r\right)^2}$$

$$(7\text{-}5)$$

where

σ_m = mean stress due to bending $\pm$ axial stress, psi
σ_r = range of stress due to bending $\pm$ axial stress, psi
τ_{ms} = mean stress due to torsion, psi
τ_{rs} = range of stress due to torsion, psi
M_m = mean applied bending moment, lb-in.
M_r = range of applied bending moment lb-in.
T_m = mean applied torque, lb-in.
T_r = range of applied torque, lb-in.
K_f = fatigue stress concentration factor due to bending, tension or compression (based on notch sensitivity)
K_{fs} = fatigue stress concentration factor due to torsion (based on notch sensitivity)
S_{syp} = yield point strength of the material in shear, psi
S_{yp} = yield point strength of the material in tension, psi
$S_e = C_R C_S C_F C_W \dfrac{1}{K_f} S_n'$ (see equation 3-32a)
$S_{es} = C_R C_S C_F C_W \dfrac{1}{K_{fs}} S_{ns}'$ (see equation 3-32b)

SECTION 7-4

Design of Shafts Subjected to Fluctuating Loads Based on the Distortion Energy Theory of Failure

The stress equation based on the distortion energy theory of failure was given in Chapter 6 (equation 6-26) as

$$\left(\frac{S_{yp}}{N}\right)^2 = \sigma_1^2 - \sigma_1\sigma_2 + \sigma_2^2$$

As was demonstrated in Section 6-1, if σ_1 and σ_2 are replaced by the relations for principal stress, equation (6-3) where the normal stress is due to uniaxial loading only, we obtain equation (6-29)

$$\frac{S_{yp}}{N} = (\sigma_x^2 + 3\tau^2)^{1/2}$$

As in the case of the maximum shear theory of failure, the Soderberg equations (6-33) and its equivalent can be substituted for σ_x and τ. The resulting equation, with a factor of safety included is

$$\frac{S_{yp}}{N} = \sqrt{\left(\sigma_m + \frac{S_{yp}}{S_e}\sigma_r\right)^2 + 3\left(\tau_{sm} + \frac{S_{syp}}{S_{es}}\tau_{sr}\right)^2} \qquad (7\text{-}6)$$

Equation (7-6) may also be expressed in terms of shaft diameter, applied bending moment, and applied torque. Repeating what we did in the case of the maximum shear theory of failure, we obtain

$$\frac{S_{yp}}{N} = \frac{32}{\pi D_o^3[1 - (D_i/D_o)^4]}\sqrt{\left(M_m + \frac{S_{yp}}{S_e}M_r\right)^2 + \frac{3}{4}\left(T_m + \frac{S_{syp}}{S_{es}}T_r\right)^2} \qquad (7\text{-}7)$$

SECTION 7-5

Comparison of Maximum Shear and Distortion Energy Theories of Failures as Applied to Shaft Design

Because the maximum distortion failure theory is less conservative than the maximum shear failure theory, the diameter calculated by using equation (7-7) will be smaller than that calculated by equation (7-5).

However, on closer inspection, these two equations are remarkably alike. Notice that if we divide both sides of equation (7-7) by 2, it is transformed exactly into equation (7-5) except for the coefficient under the radical which multiplies the applied torque components. For the maximum shear theory, this coefficient is 1, and for the distortion energy theory it is $\frac{3}{4}$. Thus, it is apparent that both theories will lead to shaft diameters not too far apart from each other. This would particularly be the result in those situations where the applied torque is much smaller in magnitude than the applied bending moment.

The reader should also note that equations (7-4), (7-5), (7-6), and (7-7) are reduced to steady load design equations when there are no fluctuating load components. Thus, these equations can be thought of as "general" equations.

SECTION 7-6

Shaft Design Equations for Fluctuating and Shock Loads

Prior to 1954, the accepted basis for shaft design was the ASME code for the "Design of transmission shafting," B17c–1927, approved by The American Standards Association. It was based on the maximum shear theory of failure, and employed combined shock and fatigue factors as multiplying coefficients for the applied bending moment and applied torque. This code was withdrawn in 1954 and has not been replaced since the time of its withdrawal. It is, therefore, not necessary to discuss this code.[3]

However, the previous discussion concerning the maximum shear failure theory and the distortion energy failure theory (both of which incorporated the Soderberg equation) resulted in equations (7-4) and (7-6) or (7-5) and (7-7). These equations are rational but include only stresses due to fluctuating loads and not shock loads. Although many shafts are not subjected to shock loads, some applications do arise where such loading does take place (for example, punch presses, shafts for ball mills, and so on).

To take account of shock conditions, it has been suggested [1] that multiplying coefficients (that is, correction factors) be used in the shaft design equation based on the distortion energy theory. However, there does not appear to be a valid argument against using these same coefficients for the shaft design equation based on the maximum shear theory of failure. Thus, equations (7-4) and (7-5) (using the maximum shear theory) become, respectively

$$\tau_{max} = \frac{0.5 S_{yp}}{N} = \sqrt{\frac{K_{sb}}{4}\left(\sigma_m + \frac{S_{yp}}{S_e}\sigma_r\right)^2 + K_{st}\left(\tau_{sm} + \frac{S_{syp}}{S_{es}}\tau_{sr}\right)^2} \qquad (7\text{-}8)$$

$$\tau_{max} = \frac{0.5 S_{yp}}{N} = \frac{16}{\pi D_o^3[1 - (D_i/D_o)^4]}$$

$$\times \sqrt{K_{sb}\left(M_m + \frac{S_{yp}}{S_e}M_r\right)^2 + K_{st}\left(T_m + \frac{S_{syp}}{S_{es}}T_r\right)^2} \qquad (7\text{-}9)$$

---

[3] The ASME code for the "Design of transmission shafting" can be found in any engineering handbook (e.g., Mark's, Kent's, etc.).

Similarly, equations (using the energy distortion theory) (7-6) and (7-7) become

$$\frac{S_{yp}}{N} = \sqrt{K_{sb}\left(\sigma_m + \frac{S_{yp}}{S_e}\sigma_r\right)^2 + 3K_{st}\left(\tau_{sm} + \frac{S_{syp}}{S_{es}}\tau_{sr}\right)^2} \qquad (7\text{-}10)$$

$$\frac{S_{yp}}{N} = \frac{32}{\pi D_o^3[1 - (D_i/D_o)^4]}\sqrt{K_{sb}\left(M_m + \frac{S_{yp}}{S_e}M_r\right)^2 + \frac{3}{4}K_{st}\left(T_m + \frac{S_{syp}}{S_{es}}T_r\right)^2}$$

$$(7\text{-}11)$$

The values for K_{sb} and K_{st} are given in the following table.

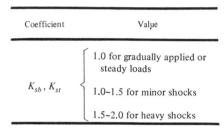

Coefficient	Value
K_{sb}, K_{st}	1.0 for gradually applied or steady loads
	1.0–1.5 for minor shocks
	1.5–2.0 for heavy shocks

SOURCE: H. A. Berchardt: A comprehensive method for designing shafts to insure adequate fatigue life. Mach. Des., (April 25, 1963).

SECTION 7-7

Shaft Diameter for Example 7-1

If the shaft is to be machined from normalized C1040 steel, we obtain from Table A-2 of Appendix A the following material properties

$$S_u = 85{,}000 \text{ psi} \qquad S_{yp} = 50{,}000 \text{ psi}$$

Since direct information about the endurance limit for C1040 is not available, we use equation (3-13). Thus

$$S_n' = 0.5S_u = 0.5(85{,}000) = 42{,}500 \text{ psi}$$

From Figure B-1 of Appendix B we determine that, for the profiled keyways at B and C, $K_f(\text{bending}) = 1.6$ and $K_{fs}(\text{torsion}) = 1.3$. For the sled-runner keyway at E, we find: $K_f(\text{bending}) = 1.3$ and $K_{fs}(\text{torsion}) = 1.3$.

The shaft is to operate in a noncorrosive atmosphere, and is to have a survival rate of 95%. Thus, from equation (3-23) and Table 3-2, we have

$$C_R = 1 - 0.08(\text{DMF}) = 1 - 0.08(1.64) = 0.869$$

From Figure B-3 of Appendix B we obtain for a machined surface

$$C_F = 0.77$$

Finally, since it is likely that the shaft diameter will be larger than $\frac{1}{2}$ in. and perhaps smaller than 2 in., we will apply equation (3-24) and so

$$C_S = 0.85$$

We now can determine the corrected endurance limit by means of equation (3-32a) (where $C_W = 1$ in this case)

$$S_e = \frac{1}{K_f} C_R C_S C_F S_n' = \frac{1}{1.6}(0.869)(0.77)(0.85)(42,500) = 15,108 \text{ psi}$$

If the shaft is to be solid (that is, $D_i = 0$), the load smooth, and the factor of safety $= 3.75$, (see Section 1-3) we now determine the diameters for the stepped shaft in Figure 7-1. The diameter between B and C is to be 25% larger than that between A and B. The pulley and gears are assembled on the shaft with a light press fit.

Consider the type of shaft load, we can conclude: (1) that since the load is smooth, $K_{sb} = K_{st} = 1.0$ (see the table Values for Shock Conditions); (2) because the bending load is repetitive, $M_m = 0$[4]; and (3) since there are no flywheels, clutches, and so on, the torque will be steady, thus $T_r = 0$. Applying this information to equation (7-11), we obtain

$$\frac{S_{yp}}{N} = \frac{32}{\pi D_{AB}^3} \sqrt{\left(\frac{S_{yp}}{S_e} M_r\right)^2 + \frac{3}{4} T_m^2} \qquad (7\text{-}12)$$

In Section 7-2, both the maximum bending moment and maximum torque were found to be at location B where the shaft diameter D_{AB} joins the larger shaft diameter D_{BC}. Possible failure can occur at the fillet joining the diameters or at the keyway. The more critical of the two possibilities will be the one with the larger product $K_f M$.

The stress concentration at the pulley is due to the profiled keyway and the light press fit. According to Peterson [2], for a press fit with an average pressure, $K_t = 1.9$ for shafts subjected to fluctuating bending loads. However, due to inconclusive evidence and fretting corrosion, we shall assume $K_f = 2.5$. Thus, for the keyway and press fit combination we obtain[5]

$$K_f M_r = (2.5)(1.6)(10,351.77) = 41,407.08 \text{ lb-in.} \qquad (7\text{-}13)$$

where

$$M_r = \frac{M_{max} - (-M_{min})}{2} = \frac{M_{max} + M_{min}}{2} = \frac{2M_r}{2} = M_r$$

Now, to obtain K_f for the fillet, it is necessary to know both r/d and D/d (see Figure B-4a in Appendix B) and q from Figure B-2 in Appendix B. Because

---

[4] $M_m = [M_{max} + (-M)_{min}]/2 = 0$.

[5] In Section 3-29, it was stated that, where two or more stress raisers exist, it was common practice to multiply the stress concentration factors for each effect.

we do not have all the data to enable us to use these figures, we will have to "guess" at a K_t and q. It is immediately apparent that unless we "guess" at a $K_f > 4$, which is the product of 2.5 and 1.6, the critical location for determining the shaft diameter d is going to be at the pulley where the keyway and press fit are the overriding factors. Since a value of K_f of such a high magnitude for a fillet is quite unlikely, we proceed with the design by using the value of the bending moment at point B. Substituting $M_r = 10{,}351.77$ in equation (7-12)

$$D_{AB} = 2.967 \text{ in.}$$

use $D_{AB} = 3.00.$[6] Thus

$$D_{BC} = 1.25(3.00) = 3.750 \text{ in.}$$

We may now check the stress condition at the fillet by assuming $r = \frac{1}{16}$ in. Thus, for $r/d = 0.0625/3 = 0.0208$ and $D/d = 1.25$, we obtain from Figure B-4a in Appendix B $K_t' \approx 2.28$. From Figure B-2 in Appendix B we determine that $q = 0.78$ (that is, for $r = 1/16$ and annealed steel). And so, using equation (3-29)

$$K_f = 1 + q(K_t - 1) = 1 + 0.78(2.28 - 1) = 2.17$$

Returning now to equation (7-12) we can determine the factor of safety, N, for the shaft diameter D_{BC}. Note that in applying equation (7-12) the value of M_r is assumed to be the same as at section B. This decision is acceptable, since the relatively wide hub of the pulley added rigidity to this section. Furthermore, as can be established from Figure 7-3, the bending moment just to the right of section B is smaller than that at B and the calculation, therefore, is conservative. Thus

$$N_{BC} = \cfrac{S_{yp}}{\cfrac{32}{\pi D_{BC}^3} \sqrt{\left(\dfrac{S_{yp}}{S_e} M_r\right)^2 + \dfrac{3}{4} T_m^2}}$$

$$= \cfrac{50{,}000}{\cfrac{32}{\pi(3.750)^3} \sqrt{\left(\dfrac{50{,}000}{15{,}108} \times 10{,}351.77\right)^2 + \dfrac{3}{4}(5250)^2}} = 7.51$$

For the purposes of completing the problem and determining the shaft deflection and critical speed, we will assume that a series 213 ball bearing (width 0.9055 in.) will be used to support the shaft at each end. To ensure a satisfactory fit, those locations of the shaft on which the bearing will be mounted are nominally 2.559-in. diameter. The fillet radius between the 3.00-in. diameter portion of the shaft and that portion which supports the bearing is $r = 0.06$ in.

[6] Since $D_{AsB} > 2$ in., one should repeat the calculation with a smaller C_s (say $C_s = 0.75$–0.80) to obtain a corrected diameter D_{AB}. However, to conserve space, this has not been done in the example given above.

From Figure 7-3 we obtain

$$M_D = \sqrt{(3591.0)^2 + (4029.9)^2} = 5398 \text{ lb-in.}$$

Now we have $r/d = 0.06/3 = 0.02$, $D/d = 3.000/2.559 = 1.17$.

From Figure B-40 in Appendix B we obtain $K_t = 2.40$, and from Figure B-2 in Appendix B we again obtain $q = 0.78$. Thus

$$K_f = 1 + q(K_t - 1) = 1 + 0.78(2.40 - 1) = 2.09$$

However, the bearing fit on a revolving shaft is likely to have a press fit with the shaft for which we can assume $K_f \approx 2.5$. Using equation (7-12), we find N for the shaft section between D and E, where

$$S_e = (0.869)(0.77)(0.85)\frac{1}{2.5}(42,500) = 9700 \text{ psi}$$

$$N_{DE} = \cfrac{50,000}{\cfrac{32}{\pi(2.559)^3}\sqrt{\left(\cfrac{50,000}{9700} \times 5398\right)^2 + \cfrac{3}{4}(3150)^2}} = 2.94$$

Thus, the shaft diameter for the ball bearings is more than satisfactory. In fact, if load, speed, and life requirements permit, it would be "in order" to consider the use of a smaller size ball bearing.

SECTION 7-8

Shaft Deflection for Example 7-1

Having determined the shaft diameter required to withstand the severest load conditions and the diameters for other parts of the shaft, the next step is to calculate the shaft deflection.

This information is most important because it is used to establish the minimum permissible clearance between the pulley, gears, and housing (or enclosure) for the shaft assembly. Also, the deflection at gear locations will increase the backlash between gear teeth, increase the pressure angle, and reduce the length of tooth contact. Excessive shaft deflection, then, impedes proper functioning of gears.

In the course of finding the shaft deflection, the slope of its elastic curve must be established. Knowing the slope will enable the designer to judge the amount of skewing between gear teeth (an additional deviation from ideal gearing theory). Furthermore, it will help him to determine the minimum bearing clearance for sleeve bearings as well as whether self-aligning bearings are required.

There are many methods[7] for obtaining the deflection of a shaft or beam. The simplest of these methods is by direct integration, particularly where a shaft has a constant diameter throughout its entire length. However, most shafts are "stepped" shafts. The use of direct integration, then, becomes cumbersome since boundary conditions at each change of diameter have to be satisfied.

The more popular methods for finding deflections are the area-moment method, graphical integration method,[8] and the numerical integration method.

We shall determine the deflection of the shaft in Example 7-1 by numerical integration. This particular method is not only compatible with modern high-speed desk calculators, but lends itself readily to computer solutions.

The bases for numerical integration are the differential equations below. The sign convention for y and the distance along the shaft-axis are shown on Figure 7-4.

$$\left.\begin{array}{ll} \text{Load equation} & \dfrac{d^4 y}{dx^4} = \dfrac{w}{EI} \\[3mm] \text{Shear equation} & \dfrac{d^3 y}{dx^3} = \dfrac{V}{EI} \\[3mm] \text{Moment equation} & \dfrac{d^2 y}{dx^2} = \dfrac{d\theta}{dx} = \dfrac{M}{EI} \\[3mm] \text{Slope equation} & \dfrac{dy}{dx} = \theta \end{array}\right\} \qquad (7\text{-}14)$$

It is apparent that by considering finite distances along a shaft length (that is, the x direction), the above equations can be integrated by numerical summation. For example, $y = \Sigma \theta \Delta x$.

The format used here to find the deflection of the shaft in Example 7-1 is based on one found in reference [3]. In accordance with this reference, Tables 7-1 and 7-2 on pages 349–350, are determined by the following step by step procedure:

---

[7] One method that is quite simple and can be used for stepped shafts with various loads employs the singularity function (also called Macauley brackets) to establish the shear, moment and deflection diagrams. The technique, once understood, becomes algebraic and is also easily adaptable for computer programming. An excellent explanation of this method can be found in *An Introduction to the Mechanics of Solids*, by S. H. Crandall and N. C. Dahl, McGraw-Hill Book Co., New York,

[8] Graphical methods of integration can be found in any good book on calculus. Specifically, one may refer to *Design of Machine Elements*, 4th ed., by Virgil M. Faires, The Macmillan Co., New York, 1965, where a problem similar to the one used in the example in our present chapter can be found. Also, it is suggested that the reader refer to *Mechanical Vibrations*, 2nd ed., by Austin H. Church, John Wiley & Sons, Inc., New York, 1964.

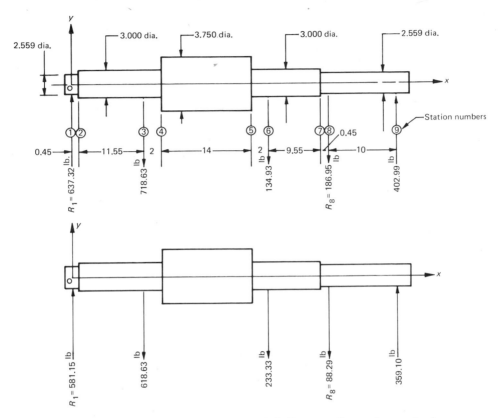

Figure 7-4 The upper sketch shows the shaft diameters, distance between loads and diameter changes, station numbers, and load magnitudes for the vertical plane. The lower sketch shows the load magnitudes for the horizontal plane. All the other data is the same as for the upper sketch and so is not repeated on the lower sketch.

Step 1. Divide the shaft into length intervals by marking a station number at each force and change of section (see Figure 7-4). Where there are relatively long sections of constant diameter, greater accuracy may be obtained by also dividing these sections into smaller length intervals.[9]

Step 2. In column 1 of the computation sheet, enter the station numbers on alternate lines.

Step 3. In column 2 of the computation sheet, enter the forces on the same line as their station number. Upward forces are taken to be positive and downward forces are taken to be negative. Note that those stations not having any forces acting at that location are blank spaces in column 2.

Step 4. Calculate the vertical shear at each station by summing the forces in column 2. Enter these shear values in column 3 one station below that

[9] This recommendation was not followed in the solution to Example 7-1 (i.e., dividing long lengths of uniform cross section) in order to conserve space. However, avoidance of this recommendation in no way alters the procedure.

for which it is calculated. As a check, the very last value for the shear should be equal in magnitude to the last force in column 2, but opposite in sign.

Step 5. Enter on the same line as the station number the distance from that station to the preceding one.

Step 6. Calculate the bending moment at each station by multiplying the shear value in column 3 by the distance to the preceding station in column 4. This product when added to the previous entry in column 5 is the bending moment at that station. Note that unless station 1 is acted upon by an outside couple or bending moment, the value at this station is zero.

Step 7. In column 6, on a line in between stations, enter the value of the area moment of inertia (I) for that section of shaft length between the two stations being considered.

Step 8. In column 7, enter on the same line as the area moment of inertia, the product of the elastic modulus (E) and the area moment of inertia (I).

Step 9. In column 8, enter the results of dividing the values in column 5 by the values in column 7 (that is, M/EI). The procedure that is followed is to divide those values in column 5 that precede by one line and follow by one line the value of EI in column 7. The first result is entered in column 8 on the line *above* the EI value, and the second result is placed on the *same* line as the EI value.

Step 10. In column 9, enter the average value of M/EI (that is, column 8) on the line in between stations. The average is obtained by summing the M/EI value at a station with the M/EI value that follows the station and dividing the total by 2.

Step 11. Calculate the slope at each station by entering the "running total" of the product of the average M/EI (that is, column 9) and the Δx value (that is, column 4) found on the very next lower line from the average M/EI value. The results are entered in column 10 on the same line as the station numbers.

Step 12. In column 11, enter the arithmetic average of the slope from station-to-station (that is, from column 10). These average slope values are recorded on the lines in between the stations.

Step 13. Next, the deflection increment is obtained by multiplying the value of the average slope (column 11) by the Δx value (column 4), entered on the next lower line from the average slope value. The product is entered in column 12 on the same line as the average slope.

Step 14. In column 12, total all the deflection increments *between bearing reactions*. Change the sign of this sum and divide it by the distance between the bearings. The result is the integration constant.

Step 15. Next, the integration constant is multiplied by the distance between stations, Δx (column 4). This product is the integration constant for each interval and is entered in column 13 on the same line as the deflection increments.

Step 16. Add the deflection increment (column 12) and the integration constant (column 13) and enter the sum as part of a "running total" in

Table 7-1 Deflection due to vertical loads for Example 7.1 (refer to Figure 7.4)

1	2	3	4	5	6	7	8	9	10	11	12	13	14
Station Number	Force or Reaction F, lb	Shear at Preceding Station V, lb	Distance between Stations Δx, in.	Bending moment $M = \Sigma V(\Delta x)$, in.-lb	Moment of Inertia I, in.^{4}	$EI \times 10^{-6}$ lb-in.^{2}	$\dfrac{M}{EI} \times 10^6$, $\dfrac{1}{\text{in.}}$	Average of Column 8 $\dfrac{M}{EI} \times 10^6$, $\dfrac{1}{\text{in.}}$	Slope Relative to Station 1 $\theta = \Sigma \dfrac{M}{EI}_{AV} 10^6(\Delta x)$, rad	Average Slope $\theta_{AV} \times 10^6$, rad	Deflection Increment $y = \theta_{AV} \times 10^6(\Delta x)$, in.	Integration Constant $C \times 10^6$, in.	Deflection $y \times 10^6$, in.
①	$R_1 = 637.52$			0	2.106	63.17	0		0			−293.419	0
		637.52	0.45				4.542	2.271		0.511	0.230		
②				286.88	3.977	119.31	2.405		1.022			−7531.097	−293.189
		637.52	11.55				64.119	33.262		193.110	2230.421		
③	−718.63			7650.24	3.977	119.31	64.119		385.198			−1304.086	−5593.869
		−81.11	2.00				62.760	63.440		448.638	897.276		
④				7488.02	9.710	291.29	25.706		512.078			−9123.602	−6000.675
		−81.11	14.00				21.808	23.757		678.377	9497.278		
⑤				6352.48	3.977	119.31	53.242		844.676			−1304.086	−5631.999
		−81.11	2.00				51.883	52.563		897.239	1794.478		
⑥	−134.93			6190.26	3.997	119.31	51.883		949.802			−6227.011	−5141.607
		−216.04	9.55				34.590	43.237		1156.259	11042.273		
⑦				4127.08	2.106	63.17	65.335		1362.715			−293.419	−326.345
		−216.04	0.45				63.796	64.566		1377.243	619.759		
⑧	$R_8 = -186.95$			4029.86	2.106	63.17	63.796		1391.770			−6520.430	0
		−402.99	10.00				0	31.885		1551.195	15511.950		
⑨	402.99			0					1710.620				8991.520

Sum of deflection increments *between* bearing supports $= \Sigma\theta \times 10^6(\Delta x) = 26081.715$

Integration constant, $C \times 10^6 = \dfrac{-26081.715}{\text{Distance between bearings}} = \dfrac{-26081.715}{40} = -652.043$ in./in.

Table 7-2 Deflection due to horizontal loads for Example 7-1 (refer to Figure 7-4.)

(1) Station Number	(2) Force or Reaction F, lb	(3) Shear at Preceding Station V, lb	(4) Distance between Stations Δx, in.	(5) Bending moment $M = \Sigma V(\Delta x)$, in.-lb	(6) Moment of Inertia I, in.⁴	(7) $EI \times 10^{-6}$, lb-in.²	(8) $\dfrac{M}{EI} \times 10^{6}$, $\dfrac{1}{\text{in.}}$	(9) Average of Column 8 $\dfrac{M}{EI} \times 10^{6}$, $\dfrac{1}{\text{in.}}$	(10) Slope Relative to Station 1 $\theta = \Sigma \dfrac{M}{EI}_{AV} 10^{6}(\Delta x)$, rad	(11) Average Slope $\theta_{AV} \times 10^{6}$, rad	(12) Deflection Increment $y = \theta_{AV} \times 10^{6}(\Delta x)$, in.	(13) Integration Constant $C \times 10^{6}$, in.	(14) Deflection $y \times 10^{6}$, in.
①	$R_1 = 581.15$			0	2.108	63.24	0	2.068	0	0.466	0.210	-273.817	0
②		581.15	0.45	261.52	3.976	119.28	4.135 / 2.192	30.329	0.931	176.081	2033.736	-7027.967	-273.607
③	-618.63	581.15	11.55	6973.80	3.976	119.28	58.466 / 58.466	58.152	351.231	409.383	818.766	-1216.964	-5267.838
④		-37.48	2.00	6898.84	9.707	291.21	57.837 / 23.690	22.789	467.535	627.058	8778.812	-8518.748	-5666.036
⑤		-37.48	14.00	6374.12	3.976	119.28	21.888 / 53.433	53.124	786.581	839.705	1679.410	-1216.964	-5405.972
⑥	-233.33	-37.48	2.00	6299.16	3.976	119.28	52.810 / 52.810	41.969	892.829	1093.231	10440.356	-5811.003	-4943.526
⑦		-270.81	9.55	3712.92	2.108	63.24	31.128 / 58.712	57.749	1293.633	1306.627	587.982	-273.817	-314.173
⑧	$R_8 = 88.29$	-270.81	0.45	3591.06	2.108	63.24	56.785 / 56.785	28.393	1319.620	1461.585	14615.850	-6084.820	0
⑨	359.10	-359.10	10.00	0			0		1603.550				8531.030

Sum of deflection increments *between* bearing supports = $\Sigma \theta \times 10^{6}(\Delta x) = 24339.272$

Integration constant, $C \times 10^{6} = \dfrac{-24339.272}{40} = \dfrac{-24339.272}{40} = -608.482$ in./in.

column 14. This "running total" is recorded on the same line as the station number and represents the deflection at that station. Because it is assumed that the bearings are rigid,[10] zeros are entered for the deflection at those stations where there are bearings.

Where the shaft loads have to be separated into horizontal and vertical components (as in our example problem), the resultant shaft deflection at each station is obtained by calculating the square root of the sum of the squares of the horizontal and vertical deflections at each station. Table 7-3 is a tabulation of these results for Example 7-1.

Table 7-3   Resultant slopes (relative to station 1) and deflections for Example 7-1.

Station number →	①	②	③	④	⑤	⑥	⑦	⑧	⑨
Slope, $\theta \times 10^6$, rad	0	1.382	521.286	693.402	1154.204	1303.555	1878.866	1917.926	2344.931
Deflection $y \times 10^6$, in.	0	401.024	7683.42	8253.036	7806.663	7132.641	453.540	0	12395.806

The method of numerical integration, as outlined above, is readily applicable to shafts without any overhanging loads, to shafts with an overhanging load at each end, and to shafts with only one overhanging load.

For shafts without overhang, all forces act between the bearing supports and the table will not contain stations outside of the bearing supports. Thus, if there is no shaft overhang, as in Example 7-1, Tables 7-1 and 7-2 will show recorded data for only eight stations.

On the other hand, shafts having an overhang at each bearing support will show recorded data for stations outside of the bearing supports. Also, it is necessary to change the algebraic sign for deflection increments and integration constants for those stations to the left of the left bearing support. This procedural change is required since the origin of the coordinate x-y axis is placed at the left bearing support, reversing, thereby, the direction of integration for those stations to the left of this support.

Of the results posted in Table 7-3, the following are of the greatest interest: The vector sum of the average slope at the left bearing is

$$\theta_{av} = 0.00000069 \text{ rad} \approx 0 \text{ deg}$$

The vector sum of the average slope at the right bearing (station 8) should be considered from the left of station 8 and from the right of station 8. The critical value is the larger of the two vector sums. Calculations show that the vector sum to the right of the bearing at station 8 is more critical. Therefore, we have

$$\theta_{av} = 0.0021314 \text{ rad} \approx 0.122 \text{ deg}$$

[10] In the strictest sense, this assumption is not valid, except for light loads.

The shaft deflections at the pulley (station 3), the 18-in. gear (station 6), and the 12-in. gear (station 9) are respectively

$$\delta(\text{pulley}) \approx 0.007684 \text{ in.}$$

$$\delta(18\text{-in. gear}) \approx 0.007133 \text{ in.}$$

$$\delta(12\text{-in. gear}) \approx 0.012400 \text{ in.}$$

The slopes at the 18-in. gear and the 12-in. gear respectively are

$$\theta(18\text{-in. gear}) = 0.0013036 \text{ rad} \approx 0.0767 \text{ deg}$$

$$\theta(12\text{-in. gear}) = 0.0023449 \text{ rad} \approx 0.134 \text{ deg}$$

The permissible misalignment tolerance for the Conrad type (also called deep groove) ball bearings is ± 0.25 deg (see Chapter 9). Thus the bearings selected are satisfactory because the slope at each bearing support is less than the possible tolerance.

There are no clearly defined standards or restrictions concerning lateral deflection of shafting. Lacking more specific information, the designer may be guided by the following criteria [4]

1. For machinery shafting, the deflection should be no greater than 0.001 in./ft of shaft length between bearing supports.
2. For shafts mounting good quality spur gears, the deflection at the gear mesh should not exceed 0.005 in. (between gears) and the slope should be limited to 0.0005 in./in. (that is, approximately 0.0286 deg).
3. For shafts mounting good quality bevel gears, the deflection at the gear mesh should not exceed 0.003 in.

Our results indicate that the first restriction, as indicated above, has been violated: 0.008253 in. $> 0.001 \times 3.3 = 0.0033$ in. The second restriction has also been violated: 0.007133 in. and 0.01239 in. > 0.005 in., 0.0767 deg and 0.134 deg > 0.0286 deg. Consequently, the shaft at both gear locations must be stiffened.

As is often the case where gearing is involved, the shaft diameter is governed by the dimensional restrictions imposed by the gearing. Thus, in Example 7-1 it is necessary to repeat the deflection calculations as performed in Tables 7-1 and 7-2. However, in repeating these calculations, the moment of inertia in column 6 is expressed in terms of the diameter: $I = \pi D^4/64$. The required diameter is then determined by equating the vector sum of the vertical and horizontal deflections at the point of interest (that is, the 18-in. and 12-in. gear) to the limiting restriction, namely, no larger than 0.005 in. In a like manner, the required diameter for a limiting slope of 0.0005 in./in. can be established. The larger of the two diameters would then be specified as the diameter to be used for the design.

SECTION 7-9

Shaft Design by Computer

In order to demonstrate the use of the computer in coping with shaft design problems, we used an RCA SPECTRA 70 machine to find a satisfactory shaft diameter for Example 7-1 in preference to repeating the above outlined numerical procedure. The results of this program are illustrated in Figure 7-5. As can be seen from Figure 7-5, the diameter at station 9 (that is, the location of the 12-in. gear) has been increased from 2.559 in. to 3.765 in. This new shaft size at the 12-in. diameter gear permits a shaft slope of 0.0005 in./in. and a shaft deflection of 0.00264 in. Both of these values satisfy the imposed restrictions. The diameters at the other shaft stations have also increased in proportion to that required at station 9. Undoubtedly, these other diameters can be reduced to 3.765 in., which would result in a single diameter shaft. However, in so doing, the designer must provide locating shoulders for the bearings and gears (for example, snap rings). This final shaft design would also have to be checked for fatigue stress, particularly at the geometric discontinuity caused by the snap ring grooves. Verification of this design is left to the reader.

The other avenue of investigation open to the designer in trying to reduce the shaft diameter is to determine whether the overhang length of 10 in. (see Figure 7-4) can be shortened. Whether this is possible depends on how this action will affect the location of other components of the machine of which this shaft is only one part.

As stated, the computer program[11] used was written for an RCA SPECTRA 70 machine, and compiled on a FAST FORTRAN COMPILER. This special version of Fortran language allows free format input and output statements. Therefore, some read and print statements will have to be changed to conform with standard Fortran language. Other than this minor adjustment, the program is completely compatible with Fortran.

The computer program is set up to calculate the shear, slope, and deflection of a simply supported, stepped shaft with or without overhang. It also offers the option of comparing the slope and deflection at a given shaft station to respective limiting values cued into the computer by the designer. Should these limiting values be exceeded (at the-station of interest), the program will automatically request the computer to increase the shaft diameter by a given percentage until the limiting values have been satisfied. The program is capable of considering as many as 20 separate stations and loads.

Input data to the program are entered in the natural sequence which is the same as that used in the numerical procedure. To assist the reader in understanding the program, a legend of symbols and description is presented in Table 7-4.

---

[11] The computer program was developed by Dr. Jeffrey Schram of The Newark College of Engineering. The authors are indebted to him for his kind assistance and contribution in helping make this portion of the book more meaningful.

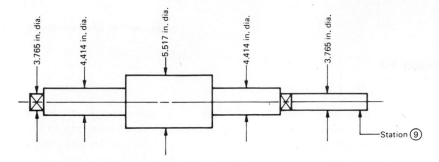

Figure 7-5 Shaft for Example 7-1 determined by computer analysis.

Table 7-4 Computer Legend

Symbol	Description
OPT	Option to check whether the slope and deflection are within given limits (ON = 2, OFF = 1)
NP	Number of stations for which the user desires to compare the slope and deflections with the limiting values (must be at least equal to 1)
LP(I)*	Station number at which the limiting values of slope and deflection are to be compared with the actual slope and deflection
DM(I)*	Maximum deflection at LP(I)
SM(I)*	Maximum slope at LP(I)
KSET	KSET = 1 means that the shaft loading is only in the vertical plane. KSET = 2 means that the shaft loading is in both the vertical and horizontal plane.
N	Number of stations
NO	Number of station up to the overhang
D(I)†	Diameter of the shaft at a given station
E(I)†	Modulus of elasticity at each station
X(I)†	Distance between stations
F(I, 1)	Forces in the vertical direction at each station
F(I, 2)	Forces in the horizontal direction at each station (This data is included only if KSET = 2)

† These quantities should appear in the following order:
D(1), E(1), X(1). D(2), E(2). X(2) . . . D(N). E(N). X(N)

* These quantities should appear in the following order:
LP(I), DM(I), SM(I)

354

The actual program used is

L&G70 FORTRAN

```
        DIMENSION D(19),E(19),X(19)         ,V(20),DBM(20),BM(20),AI(20),Y(19
        1),WK(19),WL(19),Z(19),DSL(20),SLO(20),U(19),DD(19),C(19),DEFL(20),
        2DEFX(20),SLX(20),UX(20)
        $LP(20), SM(20), DM(20) ,F(20,2)
        READ,OPT,NP
        DO   121   L =1,NP
121     READ, LP(L), DM(L), SM(L)
        READ, KSET
        READ, N,NO
        MO =NO −1
        M =N −1
        U(N) =0.0
        DO   19 J =1,M
19      READ,D(J),E(J),X(J)
        DO 491 KZ =1,KSET
        DO 22 J =1,N
22      READ, F(J,KZ)
491     CONTINUE
490     DO 100 KZ =1,KSET
49      PRINT 50
50      FORMAT ('1',16X,'SECTION',9X,'FORCE',12X,'DIAMETER',9X,'MODULUS',
        $9X,'LENGTH')
        PRINT, 1,F(1,KZ)
        DO 80 J =1,M
        K =J +1
80      PRINT,K,F(K,KZ) ,D(J) , E(J) , X(J)
        IND =0
        V(1) =0.0
        DO 1 J =2,N
        K =J −1
1       V(J) =V(K) +F(K,KZ)
        DBM(1) =0.0
        DO 2 J =2,N
        K =J −1
2       DBM(J) =V(J) *X(K)
        BM(1) =0.0
        DO 3 J =2,N
        K =J −1
        BM(J) =BM(K) +DBM(J)
        IF (ABS(BM(J)) −1.) 31,31,3
31      BM(J) =0.
3       CONTINUE
        DO 4 J =1,M
4       AI(J) =3.14159*D(J) **4/64.
        DO 5 J =1,M
5       Y(J) =E(J) *AI(J)
        DO 6 J =1,M
6       WK(J) =BM(J)/Y(J)
        DO 7 J =1,M
        K =J +1
7       WL(J) =BM(K)/Y(J)
        DO 8 J =1,M
8       Z(J) =.5*(WK(J) +WL(J))
        DO 9 J =1,M
9       DSL(J) =X(J) *Z(J)
        SLO(1) =0.0
        DO 10 J =2,N
        K =J −1
10      SLO(J) =SLO(K) +DSL(K)
        DO 28 J =2,N
```

```
28          SLO(J) = SLO(J)/1000000.
            DO 11 J = 1,M
            K = J + 1
11          U(J) = .5*(SLO(J) + SLO(K))
            DO 12 J = 1,M
12          DD(J) = U(J)*X(J)
            DDSUM = 0.0
            DO 13 J = 1,MO
13          DDSUM = DDSUM + DD(J)
            XSUM = 0.0
            DO 14 J = 1,MO
14          XSUM = XSUM + X(J)
            CF = - DDSUM/XSUM
            DO 15 J = 1,M
15          C(J) = X(J)*CF
            DEFL(1) = 0.0
            DEFL(N) = 0.0
            DO 26 J = 2,N
            K = J - 1
26          DEFL(J) = DEFL(K) + C(K) + DD(K)
            PRINT 40
40          FORMAT ('0', 16X,'SECTION',9X,'FORCE',15X,'SHEAR',
          &9X,'    SLOPE ',9X,' AVERAGE SLOPE', 9X,'DEFLECTION' )
            DO   17   J = 1,N
            ADEF = ABS(DEFL(J))
            IF (ADEF - .00001) 29,29,17
29          DEFL(J) = 0.
17          PRINT, J, F(J,KZ), V(J),SLO(J), U(J)    ,DEFL(J)
            IF(KSET - 1) 53,53,55
55          IF(KZ - 1) 56,56,57
56          DO   58 J = 1,N
            DEFX(J) = DEFL(J)
            SLX(J) = SLO(J)
58          UX(J) = U(J)
100         CONTINUE
57          DO 71 J = 1,N
            DEFL(J) = SQRT(DEFL(J)*DEFL(J) + DEFX(J)*DEFX(J))
            U(J) = SQRT(UX(J)*UX(J) + U(J)*U(J))
71          SLO(J) = SQRT(SLX(J)*SLX(J) + SLO(J)*SLO(J))
            PRINT 83
83          FORMAT('0','                                    RESULTANT SLOPE AND DEFLECTION')
            PRINT 84
84          FORMAT('0',16X,'SLOPE',8X,'AVERAGE SLOPE',8X,'DEFLECTION')
            DO 88 J = 1,N
88          PRINT, SLO(J), U(J), DEFL(J)
53          IF(OPT - 1.)99,99,160
160         DO 175 KP = 1,NP
            L = LP(KP)
            IF(ABS(DEFL(L)) - DM(KP)) 172,170,170
170         IND = 1
172         IF(SM(KP) - ABS(SLO(L))) 174,175,175
174         IND = 1
175         CONTINUE
            IF (IND) 99,99,180
180         DO 185 J = 1,M
            PRINT 240, D(J), J
240         FORMAT('0',10X,'DIAMETER  = ', F10.4,'AT SECTION  - ',I2)
            D(J) = D(J)*1.213
185         CONTINUE
            GO TO 490
99          STOP
            END
*RUN
```

SECTION 7-10

Critical Speed of Shafts

The practicalities involved in manufacturing and assembly prevent the center of mass of a symmetric, rotating system from coinciding with the actual center of rotation. In addition, the static deflection caused by the weights of the components being carried by the shaft cause a further shift of mass center from the axis of rotation. Consequently, as the shaft increases in rotational speed, the kinetic energy of the attached masses increases. When the kinetic energy reaches the potential energy of the shaft caused by the static deflection of the mounted masses, the shaft will begin to vibrate violently. The rotational speed at which this disturbance occurs is called the **fundamental frequency** or **critical speed** of the shaft. As in other vibratory systems, higher critical speeds (at smaller amplitudes) can occur at some multiple (that is, harmonic) of the fundamental frequency.

Equating the kinetic energy due to the rotation of the mounted shaft masses to the potential energy of the deflected shaft results in an equation defining the critical speed of the shaft. This equation is called the **Rayleigh equation,** and its derivation may be found in any good textbook dealing with mechanical vibrations.[12] Thus, the lowest or fundamental critical speed for a shaft simply supported at two points is

$$n_c = 187.7 \left[\frac{W_1 y_1 + W_2 y_2 + W_3 y_3 + \cdots + W_m y_m}{W_1 y_1^2 + W_2 y_2^2 + W_3 y_3^2 + \cdots + W_m y_m^2} \right]^{1/2} \tag{7-15}$$

where W_m = the weight of the rotating mass in pounds and y_m = the respective static shaft deflection due to W_m in inches.

For Example 7-1, it was suggested in Section 7.9 that the designer might be likely to consider a shaft of uniform diameter, namely 3.765-in. diameter. Considering the pulley weight of 100 lb, the 18-in. diameter gear weight of 50 lb and the 12-in. diameter gear weight of 25 lb, we can determine the static shaft deflection at each of these loads. This is simply accomplished by means of the computer or some other convenient method (that is, numerical or graphical). In this particular instance, with few loads and a uniform shaft diameter, the area-moment method would be most direct—lacking a computer. Nevertheless, the deflections at the 25-lb, 50-lb, and 100-lb loads, respectively, are 0.538×10^{-3} in., 0.427×10^{-3} in., and 0.494×10^{-3} in. Substituting in equation (7-15) we have

$$n_c = 187.7 \left[\frac{\begin{matrix}25(0.538 \times 10^{-3}) + 50(0.427 \times 10^{-3}) \\ + 100(0.494 \times 10^{-3})\end{matrix}}{\begin{matrix}25(0.538 \times 10^{-3})^2 + 50(0.427 \times 10^{-3})^2 \\ + 100(0.494 \times 10^{-3})^2\end{matrix}} \right]^{1/2}$$

$$n_c = 8560 \text{ rpm}$$

[12] W. T. Thompson: *Vibrations Theory and Applications*, Prentice-Hall, Inc., Englewood Cliffs, N.J., R. T. Anderson: *Fundamentals of Mechanical Vibrations*, The Macmillan Co., New York.

Recall that the shaft is to operate at 360 rpm—well below the critical speed. Therefore, we do not anticipate any vibration problem resulting from shaft rotation.

Actual tests have shown that the Rayleigh equation is slightly overly optimistic since self-damping of the materials and the increased stiffness attributable to gear hubs, and so on, tend to lower the calculated critical speed. Consequently, a good "rule of thumb" in practice is to keep the actual operating speed about 25% lower than the calculated critical speed.

SECTION 7-11

Torsional Stiffness

Another important aspect to consider in shaft design is torsional stiffness. Proper design requires that a shaft be able to transmit power uniformly and with a steady motion. Shafts that permit an excessive angular displacement may contribute to vibrations (both torsional and lateral), affect gear action, and cause premature bearing wear or failure. In addition, particular applications such as machine tools require that the spindles be especially rigid.

Although no standard torsional deflection has ever been established for different shaft applications, it has become standard practice to limit the torsional deflection for machinery shafting to 0.08 deg/ft of length [4] and transmission shafting to 1 deg in a length of 20 times the shaft diameter [5]. Camshafts, particularly for internal combustion engines, should be less than 0.5 deg regardless of the shaft length [5].

The equation established for torsion (see Chapter 5) is

$$\theta = \frac{TL}{JG} \tag{7-16}$$

The polar moment of inertia for a round hollow shaft is

$$J = \frac{\pi}{32}(D_o^4 - D_i^4) = \frac{\pi D_o^4}{32}\left(1 - \frac{D_i^4}{D_o^4}\right) \tag{7-17}$$

Substituting equation (7-17) into equation (7-16) and multiplying by 57.3 deg/rad, we arrive at

$$\theta = \frac{584TL}{D_o^4(1 - D_i^4/D_o^4)G} \tag{7-18}$$

where θ is the torsional deflection in degrees for a shaft length L in inches. As indicated earlier in this chapter, we can use this equation for a solid shaft by making the internal diameter, D_i identically zero.

To illustrate the application of equation (7-18), we will apply it to Example 7-1. Figure 7-6 shows a schematic representation of the torques acting on the shaft and their locations. From Figure 7-6 we have

$$T_{CB} = 5250 \text{ lb-in.}$$

$$T_{EC} = 3150 \text{ lb-in.}$$

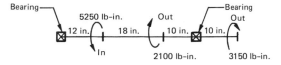

Figure 7-6 Torque distribution for shaft in Example 7-1.

Using the shaft diameter of 3.765 in. established in Section 7-9 and equation (7-18) we can calculate the torsional deflection of the shaft from E, the location of the 12-in. diameter gear to B, the location of the pulley.

$$\theta_{EB} = \theta_{EC} + \theta_{CB} = \frac{584}{12 \times 10^6(3.765)^4}[(5250)(18) + (3150)(20)]$$

$$\theta_{EB} = 0.038 \text{ deg}$$

The result is well below the torsional stiffness conditions stipulated above. Specifically for transmission shafting, we are allowed to 1 deg per 20 times the shaft diameter. Thus, in this instance,

$$\frac{1 \text{ deg}}{20(3.765)\text{in.}} \times 38 \text{ in.} = 1 \text{ deg}\left(\frac{38}{20 \times 3.765}\right) = 0.504 \text{ deg} > 0.038 \text{ deg}$$

Therefore, the shaft is sufficiently rigid. If the shaft were considered to be machinery shafting (rather than transmission shafting), we would then have

$$0.08 \text{ deg/ft} \times \frac{38 \text{ in.}}{12 \text{ in./ft}} = 0.254 \text{ deg} > 0.038 \text{ deg}$$

Again, we find that the shaft would be sufficiently stiff. It is of interest to note that, had the designer decided to use a stepped shaft (Figure 7-5), calculations would have proven it to be even stiffer than the straight shaft.

SECTION 7-12

Torsion of Shafts of Various Cross Sections

At various times, the designer must concern himself with shafts having other than round cross sections. The actual stress analysis is rather complex (see Chapter 5), with most of the results having been obtained by the membrane analysis [6, 7]. Several shapes (for example, ellipse, square, rectangle, triangle), however, have been treated rationally [6]. Table 7-5 is presented here as an aid to the designer. Nevertheless, the reader is advised to consult the many excellent references dealing with this topic for a complete "in-depth" analysis [6, 8, 9].

Table 7-5 Formulas for torsional deflection and shearing stress of various cross-sectional shapes

General formulas: $\theta = \dfrac{TL}{KG}$, $\tau = \dfrac{T}{Q}$, where θ = angle of twist, radians; T = twisting moment, in.-lb; L = length, in.; τ = unit shear stress, psi; G = modulus of rigidity, psi; K, in.^{4}; and Q, in.^{3} are functions of the cross section.

Shape	Formula for K in $\theta = \dfrac{TL}{KG}$	Formula for Shear Stress
	$K = \dfrac{\pi d^4}{32}$	$\tau = \dfrac{16T}{\pi d^3}$, max. at the boundary
	$K = {}^1\!/_{32}\pi(d^4 - d_1{}^4)$	$\tau = \dfrac{16Td}{\pi(d^4 - d_1{}^4)}$, max. at the outer boundary
	$K = {}^2\!/_3 \pi r t^3$, r = mean radius	assumed that $t \ll r$ $\tau = \dfrac{3T}{2\pi r t^2} + \dfrac{1.8Tt}{4\pi^2 r^2 t^2}$, max. at both edges away from the ends
	$K = \dfrac{\pi a^3 b^3}{a^2 + b^2}$	$\tau = \dfrac{2T}{\pi a b^2}$, max. at the boundary of the minor axis
	$K = \dfrac{\pi a_1{}^3 b_1{}^3}{a_1{}^2 + b_1{}^2}[(1 + q)^4 - 1]$ $q = \dfrac{a - a_1}{a_1}$ $q = \dfrac{b - b_1}{b_1}$	$\tau = \dfrac{2T}{\pi a_1 b_1{}^2[(1 + q)^4 - 1]}$, max. at the outer boundary of the minor axis
	$K = \dfrac{b^4 \sqrt{3}}{80}$	$\tau = \dfrac{20T}{b^3}$, max. at the midpoint of each side
	$K = 2.69b^4$	$\tau = \dfrac{1.09T}{b^3}$, max. at the midpoint of each side
	$K = \dfrac{ab^3}{16}\left[\dfrac{16}{3} - 3.36\dfrac{b}{a}\left(1 - \dfrac{b^4}{12a^4}\right)\right]$	$\tau = \dfrac{(3a + 1.8b)T}{a^2 b^2}$, max. at the midpoint of each longer side
	$K = \dfrac{2t_1 t_2 (a - t_2)^2 (b - t_1)^2}{at_2 + bt_1 - t_2{}^2 - t_1{}^2}$	$\tau = \dfrac{T}{2t_1(a - t_2)(b - t_1)}$, av. near midpoint of the longer side. $\tau = \dfrac{T}{2t_2(a - t_2)(b - t_1)}$, av. near midpoint of the shorter side. (Higher stresses occur at the inside corners.)
	$K = 0.1406b^4$	$\tau = \dfrac{4.8T}{b^3}$, max. at the midpoint of each side.

SOURCE: Colin Carmichael (ed.): *Kent's Mechanical Engineers' Handbook*. Vol. II, 12th ed., John Wiley and Sons, Inc., New York, 1961.

SECTION 7-13

Keys

Keys are used to prevent relative motion between a shaft and machine elements such as gears, pulleys, sprockets, cams, levers, flywheels, impellers, and so on. There are numerous kinds of keys (some of which have been standardized) for various design requirements. The particular type of key specified will depend upon the magnitude of the torque transmitted, type of loading (that is, steady, varying, or oscillatory), fit required, limiting shaft stress, and cost. Figure 7-7 shows the many types of keyed connections.

Of all the types shown in Figure 7-7, the keys most frequently used are the square key, the tapered key, and the Woodruff key.

Table 7-6 Dimensions of square plain parallel stock keys (dimensions in inches, see Figure 7-7a on next page)

Shaft Diameter	Width and Thickness of Key, W^*	Bottom of Keyseat to Opposite side of Shaft, S	Shaft Diameter	Width and Thickness of Key, W^*	Bottom of Keyseat to Opposite Side of Shaft, S	Shaft Diameter	Width and Thickness of Key, W^*	Bottom of Keyseat to Opposite side of Shaft, S	Shaft Diameter	Width and Thickness of Key, W^*	Bottom of Keyseat to Opposite Side of Shaft, S
$\frac{1}{2}$	$\frac{1}{8}$	0.430	$1\frac{7}{16}$	$\frac{3}{8}$	1.225	$2\frac{3}{8}$	$\frac{5}{8}$	2.021	$3\frac{7}{8}$	1	3.309
$\frac{9}{16}$	$\frac{1}{8}$	0.493	$1\frac{1}{2}$	$\frac{3}{8}$	1.289	$2\frac{7}{16}$	$\frac{5}{8}$	2.084	$3\frac{15}{16}$	1	3.373
$\frac{5}{8}$	$\frac{3}{16}$	0.517	$1\frac{9}{16}$	$\frac{3}{8}$	1.352	$2\frac{1}{2}$	$\frac{5}{8}$	2.148	4	1	3.437
$\frac{11}{16}$	$\frac{3}{16}$	0.581	$1\frac{5}{8}$	$\frac{3}{8}$	1.416	$2\frac{5}{8}$	$\frac{5}{8}$	2.275	$4\frac{1}{4}$	1	3.690
$\frac{3}{4}$	$\frac{3}{16}$	0.644	$1\frac{11}{16}$	$\frac{3}{8}$	1.479	$2\frac{3}{4}$	$\frac{5}{8}$	2.402	$4\frac{7}{16}$	1	3.881
$\frac{13}{16}$	$\frac{3}{16}$	0.708	$1\frac{3}{4}$	$\frac{3}{8}$	1.542	$2\frac{7}{8}$	$\frac{3}{4}$	2.450	$4\frac{1}{2}$	1	3.944
$\frac{7}{8}$	$\frac{3}{16}$	0.771	$1\frac{13}{16}$	$\frac{1}{2}$	1.527	$2\frac{15}{16}$	$\frac{3}{4}$	2.514	$4\frac{3}{4}$	$1\frac{1}{4}$	4.042
$\frac{15}{16}$	$\frac{1}{4}$	0.796	$1\frac{7}{8}$	$\frac{1}{2}$	1.591	3	$\frac{3}{4}$	2.577	$4\frac{15}{16}$	$1\frac{1}{4}$	4.232
1	$\frac{1}{4}$	0.859	$1\frac{15}{16}$	$\frac{1}{2}$	1.655	$3\frac{1}{8}$	$\frac{3}{4}$	2.704	5	$1\frac{1}{4}$	4.296
$1\frac{1}{16}$	$\frac{1}{4}$	0.923	2	$\frac{1}{2}$	1.718	$3\frac{1}{4}$	$\frac{3}{4}$	2.831	$5\frac{1}{4}$	$1\frac{1}{4}$	4.550
$1\frac{1}{8}$	$\frac{1}{4}$	0.956	$2\frac{1}{16}$	$\frac{1}{2}$	1.782	$3\frac{3}{8}$	$\frac{7}{8}$	2.880	$5\frac{7}{16}$	$1\frac{1}{4}$	4.740
$1\frac{3}{16}$	$\frac{1}{4}$	1.049	$2\frac{1}{8}$	$\frac{1}{2}$	1.845	$3\frac{7}{16}$	$\frac{7}{8}$	2.944	$5\frac{1}{2}$	$1\frac{1}{4}$	4.803
$1\frac{1}{4}$	$\frac{1}{4}$	1.112	$2\frac{3}{16}$	$\frac{1}{2}$	1.909	$3\frac{1}{2}$	$\frac{7}{8}$	3.007	$5\frac{3}{4}$	$1\frac{1}{2}$	4.900
$1\frac{5}{16}$	$\frac{5}{16}$	1.137	$2\frac{1}{4}$	$\frac{1}{2}$	1.972	$3\frac{5}{8}$	$\frac{7}{8}$	3.140	$5\frac{15}{16}$	$1\frac{1}{2}$	5.091
$1\frac{3}{8}$	$\frac{5}{16}$	1.201	$2\frac{5}{16}$	$\frac{5}{8}$	1.957	$3\frac{3}{4}$	$\frac{7}{8}$	3.261	6	$1\frac{1}{2}$	5.155

SOURCE: ASME: ANSI Standard B17.1-1967.

*Tolerance on W is -0.0020 in. for shafts $\frac{1}{2}$ to $1\frac{3}{4}$ in., inclusive; -0.0025 in. for shafts $1\frac{13}{16}$ to $3\frac{1}{4}$ in., inclusive; -0.0030 in. for shafts $3\frac{3}{8}$ to 6 in., inclusive.

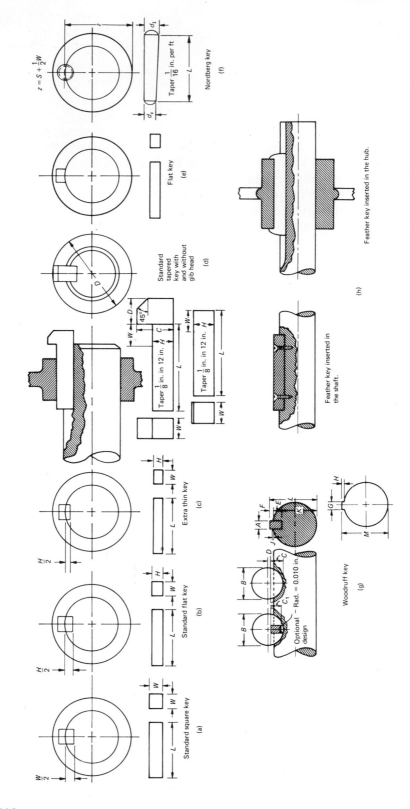

Figure 7-7 Various types of shaft keys.

362

Table 7-7 Dimensions of square and flat taper stock keys (dimensions in inches, [see Figure 7-7d])

Shaft Diameter (inclusive)	Square Type		Flat Type		Tolerance		Stock Length, L		
	Maximum Width, W	Height at Large End, H^*	Maximum Width, W	Height at Large End, H^*	On Width	On Height	Minimum	Maximum	Advancing by Increments of
$1/2 - 9/16$	$1/8$	$1/8$	$1/8$	$3/32$	-0.0020	$+0.0020$	$1/2$	2	$1/4$
$5/8 - 7/8$	$3/16$	$3/16$	$3/16$	$1/8$	-0.0020	$+0.0020$	$3/4$	3	$3/8$
$15/16-1\,1/4$	$1/4$	$1/4$	$1/4$	$3/16$	-0.0020	$+0.0020$	1	4	$1/2$
$1\,5/16-1\,3/8$	$5/16$	$5/16$	$5/16$	$1/4$	-0.0020	$+0.0020$	$1\,1/4$	$5\,1/4$	$5/8^\dagger$
$1\,7/16-1\,3/4$	$3/8$	$3/8$	$3/8$	$1/4$	-0.0020	$+0.0020$	$1\,1/2$	6	$3/4$
$1\,13/16-2\,1/4$	$1/2$	$1/2$	$1/2$	$3/8$	-0.0025	$+0.0025$	2	8	1
$2\,5/16-2\,3/4$	$5/8$	$5/8$	$5/8$	$7/16$	-0.0025	$+0.0025$	$2\,1/2$	10	$1\,1/4$
$2\,7/8 -3\,1/4$	$3/4$	$3/4$	$3/4$	$1/2$	-0.0025	$+0.0025$	3	12	$1\,1/2$
$3\,3/8 -3\,3/4$	$7/8$	$7/8$	$7/8$	$5/8$	-0.0030	$+0.0030$	$3\,1/2$	14	$1\,3/4$
$3\,7/8 -4\,1/2$	1	1	1	$3/4$	-0.0030	$+0.0030$	4	16	2
$4\,3/4 -5\,1/2$	$1\,1/4$	$1\,1/4$	$1\,1/4$	$7/8$	-0.0030	$+0.0030$	5	20	$2\,1/2$
$5\,3/4 -6$	$1\,1/2$	$1\,1/2$	$1\,1/2$	1	-0.0030	$+0.0030$	6	24	3

SOURCE: ASME: ANSI Standard B17.1–1967.
*This height of the key is measured at the distance W, equal to the width of the key, from the large end.
†$4\,1/2$ in. length instead of $4\,3/8$ in.

Because the actual stress distribution for keyed connections is not completely understood, a factor of safety of 1.5 should be used when the torque is steady. For minor shock loads, a factor of safety of 2.5 should be used, and one up to 4.5 should be used for high shock (especially if the loads are reversible). To prevent the hub from rocking on the shaft when using a straight key (that is, no taper) and to assure a good grip, the hub length should be at least 25% larger than the shaft diameter. The minimum key length should also be at least 25% larger than the shaft diameter. The hub is usually kept in place on a straight key by means of set screws. When set screws are not used, a light press fit between the hub and shaft should be specified [4].

Dimensions for various types of keys have been standardized[13] and can be found in engineering handbooks. Data for sizing only the square, tapered, and Woodruff keys are listed in Tables 7-6, 7-7, and 7-8, respectively. The letters at the top of these tables correspond to Figures 7-7a, b, and g.

[13] ANSI Standard B17.1–1967.

Table 7-8 Abbreviated list of Woodruff key dimensions (see Figure 7-7g on page 362)

Key No.	Suggested Shaft Sizes, in.	Nominal Key-Size $A^\dagger \times B$ in.	Height of Key, in. Max. C	Max. D	Distance Below Center* E in.	Shearing Area, in.^{2}
204	$\frac{5}{16} - \frac{3}{8}$	$\frac{1}{16} \times \frac{1}{2}$	0.203	0.194	$\frac{3}{64}$	0.030
305	$\frac{7}{16} - \frac{1}{2}$	$\frac{3}{32} \times \frac{5}{8}$	0.250	0.240	$\frac{1}{16}$	0.052
405	$\frac{11}{16} - \frac{3}{4}$	$\frac{1}{8} \times \frac{5}{8}$	0.250	0.240	$\frac{1}{16}$	0.072
506	$\frac{13}{16} - \frac{15}{16}$	$\frac{5}{32} \times \frac{3}{4}$	0.313	0.303	$\frac{1}{16}$	0.109
507	$\frac{7}{8} - \frac{15}{16}$	$\frac{5}{32} \times \frac{7}{8}$	0.375	0.365	$\frac{1}{16}$	0.129
608	$1 \ \ -1\frac{3}{16}$	$\frac{3}{16} \times 1$	0.438	0.428	$\frac{1}{16}$	0.178
807	$1\frac{1}{4} - 1\frac{5}{16}$	$\frac{1}{4} \times \frac{7}{8}$	0.375	0.365	$\frac{1}{16}$	0.198
809	$1\frac{1}{4} - 1\frac{3}{4}$	$\frac{1}{4} \times 1\frac{1}{8}$	0.484	0.475	$\frac{5}{64}$	0.262
810	$1\frac{1}{4} - 1\frac{3}{4}$	$\frac{1}{4} \times 1\frac{1}{4}$	0.547	0.537	$\frac{5}{64}$	0.296
812	$1\frac{1}{2} - 1\frac{3}{4}$	$\frac{1}{4} \times 1\frac{1}{2}$	0.641	0.631	$\frac{7}{64}$	0.356
1012	$1\frac{13}{16} - 2\frac{1}{2}$	$\frac{5}{16} \times 1\frac{1}{2}$	0.641	0.631	$\frac{7}{64}$	0.438
1212	$1\frac{7}{8} - 2\frac{1}{2}$	$\frac{3}{8} \times 1\frac{1}{2}$	0.641	0.631	$\frac{7}{64}$	0.517

SOURCE: ASME: AWSI Standard B17.2-1967.
*This dimension is given to help make drawings and layouts.
†The key extends into the hub a distance of $A/2$.

Standard square key

A standard square key is perhaps the most common type of key where the dimension W is equal to one quarter of the shaft diameter (see Table 7-6). As shown in Figure 7-7, it is fitted so that one half of the thickness is in the shaft and the other half is in the hub. In the hub, the keyway is cut by a key-seating machine or by broaching. The keyway in the shaft is cut by milling as shown in Figure 7-8. A plain milling cutter having a face width W is used to cut the "sled runner" keyway. An end mill with a diameter equal to the width W of the key is used to cut the profiled keyway. Where possible, the sled runner type should be used since the stress concentration for this kind of keyway is less than that for a profiled keyway. However, near a change of shaft diameter, the "sled runner" keyway may extend into the shaft shoulder and thus compound the stress concentration (that is, the fillet radius and the keyway). In such cases, it may be advisable to use a profiled keyway which would not extend to the fillet radius.

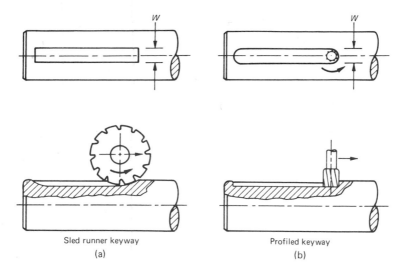

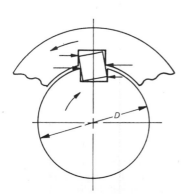

Sled runner keyway
(a)

Profiled keyway
(b)

Figure 7-8 Method of cutting keyways in shafts.

If standard square or flat plain parallel keystock is used, the fit in the shaft can be "line-to-line" or slightly loose with deliberate clearance between the top of the key and the slot in the hub. As a result, the key must be held in place with a set screw through the hub and pressed on the top of the key. For very wide keys, the key can be held in place with countersunk flat head or cap screws if the shaft is not weakened.

The possible loose fit of a key presents a complex stress analysis problem that is not completely understood. Figure 7-9 shows an exaggerated illustration of how the position of the key is rotated, producing a severe and complex stress distribution on the sides and edges of the key as well as the edges of the keyway.

When it is important to insure a tight fit for the key in the shaft, the designer cannot use standard keystock. Instead, he must specify a tolerance on the key that will provide a slight interference fit. However, for purposes

Figure 7-9 A loose fit in the keyway.

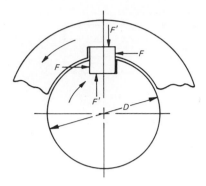

Figure 7-10 A tight fit in the keyway.

of calculation, it is assumed that a stock key is fitted as shown in Figure 7-10, implying, thereby, that the reactive forces shown are uniformly distributed along the full length of the key. The procedure followed in sizing a key is illustrated by Example 7-2.

Example 7-2. A gray cast iron gear with a 3-in. long hub transmits 1200 lb-ft of torque to a steel shaft. The gear material is ASTM 40, the 2-in. diameter shaft is made of AISI 1045 cold-drawn steel, and the key is to be cut from AISI 1020 cold-drawn square stock. If the transmitted torque produces intermittent minor shocks, find (1) the minimum length of key and (2) the length of key, if the key and shaft are to be of equal strength and of the same material.

Solution: From Table A-1 in Appendix A for ATSM 40, we obtain $S_{uc} = 140,000$ psi. From Table A-2 in Appendix A for AISI C1020 and C1045, we have, respectively, $S_{yp} = 66,000$ psi and $S_{yp} = 85,000$ psi. For intermittent shock we assume the factor of safety $N = 2.0$.

Because the precise position of the force F (see Figure 7-10) is not exactly known, the reactive force on the key is assumed to act at the outside shaft diameter.

Thus, the transmitted torque is

$$T = F(D/2) \qquad (7\text{-}19)$$

If it is assumed that the shear stress on the key acts in that plane of the key which is tangent at the shaft diameter, we have

$$S_s = \frac{F}{A} = \frac{F}{WL} \qquad (7\text{-}20)$$

where A is the shear area across the key.

Substituting equation (7-20) into equation (7-19) for F, we obtain

$$T = \frac{S_s WLD}{2} \qquad (7\text{-}21)[14]$$

where S_s is the design shear stress and L is the length of key.

[14] Careful inspection of equations (7-21) and (7-23) will show that, if the maximum shear theory of failure is used (i.e., $S_{syp} = 0.5S_{yp}$), then a square key is equally strong in shear and compression. The reader can verify this statement by equating the torques of each equation.

Since for a square or flat key one half of the thickness lies within the shaft and the other half lies within the hub of the gear (pulley, cam, and so on), there is a compressive or bearing stress on the side of the key, the side of the keyway, and the side of the hub. The compressive stress is expressed as

$$S_c = \frac{F}{A} = \frac{F}{(W/2)L} \tag{7-22}$$

where A is the bearing (that is, compression) area. Substituting equation (7-22) into equation (7-19) for F, we obtain

$$T = \frac{S_c WLD}{4} \tag{7-23}^{[15]}$$

where S_c is the design bearing (compression) stress.

Part 1. Using equation (3-6), $S_{syp} = 0.58 S_{yp}$, and with $N = 2$, we have for the key

$$S_s = \frac{0.58(66,000)}{2} = 19,150 \text{ psi}$$

Referring to Table 7-6, we find that for a 2-in. diameter shaft, a $\frac{1}{2}$-in. square key is required. Thus, using equation (7-21), the length of the key based on shear is

$$L = \frac{2T}{S_s WD} = \frac{2(1200)(12)}{19,150(0.5)(2)} = 1.5 \text{ in.}$$

Using equation (7-23) and a design stress of $S_c = S_{yp}/N = 66,000/2 = 33,000$ psi, the length of the key based on compression (that is, bearing) is

$$L = \frac{4T}{S_c WD} = \frac{4(1200)(12)}{33,000(0.5)(2)} = 1.75$$

It is obvious that further calculation for the length of key based on the bearing stress of the keyway in the shaft or bearing in the keyway slot of the cast iron hub is not necessary because in both cases the value of S_c is greater than that for the key. As a result, the length of key required for these two cases will be smaller than either of the above calculations. From these calculations, we conclude that a $\frac{1}{2}$-in. square key, 1.75 in. long is required. However, in accordance with the statement made in the earlier part of this section, the minimum key length must be at least 25% larger than the shaft diameter or 2.5 in. long in this application. To insure that the key does not rock in the axial plane of the shaft when the set screw in the hub is brought against its surface and tightened, we shall finally specify that the length of the key be 3.00 in. With a key of this length, the factor of safety in bearing (compression) becomes

$$S_c = \frac{4T}{LWD} = \frac{4(1200)(12)}{3(0.5)(2)} = 19,200 \text{ psi}$$

Thus

$$N = \frac{66,000}{19,200} = 3.45$$

[15] See footnote concerning equation (7-21).

Part 2. From tests performed at the University of Illinois it was determined that the torsional strength of a solid round shaft was reduced by a keyway in accordance with the empirical formula for relative strength given in equation (7-24).

$$e = 1.0 - 0.2w - 1.1h \qquad (7\text{-}24)$$

where e is the relative strength, w is the ratio of the width of the keyway to the diameter of the shaft, and h is the ratio of the depth of the keyway to the shaft diameter. In this case we have

$$e = 1.0 - 0.2\left(\frac{0.5}{2.0}\right) - 1.1\left(\frac{0.25}{2}\right) = 0.8125$$

Therefore the torque that the shaft can transmit is

$$T = 0.8125\frac{S_s J}{r} = 0.8125\frac{S_s \pi D^3}{16} \qquad (7\text{-}25)$$

Equating equation (7-25) to equation (7-21) (that is, the strength of the key in shear), we have

$$0.8125\frac{S_s \pi D^3}{16} = \frac{S_s WLD}{2}$$

or

$$L = 0.8125\frac{\pi D^2}{8W} = 0.8125\frac{\pi(2)^2}{8(0.5)} = 2.55 \text{ in.}$$

If we now replace S_s in equation (7-25) by $0.58S_{yp}$, we can equate this torque to equation (7-23) (that is, the strength of the key in bearing). Thus

$$0.8125\frac{0.58S_{yp}\pi D^3}{16} = \frac{S_c WLD}{4}$$

Since $S_{yp} = S_c$ for a ductile material

$$L = (0.8125)(0.58)\frac{\pi D^2}{4W} = 0.471\frac{\pi(2)^2}{4(0.5)} = 2.96 \text{ in.}$$

use $L = 3.00$ in. ●

Standard flat key

The standard flat key (Figure 7-7b) is used where the hub of the gear, pulley, and so on, is thin. The depth of the keyseat in the shaft is standard, whereas the depth in the hub is shallow. The **extra thin flat key** (Figure 7-7c) has a shallow keyseat in both the shaft and the hub. It is intended for use where the shaft is hollow and the hub is thin.

Tapered keys depend on the frictional contact between the hub and the shaft to transmit the torque. The most common type of tapered key is

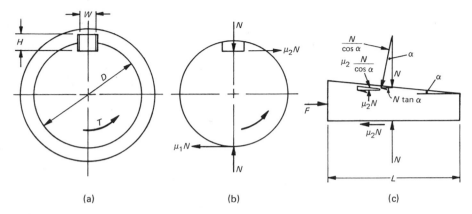

Figure 7-11 Shaft and hub assembly using a tapered key. (a) The assembly.
(b) Shaft loading. (c) Key loading.

either the Gib-Head type or the Plain type (see Figure 7-7d). This key
(tapered) is used to transmit **medium level** torques and is "locked" in place
radially and axially by the wedging action of the key between the hub and
the shaft. Sometimes, tapered keys are also designed to have bearing pressure
on the sides when fitted in the keyway. As shown in Figure (7-7d), the top
surface of the key has a standard taper of $\frac{1}{8}$ in./ft of length, which complies
with a mating taper in the hub. The lower part of the key surface is flat and
is sunk into the shaft. The Gib-Head type permits the key to be readily
removed by the prying action of a tool (for example, a screwdriver) between
the hub and the Gib head. However, it is advisable when specifying such a
key that the Gib head be so located as not to project beyond the end of a
shaft for obvious reasons of safety. If possible, a plain flat taper stock key
should be used.

As stated above, the transmitted torque between the shaft and the hub
depends upon the frictional force. This torque can be determined by balancing
the forces on the free body diagram of the shaft (refer to Figure 7-11). From
Figure 7-11b we obtain

$$T = \tfrac{1}{2}\mu_1 ND + \tfrac{1}{2}\mu_2 ND$$

But

$$N = WLS_c$$

Thus

$$T = \tfrac{1}{2}(\mu_1 + \mu_2)DWLS_c \qquad (7\text{-}26)$$

Using the values of μ_1 and μ_2 stated below, this equation becomes

$$T = 0.135DWLS_c \qquad (7\text{-}27)$$

where

T = transmitted torque, lb-in.

μ_1 = coefficient of friction between shaft and hub. A reasonable value to assume is 0.25 [5].

μ_2 = coefficient of friction between the key and the shaft keyseat. Good practice dictates that the key be greased and so μ_2 can be taken as 0.10 [5].

S_c = compressive stress in key, psi.

From Figure 7-11c we can obtain the force F required to drive the key into the assembly by summing the horizontal forces

$$F = 2\mu_2 N + N \tan \alpha = WLS_c(2\mu_2 + \tan \alpha) \tag{7-28}$$

Using $\mu_2 = 0.10$ and $\tan \alpha = 0.0104$ (that is, value of $\frac{1}{8}$ in./ft of taper), equation (7-28) becomes

$$F = 0.2104WLS_c \tag{7-29}$$

Where light, steady, nonoscillating loads are to be transmitted, and a keyseat would weaken the shaft excessively, a **flat key** (Figure 7-7e) can be used. The key can be flat or tapered on one side. When one side is flat, a set screw through the hub is necessary to keep the key in place. On the other hand, when the surface of the key that contacts the slot in the hub is tapered, a wedging action takes place at assembly, and equations (7-26) and (7-27) can be used to establish the key size and its torque capacity.

As can be observed in Figure 7-7e, the flat key requires that a flat surface be milled on the shaft to seat the key.

Woodruff key

The Woodruff key (Figure 7-7g) is a light duty key which, because of its deeper keyseat, weakens the shaft but has the advantage of being able to align itself readily with the hub, as it is free to rotate within the semicircular keyseat. It is widely used in the automotive and machine tool industries, and is usually limited to shafts no larger in diameter than $2\frac{1}{2}$ in. This type of key has the advantage of (1) not tipping or rolling over because of the deep keyseat, (2) readily adjusting itself to the mating hub due to its ability to rotate freely within the keyseat, and (3) being well adapted for use in fitting tapered shafts to hubs. Where a shaft is too weakened by the use of a certain size of Woodruff key, the problem can be reduced in severity by using two or more keys (in line) with a longer hub. A special milling cutter is used to cut the keyway in the shaft, allowing for clearance in both the diameter and width.

Dimensions for standard Woodruff keys are given in Table 7-8. From this table, it is possible to calculate the torque carrying capacity of a Woodruff key.

Example 7-3. A gear that transmits 4000 lb-in. of torque is to be keyed to a $1\frac{1}{4}$-in. diameter shaft by a $\frac{1}{4}$ by $1\frac{1}{8}$ (that is, Key No. 809) Woodruff key. What is the factor of safety of the key for both shear and bearing? The key material is AISI 1030.

Solution: From Table A-2 in Appendix A for cold-drawn 1030 steel $S_{yp} = 76,000$ psi. Thus, to obtain the allowable shearing stress we use equation (3-6)

$$S_{syp} = 0.58S_{yp} = 0.58(76,000) = 44,100 \text{ psi}$$

Now, the torque capacity of the key in shear is

$$T = S_{syp}A_s\frac{D}{2} = (44,100)(0.262)\left(\frac{1.25}{2}\right) = 7220 \text{ lb-in.}$$

To obtain the torque carrying capacity of the key in bearing, we need to know the bearing area. From the second footnote in Table 7-8, we know that the portion of the key that projects into the hub is equal to one half of the A dimension in Table 7-8. With this information, we can establish the bearing area A_b. Thus, the torque carrying capacity of the key in bearing is

$$T = S_{yp}A_b\frac{D}{2} = 76,000\left(\frac{0.25}{2} \times 1.125\right)\left(\frac{1.25}{2}\right) = 6670 \text{ lb-in.}$$

Finally,

$$N(\text{shear}) = 7220/4000 = 1.81$$

$$N(\text{bearing}) = 6670/4000 = 1.67. \quad \bullet$$

For light duty or medium operation, it is also possible to use a **taper pin**[16] as a key, as shown in Figure 7-7f, but the taper is $\frac{1}{4}$ in./ft (that is, Morse standard paper pins) rather than $\frac{1}{16}$ in./ft as indicated in the figure.

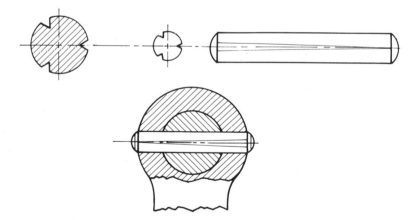

Figure 7-12 A grooved pin used for holding a hub to a shaft. These pins do not require the hole to be reamed. The assembly is held in place by elastic deformation of the edges of the three sectors, and the effective diameters of these edges are enlarged by the three axial grooves.

[16] For sizes and data on taper pins, see ANSI Standard B4.20–1958.

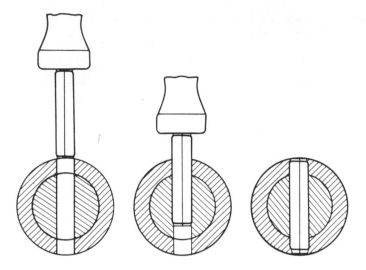

Figure 7-13 A roll pin as used to fix a hub to a shaft. The assembly is held together by the spring action of the pin.

The tapered hole is reamed at assembly so that half the pin diameter is in the hub and the other half of the diameter is in the shaft.

Quite often, straight dowel pins, grooved pins (see Sigure 7-12) or roll pins (see Figure 7-13) are used to fix a hub to a shaft. These methods of fixing a hub to a shaft are limited to light duty service.

Heavy duty keys

Heavy duty keys are the Nordberg key (Figure 7-7f), the Kennedy key, the Lewis key, and the Barth key, of which the latter three are not shown in Figure 7-7.

The **Nordberg key** (Nordberg Manufacturing Company) is a pin type key that is available both in straight and tapered shapes. However, for heavy duty service, the tapered shape is used. The key is driven into a reamed hole at the end of the shaft. As with the Morse taper pin, half of the pin diameter is located in the shaft, and half is located in the hub. As indicated in Figure 7-7f, the taper is $\frac{1}{16}$ in./ft.

A **feather key** (Figure 7-7h) is used when it is necessary to permit a hub to have axial movement along the shaft and to prevent any rotation between the shaft and the hub. The key is either screwed to the shaft with a running fit in the hub or is held in the hub with a running fit in the shaft. Generally, the former design is preferred. When two keys 180 deg apart are used, analysis indicates [5] that the axial friction force required to move the hub along the shaft is one half of that required when one key is used. As a guide in sizing a feather key, the bearing pressure on its side should not exceed 1000 psi [12].

SECTION 7-14

Splines

The keys discussed in Section 7.13 tend to weaken a shaft because of the keyway. By cutting splines, which are integral with the shaft, the effect is the same as having added multiple keys without having weakened the shaft to the same degree. There are two forms of splines: (1) straight splines and (2) involute splines.

Straight splines

Straight splines are the older of the two forms (adopted by the SAE in 1914) and are generally being replaced by the stronger involute forms. Nevertheless, many machine tools, automotive equipment, and so on, employ this form, and some designers continue to use it because of its relative simplicity. Figure 7-14 shows the standard SAE 4, 6, 10, and 16 spline fittings. Table 7-9 establishes the maximum dimensions for these splines based on the nominal shaft diameter D.

To obtain a particular class of fit, the shaft dimensions are varied and reflect the type of material used, its heat treatment, and the machining method employed. The splined fittings (for which the dimensions in Table 7-9 and the *SAE Handbook* apply) are soft broached. The machine tool industry varies the aforementioned method of establishing fits by varying the spline fitting dimensions rather than the splined shaft dimensions. This

Table 7-9 Formulas for Dimensions of Splines

No. of Splines	Standard Sizes, Nominal	All Fits	Permanent Fit		Not Slide Under Load		Slide Under Load	
		W	h	d	h	d	h	d
4	by $\frac{1}{8}$-in. from $\frac{3}{4}$	$0.241D$	$0.075D$	$0.850D$	$0.125D$	$0.075D$		
6	in. to $1\frac{3}{4}$; 2, $2\frac{1}{4}$, $2\frac{1}{2}$, 3	$0.250D$	$0.050D$	$0.900D$	$0.075D$	$0.850D$	$0.100D$	$0.800D$
10	Same as above, plus by $\frac{1}{2}$ in. from 3 to 6 in.	$0.156D$	$0.045D$	$0.910D$	$0.070D$	$0.860D$	$0.095D$	$0.810D$
16	by $\frac{1}{2}$ in. from 2 to 6 in.	$0.098D$	$0.045D$	$0.910D$	$0.070D$	$0.860D$	$0.095D$	$0.810D$

SOURCE: *SAE Handbook*. Society of Automotive Engineers, New York, 1948.

For D and d, tolerance allowed of −0.001 in. for shafts $\frac{3}{4}$ to $1\frac{3}{4}$ in., inclusive; −0.002 for shafts 2 to 3 in., inclusive; −0.003 in. for shafts $3\frac{1}{2}$ to 6 in., inclusive, for 4-, 6-, and 10-spline fittings; tolerance of −0.003 in. allowed for all sizes of 16-spline fittings.

For W, tolerance allowed of −0.002 in. for shafts $\frac{3}{4}$ to $1\frac{3}{4}$ in., inclusive; −0.003 in. for shafts 2 to 6 in., inclusive, for 4-, 6-, and 10-spline fittings; tolerance of −0.003 allowed for all sizes of 16-spline fittings.

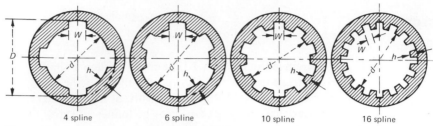

4 spline   **6 spline**   **10 spline**   **16 spline**

Figure 7-14 SAE standard straight spline fittings.

approach is preferred because a uniform grinding operation can be performed on the shaft. Thus, should a splined shaft have a free fit and a press fit with two different spline fittings, only one shaft grinding operation is needed—the required fits being obtained by varying the dimensions of the fittings. The machine tool industry requires a wider range of fits than those listed in Table 7-9 and has, therefore, designated the following fits: free fit, sliding fit, push fit, light drive fit, and press fit. Specifications concerning these fits may be obtained from reference [13].

According to the SAE, the equation for the theoretical torque capacity of straight sided splines with sliding (based on 1000-psi spline pressure) is

$$T = 1000nr_mhL \qquad (7\text{-}30)$$

where

T = theoretical torque capacity, lb/in.
n = number of splines
$r_m = (D + d)/4$ in. (see Figure 7-14)
h = depth of spline, in. (see Figure 7-14)
L = length of spline contact, in.

Involute splines

Involute splines are becoming the predominant spline form because they are stronger than straight sided splines and are easier to cut and to fit. These splines have the general form of internal and external involute gear teeth (see Chapter 10) with a 30 deg pressure angle[17] and one half the depth of a standard gear tooth. The external spline can be formed either by hobbing or by a gear shaper. Internal splines are formed by broaching or by a gear shaper. To control tolerances, the minimum effective space width and the minimum major diameter of the internal spline are held to basic dimensions. The external spline, however, is varied to obtain the desired fit. The advantages of involute splines are (1) maximum strength at the base of the tooth, (2) accuracy of spacing and the equalizing of the bearing pressure stresses among the teeth, and (3) the elimination of the need for grinding due to the smooth cutting action of a gear hob. The nomenclature associated with involute splines is shown in Figure 7-15.

[17] Pressure angles of 45, 20, 25, and $14\frac{1}{2}$ deg are also sometimes used. However both the SAE and ANSI specify only the 30 deg pressure angle in their standards.

Splines are made having a flat root or a fillet root (see Figure 7-15) and are available in 14 diametral pitches designated as fractions, namely $\frac{2.5}{5}$, $\frac{3}{6}$, $\frac{4}{8}$, $\frac{5}{10}$, $\frac{6}{12}$, $\frac{8}{16}$, $\frac{10}{20}$, $\frac{12}{24}$, $\frac{16}{32}$, $\frac{20}{40}$, $\frac{24}{48}$, $\frac{32}{64}$, $\frac{40}{80}$, and $\frac{48}{96}$. Within each fractional designation, splines can be cut having 6 to 50 teeth. The numerator of these fractions is the diametrical pitch P (see Chapter 10), and the denominator (always double the numerator) controls the depth of the tooth.

There are two types of spline fits[18] (see Figure 7-16):

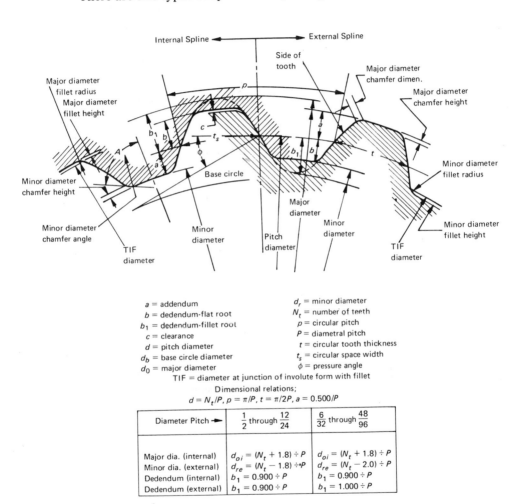

a = addendum
b = dedendum-flat root
b_1 = dedendum-fillet root
c = clearance
d = pitch diameter
d_b = base circle diameter
d_0 = major diameter

d_r = minor diameter
N_t = number of teeth
p = circular pitch
P = diametral pitch
t = circular tooth thickness
t_s = circular space width
ϕ = pressure angle

TIF = diameter at junction of involute form with fillet

Dimensional relations;
$$d = N_t/P, \; p = \pi/P, \; t = \pi/2P, \; a = 0.500/P$$

Diameter Pitch ➤	$\frac{1}{2}$ through $\frac{12}{24}$	$\frac{6}{32}$ through $\frac{48}{96}$
Major dia. (internal)	$d_{oi} = (N_t + 1.8) \div P$	$d_{oi} = (N_t + 1.8) \div P$
Minor dia. (external)	$d_{re} = (N_t - 1.8) \div P$	$d_{re} = (N_t - 2.0) \div P$
Dedendum (internal)	$b_1 = 0.900 \div P$	$b_1 = 0.900 \div P$
Dedendum (external)	$b_1 = 0.900 \div P$	$b_1 = 1.000 \div P$

Figure 7-15 Nomenclature and some dimensional relations for the involute spline profile. Note that the vertical line separates the internal spline form from the external spline form. The dotted curve is the outline of the optional fillet root form. [From H. L. Horton (ed.): *Machinery's Handbook*, 15th ed. The Industrial Press, New York, 1957.]

[18] Prior to 1959, the minor diameter was also used for tolerance control, but this basis of control has since been deleted from the standards.

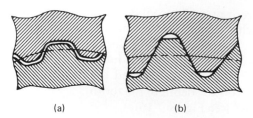

Figure 7-16 (a) Major diameter fitted spline.
(b) Side fitted spline.

(a)   (b)

1. **Major diameter fitted** splines where the fit is controlled by variation of the major diameter of the external splines.
2. **Side fitted** splines where the fit is controlled by varying the tooth thickness. It is customary to use this type of fit for fillet root type splines. However, it also can be used for the flat root type spline.

The two types of fits are divided into two classes:

Class 1. A loose fit where there is clearance at all points.
Class 2. A close fit, which is close on either the major diameter or the sides of the tooth.

According to reference [14], "for carrying of any load or to obtain stability, there is seldom need to have a spline longer than its pitch diameter." The spline length (L), required to transmit a torque (T) is obtained as follows.

We found in Chapter 5 that the torque carrying capacity of a shaft (based on shearing stress) was

$$T = \frac{\pi D_{re}^3 (1 - D_i^4/D_{re}^4)S_s}{16} \qquad (7\text{-}31)[19]$$

where the terms are those defined in Figure 7-15 except for D_i, which is the internal diameter of a hollow shaft. If we assume that all the teeth are in uniform contact,[20] the torque carrying capacity of the shaft (based on the compressive strength of the teeth) is

$$T = \frac{S_c AND}{2} = \frac{S_c LhND}{2} \qquad (7\text{-}32)$$

where

A = area of contact of one tooth = Lh
h = height of tooth contact = $0.8/P = 0.8D/N_t$ (from reference [14])

Replacing h in equation (7-32), we get

$$T = 0.4S_c LD^2 \qquad (7\text{-}33)$$

[19] Again we note that this equation can also be used for a solid shaft, namely, $D_i \equiv 0$.

[20] This assumption is *not* strictly true, since manufacturing accuracy plays a decisive role in determining spacing errors. Furthermore, shaft alignment also affects tooth contact and tooth load distribution.

The shear area at the pitch diameter of the splines is $\pi DL/2$ and so the shearing stress is

$$S_s = \frac{4T}{\pi D^2 L} \tag{7-34}$$

Solving equation (7-34) for T and equating it to equation (7-33), we find that $S_s/S_c = 0.5093$. Therefore, we conclude that the splines are more highly stressed in shear than in compression (that is, bearing). Thus, shearing stress becomes the basis for design of splines.

If we now suggest that the strength of the spline teeth in shear should be the same as the shaft strength in shear, we can equate the shearing stress of equation (7-34) with that of equation (7-31) to obtain

$$L = \frac{D_{re}^3(1 - D_i^4/D_{re}^4)}{4D^2} \tag{7-35}$$

For a solid shaft, equation (7-35) becomes

$$L = \frac{1}{4} \frac{D_{re}^3}{D^2} \tag{7-36}$$

However, according to the SAE, "actual practice has shown that due to inaccuracies in spacing and tooth form, the equivalent of about 25% of teeth are in contact, so that a good approximate formula for a splined shaft is"

$$L_e = \frac{D_{re}^3(1 - D_i^4/D_{re}^4)}{D^2} \tag{7-37}$$

where L_e = effective spline length, and $D_i = 0$ for a solid shaft.

Involute serrations are involute splines that have a 45 deg pressure angle and are used mainly for close fits not subjected to sliding. However, it is possible to use other classes of fits. The nomenclature used for splines applies directly to involute serrations. Involute pitches listed in the *SAE Handbook* are $\frac{10}{20}$, $\frac{16}{32}$, $\frac{24}{48}$, $\frac{32}{64}$, $\frac{40}{80}$, $\frac{48}{96}$, $\frac{64}{128}$, $\frac{80}{160}$, and $\frac{128}{256}$, and complete tables for involute serration specifications are provided.

Involute serrations have teeth that are shallower than involute splines and also have broader bases, less depth of contact, and quite frequently provide manufacturing advantages. Compared to involute splines, involute serrations have greater contact pressures, sliding resistance, and radial forces for the same loads. By using finer pitches, a wider range of index positions is possible by virtue of the greater number of teeth. For more detailed information, the reader is again referred to the *SAE Handbook*.

SECTION 7-15

Couplings

Couplings are used to connect two shafts. For example, a coupling is used to join the shaft of an electric motor to the line shaft of a machine or a hydraulic turbine to an electric generator or, for practical reasons, is used to sectionalize a long shaft, and so on. Couplings used for such typical applications are called **permanent couplings** because their connections would only be broken for repairs and/or general maintenance. Those applications which require the shafts to periodically disengage are called clutches, and are discussed in Chapter 13.

Permanent couplings are classified into two groups (1) rigid couplings and (2) flexible couplings.

Rigid couplings

Rigid couplings are used for shafts having good collinear alignment and must be installed with care and forethought. Connecting misaligned shafts with a rigid coupling can lead to bearing failure, fatigued shafts, worn flanges, or broken flange bolts. When used on line shafting, support bearings should be located near the coupling and checked for both static and dynamic balance. Although simple in design, rigid couplings are generally restricted to relatively low speed applications where good shaft alignment or shaft flexibility can be expected.

There are three important types of rigid couplings. These are the compression, ribbed, and flange type couplings (see Figure 7-17). Figure 7-17a shows a compression coupling (also called the Seller's coupling) that has two split cones keyed to the shafts. By tightening the bolts, the cones are forced to "squeeze" the shaft by the wedging action of the double conical shell. These couplings are used on shafts from $1\frac{7}{16}-8\frac{5}{16}$ in. diameter. The inspection hole in the conical shell permits an observer to see when the cones are drawn together.

Figure 7-17b shows a flanged compression coupling in which the split double cone does not move axially but is squeezed against the shaft by the wedging action of flanges drawn together by the bolts. This type of coupling transmits torque only by the frictional force between the shaft and the split double cone eliminating, thereby, the need for a key and keyway. The flange dimensions D_1 and L are approximately the same as those for flanged couplings (see Figure 7-17b).

Compression couplings are available for shafts up to 3-in. diameters, and can be made to order for nonstandard or oversized shafts.

Figure 7-17c is made in two axial parts clamped together by means of bolts as shown. A square key is used to maintain shaft alignment as well as to locate one half of the coupling. Torque is transmitted mainly by friction (due to the clamping action of the bolts) and partially by the key. This

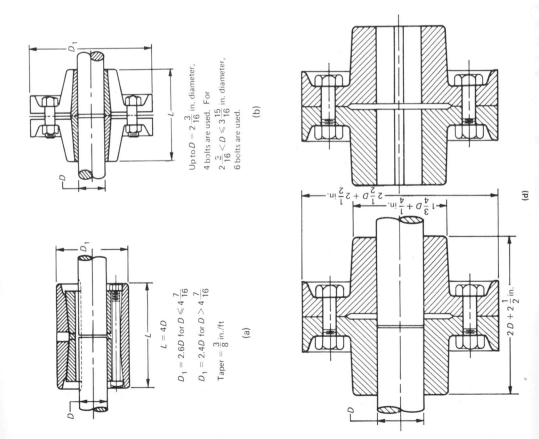

Figure 7-17 Types of rigid coupling. (a) Sellers conevise coupling. (b) Flanged compression coupling. (c) Ribbed coupling. (d) Flange coupling. [Courtesy Link-Belt Enclosed Drive Division, FMC Corporation.]

(c)

$L = 4D$

$D_1 = 2.6D$ for $D \leqslant 4\frac{7}{16}$

$D_1 = 2.4D$ for $D > 4\frac{7}{16}$

Taper $= \frac{3}{8}$ in./ft

(a)

Up to $D = 2\frac{3}{16}$ in. diameter, 4 bolts are used. For $2\frac{3}{16} < D \leqslant 3\frac{15}{16}$ in. diameter, 6 bolts are used.

(b)

$1\frac{3}{4}D + \frac{1}{4}$ in.

$2\frac{1}{2}D + 2\frac{1}{2}$ in.

$2D + 2\frac{1}{2}$ in.

(d)

type of coupling is intended for heavy duty service. Standard units are available for shafts up to 7-in. diameters and can transmit the torque based on AISI C1018 shaft strength.

The most widely used of the rigid couplings is the flange coupling (Figure 7-17d), which is capable of transmitting large torques. These couplings, although larger in diameter than the two types previously described, are shorter and about 20–25 % lighter. Although flange couplings have not been standardized,[21] they are commercially available to fit shafts up to 8-in. diameters, and are rated at a torque capacity equivalent to AISI C1018 shafting.

As can be seen in Figure 7-17d, flange alignment (called register) is obtained in one of two ways. One way is to permit one shaft to act as a pilot and enter the mating flange to about $\frac{3}{8}$ in. The second way (not shown in Figure 7-17d) is to machine a shallow projection (that is, rabbet) on one flange face and fit it to a female recess cut in the face of the other flange. Alignment is obtained by carefully machining the diameter of male projection and female recess.

Best results from this kind of coupling are obtained when the flanges are shrunk on the shaft and then finish machined with the shafts straightened afterwards. For greater reliability and strength (for example, marine and automotive drive shafts), flanges are often forged integrally with the shafting. When flanges are force fitted onto shafts, square keys are used, but tapered keys are used when flanges are placed on the shafts with a slip fit.

Torque is assumed to be transmitted in one of two ways, (1) by means of carefully fitted (that is, ground) bolts in holes that are line reamed at assembly or (2) by the frictional force produced between the two flange faces when bolted together. The first method, requiring selective assembly, needs a dowel pin and hole (or some other marker) on each half of the flange. This will guarantee the realignment of the same bolt holes if the flanges have to be disconnected and then reassembled. With virtually no clearance between the bolt holes and bolts, the bolts are subjected to shearing stress.[22] By assuming that the torque is transmitted by virtue of the friction force between the flange faces, there is no need for ground bolts and line reamed bolt holes. In fact, enough clearance can be allowed between bolts and holes to assure that the flange can be assembled in any angular orientation of the bolt holes. Therefore, the bolts are only subjected to a tensile stress. Transmittal of torque by friction is not recommended where loads are unsteady or reversible.

The flange surface that seats the bolt heads and nuts is machined or spot faced perpendicularly to the bolt hole axis, assuring that the bolts are not

---

[21] An exception is ANSI B49.1–1969 "Shaft couplings, integrally forged flange type for hydro-electric units." These flanges are standard for shafts ranging from $3\frac{1}{2}$–48-in. diameters.

[22] In the strictest sense, this is not completely true. It is more likely that the bolts would be subjected to the combined stress of bending and shear. The bending component would be caused by any relative displacement of the flange halves up to the minimal clearance between a bolt and hole.

deliberately subjected to bending when tightened. As can be seen from Figure 7-17d, the heads of the bolts and nuts are covered by projecting flanges as a safety measure to protect workmen. Because of these projections, flange couplings are also known as "safety flange couplings."

As "a rule of thumb" guide, the length of hub, diameter of hub, and flange diameter can be based on the relations in Figure 7-17d. It is also common practice to use a number of bolts in accordance with empirical equation (7-38)

$$n = 0.5D + 3 \tag{7-38}$$

where n is the number of bolts and D is the shaft diameter. Dimensions of safety flange couplings for shaft diameters from 1–12 in. are listed in *Machinery's Handbook* [15]. Before specifying such flanges, the designer would be well advised to check the coupling strength.

If a flange coupling is to be designed (or specified) using ground and fitted flange bolts, the designer should check the strength of the following areas:

1. *Direct shear failure of the bolts.* The bolts are assumed to carry their fractional part of the load which, when divided by the cross-sectional area, should result in a shear stress below that of the material strength divided by the factor of safety. Due account should also be taken of any service factors based on industry experience.[23] A particular approach is to make the bolts as strong in direct shear as is the shaft in torsion. Note that, if in the designer's judgement "excessive" bolt clearance would introduce a bending stress, then the bolts must be designed on the basis of combined stress (that is, transverse shear and bending).

2. *Bearing of the bolts.* Bearing of the projected area of the bolt in contact with the side of the flange hole. For steel, the allowable stress in crushing can be assumed as twice the yield value in tension.

3. *Shearing of the flange at the hub.* The shear area resisting failure is the hub circumference times the web thickness of the flange.

4. *Shearing or crushing of the key.* The calculations for these possible modes of failure are described for a square or tapered key in Section 7.13 of this chapter.

In contrast to fitted bolts, a flange coupling designed on the basis of friction-torque capacity requires a somewhat different analysis than that described above. To assure no slip, we must have

$$T_f > T$$

where T_f is the frictional torque and T is the applied torque. If F_0 is the bolt tension, μ the coefficient of friction between the flange faces, D_o the

---

[23] See manufacturers' catalogs.

outside diameter of the flange friction face, D_i the inside diameter of the flange friction face, and n the number of bolts, T_f is

$$T_f = F_f r = \mu F_0 n \left(\frac{D_o + D_i}{2} \right) \frac{1}{2} \geqslant T \tag{7-39}$$

where F_f is the frictional force and r is the mean radius at which F_f is applied. If we now determine the torque-capacity of the shaft, we may derive an equation determining the bolt load F_0 required. Thus for a yield in shear of $0.5 S_{yp}$ for steel (that is, using the maximum shear theory) and a factor of safety N, we have

$$S_s = \frac{0.5 S_{yp}}{N} = \frac{T D_o}{J} = \frac{32T}{\pi D_o^3 (1 - D_i^4 / D_o^4)}$$

or

$$T = \frac{\pi S_{yp} D_o^3 (1 - D_i^4 / D_o^4)}{64N}$$

Thus, relation (7-39) becomes

$$\mu F_0 n \frac{D_o + D_i}{4} \geqslant \frac{\pi S_{yp} D_o^3 (1 - D_i^4 / D_o^4)}{64N}$$

Solving for F_0,

$$F_0 \geqslant \frac{\pi S_{yp} D_o^3 (1 - D_i^4 / D_o^4)}{16 \mu n (D_o + D_i) N} \tag{7-40}$$

where $D_i \equiv 0$ for a solid shaft. From relation (7-40), we can calculate the minimum bolt force required to transmit a torque by the friction force between the flange faces.

In a similar fashion, we can obtain the bolt force required to transmit a torque by friction based on the shearing of a key by means of equations (7-21) and (7-39) or that which is based on the bearing of a key by means of equations (7-23) and (7-39). The resulting relations are respectively

$$F_0 \geqslant \frac{S_{yp} W L D_o}{\mu n (D_o + D_i) N} \tag{7-41}$$

$$F_0 = \frac{S_c W L D_o}{\mu n (D_o + D_i) N} \tag{7-42}$$

The required bolt area is determined by the largest F_0 found by equations (7-40), (7-41), and (7-42) and then dividing this load by the tensile yield strength of the bolt material specified or selected.

Flexible couplings

Flexible couplings are used to connect shafts subject to one or more kinds of misalignment (see Figure 7-18) and to reduce the effect of shock and impact loads that could be transferred between shafts. Flexible couplings are broadly classified into two groups, (1) couplings with kinematic flexibility that employ rigid parts, and (2) couplings that have resilient parts.

Flexible couplings employing rigid parts are designed for specific shaft misalignments and so do not possess constraints in the misaligned directions. Such couplings transmit torque without backlash or angular play (that is, no torsional flexibility) other than that due to manufacturing tolerances and wear. As a consequence of this type of construction, couplings with kinematic flexibility (that is, lacking torsional flexibility) are incapable of dampening the transmittal of shock and impact loads. Figures 7-19, 7-20, 7-21, 7-22, and 7-23 are common types of flexible couplings having rigid members.

Flexible couplings that contain **resilient components** are capable of accommodating shaft misalignments as well as shock and impact loads. Because these types of couplings possess torsional flexibility, they also act as "detuning" devices, thereby altering the vibration properties of the connected system. Figures 7-24, 7-25, and 7-26 are photographs of different types of flexible couplings that contain metallic resilient components.

Another large group of flexible couplings contain nonmetallic flexible members. In this group, there are two types of designs, (1) where the nonmetallic flexible material is subjected to compression by being held between projections from the coupling flanges and, (2) where the nonmetallic flexible

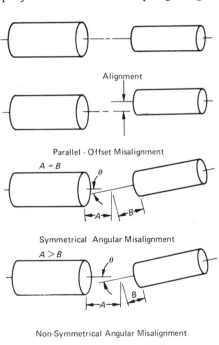

Alignment

Parallel - Offset Misalignment

$A = B$

θ

Symmetrical Angular Misalignment

$A > B$

θ

Non-Symmetrical Angular Misalignment

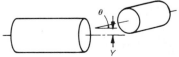

θ

Y

Figure 7-18 Types of shaft misalignment.

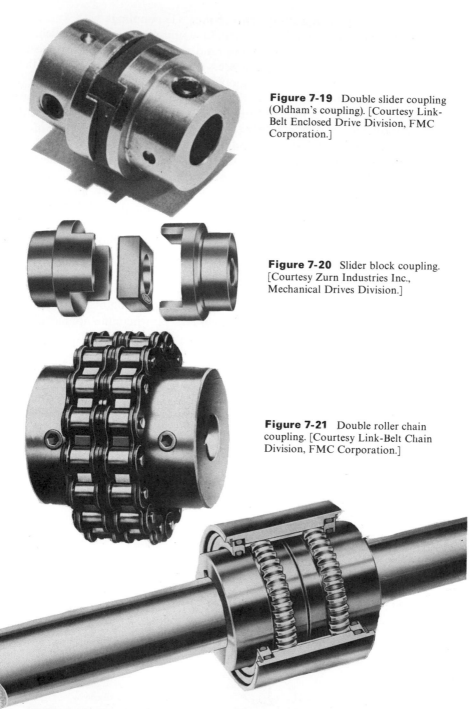

Figure 7-19 Double slider coupling (Oldham's coupling). [Courtesy Link-Belt Enclosed Drive Division, FMC Corporation.]

Figure 7-20 Slider block coupling. [Courtesy Zurn Industries Inc., Mechanical Drives Division.]

Figure 7-21 Double roller chain coupling. [Courtesy Link-Belt Chain Division, FMC Corporation.]

Figure 7-22 Gear coupling. [Courtesy Zurn Industries, Inc., Mechanical Drives Division.]

Figure 7-23 Flexible disc coupling. [Courtesy of Thomas Coupling Division, Rex Chainbelt Corp.]

material is fastened (or bonded) to the coupling flanges and thereby subjected to shear. The latter type of design results in a coupling having a "softer" torsional spring constant than a compression type design. This important difference is attributable to the fact that the nonmetallic flexible member (usually an elastomer) is not confined in the "shear type" design, whereas

Figure 7-24 Franke pin coupling. [Courtesy Waldron Coupling Division, Midland-Ross Corp.]

Figure 7-25 Laminated metal radial spoke coupling. [Courtesy Brown Engineering Company.]

the nonmetallic material is squeezed between the flange projections in the "compression type" design.

Figures 7-27, 7-28, and 7-29 are illustrations of the compression type, nonmetallic flexible member couplings. Figures 7-30, 7-31, 7-32, and 7-33 are illustrations of the shear type, nonmetallic flexible member couplings.

Figure 7-26 Steelflex coupling. [Courtesy of Folk Corporation, Subsidiary Sunstrand Corporation.]

Figure 7-27 Ajax rubber-cushioned sleeve bearing coupling. [Courtesy Ajax Flexible Coupling Co. Inc.]

It is obvious from the many flexible couplings shown, that there is a coupling that will satisfy almost any design requirement. The designer will find that each manufacturer's catalog contains the specialized information required to size a proper unit for any particular coupling. Although the designer would normally not be confronted with the detailed design of a coupling, he should, on such occasions, work closely with the manufacturer.

Figure 7-28 Sure-Flex coupling. [Courtesy of Gerbing Manufacturing Co.]

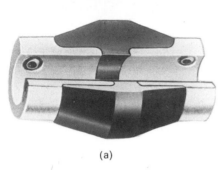

(a)

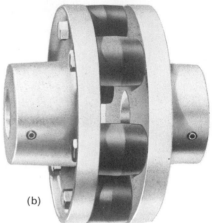

(b)

Figure 7-29 Rubber insert coupling. [Courtesy of Metal Products Division, Koppers Company, Inc.]

Figure 7-30 Bonded rubber disc couplings. [Courtesy Lord Kinematics, Lord Corporation, Erie, Pa.]

(a)

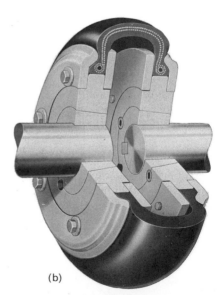

(b)

Figure 7-31 Para-flex coupling. [Courtesy Dodge Manufacturing Division, Reliance Electric Company.]

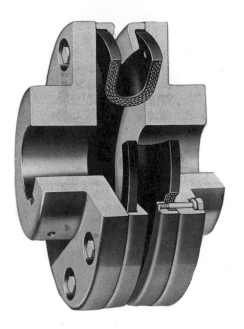

Figure 7-32 Airflex coupling. [Courtesy the Falk Corporation, subsidiary Sunstrand Corporation.]

Figure 7-33 Morflex coupling. [Courtesy Morse Chain, Division of Borg-Warner Corp.]

SECTION 7-16

Universal Joints

A universal joint (also known as **Hooke's joint** or **Cardan's joint**) is a kinematic linkage used to connect two shafts that have a permanent angular misalignment.[24] As illustrated in Figure 7-34, a universal joint consists of a driving yoke 1, which can be connected to an input drive shaft, a cross link C, and a driven yoke 2, which can be connected to an output shaft. Note that both yokes are free to pivot about pins AB and MN of the cross link C.

A severe disadvantage of the universal joint is that it produces a variable velocity ratio, (i.e., if the input shaft has a constant angular velocity ω, the output shaft will have a non-constant angular velocity ω_2). We can demonstrate this fact by referring to Figure 7-34 where illustration (b) is the top view of illustration (a) and illustration (c) is a view of illustration (b) after it has been rotated by 90 deg. From Figure 7-34b we find that the velocity of point M is $v_m = \omega_1 r \cos \delta$, perpendicular to pin MN which is in the plane of yoke 2. Thus, we obtain the angular velocity of yoke 2 as

$$\omega_2 = v_m/r = \omega_1 r \cos \delta / r = \omega_1 \cos \delta$$

We now can write the velocity ratio as

$$\frac{\omega_1}{\omega_2} = \frac{\omega_1}{\omega_1 \cos \delta} = \frac{1}{\cos \delta} \qquad (7\text{-}43)$$

Now looking at Figure 7-34c, we see that a rotation of 90 deg has caused pins AB and MN (perpendicular to the page) to assume the positions shown. From Figure 7-34c we obtain $v_a = r\omega_1$ which is represented by the velocity

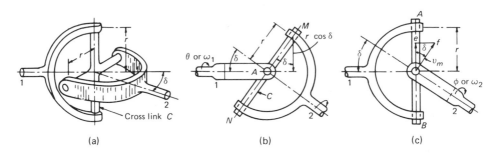

| (a) | (b) | (c) |

Figure 7-34 Basic components of Hooke's joint. When 1 has turned $\theta = 90$ deg (and 180, 270, 360 deg), the driven member 2 has turned $\phi = 90$ deg (and 180, 270, 360 deg); but at other values of θ, θ and ϕ are not the same.

---

[24] The universal joint can be used in place of couplings where the *only* misalignment between shafts is angular. It *cannot* be used to compensate for offset shaft alignment or axial play, although the latter condition can be accommodated by use of telescoping shafts.

vector $\bar{e}$. Since the pin joint at N cannot have two separate velocities, velocity vector $\bar{e}$ must be a component of velocity vector $\bar{v}_m$. Hence, we have

$$v_m = \frac{r\omega_1}{\cos \delta}$$

and obtain

$$\omega_2 = \frac{v_m}{r} = \frac{r\omega_1}{r \cos \delta} = \frac{\omega_1}{\cos \delta}$$

The velocity ratio of this 90 deg rotated position then is

$$\frac{\omega_1}{\omega_2} = \frac{\omega_1}{\omega_1/\cos \delta} = \cos \delta \qquad (7\text{-}44)$$

We can readily see by comparing equations (7-44) and (7-45) that the speed of the driven shaft 2 varies from a minimum of $\omega_1 \cos \delta$ to a maximum of $\omega_1/\cos \delta$ for a 90 deg rotation. From 90 deg to 180 deg, the driven shaft speed becomes a minimum. This cycle repeats itself every 180 deg. Now, from spherical trigonometry, it can be shown[25] that

$$\tan \varphi = \tan \theta \cos \delta \qquad (7\text{-}45)$$

Next, we differentiate equation (7-45) with respect to time t for some fixed angle δ between shafts.

$$\sec^2 \varphi \frac{d\varphi}{dt} = \sec^2 \theta \frac{d\theta}{dt} \cos \delta$$

or

$$\omega_2 = \frac{\omega_1 \cos \delta/\cos^2 \theta}{1 + \tan^2 \varphi} = \frac{\omega_1 \cos \delta/\cos^2 \theta}{1 + \tan^2 \theta \cos^2 \delta}$$

$$= \frac{\omega_1 \cos \delta/\cos^2 \theta}{\left(\dfrac{\cos^2 \theta}{\sin^2 \theta} + \cos^2 \delta\right)\dfrac{\sin^2 \theta}{\cos^2 \theta}} = \frac{\omega_1 \cos \delta}{(\cos^2 \theta + \sin^2 \theta \cos^2 \delta)}$$

But $\sin^2 \theta = 1 - \cos^2 \theta$. We finally obtain a relation for the output shaft velocity ω_2 as a function of the input velocity ω_1 the angle between the shafts δ and the angular displacement of the input shaft θ.

$$\omega_2 = \frac{\omega_1 \cos \delta}{1 - \sin^2 \delta \sin^2 \theta} \qquad (7\text{-}46)$$

Differentiating ω_2 with respect to t produces the equation for the acceleration

[25] For example see *Mechanics of Machinery* by C. W. Ham and E. J. Crane, McGraw-Hill Book Company, New York, 1948; or *Kinematics of Machines* by R. T. Hinkle, Prentice-Hall, Inc., Englewood Cliffs, N.J., 1964.

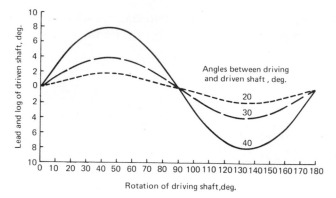

Figure 7-35 Plot of how the speed of the output shaft leads and lags the speed of the driver shaft $\delta = 20$, 30, and 40 deg.

of shaft 2 (note that ω_1 and δ are constant).

$$\alpha_2 = \frac{d\omega_2}{dt} = \frac{\omega_1^2 \sin^2 \delta \cos \sin 2\theta}{(1 - \sin^2 \delta \sin^2 \theta)^2} \qquad (7\text{-}47)$$

We can readily ascertain from equation (7-46) that ω_2 varies with the angular position θ of shaft 1 (for a constant ω_2 and δ). We also observe from this same equation that the magnitude of the variation of ω_2 is larger, with larger angles δ between shafts. This variation is vividly illustrated by Figure 7-35, which is a plot of equation 7-46 showing how the driven shaft speeds up and slows down for each revolution of the driver shaft 1.

This phenomenon can further be verified by equation (7-47), which shows that the angular acceleration of the driven shaft increases with increasing angles δ. As a result of these output velocity variations, severe vibrations may be introduced into the driven machinery or equipment. To counter this undesirable effect, the designer should avoid using a single universal joint for shafts at an angle greater than 15 deg, although well constructed "joints" can accommodate angular shaft misalignments as large as 40 deg. Also, depending on the quality of the universal joint, the designer should plan to use these connections for low or moderate shaft speeds and power.

By using a double universal joint (Figure 7-36b) or two single universal joints connected by a short shaft (Figure 7-37) it is possible to connect two shafts having considerable angular misalignment. This arrangement of universal joints can also provide a constant velocity ratio between input and output shafts. To achieve this desirable condition when both the driver and driven shaft are in the same plane, it is necessary for the yokes of the input and output shafts to be in the same plane and for the angles between the driver shaft, the driven shaft, and the connecting shaft to be equal. Figures 7-38 and 7-39 illustrate two arrangements for achieving this constant speed ratio arrangement.

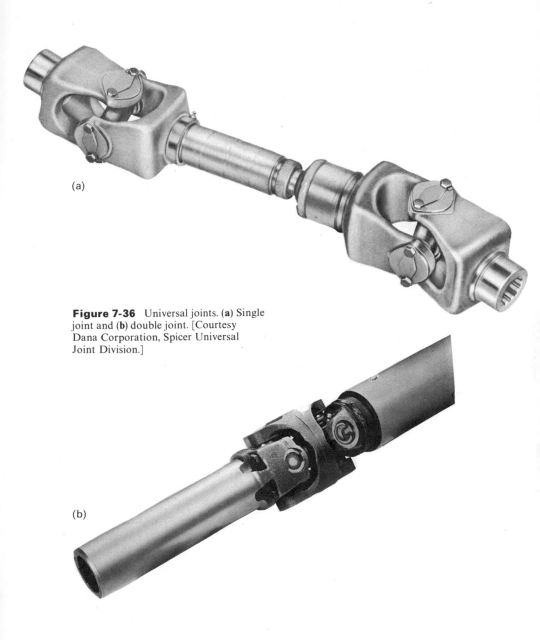

(a)

(b)

Figure 7-36 Universal joints. (**a**) Single joint and (**b**) double joint. [Courtesy Dana Corporation, Spicer Universal Joint Division.]

Figure 7-37 Two universal joints joined by a short shaft. [Courtesy Lovejoy Inc.]

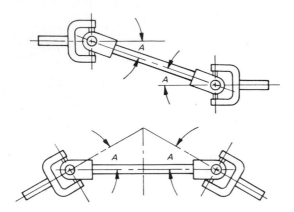

Figure 7-38 Two arrangements of a double universal joint system for achieving a constant velocity ratio.

Sometimes, design circumstances require that the double universal shaft assembly connect input and output shafts that cannot be in the same plane. In such cases, it is still possible to obtain an arrangement that will result in a constant velocity ratio, but it is imperative that (1) the yoke at each end of the connecting shaft be so oriented that the planes *containing* them be at the same angle γ formed by the planes of the driving and driven shafts (that is, the connecting shaft yokes are perpendicular to planes A and B as shown in Figure 7-39), (2) that the angles formed at joints of the connecting shaft with the input shaft and the output shaft be equal (that is, $\beta_1 = \beta_2$ in Figure 7-39).

Because universal joints do not provide for axial play, provision for this requirement can be made in the connecting shaft or at the connection between the driver or driven shaft.

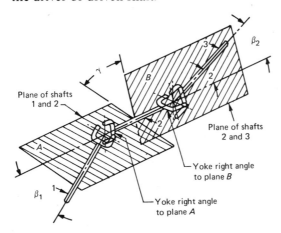

Figure 7-39 Correct angular arrangement for achieving a constant velocity ratio when three shafts are not in the same plane. *Note*: For this arrangement to *function* as desired, β_1 must be equal to β_2.

Several types of universal joints have been developed by various manufacturers because of their wide application (for example, in automotive, agricultural, aircraft, industrial, and instrument applications) and because of the need for one that has a constant velocity ratio as well as for one that is able to operate satisfactorily under high speeds.

SECTION 7-17

Flexible Shafting

Where power is to be transmitted between two points located in such a manner or configuration that a connection by shafting is not simple or feasible, and combinations of belts, chains, and/or gears would be complicated or costly, the designer might consider the use of a flexible shaft. There are two principal kinds of flexible shafting, (1) the shaft designed to transmit power in one rotational direction and (2) the shaft designed primarily to transmit motion for remote control applications that can be worked rotationally in both directions. Typical power transmission applications are business machines, food handling machines, multiple spindle drills, portable tools, tachometers, indicator mechanisms, and speedometers. Typical remote control applications are power operated automobile seats, automobile windows and convertible tops, aircraft controls, medical and dental equipment, and so on.

Flexible shafts are constructed of 1 to 12 layers of wire which are helically wound on a mandrel. Each layer is wound in an opposite direction (that is, the same as a right hand or left hand screw), and the top layer determines whether the cable is either a "right lay" or a "left lay" cable. The shaft is then encased in a sheath and end fittings are attached. Wires used to fabricate flexible shafts can be wrought steel, stainless steel, phosphor bronze, Monel, and Inconel. For high temperature application, stainless steel is used. Monel and phosphor bronze are used respectively for applications requiring corrosion resistance and nonmagnetic properties.

Shaft diameters ranging from a 0.043-in. to 2-in. diameter are available and are rated in accordance with the dynamic torque capacity in the winding direction corresponding to the radius of curvature. The larger the shaft diameter, the more pronounced is the reduction of the torque capacity with the smaller radii. For example, a 0.050-in. diameter shaft which has a torque capacity of 0.26 lb-in. for a 10-in. radius of curvature decreases to 0.16 lb-in. for a 4-in. radius of curvature—a reduction of 38.5%. On the other hand, a 0.187-in. diameter shaft has a torque capacity of 11.0 lb-in. for a 10-in. radius of curvature and a 4.0 lb-in. torque capacity for a 4-in. radius of curvature—a 63.6% reduction of torque capacity.

Flexible shafts for power transmission should have a left-hand lay for clockwise rotation and a right-hand lay for counterclockwise rotation. These directions are given as viewed from the power source. Figure 7-40 shows a typical shaft construction and assembly.

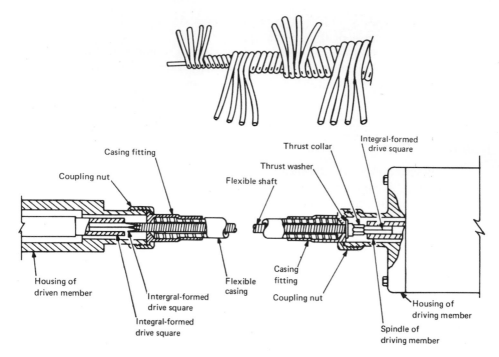

Figure 7-40 Typical flexible shaft construction showing connections. [Courtesy S. S. White Industrial Products, Pennwalt Corp.]

As with couplings, manufacturers' catalogs[26] describe the proper procedure and considerations required to select an appropriate flexible shaft.

PROBLEMS

1. A solid transmission shaft made of AISI Type 316 cold-drawn stainless steel is used to transmit 95 hp to a series of chemical mixing vats at 100 rpm. Since the atmosphere may be corrosive or at best unknown, assume a factor of safety of 4 (see Section 1.3). What is the shaft diameter?

2. Assume you wish to replace the solid shaft of Problem 1 with a hollow shaft having an inside diameter equal to the diameter of the solid shaft. What is the wall thickness of the hollow shaft? What is the per cent difference in weight per foot of shaft length between the hollow and solid shafts?

3. It has been decided because of atmospheric corrosion to replace a AISI 1030 cold-drawn steel shaft with an aluminum alloy 2017-T4 shaft. What diameter aluminum shaft must be used? If the aluminum shaft is to have the same angular stiffness as the steel shaft, what is the weight ratio of the shafts?

4. A horizontal power transmission shaft is supported by two bearings 40 in. apart. The shaft overhangs the right bearing by 12 in. and supports a 30-in. pitch diameter straight-toothed spur gear. On the left side there is a shaft overhang of 10 in.

[26] For example, F. W. Stewart Corp., S. S. White Ind. Products, Elliot Mfg. Co., Stow Mfg. Co.

supporting a 50-in. diameter flat belt pulley. The respective weights of the gear and pulley are 200 and 600 lb. The gear is driven by a pinion in a rotational direction such that the tangential turning force on the gear tooth acts upwards (ignore the radial force tending to separate the gears in this problem). The pulley that delivers the power vertically downward has a belt tension ratio (that is, tight side to loose side) of 2.5. The shaft must transmit 25 hp at 150 rpm. Assume 100% transmission efficiency (that is, no belt slips and no losses at the gears). (a) Draw the loading, shear, and moment diagrams. (b) Determine the shaft diameter by the maximum shear failure theory. The material is AISI 1040 annealed steel and both the gear and pulley are held on the shaft by a sled-runner key. (c) What would the shaft diameter be if it were subjected to a definite minor shock caused by a single revolution clutch located on the pinion shaft (that is, before the gear input)?

5. Schematic Problem Figure 5 shows a straight tooth, involute gear mounted midway between ball bearing supports with an overhanging flat belt pulley. Power input to the pulley is 15 hp at 1000 rpm under steady load. The pulley weighs 80 lb and the gear weighs 40 lb. Determine the shaft diameter (that is, configuration) if lengths AB and CD are to be the same diameter and length BC is 50% larger. The radius of the fillet joining sections AB and BC is 0.0625 in. The radius of the fillet joining sections CD and BC (that is, where the bearing is shouldered) is 0.010 in. The gear is keyed to the shaft by a square profiled key and the pulley by a sled-runner key. The shaft material is AISI 1020 cold-drawn steel. Assume zero pulley slip. Base your design on the maximum shear theory of failure. See equations (10-12) and (10-13) for gear forces.

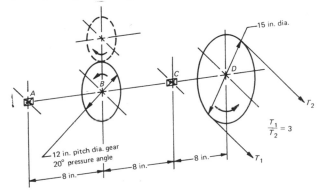

Problem Figure 5

6. Problem Figure 6 shows a fixed gear train in which the shaft is machined from AISI 2330 cold-drawn steel. Power input to the system is at gear A, and the output is at gear D. Gear C is mounted on the outside diameter of a single revolution clutch that transfers power to gear D. This power changes from 20 hp to 120 hp and back to 20 hp for each revolution of the shaft. Gear B is keyed to the shaft by a sled-runner key and the clutch by a profiled key. If the shaft is not stepped and a safety factor of 1.5 is assumed, determine the shaft diameter. In this problem, the radial forces tending to separate the gears are to be ignored and only the tangential turning force components are considered. Assume also that minor shock is contributed by the engaging clutch for each revolution of the shaft. Ignore the weights of the gears.

7. Solve Problem 6 taking into account the forces tending to separate the gears. The gears have a 20 deg pressure angle.

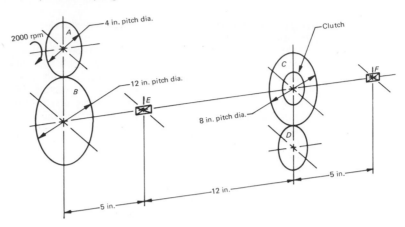

Problem Figure 6

8. Problem Figure 8 shows a schematic for a shaft of a punch press which mounts
a flywheel, a flat belt pulley, and a gear *D*. The pulley weighing 120 lb is driven by a
belt located at 45 deg with the horizontal, as shown. The input to the pulley is 30 hp
and it rotates at 300 rpm. A straight toothed involute spur gear located at *D* and
having a 20 deg pressure angle drives a gear *F*. This gear, in turn, drives a crank and
connecting rod that operates the punch. The weight of the gear is 30 lb. As in all
mechanical presses, the stored energy of a flywheel is used during the punching
operation. In this case, a flywheel weighing 1000 lb and having a radius of gyration
of 20 in. is located at *A*. During the punching part of the cycle, it is assumed that
the power delivered to gear *D* is doubled—namely, 30 hp is obtained from the
flywheel and 30 hp is obtained from the belt. The timing of the cycle is such that
the location on the shaft at which the moment is a maximum experiences an
alternating tensile and compressive stress. The flywheel is locked to the shaft by
a sled-runner keyway, whereas the pulley and gear are both held by a profiled
keyway. Using a safety factor of 2.5 and AISI 3140 cold-drawn alloy steel, determine
the shaft diameter by the distortion energy failure theory accounting for the impact
load due to punching.

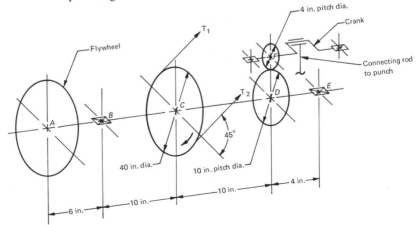

Problem Figure 8

9. The worm drive shown in Problem Figure 9 supplies 60 hp steadily at 1600 rpm and is driven by a 10-in. pitch diameter 20 deg pressure angle gear. The pitch diameter of the worm is 3 in. and it is desired to make the worm an integral part of the shaft if possible. The figure shows the forces acting on the worm and input gear where the thrust load is taken by the bearing at B. The shaft is to be made of AISI 1040 hot-rolled steel. The fatigue stress concentration factor for the worm threads can be taken as $K_f = 1.5$ for both bending and shear. Determine the following: **(a)** the minimum root diameter of the worm thread by the energy distortion theory of failure (assume a safety factor of 2.0); **(b)** the shaft diameter D at the change of section where the shaft joins the worm; **(c)** the safety of the shaft diameter found in part (b) at the gear A.

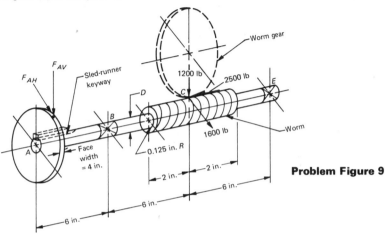

Problem Figure 9

10. Problem Figure 10 shows a shaft that is a component of a parts feeder for a production machine. The shaft is supported by a split sleeve bearing at B and a regular sleeve bearing at D and mounts two $14\frac{1}{2}$-deg pressure angle straight tooth involute spur gears at A and C. Gear C is keyed to the shaft by a profiled keyway, and gear A is held by a sled-runner keyway. Input to gear A is 10 hp at 300 rpm. Output is at gear C. The shaft material is made of AISI 1340 quenched in oil and tempered at 1200°F. **(a)** Determine the factor of safety N at the $\frac{1}{8}$-in. fillet radius. **(b)** Determine the factor of safety of that portion of the shaft which holds gear C. Use the maximum distortion theory of failure in determining both (a) and (b).

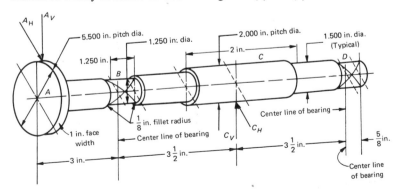

Problem Figure 10

11. The worm shown in Problem Figure 11 is made of AISI 8740 alloy steel quenched in oil and tempered at 1000°F. An input torque of 60,000 in./lb is applied to the right end of the shaft. The pitch diameter of the worm is 6.923 in. and is the diameter at which it is assumed the forces R, E, and T are acting. The root diameter is 5.701 in. The force opposing rotation T (shown as coming out of the paper in a perpendicular direction) is 6200 lb. R is 1950 lb and is the force that tends to cause the worm and worm gear to separate. E is 6600 lb and is the reactive thrust force acting on the worm. The fatigue stress concentration factor at the root of the worm thread can be taken as 1.5 for shear and bending. Using the distortion energy theory of failure, determine the factor of safety N at the critical points of the shaft.

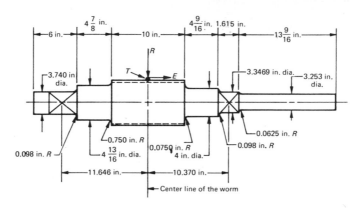

Problem Figure 11

12. The input to pulley A in Problem Figure 12 varies from 20 to 30 hp and back to 20 hp for each revolution at a speed of 200 rpm. Pulley A weighs 150 lb and pulley C weighs 300 lb. Both are keyed to the shaft by a profiled key. The shaft is machined from AISI 1020 hot-rolled steel. Determine the following: **(a)** The shaft diameter required for a factor of safety of 2.5. **(b)** The slope of the shaft at bearing D. **(c)** The maximum deflection of the shaft between bearings B and D. **(d)** The shaft deflection at pulley A. **(e)** The lowest critical speed of the shaft.

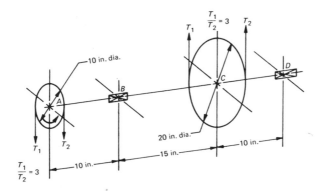

Problem Figure 12

13. Power is delivered to the pulley and taken out at the gear. The forces acting on each of the elements are shown on the Problem Figure 13. The pulley weighs 350 lb and the gear weighs 150 lb. If the shaft material is AISI 1030 normalized steel, determine the required shaft diameter by the maximum shear theory of failure. The load is steady and both the gear and pulley are fixed to the shaft by a profiled key.

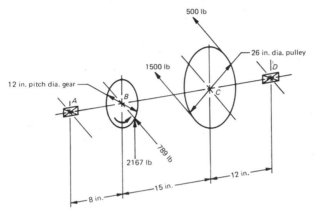

Problem Figure 13

14. In Problem Figure 14, a 20-in. diameter flat belt pulley receives 25 hp at 500 rpm. This power is transferred to a straight toothed 20-deg pressure angle spur gear with a pitch diameter of 10 in. The pulley weighs 250 lb and the gear 150 lb. If the loads are steady, determine the shaft diameter required based on the maximum shear theory of failure. The shaft is turned from AISI 1030 hot-rolled steel. Use a factor of safety of 2. Both the gear and pulley are held on the shaft by a profiled key.

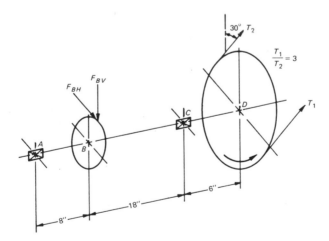

Problem Figure 14

15. The steel shaft shown in Problem Figure 15 is simply supported by bearings at reactions R_L and R_R. Determine the slope at each bearing and the maximum deflection. Use the numerical method of Section 7-8. Check your answer by using the computer program of Section 7-9.

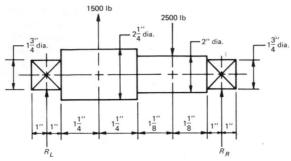

Problem Figure 15

16. For the shaft diameter found in Problem 5, determine the following: **(a)** The slope at the bearing supports. **(b)** The maximum shaft deflection. **(c)** The lowest critical speed. Is the shaft in danger of vibrating excessively? Solve parts (a) and (b) by the computer using the program found in Section 7-9.

17. Solve parts (b), (c) and (d) of Problem 12 using the numerical method described in Section 7-8.

18. Solve parts (b), (c), and (d) of Problem 12 using the area moment method.

19. Solve parts (b) and (c) of Problem 12 by graphical integration.[27]

20. Determine the slope at bearing *D* and the maximum shaft deflection for Problem 10.

21. Determine the following for Problem 13: **(a)** The slope of the shaft at bearings *A* and *D*. **(b)** The maximum shaft deflection. **(c)** The lowest critical speed of the system.

22. Determine the following for Problem 14: **(a)** The slope of the shaft at bearing *A*. **(b)** The maximum shaft deflection. **(c)** The lowest critical speed of the system. For parts (b) and (c), use the area moment method.

23. Verify the statement that "a square key is equally strong in shear as it is in compression."

24. If the shaft and key are made of the same material, determine the length of square key required as a function of the shaft diameter.

25. A plain standard square key is used to hold a $2\frac{1}{2}$-in. long hub on a $1\frac{7}{16}$-in. diameter shaft. If the key and shaft are of the same material, having an allowable stress of 8000 psi, what is the factor of safety against shear failure of the key if the torque being transmitted is 3500 in.-lb? The length of key is $2\frac{1}{4}$ in.

26. A gear is keyed to a $3\frac{1}{4}$-in. diameter shaft, and delivers 80 hp at 200 rpm to the punch of a mechanical press. The gear material is class 60,000 cast carbon steel, the shaft material is AISI 1040 hot-rolled steel, and the key material is AISI 1020 cold-drawn steel. Because of the shock loading, a safety factor of 4 is suggested. Determine the length of a standard square key. What is the torque carrying capacity of the shaft due to the keyway?

[27] For example, see (1) *Design of Machine Elements* by V. M. Faires, The Macmillan Company, New York, 1965. (2) *Design of Machine Elements* by A. Vallance and V. L. Doughtie, The McGraw-Hill Book Company, New York, 1951. (3) *Mechanical Engineering Design* by J. E. Shigley, The McGraw-Hill Book Company, New York, 1972.

27. An electric motor for a chemical blender supplies 60 hp at 1750 rpm to a $1\frac{3}{4}$-in. diameter shaft made of AISI 1045 cold-drawn steel. A cast steel gear with a $2\frac{1}{4}$-in. long hub is keyed to the shaft by a square key. The gear material is class 85,000 carbon steel. Select a standard square key and determine its length if the key material is AISI 1020 cold-drawn steel. Assume a factor of safety of 2.5 (mild shock) since the viscosity of the material being mixed varies. By what percentage has the torque capacity of the shaft been reduced due to the keyway?

28. A cast iron pulley is keyed by a number 812 Woodruff key to a $1\frac{1}{4}$-in. diameter shaft made of AISI 1040 cold-drawn steel. If the shaft rotates steadily at 200 rpm, what horsepower can the key transmit if it is made of (a) AISI 1020 cold drawn steel, and (b) AISI 1060 quenched in oil and tempered at 1200°F.

29. A foot pedal lever of a kick press is keyed to a 2-in. diameter shaft made of AISI 1040 cold-drawn steel by a radial taper pin with a 0.5-in. mean diameter. The pin is made of AISI 1060 steel, oil quenched and tempered at 600°F. The lever, which is 22 in. long, is subjected to a reversing load. For a factor of safety of 2 based on the endurance strength, determine: (a) The safe lever load for the shaft. (b) The safe lever load for the pin (direct shear only). (c) The safe lever load for the combination of the shaft and pin.

30. In some instances, a key is so designed that it will fail if a limiting horsepower, torque, or stress is exceeded. This is deliberately intended to protect equipment "downstream" from the key in case there is a jam or overload. Thus, consider a 2-in. diameter shaft made of AISI 1040 cold-drawn steel subjected to torsion only. If it is desired that the key shear at 75 % of the shaft strength (based on ultimate strength), how long would a standard square key have to be? The key material is AISI 1020 cold-drawn steel.

31. A straight sided splined shaft of an automotive rear axle has 16 splines. The shaft diameter D is 2.00 in. For a "not slide under load" fit, determine the torque carrying capacity of this shaft and horsepower at 3000 rpm. The splines are 1.75 in. long and are cut from AISI 1040 cold drawn steel.

32. A solid shaft for an automobile transmission has a 10-tooth involute spline with a diametral pitch of $\frac{10}{20}$. The shaft is made of AISI 4340 steel quenched in oil and tempered at 1000°F. Based on yield, what is the factor of safety if the shaft transmits 150 hp at 3000 rpm?

33. A rigid flange coupling connects two 5-in. diameter AISI 1040 cold-drawn shafts. The two halves of the coupling are held together by six evenly spaced 1-in. diameter bolts located on a 12-in. bolt circle. Each flange half is keyed to the shaft by a standard AISI 1020 cold-drawn square key. The flange web thickness is $1\frac{1}{2}$ in. The flange material is class 60,000 annealed cast carbon steel and the bolts are made of AISI 1030 cold-drawn steel. Because the coupling can be expected to experience moderate shock, a factor of safety of 3 with respect to the yield strength should be applied to the torque capacity of the shaft (see Section 1-3). (a) Assuming that the bolts fit the bolt holes with zero clearance and are "finger tight" when assembled, determine the factor of safety for each possible mode of failure. (b) If the bolts fit the holes with clearance, determine the factor of safety based on yield strength for the bolt tension force (that is, minimum tightening force) required to prevent slip in the coupling. Also determine the factor of safety for the bolt tension force based on (c) shearing of the key, and (d) compression of the key. For the flange configuration see Figure 7-17d.

REFERENCES

[1] H. A. Berchardt: A comprehensive method for designing shafts to insure adequate fatigue life. *Mach. Des.*, (April 25, 1963).

[2] R. E. Peterson: *Stress Concentration Design Factors*. John Wiley & Sons, Inc., New York, 1962.

[3] R. Bruce Hopkins: Calculating deflections in stepped shafts and nonuniform beams. *Mach. Des.*, **33**(14): 159–164 (1961).

[4] Virgil F. Faires: *Design of Machine Elements*, 4th ed. The Macmillan Co., New York, 1965.

[5] M. J. Siegel, V. L. Maleev, and J. B. Hartman: *Mechanical Design of Machine Elements*, 4th ed. International Textbook Co., Scranton, Pa., 1968.

[6] S. P. Timoshenko and J. N. Goodier: *Theory of Elasticity*. McGraw-Hill Book Co., New York, 1951.

[7] Sir Geoffrey Taylor: The use of soap films in solving torsion problems. *Scientific Papers of Sir Geoffrey Taylor*, Vol. 1. Cambridge University Press, London, 1958, pp. 1–23.

[8] I. S. Sokolnikoff: *Mathematical Theory of Elasticity*. McGraw-Hill Book Co., New York, 1956.

[9] C. T. Wang: *Applied Elasticity*. McGraw-Hill Book Co., New York, 1953.

[10] Colin Carmichael (ed.): *Kent's Mechanical Engineers' Handbook*, Vol. II, 12th ed. John Wiley & Sons, New York, 1961.

[11] R. R. Moore: *Bulletin No. 42, Engineering Experiment Station*, University of Illinois, Urbana, Ill.,

[12] Harold A. Rothbart (ed.): *Mechanical Design and Systems Handbook*, Sect. 27. McGraw-Hill Book Co., New York, 1964.

[13] J. B. Armitage: Straight splined shaft. *Mech. Eng.*, **70**: 738–742 (Sept. 1948).

[14] *SAE Handbook*. Society of Automotive Engineers, Inc., New York, 1954.

[15] H. L. Horton (ed.): *Machinery's Handbook*, 15th ed. The Industrial Press, New York, 1957.

Journal Bearings and Lubrication

This chapter will present a discussion of the fundamentals of lubrication, with particular emphasis upon the design of journal bearings. The analytical approach as well as the use of design charts will be discussed.

SECTION 8-1

Introduction

A major problem faced by engineers through the years has been how to prevent the loss of useful energy due to friction. It has been estimated that of all the energy produced throughout the world, as much as one third to one half is wasted because of friction. **Friction** may be defined as the opposing force that is developed when two surfaces move relative to each other. **Lubrication** has then been defined as the art of reducing the friction developed between two surfaces moving relative to each other. This is usually done by placing a substance between the moving surfaces. Although the material that is called a lubricant is usually in the liquid state, solids and gases are also used as lubricants.

Plain bearings, as distinguished from the rolling element bearings to be discussed in the next chapter, are usually classified as plain journal or sleeve, thrust, spherical, pivot, or shoe-type thrust. Another method of classification is to designate the bearing according to the type of lubrication used.

A hydrodynamically lubricated bearing is one that uses a fluid lubricant (liquid or gas) to separate the moving surfaces completely. When this ideal condition is attained, we speak of the lubrication as being thick film. Other commonly used terms for this type of lubrication are fluid film, stable, or perfect. In order for hydrodynamic lubrication to exist, relative motion must exist between the two surfaces and a pressure must be developed. The pressure development is accomplished by the wedging action that results when the two surfaces are not parallel. Figure 8-1 illustrates the situation just described.

If the fluid film gets thinner and is no longer able to separate the moving surfaces, partial metal-to-metal contact can occur; this type of lubrication is

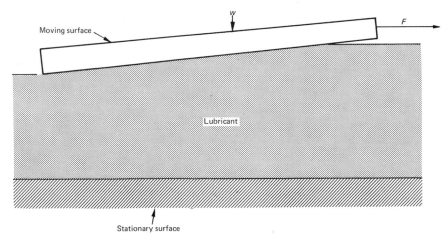

Figure 8-1 The conditions necessary for hydrodynamic lubrication to exist are shown. Pressure is developed in the lubricant due to the wedging action between the two surfaces having relative motion.

called boundary lubrication. As more metal-to-metal contact takes place the friction developed becomes greater, and, unless the bearing was designed to operate under this thin film type of lubrication, failure will occur. One of the design criteria which is very often used is the so-called minimum film thickness. In this method, the designer makes certain that the film thickness does not become less than some minimum safe value.

Boundary lubrication is usually not planned by the designer. It depends on such factors as surface finish, wear-in, and surface chemical reactions. Low revolution per minute, heavily loaded bearings, misaligned bearings, and improperly lubricated bearings are usually more prone to operate under boundary lubrication. If a bearing operates under boundary lubrication but does not fail, it is possible that the wearing-in that takes place will then allow the bearing to operate with hydrodynamic lubrication.

Boundary lubrication presents yet another problem to the designer: it cannot be analyzed by mathematical methods but must be dealt with on the basis of test data.

SECTION 8-2

Types of Journal Bearings

A bearing that supports a load in the radial direction is known as a **journal bearing.** As can be seen from Figure 8-2, a journal bearing consists of two main parts, a shaft called the journal and the hollow cylinder that supports the shaft known as the bearing. In most applications, the journal rotates while the bearing is stationary. However, there are applications where the journal is stationary and the bearing rotates, and even some where both the journal and bearing rotate.

As will be seen in Section 8-10, the pressure distribution around a journal bearing varies greatly. As a result, journal bearings can be made with the full bearing thickness around the whole circumference (a **full journal bearing**)

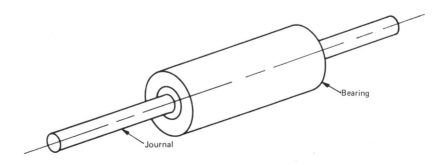

Figure 8-2 An example of a journal bearing.

or with the full bearing thickness around a portion of the circumference and an oil cap around the remainder of the circumference (**partial bearing**). Figure 8-3A shows a full journal bearing, whereas a partial journal bearing is depicted in Figure 8-3B. A partial bearing having zero clearance is known as a **fitted bearing.** Zero clearance simply means that the radii of the journal and bearing are equal.

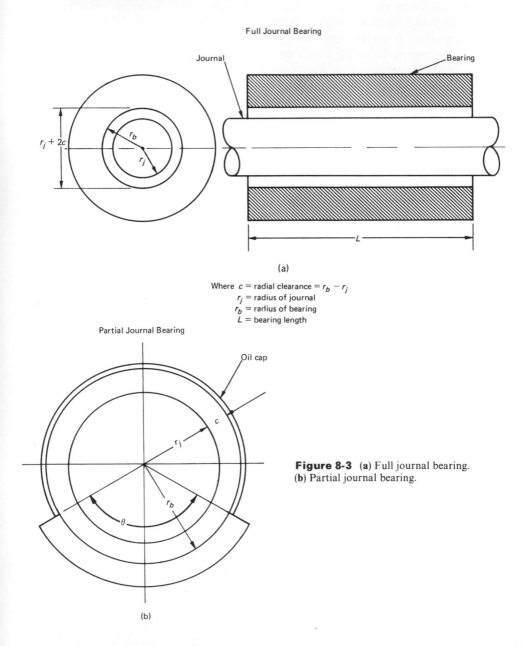

Full Journal Bearing

Where c = radial clearance = $r_b - r_j$
r_j = radius of journal
r_b = radius of bearing
L = bearing length

Partial Journal Bearing

Figure 8-3 (a) Full journal bearing. (b) Partial journal bearing.

SECTION 8-3

Newton's Law of Viscous Flow (Viscosity)

One of the fundamental problems involved in lubrication theory is the effect of the internal resistance of the fluid being used as a lubricant. The expression for this internal resistance, called viscosity, can be obtained by applying Newton's law of viscous flow to the system shown in Figure 8-4. In the figure, the lower plate is stationary, while the upper plate is moving to the right with a velocity U. The two parallel plates are separated by a lubricant film of thickness h.

When two plates, having relative motion, are separated by a lubricant, in this case an oil film, a flow of oil takes place. In most lubrication problems, conditions are such that the flow that occurs is laminar. By **laminar flow** we mean that the fluid is in layers or laminae, which are maintained as the flow progresses. When this condition is not met, we speak of the flow as being **turbulent.**

Under conditions of laminar flow, we may assume that perfect adhesion is achievable. In other words, the lamina immediately adjacent to the moving plate moves with the same velocity as the plate, whereas that immediately adjacent to the stationary plate has zero velocity. The intermediate laminae move with velocities that vary linearly from 0 to U. Because the laminae have

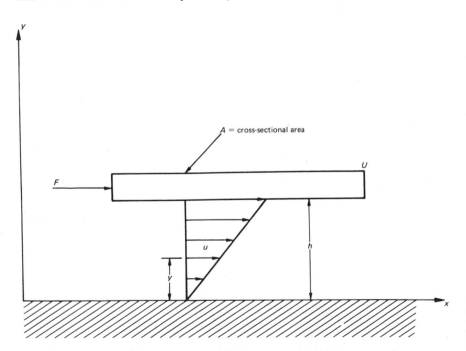

Figure 8-4 Two plates having a relative velocity, which are separated by an oil film and under laminar flow, have a linear velocity gradient, as shown.

different velocities, each layer must slide upon the adjacent layer. A force, F, is required to produce this sliding. The resistance the fluid offers to this force, is known as the shear stress, which in turn causes fluid friction.

Newton's law of viscous flow states that at any point in the fluid film, the shearing stress is proportional to the velocity gradient.

$$\tau(\text{stress}) \propto \frac{du}{dy}$$

or

$$\tau = \mu\frac{du}{dy} \tag{8-1}$$

where μ is a proportionality constant called either the coefficient of absolute viscosity, absolute viscosity, or more usually simply viscosity, du is the change in velocity, and dy is the change in film thickness.

Because the velocity varies linearly across the film,

$$\frac{du}{dy} = \frac{U}{h}$$

The shearing stress may be written as

$$\tau = \frac{F}{A}$$

where A is the cross-sectional area being sheared. Therefore

$$\frac{F}{A} = \mu\frac{U}{h}$$

or

$$F = \mu\frac{AU}{h} \tag{8-2}$$

Thus the shearing or frictional force required increases with velocity and area. It will be recalled that solid friction is relatively independent of speed and area but dependent on load.

Viscosity, a fluid's resistance to flow, can be expressed dimensionally by solving equation (8-2) for μ.

$$\mu = \frac{Fh}{AU} = \frac{(\text{force})(\text{length})}{(\text{length}^2)(\text{length/time})}$$

In the English system

$$\frac{(\text{lb})(\text{in.})}{(\text{in.}^2)(\text{in./sec})} = \frac{\text{lb-sec}}{\text{in.}^2} = \text{reyn}$$

The reyn, named in honor of the English physicist Reynolds is the viscosity unit used in the English system. In the metric system the standard unit is the poise, named after the French physician Poiseuille.

$$\frac{(\text{force})(\text{time})}{\text{length}^2} = \frac{\text{dyne-sec}}{\text{cm}^2} = \text{poise}$$

A smaller unit, the centipoise, $\frac{1}{100}$ poise, is frequently used.
The simple conversion between reyns and centipoises (cp) is

$$1 \text{ reyn} = 6.9 \times 10^6 \text{ cp}$$

SECTION 8-4

Hagan-Poiseuille Law (Flow Through Capillary Tube)

Because many methods that are commonly used to measure viscosity make use of the flow through a capillary tube, it is important to discuss the Hagan-Poiseuille law for laminar flow through a capillary tube. The following assumptions will be made and refer to the tube shown in Figure 8-5. The pressure drops gradually along the tube in going from left to right, the flow is steady and laminar, the fluid is incompressible, the fluid completely fills the interior of the tube, the capillary diameter is small enough so that the pressure drop across the tube can be ignored, and the fluid does not accelerate as it flows through the tube.

A cylindrical element of fluid of radius r and length dx is shown in Figure 8-5 with the pressure (p) and shearing stress (τ) drawn in. Because the element is in static equilibrium, the summation of forces along the x axis must equal zero.

$$p\pi r^2 - (p - dp)\pi r^2 - \tau 2\pi r \, dx = 0$$

$$dp = \frac{\tau}{r} 2 \, dx \tag{8-3}$$

Newton's law of viscous flow may be written

$$\tau = -\mu \frac{du}{dr} \tag{8-4}$$

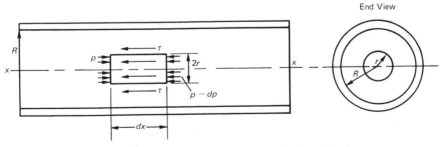

Figure 8-5 The free body diagram of the forces acting in the x direction, on an element dx, of the lubricant flowing through a capillary tube.

the minus sign is used since the velocity u decreases as the radius increases. Substituting equation (8-4) into equation (8-3) and solving for du, we get

$$dp = -\frac{\mu}{r}\frac{du}{dr}2\,dx$$

and

$$du = -\frac{r}{2\mu}\frac{dp}{dx}\,dr$$

Integrating with respect to r gives

$$u = -\frac{1}{2\mu}\frac{dp}{dx}\int r\,dr$$

$$= -\frac{1}{2\mu}\frac{dp}{dx}\frac{r^2}{2} + C$$

where C is a constant of integration. Using the boundary condition that the velocity $= 0$, when $r = R$ we get

$$0 = -\frac{1}{2\mu}\frac{dp}{dx}\frac{R^2}{2} + C$$

$$C = \frac{1}{4\mu}\frac{dp}{dx}R^2$$

Therefore

$$u = \frac{R^2 - r^2}{4\mu}\frac{dp}{dx} \tag{8-5}$$

Since equation (8-5) is the equation of a parabola, the velocity distribution across a capillary tube is a paraboloid.

The flow rate (Q) can be determined by integrating the product of the velocity at some radius r by the cross-sectional area of the differential element at that radius. A cylindrical shell must be used because it has uniform velocity over its cross-sectional area, whereas the cylindrical element used previously will not have uniform velocity. Figure 8-6 shows the element we will consider.

$$dQ = u\,dA$$

$$Q = \int_0^R \frac{dp}{dx}\frac{(R^2 - r^2)}{4\mu}2\pi r\,dr$$

$$= \frac{\pi}{2\mu}\frac{dp}{dx}\left[\frac{R^2 r^2}{2} - \frac{r^4}{4}\right]_0^R$$

$$Q = \frac{\pi R^4}{8\mu}\frac{dp}{dx} \tag{8-6}$$

End View

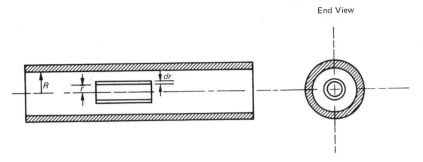

Figure 8-6 The cylindrical shell free body diagram used to derive the expression for the flow rate through a capillary tube.

Equation (8-6) could be used as the basis for determining values for the absolute viscosity μ.

Another interesting flow equation results, when an inclined, open ended capillary tube is considered. Because the tube shown in Figure 8-7 is open to the atmosphere at both ends, the pressure difference between the two ends is due only to the vertical height, h. Thus,

$$\frac{dp}{dx} = \frac{\rho g h}{L}$$

where ρ is the mass density, g is the acceleration of gravity, and L is the length of the tube. Substituting into equation (8-6) we get

$$Q = \frac{\pi R^4}{8\mu} \frac{\rho g h}{L}$$

or

$$\frac{\mu}{\rho} = \frac{\pi R^4 g h}{8 Q L}$$

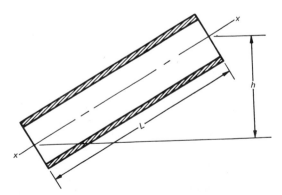

Figure 8-7 Sketch of an inclined, open ended capillary tube.

Here μ/ρ defined as the kinematic viscosity, is represented by the greek letter ν, and is expressed in stokes. Obviously the conversion between absolute and kinematic viscosity involves only the mass density.

$$\nu = \frac{\mu}{\rho}$$

(8-7)

where ν = kinematic viscosity in stokes, μ = absolute viscosity in poises, and ρ = mass density.

SECTION 8-5

Viscosity Measuring Devices

The Saybolt Universal viscometer is perhaps the most widely used viscosity measuring instrument. It utilizes the equation for flow through a capillary tube to measure the kinematic viscosity of lubricating oils. The instrument itself consists of a standard 60-cm^3 receiving flask and a reservoir surrounded by a constant temperature bath. The oil sample to be tested is placed in the reservoir and, when the bath and the reservoir reach the desired test temperature, a stopper at the bottom is removed. The time required for 60-cm^3 of the oil to flow through a capillary tube is recorded. This time, measured in seconds, has become a standard unit of viscosity known as Saybolt Universal Seconds, or simply SUS.

A rather simple formula may be used to convert SUS to absolute viscosity.

$$Z = \rho_t \left(0.22S - \frac{180}{S} \right)$$

(8-8)

where Z = absolute viscosity in centipoise at test temperature t, S = Saybolt Universal Seconds, and ρ_t = specific gravity at test temperature, t.

The specific gravity at the test temperature may be obtained from equation (8-9)

$$\rho_t = \rho_{60} - 0.00035(t - 60)$$

(8-9)

where ρ_{60} = specific gravity at 60°F (standard) and t = test temperature, °F.

Example 8-1. Determine the absolute and kinematic viscosity in reyns and centistokes (cs) of an oil that had an SUS rating of 120 at 100°F (the specific gravity at 60°F can be taken as 0.89).

Solution:

$$\rho_t = \rho_{60} - 0.00035(t - 60)$$

$$= 0.89 - 0.00035(100 - 60)$$

$$= 0.89 - 0.014$$

$$= 0.876$$

$$Z = \rho_t \left(0.22S - \frac{180}{S} \right)$$

$$= 0.876\left(0.22 \times 120 - \frac{180}{120}\right)$$

$$= 0.876(24.9)$$

$$= 21.8 \text{ cp}$$

$$\mu = 21.8 \times (1.45 \times 10^{-7})$$

$$= 31.6 \times 10^{-7} \text{ reyns}$$

$$v = \frac{Z}{\rho} = \frac{21.8}{0.876} = 24.9 \text{ cs}$$

v can also be obtained directly from

$$v = 0.22S - \frac{180}{S} = 0.22 \times 120 - \frac{180}{120} = 24.9 \text{ cs} \quad \bullet$$

SECTION 8-6

Temperature Effect on Viscosity

Unfortunately the viscosity of lubricants varies with changes in temperature. In fact, gases such as air have an increased viscosity with increased temperature, whereas the viscosity of liquids decreases with increased temperature. Clearly, the designer would prefer lubricants that have as small a viscosity change as possible with respect to temperature change.

A means of rating the response of an oil's viscosity variation to temperature change was worked out in 1929 by Dean and Davis [1]. They introduced the concept of a viscosity index. Equation (8-10) is used for calculating the viscosity index.

$$\text{VI} = \frac{L - U}{L - H} \times 100 \tag{8-10}$$

where VI = viscosity index in per cent, L = viscosity of a standard 0% VI oil at 100°F, H = viscosity of a standard 100% VI oil at 100°F, U = viscosity of the unknown VI oil at 100°F.

The procedure for determining the viscosity index of an unknown oil is as follows:

1. Measure the viscosity of a sample of the unknown oil at 100 and 210°F. The viscosity at 100°F is used as U.
2. From the standard oils having a VI of 100%, select one that has the same viscosity at 210°F as the unknown oil. The viscosity of this oil at 100°F is then used as H.
3. From the standard oils having a VI of 0%, select one that has the same viscosity at 210°F as the unknown oil. The viscosity of this standard oil at 100°F is then used as L.

Substitution of these values into equation (8-10) will give the value of the viscosity index for the unknown oil. This procedure can be represented graphically as shown in Figure 8-8. Table 8-1 is a listing of L and $L - H$

values to be used in equation (8-10). The table can be interpolated to give reasonably good results. Equations for determining L and H when the viscosity at 210°F is above those given in the table as well as procedures for determining viscosity indexes over 100% can be found in the ASTM handbook.

Table 8-1 Values of L and D for Calculating Viscosity Index from Saybolt Universal Viscosity.

Saybolt Universal Viscosity at 210°F. SUS	L	D $(L-H)$	Saybolt Universal Viscosity at 210°F. SUS	L	D $(L-H)$
40	137.9	30.8	110	3220	1819
45	265.1	88.8	115	3523	2013
50	422.0	166.9	120	3838	2218
55	596.0	256.8	125	4163	2430
60	780.6	355.0	130	4498	2650
65	976.1	462.1	135	4845	2880
70	1182	578	140	5202	3118
75	1399	702	145	5570	3365
80	1627	836	150	5945	3621
85	1865	977	155	6339	3886
90	2115	1129	160	6740	4160
95	2375	1288	165	7151	4442
100	2646	1457	170	7573	4733
105	2928	1634	175	8006	5032

Table 8-1. (continued)

Saybolt Universal Viscosity at 210°F. SUS	L	D $(L-H)$	Saybolt Universal Viscosity at 210°F. SUS	L	D $(L-H)$
180	8450	5341	295	21637	14854
185	8904	5658	300	22340	15373
190	9370	5985	305	23054	15901
195	9846	6319	310	23778	16436
200	10333	6663	315	24513	16981
205	10831	7015	320	25260	17536
210	11339	7376	325	26017	18098
215	11858	7745	330	26784	18669
220	12389	8125	335	27563	19249
225	12930	8512	340	28352	19838
230	13481	8907	345	29152	20435
235	14044	9313			
240	14617	9726			
245	15201	10148			
250	15796	10579			
255	16402	11020			
260	17019	11469			
265	17646	11926			
270	18284	12392			
275	18933	12867			
280	19593	13351			
285	20263	13843			
290	20945	14344			

SOURCE: Extracted from ASTM D567, Standard Method for Calculating Viscosity Index.

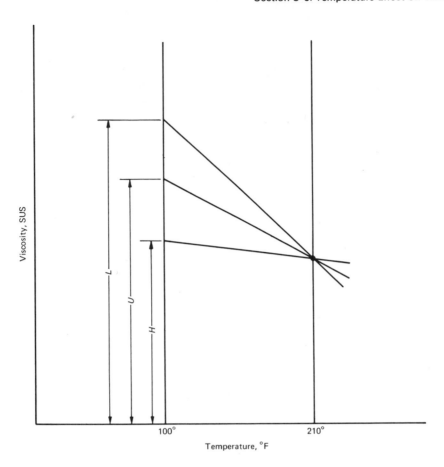

Figure 8-8 Illustration of graphic procedure that can be used to determine the viscosity index.

Example 8-2. Determine the viscosity index of an unknown oil having a viscosity of 89 SUS at 210°F and 1400 SUS at 100°F.

Solution: From Table 8-1, for 89 SUS, interpolation gives $L = 2065$, $L - H = 1099$. Substituting into equation (8-10) we get

$$VI = \frac{L - U}{L - H} \times 100 = \frac{2065 - 1400}{1099} \times 100$$

$$= \frac{665}{1099} \times 100 = 60\% \quad \bullet$$

SECTION 8-7

Petroff's Law

Petroff's equation can be used to determine frictional losses in a journal bearing operating under no load. Under this condition, the journal is concentric in the bearing. Obviously, these conditions of operation could not be applied to an actual bearing. However, if the load applied is low and the rotative speed is fairly high, reasonable values are obtained. The designer usually uses Petroff's equation to obtain a first approximation of the frictional losses and from then on uses more exact methods (to be discussed in Section 8-10) to obtain frictional values. Two concentric cylinders representing a journal rotating in a bearing are shown in Figure 8-9.

From Newton's law

$$\tau = \mu \frac{U}{h}$$

and the frictional force is

$$F = \mu A \frac{U}{h}$$

so that the frictional torque is

$$T_f = Fr = \mu A \frac{U}{h} r$$

Since $U = r\omega$, $\omega = 2\pi n/60$, and $A = 2\pi r L$

$$T_f = \mu 2\pi r L r \frac{2\pi n}{60h} r$$

$$= \frac{\pi^2 \mu L r^3 n}{15h} \tag{8-11}$$

where

T_f = frictional torque, in.-lb
μ = absolute viscosity, reyns
L = length of bearing, in.
r = journal radius, in.
n = journal speed, rpm
h = radial clearance or film thickness, in.

The frictional horsepower can be obtained from equation (8-12).

$$F_{hp} = \frac{T_f n}{63,000} \tag{8-12}$$

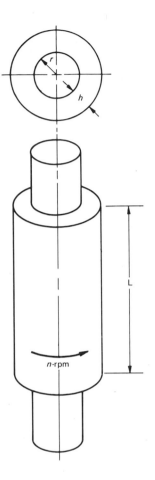

Figure 8-9 The two concentric cylinders shown represent a journal rotating in a bearing with zero eccentricity.

SECTION 8-8

Hydrostatic Lubrication

Although most of the applications involving journal bearings are of the hydrodynamic type, to be discussed in Section 8-9 of this chapter, there are enough instances involving hydrostatic lubrication to warrant a brief discussion. Some of the more common examples are thrust bearings, oil lifts needed during starting of heavily loaded bearings, bearings used in low speed applications, and many others too numerous to mention.

In order to illustrate this type of lubrication in a little more detail, consider the vertical shaft thrust bearing shown in Figure 8-10. The sketch is merely to be used to demonstrate the principle upon which this form of lubrication operates because an actual thrust bearing of this type would be of a much more complicated construction. The vertical shaft, rotating at n rpm is to support a vertical load W. Oil at an inlet pressure p_0, is pumped into the

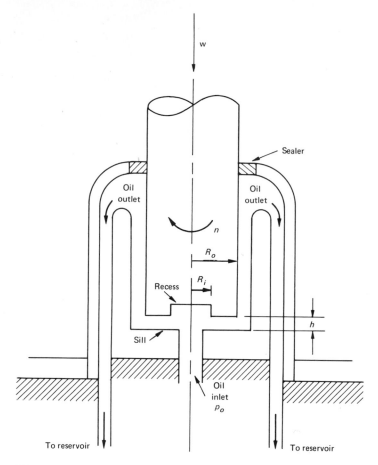

Figure 8-10 Simplified sketch of a vertical shaft thrust bearing.

recess of radius R_i. The oil is forced outward under continuously decreasing pressure, then upward along the sides of the shaft, and then finally returns through a system of piping to the reservoir.

Another type of hydrostatic problem concerns hydrostatic lifts. This problem arises when journal bearings are starting, stopping, or operating at low speeds. The problem can usually be resolved by supplying oil under pressure to the bearing.

The final type of hydrostatic lubrication we will consider is the so-called squeeze film problem. For example, when a machine is temporarily shut down, the load carrying capacity should become zero because the relative motion needed to develop the pressure to support the load is no longer present. However, it was observed that, contrary to expectations, a load carrying capacity did indeed exist. The explanation was that the squeezing out of the lubricant as the surfaces approached each other developed a pressure which was capable of supporting a load for a certain interval of time. The designer is interested in knowing how much time is required for the film to reach a predetermined minimum value. Clearly, this information can be used to determine whether the film will break down before the machine is started up again. If it is determined that the film would have broken down (resulting in metal-to-metal contact), an external supply of pressure may be needed to lift the surface before the machine is started.

A much more complete discussion of hydrostatic lubrication, including the derivation of equations needed to compute such items as load carrying capacity, flow, and supply pressure required, can be found in reference [2].

SECTION 8-9

Hydrodynamic Lubrication

The hydrodynamic theory of lubrication has been in existence since the 1880s. Beauchamp Tower's experimental work on railroad journal bearings induced Osborne Reynolds to perform the mathematical analysis that led to the formulation of the differential equation bearing Reynolds' name. A simple definition of what is meant by hydrodynamic lubrication is to say that the pressure built up by the wedging action produced by two nonparallel surfaces, having relative motion, is sufficient to support an applied load without causing metal-to-metal contact.

We will now proceed to derive the two-dimensional (one-dimensional flow) Reynolds equation. There are several assumptions that are necessary to the derivation.

1. The lubricant is Newtonian; in other words, it obeys Newton's law of viscous flow.
2. The flow is laminar.
3. The lubricant is incompressible.
4. The pressure across the depth and the width of the lubricant film is constant.
5. The viscosity of the lubricant is constant throughout the film
6. The inertia forces due to the acceleration of the lubricant are small enough to be considered negligible.
7. The lubricant film is thin enough so that any effect of bearing curvature may be ignored.
8. The bearing is assumed to have an infinite width. In other words, there is no end leakage (flow along width of bearing).
9. Perfect adhesion exists between the lubricant and the bearing surfaces. This means that the layer of lubricant immediately adjacent to a bearing surface moves with the same velocity as the surface.

Let us consider the situation represented in Figure 8-11. The moving surface supports a load W, and has a velocity in the x direction of U. We will be

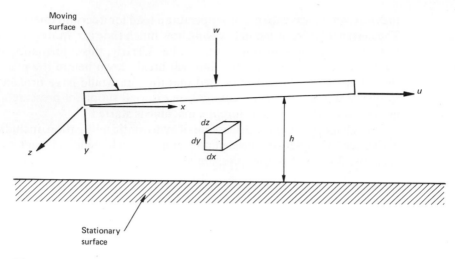

Figure 8-11 A lubricant separates the stationary plate from the plate moving with a velocity U. The load supported is W.

interested in drawing a free body diagram of the forces acting in the x direction on the element of sides dx, dy, and dz as shown. The free body diagram is shown in Figure 8-12.

Summing the forces in the x direction, we get

$$\Sigma F_x = 0 = \left(p + \frac{\partial p}{\partial x}\,dx\right) dy\,dz - p\,dy\,dz - \tau_x\,dx\,dz + \left(\tau_x + \frac{\partial \tau_x}{\partial y}\,dy\right) dx\,dz$$

$$= \frac{\partial p}{\partial x}\,dx\,dy\,dz + \frac{\partial \tau_x}{\partial y}\,dx\,dy\,dz = 0$$

or

$$\left(\frac{\partial p}{\partial x} + \frac{\partial \tau_x}{\partial y}\right) dx\,dy\,dz = 0$$

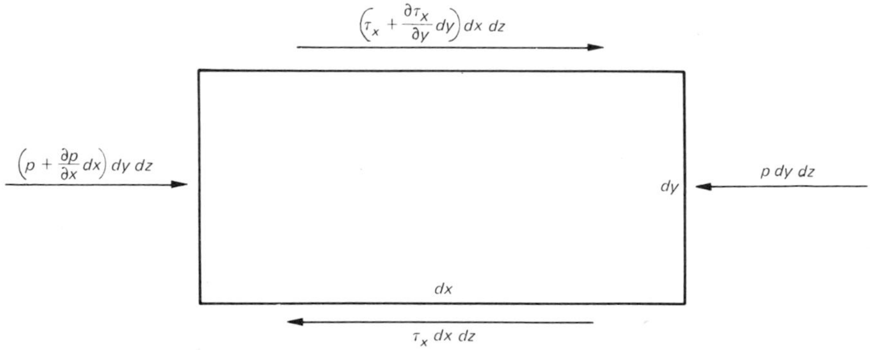

$\left(\tau_x + \frac{\partial \tau_x}{\partial y}\,dy\right) dx\,dz$

$\left(p + \frac{\partial p}{\partial x}\,dx\right) dy\,dz$

$p\,dy\,dz$

dy

dx

$\tau_x\,dx\,dz$

Figure 8-12 A free body drawing of the forces acting on the elemental volume shown in Figure 8-11.

Therefore

$$\frac{\partial p}{\partial x} = -\frac{\partial \tau_x}{\partial y}$$

From Newton's law

$$\tau_x = -\mu \frac{\partial u}{\partial y}$$

where the minus sign is used to indicate a negative velocity gradient

$$\frac{\partial \tau_x}{\partial y} = -\mu \frac{\partial^2 u}{\partial y^2}$$

Therefore,

$$\frac{\partial p}{\partial x} = \mu \frac{\partial^2 u}{\partial y^2}$$

or

$$\frac{\partial^2 u}{\partial y^2} = \frac{1}{\mu} \frac{\partial p}{\partial x}$$

It is now possible to obtain an equation for the velocity, u, by integrating the above equation twice.

$$\frac{\partial u}{\partial y} = \frac{1}{\mu} \frac{\partial p}{\partial x} y + c_1$$

$$u = \frac{1}{\mu} \frac{\partial p}{\partial x} \frac{y^2}{2} + c_1 y + c_2 \tag{8-13}$$

The two boundary conditions we will use to evaluate the constants of integration are (1) $u = U$ when $y = 0$, (2) $u = 0$ when $y = h$ where U is the velocity of the moving plate.

Applying (1) to equation (8-13) we get $c_2 = U$ and applying (2) to equation (8-13) we get

$$0 = \frac{1}{\mu} \frac{\partial p}{\partial x} \frac{h^2}{2} + c_1 h + U$$

or

$$c_1 = -\frac{1}{2\mu} \frac{\partial p}{\partial x} h - \frac{U}{h}$$

Therefore

$$u = \frac{1}{\mu} \frac{\partial p}{\partial x} \frac{y^2}{2} - \frac{1}{2\mu} \frac{\partial p}{\partial x} hy - \frac{U}{h} y + U$$

$$= \frac{1}{2\mu} \frac{\partial p}{\partial x} (y^2 - hy) + U\left(1 - \frac{y}{h}\right) \tag{8-14}$$

We now make use of the assumption of incompressibility to write an equation stating that the quantity of fluid entering the elemental cube shown in Figure 8-12, must equal the volume of fluid leaving the cube. In the following equations, u = velocity along x axis, v = velocity along y axis, and w = velocity along z axis.

$$u\,dy\,dz + v\,dx\,dz + w\,dx\,dy = \left(u + \frac{\partial u}{\partial x}dx\right)dy\,dz + \left(v + \frac{\partial v}{\partial y}dy\right)dx\,dz$$

$$+ \left(w + \frac{\partial w}{\partial z}dz\right)dx\,dy$$

$$\left(\frac{\partial u}{\partial x} + \frac{\partial v}{\partial y} + \frac{\partial w}{\partial z}\right)dx\,dy\,dz = 0$$

or

$$\frac{\partial u}{\partial x} + \frac{\partial v}{\partial y} + \frac{\partial w}{\partial z} = 0$$

But since we assumed no end leakage, $\partial w/\partial z = 0$. Therefore

$$\frac{\partial v}{\partial y} = -\frac{\partial u}{\partial x}$$

We now differentiate equation (8-14) to get

$$\frac{\partial u}{\partial x} = \frac{\partial}{\partial x}\left[\frac{1}{2\mu}\frac{\partial p}{\partial x}(y - h)y + U\left(1 - \frac{y}{h}\right)\right]$$

Therefore

$$\frac{\partial v}{\partial y} = -\frac{\partial}{\partial x}\left[\frac{1}{2\mu}\frac{\partial p}{\partial x}(y - h)y + U\left(1 - \frac{y}{h}\right)\right]$$

Upon integrating with respect to y, with y going from 0 to h, we get

$$\int_0^h \frac{\partial v}{\partial y} = -\int_0^h \frac{\partial}{\partial x}\left[\frac{\partial p}{\partial x}\frac{y(y - h)}{2\mu}\right]dy - \int_0^h \frac{\partial U}{\partial x}\left(1 - \frac{y}{h}\right)dy$$

$$v\Big|_{y=0}^{y=h} = -\frac{\partial}{\partial x}\left[\frac{\partial p(y^3/3 - hy^2/2)}{\partial x\,2\mu}\right]_0^h - \frac{\partial}{\partial x}\left[U\left(y - \frac{y^2}{2h}\right)\right]_0^h$$

Because we assume that perfect adhesion exists between lubricant and bearing, $v = 0$, when $y = 0$, and $y = h$. Therefore

$$0 = -\frac{\partial}{\partial x}\left[\frac{\partial p}{\partial x\,2\mu}\left(\frac{h^3}{3} - \frac{h^3}{2}\right)\right] - \frac{\partial}{\partial x}U\left(h - \frac{h}{2}\right) \quad \text{and}$$

$$\frac{\partial}{\partial x}\left(\frac{h^3}{12\mu}\frac{\partial p}{\partial x}\right) = \frac{U}{2}\frac{\partial h}{\partial x}$$

and

$$\frac{\partial}{\partial x}\left(h^3\frac{\partial p}{\partial x}\right) = 6\mu U\frac{\partial h}{\partial x} \tag{8-15}$$

Equation (8-15) is the one-dimensional flow Reynolds' equation. If end leakage is not ignored, an analysis similar to the above will yield the following form of Reynolds' equation shown as equation (8-16).

$$\frac{\partial}{\partial x}\left(h^3\frac{\partial p}{\partial x}\right) - \frac{\partial}{\partial z}\left(h^3\frac{\partial p}{\partial z}\right) = -\,6\mu U\frac{\partial h}{\partial x} \tag{8-16}$$

This equation has been solved by numerical methods.

SECTION 8-10

Design Charts

Raimondi and Boyd were able to apply digital computer techniques toward the solution of the fundamental lubrication equations, and present the results in the form of design charts and tables [4]. The solutions obtained are mathematical and thus give the theoretical results that the designer can expect. The charts are plotted with the bearing characteristic number, also known as the Sommerfeld number, S', as the abscissa.

$$S' = \left(\frac{r_j}{c}\right)^2\frac{\mu n'}{P} \tag{8-17}$$

where

S' = bearing characteristic number, dimensionless
r_j = radius of journal, in.
c = radial clearance, in.
μ = absolute viscosity, reyns
n' = relative speed between journal and bearing, rps. In some cases n is expressed in rpm, with the result that S' is in sec/min, instead of being dimensionless
P = load per projected area of journal, psi

Figure 8-13 is a plot of temperature versus viscosity for various SAE oils, and Figure 8-14 is a diagram of the pressure distribution around a journal bearing and also shows some of the nomenclature commonly used.

Before proceeding to the presentation of the design charts, some of the problems of presentation must be discussed. Boyd and Raimondi first published a paper [6] in which they considered bearings having no end leakage; in other words, bearings having L/D (length of bearing to diameter of bearing) ratios equal to infinity. Then in reference [4], part I, they extended the work to bearings having L/D ratios of 1, and in part II, L/D ratios of $\frac{1}{2}$ and $\frac{1}{4}$ were discussed. In all their papers to this point, they assumed that the lubricant

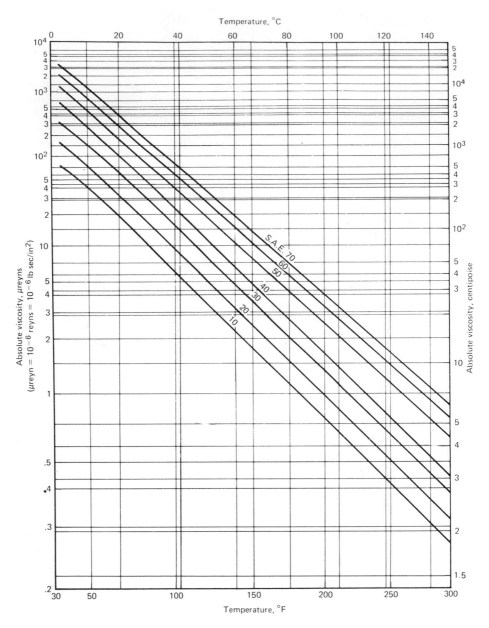

Figure 8-13 Viscosity-temperature chart for determining viscosity of typical SAE numbered oils at various temperatures. [From A. A. Raymondi and J. Boyd: A solution for the finite journal bearing and its application to analysis and design, Parts I, II, III. *Trans. American Society of Lubrication Engineers*, **1**(1): 159–209 (1958).]

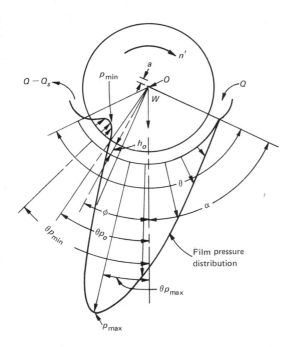

Figure 8-14 The pressure variation around a journal bearing is shown. [From A. A. Raymondi and J. Boyd: A solution for the finite journal bearing and its application to analysis and design, Parts I, II, III. *Trans. American Society of Lubrication Engineers*, **1**(1):159–209 (1958).]

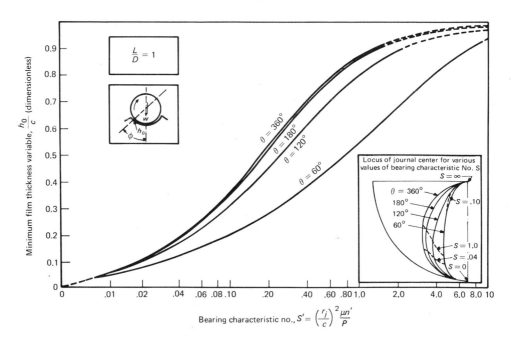

Figure 8-15 Minimum film thickness variable versus bearing characteristic number ($L/D = 1$). [From A. A. Raymondi and J. Boyd: A solution for the finite journal bearing and its application to analysis and design, Parts I, II, III. *Trans. American Society of Lubrication Engineers*, **1**(1):159–209 (1958).]

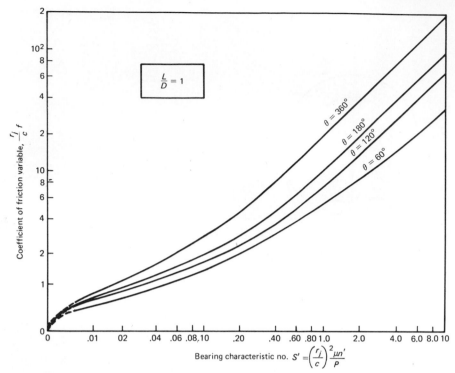

Figure 8-16 For determining friction coefficient. [From A. A. Raymondi and J. Boyd: A solution for the finite journal bearing and its application to analysis and design, Parts I, II, III. *Trans. American Society of Lubrication Engineers*, **1**(1): 159–209 (1958).]

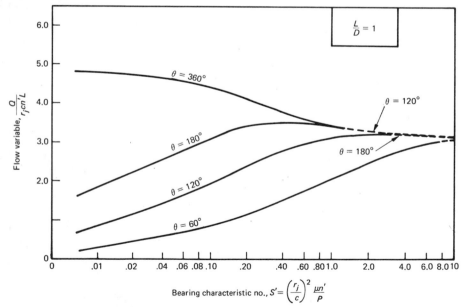

Figure 8-17 For determining lubricant flow. [From A. A. Raymondi and J. Boyd: A solution for the finite journal bearing and its application to analysis and design, Parts I, II, III. *Trans. American Society of Lubrication Engineers*, **1**(1): 159–209 (1958).]

film was continuous throughout the bearing circumference and that the film pressure was high enough to prevent rupture. Although this assumption was valid for lightly loaded or high speed bearing applications, many bearings operate under conditions that do cause film rupture. For this reason, part III, was devoted to the results obtained when film rupture was considered. The designer can therefore use the results of parts I or II to ascertain whether subatmosphere pressure exists (with consequent film rupture). If rupture does occur, the results of part III are to be used.

A major difficulty encountered in presenting this material in a text of this kind is the question of space limitation. The solution finally arrived at was to present a series of charts from part III for L/D ratios equal to 1. Figures 8-15 through 8-19 present design charts that are sufficient for classroom purposes. Those desiring more complete information, can find it in the references cited. The best way to explain the use of the charts is to do an example.

Example 8-3. Analyze a 180-deg partial journal bearing operating under the following conditions: $n = 3600$ rpm; $n' = 60$ rps; $W = 1600$ lb; $\mu = 2 \times 10^{-7}$ reyn; $c = 0.002$ in.; $r_j = 2$ in.; $L = 4$ in.

Solution:

$$S' = \left(\frac{r_j}{c}\right)^2 \frac{\mu n'}{P}$$

$$P = \frac{W}{2r_j L} = \frac{1600}{(2)(2)(4)} = 100 \text{ psi}$$

$$S' = \left(\frac{2}{0.002}\right)^2 \frac{(2 \times 10^{-7})(60)}{100} = 0.12$$

$$L/D = 4/4 = 1$$

$$\theta = 180 \text{ deg}$$

where $D = 2r_j$, and where θ is the partial bearing angle shown in Figure 8-3.
  Part 1: To determine the minimum film thickness, refer to Figure 8-15.

$$\frac{h_0}{c} = 0.39$$

Therefore

$$h_0 = 0.39 \times 0.002 = 0.00078 \text{ in.}$$

Since $a = \varepsilon c = c - h_0$, $h_0 = c(1 - \varepsilon)$. Therefore

$$\varepsilon = 1 - \frac{h_0}{c} = 1 - 0.39$$

$$= 0.61$$

If this value for minimum film thickness is less than the value the designer has chosen as a minimum, the design must be changed.

  Another way in which the chart can be used is to decide on a minimum film thickness and read the corresponding Sommerfeld number. Bearing dimensions or viscosity can then be adjusted to conform to this Sommerfeld number.

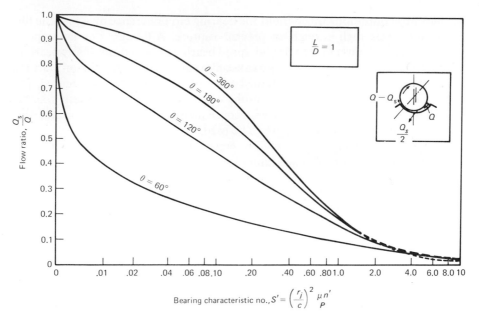

Figure 8-18 For determining end leakage. [From A. A. Raymondi and J. Boyd:
A solution for the finite journal bearing and its application to analysis and design,
Parts I, II, III. *Trans. American Society of Lubrication Engineers*, **1**(1): 159–209
(1958).]

Part 2: The frictional power loss will next be determined. This is the power
needed to overcome the fluid friction in the bearing.
From Figure 8-16 for $S' = 0.12$

$$\frac{r_j}{c}f = 2.2$$

$$f = 2.2 \times \frac{0.002}{2} = 0.0022$$

Then frictional torque, T_f is

$$T_f = fWr_j = 0.0022 \times 1600 \times 2 = 7.04 \text{ in.-lb}$$

and

$$F_{hp} = \frac{T_f n}{63,000} = \frac{7.04 \times 3600}{63,000} = 0.4 \text{ hp}$$

Part 3: Another variable of some interest to the designer is the flow, Q. The
chart for determining the flow requirement is given in Figure 8-17. If the
lubricant is supplied to the bearing from some external source, say an oil
reservoir, the rate at which the lubricant must be supplied can be determined
from the figure.
It should be pointed out that the failure to supply a flow Q will not necessarily
cause a bearing failure but will change the performance characteristics of the
bearing. In other words, if the bearing is to have the performance characteristics
indicated by the charts, the amount of oil supplied to the bearing must equal Q.

It must be emphasized that, when bearings are lubricated by external means under pressure, special methods of solution must be used.

From Figure 8-17, for $S' = 0.12$

$$\frac{Q}{r_j c n' L} = 3.2$$

Therefore

$$Q = 3.2 \times 2 \times 0.002 \times 60 \times 4$$

$$= 3.07 \text{ in.}^3/\text{sec}$$

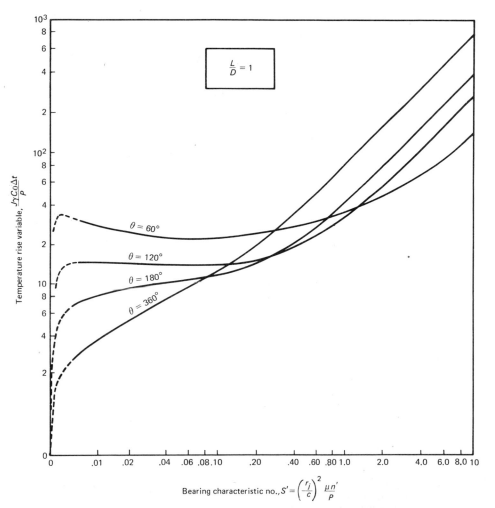

Figure 8-19 For determining film temperature rise. [From A. A. Raymondi and J. Boyd: A solution for the finite journal bearing and its application to analysis and design, Parts I, II, III. *Trans. American Society of Lubrication Engineers,* **1**(1): 159–209 (1958).]

Part 4: Another consideration with regard to flow is the amount of end leakage. This end flow will cause a decrease in pressure along the bearing. The quantity of oil flowing can be obtained by using Figure 8-18 and the ratio Q_s/Q. For $S' = 0.12$

$$\frac{Q_s}{Q} = 0.58$$

$$Q_s = 0.58 \times Q = 0.58 \times 3.07 = 1.78 \text{ in.}^3/\text{sec}$$

Part 5 : The temperature rise that occurs in the oil film due to fluid friction is of obvious interest to the designer. It is almost impossible to get a precise value for this temperature rise because some of the heat developed is carried away by the oil and some heat is transferred by conduction, convection, and radiation. Figure 8-19 may be used to obtain conservative estimates of temperature rise. The curves are based upon the assumptions that all of the heat generated by the fluid friction is effective in raising the temperature of the lubricant and that none of the lubricant leaving the trailing edge of the film is carried over to the leading edge. In Section 8-11 we will discuss the question of temperature rise in greater detail, but for the moment we will use the chart to obtain a first estimate of temperature rise.

For $S' = 0.12$ and where $C_0 =$ specific heat, 0.42 Btu/(lb)(°F); $J =$ mechanical equivalent of heat, 778 ft-lb/Btu; and $\gamma =$ weight density, 0.03 lb/in.^{3}

$$\frac{J\gamma C_0 \Delta t}{P} = 12$$

$$\Delta t = \frac{12P}{J\gamma C_0} = \frac{12 \times 100}{778 \times 12 \times 0.03 \times 0.42}$$

$$= 10.2°F \quad \bullet$$

SECTION 8-11

Heat Balancing of Bearings

By heat balancing a bearing, we simply mean the determination of the balance that exists between the heat developed and the heat dissipated in a bearing. There are two general types of bearings to be considered, the self-contained bearing and the pressure-fed bearing. We will devote our attention first to the self-contained type. A **self-contained bearing** is one in which the lubricant is contained in the bearing housing, which is sealed to prevent oil loss. Obviously, the self-contained bearing is economically more desirable because it does not require expensive cooling or lubricant-circulating systems. Bearings of this type dissipate heat to the surrounding atmosphere by means of conduction, convection, and radiation. They are widely used in industry, and are known as **pillow-block** or **pedestal bearings.**

The important question to be answered from the designer's point of view, is what will be the equilibrium temperature of the oil film. In other words, after an interval of operation, what will be the film temperature when the heat developed is exactly equal to the heat dissipated. The usual desired value for average film temperature is 160°F. If the temperature rises above 200°F, harmful deterioration of the lubricant as well as damage to the bearing material can take place.

The heat dissipated from the bearing housing may be approximated by equation 8-18

$$H = CA(t_b - t_a) \tag{8-18}$$

where

H = heat lost, Btu/hr
C = heat transfer coefficient, Btu/(hr)(ft^2)(°F)
A = effective area of bearing housing through which heat is being transferred, ft^2
t_b = temperature of the bearing housing, °F
t_a = ambient air temperature, °F.

The heat transfer coefficient depends on many factors, such as the surface condition of the housing, the material and shape of the housing, and the velocity of the surrounding air. A value for C of 2 Btu/(hr)(ft^2)(°F) for still air is widely used; a value of 5.9 Btu/(hr)(ft^2)(°F) is suggested for air having a velocity of 500 ft/min.

The bearing housing area, which is dissipating heat, is sometimes difficult to calculate. A reasonable estimate for this area is that suggested by Fuller [2]. For simple pillow-block bearings, the effective area in square inches may be taken as 12.5DL and for pillow-blocks with separate shells 20DL is recommended.

Another difficulty the designer faces is that, although equation (8-18) may give the rate at which the housing is dissipating heat, the average oil film temperature rise may be greater than this value. The construction of the bearing and lubrication method used are the factors to be considered. Faires [8] suggests the following approximations.

For oil-ring bearings in still air

$$t_o - t_a = 2(t_b - t_a) \tag{8-19a}$$

where t_o is the oil film temperature.

For oil-bath bearings in still air

$$t_o - t_a = 1.3(t_b - t_a) \tag{8-19b}$$

For waste-packed bearings in still air

$$t_o - t_a = 2.5(t_b - t_a) \tag{8-19c}$$

For air moving at 500 ft/min, the oil-ring bearing constant should be increased by 15–20%. We will demonstrate the procedure that can be followed to determine the oil film temperature in Example 8-4.

Example 8-4. An oil-ring full journal bearing is to operate in still air. The bearing diameter is 3 in., and the length is also 3 in. The bearing is subjected to a load of 1000 lb and is rotating at 500 rpm, the radial clearance is 0.0025 in., the oil is an SAE 30, and the ambient air temperature is 80°F. What is the value of the viscosity of the oil.

Solution: Assume the average oil temperature is 160°F. Then from Figure 8-13

$$\mu = 2.8 \times 10^{-6} \text{ reyns}$$

$$S' = \left(\frac{r_j}{c}\right)^2 \left(\frac{\mu n'}{P}\right) = \left(\frac{1.5}{0.0025}\right)^2 \left(\frac{2.8 \times 10^{-6} \times \frac{500}{60}}{\frac{1000}{3 \times 3}}\right)$$

$$= 0.0758$$

From Figure 8-16

$$\frac{r_j}{c} f = 2.4$$

$$f = 2.4 \frac{c}{r_j} = \frac{2.4 \times 0.0025}{1.5} = 0.004$$

Therefore, the heat developed is

$$H = fWV = 0.004 \times 1000 \text{ lb} \times 500 \frac{\text{rev}}{\text{min}} \times 2\pi \frac{\text{rad}}{\text{rev}} \times \frac{1.5}{12} \text{ ft}$$

$$= 1570 \text{ ft-lb/min}$$

Then from equation (8-18)

$$H = CA(t_b - t_a)$$

$$C = \frac{2 \text{ Btu}}{(\text{hr})(\text{ft}^2)(°F)} \times 778 \frac{\text{ft-lb}}{\text{Btu}} \times \frac{1 \text{ hr}}{60 \text{ min}}$$

$$= 25.93 \, [\text{ft-lb}/[(\text{min})(\text{ft}^2)(°F)]$$

$$A = 12.5DL = 12.5 \times 3 \times 3 = 112.5 \text{ in.}^2$$

$$t_b - t_a = \frac{H}{CA}$$

$$= \frac{1570 \frac{\text{ft-lb}}{\text{min}}}{25.93 \frac{\text{ft-lb}}{(\text{min})(\text{ft}^2)(°F)} \times 112.5 \text{ in.}^2 \times \frac{1 \text{ ft}^2}{144 \text{ in.}^2}}$$

$$= 78.1°F$$

$$t_b = 78.1 + t_a = 78.1 + 80 = 158.1°F$$

From equation (8-19a)

$$t_o - t_a = 2(t_b - t_a) = 2 \times 78.1°F = 156.2°F$$

$$t_o = 156.2 + t_a = 156.2 + 80 = 236.2°F$$

This does not agree with the assumed value of 160°F. Therefore, assume $t_o = 200°F$. Then from Figure 8-13

$$\mu = 1.3 \times 10^{-6} \text{ reyns}$$

$$S' = \left(\frac{r_j}{c}\right)^2 \frac{\mu n'}{P} = \left(\frac{1.5}{0.0025}\right)^2 \left(\frac{1.3 \times 10^{-6} \times \dfrac{500}{60}}{\dfrac{1000}{3 \times 3}}\right)$$

$$= 0.0352$$

From Figure 8-16

$$\frac{r_j}{c} f = 1.5$$

$$f = \frac{1.5 \times 0.0025}{1.5} = 0.0025$$

Therefore

$$H = fWV = 0.0025 \times 1000 \times 500 \times \frac{2\pi}{12} \times 1\tfrac{1}{2}$$

$$= 982 \text{ ft-lb/min}$$

$$t_b - t_a = \frac{H}{CA} = \frac{982}{25.93 \times \dfrac{112.5}{144}} = 48.5°F$$

$$t_b = 48.5 + 80 = 128.5°F$$

$$t_o - t_a = 2(t_b - t_a) = 2 \times 48.5 = 97 \text{ F}$$

$$t_o = 97 + 80 = 177°F$$

This is closer to the assumed value of 200°F.

The next trial would be 190°F. In any event, because the film temperature is less than 200°F, external cooling will not be required.

We will now turn our attention to the heat balance in forced-feed bearings. As was stated in Example 8-4, in those cases when oil film temperature exceeds 200°F, some external source of cooling is required. The usual method of solving this problem is to supply oil under pressure to the bearing. As the oil flows through the bearing, it picks up heat from the bearing. The oil is then returned to a reservoir or sump where it is cooled before being recirculated.

A common method used for pressure lubrication is the so-called circumferential groove method. Figure 8-20 is an illustration of a circumferential groove bearing. As the name implies, a circumferential groove is cut at the center of the bearing, the oil is forced into the groove through an oil supply hole placed in the groove, opposite the portion of the oil film that is supporting the load. The groove, however, has the disadvantage of breaking up the active length of the oil film. As a result, the pressure distribution does not vary as

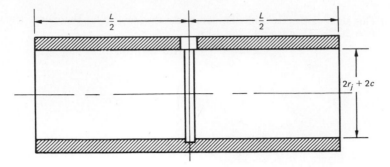

Figure 8-20 Circumferential groove going completely around the circumference of the bearing gives this bearing its name.

the smooth curve in Figure 8-21 but rather is more like the curve b in the same figure.

Despite breaking the oil film in half, the efficient cooling obtained allows larger loads to be applied to the bearing. Equation (8-20) can be used for determining the theoretical flow through a 360-deg circumferentially grooved bearing.

$$Q = \frac{2\pi r_j p_0 c^3}{3\mu L}(1 + 1.5\varepsilon^2) \tag{8-20}$$

where the symbols have the same meaning as in Section 8-10.

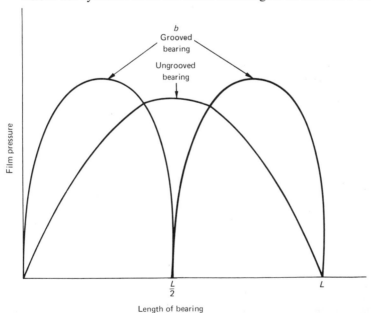

Figure 8-21 Comparison of pressure distribution along the length of a journal bearing with and without a groove.

Other types of pressurized oil supply bearings are the axial groove and inlet hole. In the inlet hole type, the oil is introduced under pressure by means of a single hole in the bearing, whereas the axial groove is similar to the circumferential groove type except that the groove is placed 90 deg away, or in other words, parallel to the axis of the bearing. There are many types that involve combinations of axial and circumferential grooves as well as a wide variety of groove types.

SECTION 8-12

Methods of Lubrication

There are a variety of methods used to lubricate bearings. The method chosen for a specific problem depends to a large extent upon the type of service the bearing is to perform and also how important the bearing is to the system of which it is a part.

Bearings that are to be used in low speed, light load applications can be lubricated by the **hand oiling** method. It is not a very desirable method because it tends to result in an excessive supply of oil, with the resultant leakage problem, at the time of application and later, before the next oiling, there may not be sufficient lubricant present to maintain the oil film. A good general rule to follow is that hand oiling should be used only if no other alternative is available, and then only if the bearing plays a relatively minor role in the operation of the system it is a part of.

A **wick-feed oiler,** as the name implies, depends upon an absorbant material acting as a wick to supply the oil to the bearing. While one end of the wick is immersed in a reservoir of oil, the other end is in contact with the journal. The oil is thus drawn from the reservoir, through the wick, to the bearing. The flow rate can be controlled because it will depend on the kind of material and construction of the wick. The wick-feed oil method is better than the hand oiling method because of the more uniform supply of oil.

A **drop-feed oiler** allows oil from a reservoir to flow through a needle valve to the bearing. Clearly, the valve can be adjusted to control the amount of oil flow. While this method is also better than hand-oiling because of a more uniform rate of flow, it does have the danger of the valve clogging, if any impurities are present in the oil.

The **ring-oiled bearing** makes use of a ring or chain that is placed over the journal near or at the center of the bearing. As the ring rotates, it dips into a reservoir and carries the oil to the top of the bearing. The method is quite reliable, and is widely used in medium to relatively high speed applications.

When a machine has a rotating part such as a crank or gear enclosed in a housing, the **splash system** of lubrication is very useful. The moving part runs through a reservoir of oil formed in the enclosed casing. This causes a spray of oil to drench the casing, thus lubricating the bearing. It is also possible to have channels and ducts that lead directly to the bearing. The oil, in this system, is sprayed into these channels. As long as the proper oil level is maintained, a continuous supply of oil is ensured.

In **pressure fed systems,** a continuous supply of oil is furnished to the bearing by a pump. This method was discussed earlier, and it will be remembered that oil is returned to a reservoir after being circulated through the bearing. As a result, if sufficient flow is available, much of the heat developed in the bearing is carried away by the oil. The pressure lubricated system is the most extensively used method.

In those applications involving heavy loads, low speeds, high temperature, and designs for which it would be difficult to retain oil, grease is recommended as a lubricant. The grease must usually be applied under pressure to the surface to be lubricated. An example everyone is familiar with is the use of grease to lubricate the chassis of an automobile.

SECTION 8-13

Bearing Materials

The operating conditions for bearings are such that rather stringent requirements must be set forth in regard to the material to be used. Some of the properties a good bearing material should possess are mentioned in the following list.

1. The material should have good compatibility, which means good antiweld and antiscoring properties. Since most journal bearings will experience occasional metal-to-metal contact, it is important that the bearing material be one that does not readily weld itself to the shaft material.

2. Conformability is a measure of the bearing's ability to adjust to misalignment or other geometric errors. Materials having a low modulus of elasticity usually have good conformability.

3. Embeddability, means the material is soft enough to absorb foreign materials that are too large to pass through the oil film. By allowing this embedding, wear and scoring can be prevented.

4. The material should have good fatigue strength because of the many applications for which the bearing loads change directions.

5. Resistance to corrosion is required in those applications where the lubricating oil used may oxidize and thus corrode the bearing.

6. Clearly, from the discussion in Section 8-11, good heat conductance is desirable.

7. Last, but certainly not least important, the cost should be as low as possible.

Let us now consider some of the more important types of materials.

1. **Babbitt alloys,** of either tin or lead base, are perhaps the most commonly used material. They have excellent embeddability and compatibility characteristics. However, babbitt alloys have the disadvantage of being relatively weaker than other bearing materials, lose strength rapidly with increasing temperature, and have lower fatigue strength. These shortcomings can generally be remedied by using a thin internal babbitt surface on steel backing.

2. **Copper alloys** are also widely used and are primarily bronzes. They are generally stronger, have a greater load capacity, have good fatigue strength, are harder, but less score resistant than babbitt bearings.

3. **Aluminum alloys,** because of their fatigue strength, load carrying capacity, thermal conductivity, corrosion resistance, and low cost, are widely used for bearings in internal combustion engines. Their disadvantages are that they require hardened journals, and have poor compatibility, conformability, and embeddability. When a thin layer of babbitt is placed inside an aluminum bearing, the antiscoring and embeddability characteristics are improved.

4. **Porous metal** bearings of either bronze or iron have found wide acceptance. These sintered-metal, self-lubricated bearings have interconnecting pores in which oil is stored and then fed to the bearing surface. The low cost and long time between lubricant supply are their prime advantages.

5. **Silver** bearings are extremely useful for heavy duty applications. The bearings are made by electrodepositing silver on a steel backing with an overlay of lead 0.001–0.005 in. thick. A thin layer of indium is then deposited on the lead to provide corrosion protection.

6. **Cast iron and steel** are used in bearings subjected to relatively light loads. The prime advantage of these bearings is low cost. However, because of poor embeddability and conformability, these bearings require very good alignment and freedom from foreign matter.

7. Various **plastics,** such as phenolics, nylon, fluorocarbons, acetal, and so on, are used as bearing materials. The advantages of using plastics are no corrosion, quiet operation, moldability, and excellent compatibility. The last named characteristic usually means that no lubrication is required. However, when used in heavy load applications, their low heat conductivity may result in buildup of heat which will then require external cooling.

8. **Rubber** and other elastomeric materials are used in such applications as ship propellor shafts and rudders, hydraulic pumps, sand dredges, and so on. They provide vibration isolation, can compensate for misalignment, and have good conformability. They are generally made fluted and placed inside a noncorrodible metal shell. A water flush will thus permit sand and grit to pass through the bearing without scoring it.

9. **Other materials,** which are used in specialty applications, are wood (lignum vitae and oil-impregnated oak), ceramics and cermets, sapphire, and glass.

SECTION 8-14

Design Considerations

When a bearing is still in the design stage, the effects of varying dimensions and parameters should be investigated. A general design procedure would involve choosing values for those quantities which are under the control of the designer or which are given. These quantities are usually designated as independent variables and include the viscosity of the lubricant, load, speed of rotation, radius and length of bearing, clearance, and whether it is to be a full or partial bearing. These values are then used to determine the so-called dependent variables such as minimum film thickness, temperature rise, coefficient of friction, and oil flow. We will now briefly discuss these quantities as well as some of the more important design parameters.

1. **Lubricants.** These can be either solid, liquid, or gas. Designers usually base their choice upon such factors as type of machine, method of lubricant supply, and load characteristics.

2. **Bearing Load.** The load acting on a bearing is usually specified, but by choosing the length and diameter of the bearing, the designer can choose the value of the load per projected area. The desired life of the bearing will usually dictate the magnitude of the load per projected area. Clearly, the smaller the load per projected area, the greater the bearing life.

3. **Length/Diameter Ratio.** The L/D or length-to-diameter ratio is an extremely important bearing parameter. The usual practice is to choose L/D values from 0.8 to 1.5, with a value of unity most generally used. As a guide in choosing the magnitude of an L/D ratio the following factors should be considered.

Bearings with L/D ratios greater than 1 (long bearing) are usually used in applications where misalignment must be avoided and a reduced load carrying capacity can be tolerated. When the L/D ratio is less than 1 (short bearing), the danger of metal-to-metal contact because of large shaft deflections is greatly reduced. There are other factors to be considered, but a rough rule to be followed might be as follows: use an L/D of unity, decrease it if deflections are expected to be severe, increase it if shaft alignment is important.

4. **Clearance.** Proper values to be used for journal bearing clearance depend on factors such as materials, manufacturing accuracy, load carrying capacity, minimum film clearance, oil flow, film temperature, and so on. Clearly a complete analysis is needed to obtain a proper value for the clearance. If a reasonable value is desired with a minimum of analysis, a clearance ratio, c/r, of 0.001 has been successfully used for many years.

Clearance value can be obtained by optimization techniques. The problem is that large clearances will permit foreign materials to pass easily through the bearings, the increased flow will reduce film temperature and thus increase bearing life. But too large a clearance will result in a loose, noisy bearing and a resulting decrease in minimum film thickness.

PROBLEMS

1. Two storage tanks are connected by a horizontal capillary tube. The liquid stored in the tanks is an SAE 10 oil at a temperature of 70°F. The tube has a bore of 0.03 in. and is 90 in. long. If the difference in pressure in the two tanks (at the points where the tube is connected to the tanks) is 10 psi, what is the flow in gallons per minute if the flow is laminar?

2. What will be the absolute viscosity in reyns and the kinematic viscosity in SUS for a fluid having a viscosity of 30 cs at 90°F and a specific gravity of 0.9 at 60°F.

3. What is the viscosity index of an oil with an SUS of 2900 at 100°F and 140 SUS at 210°F.

4. A lightly loaded (Petroff's equation may be used) journal bearing is 3 in. long, has a 3 in. diameter, is acted on by a 400-lb radial load, the radial clearance is 0.003 in., is rotating at 30,000 rpm and is supplied with a lubricant having a viscosity of 0.5×10^{-6} reyns. Determine (**a**) the frictional torque developed, (**b**) the frictional horsepower, and (**c**) the coefficient of friction.

5. A lightly loaded full journal bearing has a 5-in. length, a 5-in. diameter, a 0.0015-in. radial clearance, a rotative speed of 500 rpm, and a radial load of 1500 lb. For a coefficient of friction of 0.01, determine the average viscosity of the oil. If the average film temperature is 155°F, what is the approximate grade of oil being used?

6. A hydrostatic step bearing, similar to the one shown in Section 8-8, has a thrust load of 100,000 lb applied to it. The bearing dimensions are as follows: journal radius = 10 in., recess radius = 5 in., viscosity of lubricant = 2.5×10^{-6} reyns, minimum film thickness = 0.004 in. What will be the vlaue of the supply pressure required, and what is the required flow? The load carrying capacity is given by

$$W = \frac{p_o \pi}{2} \left[\frac{R_o^2 - R_i^2}{\ln (R_o/R_i)} \right]$$

and the required flow is given by

$$Q = \frac{p_o \pi h^3}{6\mu \ln (R_o/R_i)}$$

7. The following problem is presented as a means of introducing an elementary concept of hydrostatic lift.

A 180-deg partial journal bearing is found to require a hydrostatic lift. The journal, of length 5 in., has a 2.500-in. radius, a bearing radius of 2.508-in., and a 5000-lb load applied to it. Oil having a viscosity of 20×10^{-6} reyns is supplied to a 3-in. long rectangular groove in the bearing. What will be the required supply pressure in order to assure a minimum film thickness of 0.003 in.?

The load carrying capacity equation is given by

$$W = \frac{Q6\mu\varepsilon^3 r_j^2[2 + 3\varepsilon - \varepsilon^3]}{a^3(1 - \varepsilon^2)^2}$$

and the flow equation is

$$Q = \frac{p_o b a^3}{6\mu\varepsilon^3 r_j} \left[\frac{\varepsilon(4 - \varepsilon^2)}{2(1 - \varepsilon^2)} + \frac{2 + \varepsilon^2}{(1 - \varepsilon^2)^{5/2}} \tan^{-1} \left(\frac{1 + \varepsilon}{\sqrt{1 - \varepsilon^2}} \right) \right]^{-1}$$

where a = eccentricity; ε = eccentricy ratio = $a/(r_b - r_j)$; b = length of oil slot in bearing.

8. A journal bearing has the following specifications: journal radius $= \frac{1}{2}$ in.; radial clearance $= 0.0005$ in.; bearing length $= 1$ in.; viscosity of oil $= 15 \times 10^{-7}$ reyns; load acting on bearing $= 1000$ lb. If the load on the bearing is stopped for 0.1 sec and the minimum film thickness is to be at least 0.00045 in., will a hydrostatic lift be needed before the load is again applied?

The equation for determining the time in seconds, for the eccentricity ratio to go from a value of ε_1 to ε_2 is

$$\Delta t = \frac{24\mu b r_j^3}{Wc^2}\left[\tan^{-1}\left(\frac{1+\varepsilon}{1-\varepsilon}\right)^{1/2} \frac{\varepsilon}{\sqrt{1-\varepsilon^2}}\right]_{\varepsilon_1}^{\varepsilon_2}$$

where $b =$ bearing length; and $c =$ radial clearance.

9. A 360-deg journal bearing with a diameter of 2 in. and a length of 2 in. consumes 0.116 hp in friction at an operating speed of 1432 rpm. SAE 10 oil is used, and the film temperature is 173°F. The radial clearance of the bearing equals 0.001 in. Determine (**a**) the eccentricity ratio. (**b**) The minimum film thickness. (**c**) The total load for the bearing.

10. To demonstrate the use of the Boyd and Raimondi design charts, determine the quantities asked for in regard to the following journal bearing problem. A 180-deg partial journal bearing has an L/D ratio of 1, a 4-in. diameter, a radial clearance of 0.003 in., an operating speed of 600 rpm and an applied load of 1500 lb. If the film thickness is to be no less than 0.0009 in., find (**a**) required viscosity, (**b**) frictional force developed, (**c**) amount of oil flow through bearing, (**d**) the end flow, (**e**) temperature rise of the oil, (**f**) the heat developed.

11. A full journal bearing having a 5-in. diameter, a 5-in. length, and a radial clearance of 0.001 in. is subjected to a radial load of 2500 lb. When the rotative speed is 200 rpm, a frictional force of 15 lb is developed. If the average film temperature is maintained at 160°F, what will be the viscosity of the oil? (**a**) Using Petroff's equation (**b**) using the design charts.

12. In order to gain more insight into the differences between full and partial bearings, consider the following problem. A journal bearing has an L/D ratio of 1, a 3-in. diameter, an oil viscosity of 4×10^{-6} reyns, and an r/c ratio of 1000. A minimum film thickness of 0.0006 in. is to be maintained and the rotative speed is 3000 rpm. Determine the following quantities for a 360-deg bearing. (**a**) Flow entering in cubic inches per second. (**b**) End leakage in cubic inches per second. (**c**) Load. (**d**) Coefficient of friction. (**e**) Frictional horsepower. (**f**) Temperature rise of the oil.

13. Same as Problem 12 for a 180 deg bearing.

14. Same as Problem 12 for a 120 deg bearing.

15. Same as Problem 12 for a 60 deg bearing.

16. A 4000 lb load is applied to a 180 deg partial bearing having a 2-in. diameter and length, and a 0.001-in. radial clearance. The journal is rotating at 4000 rpm, and uses an SAE 30 oil with an inlet temperature of 100°F. What will be the average film temperature?

17. An oil bath journal bearing rotating at 1000 rpm in an ambient air temperature of 90°F is subjected to a load of 6000 lb. The 180 deg partial bearing has an L/D ratio of 1, a journal radius of 2 in., a bearing radius of 2.006 in. and a minimum film thickness of 0.0024 in. Assume pillow-blocks with separate shells and a surrounding air velocity of 500 ft/min. Determine (**a**) the viscosity (**b**) the frictional loss (**c**) the proper SAE grade of oil to use, and (**d**) the increase in temperature of the oil between entrance and exit from the bearing.

18. A full journal bearing is rotating at 500 rpm, and is supporting a load of 4000 lb. The L/D ratio is 1, the journal radius 3 in., and the bearing radius is 3.006 in. A minimum film thickness of 0.0024 in. is to be maintained. Oil is supplied to the bearing by means of a circumferential groove at the center of the bearing at a supply pressure of 60 psi gage. What is the average temperature rise of the oil?

19. A 360 deg journal bearing with a diameter of 4 in. and a length of 4 in. consumes 0.2 hp in friction at an operating speed of 1500 rpm. SAE 20 oil is used, and the film temperature is 175°F. The radial clearance of the bearing equals 0.0015 in. Determine: **(a)** The eccentricity ratio. **(b)** The minimum film thickness. **(c)** The total load for the bearing.

REFERENCES

[1] E. W. Dean and G. H. B. Davis: Viscosity variation of oils with temperature. *Chem. Met. Eng.*, **36**: 618–619 (1929).

[2] D. D. Fuller: *Theory and practice of lubrication for engineers.* John Wiley & Sons, New York, 1956.

[3] O. Reynolds: On the theory of lubrication and its application to Mr. Beauchamp Tower's experiments. *Phil. Trans. Roy. Soc. (London)*, **177**: 157–234 (1886).

[4] A. A. Raimondi and J. Boyd: A solution for the finite journal bearing and its application to analysis and design, Parts I, II, and III. *Trans. ASLE*, **1**(1): 159–209 (1958).

[5] A. Sommerfeld: Zur Hydrodynamischen Theorie der Schmiermittelreibung, 2. *Math. Phys.*, **50**: 97–155 (1904).

[6] J. Boyd and A. A. Raimondi: Bearing theory in analysis and design of journal bearings. *J. Appl. Mech.*, **73**: 298–316 (1951).

[7] G. B. Karelitz: Performance of ring bearings. *Trans. ASME*, **J2**: 57–70 (1930).

[8] V. M. Faires: *Design of Machine Elements.* The Macmillan Company, New York, 1965.

[9] *Seals Handbook, Machine Design.* Penton, Cleveland, Ohio, 45 (1973).

[10] R. R. Slaymaker: *Bearing Lubrication Analysis.* John Wiley & Sons, New York, 1955.

[11] M. C. Shaw and E. F. Macks: *Analysis and Lubrication of Bearings.* McGraw-Hill Book Co., 1949.

[12] *The Bearings Book, Machine Design* Penton, Cleveland, Ohio, 44 (1972).

[13] E. I. Radzimovsky: *Lubrication of Bearings.* The Ronald Press, New York, 1959.

[14] P. R. Trumpler: *Design of Film Bearings.* The Macmillan Company, New York, 1966.

Rolling Bearings

A = a value depending on the bearing type (see Table 9-11)
a_1 = life adjustment reliability factor
a_2 = life adjustment material factor
a_3 = life adjustment application factor
b = an exponent
C = basic dynamic load rating, lb
C_0 = basic static load rating, lb
D = bearing outer diameter, mm or in.
d = bearing bore, mm or in.
d_m = mean bearing diameter, mm
e = a constant (see Tables 9-5, 9-6, or 9-7)
F_a = thrust load, lb
F_r = radial load, lb
F_s = bearing service factor
f_1 = a coefficient depending on bearing size (see Figure 9-47)
f_2 = a coefficient depending on relative bearing load (see Figure 9-48)
H = bearing height for a thrust bearing, mm

hp = horsepower
i = number of rows of balls
L_{10} = rating life in millions of revolutions (based on 10% failure)
N_m = rpm during the mth fraction of a cycle
n = number of balls
n = shaft speed, rpm
P = equivalent load, lb
P_m = equivalent load during the mth fraction of a cycle
p_m = mth fraction of a cycle
SUS = viscosity in Saybolt Universal Seconds
T = frictional torque, lb-in.
V = a factor determined by whether the inner or outer ring is rotating
X = a radial load factor
Y = a thrust load factor
μ = coefficient of friction

The advent of the automobile, high speed engines, and automatic production machinery provided the impetus for extensive research and development of the rolling bearing (also called the antifriction bearing) see Figure 9-1. As a result, the Anti-Friction Bearing Manufacturers Association (AFBMA) standardized bearing dimensions and the basis for their selection. Thus, it is

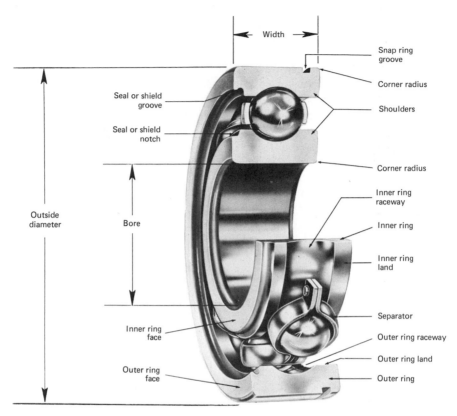

Figure 9-1 Ball bearing nomenclature. [Courtesy New Departure-Hyatt Bearings Division, General Motors Corporation.]

possible for a designer to select a bearing from the catalog of one manufacturer and successfully replace it with a bearing having identical dimensions from a different manufacturer. The designer will also find that, although the AFBMA has standardized the method for selecting a bearing based on load and life requirements, not all manufacturers interpret these standards uniformly. However, the catalogs contain sufficient explanation so that one can always relate his results to equivalent AFBMA values.

Before deciding to use rolling bearings, the designer should give careful consideration to their relative advantages and disadvantages in comparison to journal bearings.

Advantages of rolling bearings compared to journal bearings

1. Starting friction torque is low—not much greater than the running frictional torque (see Section 9.7).
2. Ease of lubrication either with prepacked grease or with relatively simple oil systems.
3. Less axial space for a comparable shaft diameter.

4. With the exception of straight rollers, capable of supporting both radial and thrust loads. (Journal bearings can support only a radial load, if a thrust bearing is not also provided.)

5. Early warning of impeding failure signalled by increasing noisiness at the same speed of rotation. (Journal bearings do not provide such a signal and can suddenly fail.)

6. Readily replaceable as stock items (except for some special applications).

7. Standardization and the employment of close tolerances make preferable their use in the satisfactory operation of cams and gears.

8. Can be preloaded causing a shaft to become stiffer—very important in machine tool applications.

9. Can be used for mounting a shaft placed in any position in space.

10. Wide versatility with respect to mounting because they are supplied in special housings (for example, pillow-blocks, flanges, and so on).

Disadvantages of rolling bearings compared to journal bearings

1. Greater diametral space required for a comparable shaft diameter.
2. Initial cost is usually higher.
3. Noisier in normal operation.
4. Dirt, metal chips, and so on, entering the bearings can limit their life causing early failure. (Journal bearings do not suffer from this malady because foreign matter is either washed away by the lubricant or becomes embedded in the softer bearing material.)
5. Finite life due to eventual failure by fatigue. (Journal bearings, properly maintained, can run "forever.")
6. Lesser capacity to withstand shock.

The stresses developed between the ball(s) and the races or the roller(s) and the races are very complex and were first studied by Stribeck [1] who based his analysis on the earlier work of H. Hertz [2] (that is, contact stresses). Space limitations preclude further discussion here, but the interested reader is directed to references [3], [4], and [5] for a mathematical treatment of the stress in rolling bearings.

In this chapter, we shall describe the most common types of bearings and explain the procedure for selecting a bearing based upon load and life requirements. In addition, we shall also discuss and illustrate some important "schemes" for mounting bearings as well as their methods of lubrication.

SECTION 9-1

Bearing Nomenclature and Types of Ball Bearings

Figure 9-1 is an illustration naming the various parts, surfaces, and edges of a ball bearing. Note that the basic bearing consists of four parts: (1) the outer ring, (2) the inner ring, (3) the balls, and (4) the separator

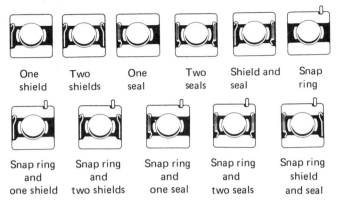

One shield | Two shields | One seal | Two seals | Shield and seal | Snap ring

Snap ring and one shield | Snap ring and two shields | Snap ring and one seal | Snap ring and two seals | Snap ring shield and seal

Figure 9-2 Bearings with seals and shields. [Courtesy New Departure-Hyatt Bearings Division, General Motors Corporation.]

(that is, ball retainer). The separator serves the purpose of always keeping the balls separated and thereby preventing them from rubbing against each other. Some special ball (and also needle) bearings do not have an inner ring. Instead, the balls are permitted to "ride" in a race directly cut in a hardened shaft.

Bearings are available with (1) shields to prevent dirt from entering and to retain grease, (2) shields and seals to contain lubricant for self-lubrication, and (3) snap rings and flanges that provide for simple bearing containment (see Figure 9-2).

One of the important aspects to successful bearing design is the conformity of the ball radius to the raceway radius. Figure 9-3 is a photograph illustrating

Figure 9-3 Conformity of ball radius to that of the raceway. [Courtesy New Departure-Hyatt Bearings Division, General Motors Corporation.]

what is meant by conformity. The figure shows an example of low conformity of ball to raceway. If conformity is increased, the contact area between the ball and raceway, when loaded, is increased. Thus, the unit surface stress is reduced and greater loads can be supported. However, increasing conformity increases bearing friction; thus, the resultant "fit" of the ball and raceway curvature becomes a matter of design compromise. Bearing manufacturers establish their own conformity values based upon their individual experiences and research data. Because of conformity, and elastic and plastic deformation of the balls and races when loaded, the balls do not have pure rolling motion. Instead, a small amount of sliding occurs, which affects both the frictional loss and life of the bearing.

Ball bearings are categorized into three areas, namely, (1) radial ball bearings, (2) angular-contact ball bearings, and (3) thrust ball bearings.

Radial ball bearings

Figure 9-4 illustrates the various types of radial ball bearings commonly available. The most widely used radial ball bearing is the **Conrad** or **deep groove bearing.** This bearing, primarily designed to support radial loads, has deep raceways that are continuous (that is, there are no openings, recesses, and so on) over all of the ring circumference. This type of construction permits the bearing also to support relatively high thrust loads in either direction. In fact, the thrust load capacity is about 70% of the radial load capacity, as noted in Figure 9-4. The reason that a ball bearing designed primarily for a radial load can also support a high thrust load is that only several balls (sometimes only one) carry the radial load, whereas all the balls act to withstand the thrust load. Figure 9-5 shows, in an exaggerated manner, how only some of the balls sustain a radial load.

As shown in Figure 9-6, Conrad bearings are assembled in four steps. Conrad bearings that are intended for high speed operation are usually made with machined bronze or phenolic-cloth laminate separators.

To increase the radial load carrying capacity of the ball bearing, more balls are used. This is the concept behind the **maximum capacity** or **filling notch** type of bearing. These bearings have the same basic radial construction as the Conrad type. However, as shown in Figure 9-4, a filling notch (or loading groove) permits more balls to be used than a Conrad bearing of comparable size.

Because the loading groove in each ring interrupts the ball raceway shoulders, the thrust capacity of the bearing is limited. As noted in Figure 9-4, the thrust capacity of the filling notch type is only 20% of the thrust capacity of the Conrad bearing, whereas the radial capacity is 20–40% higher than the radial bearing.

The **magneto** or **counterbored** type bearing is similar to the deep groove bearing except that the outer ring has but one shoulder, which makes the bearing separable. Thus, this type of bearing permits the inner and outer rings to be mounted separately. Magneto bearings are extra-light, being

Figure 9-4 Common types of radial ball bearings and some of their important characteristics. (1) The approximate range of bore sizes, although stated in inches, is given in millimeters in manufacturers' catalogs along with the equivalent inch dimension. To accommodate American availability of bar stock for shafting, manufacturers also supply some bearings with bores having inch dimensions. (2) The columns "Relative Capacity" and "Limiting Speed Factor" are based on the value of unity for the Conrad or deep groove bearing since this type of bearing is the one most widely selected by designers. [From *Machine Design*, 1970 *Bearings Reference Issue*). The Penton Publishing Co., Cleveland, Ohio.]

Type	Approx Range of Bore Sizes (in.)		Relative Capacity		Limiting Speed Factor	Tolerance to Misalignment
	Min	Max	Radial	Thrust		
Conrad or deep groove	 0.1181	41.732	1.00	0.7 (2-direction)	1.0	±0°15′
Maximum capacity or filling notch	 0.3937	5.1181	1.2–1.4	0.2 (2-direction)	1.0	±0°3′
Magneto or counterbored outer	 0.1181 0.3937	1.181 7.874	0.9–1.3	0.5–0.9 (1-direction)	1.0	±0°5′
Airframe or aircraft control	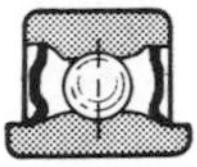 0.1900	1.250	High static capacity	0.5 (2-direction)	0.2	0°
Self-aligning internal	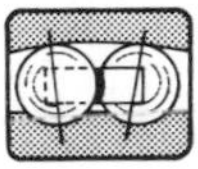 0.1969	4.7244	0.7	0.2 (1-direction)	1.0	±2°30′
Self-aligning, external	—	—	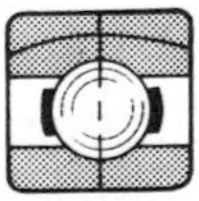 1.0	0.7 (2-direction)	1.0	High
Double row, maximum	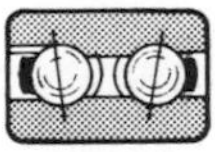 0.3937	4.3307	1.5	0.2 (2-direction)	1.0	±0°3′
Double row, deep groove	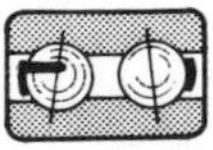 0.3937	4.3307	1.5	1.4 (2-direction)	1.0	0°

supplied to a bore size of only 1.181 in. Counterbored bearings, however, are available in much larger bore sizes (see Figure 9-4). It is apparent that these bearings can only support unidirectional thrust loads. Counterbored types are widely employed in fractional horsepower motors.

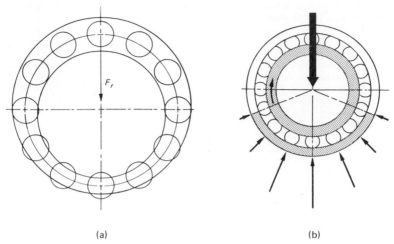

(a) (b)

Figure 9-5 (a) Radial displacement in a ball bearing when carrying a radial
load on the inner ring. [Courtesy of Link-Belt Division, FMC Corp.]
(b) Nonfluctuating load distribution within a bearing. [Courtesy SKF
Industries, Inc.]

Airframe or **aircraft control** bearings are designed to withstand heavy
radial loads in oscillating or slow turning applications. These bearings are
often supplied with a full complement of balls to provide high load capacity.
However, where torque requirements are not too severe and the operation
is smooth, the bearing can be obtained with ball separators. The bearings
are grease-packed and sealed with special synthetic rubber to withstand
adverse environmental conditions. The external surfaces are usually cadmium
plated to resist corrosion, depending upon specifications (usually military).

Airframe bearings are also available in double row, extra-wide, self-
aligning, and rod end types.

Self-aligning bearings are intended to compensate for misalignments
arising from shaft deflection, frame distortion, or foundation deflection.
They are available in two types: self-aligning internal and self-aligning

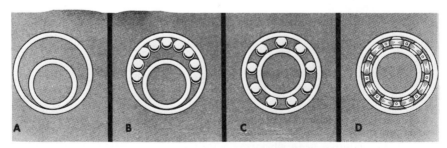

Figure 9-6 Steps in the assembly of the Conrad or deep groove type ball bearing.
[Courtesy of New Departure-Hyatt Bearings Division, General Motors
Corporation.]

external. The basic difference between the two types is made clear by inspection of Figure 9-4. Because of conformity between the balls and the outer raceway, higher contact stresses are produced in the internal type of self-aligning bearing. The external self-aligning bearing does not suffer from this handicap because alignment is achieved by grinding a spherical surface on the outside diameter of the outer ring and matching it to a similarly ground surface of a housing. The penalty paid in using the external type of bearing is the greater mounting space required in the radial direction.

Double row ball bearings are available as double row, deep groove bearings and as double row maximum ball bearings. The latter type of bearing is of the filling notch type, whereas the former bearing is of the Conrad or deep groove type.

The double row maximum bearing possesses a larger ball capacity than the deep groove type, giving it good radial load capacity at the expense of thrust load capacity. Note from Figure 9-4 that the lines of contact converge with the envelope of the bearing.[1] This type of geometry reduces the resistance of the bearing to the angular deflection, and therefore it should not be used in a design requiring a single bearing mounting. In fact, this bearing is particularly suited for applications having heavy loads and where slight misalignments are expected (for example, gear reducers).

The double row deep groove bearing can be used not only with high radial loads, but also with high thrust loads. Figure 9-4 shows the lines of contact for this type of bearing converging outside of the bearing envelope. This type of geometry produces a rigid bearing. Thus, the double row deep groove bearing has a propensity for effectively resisting axial, radial, and overturning deflections. Consequently, these bearings are often used singly in mounting idler pulleys, gears, wheels, and so on. As indicated in Figure 9-4, the permissible misalignment tolerance is 0 deg, and they cannot be used where angular shaft deflection is permitted.

Both types of bearings can be supplied with a light, medium, or heavy preload, thereby providing a wide range of loading and stiffness.

Angular-contact ball bearings

A second category of ball bearings is the angular-contact ball bearing. Figure 9-7 illustrates the various types of angular-contact bearings available, their range of bore sizes, relative radial and thrust load capacities, limiting speed factor, and misalignment tolerance.

The primary type of angular-contact bearing is the **one-directional thrust** type, which has a single row of balls and is so designed that the centerline of contact between the balls and the raceway is at an angle to a plane perpendicular to the axis of rotation. This angle, called the contact angle, is shown in Figure 9-8.

---

[1] Theoretically, the lines of contact converge on the shaft center line.

| Type | | Approx Range of Bore Sizes (in.) | | Relative Capacity | | Limiting Speed Factor | Tolerance to Misalignment |
		Min	Max	Radial	Thrust		
One-directional, thrust		0.3937	12.5984	1.00–1.15*	1.5–2.3* (1–direction)	1.1–3.0*	±0°2'
Duplex, back-to-back		0.3937	12.5984	1.85	1.5 (2-direction)	3.0	0°
Duplex, face-to-face		0.3937	12.5984	1.85	1.5 (2-direction)	3.0	0°
Duplex, tandem		0.3937	12.5984	1.85	2.4 (1-direction)	3.0	0°
Two directional or split ring		0.3937	4.3307	1.15	1.5 (2-direction)	3.0	±0°2'
Double row		0.3937	5.5118	1.5	1.85 (2-direction)	0.8	0°
Double row, maximum		0.3937	4.3307	1.65	0.5 (in 1 direction) 1.5 (in other direction)	0.7	0°

*Depends on contact angle.

Figure 9-7 Typical forms of angular-contact bearings and some of their important characteristics. [From *Machine Design*, 1970 *Bearing Reference Issue*. The Penton Publishing Co., Cleveland, Ohio.]

The reader can observe from Figure 9-8 that the outer ring has one "heavy" raceway shoulder and another raceway shoulder which has been removed by counterboring. The counterbore is cut to within a few thousandths of the bottom of the raceway. The bearing is assembled by thermally expanding the

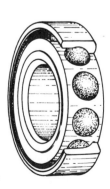

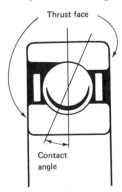

Figure 9-8 Section through an angular-contact bearing illustrating the contact angle. [Courtesy New Departure-Hyatt Bearings Division, General Motors Corporation.]

outer ring so that the inner ring, a full complement of balls, and the ball separator are "snapped" into place. Upon cooling the outer ring, the bearing assembly becomes nonseparable, being held together by the small "snap" shoulder formed by the counterboring operation. This design, which uses a full complement of balls, permits the bearing to carry a higher radial load than a comparable deep groove bearing and a high unidirectional thrust load.

These bearings are made with an initial internal looseness which is necessary to obtain angular contact. They become rigid when loaded axially and have contact angles ranging between 15 and 40 deg.[2] For example, New Departure-Hyatt Bearings supplies angular-contact bearings with 15-, 25-, or 35-deg contact angles. The higher contact angle bearings can support greater axial loads but at reduced radial loads.

The **two-directional** or **split ring** angular-contact bearing was originally developed for use in high speed turbines. The bearing consists of a solid one-piece outer ring and a two-piece inner ring. Because the inner ring is split, it is possible to assemble this bearing with a full complement of balls for maximum load carrying capacity. The ball separator is of one-piece construction, usually made of bronze.

This type of bearing can carry a substantial amount of radial load provided a sufficiently high thrust load is being simultaneously carried. Should a high thrust load be absent, the balls would slip and rapid bearing deterioration would follow.

Duplexing of angular-contact ball bearings arises because there is a need for maintaining very rigid bearing supports that act to minimize both axial and radial shaft deflections. This need is most obvious in machine tool applications (for example, lathe headstock spindles, grinding wheel spindles, boring bar spindles, and so on), instruments, or in any machine or device where shaft rigidity is a necessity for accurate performance.

Rigidity of the bearing assembly can be achieved by introducing a controlled axial preload. This intentional preload is introduced in one of three ways: (1) Using a set of matched ball bearings having a specific ring "stickout"

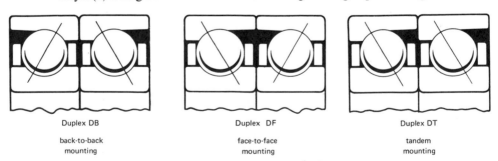

| Duplex DB | Duplex DF | Duplex DT |
| back-to-back mounting | face-to-face mounting | tandem mounting |

Figure 9-9 Duplex mounting arrangements. [Courtesy New Departure-Hyatt Bearings Division, General Motors Corporation.]

[2] For high speed applications, the contact angle should not exceed 30 deg.

Figure 9-10 Duplex mounting arrangements showing face stickouts before assembly. [Courtesy New Departure-Hyatt Division, General Motors Corporation.]

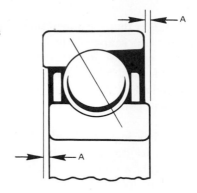

Single bearing showing equal face stickout on either side.

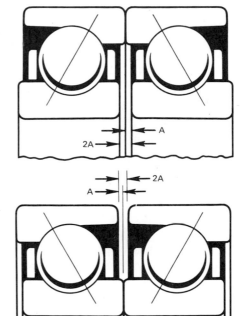

DB mounting before clamping. When inner rings are abutted, a preload corresponding to an axial deflection of "A" will exist.

DF mounting before clamping. When outer rings are abutted, a preload corresponding to axial deflection of "A" will exist.

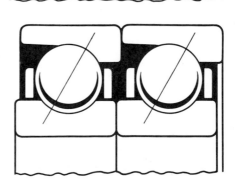

DT mounting in which both bearings share thrust load. DT pairs may be preloaded against single angular contact bearings or duplex (DT) pairs.

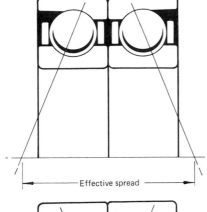

Effective spread

Figure 9-11 DB mounting showing the effective spread as greater than the distance between the bearings. [Courtesy New Departure-Hyatt Bearings Division, General Motors Corporation.]

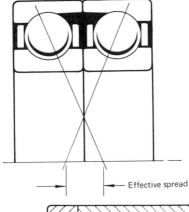

Effective spread

Figure 9-12 DF mounting showing the effective spread as less than the distance between the bearings. [Courtesy New Departure-Hyatt Bearings Division, General Motors Corporation.]

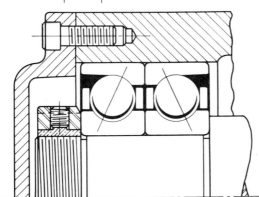

Figure 9-13 Maximum resistance to the misalignment of cocking loads is obtained by utilizing a set of angular-contact bearings in the DB (back-to-back) style of mounting. The figure illustrates a DB mounting that is free to float axially in the housing. The preload predetermined for the duplex set is applied by locking the inner rings of the pair together. A DF mounting cannot be similarly floating because the preload is obtained by clamping the outer rings. Note that the rigidity of the DB mounting necessitates an accurate alignment of the housing bore with respect to the spindle and careful control of the squareness of the spindle shoulders. [Courtesy New Departure-Hyatt Bearings Division, General Motors Corporation.]

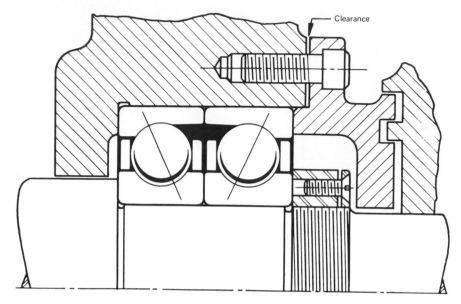

Figure 9-14 A fixed mounting in which the inner rings of the pair of DF bearings are clamped between the spindle shoulder and a locknut. The predetermined preload is applied by tightening the housing end cap until the two outer rings are locked together. The DF mounting tolerates slightly more operating misalignment than the DB mounting. Whenever optimum results are expected, misalignment should be held to minimum values. [Courtesy New Departure-Hyatt Bearings Division, General Motors Corporation.]

on the faces of the inner or outer rings. When the gap between the rings without "stickout" is closed, the bearing assembly receives a controlled axial preload. This method of introducing a preload is called duplexing. (2) Using a nut on the shaft or housing which, when turned, causes the rings of the angular-contact bearing to move relative to one another in an axial direction. All looseness within the bearing is removed and the axial preload is determined by the number of turns made by the nut. (3) Using a thrust washer, shims, or a spring to introduce the relative ring displacement resulting in an axial load.

The first method (that is, duplexing) is the most reliable because it depends only upon the dimensional accuracy of the duplex bearing sets that are used. As in the manufacture of all bearing components, paired sets of duplex bearings are carefully controlled dimensionally, and so this method of preloading is the one which is most widely used.

Figure 9-7 shows three ways in which angular-contact ball bearings can be duplexed. To assist in explaining the three bearing arrangements in Figure 9-7, we shall refer to Figures 9-9 and 9-10.

As shown in Figures 9-7 and 9-9, duplex bearings may be mounted as follows: (1) back-to-back (that is, DB), (2) face-to-face (that is, DF) or (3) in tandem (that is, DT). Figure 9-10 illustrates how "stickout" (that is,

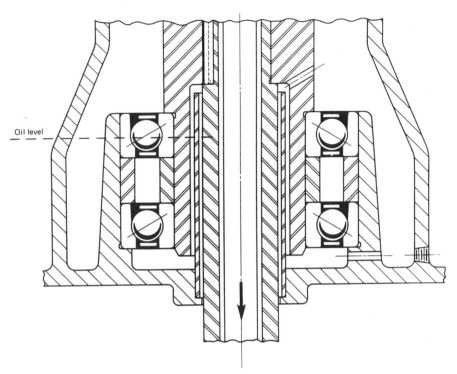

Oil level

Figure 9-15 The DT mounting is intended for combined loads with very heavy thrust in one direction (indicated by arrow). When correctly and accurately applied, two bearings of a DT set share the applied load. For most applications, it is usually desired to preload the DT set against an opposed angular contact bearing or an opposed DT set at the other end of the shaft. However, in most vertical mountings where the applied thrust load is constant in one direction, preloading may not be necessary. [Courtesy New Departure-Hyatt Bearings Division, General Motors Corporation.]

offset) is used to achieve one of the mounting arrangements shown in Figure 9-9. The amount of "stickout" needed depends upon the magnitude of the axial preload required. As a result, bearing manufacturers supply duplex pairs for light, medium, or heavy preloads.

The selection of a DB, DF, or DT mounting depends on the rigidity and thrust load design requirements. In the DB arrangement (see Figure 9-11), contact lines converge outside of the bearing envelope resulting in an "effective spread" that is greater than the axial distance between both bearings. Consequently, this arrangement results in a very rigid assembly and provides greater resistance to shaft bending moments and deflections.[3] Thus, where a designer is aware of unavoidable shaft bending or housing misalignments that must be tolerated, he should select the DF arrangement (see Figure 9-12).

[3] The reader may readily verify this argument by imagining a loaded shaft in each arrangement and drawing the free body forces acting on the balls.

The DT arrangement (see Figure 9-10) is used for applications requiring the bearings to withstand extremely high thrust loads in one direction where high speeds or space limitations preclude the use of a larger bearing or simpler arrangement. For unusually high uniaxial thrust loads, it is possible to use three (or more) DT bearings. Where a heavy thrust load is carried in one direction and a lesser, but considerable, reversed load also exists, then an arrangement using a pair of DT bearings mounted in a DB arrangement with a single bearing should be used. When severe axial loads are expected in both directions, two pairs of DT bearings mounted in a DB arrangement should be used.

Representative arrangements showing the application of DB, DF, and DT mounted bearings are shown in Figures 9-13, 9-14, 9-15 and 9-16.

The **double row angular-contact** bearings shown in Figure 9-7 act in the same manner as two single opposed angular-contact bearings. They are available with the contact lines converging outside the bearing envelope (as with DB bearings), making the bearing more rigid, or with the contact lines converging within the bearing envelope (as with DF bearings), which allows for minor shaft and bearing support misalignment.

The double row maximum angular-contact bearing is of the filling notch type and thus has a reduced thrust capacity in one direction but a higher radial load capacity in comparison to the regular double row bearing.

These bearings are normally manufactured with a built-in preload.

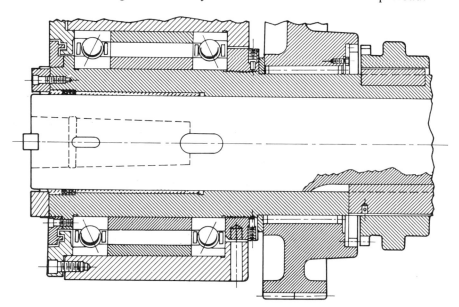

Figure 9-16 A modified DB mounting at the nose of a precision spindle. The bearings of the duplex set are separated by spacers, increasing the spindle's resistance to shaft bending moments. Both the inner and outer ring spacers must be exactly the same length to obtain the predetermined preload for the duplex set of bearings. [Courtesy New Departure-Hyatt Bearings Division, General Motors Corporation.]

Thrust ball bearings

As indicated in Figure 9-17, there are three types of thrust ball bearings, (1) the one-directional flat race bearing, (2) the one-directional grooved race bearing, and (3) the two-directional grooved race bearing.

Thrust ball bearings are designed to carry pure thrust loads and, if any radial load is present, separate radial bearings must be used. From the viewpoint of both economics and simplicity of design, it is wise to seek the use of an angular-contact bearing where both radial and thrust loads are present.

The **one-directional flat race** thrust ball bearing consists of two ungrooved washers, balls, and a ball separator. The separator is kept in place by the shaft, permitting the balls and the washers some slight radial movement but *no radial load support*. Although the friction in this bearing is quite small, its speed is limited by the centrifugal force acting on the balls, which under high speeds cannot be contained by the separator.

The **one-directional grooved race** thrust ball bearing is different than the flat race bearing in one respect, namely, the races are grooved, providing containment for the balls. Because of this containment, this type of thrust ball bearing can function under higher thrust loads and speeds than the flat washer type of bearing. However, the frictional torque of this bearing is higher than that of the flat washer type. The one-directional grooved race thrust bearing is also available with one washer that has a convex spherical seat that mates with a third washer having a concave spherical seat. The whole bearing assembly thus becomes self-aligning.

Figure 9-17 Typical forms of ball thrust bearings and some of their important characteristics. [From *Machine Design*, 1970 *Bearings Reference Issue*. The Penton Publishing Co., Cleveland, Ohio.]

Type	Approx Range of Bore Sizes (in.) Min	Max	Relative Capacity Radial	Thrust	Limiting Speed Factor	Tolerance to Misalignment
One-directional, flat race	 0.254	3.500	0	0.7 (1-direction)	0.10	0° (accepts eccentricity)
One-directional, grooved race	 0.254	46.4567	0	1.5 (1-direction)	0.30	0°
Two-directional, grooved race	 0.5906	8.6614	0	1.5 (2-direction)	0.30	0°

The **two-directional grooved race** thrust ball bearing has two separators and a middle grooved race that rotates with the balls. This bearing possesses the same characteristics as the one-directional grooved bearing but can withstand axial loads in two directions. These bearings can also be furnished with spherically dished alignment washers.

SECTION 9-2

Roller Bearings

Roller bearings serve the same purpose as ball bearings, but they can support much higher loads than comparably sized ball bearings because they have line contact instead of point contact. Most types of radial roller bearings cannot resist thrust loads of any significant magnitude and, with the exception of the cylindrical type, operate at speeds lower than those for ball bearings.[4] Roller bearings are also capable of withstanding moderate to heavy shock loads depending on the roller size.

It is important to note that roller bearings are not supplied in sealed, self-lubricated form as are the bearings of the Conrad type. Thus, careful consideration must be given to their lubrication, although many can function adequately under limited speed and load combinations with only a periodic greasing. The manufacturer should be consulted before adopting this mode of lubrication.

Roller bearings can be classified into four basic types: (1) cylindrical roller bearings, (2) needle roller bearings, (3) tapered roller bearings, and (4) spherical roller bearings. Figures 9-18, 9-19, 9-20 and 9-25 respectively illustrate the different forms that exist in each class as well as their bore sizes and other important characteristics.

Cylindrical roller bearings

Cylindrical roller bearings come in a variety of forms as indicated in Figure 9-18. They are available in a wide range of bore sizes, and function with rollers having length-to-diameter ratios from 1 : 1 to 3 : 1. The outside diameter of the roller is often crowned to increase the load carrying capacity by eliminating any edge loading. The variety of types available permits the consideration of a wide range of shaft and housing designs.

When the loads are high and a reduction in the diametral size of the bearing is desirable, it is possible to permit the rollers to operate directly on the shaft journal.[5] In these applications, it is imperative that high loads be present to prevent the rollers from slipping in the races, which can lead to early failure.

---

[4] Cylindrical roller bearings with roller length-to-diameter ratios of 1 : 1 can operate at the same speeds as comparably sized ball bearings.

[5] The journal must be properly hardened (e.g., a minimum of Rockwell C58), and the reader is advised to seek the counsel of the manufacturer before proceeding with this design.

Figure 9-18 Typical forms of cylindrical roller bearings and some of their important characteristics. [From *Machine Design*, 1970 *Bearings Reference Issue*. The Penton Publishing Co., Cleveland, Ohio.]

Type	Approx. range of bore sizes (in.) Min.	Max.	Relative capacity Radial	Thrust	Limiting speed factor	Tolerance to misaligment
Separable outer ring, nonlocating RN, RIN	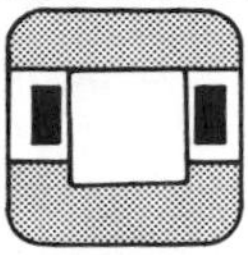 0.3937	12.5984	1.55	0	1.20	±0°5'
Separable inner ring, nonlocating RU, RIU	 0.4724	19.6850	1.55	0	1.20	±0°5'
Separable outer ring, one-direction locating RF, RIF	 1.5748	7.000	1.55	Locating (1-direction)	1.15	±0°5'
Separable inner ring, one-direction locating FJ, RIJ	 0.4724	12.5984	1.55	Locating (1-direction)	1.15	±0°5'
Self-contained two-direction locating	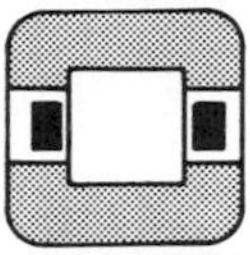 0.4724	3.9370	1.35	Locating (2-direction)	1.15	±0°5'
Separable inner ring, two-direction locating RT, RIT	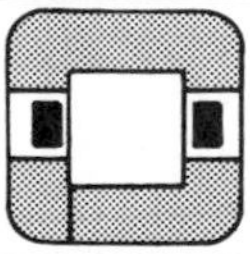 0.7874	12.5984	1.55	Locating (2-direction)	1.15	±0°5'
Nonlocating, full complement RK, RIK	 0.6693	2.9528	2.10	0	0.20	±0°5'
Double-row, separable outer ring, nonlocating RD	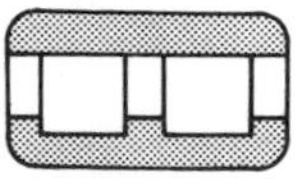 1.1811	41.7323	1.85	0	1.00	0°
Double row, separable inner ring, nonlocating	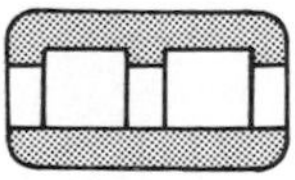 2.7559	41.7323	1.85	0	1.00	0°

Needle roller bearings

Needle roller bearings are like cylindrical roller bearings in that they can withstand high radial loads, but are different in that their rollers (called needles) have a much greater length-to-diameter ratio. Also, needle bearings have a much smaller diametral silhouette than cylindrical roller bearings.

It can be observed from Figure 9-19 that there are two basic forms of needle bearings. In one form, the needles are not separated by a roller cage, and in the other form the needles are separated by a cage. The bearing that does not have the roller separator has a full complement of rollers and, therefore, can handle a higher load than the bearing having a roller separator. However, the latter type of needle bearing is capable of operating at much higher speeds because the needles are kept from rubbing against one another (causing skidding) by the separator.

Both forms of needle bearings can be mounted with the needles in direct contact with the shaft, making for a rather small diametral bearing. As with the cylindrical roller bearing, when the rollers (that is, needles) are in direct contact with the shaft, the shaft should be heat treated to a minimum hardness of Rockwell C 58.

Figure 9-19 Typical forms of needle roller bearings and some of their important characteristics. [From *Machine Design*, 1970 *Bearings Reference Issue*. The Penton Publishing Co., Cleveland, Ohio.]

Type	Bore Sizes (in.) Min Max	Relative Load Capacity Dynamic State		Limiting Speed Factor	Misalignment Tolerance
Drawn cup, needle	 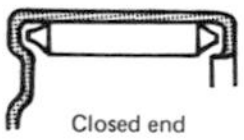 0.125 7.250	High	Moderate	0.3	Low
Drawn cup, needle, grease retained	 0.156 1.000	High	Moderate	0.3	Low
Drawn cup, roller	 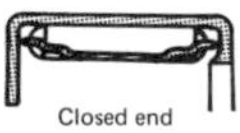 0.187 2.750	Moderate	Moderate	0.9	Moderate
Heavy-duty roller	 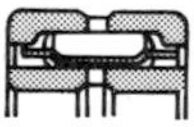 0.625 9.250	Very high	Moderate	1.0	Moderate
Caged roller	 0.500 4.000	Very high	High	1.0	Moderate
Cam follower	 0.500 6.000	Moderate to high	Moderate to high	0.3-0.9	Low
Needle thrust	 0.252 4.127	Very high	Very high	0.7	Low

Needle bearings are mainly lubricated by grease. For high load or high speed application, some form of oil lubrication is required if the bearing is not to fail prematurely. Some bearings can be obtained with oil seals, but the range of selection available is limited (for example, cam followers). Where oil is mandatory in a needle bearing (for example, heavy duty) holes are provided for lubrication supply.

A group of aircraft needle bearings specifically designed for heavy duty operation and very low speeds will not be described in this text. It should be noted, however, that all of these type bearings are provided with oil holes for lubrication. For more detailed data concerning these bearings, the reader is advised to refer to the manufacturers' catalogs (for example, Torrington Company).

Tapered roller bearings

Tapered roller bearings are available in the forms shown in Figure 9-20. These bearings are designed specifically to withstand high radial loads, high thrust loads, and combined high radial and thrust loads at moderate to high speeds. The various parts that constitute a tapered bearing are illustrated in Figure 9-21. It can be easily observed that the single-row tapered roller bearing is capable of resisting thrust in one direction only. Consequently, shafts mounting single-row tapered bearings must also mount an opposed single-row tapered bearing, an opposed angular-contact ball bearing, or a Conrad (that is, deep groove) type ball bearing. Where double- or four-row tapered roller bearings are used, thrust in both directions can be withstood, and the additional types of bearing just mentioned would not be needed.

The principle of operation of tapered roller bearings is similar to that of bevel gear operation. Note that Figure 9-22 illustrates this idea. This figure shows that the tapered surfaces of the cup, rollers, and cone represent frustrums of cones, the elements of which converge to a common apex on the bearing axis. As with bevel gears, pure rolling (or close to it because of tolerances) action takes place. When under any type of load, whether radial, thrust, or combined, the rollers are forced against the cone back face rib (see Figure 9-21), which also provides guidance for the rollers.

Tapered roller bearings are ideally suited to withstand repeated shock loads that can be expected from service applications (for example, automotive wheels and transmissions, rolling mill shafts, railroad car trucks, and so on). Also, the way in which a pair of single-row tapered bearings is mounted plays a significant role in determining the rigidity of the bearing assembly. This is best explained by referring to Figure 9-23 which shows two mounting arrangements. The schematic arrangement of the two bearings above the centerline is called an "indirect" mounting (note that the cone elements converge towards apexes between the bearings). The schematic arrangement below the centerline is called a "direct" mounting (note that in this case, the cone elements converge at apexes outside of the bearings).

Figure 9-20 Typical forms of tapered roller bearings and some of their important characteristics. [From *Machine Design*, 1970 *Bearings Reference Issue*. The Penton Publishing Co., Cleveland, Ohio.]

Type		Subtype	Approx Range of Bore Sizes (in.)	
Single row TS		TST—tapered bore	0.3125	66.5000
		TSS—steep angle	0.9375	17.0000
		TS—pin cage	0.6250	50.0000
		TSE, TSK—keyway cones		—
		TSF, TSSF—flanged cup	0.4720	14.8750
		TSG—steering gear (without cone)	0.3125	42.0000
Two row, double cone, single cups TDI	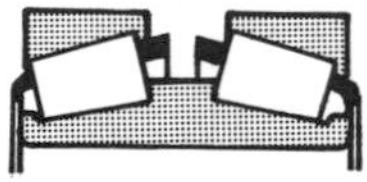	TDIK, TDIT, TDITP—tapered Bore	1.1875	47.2500
		TDIE, TDIKE—slotted double cone	1.1866	33.7656
		TDIS—steep angle	0.9375	27.0030
			2.1650	20.5000
Two row, double cup, single cones, adjustable TDO	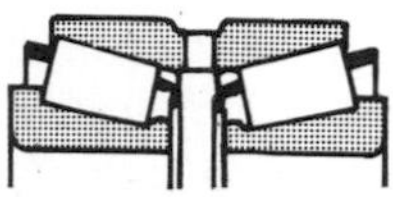		0.3125	72.0000
		TDOC, TDOD (only one lubricant hole in cup)	0.9600	56.3750
		TDOS—steep angle	0.7500	56.3750
Two row, double cup, single cones, nonadjustable TNA	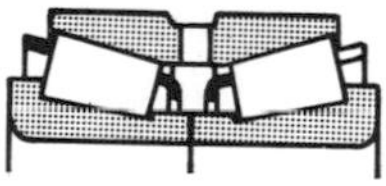		0.7500	24.0000
		TNAD, TNADC (only one lubricant hole in cup)	1.3125	24.0000
		TNASW—slotted cones	1.1805	10.2500
		TNAU, TNASWE—extended cone rib	0.7500	12.0000
		TNAH, TNASWH—slotted cones, sealed	0.3125	2.7559
		TNAS—steep angle	0.7500	4.5000
Four row, cup adjusted, TQO	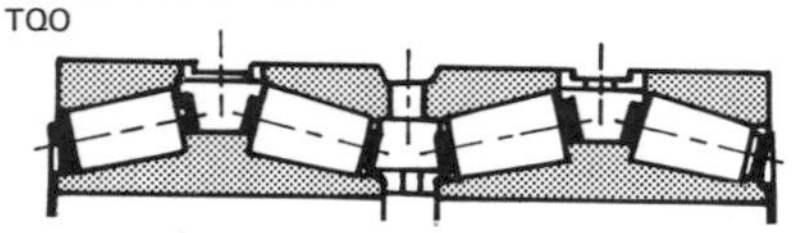		2.7500	47.2500
		TQOK, TQOT—tapered bore	9.7500	47.2500
Four row, cup adjusted, TQI	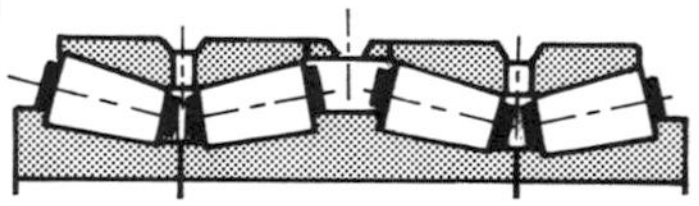	TQIK, TQIT—tapered bore	—	—

In Figure 9-23, we see that perpendiculars have been drawn respectively from point A_c on bearing A, and point B_c on bearing B to points A_0 and B_0 on the shaft centerline. Points A_c and B_c are the centerpoints of the respective bearing roller cups. Thus, we obtain a distance a_a (that is, effective bearing spread) that is a measure of the rigidity of the bearing mounting. It is

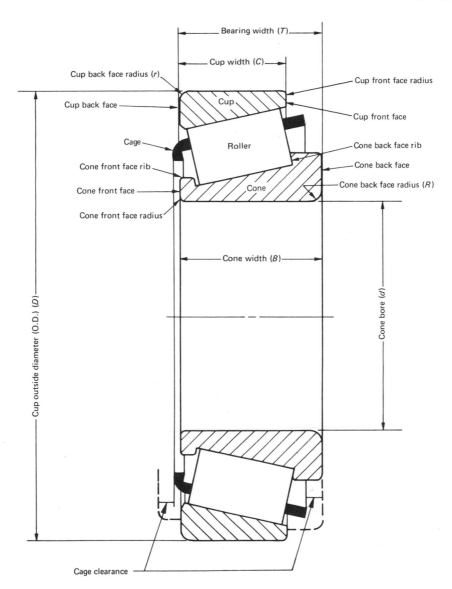

Figure 9-21 Nomenclature for a tapered roller bearing. [Courtesy The Timken Company.]

readily seen that the actual bearing spacing a_b for the "direct" mounting (below the centerline) is longer than the actual bearing spacing a_b for the indirect mounting (above the line). From this geometric comparison, we see that "indirect" mountings provide greater rigidity when the pair of bearings is closely spaced when used, for example, with idler pulleys, drums, sheaves, spindles, front wheel automobile axles, stub gear shafts, and so on. On the other hand, the "direct" mounting provides greater rigidity when

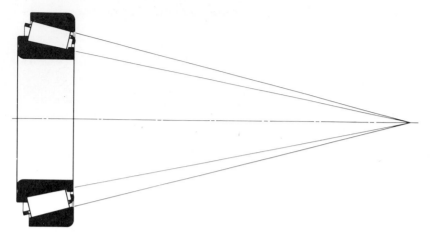

Figure 9-22 The basic principle for the correct operation of the tapered roller bearing is for the tapered surfaces to converge to a common apex on the axis of the bearing. [Courtesy The Timken Company.]

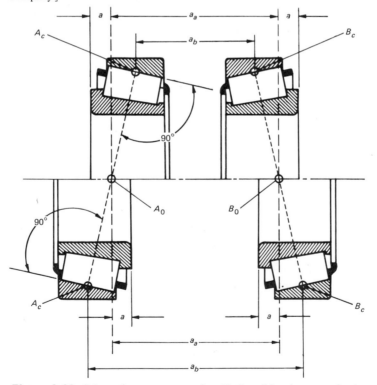

Figure 9-23 Schematic arrangement of an "indirect" bearing mounting is shown above the centerline, and that for "direct" mounting is shown below the centerline. A complete explanation of the meaning and use of all the letters shown can be found in the *Timken Engineering Journal*, Vol. I. [Courtesy The Timken Company.]

the bearings are not closely spaced and are used for mounting automobile transmissions, machine tool gear boxes, speed reducers, machinery rollers, and so on.

It is also of interest to observe that the two-row double-cone single-cup and two-row double-cup single-cone adjustable bearings (see Figure 9-20), which can withstand two-directional thrust loads, are similar to the DF and DB duplex bearing mounting described in Section 9.1. These bearings can be preloaded to provide greater rigidity at the shaft support. Preloading of the double-cup bearing produces a stiffer (that is, high radial rigidity) shaft assembly than the preloading of a double-cone bearing. The four-row cup-adjusted bearings (Figure 9-20) are intended for extra-heavy duty service (for example, rolling mills in the steel industry).

Tapered roller bearings to withstand pure thrust loads (not shown in Figure 9-20) are also manufactured in standard forms. These are shown in Figure 9-24.

For continuous reliable operation, the designer must provide for lubrication with grease or a less viscous oil. Before deciding on his final design, he should carefully review the recommendations concerning proper lubrication found in the manufacturers' catalogs and consult the particular manufacturer concerning any special or unusual requirements.

Figure 9-24 Typical forms of tapered roller thrust bearings. [Courtesy The Timken Company.]

Approx. range of bore size, in.			Load range, lb
	TTSP	Rollers are spaced by a stamped cage (i.e., separator). The bearing is held together as an assembly by a metal retainer. Used for oscillating or slowly rotating installations.	
0.6350–5.8125			2500–11,700*
	TTC		
1.2600–3.0100		Rollers are not separated by a cage. The bearing is held together as an assembly by a metal retainer. Used for oscillating or slowly rotating motion.	
	TTCS		7650–32,400†
1.2600–3.0100 			
	TTHD	This is a heavy duty thrust bearing designed for moderately high speeds and continuous rotation. The rollers operate between two symmetric raceways having inner and outer ribs. The ground rollers are held in a bronze cage.	
1.3750–48.0000			12000–1,930,000†

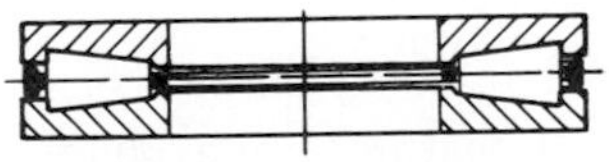

*For slow turning speeds (e.g. steering pivots)
†Load rating is at 50 rpm

Spherical roller bearings

Spherical roller bearings (Figure 9-25) are available in single-row, double-row or single-row thrust types. The important characteristic common to all spherical roller bearings is their self-aligning property. The ability of this type of bearing to adjust itself readily to shaft misalignment is found in its fundamental construction, namely, grinding either the inner or outer raceway to a spherical contour. Where the load is one that is predominantly thrust with a small radial component, the thrust type spherical roller bearing is recommended.

As in all the previous discussion relating to bearings, lubrication is of primary importance in achieving reliable performance. Where the appropriate lubricant or method of lubrication is not listed in the manufacturer's catalog, the designer should discuss his particular problem with the manufacturer's engineering department.

Figure 9-25 Typical forms of spherical roller bearings and some of their important characteristics. [From *Machine Design*, 1970 *Bearings Reference Issue*. The Penton Publishing Co., Cleveland, Ohio.]

Type	Approx Range of Bore Sizes (in.)		Relative Capacity		Limiting Speed Factor	Tolerance to Misalignment
	Min	Max	Radial	Thrust		
Single row, barrel or convex	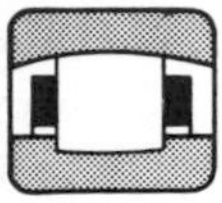 0.7874	12.5984	2.10	0.20	0.50	±2°
Double row, barrel or convex	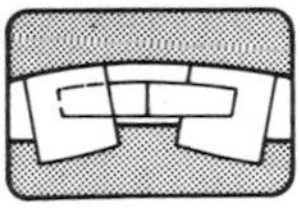 0.9843	49.2126	2.40	0.70	0.50	+1°30'
Thrust	 3.3622	14.1732	0.10* 0.10†	1.80* 2.40†	0.35–0.50	±3°
Double row, concave	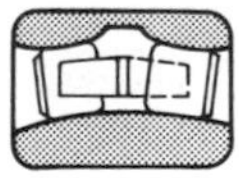 1.9680	5.1171	2.40	0.70	0.50	±1°30'

*Symmetric rollers. †Asymmetric rollers.

SECTION 9-3

Miscellaneous Bearing Configurations

All of the aforementioned types of bearings are available in a variety of housing and mounting forms. In addition, special application type bearings are also available. Figures 9-26 to 9-33 inclusive are illustrative of some of the various types and forms available.

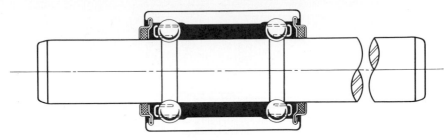

Figure 9-26 Fan and pump shaft bearings. [Courtesy New Departure-Hyatt Bearings Division, General Motors Corporation.]

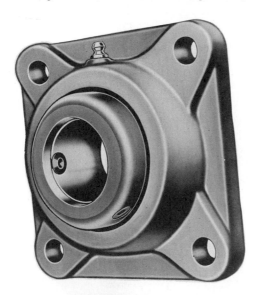

Figure 9-27 Flange ball bearing. [Courtesy Dodge Manufacturing Division, Reliance Electric Co.]

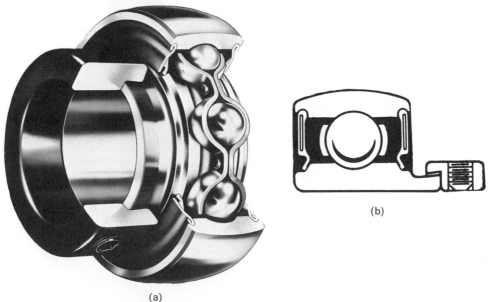

(a)

(b)

Figure 9-28 Adapter bearing makes it possible to mount a ball bearing on commercial steel shafting without machining a bearing seat. [Courtesy New Departure-Hyatt Bearings Division, General Motors Corporation.]

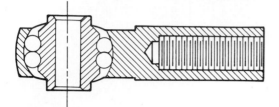

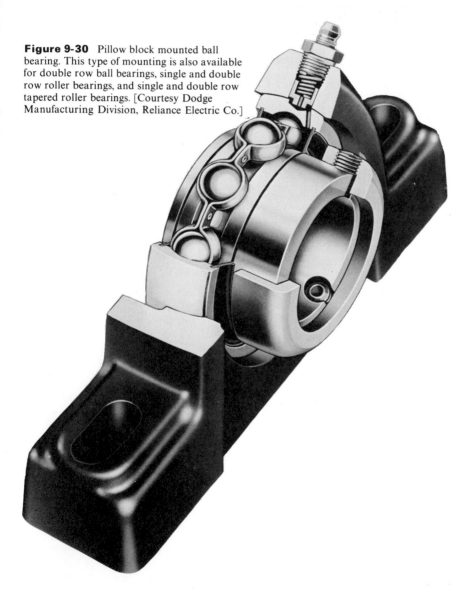

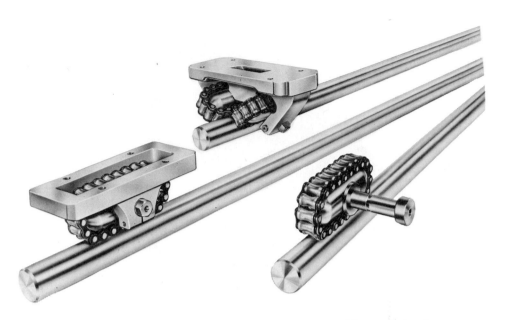

Figure 9-31 Recirculating roller chain bearing. [Courtesy Thomson Industries, Inc., Manhasset, N.Y.]

Figure 9-32 Ball bushing. [Courtesy Thomson Industries, Inc., Manhasset, N.Y.]

Figure 9-33 Ball bearing spline. [Courtesy Saginaw Steering Division, General Motors Corporation.]

SECTION 9-4

Standard Dimensions for Roller Bearings

For obvious reasons, standardization of common and widely used mechanical elements is desirable in promoting economy in the design, production, and maintenance of all kinds of equipment, machinery, and devices. As mentioned at the beginning of this chapter, in the United States, the Anti-Friction Bearing Manufacturers Association (AFBMA) is the responsible organization for establishing and publishing the various roller bearing standards and releasing revisions as required. The actual work in preparing the standards was carried out by three engineering committees appointed by the AFBMA, namely, The Annular Bearing Engineers Committee (ABEC), The Roller Bearing Engineers Committee (RBEC), and The Ball Manufacturers Engineers Committee (BMEC). The committees worked in close cooperation with The American National Standards Institute (ANSI) and The International Standards Organization (ISO). This major contribution by the AFBMA has been most significant in promoting the wide use and acceptance of uniform bearing standards. It is obvious that we cannot here enter into a description of all the standards, and we will therefore confine ourselves to data dealing with size specification.[6]

The dimensional system permits the interchangeability of the same size bearing made by any manufacturer. However, there are special bearings,

---

[6] These specifications apply to ball and roller (straight, spherical, and needle) bearings in millimeter dimensions only. Standards for inch series bearings have been standardized in the United States. To date, specifications for tapered roller bearings have not been established. However, all the manufacturers have numbered tapered roller bearings similarly, and those numbers are included in the *AFBMA Standards*, Section 5.

limited application bearings, inch sizes, and so on, which are not standardized but are subject entirely to the manufacturer's control. In order to initiate a uniformly standard system, it was first necessary to establish a range of bore diameters. Starting with a diameter of 4 mm, bearing bores increase by 1 mm up to and including 10 mm after which they increase by 5 mm to 120 mm.[7] Beyond this diameter, bearing bores increase by 10 mm to a maximum bore diameter of 500 mm.

In order to satisfy the different bearing capacities that might be needed, a series of outside diameters was chosen for each bearing bore diameter. These outside diameters (O.D.) called the **diameter series** are numbered consecutively 8, 9, 0, 1, 2, 3, and 4, where 8 is the smallest O.D., and 4 is the largest O.D. Thus, diameter series represent different size bearings having the same section height to bore diameter (see Figure 9-34). Also, it can be seen from Figure 9-34 that a **width series** 0, 1, 2, and 3 was established whereby each successive number indicates and increasing ratio of width to bearing section height.

The consequence of this system is that any two bearings belonging to the same diameter and width series belong to the same **dimension series** (Figure 9-34). The dimension series is denoted by two digits—the first digit representing the width series, and the second digit representing the diameter series. The system just described establishes standard external dimensions without restricting the internal design of the bearing. The manufacturer is thereby free to establish the ball or roller diameter, the quantity used, raceway conformity, and so on, allowing the designer to choose from a variety of bearing types that all have the same boundary dimensions.

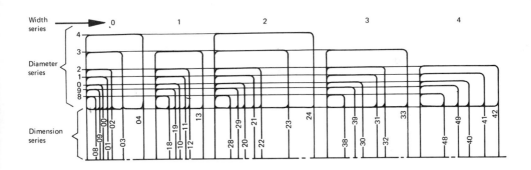

Figure 9-34 Relative proportions of boundary dimensions of different bearing dimension series.

---

[7] Exceptions to this rule are the 12-mm and 17-mm bearing bore diameters. Also, manufacturers list the 4–9-mm bore bearings as "extra small series," and start with the 10-mm size when listing the more commonly used bearings.

To illustrate the AFBMA procedure, suppose a ball bearing is designated as 10BC02. The letters BC are an indication of the type[8] of bearing. The letters BC[9] also denote a single-row radial contact bearing having metric dimensions. The prefix 10 indicates a bearing have a 10-mm bore diameter, and the suffix 02 indicates that the bearing falls within the 02 dimension series. Reference to Table 9-1 indicates that this bearing has an O.D. 1.1811 in., and is 0.3543 in. wide. This same size bearing as a filling slot type (in metric dimensions) would be specified as 10BL02.

Thus, any type of bearing having the same dimensions can be specified by the appropriate letter designation separating the prefix and suffix numbers. As indicated, these letter-bearing type associations are not listed in this text. The designer is advised to consult the *AFBMA Standards* to obtain complete information. However, he can specify a bearing size by using the information in this chapter. For example, he may call for the use of a 10-mm (0.3937-in.) single-row, deep-groove ball bearing of the 02 series.

Recognizing that designers do have available for their use the catalogs of several bearing manufacturers, we will say a few words about their coding procedure and how it relates to the AFBMA description. Although manufacturers adhere to AFBMA boundary dimensions, load and life ratings have followed the older SAE standard of designating bearings as follows:

Extra light series or 100 series[10] (equivalent to dimension series 01)
Light series or 200 series (equivalent to dimension series 02)
Medium series or 300 series (equivalent to dimension series 03)
Heavy series or 400 series (equivalent to dimension series 04)

Following traditional practice, manufacturers designate bearings by a number-letter system that contains as a core one of the above number series. The system is otherwise unique with respect to the company concerned. The last two digits (that is, X00) of the core number are used to indicate the bearing bore.[11] Thus, starting with a bearing bore of 20 mm, the last two digits when multiplied by 5 yield the bore diameter in millimeters. Other prefix or suffix numbers and/or letters that appear in the manufacturer's

---

[8] The AFBMA has also established a bearing type identification code. This code has not been included in this text because of the lack of space and also because the manufacturers persist in identifying the *type* of bearing by their own systems. Nevertheless, the designation described here should be familiar to the designer because various handbooks do contain the system. Also, if the manufacturer's catalog is not at hand a bearing designated by this code is easily translated by the manufacturer or supplier to his own identification code.

[9] If the designation had been 10BIC02, an inch-size single-row radial contact bearing having a $\frac{10}{16}$-in. bore diameter would be indicated. The 02 still signifies the same dimension series.

[10] (1) New Departure-Hyatt calls this the 3L series. (2) Manufacturers' catalogs also list an extremely light series (equivalent to a diameter series 0). The numbering method for this series is not consistent with all manufacturers. For example, New Departures-Hyatt uses 3LL00 as a designation, and Marlin-Rockwell uses 1900. There is also lack of manufacturers' (not AFBMA) uniformity in designating instrument and extra small bearings.

[11] This rule is not applicable to bearings with bores smaller than 20 mm.

Table 9-1 Standard Dimensions and Load Ratings of Radial Rolling Bearings (C_o = basic static load rating, lb; C = basic dynamic load rating, lb)

Dimension Series 02 bearings are shown at left; Dimension Series 22 and Dimension Series 32 at right. The steep‑angle, cylindrical, and series‑22 spherical columns apply to Diameter series 2.

Bore d (mm)	d (in.)	Outside dia. D (mm)	D (in.)	Max Fillet Radius (in.)	Width B (mm)	B (in.)	Self-aligning Ball Bearing C_o	Self-aligning C	Single-Row Deep-Groove C_o	Deep-Groove C	Angular-Contact Small-Angle C_g	Small-Angle C	Angular-Contact Steep-Angle C_o	Steep-Angle C	Cylindrical Roller C_p	Cylindrical C	Ser.22 Width B (mm)	Ser.22 B (in.)	Ser.22 Spherical Roller C_o	Ser.22 Spherical C	Ser.32 Width B (mm)	Ser.32 B (in.)	Ser.32 Double-Row Non-Filling-Notch C_o	Double-Row C	Ser.32 Spherical Roller* C_o	Spherical* C
4	0.1575	13	0.5118	0.012	5	0.1969	—	—	128	268																
5	0.1969	16	0.6299	0.012	5	0.1969	—	—	211	415																
6	0.2362	19	0.7480	0.012	6	0.2362	118	435	211	415																
7	0.2756	22	0.8661	0.012	7	0.2756	148	460	304	565																
8	0.3150	—	—	—	—	—	148	460	304	565																
9	0.3543	26	1.0236	0.024	8	0.3150	208	465	440	785	—	—									14.3	0.5625	800	1,240		
10	0.3937	30	1.1811	0.024	9	0.3543	300	950	440	805	735	1,240									15.9	0.6250	1,250	1,820		
12	0.4724	32	1.2598	0.024	10	0.3937	332	965	685	1,180	920	1,470									15.9	0.6250	1,430	2,030		
15	0.5906	35	1.3780	0.024	11	0.4331	452	1,290	790	1,320	1,180	1,840									17.5	0.6875	1,840	2,540		
17	0.6693	40	1.5748	0.024	12	0.4724	545	1,370	1,000	1,650	—	—														
20	0.7874	47	1.8504	0.039	14	0.5512	715	1,710	1,390	2,210	1,960	2,470	1,730	2,560	1,620	2,980					20.6	0.8125	2,540	3,410		
25	0.9843	52	2.0472	0.039	15	0.5906	905	2,100	1,560	2,420	1,960	2,820	2,490	3,550	2,220	3,970					20.6	0.8125	2,860	3,700		
30	1.1811	62	2.4409	0.039	16	0.6299	1,310	2,710	2,250	3,360	2,820	3,910	3,390	4,690	3,450	5,900					23.8	0.9375	4,120	5,140		
35	1.3780	72	2.8346	0.039	17	0.6693	1,500	2,740	3,070	4,440	3,340	5,160	4,190	5,560	4,660	7,670					27.0	1.0625	5,600	6,780		
40	1.5748	80	3.1496	0.039	18	0.7087	1,930	3,330	3,520	5,040	4,780	6,160	—	—	—	—	23	0.9055	9,870	13,600	30.2	1.1875	6,430	7,680		
45	1.7717	85	3.3465	0.039	19	0.7480	2,160	3,780	4,010	5,660	5,440	6,920	4,770	6,230	5,010	8,070	23	0.9055	11,300	14,200	30.2	1.1875	7,320	8,620		
50	1.9685	90	3.5433	0.039	20	0.7874	2,370	3,930	4,450	6,070	5,850	7,260	5,110	6,470	5,370	8,440	23	0.9055	12,000	14,700	30.2	1.1875	8,130	9,220		
55	2.1654	100	3.9370	0.050	21	0.8268	3,010	4,630	5,630	7,500	7,410	8,980	6,470	8,010	6,710	10,300	25	0.9843	15,000	18,300	33.3	1.3125	10,300	11,400		
60	2.3622	110	4.3307	0.059	22	0.8661	3,490	5,200	6,950	9,070	9,150	10,900	7,990	9,700	8,460	12,600	28	1.1024	18,700	22,300	36.5	1.4375	12,700	13,800		
65	2.5591	120	4.7244	0.059	23	0.9055	3,870	5,360	7,670	9,900	11,100	11,800	9,400	11,000	10,200	14,900	31	1.2205	22,800	26,200	38.1	1.5000	14,000	15,000		
70	2.7559	125	4.9213	0.059	24	0.9449	4,220	5,990	8,410	10,800	11,800	12,900	10,300	12,000	10,200	14,800	31	1.2205	23,800	27,200	39.7	1.5625	15,400	16,300		
75	2.9528	130	5.1181	0.059	25	0.9843	4,810	6,710	9,250	11,400	12,700	14,000	11,000	12,800	12,800	18,200	31	1.2205	25,100	28,200	41.3	1.6250	16,900	17,300		
80	3.1496	140	5.5118	0.059	26	1.0236	5,290	6,820	10,000	12,600	14,100	15,700	12,300	13,900	13,700	19,600	33	1.2992	29,000	32,300	44.4	1.7500	18,300	19,100		
85	3.3465	150	5.9055	0.079	28	1.1024	6,390	8,500	12,000	14,400	16,300	17,700	14,100	15,500	15,900	22,400	36	1.4173	33,600	37,400	49.2	1.9375	19,500	19,700		
90	3.5433	160	6.2992	0.079	30	1.1811	7,140	9,840	13,600	16,600	19,200	20,800	16,700	18,500	20,600	28,600	40	1.5748	40,400	44,000	52.4	2.0625	22,100	22,600		
95	3.7402	170	6.6929	0.079	32	1.2598	8,280	11,000	15,600	18,800	20,600	22,500	17,500	19,700	22,800	31,400	43	1.6929	49,700	53,000	55.6	2.1875	28,600	28,600		

SOURCE: *Standards of the Anti-Friction Bearing Manufacturers Association,* New York, 1972.

*Spherical roller bearings begin at a 100 mm bore for this dimension series and are not listed here.

Table 9-2 Standard Dimensions and Load Ratings of Radial Rolling Bearings

Bore d (mm)	Bore d (in.)	Outside Dia D (mm)	Outside Dia D (in.)	Max Fillet Radius (in.)	Series 03 Width B (mm)	Series 03 Width B (in.)	03 Self-aligning C_o	03 Self-aligning C	03 Single-Row Deep-Groove C_o	03 Single-Row Deep-Groove C	03 Angular-Contact C_o	03 Angular-Contact C	03 Cylindrical Roller C_o	03 Cylindrical Roller C	03 Spherical Roller C_o	03 Spherical Roller C	Series 23 Width B (mm)	Series 23 Width B (in.)	23 Self-aligning C_o	23 Self-aligning C	23 Spherical Roller C_o	23 Spherical Roller C	Series 33 Width B (mm)	Series 33 Width B (in.)	33 Single-Row Deep-Groove C_o	33 Single-Row Deep-Groove C	33 Double-Row Nonfilling-Notch C_o	33 Double-Row Nonfilling-Notch C
4	0.1575	16	0.6299	0.012	5	0.1969																						
5	0.1969	19	0.7480	0.012	6	0.2362																						
6	0.2362																											
7	0.2756																											
8	0.3150																											
9	0.3543																											
10	0.3937	35	1.3780	0.024	11	0.4331	—	—	845	1,400																		
12	0.4724	37	1.4567	0.039	12	0.4724	530	1,630	1,040	1,680																		
15	0.5906	42	1.6535	0.039	13	0.5118	590	1,650	1,220	1,960																		
17	0.6693	47	1.8504	0.039	14	0.5512	820	2,170	1,470	2,340							19	0.7480	895	2,500			22.2	0.8750			2,690	3,630
20	0.7874	52	2.0472	0.039	15	0.5906	900	2,150	1,750	2,750	1,920	3,000					21	0.8268	1,190	3,210			22.2	0.8750	1,750	2,750	3,200	4,270
25	0.9843	62	2.4409	0.039	17	0.6693	1,350	3,110	2,390	3,660	2,870	4,220	2,870	5,130	6,000	6,700	24	0.9449	1,680	4,210			25.4	1.0000	2,390	3,660	4,360	5,660
30	1.1811	72	2.8346	0.039	19	0.7480	1,740	3,700	3,340	4,850	3,840	5,370	3,940	6,760	8,500	9,500	27	1.0630	2,250	5,420			30.2	1.1875	3,340	4,850	6,100	7,490
35	1.3780	80	3.1496	0.059	21	0.8268	2,210	4,350	4,020	5,750	4,620	6,340	5,370	8,830	9,800	10,800	31	1.2205	2,870	6,820			34.9	1.3750	4,020	5,750	7,340	8,860
40	1.5748	90	3.5433	0.059	23	0.9055	2,740	5,110	5,020	7,040	5,770	7,740	6,340	10,300	12,900	13,700	33	1.2992	3,530	7,750	16,100	20,400	36.5	1.4375	5,020	7,040	9,170	10,800
45	1.7717	100	3.9370	0.059	25	0.9843	3,580	6,600	6,730	9,120	7,730	10,100	9,030	14,200	17,300	17,000	36	1.4173	4,470	9,430	20,600	25,000	39.7	1.5625	6,730	9,120	12,300	14,100
50	1.9685	110	4.3307	0.079	27	1.0630	3,930	7,510	8,010	10,700	9,200	11,800	11,100	17,000	18,300	19,300	40	1.5748	5,280	11,100	26,500	31,600	44.4	1.7500	8,010	10,700	14,600	16,500
55	2.1654	120	4.7244	0.079	29	1.1417	5,060	8,800	9,400	12,400	10,800	13,600	13,600	20,700	21,600	22,800	43	1.6929	6,300	13,000	32,600	37,800	49.2	1.9375	9,400	12,400	17,200	19,000
60	2.3622	130	5.1181	0.079	31	1.2205	5,980	9,860	10,900	14,100	12,500	15,600	15,500	23,300	25,000	26,000	46	1.8110	7,400	15,100	38,000	44,300	54.0	2.1250	10,900	14,100	19,900	21,800
65	2.5591	140	5.5118	0.079	33	1.2992	6,600	10,700	12,500	16,000	14,400	17,600	17,100	25,600	30,500	31,000	48	1.8898	8,680	16,600	42,100	48,100	58.7	2.3125			22,900	24,600
70	2.7559	150	5.9055	0.079	35	1.3780	7,980	12,900	14,200	18,000	16,400	19,800	20,800	30,100	34,000	34,500	51	2.0079	10,000	18,900	49,500	55,800	63.5	2.5000			26,000	27,700
75	2.9528	160	6.2992	0.079	37	1.4567	8,620	13,700	16,100	19,600	18,500	21,500	25,600	36,500	38,000	39,000	55	2.1654	10,500	19,600	56,200	62,400	68.3	2.6875			29,400	30,200
80	3.1496	170	6.6929	0.098	39	1.5354	9,490	15,300	18,000	21,300	20,700	23,300	25,600	36,500	43,000	43,000	58	2.2835	13,000	23,900	64,400	71,400	68.3	2.6875			32,900	32,700
85	3.3465	180	7.0866	0.098	41	1.6142	10,900	16,900	20,100	22,900	23,100	25,200	30,500	42,900	—	—	60	2.3622	13,800	24,300	68,800	76,400	73.0	2.8750			32,000	32,100
90	3.5433	190	7.4803	0.098	43	1.6929	12,600	20,200	22,300	24,700	25,600	27,000	33,300	46,500	—	—	64	2.5197	15,400	26,400	85,200	90,600	73.0	2.8750			35,600	34,600

SOURCE: *Standards of the Anti-Friction Bearing Manufacturers Association.* New York, 1972.

Table 9-3 Standard Dimensions and Load Ratings of Radial Rolling Bearings

Bearing Bore d		Diameter Series 0 — Dimension Series 10									Diameter Series 1 — Dimension Series 30						Diameter Series 1 — Dimension Series 31						
mm	in.	Outside Dia. D (mm)	Outside Dia. D (in.)	Max Fillet Radius, in.	Width B (mm)	Width B (in.)	Single-Row Deep-Groove Ball Bearing C_o	Single-Row Deep-Groove Ball Bearing C	Angular-Contact Small-Angle Ball Bearing C_o	Angular-Contact Small-Angle Ball Bearing C	Width B (mm)	Width B (in.)	Double-Row Cylindrical Roller Bearing C_o	Double-Row Cylindrical Roller Bearing C	Spherical Roller Bearing C_o	Spherical Roller Bearing C	Outside Dia. D (mm)	Outside Dia. D (in.)	Max Fillet Radius, in.	Width B (mm)	Width B (in.)	Spherical Roller Bearing C_o	Spherical Roller Bearing C
4	0.1575																						
5	0.1969																						
6	0.2362																						
7	0.2756	19	0.7480	0.012	6	0.2362	—	340															
8	0.3150	22	0.8661	0.012	7	0.2756	—	565															
9	0.3543	24	0.9449	0.012	7	0.2756	—	585															
10	0.3937	26	1.0236	0.012	8	0.3150	440	790															
12	0.4724	28	1.1024	0.012	8	0.3150	500	880															
15	0.5906	32	1.2598	0.012	9	0.3543	565	965															
17	0.6693	35	1.3780	0.012	10	0.3937	625	1,040															
20	0.7874	42	1.6535	0.024	12	0.4724	1,000	1,620			16	0.6299	2,440	3,690									
25	0.9843	47	1.8504	0.024	12	0.4724	1,110	1,740	—	—	19	0.7480	3,160	4,610									
30	1.1811	55	2.1654	0.039	13	0.5118	1,550	2,290	—	—	20	0.7874	4,410	6,070									
35	1.3780	62	2.4409	0.039	14	0.5512	1,910	2,760	2,450	3,250	21	0.8268	5,410	7,260									
40	1.5748	68	2.6672	0.039	15	0.5906	2,090	2,900	2,780	3,490													
45	1.7717	75	2.9528	0.039	16	0.6299	2,730	3,630	3,360	4,140	23	0.9055	6,510	8,530									
50	1.9685	80	3.1496	0.039	16	0.6299	2,940	3,770	3,760	4,410	23	0.9055	7,160	9,050									
55	2.1654	90	3.5433	0.039	18	0.7087	3,820	4,890	4,970	4,890	26	1.0236	9,540	11,800									
60	2.3622	95	3.7402	0.039	18	0.7087	4,110	5,090	5,250	5,940	26	1.0236	10,400	12,500									
65	2.5591	100	3.9370	0.039	18	0.7087	4,410	5,280	5,800	6,290	26	1.0236	11,300	13,200									
70	2.7559	110	4.3307	0.039	20	0.7874	5,480	6,580	6,980	7,680	30	1.1811	15,000	17,000									
75	2.9528	115	4.5276	0.039	20	0.7874	5,870	6,830	7,720	8,140	30	1.1811	15,000	16,900									
80	3.1496	125	4.9213	0.039	22	0.8661	7,030	8,240	9,440	9,950	34	1.3386	18,600	20,800									
85	3.3465	130	5.1181	0.039	22	0.8661	7,540	8,560	9,910	10,200	34	1.3386	20,100	21,800									
90	3.5433	140	5.5118	0.059	24	0.9449	8,790	10,000	11,800	12,200	37	1.4567	23,300	25,400									
95	3.7402	145	5.7087	0.059	24	0.9449	9,410	10,500	12,400	12,500	37	1.4567	25,000	26,700									
100	3.9370	150	5.9055	0.059	24	0.9449	9,410	10,400	13,000	12,800	37	1.4567	26,800	27,900									

SOURCE: *Standards of the Anti-Friction Bearing Manufacturers Association.* New York, 1972.
*Spherical roller bearings for dimension series 30 begins with a 120-mm bearing bore and is not listed here.
†Spherical roller bearings for dimension series 31 begins with a 110-mm bearing bore and is not listed here.

designation of a bearing are used to indicate features such as bearing type, self-lubricating, type of seals, snap ring for mounting, material differences, and so on.[12]

As an illustration, a New Departure-Hyatt bearing having a basic bearing number 3212 indicates that it belongs to the 200 series (that is, light series), has a bore diameter of 60-mm (12×5), and is a Conrad (that is, deep groove) single-row bearing open on the sides. The last part of this description is based on the use of 3000 by New Departure-Hyatt to indicate this type of bearing. This same bearing is designated by the Marlin-Rockwell Company as 212-S, where the 212 has the same meaning as described above. However, the S is used to indicate a single-groove, Conrad type bearing.[13] The same bearing is designated by SKF as bearing number 6212. Notice that SKF uses 6000 as the basic number to indicate single-groove, Conrad bearings. Nevertheless, the important numerical characteristic to observe is that in all cases the number 212 appears. This common basic number makes it simple to substitute the bearing of one manufacturer for that of another. As a service, many companies list bearing conversion tables at the end of their catalogs. This same bearing designated by AFBMA standards would be 60BC02.[14]

It is obvious from Figure 9-34 that the number of bearings represented by the dimension series is very extensive, and to reproduce them here is not feasible. Therefore, Tables 9-1, 9-2, and 9-3 represent portions of the more widely used bearings, and the reader is advised to consult the *AFBMA Standards* or a manufacturer's catalog for a complete listing.

SECTION 9-5

Bearing Tolerances

The Annular Bearing Engineers' Committee (ABEC) of the AFBMA has established five basic grades of ball bearing precision. These grades are ABEC 1, 3, 5, 7, and 9. Grade 1 has the widest tolerance; as the numbers increase, the tolerance becomes smaller. For most normal applications, ABEC 1 is satisfactory. Where closer tolerances are needed, ABEC 3 and 5 can be specified. ABEC 7 and 9 are super precision grades reserved for

---

[12] Here again, there are some exceptions to the practice of bearing designations by manufacturers. For example, the New Departure-Hyatt basic bearing number 3212 becomes 7512 with one shield, Z 97512 with one shield and one seal, 477512 with a snap ring and two shields, etc. Note that the only numbers remaining of the basic bearing numbers are the last two digits (i.e., 12 which indicates a bearing bore of 60 mm).

[13] The Marlin-Rockwell Company is one that continues to use the same basic number regardless of special features. For example, a 212-S bearing with one shield is designated as 212SF, as 212SF2 with one shield and one seal, as 212SFFG with two shields and a snap ring, etc.

[14] The reader using the standard dimension and load rating tables of the AFBMA listed in this text would, in selecting this bearing, call for a "60-mm (2.3622-in.) bore, single-row deep-groove (i.e., Conrad) ball bearing of the 02 dimension series."

applications requiring extreme accuracy. Such applications are found in the design of instruments, aircraft controls, servosystems, and machine tools. Considering the discussion in Chapter 4 concerning tolerances and costs, the designer must be able to justify specifying high ABEC grades. For example, in the bearing bore range of 11 to 16 inclusive, the ABEC tolerances are as follows:

ABEC Grade	Tolerance
1	+0.0000 −0.0006
3	+0.0000 −0.0004
5	+0.0000 −0.0003
7	+0.0000 −0.0002
9	+0.0000 −0.00015

From this list, it is readily seen that the ABEC grade 9 has only one quarter the allowance of the ABEC grade 1. Reference to Figure 4-69 shows the relative time to produce the tolerance for ABEC 9 as 11.5, and the tolerance for ABEC 1 as 7.9. Thus, to produce grade 9, a 45.6% longer period of time (that is, increased cost) is required than to produce grade 1.

Manufacturers' catalogs contain the complete ABEC tolerance tables both for bore diameter and radial runout. Tolerance grades have also been established for cylindrical roller bearings by The Roller Bearing Engineers' Committee (RBEC) of the AFBMA. For cylindrical roller bearings, there are only two grades, RBEC 1 and 5. These grades have the same tolerance values that have been assigned to ABEC 1 and 5. Tapered roller bearing tolerances have also been graded. These grades are 4, 2, 3, 0, and 00 with 4 having the lowest precision and 00 having the highest precision.[15]

SECTION 9-6

Rolling Bearing Materials

Ball bearings (except for the retainers, seals, and ball separators) are commonly made of SAE 52100 (or AISI E-52100), a high carbon chromium steel that is through hardened to Rockwell C 58–65. Due to the loss of hardness with increasing temperatures, SAE 52100 cannot be used where the temperature is above 350°F.

[15] See Section 1 of *The Timken Engineering Journal*, The Timken Roller Bearing Company, Canton, Ohio.

Bearing steels are produced by the vacuum-melting (VM) process and, in particular, by the consumable electrode vacuum-melted process (CVM) in contrast to air melted steels. Steel produced by these methods is more uniform in structure and contains fewer impurities. As a result, the reliability of bearings has been improved.

High temperature bearing problems are not uncommon and in the past years have served to prevent the development of both industrial and military hardware. However, continuing research has led to the development of materials capable of maintaining a through hardness greater than Rockwell C 58 at higher than normal temperatures.

Figure 9-35 illustrates how some materials vary with temperature. The maximum operating temperature of each material is that point at which the curve crosses the Rockwell C 58 line.

For mildly corrosive applications, it is quite common to use grade 440C, a martensitic stainless steel. Notice that in Figure 9-35 the anticorrosion steel is "restricted" to an operating temperature no higher than 300°F. At a temperature above 300°F, its hardness drops below Rockwell C 58 and the raceways may begin to "brinell."

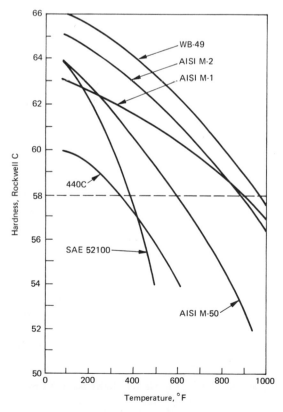

Figure 9-35 Hardness versus temperature of some through hardened bearing steels. [From *Machine Design*, 1970 *Bearings Reference Issue*. The Penton Publishing Co., Cleveland, Ohio.]

Roller bearings are usually fabricated of case hardening (that is, carburizing grade) steels. These steels are surface hardened to Rockwell C 58–63 to a depth of no greater than 0.015 in., past which there is a softer core with a hardness of Rockwell C 25–40. Carburizing grades (for example, AISI 4620) are limited to an operating temperature no higher than about 300°F. Continuing metallurgical research, however, has led to the development of carburizing grade bearing steels that are suitable for higher operating temperatures. Figure 9-36 shows the hardness-temperature plot of two such steels in comparison with AISI 4620. These curves illustrate the marked increase in operating temperatures attainable by special steels.

Ball separators (that is, cages) are normally fabricated of 1010 steel. However, for use at elevated temperatures (up to 700°F), separators made of M-1, S-Monel, 440C, polyimide polymer (under 700°F), cobalt alloy, and copper alloy (for example, bronze or silver-plated silicon iron bronze) have been successfully used.

For mildly corrosive environments it is customary to use grade 302 or grade 410 stainless steel as ball separator material. Most angular-contact bearings and high speed bearings use ball separators made of cotton woven fabric impregnated with a phenolic resin.

Seals used to retain the lubricant in "self-lubricating" bearings are stamped from a low carbon steel (for example, 1010). Depending upon the manufacturer and the particular bearing, the seals are either completely molded into a synthetic rubber compound or just edged with this material. Also a seal made of felt pressed between two metal rings is quite popular.

Shields that help both to retain grease and to prevent chips, dirt, or large particles from entering the bearing are also made of a low carbon steel which is crimped into a groove in the outer ring and maintains a close running fit with the inner ring.

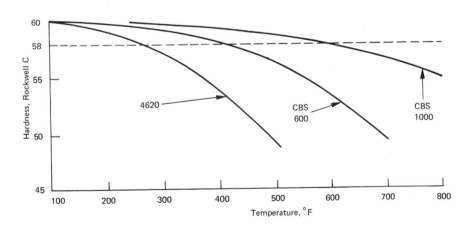

Figure 9-36 Hardness versus temperature of three carburized bearing steels. [Courtesy The Timken Company.]

Where extreme temperature (for example, 1500°F) and environmental conditions have precluded the use of available stock bearings, materials such as alumina, zirconium oxide, titanium carbide, pyroceram,[16] and so on, have been used in place of steels.

SECTION 9-7

Rolling Bearing Friction

Bearing friction is greatly influenced, among other things (for example, hysteresis, slip), by the coefficient of friction between the rolling members [3]. Table 9-4, based on years of accumulated test data, lists the average coefficient of friction (μ) for several types of bearings measured at the shaft surface.

It is important to emphasize that the values for μ given in Table 9-4 require modification should there be a marked change of temperature, load, speed and lubrication from the normal operating ranges of any of these factors.

Table 9-4   Average coefficients of friction

Type of Bearing	Starting		Running	
	Radial	Thrust	Radial	Thrust
Ball bearing	0.0025	0.0060	0.0015	0.0040
Spherical roller bearing	0.0030	0.120	0.0018	0.0080
Cylindrical roller bearing	0.0020	—	0.0011	—

SOURCE: *Bearing Technical Journal*. FMC Corporation, Link-Belt Bearing Division, Indianapolis, Ind., 1970.

Actually, the greatest contribution to bearing friction is made by the seals which can produce several times greater friction than the bearing torque. Where the designer feels that the total bearing friction (that is, including seal friction) is a significant factor affecting his design, then consultation with the manufacturer becomes necessary.

Although insignificant in many designs, the horsepower lost due to frictional torque is

$$\text{hp} = \frac{Tn}{63,025} = \frac{\mu F_r \, dn}{126,050} \qquad (9\text{-}1)$$

where

T = frictional torque, lb-in.
n = shaft speed, rpm
d = bearing bore, in.
F_r = radial bearing load, lb

[16] Product of Corning Glass Company.

SECTION 9-8

Basis for Bearing Failure

Carefully installed bearings that are properly lubricated, kept free of foreign matter, and are not overloaded will fail by fatigue. Evidence of this failure appears as spalling or flaking of a raceway or rolling element(s). As the rolling elements revolve within the raceways, they are subjected to a repeating contact (that is, Hertzian) stress. In addition, those areas of the raceways that support the shaft load as the rolling elements pass over them are also subjected to a repeating contact stress. Because these stresses are greater than the endurance limit of the material, it is obvious that the bearing will have a limited life. In fact, if one considers that pure rolling does not occur in the bearing but that some sliding of the balls or rollers takes place, it is readily understood why particles of metal are removed from the raceway surfaces. The removal of this metal is called spalling and, when this condition arises in a bearing, the bearing has failed.

The statistical analysis concerning the fatigue failure of rolling bearings presented in 1947 by Lundberg and Palmgrem [9, 10] provided the ground work for the adoption in 1950 by the AFBMA of a "Standard method of evaluating the load ratings of annular ball bearings." This standard has also been approved by the American National Standards Institute (ANSI B3.11–1959) and is the basis for selecting a bearing as described in this text. A similar standard for evaluating roller bearings was also adopted.

SECTION 9-9

Life, Rating Life, and Basic Load Rating

Notwithstanding modern manufacturing methods and the use of quality control procedures, no group of seemingly identical bearings is exactly alike. Each may differ, however slightly, metallurgically, in surface finish, roundness of balls, and so on. As a result, no two bearings within the same family may have the exact number of operating hours to fatigue failure after having been subjected to the same speed and load conditions. Thus, the life of a bearing is established on a purely statistical basis (see reference [3]) and the AFBMA has established the following definitions to ensure a uniform understanding and procedure when selecting a bearing:

1. The **life**[17] of a radial ball bearing is the number of revolutions (or hours, at some given constant speed) that the bearing runs before the first evidence of fatigue develops in the material of either ring or in a ball.
2. The **rating life** of a group of apparently identical radial ball bearings, thrust ball bearings, radial roller bearings, or thrust roller bearings is

---

[17] This same definition is also applicable to thrust ball bearings, radial roller bearings and thrust roller bearings by just replacing "ball" with "roller," and "ring" with "washer."

defined as the number of revolutions (or hours at some given constant speed) that 90% of a group of apparently identical bearings will complete or exceed before the first evidence of fatigue develops. (Rating life is commonly referred to as L_{10} life, B-10 life, or minimum life.) As presently determined, the **median life**[18] that this same group of bearings would complete or exceed is 5 times the rating life (that is, median life $= 5L_{10}$).

3. The **basic load rating**[19] (also called the **dynamic load rating, basic dynamic capacity,** and the **specific dynamic capacity**) of radial ball bearings is that constant stationary radial load which a group of apparently identical ball bearings with stationary outer rings can endure for a rating life of 1 million (that is, 10^6) revolutions of the inner rings. In single-row angular-contact bearings, the basic load rating relates to the radial component of the load which results in a purely radial displacement of the bearing rings in relation to each other. Load ratings, if given for specific speeds, are to be based on a rating life of 500 hr. (This is equivalent to running a bearing for 500 hr at $33\frac{1}{3}$ rpm or for a total of 10^6 revolutions. On the basis of median life, this is equivalent to having run a bearing for 2500 hr at $33\frac{1}{3}$ rpm for a total of 5×10^6 revolutions.)

4. The **basic static load rating**[19] is defined as that radial load which corresponds to a total permanent deformation of rolling element and race (or washer) at the most heavily stressed contact of 0.0001 of the ball or roller diameter. In single-row angular-contact ball bearings, the basic static load rating relates to the radial component of that load which causes a purely radial displacement of the bearing rings in relation to each other.

Basic static load rating

The basic static load ratings for different types of bearings, symbolized by C_0, are given in Tables 9-1, 9-2, and 9-3. The value of C_0 depends on the bearing material, the number of rows of rolling elements in a bearing, the number of rolling elements per row, the bearing contact angle (see Figure 9-8), and the ball or roller diameter. Those readers wishing to know how C_0 is calculated should refer to Section 9 of reference [7] for specific equations and data.

Normally the basic static load rating has little influence in the selection of a rolling bearing. However if a bearing in a machine is stationary for extended periods of time, local permanent deflection can occur. This is particularly

---

[18] Various manufacturers' catalogs and texts mistakenly call this "average life." The designer must be careful in using this term since this usage is quite prevalent. The AFBMA defines **average life** of an antifriction bearing as the summation of all bearing lives in a series of life tests divided by the number of life tests. Some manufacturers define average life as being equal to 7 times the rating life.

[19] This same definition applies to radial roller bearings, thrust ball bearings, and thrust roller bearings. However, for thrust bearings, the loads are not radial but are thrust loads, and the word "ring" is replaced by the word "washer."

true where the load exceeds C_0. Where operating speeds are very low, higher loads than C_0 can be allowed but should be checked with the bearing manufacturer.

Basic load rating

The basic load ratings for different bearings, symbolized by C, are listed in Tables 9-1, 9-2, and 9-3. The value of C depends on the same factors as those which determine C_0, except for an additional parameter concerning the loading geometry. As with C_0, Section 9 of reference [7] contains the specific relationships and data needed to compute C.

The basic load rating C enters directly into the process of selecting a bearing, which will subsequently be explained.

Extensive testing of rolling bearings and subsequent statistical analysis have shown that load and life of a bearing are related statistically [3]. In particular this relationship is defined by the expression

$$L_{10} = \left(\frac{C}{P}\right)^b \tag{9-2[20]}$$

where L_{10} = rating life in millions of revolutions (that is, the number of revolutions resulting in 10% failure); C = basic load rating in pounds (obtained from Tables 9-1, 9-2, 9-3, or a manufacturer's catalog); P = equivalent load in pounds (see Section 9-10); $b = 3.0$ for ball bearings[21] and $\frac{10}{3}$ for roller bearings.

In terms of hours of life, equation (9-2) becomes

$$L_{10} = \frac{10^6}{60n} \left(\frac{C}{P}\right)^b \tag{9-3}$$

where n = rotational speed in revolutions per minute.

Again, we urge the designer to read carefully that portion of the manufacturer's catalog that explains how load rating and life are established. Although most manufacturers adhere to the recommendations of the AFBMA, there are some exceptions. For example, New Departure-Hyatt list their load ratings on an average (that is, median) life of 3800 hr instead of 2500 hr as specified by the AFBMA. Regardless of catalog variations, however, the designer can always convert the data to the AFBMA standard.

SECTION 9-10

Equivalent Load

As defined by the AFBMA, the equivalent load is that constant stationary radial load which, if applied to a bearing with rotating inner and stationary outer ring, would give the same life as that which the bearing would attain under the actual conditions of load and rotation.

[20] Equation (9-2) is not applicable to filling slot type bearings.

[21] New Departure-Hyatt uses an exponent of 4.

In many applications, bearings have to carry a load composed of axial and radial components. In addition, they are sometimes required to operate with a rotating outer and a stationary inner ring. It then becomes necessary to express these conditions by an equivalent load satisfying the above definition. The expression used to define this equivalent load, which is applicable to ball (that is, radial and angular-contact) bearings and roller bearings (not applicable to filling-slot bearings) is

$$P = XVF_r + YF_a \qquad (9\text{-}4)$$

where

P = equivalent load, lb
F_r = radial load, lb
F_a = thrust (that is, axial) load, lb
V = a rotation factor: 1.0 for inner ring rotation, 1.2 for outer ring rotation. For self-aligning ball bearing use 1 for inner or outer ring rotation.
X = a radial load factor (see Table 9-5, 9-6, or 9-7 as applicable).
Y = a thrust factor (see Table 9-5, 9-6, or 9-7 as applicable).

Looking at Table 9-5, we observe that the radial factor X can in some cases be less than unity. Thus, it is possible to have a combination where, if the thrust component is much smaller than the radial component, the radial component without the radial factor X is the larger of the two equivalent radial loads P. It therefore becomes necessary to also calculate

$$P = VF_r \qquad (9\text{-}5)$$

The equivalent load used in selecting a bearing is then the larger of the two values obtained from equations (9-4) and (9-5).

Equations (9-4) and (9-5) are also used to determine the equivalent load for *single-row and double-row spherical bearings*. For single-row spherical bearings, values of X and Y are found in Table 9-6. For double-row spherical bearings, values of X and Y are found in Table 9-7.

Since *straight cylindrical roller bearings* are not intended to be used to withstand thrust loads,[22] the equivalent load for this type of bearing can also be calculated by means of equation (9-5).

Equivalent loads for *thrust ball bearings* and *thrust roller bearings* can be calculated from equation (9-4) where V is unity.

Space limitations make it impossible to list the V factors for straight cylindrical roller bearings, the X, Y factors for both types of thrust bearings, and the respective bearing tables which give the values for C_0 and C (that is, tables like Tables 9-1, 9-2, and 9-3). Such information is readily available in the *AFBMA Standards*, engineering handbooks, and manufacturers' catalogs.

---

[22] For those straight cylindrical roller bearings that have a locating flange or flanges (see Figure 9-18), the maximum thrust load should not exceed the value determined by, $F_a \leqslant 0.2F_r$.

Table 9-5 Factor *X* and *Y* for ball and roller bearings

Contact Angle α, deg	$\dfrac{iF_a{}^1}{C_o}$	Single-Row Bearing[2] $F_a/VF_r > e$ X	Y	Double-Row Bearing[3] $F_a/VF_r \le e$ X	Y	$F_a/VF_r > e$ X	Y	e	
									F_a/ind^2
Radial-contact groove ball bearing[4]									
	0.014		2.30				2.30	0.19	25
	0.028		1.99				1.99	0.22	50
	0.056		1.71				1.71	0.26	100
	0.084		1.55				1.55	0.28	150
	0.11	0.56	1.45	1.0	0	0.56	1.45	0.30	200
	0.17		1.31				1.31	0.34	300
	0.28		1.15				1.15	0.38	500
	0.42		1.04				1.04	0.42	750
	0.56		1.00				1.00	0.44	1000
Angular-Contact groove ball bearings[4]									F_a/nd^2
	0.014		Use X, Y,		2.78		3.74	0.23	25
	0.028		and e val-		2.40		3.23 ·	0.26	50
	0.056		ues appli-		2.07		2.78	0.30	100
	0.085		cable to		1.87		2.52	0.34	150
5	0.11	0.56	single-row	1.0	1.75	0.78	2.36	0.36	200
	0.17		radial-		1.58		2.13 .	0.40	300
	0.28		contact		1.39		1.87	0.45	500
	0.42		bearings		1.26		1.69	0.50	750
	0.56				1.21		1.63	0.52	1000
	0.014		1.88		2.18		3.06	0.29	25
	0.029		1.71		1.98		2.78	0.32	50
	0.057		1.52		1.76		2.47	0.36	100
10	0.086	0.46	1.41	1.0	1.63	0.75	2.29	0.38	150
	0.11		1.34		1.55		2.18	0.40	200
	0.17		1.23		1.42		2.00	0.44	300
	0.29		1.10		1.27		1.79	0.49	500
	0.43		1.01		1.17		1.64	0.54	750
	0.57		1.00		1.16		1.63	0.54	1000
	0.015		1.47		1.65		2.39	0.38	25
	0.029		1.40		1.57		2.28	0.40	50
	0.058		1.30		1.46		2.11	0.43	100
15	0.087	0.44	1.23	1.0	1.38	0.72	2.00	0.46	150
	0.12		1.19		1.34		1.93	0.47	200
	0.17		1.12		1.26		1.82	0.50	300
	0.29		1.02		1.14		1.66	0.55	500
	0.44		1.00		1.12		1.63	0.56	750
	0.58		1.00		1.12		1.63	0.56	1000
20		0.43	1.00	1.0	1.09	0.70	1.63	0.57	
25		0.41	0.87	1.0	0.92	0.67	1.41	0.68	
30		0.39	0.76	1.0	0.78	0.63	1.24	0.80	
35		0.37	0.66	1.0	0.66	0.60	1.07	0.95	
40		0.35	0.57	1.0	0.55	0.57	0.93	1.14	
Self-aligning ball bearings									
		0.40	0.4 cot α	1.0	0.42 cot α	0.65	0.65 cot α	1.5 tan α	
Roller-bearings, self-aligning, tapered[5]									
α ≠ 90		0.4	0.4 cot α	1.0	0.45 cot α	0.67	0.67 cot α	1.5 tan α	

SOURCE: Frank W. Wilson (ed.): *Tool Engineers Handbook*, 2nd ed. McGraw-Hill Book Co., New York, 1959.
NOTE: Values of X, Y, and e for a load or contact angle other than shown are obtained by linear interpolation.
[1] C_o is the static basic load rating; i is the number of rows of balls (not used for radial contact bearings).
[2] For single-row bearings, when $Fa/VF_r \le e$, use X = 1 and Y = 0.
   When calculating the equivalent load for a unit consisting of two similar single-row angular-contact ball bearings in a duplex mounting, "face to face" or "back to back," the pair is considered as one double-row angular-contact ball bearing.
   When calculating the equivalent load for a unit consisting of two or more single-row radial or angular-contact ball bearings mounted "in tandem," the bearings are calculated individually as single-row ball bearings.
[3] Double-row bearings are presumed to be symmetrical.
[4] Permissible maximum value of F_a/C_o depends on the bearing design.
[5] For α = 0; $F_a = 0$ and X = 1.

Table 9-6 Load ratings and values of **X** and **Y** for single row, spherical roller bearings (inch size) (C_o = basic static load rating; C = basic load rating, i.e. basic dynamic load rating)

Bore dia., in.	O.D., in.	Assembly Width, in.	e	$\frac{F_a}{VF_r} > e$ * X	Y	C_0, lb	C, lb	Bore dia., in.	O.D., in.	Assembly Width, in.	e	$\frac{F_a}{VF_r} > e$* X	Y	C_0, lb	C, lb
1.0000	2.3750	0.781	0.51		1.17	4650	6060	2.5000	4.3307	0.866	0.38		1.60	15500	16400
1.1250	2.3750	0.781	0.51		1.17	4650	6060	2.6250	4.4677	0.948	0.37		1.61	17800	18600
1.1875	2.6250	0.812	0.48		1.25	5590	7170	2.6250	5.0000	1.094	0.42		1.44	20300	22800
1.2500	2.6250	0.812	0.48		1.25	5590	7170	2.7500	5.1172	1.062	0.33		1.59	20700	21700
1.3775	2.8345	0.670	0.44		1.37	6300	7640	2.7553	5.9045	1.188	0.40		1.49	26000	30000
1.5000	2.8345	0.670	0.44		1.37	6300	7640	2.9522	5.1172	1.062	0.38		1.59	20700	21700
1.5743	3.1496	0.828	0.47		1.27	7470	9130	3.0000	5.1172	1.062	0.38		1.59	20700	21700
1.7500	3.3464	0.812	0.45		1.34	8650	10500	3.0000	5.9045	1.109	0.38		1.57	25800	26200
1.7712	3.3464	0.812	0.45		1.34	8650	10500	3.3457	5.9045	1.109	0.38		1.57	25800	26200
1.9375	3.5433	0.787	0.40	0.40	1.49	9700	11100	3.4375	6.0000	1.562	0.43	0.40	1.39	33000	31700
1.9680	3.5433	0.787	0.40		1.49	9700	11100	3.5000	6.0000	1.562	0.43		1.39	33000	31700
1.9680	3.9370	0.828	0.45		1.34	13600	15800	3.5100	6.0000	1.562	0.43		1.39	33000	31700
1.9680	4.3299	1.063	0.48		1.24	16800	19200	3.5425	7.4792	1.419	0.38		1.60	50500	48100
2.0000	3.9370	0.828	0.40		1.49	12900	13800	3.6250	6.0000	1.562	0.43		1.39	33000	31700
2.1648	3.9370	0.828	0.40		1.49	12900	13800	3.6250	7.0866	1.339	0.36		1.67	39700	40600
2.1875	3.9370	0.828	0.40		1.49	12900	13800	3.7402	7.0666	1.339	0.36		1.67	39700	40600
2.2500	3.9370	0.828	0.40		1.49	12900	13800	3.9375	7.0856	1.495	0.36		1.67	39700	40600
2.2500	4.3307	0.866	0.38		1.60	15500	16400	4.0000	7.4792	1.419	0.38		1.60	50500	48100
2.3616	4.3307	0.866	0.38		1.60	15500	16400	4.1331	7.4792	1.419	0.38		1.60	50500	48100
2.4375	4.3307	0.866	0.38		1.60	15500	16400	4.7236	8.4634	1.718	0.37		1.63	61500	59500

SOURCE: Data from *Bearing Technical Journal*, FMC Corporation, Link-Belt Bearing Division, Indianapolis, Ind., 1970. The data applies to Link-Belt series A 2000S.

*For $F_a/VF_r \leqslant e$, $x = 1.0$ and $y = 0$.

Table 9-7 Value of **Y** for double row, spherical roller bearings*

Bearing Bore, mm	Dimension Series 22 e	$\frac{F_a}{VF_r} \leqslant e$ Y	$\frac{F_a}{VF_r} > e$ Y	Dimension Series 23 e	$\frac{F_a}{VF_r} \leqslant e$ Y	$\frac{F_a}{VF_r} > e$ Y	Dimension Series 30 e	$\frac{F_a}{VF_r} \leqslant e$ Y	$\frac{F_a}{VF_r} > e$ Y	Dimension Series 31 e	$\frac{F_a}{VF_r} \leqslant e$ Y	$\frac{F_a}{VF_r} > e$ Y	Dimension Series 32 e	$\frac{F_a}{VF_r} \leqslant e$ Y	$\frac{F_a}{VF_r} > 1$ Y
40	—	—	—	0.40	1.70	2.53									
45	0.28	2.39	3.56	0.39	1.74	2.59									
50	0.26	2.57	3.83	0.39	1.73	2.57									
55	0.26	2.64	3.93	0.38	1.76	2.62									
60	0.26	2.58	3.84	0.38	1.79	2.66									
65	0.26	2.55	3.80	0.37	1.84	2.74									
70	0.25	2.69	4.00	0.36	1.86	2.77									
75	0.24	2.82	4.20	0.38	1.79	2.67									
80	0.24	2.84	4.24	0.36	1.86	2.76									
85	0.24	2.80	4.17	0.36	1.86	2.77									
90	0.25	2.69	4.00	0.36	1.89	2.82									
95	0.26	2.57	3.83	0.36	1.86	2.77									
100	0.27	2.54	3.79	0.37	1.83	2.72									
110	0.27	2.46	3.66	0.36	1.90	2.82	—	—	—	0.31	2.15	3.20	0.34	1.98	2.95
120	0.27	2.50	3.72	0.35	1.92	2.85	0.24	2.80	4.16	0.31	2.16	3.22	0.35	1.91	2.84
130	0.28	2.44	3.63	0.35	1.91	2.84	0.25	2.76	4.11	0.30	2.25	3.35	0.36	1.89	2.81
140	0.27	2.48	3.69	0.36	1.87	2.79	0.24	2.82	4.20	0.30	2.28	3.40	0.35	1.93	2.87
150	0.27	2.48	3.71	0.36	1.89	2.81	0.24	2.86	4.26	0.32	2.13	3.17	0.36	1.90	2.83
160	0.28	2.44	3.63	0.35	1.90	2.83	0.24	2.84	4.22	0.32	2.14	3.19	0.36	1.89	2.81
170	0.28	2.42	3.60	0.35	1.93	2.87	0.25	2.75	4.09	0.31	2.19	3.26	0.36	1.89	2.81
180	0.27	2.51	3.73	0.35	1.95	2.91	0.25	2.66	3.96	0.31	2.15	3.20	0.36	1.88	2.80
190	0.27	2.48	3.70	0.34	1.96	2.91	0.25	2.74	4.08	0.32	2.10	3.13	0.35	1.92	2.85
200	0.27	2.46	3.67	0.35	1.95	2.90	0.25	2.67	3.98	0.32	2.11	3.14	0.36	1.90	2.83
220	0.27	2.48	3.70	0.33	2.03	3.02	0.25	2.67	3.97	0.32	2.13	3.17	0.36	1.88	2.80
240	0.27	2.47	3.68	—	—	—	0.24	2.78	4.13	0.31	2.17	3.24			
260							0.25	2.74	4.08						
280							0.24	2.81	4.17						
300							0.24	2.79	4.15						

SOURCE: Data from *Bearing Technical Journal*, FMC Corporation, Link-Belt Bearing Division, Indianapolis, Ind., 1970.

*For all dimension series, $X = 1.00$ for $F_a/VF_r \leqslant e$ and $X = 0.67$ for $F_a/VF_r > e$.

Table 9-8 Ball bearing service factors, F_s

Type of Service	Multiply Calculated Load by Following Factors	
	Ball Bearings	Roller Bearings
Uniform and steady load	1.0	1.0
Light shock load	1.5	1.0
Moderate shock load	2.0	1.3
Heavy shock load	2.5	1.7
Extreme and indeterminate shock load	3.0	2.0

Nevertheless the following procedure, used to illustrate the selection of ball and spherical roller bearings, is the same as that which would be used to select a straight cylindrical roller bearing or a thrust bearing.

The equivalent load calculated from equations (9-4) or (9-5) does not account for any shock or impact forces a bearing may experience. As a precaution against possible damage or early bearing failure, it is suggested that the equivalent load be multiplied by an appropriately selected service factor

Table 9-9 Guide to values of life requirements for different classes of machines

Type of Machine	Life in Hours of Operation
Instruments and apparatus that are only infrequently used Ex.: Demonstration apparatus, devices for operation of sliding doors	500
Aircraft engines	500–2,000
Machines for service of short duration or intermittent operation, where service interruptions are of minor importance Ex.: Hand tools, lifting tackle in machinery shops, hand driven machines in general, farm machinery, assembly cranes, charging machines, foundry cranes, household machines	4,000–8,000
Machines for intermittent service where dependable operation is of great importance Ex.: Auxiliary machines in power stations, conveying equipment in production lines, elevators, general cargo cranes, machine tools less frequently used	8,000–12,000
Machines for 8-hr service that are not always fully utilized Ex.: Stationary electric motors, gear drives for general purposes	12,000–20,000
Machines for 8-hr service that are fully utilized Ex.: Machines in general in the mechanical industries, cranes for continuous service, blowers, jackshafts	20,000–30,000
Machines for continuous operation (24-hr service) Ex.: Separators, compressors, pumps, main line shafting, roller beds and conveyor rollers, mine hoists, stationary electric motors	40,000–60,000
Machines for 24-hr service where dependability is of great importance Ex.: Pulp and paper machines, public power stations, mine pumps, public pumping stations, machines for continuous service aboard ship	100,000–200,000

SOURCE: General Catalogue and Engineering Data, SKF Industries, Phila., Pa.

from Table 9-8. The factors in this table are based upon accumulated years of experience for a variety of design conditions.

In choosing a bearing, a designer must base his selection on life and load requirements. As is often the case, data concerning the expected life of a bearing to be used in a particular application are not readily available. Table 9-9, based upon accumulated industrial experience, can be used to assist the designer in selecting a reasonable design life for a 90% probability of survival.

Example 9.1. A 309 single-row deep groove ball bearing which is to operate at 1500 rpm, is acted on by a 1890-lb radial load and a 1250-lb thrust load. The inner ring rotates, the load is steady, and the service is continuous. Determine the rating life and the median life of the bearing.

Solution: A 309 bearing belongs to the medium series (that is, 300 series) and is equivalent to dimension series 03. Referring to Table 9-2, we find that for a 45-mm (that is, 9×5) bore bearing: $C = 9120$ lb, and $C_0 = 6730$ lb.

To determine the equivalent load P, we need to know the value of X and Y from Table 9-5.

$$\frac{iF_a}{C_0} = \frac{1(1250)}{6730} = 0.186 \qquad \frac{F_a}{VF_r} = \frac{1250}{1(1890)} = 0.672$$

We see that F_a/VF_r is larger than e, so we must obtain X and Y from Table 9-5. (*Note:* $X = 1$ and $Y = 0$ for $F_a/VF_r \leqslant e$). By interpolating values of iF_a/C_0 we obtain $Y = 1.287$. The value of X is constant and equals 0.56.

Applying equation (9-4)

$$P = XVF_r + YF_a = (0.56)(1)(1890) + (1.287)(1250) = 2668 \text{ lb}$$

and applying equation (9-5)

$$P = VF_r = 1(1890) = 1890 \text{ lb}$$

Since 2668 lb is larger than 1890 lb, the larger value is used for life calculations. Applying equation (9-2)

$$L_{10} = \left(\frac{C}{P}\right)^b = \left(\frac{9120}{2668}\right)^3 = 40 \text{ million revolutions} = 40 \times 10^6 \text{ rev}$$

or

$$L_{10} = \frac{40 \times 10^6}{1500 \times 60} = 445 \text{ hr}$$

$$\text{median life} = 5(445) = 2225 \text{ hr} \quad \bullet$$

Example 9-2. For the bearing in Example 9-1, how does the rating life and median life change if the bearing is subjected to a light shock load as the outer ring is rotating?

Solution: For a rotating outer ring, $V = 1.2$. Thus, we have

$$\frac{F_a}{VF_r} = \frac{1250}{(1.2)(1890)} = 0.560$$

we see that F_a/VF_r is still larger than any value of e applicable to a single-row ball bearing in Table 9-5; thus, we still must choose an X and Y from Table

9-5. With the ratio $(iF_a/C_0$ remaining the same, $X = 0.56$ and $Y = 1.287$. From Table 9-8 and equation (9-4)

$$P = F_s(XVF_r + YF_a) = 1.5(0.56 \times 1.2 \times 1890 + 1.287 \times 1250) = 4320 \text{ lb}$$

From equation (9-5)

$$P = F_s VF_r = 1.5(1.2 \times 1890) = 3400 \text{ lb}$$

Since 4320 lb is larger than 3400 lb, we use $P = 4320$ lb for calculating the rating life. Now, using equation (9-2)

$$L_{10} = \left(\frac{C}{P}\right)^b = \left(\frac{9120}{4320}\right)^3 = 9.37 \times 10^6 \text{ rev}$$

$$\text{rating life} = \frac{9.37 \times 10^6}{1500 \times 60} = 104 \text{ hr}$$

$$\text{median life} = 5(104) = 520 \text{ hr}$$

Note: for a 62% increase in equivalent load, the rating life was reduced by 76.5%. ●

Example 9-3. As another example, consider the case of selecting a bearing for a $2\frac{1}{2}$-in. diameter shaft that rotates uniformly and steadily at 1800 rpm. Due to a bevel gear mounted on the shaft, the bearing will have to withstand a 1000-lb radial load and a 350-lb thrust load. Without any restriction as to the type of bearing, select one that is satisfactory for a rating life of at least 20,000 hr.

Solution: Observing that the thrust load is greater than 20% of the radial load, we can eliminate the possibility of using a straight roller bearing. We can also eliminate from consideration the tapered roller bearing. This type of bearing is primarily used for applications where there is high thrust load and a moderately high radial load. We will, therefore, consider using one of the following types of bearings: (1) a single-row deep groove bearing, (2) a single-row spherical roller bearing, and (3) a double-row spherical roller bearing. The bearing bore diameter is selected so that it will be compatible for mounting on the $2\frac{1}{2}$-in. diameter shaft (that is, the shaft diameter can be "turned down" to fit the bearing bore and provide a shoulder for the inner ring). In this case, we shall specify a bearing bore of 50 mm (1.9685 in.).

Part 1. Consider a 310 single-row, deep groove bearing. From Table 9-2 we establish that $C = 10,700$ lb, and $C_0 = 8010$ lb. We now need to determine the equivalent load P. To do so, the values of X and Y are needed from Table 9-5. To obtain the values of X and Y, it is necessary to calculate iF_a/C_0 and find e. Thus

$$\frac{iF_a}{C_0} = \frac{1(350)}{8010} = 0.0437; \qquad e = 0.2424 \text{ by linear interpolation}$$

$$\frac{F_a}{VF_r} = \frac{350}{1(1000)} = 0.350 > 0.2424 = e$$

Thus, from Table 9-5, $X = 0.56$, $Y = 1.833$ by linear interpolation. Applying equation (9-4), we obtain

$$P = XVF_r + YF_a = (0.56)(1)(1000) + 1.833(350) = 1202 \text{ lb}$$

Then applying equation (9-5)

$$P = VF_r = 1(1000) = 1000 \text{ lb}$$

Using the higher equivalent load we proceed directly to calculate rating life. By means of equation (9-2), we get

$$L_{10} = \left(\frac{C}{P}\right)^b = \left(\frac{10,700}{1202}\right)^3 = 705 \times 10^6 \text{ rev}$$

or by using equation (9-3) we obtain the rating life L_{10} in hours

$$L_{10} = \frac{10^6}{60n}\left(\frac{C}{P}\right)^3 = \frac{10^6(705)}{60(1800)} = 652 \text{ hr.}$$

Part 2. Consider a single-row spherical roller bearing. This bearing is ordinarily available in bore sizes that are in inches. To fit the shaft diameter and to be comparable with other bearings reviewed in this problem, we shall select a spherical roller bearing from Table 9-6 with a bore diameter of 1.9680 in., an O.D. of 3.5433 in., and a width of 0.787 in. We also note that $C = 11,100$ lb, and $C_0 = 9700$ lb. Following the same procedure as with the deep groove ball bearing, we have

$$\frac{F_a}{VF_r} = 0.350 < 0.40 = e \text{ (from Table 9-6)}$$

and so we use $X = 1$ and $Y = 0$

$$P = XVF_r + YF_a = (1)(1)(1000) + 0(350) = 1000 \text{ lb}$$
$$P = VF_r = 1000 \text{ lb}$$

$$L_{10} = \left(\frac{C}{P}\right)^b = \left(\frac{11,100}{1000}\right)^{3.33} = 3020 \times 10^6 \text{ rev}$$

or,

$$L_{10} = \frac{10^6(3020)}{60(1800)} = 27,900 \text{ hr}$$

Part 3. Consider a double-row spherical roller bearing of the dimension series 22. From Table 9-1 we note that $C = 14,700$ lb, and $C_0 = 12.000$ lb. Values of X and Y are obtained from Table 9-7 for a 50-mm bearing bore

$$\frac{F_a}{VF_r} = 0.350 > 0.26 = e \qquad Y = 3.83, X = 0.67 \text{ (see footnote of Table 9-7)}$$

$$P = XVF_r + YF_a = (0.67)(1)(1000) + 3.83(350) = 2010 \text{ lb}$$

$$P = VF_r = 1000 \text{ lb}$$

Using the larger of the two calculated equivalent loads,

$$L_{10} = \left(\frac{C}{P}\right)^b = \left(\frac{14,700}{2010}\right)^{3.33} = 758.5 \times 10^6 \text{ rev}$$

or

$$L_{10} = \frac{10^6(758.5)}{60(1800)} = 7020 \text{ hr}$$

Part 4. Consider a double-row spherical roller bearing of dimension series 23. From Table 9-2, we note that $C = 31,600$ lb, and $C_0 = 26,500$ lb. Values of X and Y are obtained from Table 9-7 for a 50-mm bearing bore.

$$\frac{F_a}{VF_r} = 0.350 < 0.39 \qquad Y = 1.73, \text{ and } X = 1.00 \text{ (see footnote of Table 9-7)}$$

$$P = XVF_r + YF_a = (1)(1)(1000) + 1.73(350) = 1605 \text{ lb}$$

$$P = VF_r = 1000 \text{ lb}$$

Using the larger of the two calculated equivalent loads,

$$L_{10} = \left(\frac{C}{P}\right)^b = \left(\frac{31,600}{1605}\right)^{3.33} = 20,418 \times 10^6 \text{ rev}$$

or

$$L_{10} = \frac{10^6(20,418)}{60(1800)} = 189,000 \text{ hr}$$

From the above calculations, it is readily seen that the single-row deep groove ball bearing and the double-row spherical roller bearing (dimension series 22) do not satisfy the life requirement of 20,000 hr. Therefore, they are eliminated from consideration. Both the single-row spherical roller bearing and the double-row spherical roller bearing (dimension series 23) satisfy the life requirement. However, the double-row spherical bearing is 9.45 times overdesigned. In addition, it is more expensive than the single-row spherical roller bearing. Our choice, therefore, is *the single-row, spherical bearing.* ●

SECTION 9-11

Bearing Survival with Probabilities Higher than 90%

As previously indicated, the definition of rating life was based upon a 10% failure rate (or a 90% survival rate). The AFBMA and manufacturers' catalogs list the bearing capacities to be compatible with this definition. The question that arises is "how can the designer select a bearing with a probability of survival greater than 90%"? Certainly, there are many applications in which the likelihood of failure or catalog survival rate cannot be tolerated (for example, manned space vehicles, medical and hospital equipment, nuclear power plant controls, and so on).

The AFBMA has recognized the need for providing reliability adjustment factors and has published such data in its latest (1972) standards. These data are given for reliabilities of 90, 95, 96, 97, 98, and 99%. To avoid the need for interpolation, we have plotted these values in Figure 9-37. This curve can be applied to both ball and roller bearings but is restricted to reliabilities no greater than 99%.

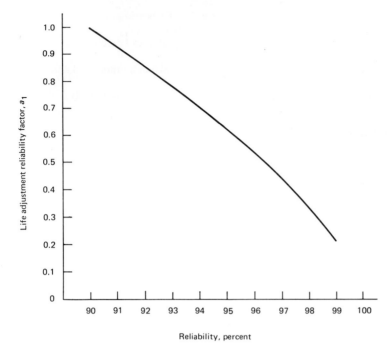

Figure 9-37 Life adjustment relating factor, a_1.

Example 9-4. Let us assume that in Example 9-1 only a 5% probability of failure can be permitted (that is, 95% reliability). What can the designer expect the rating life to be for this 309 bearing?

Solution: From Figure 9-37, for a reliability of 95.0%, $a_1 = 0.62$. Thus

$$L_5 = a_1 L_{10} = a_1 \left(\frac{C}{P}\right)^3 = 0.62(40 \times 10^6) = 24.8 \times 10^6 \text{ rev}$$

or

$$L_5 = 0.62(445) = 276 \text{ hr} \quad \text{and} \quad \text{median life} = 5(276) = 1380 \text{ hr}$$

In order to improve the reliability of the 309 bearing of Example 9-1 from 90 to 95.0%, a reduction of rating life from 40×10^6 rev to 24.8×10^6 rev is required. ●

Example 9-5. A single-row deep groove ball bearing with a bore diameter not to exceed 45 mm (1.7717 in.) is to be selected. The bearing is to withstand a 400-lb radial load and a 100-lb thrust load at 1000 rpm. It is desired that the bearing have a rating life of 5000 hr with a failure probability of 6.0%. Select the bearing if the inner ring is rotating.

Solution:

$$\frac{F_a}{VF_r} = \frac{100}{1(400)} = 0.250$$

Inspection of Table 9-5 leads us to a first guess, namely that

$$\frac{F_a}{VF_r} = 0.250 < e$$

Thus, we use $X = 1$ and $Y = 0$

$$P = XVF_r + YF_a = (1)(1)(400) + (0)(100) = 400 \text{ lb}$$

$$P = VF_r = 400 \text{ lb}$$

From equation (9-3), we have

$$C = P\left(\frac{n \times 60 \times L_{10}}{10^6}\right)^{1/3} = 400\left(\frac{1000 \times 60 \times 5000}{10^6}\right)^{1/3} = 2680 \text{ lb}$$

From Figure 9-37 for a 6.0% probability of failure, we find $a_1 = 0.70$. Thus we must find a single-row deep groove bearing with $C = 2680/(0.70)^{1/3} = 3018$ lb. ●

Inspecting Table 9-1 under the column for dimension series 02, we find a bearing with the following data: bore diameter $= 30$ mm (1.1811 in.); $C = 3360$ lb; $C_0 = 2250$ lb.

As a check of our original guess, we calculate

$$\frac{iF_a}{C_0} = \frac{1(100)}{2250} = 0.0444$$

Inspection of Table 9-5 shows that for this value of iF_a/C_0, e is greater than 0.250. Thus our original assumption is justified, namely $X = 1$ and $Y = 0$ when $F_a/VF_r \leqslant e$. Thus the bearing selected is satisfactory.

SECTION 9-12

Life Adjustment Factors for Materials

The basic dynamic capacity ratings as defined by the AFBMA (see Section 9-9) are predicated on the use of air-melted AISI 52100 steel with a minimum through hardness of 58 Rockwell C. However, an improved air-melting process and the introduction of carbon-vacuum degassed (CVD)[23] steel has resulted in steels of higher quality.

Thus better steels, higher quality forming methods, improved control of heat treatment and overall manufacturing techniques have resulted in life increases of 3–8 times that of L_{10} [13]. In fact in using consumable electrode vacuum-remelted (CVM)[24] steel, extraordinarily long bearing lives were experienced.

The AFBMA, has recognized this life improvement but considers all of these improved steels as a special category and therefore suggests that the

[23] This is currently the most common process for producing bearing steels.

[24] The process called CVM (consumable electrode vacuum remelting) results in a steel of even higher quality than that produced by the CVD process (see reference [13]).

designer obtain the materials adjustment factor a_2 from the manufacturer.

However, the *AFBMA Standard* does indicate that "the ball bearing industry currently uses an a_2 factor of 3 for radial ball bearings of good quality."[25]

For CVM steels, reference [13] also recommends a factor of 3. For a "normal" bearing material (that is, air-melted and through-hardened steel), reference [13] lists factors that range from 0.2 to 2.0. Of particular significance is the fact that the most common bearing material, AISI 52100 is assigned the factor of 2.0 based on the results of having fatigue tested a 207 ball bearing. This results in a bearing life 100% longer than would be normally calculated from equation (9-2). The reader is advised to use this factor a_2 with caution and only after careful consideration of all the parameters that can affect the fatigue life of a bearing.

SECTION 9-13

Life Adjustment Factor for Application Conditions

By deductive reasoning, it is not difficult to realize that bearing life can be (and is) significantly affected by application conditions. Accordingly the AFBMA suggests the following be considered in determining the life of a bearing: (1) lubrication, (2) load distribution (including the effects of clearance, misalignment, housing and shaft stiffness, type of loading, and thermal gradients), and (3) temperature. The life factor determined by (2) and (3) should be obtained from the bearing manufacturer.[26]

Where lubrication (that is, item 1) is adequate, an a_3 factor of 1 is recommended. However, a_3 might conceivably be less than 1 when any of the following conditions prevail:

1. Exceptionally low values of nd_m (revolutions per minute times ball pitch diameter in millimeters), for example, $nd_m < 10,000$. This requirement is applicable to both ball and roller bearings.
2. Lubricant viscosity is less than 70 SUS (100 SUS for roller bearings) at operating temperature.
3. Excessively high operating temperature.

If any of these conditions exist in a particular application, the designer should obtain an appropriate value of a_3 from the manufacturer before making a final bearing selection.

---

[25] Although not a part of the *AFBMA Standard*, reference [13] contains a list of adjustment factors which makes a distinction between bearing materials and processes.

[26] Reference [13] contains quantitative values for such parameters as lubrication, speed, and misalignment. However, these values have not been sanctioned by the AFBMA and if used should be applied with caution.

SECTION 9-14

Summary of Life Adjustment Factors

From the previous discussion an adjusted fatigue life equation can be expressed as

$$L'_n = a_1 a_2 a_3 \left(\frac{C}{P}\right)^b \tag{9-6}$$

where L'_n = the adjusted fatigue life of the bearing with a failure probability of n, and $a_1 a_2 a_3$ = factors as defined respectively in Sections 9-11, 9-12, and 9-13.

The designer should be forewarned not to apply the life adjustment factors indiscriminately because this may lead to an overly optimistic estimation of the bearing endurance life. Uncertain parameters such as shaft size, misalignment, temperature gradients, and so on, can cause equation (9-6) to be invalid.

Most situations requiring the selection of a bearing are routine. But where special requirements must be satisfied, the designer would do well to discuss his problem(s) with the manufacturer.

SECTION 9-15

Rolling Element Bearings Subjected to Variable Loads

There are many applications where a bearing is subjected to both variable loading and changing speed during each revolution. A designer could select a bearing for the most severe loading condition. However, this viewpoint is rather conservative and could be unnecessarily expensive, particularly if production required the use of many such bearings. What is needed, therefore, is a relationship that will relate load rating C and rating life L_{10} for varying loads.

Rearranging equation (9-2), we have

$$C^3 = \frac{60 n L_{10}}{10^6} P^3 \tag{9-7}$$

If during a fraction of cycle p_m the speed n_m and equivalent load P_m are constant, we express equation (9-7) as a summation of the effect of n_m and P_m on each fraction of a cycle. Thus, we obtain

$$C^3 = \frac{60 L_{10}}{10^6} \sum_{m=1}^{q} p_m n_m P_m^3 \tag{9-8}$$

where

C = the required basic load rating, lb
L_{10} = rating life, hr (for a probability of failure of 10%)
p_m = fraction of a cycle
n_m = speed during fraction of a cycle, rpm
P_m = equivalent load during a fraction of a cycle, lb

Example 9-6. A $2\frac{1}{2}$-in. diameter shaft of a machine operates continuously for 8 hr daily. Because of an overrunning clutch, one of the shaft bearings will be subjected to a varying load and speed cycle as follows:

Fraction of the Cycle	F_r, lb	F_a, lb.	RPM	Load Conditions
$\frac{1}{10}$	800	400	1000	Steady
$\frac{1}{10}$	400	400	1500	Light shock
$\frac{1}{2}$	1000	400	1200	Light shock
$\frac{3}{10}$	500	400	1500	Steady

Find a ball or roller bearing that will satisfy the given conditions. The inner ring rotates.

Solution: Referring to Table 9-9, we shall assume a design life of 25,000 hr (based upon a reliability of 90%). Also, from Table 9-8, shock factors for the given conditions are:
For ball bearings:

$$F_s(\text{steady load}) = 1.0$$

$$F_s(\text{light shock}) = 1.5$$

For roller bearings:

$$F_s(\text{steady load}) = 1.0$$

$$F_s(\text{light shock}) = 1.0$$

As a trial selection, we shall try a 312 single-row deep groove ball bearing. From Table 9-2 for a 60-mm ($12 \times 5 = 60$) bearing bore, we have $C = 14,100$ lb and $C_0 = 10,900$ lb. We now proceed to calculate the equivalent load for each fraction of the cycle.

For the first tenth of the cycle:

$$\frac{F_a}{VF_r} = \frac{400}{(1)(800)} = 0.50$$

For the second tenth of the cycle:

$$\frac{F_a}{VF_r} = \frac{400}{(1)(400)} = 1.00$$

For the next half of the cycle:

$$\frac{F_a}{VF_r} = \frac{400}{(1)(1000)} = 0.40$$

For the remaining three tenths of the cycle:

$$\frac{F_a}{VF_r} = \frac{400}{(1)(500)} = 0.80$$

$$\frac{iF_a}{C_6} = \frac{(1)(400)}{10,900} = 0.0367$$

and by interpolation, $e = 0.232$.

We can readily see that all of the values of F_a/VF_r are greater than $e = 0.232$. Thus, from Table 9-5, $X = 0.56$ and, by interploation, $Y = 1.922$. From equation (9-4), we now can calculate the equivalent load P for each fraction of the cycle.

$$P = XVF_r + YF_a$$

$$P(\tfrac{1}{10}\text{ cycle}) = (0.56)(1)(800) + (1.922)(400) = 1217\text{ lb}$$

$$P(\tfrac{1}{10}\text{ cycle}) = (0.56)(1)(400) + (1.922)(400) = 993\text{ lb}$$

$$P(\tfrac{1}{2}\text{ cycle}) = (0.56)(1)(1000) + (1.922)(400) = 1329\text{ lb}$$

$$P(\tfrac{3}{10}\text{ cycle}) = (0.56)(1)(500) + (1.922)(400) = 1049\text{ lb}$$

Now, we can substitute into equation (9-8), remembering to account for the shock factors, F_s.

$$C^3 = \frac{60(25,000)}{10^6}[\tfrac{1}{10}(1000)(1.0 \times 1217)^3 + \tfrac{1}{10}(1500)(1.5 \times 933)^3$$

$$+ \tfrac{1}{2}(1200)(1.5 \times 1329)^3 + \tfrac{3}{10}(1500)(1.0 \times 1049)^3]$$

$$C = 20,650\text{ lb}$$

Because the required basic load rating is larger than the load rating of the 312 bearing (that is, $20,650 > 14,100$), we cannot use this bearing. Inspection of Table 9-2 discloses that a 316 single-row deep groove bearing with a $C = 21,300\text{ lb}$ is the smallest one that can be used. But its bore diameter is 80 mm (3.1496 in.), exceeding the $2\tfrac{1}{2}$-in. shaft diameter, so it cannot be considered.

Referring again to Table 9-2 under the dimension series 23, we now try a double-row spherical roller bearing with a 45-mm (1.7717 in.) bore. For this bearing $C = 25,000\text{ lb}$ and $C_0 = 20,600\text{ lb}$. As above, we must calculate the equivalent load for each fraction of the cycle.

The value of F_a/VF_r for each fraction of the cycle calculated above remains the same for the spherical roller bearing. We see that each of the values for F_a/VF_r is greater than the value of $e (= 0.39)$ found in Table 9-7 for a 45-mm bore bearing of the dimension series 23. Thus, $X = 0.67$ and $Y = 2.59$. The equivalent load for each cycle fraction can now be calculated.

$$P(\tfrac{1}{10}\text{ cycle}) = (0.67)(1)(800) + (2.59)(400) = 1572\text{ lb}$$

$$P(\tfrac{1}{10}\text{ cycle}) = (0.67)(1)(400) + (2.59)(400) = 1302\text{ lb}$$

$$P(\tfrac{1}{2}\text{ cycle}) = (0.67)(1)(1000) + (2.59)(400) = 1706\text{ lb}$$

$$P(\tfrac{3}{10}\text{ cycle}) = (0.67)(1)(500) + (2.59)(400) = 1371\text{ lb}$$

Substituting these values into equation (9-8) and accounting for the shock factors F_s, we obtain

$$C^3 = \frac{60(25{,}000)}{10^6} [\tfrac{1}{10}(1000)(1.0 \times 1572)^3 + \tfrac{1}{10}(1500)(1.0 \times 1302)^3$$

$$+ \tfrac{1}{2}(200)(1.0 \times 1706)^3 + \tfrac{3}{10}(1500)(1.0 \times 1371)^3]$$

$$C = 19{,}400 \text{ lb}$$

Because 19,400 lb is less than 25,000 lb, the choice of the double-row spherical roller bearing with a 45-mm bore diameter is satisfactory. ●

SECTION 9-16

Lubrication of Rolling Bearings

Satisfactory performance of rolling bearings depends greatly upon the use of the proper lubricant, lubrication frequency, and a housing design that provides adequate lubricant flow. Although the frictional forces produced by a rolling element are comparatively low (see Section 9-7), sliding between the elements, races, and separator (that is, retainer or cage) is a major source of frictional resistance. Two other factors contributing to frictional resistance are the movement of the bearing elements through the lubricant and the deformation of the rolling elements and race when under load. The latter consideration has, in recent times, become a topic of great research interest, particularly when the bearing elements are highly loaded. It is called elastohydrodynamic lubrication.[27]

Specifically, a proper lubricant should satisfy the following requirements:

1. Form a film between the rolling elements and raceways and between the rolling elements and separator.
2. Protect the bearing components against corrosion.
3. Remove the heat generated by the bearing when in operation.
4. Prevent the infiltration of dirt and/or other foreign matter from entering the bearing.

Depending upon load, speed, and temperature requirements, lubricants are either greases or oils. Synthetic and dry lubricants are also widely used for special applications (for example, extreme temperatures, inaccessibility to continuous lubrication, and so on). Greases are suitable for low speed operation and do not require complicated sealing or lubricating systems such as when oils are used. Also, grease permits bearings to be prepacked.

Greases are a mixture of a lubricating oil and a metallic soap or some other vehicle that will keep the oil in suspension (for example, synthetic thickener).

[27] The problems of interest in this area also involve gear tooth contact stress. A good introduction to this subject is a book entitled *Elasto-Hydrodynamic Lubrication*, by D. Dawson and G. R. Higginson, Pergamon Press, New York. It contains an excellent list of references. The reader should also refer to recent papers published in the *Transactions of the ASME* and *The Journal of Lubrication Technology*, published by the American Society of Lubrication Engineers.

Thickeners used are calcium (that is, lime), sodium, lithium, barium, bentone, aluminum, or synthetic soap bases. Greases are graded according to a hardness rank scale established by the National Lubrication Grease Institute (NGLI), which ranges from 0 to 6 in order of increasing hardness. Hardness grade numbers are determined by standard ASTM penetration tests. Table 9-10 indicates the important operating characteristics and operating conditions of greases having various soap bases.

To prevent "churning" of grease at operating temperature, the bearing housing volume should not be filled with more than one third to one half of its capacity. The housing and shaft design should be such as to "urge" the grease into contact with the bearing. The time periods between regreasing depend upon the load, speed, operating temperature, type of grease used, and environment. These periods can range from 6 months to 2 years. Manufacturers' catalogs usually give regreasing recommendations for normal applications. Typical bearing mountings employing grease as a lubricant are shown in Figures 9-38 and 9-39.

Where bearing speeds are higher or loads are severe, oil becomes the preferred method of lubrication. The most common type of lubricating oil is a mineral oil. Oil, depending upon the desired properties, contains different kinds and quantities of extreme pressure additives, antifoaming, and antioxidation agents. Viscosity ratings for the lubricating oils are usually stated in Saybolt Universal Seconds (SUS) at 100°F, and are graded by SAE, ASTM, or AGMA numbers.

Table 9-10 Important operating characteristics of various greases

Operating Conditions							Characteristics				
Temperature °F			Load		Speed		Grease	NLGI	Dropping Point, °F	Max Operating Temp- °F	Water
Below 40	40–150	Above 150	Low	High	Low	High	Recommended	Number			Resistance
							Lime base	0, 1 or 2	200	150	Good
								2, 3, 4, or 5			
							Sodium base	0, 1 or 2	325	250	Poor
								2, 3 or 4			
							Lithium base	0, 1 or 2	Above 350	300	Good
								2 or 3			
							Barium base	0, 1 or 2	> 400	300	
								2 or 3			
							Bentone base	1	> 500	450	
								2			

SOURCE: *Bearings Book Issue, Machine Design.* The Penton Publishing Co., Cleveland, Ohio, 1963.

NOTES: 1. Grease should contain oxidation inhibitor.
2. Grease should contain EP additives if loads are abnormally high.
3. Under operating conditions, use areas that are cross hatched.

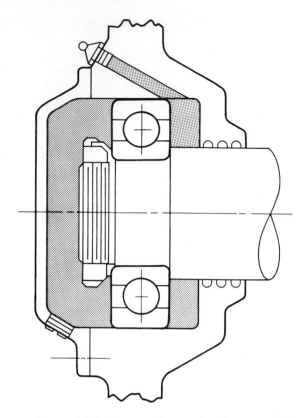

Figure 9-38 Regreaseable mounting. Recommended for moderate speeds and loads. Where prelubricated sealed bearings are not suitable for a particular reason, consideration must be given to the use of an open type bearing with provision for relubrication. The grease plug at the bottom should be removed while the grease is being inserted through the fittings at the top. The direction of flow tends to remove the old grease. [Courtesy Marlin-Rockwell Division of TRW, Inc. Jamestown, N.Y.]

Methods of selecting a lubricating oil vary with different manufacturers. For example, Link-Belt Company makes its selection based on speed, per cent of basic load rating, and operating temperature. The Torrington Company uses operating temperature and speed, where the speed is limited by the bearing size and type. SKF Industries, Inc. attempts to select a lubricant by considering the elastohydrodynamic film formed between the rolling elements and the raceway. The procedure is rather involved and cannot be entered into in this text. Interested readers are advised to contact SKF for specific information. Figure 9-40 is offered here as a simple and straightforward method of selecting a lubricating oil for a rolling bearing. The heavy, dotted line in Figure 9-40 is an example of how to use the chart.

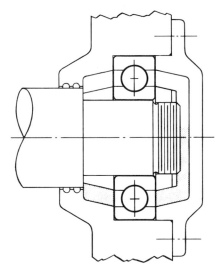

Figure 9-39 High temperature grease mounting. The life of permanently lubricated installations at high temperatures is a function of the volume of grease present, and the design of the mounting. Note that ample grease space has been provided, and that the configuration of parts adjacent to the bearing is such as to urge the lubricant into contact with the active bearing parts. [Courtesy Marlin-Rockwell, Division of TRW, Inc. Jamestown, N.Y.]

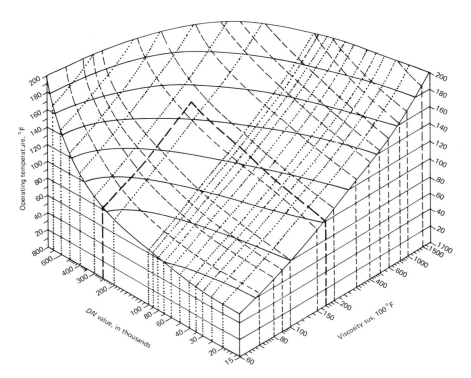

Figure 9-40 Oil viscosity selection chart. The heavy dotted line is an example (that is, a 50-mm bore ball bearing (D), running at a shaft speed of 5000 rpm (N) is to operate at 150°F). Enter the chart at $DN = 50 \times 5000 = 250,000$. Move upward and onto the top surface until the operating temperature of 150°F is reached. Move parallel and down to the right and then vertically down as shown to read the required viscosity is 170 SUS. [Courtesy the Fafnir Bearing Company.]

The amount of oil necessary for adequate lubrication is such that no more than a thin film is provided. When the quantity of oil exceeds that which is required to just form a film on the bearing, frictional torque increases. Only in those cases where the heat generated is an important factor should increased quantities of oil be used—then only where the oil can be circulated or mist sprayed. There are six methods commonly employed for oil lubrication. These are described by the Marlin-Rockwell Company as:

1. **Jet Oil Lubrication.** Oil, under pressure, is forced through an orifice into the bearing. The oil jet is directed at the space between the bore of the cage (that is, separator) and the outer diameter of the inner ring. This means of application is particularly advantageous for heavily loaded, high speed operation. For extremely high speeds, means for scavenging the oil should be provided on each side of the bearing (see Figure 9-41).

2. **Circulating Oil Lubrication.** In this system, oil is circulated through the bearing by slingers or other means. Circulating systems provide a reliable, relatively low cost method of lubricating heavily loaded bearings. More expensive systems use a circulating pump to assure a positive supply of lubricant (see Figure 9-42).

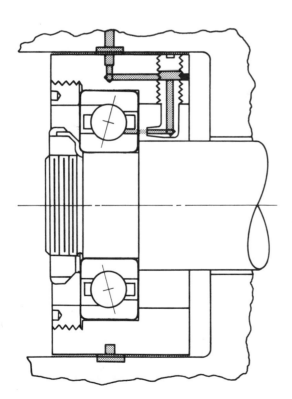

Figure 9-41 Jet oil lubrication. [Courtesy Marlin-Rockwell, Division of TRW Inc., Jamestown, N.Y.

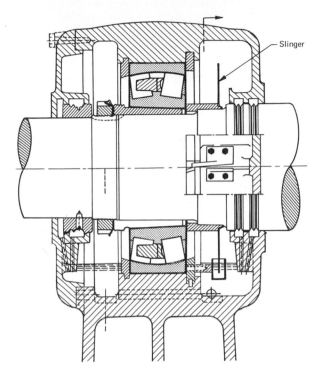

Figure 9-42 Circulating oil lubrication by means of a slinger. [Courtesy SKF Industries, Inc.]

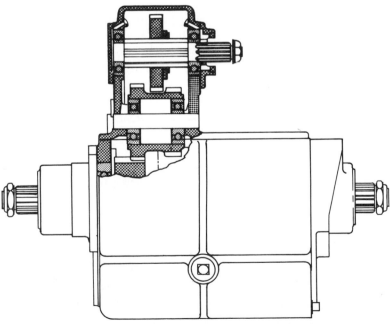

Figure 9-43 Oil splash lubrication. Note the feeder trails in the case to direct the oil washdown into the bearings. [Courtesy Fafnir Bearing Co.]

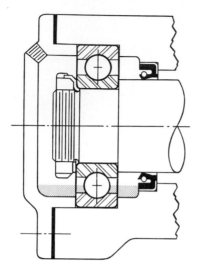

Figure 9-44 Oil bath lubrication. Note that the oil depth is maintained at approximately the level of the midpoint of the lowest ball. [Courtesy Marlin-Rockwell, Division of TRW, Inc., Jamestown, N.Y.]

3. **Oil Splash Lubrication.** The splash system is particularly suitable for oil lubricated gear boxes. The splash from the gears serves to lubricate the bearings. Because the oil carries the debris of wear, the use of filters and magnetic drain plugs is helpful in reducing possible contamination of bearings (see Figure 9-43).

4. **Oil Bath Lubrication.** This form of lubrication is suitable for slower speed applications where an oil reservoir keeps the bearing partially immersed. The oil level should never be higher than the midpoint of the lowest ball (or roller) being lubricated. A larger amount of oil can cause "churning," which increases fluid friction and can cause excessive operating temperatures (see Figure 9-44).

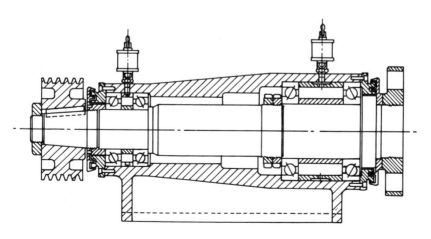

Figure 9-45 Drop feed lubrication. [Courtesy Fafnir Bearing Co.]

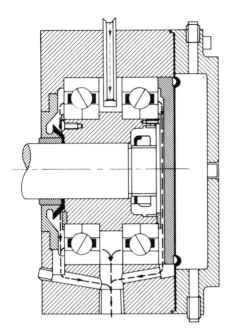

Figure 9-46 Oil-air mist lubrication of a machine tool spindle. The lubricant used is a spindle oil rated at 100 SUS at 100°F. It is delivered at the rate of 40 drops/min into the system under 20 psi air pressure. Precleaning of the air and lubricating lines and effective air filtering is a must for successful operation. [Courtesy Fafnir Bearing Co.]

5. **Drop Feed Lubrication.** This system uses a commercial drop feed oil. It is used where moderate loads and speeds are encountered. The principal disadvantages are the refilling of the oil cup and the provision for the disposal of waste oil (see Figure 9-45).

6. **Air-Oil Mist Lubrication.** In this system, tiny droplets of oil are suspended in an air stream that passes through the bearing. Commercial units are available which provide excellent lubrication for high speed units such as machine tool spindles (see Figure 9-46).

SECTION 9-17

Speed Limitations of Rolling Bearings

Some manufacturers' catalogs provide information concerning the speed limitation imposed on bearings. However, lacking such information, we can determine the approximate limiting speed for rolling bearings. Such information is important because excessive speed for an extended time period can increase the bearing temperature and cause a breakdown in lubrication. This situation would ultimately lead to bearing failure. The temperature rise, caused by friction, is a function of the type of bearing construction, the size of the bearing, and the load it has to carry.

The approximate limiting speed of a ball or roller bearing is given by [11]

$$n = \frac{f_1 f_2 A}{d_m} \tag{9-9}$$

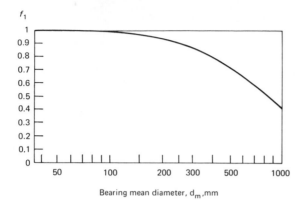

Figure 9-47 Factor f_1 to be used in equations
(9-9) and (9-10). [From Frank W. Wilson (ed.): *Tool
Engineers Handbook*, 2nd ed. McGraw-Hill Book
Co. New York, 1959.]

and for a thrust bearing is

$$n = \frac{f_1 f_2 A}{\sqrt{DH}} \tag{9-10}$$

where

n = approximate speed, rpm, when using oil lubrication (when using grease, reduce this value to $\frac{2}{3}$ for ball bearings, and $\frac{1}{2}$ for roller bearings)

f_1 = a coefficient depending on bearing size, from Figure 9-47

f_2 = a coefficient depending on relative bearing load, from Figure 9-48

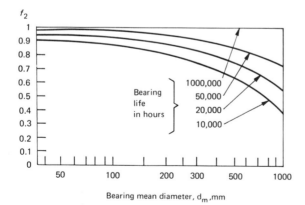

Figure 9-48 Factor f_2 to be used in equations
(9-9) and (9-10). [From Frank W. Wilson (ed.): *Tool
Engineers Handbook*, 2nd ed. McGraw-Hill Book
Co., New York, 1959.]

Table 9-11   Factor A for determining approximate
bearing speed limitation

Bearing Type	Factor A
Radial bearings	
Single-row deep-groove ball bearings	
Ball-centered pressed-steel cage	500,000
Ring-centered machined cage	800,000
Angular-contact ball bearings	
Large-angle ball-centered cage, single	500,000
Large-angle ball-centered cage, duplex	350,000
Small-angle ring-centered cage, single	800,000
Small-angle ring-centered cage, duplex	600,000
Single-row filling-slot ball bearings	500,000
Double-row deep-groove ball bearings	350,000
Self-aligning ball bearings	
Dimension series 02, 12, 22, 03, 04	500,000
Dimension series 23	450,000
Cylindrical roller bearings	
Single-row	500,000
Double-row	450,000
Self-aligning roller bearings	
Dimension series 13, 22, 23	300,000
Dimension series 30, 31, 32	280,000
Tapered roller bearings	
Single-row	300,000
Double-row	280,000
Thrust bearings:	
Ball thrust bearings	
Pressed-steel cage	150,000
Machined-brass cage	200,000
Spherical roller thrust bearings	200,000

SOURCE: Frank W. Wilson (ed.): *Tool Engineers Handbook*, 2nd ed. McGraw-Hill
Book Company, New York, 1959.

A = a value depending on bearing type, from Table 9-11
d_m = bearing mean diameter, mm
D = bearing outer diameter, mm
H = bearing height for a thrust bearing, mm

SECTION 9-18

Seals

Seals perform two very important functions, containment of the lubricant
and keeping foreign matter from entering the bearing area. Earlier in our
description of bearings, we described how some of them are provided with
seals and shields to contain the lubricant and exclude contaminants. However, where bearings are not "self-sealed," provision must be made for
sealing. There are many seal designs, and the selection of any one design
depends on what is expected of the seal, for example, (1) the nature of the
material to be excluded (that is, liquid, solid, powder, and so on, (2) shaft

surface speed, (3) temperature conditions, (4) type of lubricant, (5) permissible leakage, and (6) other environmental and operational conditions.

Due to limitations of space, we cannot enter into a detailed analysis and description of seals.[28] Basically, there are three categories of seals : (1) contact seals, (2) labyrinth or clearance seals, and (3) combinations of contact and labyrinth seals.

Contact seals are available from simple felt stripping to spring loaded lip assemblies. Seals within this category are in intimate contact with the shaft, and require quality shaft finishes. In some cases, surface flatness is within twenty millionths of an inch. Contact seals limit the surface speed of the shaft because of frictional drag and the resulting temperature increase in the bearing area. Depending upon the shaft diameter, seal material, and seal design, shaft rubbing (that is, surface) speeds range between 500 and 1000 ft/min for felt, and from 2000 to 3000 ft/min for lip seals.

Lip seals are made of various materials such as leather, synthetic elastomers, plastics, or laminates. Figure 9-49 illustrates how a felt seal is used in conjunction with a lip seal. Felt seals are used in combination with lip seals and labyrinth seals because of their "wicking effect," which tends to absorb a contaminating liquid that is to be "sealed out" or an oil which is to be "sealed in." Felt seals are good for excluding dirt and foreign solid matter. Lip seals are excellent for sealing solids, liquids, and gases at moderate pressures. For sealing liquids and gases at medium to high pressures and high speeds, an axial type of seal is often used. Although expensive and requiring very precise alignment, the axial type seal is quite effective (see Figure 9-50).

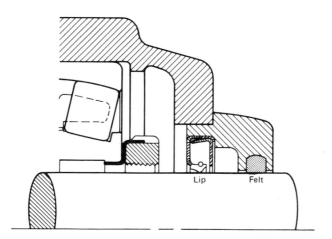

Lip   Felt

Figure 9-49 Felt used in combination with a lip seal. [Courtesy of Link-Belt Bearing Division, FMC Corporation.]

[28] For an in-depth discussion, see the *Seals Symposium Issue, Transactions of the ASME*, Series F, Vol. 90, No. 2, 1968. Also see *Machine Design, 1971 Seals and Reference Issue*, Vol. 43, No. 2.

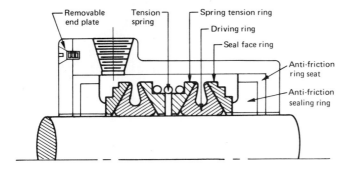

Figure 9-50 Mechanical axial seal. [Courtesy Link-Belt Bearing Division, FMC Corporation.]

Labyrinth or clearance type seals are deliberately designed to provide clearance between the seal and the rotating shaft. Unlike the contact type seal, friction due to rubbing and the subsequent heat generation present no problem for the labyrinth type seal. Consequently, labyrinth seals do not restrict the speed of the rotating shaft. Labyrinth seals are generally not used to seal against pressure or for applications that require the bearing to be submerged in liquids or solids. Labyrinth type seals range from simple low-clearance shaft openings (see Figure 9-51) to a complex system of labyrinths, flingers, and baffles (see Figure 9-52). Labyrinth seals are constructed of metal or plastic, the choice depending upon corrosive environments, temperature conditions, abrasive materials, and so on.

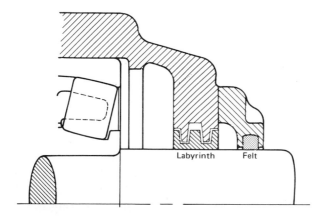

Figure 9-51 Felt used in combination with a labyrinth seal. [Courtesy Link-Belt Bearing Division, FMC Corporation.]

Figure 9-52 Variations of labyrinth seals. [Courtesy Link-Belt Division, FMC Corporation.]

SECTION 9-19

Typical Bearing Assemblies

It is important that the designer specify the correct shaft and housing tolerances for mounting a bearing. For a rotating shaft, the inner ring of a bearing has a tight (that is, interference) to a *slightly* loose fit with the shaft, whereas the outer ring has a loose to *slightly* tight fit with the housing. For a mounting with a rotating housing, the converse of these fits applies. The type of fit depends upon the bearing size and the ABEC number. Manufacturers' catalogs contain detailed tables specifying the shaft and housing tolerances for each ABEC number. A design that does not use the data in these tables invariably leads to early or even immediate bearing failure.

Actual mounting arrangements vary widely and depend upon the type of bearing used and the application being considered. The Marlin-Rockwell Company suggests five basic mounting designs for single-row and double-row ball bearings which are used in the majority of applications. These mounting designs are shown in Figures 9-53 to 9-57. Aspects of these designs can also be used for rolling bearings. It would be wiser, however, to consult the manufacturers' catalogs for specific recommendations.

The standard mounting (Figure 9-53) is the ideal mounting for a shaft supported by two ball bearings. It has the following advantages:

1. Permits one bearing to take an axial load in either direction.
2. Axial shaft expansion is provided for by the "floating" of the unclamped bearing.
3. Bearings cannot be axially preloaded through improper adjustment of the lock nuts. The lock nuts serve to clamp the bearing inner rings against the shaft shoulder.
4. Mounting arrangement is suitable for a wide range of speed and temperature conditions.

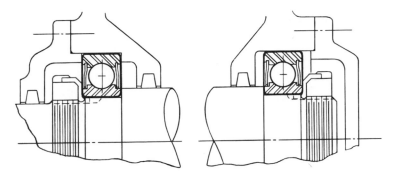

Figure 9-53 Standard mounting. [Courtesy Marlin-Rockwell Division of TRW, Inc., Jamestown, N.Y.]

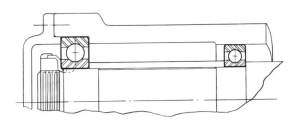

Figure 9-54 Standard mounting with a spacer. [Courtesy Marlin-Rockwell Division of TRW, Inc., Jamestown, N.Y.]

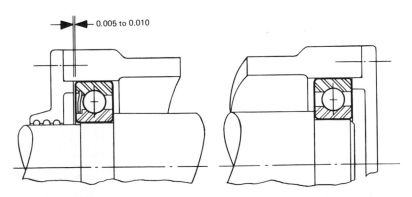

Figure 9-55 Mounting using no lock nut or snap-rings. [Courtesy Marlin-Rockwell Division of TRW, Inc., Jamestown, N.Y.]

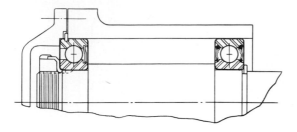

Figure 9-56 Mounting with a lock nut and snap-ring. [Courtesy Marlin-Rockwell Division of TRW, Inc., Jamestown, N.Y.]

An alternate bearing mounting to that shown in Figure 9-53 is the one shown in Figure 9-54. This design is used where the bearings are assembled from one end of the shaft. Note that the inner rings of both bearings, along with the spacer which separates them, are clamped against the shaft shoulder by means of only one lock nut at the end of the shaft. The advantages of this mounting design are the same as the ones cited above.

The bearing mounting design shown in Figure 9-55 does not use nuts on the shaft and permits a "through" bore in the housing. Because of tolerance buildup of the various components, it is difficult to control the axial play of the shaft unless shims are used. These shims are usually mounted between the face of the bearing outer ring and the end cover shoulder. The axial play of the shaft should be sufficiently large to eliminate any possibility of preloading due to thermal expansions, yet small enough to eliminate the effects of any reversing thrust loads. Preferably, this design should be avoided where reversing thrust loads may occur. This mounting design is also adaptable for locations where the shaft length is short.

Another alternate to the mounting illustrated in Figure 9-53 is the one shown in Figure 9-56. Note that this design differs from that shown in Figure

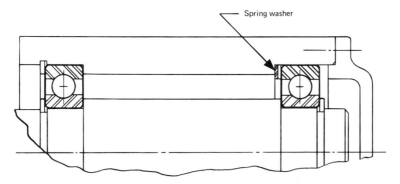

Spring washer

Figure 9-57 Mounting with snap rings and a spring washer. [Courtesy Marlin-Rockwell Division of TRW, Inc., Jamestown, N.Y.]

9-53 in that the bearing on the right end is held on the shaft by a snap-ring which eliminates the lock nut and the necessity of threading the shaft. Also, the use of a snap-ring bearing (shown on the left in Figure 9-56) makes possible a "through" bore housing reducing, thereby, the cost of manufacture.

The last of the five most commonly used bearing mounting designs is shown in Figure 9-57. This particular mounting can be used where both the shaft and housing have shoulders and where the thrust load is minimal. A commercially available spring washer is used to provide a small preload on the bearings, which acts to eliminate shaft end play and contributes to quiet bearing operation.

SECTION 9-20

Selection of Tapered Roller Bearings

Limitations of space preclude a discussion of the procedure required to select a tapered roller bearing. However, bearing manufacturers such as The Timken Bearing Company and The Torrington Company provide literature which in "stepwise" fashion clearly illustrates the selection of this type of bearing.

PROBLEMS

1. Explain why deep groove bearings are capable of supporting relatively high thrust loads.

2. Explain why filling notch bearings can support higher radial loads than deep groove bearings of comparable size.

3. Why is the thrust capacity of the filling notch bearing less than a deep grove bearing of comparable size?

4. With double-row bearings, the lines of contact converge either inside or outside the bearing envelope depending on the bearing type. Explain how this convergence affects the rigidity of the shaft and how it may be used to advantage for particular applications.

5. What is the primary characteristic difference between a deep groove bearing and an angular-contact bearing?

6. Explain duplexing of angular-contact bearings. What is the purpose of duplexing?

7. Why are roller type bearings used? What magnitude of thrust load can they withstand?

8. What is the most important advantage gained in using needle bearings? Can you cite any examples?

9. List some applications where tapered roller bearings are used. Explain why they are used for these applications.

10. What is the most common material used for making ball bearings? What material is used for making roller bearings? For each of the above bearing types, what is the approximate hardness for the material indicated? What temperature limits the use of these materials?

11. Explain the purpose of having seals on bearings. Explain the purpose of having shields on bearings.

12. Why are ball separators used? Why is it detrimental when they are not in the bearing?

13. Explain the basis for bearing failure. What is meant by spalling?

14. What is the meaning of L_{10} (or B-10) life of a roller bearing? How does this compare with the median life of a bearing?

15. Explain rating life and basic load rating.

16. (a) A single-row deep-groove ball bearing with a 60-mm bore rotates at 1000 rpm while having to withstand a 1000-lb radial load. Calculate the horsepower lost due to friction. (b) What is the torque at starting? (c) Calculate the starting and running friction horsepower if, in addition to the radial load, a 400-lb thrust load also had to be withstood by the bearing. (d) Repeat the calculation of part (c) for a spherical roller bearing.

17. For a 60-mm bore single-row deep-groove ball bearing of dimension series 02, Table 9.1 lists the following values for the basic dynamic and static load ratings as $C = 9070$ lb, and $C_0 = 6950$ lb. Two of these bearings are to be used to support a shaft with a stationary center load of 2000 lb. The right hand bearing must also support a stationary thrust load of 300 lb. If the speed of the shaft is constant at 1000 rpm, determine (a) the L_{10} rating life in revolutions and in hours for each bearing, (b) the median life in hours for each bearing, (c) the expected life of each bearing if the equivalent load for each were increased by 50%, (d) the equivalent load for each bearing if operating life were increased 100% above the L_{10} rating life, and (e) the basic number of this bearing that one finds listed in industrial catalogs.

18. Repeat Problem 17 (except part e) using the same loading and speed conditions but for a 1.5-in. bore single-row spherical bearing.

19. Repeat Problem 17 (except part e) using the same loading and speed conditions for a 60-mm bore (dimension series 22), double-row spherical roller bearing.

20. Repeat Problem 17 (except part e) for a rotating outer ring, but stationary inner ring.

21. A 30-mm bore (dimension series 02) single-row angular-contact ball bearing has a 30 deg contact angle (assume this as a steep angle). If the bearing carries a 700-lb radial load and a 1200-lb thrust load and the inner ring rotates at 1500 rpm, determine the rating life in hours.

22. Repeat Problem 21 if the contact angle is 5 deg (that is, considered small).

23. Repeat Problem 21 if the bearing is a single-row deep-groove type.

24. A vertically mounted centrifuge basket and shaft weighs 500 lb and can be filled with as much as 1000 lb of material. If the load is centered on the shaft, select an angular contact ball bearing (from Table 9-2) which will fit a nominal shaft diameter of $3\frac{3}{4}$ in. which rotates at 3000 rpm. Considering the application, select an appropriate service factor from Table 9-8. What is the rating life of the bearing selected? If the centrifuge is used intermittently, how does this life compare to that which is recommended in Table 9-9? To increase the life of the bearing, could you recommend another type of bearing from Table 9-2? If so, what would be the new rating life? For each of the bearings selected, specify the bearing number that would identify either of these bearings in any commercial catalog.

25. For Problem 24, select a bearing to support the upper part of the vertical shaft. Keep in mind that all of the thrust load is carried by the lower bearing.

26. (a) An overhead crane trolley runs at 60 ft/min on four 8-in. diameter wheels and is to have a capacity of 4 tons. The wheels are to be mounted on cylindrical type roller bearings which are supported by nonrotating shafts $1\frac{3}{4}$ in. in diameter. Assuming that the type of service will, at times, subject the crane to moderate shock, select an appropriate bearing for a minimum life of 8000 hr of operation. (b) What would be the expected life of the bearing selected in part (a) if the following considerations were explored: (1) Desired reliability is 96%. (2) Full advantage is taken of the AISI 52100, CVM type steel. (3) Normal application conditions (however, check nd_m value).

27. A spindle for a deburring machine is to be supported by two bearings. The burr, located outside of the bearing supports, is to rotate at 4000 rpm. Under the most severe conditions, the bearing closest to the burr will experience a radial load of 250 lb and an axial load of 150 lb. The bearing furthest from the burr will experience only a radial load of 200 lb. If the shaft is subjected to a light shock loading and cannot exceed $1\frac{1}{2}$ in. in diameter, select suitable bearings for this operation. What is the rating life in hours for the bearings selected? Compare this life to the suggested hours of operation indicated in Table 9-9 assuming the machine will be in continuous operation for 8 hr/day. If the operating temperature of the bearings is not to exceed 120°F, what must the viscosity of the lubricating oil be? Check the bearings selected to see if the required operating speed exceeds its speed limitation.

28. A deep groove ball bearing is subjected to the following cyclic radial loading: 500 lb for $\frac{2}{3}$ of a revolution, and 250 lb for $\frac{1}{3}$ of a revolution. If the shaft is rotating at a speed of 500 rpm, determine the basic load rating to be used in selecting a bearing with a life of 10,000 hrs.

29. A shaft is subjected to the varying radial load per cycle as follows: 600 lb for 1 sec, 200 lb for 2 sec, and 100 lb for 3 sec. If the shaft rotates at a constant speed of 500 rpm what basic load rating for each fraction of the cycle should be used in selecting a bearing with a life of 15,000 hrs?

30. Determine the equivalent load for the following cyclic radial loading for a life of 20,000 hr: 100 lb at 1000 rpm for 30% of the time, 80 lb at 5000 rpm for 60% of the time, and 50 lb at 2000 rpm for 10% of the time. Select the smallest possible deep groove ball bearing that will satisfy this load. What is the "core number" of this bearing that would appear in a commercial bearing designation? Check the bearing for speed limitation.

31. A number 312 deep groove ball bearing is subjected to the following loading cycle: for 20% of the time, the radial load is 1000 lb and the axial load is 500 lb at 700 rpm, for 50% of the time, the radial load is 1200 lb, and the axial load is 300 lb at 1000 rpm, for 30% of the time, the radial load is 600 lb, and the axial load is 400 lb at 1500 rpm. Determine (a) the equivalent load, (b) the rating life, (c) the mean life. The loads are steady and the inner ring rotates.

32. Repeat Problem 31 but this time account for mild shock for the initial 20% of the time, and heavy shock for the last 30% of the time. In addition to answering the same questions asked in Problem 31, determine the bearing life for 97% reliability.

REFERENCES

[1] Stribeck (H. Hess, tr.): Ball bearings for various loads. *Trans. ASME*, **29**: 420–463 (1907).

[2] H. Hertz: *Gesamlte Werke (Collected Works)*, Vol. 1. Leipzig, Germany, 1895, p. 157.

[3] Arvid Palmgren: *Ball and Roller Bearing Engineering*, 3rd ed. SKF Industries, Inc., Philadelphia, Pa., 1959.

[4] Tedric A. Harris: *Rolling Bearing Analysis: Theory and Analysis*. John Wiley & Sons, Inc., New York, 1966.

[5] Harold A. Rothbart (ed.): *Mechanical Design and Systems Handbook*, Sect. 13. McGraw-Hill Book Co., New York, 1964.

[6] 1970 Bearings Reference Issue, *Machine Design*. The Penton Publishing Co., Cleveland, Ohio.

[7] *Standards of the Anti-Friction Bearing Manufacturers Association*. New York, 1972.

[8] *Bearing Technical Journal*. FMC Corp., Link-Belt Bearing Division, Indianapolis, Ind., 1970.

[9] G. Lundberg and A. Palmgren: Dynamic capacity of roller bearings, *Acta Polytech., Mech. Eng. Ser. (Stockholm)*, **1**(3), 1947.

[10] G. Lundberg and A. Palmgren: Dynamic capacity of roller bearings. *Acta Polytech. Mech. Eng. Ser. (Stockholm)*, **2**(4), 1947.

[11] Frank W. Wilson (ed.): *Tool Engineers Handbook*, 2nd ed. McGraw-Hill Book Co., New York, 1959.

[12] *Central Catalogue and Engineering Data*. SKF Industries, Philadelphia, Pa.,

[13] E. N. Bamber, et al.: *Life Adjustment Factors for Ball and Roller Bearings*. American Society of Mechanical Engineers, New York, 1971.

[14] *Bearings Book Issue, Machine Design*. The Penton Publishing Co., Cleveland, Ohio, 1963.

10

Spur Gears

SYMBOLS

a = addendum
b = width of gear
C = clearance
c = center distance
C_f = surface condition factor
C_m = load distribution factor
C_o = overload factor
C_p = elastic properties coefficient
C_s = size factor
C_v = dynamic factor
d = pitch diameter
d_b = base circle diameter
d_o = outside diameter
E = modulus of elasticity
F_b = bending load
F_d = dynamic load
F_n = normal load
F_r = radial load
F_t = tangential force
F_w = wear load
hp = horsepower
I = geometry factor for wear
J = geometry factor for bending
K = wear load factor
K_f = fatigue stress concentration factor
K_L = life factor
K_m = load distribution factor
K_o = overload factor

K_R = factor of safety (reliability factor)
K_S = size correction factor
K_T = temperature factor
K_t = theoretical stress concentration factor
n = speed, rpm
N_t = number of teeth
P = diametral pitch
p = circular pitch
q = notch sensitivity factor
R = carburized Rockwell hardness number
r = pitch circle radius
r_a = addendum circle radius
r_b = base circle radius
r_c = radius of curvature
r_v = velocity ratio
S_o = allowable static stress
S_e = allowable surface endurance limit
T = torque
t = tooth thickness
V_p = pitch line velocity
Y, y = Lewis form factor
μ = Poisson's ratio
σ = actual stress
ϕ = pressure angle
ω = angular velocity

This chapter will present a detailed analysis of spur gears. A brief review of terminology and kinematics will be followed by a complete discussion of the stresses and other factors that influence spur gear design.

SECTION 10-1

Spur Gear Terminology

Because it is assumed that the reader already has an understanding of the kinematics of spur gearing, only a brief review of this topic will be given. Although many good texts are available, reference [1] is suggested for those who wish a more detailed review.

Spur gears are used to transmit power and rotary motion between parallel shafts. As can be seen in Figure 10-1, the teeth are cut parallel to the axis of the shaft on which the gears are mounted. The smaller of two gears in mesh is called the **pinion,** and the larger is customarily designated as the **gear.** In most applications the pinion is the driving element whereas the gear is the driven element. There are some applications, as in epicyclic gear trains, Figure 10-2, for which gears with teeth cut on the inside of the rim are needed. Such a gear is known as an **internal gear.**

The important definitions and geometric properties of external and internal spur gears are presented in Figures 10-3 and 10-4.

The circular pitch, p, of a spur gear is defined as the distance, on the pitch circle, from a point on a tooth to the corresponding point of the adjacent tooth. The diametral pitch is defined as the number of teeth of the gear divided by the pitch circle diameter.

From these definitions it is clear that the following equations hold:

$$p = \frac{\pi d}{N_t} \tag{10-1}$$

Figure 10-1 The spur gears shown have their teeth cut parallel to the axis of the shaft on which the gears are mounted. The smaller of the two meshing gears is called the pinion; the larger is simply designated as the gear. [Courtesy Illinois Gear Division, Wallace Murray Corporation.]

Figure 10-2 The large gear, in the epicyclic gear set shown, has its teeth cut on the inside and is known as an internal gear. [Courtesy Fairfield Manufacturing, La Fayette, Ind.]

where p = circular pitch in inches; d = diameter of pitch circle in inches; and N_t = number of teeth of the gear.

$$P = \frac{N_t}{d} \qquad (10\text{-}2)$$

where P = diametral pitch, and

$$Pp = \pi \qquad (10\text{-}3)$$

The diametral pitch determines the relative size of gear teeth as can be seen from Figure 10-5. In order for two gears to mesh, they must have the same pitch.

When two gears are in mesh, the distance between the centers of the two gears, is equal to one half the sum of their pitch diameters. In equation form

$$c = \frac{d_1 + d_2}{2} \qquad (10\text{-}4)$$

In Figure 10-3, the center distance, c, is shown.

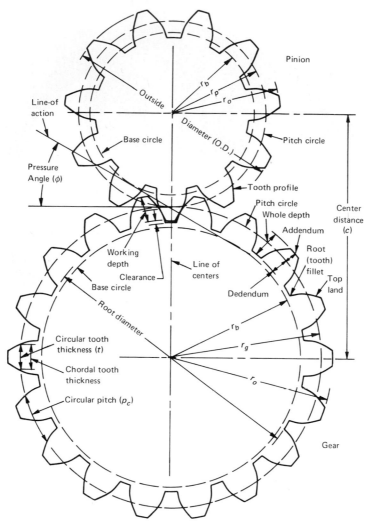

Figure 10-3 The basic geometry and nomenclature of a meshed spur gear set is shown. Some of the important features of gear design that are shown include center distance, pitch circle diameters, tooth size, number of teeth, and pressure angle. [Courtesy Designatronics, Mineola, N.Y.]

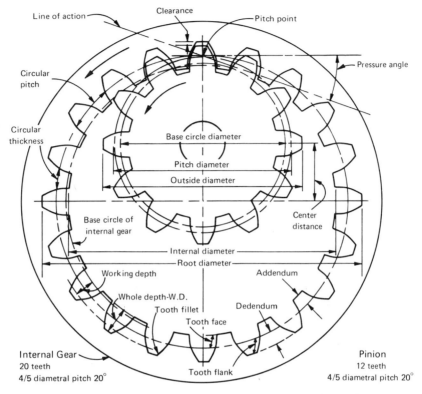

Figure 10-4 The basic geometry and nomenclature of a meshed internal gear and pinion are shown. [Courtesy Fellows Corporation.]

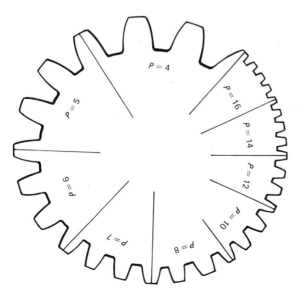

Figure 10-5 The effect of the value of the diametral pitch in the relative size of gear teeth is shown. Clearly, for a given pitch diameter, the smaller the diametral pitch the larger the gear tooth.

SECTION 10-2

Backlash

The space between teeth must be made larger than the gear teeth width as measured on the pitch circle. If this were not the case, the gears could not mesh without jamming. The difference between toothspace and tooth width is known as backlash. Figure 10-6 shows the backlash present between two meshing spur gears. Backlash will be discussed in greater detail in Section 10-19 of this chapter.

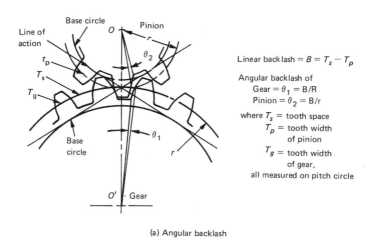

Linear backlash $= B = T_s - T_p$

Angular backlash of
$$\text{Gear} = \theta_1 = B/R$$
$$\text{Pinion} = \theta_2 = B/r$$

where T_s = tooth space
T_p = tooth width
of pinion
T_g = tooth width
of gear,
all measured on pitch circle

(a) Angular backlash

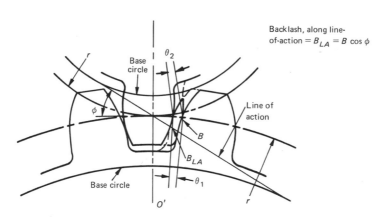

Backlash, along line-
of-action $= B_{LA} = B \cos \phi$

(b) Linear backlash

Figure 10-6 Backlash, the amount by which the width of a tooth space exceeds the thickness of the engaging tooth on the pitch circles is shown. Backlash can be designated as (a) angular, or (b) linear. [Courtesy Designatronics, Mineola, N.Y.]

SECTION 10-3

Fundamental Law of Gearing and Velocity Ratio

In order for two meshing gears to maintain a constant angular velocity ratio, they must satisfy the fundamental law of gearing. This law may be stated as follows: *The shape of the teeth of a gear must be such that the common normal at the point of contact between two teeth must always pass through a fixed point on the line of centers.* When two gears in mesh satisfy the fundamental law, the gears are said to produce conjugate action.

The velocity ratio mentioned in connection with the fundamental law is defined as the ratio of the angular speed of the driven gear to the angular speed of the driver gear. Or, stated another way, it is the ratio of the output speed divided by the input speed. As is obvious from the above definition, the velocity ratio is less than 1 when the pinion is the driver and greater than 1 when the gear is the driver.

There are several useful equations for determining the velocity ratio as indicated by equations (10-5).

$$r_v = \frac{\omega_2}{\omega_1} = \frac{n_2}{n_1} = \frac{N_{t_1}}{N_{t_2}} = \frac{d_1}{d_2} \qquad (10-5)$$

where

r_v = velocity ratio
ω = angular velocity, rad/sec
n = angular velocity, rpm
N_t = number of teeth
d = pitch circle diameter, in.
subscript 1 refers to the driver and subscript 2 refers to the driven gear.

SECTION 10-4

Involute Gear Teeth

In order to obtain conjugate action, most gear profiles are cut to conform to an involute curve. There are a few gears in existence that are cut wholly or partly in the form of a cycloidal curve and are thus able to obtain conjugate action. However, these gears are so few in number that we will consider only the properties of the involute curve.

The involute curve may be constructed graphically by wrapping a string around a cylinder and then tracing the path a point on the string makes as the string is unwrapped from the cylinder. When the involute is applied to gearing, the cylinder around which the string is wrapped is defined as the base circle. Gear teeth are cut in the shape of an involute curve between the base and addendum circles, whereas that part of the tooth between the base and the dedendum circle is generally a radial line.

SECTION 10-5

Gear Tooth Action

To clarify the action that takes place when two gears are in mesh, consider Figure 10-7. Gear number 1 (pinion) is the driver and has its center at O_1, gear number 2 whose center is at O_2 is the driven gear. The pitch circle radii

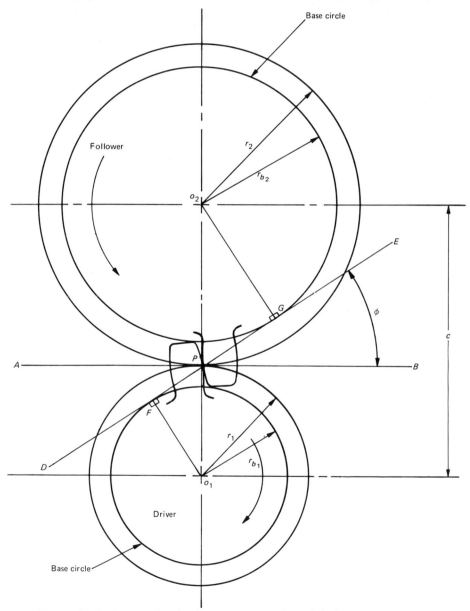

Figure 10-7 Gear tooth action between two gears in mesh is shown.

are r_1 and r_2, and they are mutually tangent along the line of centers, O_1O_2, at the pitch point P.

Line DE is tangent to both base circles, passes through the pitch point, and is normal to the teeth that are in contact because these are the properties of an involute curve. Line DE is, therefore, the line along which all points of contact of two teeth must lie, and also the line along which the normal load that one tooth exerts on the other lies. For these reasons DE is commonly known as the **line of action** or the **pressure line.** Line AB is perpendicular to the line of centers at the pitch point. The angle ϕ, between AB and DE is known as the **pressure angle.** Most gears are cut to operate with standard pressure angles of 20 or 25 deg. A few gears are still manufactured with pressure angles of $14\frac{1}{2}$ deg, but they are used primarily as replacements for gear systems already in existence.

It is extremely important to locate the pressure line properly. The rule to be used is as follows: The pressure line is properly located by rotating from the line perpendicular to the line of centers at the pitch point through an angle equal to the pressure angle ϕ and in a direction opposite to the direction of rotation of the driver. To illustrate, refer again to Figure 10-7. The pressure line, DE, was located by rotating AB through an angle ϕ in the counterclockwise direction, since the driver (gear number 1) was rotating in the clockwise direction.

Finally, by considering triangles O_1FP and O_2GP, the following equations hold

$$r_{b_1} = r_1 \cos \phi$$

$$r_{b_2} = r_2 \cos \phi$$

or, in general

$$r_b = r \cos \phi \tag{10-6}$$

where r_b is the base circle radius in inches.

Example 10-1. A gear has 45 teeth, a diametral pitch of 3, and is cut with $14\frac{1}{2}$ deg full depth teeth. (Table 10-1 is to be used for tooth proportions.)

Determine: (a) The diameter of the base circle and outside diameter, (b) circular pitch, and (c) the clearance as determined by calculating the addendum and dedendum.

Solution:

$$d = \frac{N_t}{P} = \frac{45}{3} = 15 \text{ in.}$$

Part a:

Now

$$d_b = d \cos \phi = 15 \cos 14\frac{1}{2} \text{ deg}$$

$$= 15 \times 0.968 = 14.52 \text{ in.}$$

Table 10-1 Tooth System

	$14\frac{1}{2}$-deg Full Depth	$14\frac{1}{2}$-deg Composite	20-deg Full Depth Involute	20-deg Stub Involute	20-deg Coarse Pitch	20-deg Fine Pitch	25-deg Full Depth Involute
Addendum	$\frac{1}{P}$	$\frac{1}{P}$	$\frac{1}{P}$	$\frac{0.8}{P}$	$\frac{1}{P}$	$\frac{1}{P}$	$\frac{1}{P}$
Dedendum	$\frac{1.157}{P}$	$\frac{1.157}{P}$	$\frac{1.25}{P}$	$\frac{1}{P}$	$\frac{1.25}{P}$	$\frac{1.2}{P} + 0.002$ in.	$\frac{1.25}{P}$
Clearance	$\frac{0.157}{P}$	$\frac{0.157}{P}$	$\frac{0.25}{P}$	$\frac{0.2}{P}$	$\frac{0.25}{P}$	$\frac{0.2}{P} + 0.002$ in.	$\frac{0.25}{P}$
Working depth	$\frac{2}{P}$	$\frac{2}{P}$	$\frac{2}{P}$	$\frac{1.6}{P}$	$\frac{2}{P}$	$\frac{2}{P}$	$\frac{2}{P}$
Whole depth	$\frac{2.157}{P}$	$\frac{2.157}{P}$	$\frac{2.25}{P}$	$\frac{1.8}{P}$	$\frac{2.25}{P}$	$\frac{2.2}{P} + 0.002$ in.	$\frac{2.25}{P}$

and

$$d_0 = d + 2a$$

From table 10-1 $a = 1/P = 0.333$. Then

$$d_0 = 15 + 2 \times 0.333 = 15.667 \text{ in.}$$

Part b:

$$p = \frac{\pi}{P} = \frac{3.1416}{3} = 1.0472 \text{ in.}$$

Part c:

$$\text{clearance} = d_e - a$$

where d_e = dedendum; and a = addendum.

From Table 10-1 $d_e = 1.157/P = 1.157/3 = 0.386$ in.

$$c = 0.386 - 0.333 = 0.053 \text{ in.}$$

As a check, From table 10-1

$$\text{clearance} = \frac{0.157}{P} = \frac{0.157}{3} = 0.052 \text{ in.} \quad \bullet$$

Example 10-2. A gear having a diametral pitch of 4 is to drive another gear at 600 rpm. The velocity ratio is to be $\frac{1}{3}$ and the center distance between the shafts must be 8 in. (a) Determine the number of teeth of each gear. (b) Find the value of the pitch line velocity.

Solution:
Part a:

$$r_v = \frac{d_1}{d_2} = \frac{1}{3}$$

therefore

$$d_2 = 3d_1$$

Because

$$c = \frac{d_1 + d_2}{2} = 8$$

$$d_1 + 3d_1 = 16$$

Therefore

$$d_1 = 4 \text{ in.}$$

and

$$d_2 = 3d_1 = 3 \times 4 = 12 \text{ in.}$$

Now

$$N_{t_1} = d_1 P = 4 \times 4 = 16 \text{ teeth}$$
$$N_{t_2} = d_2 P = 12 \times 4 = 48 \text{ teeth}$$

Part b:

$$V_p = r_1 \omega_1 = \frac{d_2}{2} n_2 \times \frac{2\pi}{60} \times \frac{1}{12}$$

$$= \frac{12}{2} \times \frac{600}{12} \times \frac{2\pi}{60} = 31.416 \text{ ft/sec} \quad \bullet$$

SECTION 10-6

Contact Length and Contact Ratio

When two gear teeth come into mesh, the initial point of contact occurs when the flank of the driver comes into contact with the tip of the driven gear. The contact ends when the tip of the driver tooth comes into contact with the flank of the driven tooth.

Because the tips of gear teeth lie on the addendum circle, contact between two gear teeth starts when the addendum circle of the driven gear intersects the pressure line and ends when the addendum circle of the driver intersects the pressure line.

Figure 10-8 shows the important points in the previous discussion. Contact occurs at point A and ends at point B. The length of contact AB, which can be derived geometrically, is given by equation (10-7)

$$AB = \sqrt{(r_2 + a_2)^2 - r_2^2 \cos^2 \phi} - r_2 \sin \phi$$
$$+ \sqrt{(r_1 + a_1)^2 - r_1^2 \cos^2 \phi} - r_1 \sin \phi \tag{10-7}$$

where r = pitch circle radius in inches; a = length of addendum in inches; and ϕ = pressure angle, degrees.

When two gears are in mesh, it is desirable to have at least one pair of teeth in contact at all times. The method usually employed to indicate how many teeth are in contact is the **contact ratio.** This ratio is defined as the length of contact divided by the base pitch, where the base pitch is defined as the distance measured on the base circle between corresponding points of adjacent teeth. The relationship between the circular pitch and the base pitch is

$$p_b = p \cos \phi \tag{10-8}$$

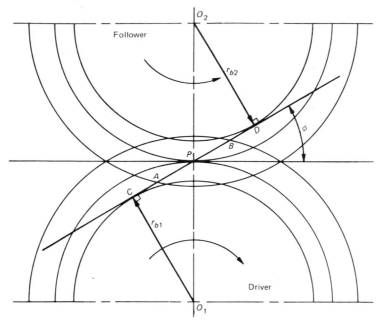

Figure 10-8 The contact length for two gears in mesh is shown.
Contact starts when the flank of the driver touches the tip of the driven
gear and ends when the tip of the driver tooth touches the flank of the
driven tooth.

The contact ratio is therefore given by equation (10-9).

$$\text{contact ratio} = \frac{\sqrt{(r_2 + a_2)^2 - r_2^2 \cos^2 \phi} - r_2 \sin \phi}{p_b}$$
$$+ \frac{\sqrt{(r_1 + a_1)^2 - r_1^2 \cos^2 \phi} - r_1 \sin \phi}{p_b} \qquad (10\text{-}9)$$

Most gears are designed with contact ratios between 1.2 and 1.6. For
example, a ratio of 1.4 means that one pair of teeth is always in contact, and
a second pair is in contact 40% of the time.

Example 10-3. How many teeth will be in contact for a gear set in which the driver
is a 24-tooth 4-diametral pitch 25-deg full depth spur gear and the driven
gear has 48 teeth.

Solution:

$$\text{contact ratio} = \frac{\sqrt{(r_2 + a_2)^2 - r_2^2 \cos^2 \phi} - r_2 \sin \phi}{p_b}$$
$$+ \frac{\sqrt{(r_1 + a_1)^2 - r_1^2 \cos^2 \phi} - r_1 \sin \phi}{p_b}$$

Now

$$r_2 = \frac{d_2}{2} = \frac{N_{t_2}}{2P} = \frac{48}{2 \times 4} = 6 \text{ in.}$$

$$r_1 = \frac{d_1}{2} = \frac{N_{t_1}}{2P} = \frac{24}{2 \times 4} = 3 \text{ in.}$$

From Table 10-1 $a_2 = 1/P = 1/4 = 0.25$ in.; $a_1 = 1/P = 1/4 = 0.25$ in.: $p = \pi/P = 3.1416/4 = 0.7854$ in.; and $p_b = p \cos \phi = 0.7854 \times \cos 25 \deg = 0.7854 \times 0.906 = 0.712$. Therefore

$$\text{contact ratio} = \frac{\sqrt{(6 + 0.25)^2 - 6^2(0.906)^2} - 6 \times 0.423}{0.712}$$

$$+ \frac{\sqrt{(3 + 0.25)^2 - 3^2(0.906)^2} - 3 \times 0.423}{0.712}$$

$$= \frac{\sqrt{39.2 - 29.5} - 2.5 + \sqrt{10.6 - 7.4} - 1.3}{0.712}$$

$$= \frac{3.1 - 2.5 + 1.8 - 1.3}{0.712} = \frac{1.1}{0.712}$$

$$= 1.54 \text{ teeth in contact} \quad \bullet$$

SECTION 10-7

Interference

Because the portion of a gear tooth below the base circle is cut as a radial line and not an involute curve, if contact should occur below the base circle, nonconjugate action would result (fundamental law of toothed gearing would not hold).

The condition for which interference will occur can be demonstrated graphically by considering Figure 10-9. Points A and B, the points of tangency of the base circles with the pressure line, are known as the interference points. If contact occurs outside of these points (if the addendum circle intersects the line of action outside these points), interference will occur. The gears shown in Figure 10-9 will have interference (nonconjugate action) because the points of intersection of the addendum circles C and D lie outside the interference points.

Equation (10-10), derivable from a geometric consideration of Figure 10-9, can be used to determine whether interference will occur.

$$r_a = \sqrt{r^2 \cos^2 \phi + c^2 \sin^2 \phi}$$

$$= \sqrt{r_b^2 + c^2 \sin^2 \phi} \tag{10-10}$$

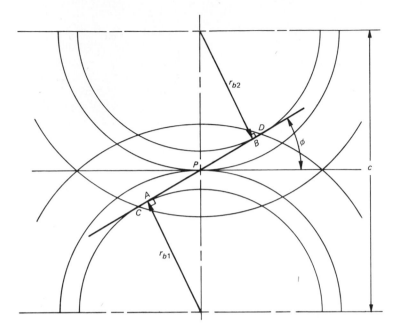

Figure 10-9 When contact between two gears in mesh occurs below the base circle, nonconjugate action results; the resulting condition is called interference. In the figure, interference will occur if contact takes place outside of points *A* or *B*. Since contact for the gears shown occurs at *C* and *D*, interference will result.

where

r_a = radius of addendum circle, in.
c = center distance, in.
ϕ = pressure angle, deg
r_b = base circle radius, in.

Interference will occur when the actual addendum circle radius exceeds the value as calculated by equation (10-10). No interference will occur if the actual is equal to or less than the calculated value.

Example 10-4. Determine whether or not interference will occur for the following gear set. Both driver and driven gear are 2-diametral pitch $14\frac{1}{2}$ deg full depth, with 16 teeth.

Solution:

$$d_1 = d_2 = \frac{N_t}{P} = \frac{16}{2} = 8 \text{ in.}$$

$$c = \frac{d_1 + d_2}{2} = \frac{8 + 8}{2} = 8 \text{ in.}$$

$$r_{b_1} = r_{b_2} = \frac{d_1}{2} \cos \phi = 4 \times \cos 14\tfrac{1}{2} \deg = 4 \times 0.968 = 3.9 \text{ in.}$$

$$r_{a_1} = r_{a_2} = \sqrt{r_{b_1}^2 + c^2 \sin^2 \phi} = \sqrt{(3.9)^2 + 8^2(0.25)^2}$$

$$= \sqrt{15.2 + 4} = 4.38 \text{ in.}$$

the maximum allowable value for radius of the addendum circle. From Table 10-1, $a_1 = 1/P = \tfrac{1}{2} = 0.5$ in. Then the actual

$$r_a = r_1 + a_1 = 4 + 0.5 = 4.5 \text{ in.}$$

Therefore, interference will occur because the actual radius of the addendum circle is greater than the maximum allowable radius. ●

There are several methods available to prevent interference.

1. Undercutting is a procedure in which the portion of the tooth below the base circle causing interference is cut away. Contact therefore does not occur on noninvolute portions of the tooth and, of course, there is no interference. This method has two distinct disadvantages. First, the contact ratio is reduced, resulting in noisier and rougher gear action. Second, the section modulus is reduced at the base of the tooth (increasing the stress), which is already the weakest portion of the tooth.

2. The tooth may be stubbed or, in other words, have a portion of the tip removed. Again, although interference is prevented, the resulting reduced contact ratio produces noisier and rougher gear action.

3. Increasing the pressure angle will decrease the base circle. This in turn increases the involute portion of the tooth profile and thus eliminates interference. However, the increased pressure angle increases the separating force (to be discussed in Section 10-12). Again, the result is poorer gear action.

4. Gears may be cut with long and short addendum gear teeth. For example, the driver may be cut with an increased addendum (the dedendum is decreased proportionately) while the driven gear is cut with a decreased addendum. Obviously, such gears are not standard, therefore not interchangeable, and thus more expensive.

To sum up this discussion, interference must be eliminated, but the method to be used depends largely upon the application and the designer's experience.

SECTION 10-8

Standard Gear Systems

Most gears are manufactured to conform to the standard gear systems set up by national associations such as the American Gear Manufacturers Association (AGMA), the American Standards Association (ASA), and the American Society of Mechanical Engineers (ASME). Obviously, such standardized gears are not only interchangeable but can also be manufactured much more economically. Modern gears are usually manufactured with 20 or 25 deg pressure angles. However, because some gear systems in existence use $14\frac{1}{2}$ deg gears, this type of gear is also manufactured. Table 10-1 lists the proportions for some of the more important standard gear systems. The composite system mentioned in the table has a tooth profile that is an involute for a portion of the tooth and a cycloidal profile for the remainder.

As can be seen in Table 10-1, gears are classified according to type of pitch. Although no standards exist regarding pitch the following list is a good rule of thumb to use

Coarse pitch	$\frac{1}{2} < P < 10$
Medium coarse	$12 < P < 18$
Fine	$20 < P < 128$
Ultra fine	$150 < P < 200$

SECTION 10-9

Common Gear Manufacturing Methods

In this section we will discuss some of the more common methods of manufacturing gears.

Milling cutter

In this procedure, a milling cutter is machined so that it will cut the desired gear tooth space. The cutter is then passed across the gear blank to cut out a space. Then the gear blank is rotated to the proper position and the next space is cut. This procedure is repeated until all of the tooth spaces have been cut. In Figure 10-10 is shown a typical form milling cutter.

There is a disadvantage to this method of manufacture that is sufficiently important as to limit severely the uses of gears cut by this method. Clearly, the cutter can only be used to cut a gear of a certain pitch and a certain number of teeth. In other words, a separate cutter must be used not only for every pitch but for every number of teeth. If the gear manufacturer did this, the cost of a gear would be prohibitive. The usual procedure is to use the same cutter for eight to ten different numbers of teeth at a given pitch. This enables the gears to be manufactured at a more reasonable cost, but obviously only one out of eight or ten gears will be properly cut. As a result the milling cutter method is seldom used, and then only for those applications where accuracy is relatively unimportant.

Generating rack-cutter

In this method, a gear rack is reciprocated across the gear blank-face. After each cut, the rack-cutter is simultaneously rotated through a small angle, and the next cut is made. This procedure is followed until the end of the rack is reached, at which time the rack and blank are repositioned. Figure 10-11 shows a rack-cutter and the gear blank upon which the teeth are being cut.

Figure 10-10 The formed disc cutter shown is usually used to manufacture gears for rough, heavy duty, slow speed applications. The process, which cuts teeth one at a time, is quite economical. [Courtesy Horseburgh-Scott.]

The disadvantages of the rack-cutter are the length of time needed to cut the gear and the inaccuracy that results from the need to reposition the rack. Despite the disadvantages previously mentioned, the rack-cutter is very often used for cutting large gears. This is primarily the case because of the inefficiency of other cutting methods when used to cut very large gears.

Generating gear shaper cutter

This cutting procedure is very similar to the rack-cutter process previously discussed. The primary difference is that the cutting tool is in the form of a gear. The advantages of this type cutter are that it is a true generating procedure because there is no need to reposition the cutter during the cutting operation and the shaping operation permits the generation of internal gears. Figure 10-12 illustrates how an external spur gear is generated with a gear shaper cutter.

The primary disadvantage of this method is that the tooth shape of the cutter is transferred directly to the gear blank, and any error in profile of even one tooth of the cutter will result in errors in the corresponding teeth cut on the blank. However, with care in manufacturing procedures, the generating shaper method is probably the best of the methods discussed to this point.

Figure 10-11 The rack-shaped cutter in the figure is generating an external gear. [Courtesy Horseburgh-Scott.]

Generating hob

Hob generating is another method similar to the rack generation and shaper generation processes previously discussed. The cutting tool is a hob or worm. The hob is drawn across the gear blank, while both hob and blank are being synchronously rotated. The essentials of the hobbing operation are illustrated in Figure 10-13. The primary advantage of the hobbing process is that no repositioning of the hob is required, as was the case with the rack generation. Also, because each gear blank tooth is cut by several hob teeth, the effect of any one hob tooth profile error can be minimized. Hobbing is probably the most popular of the gear cutting methods.

SECTION 10-10

Other Gear Production Methods

The methods to be discussed in this section produce gears that are low in cost, can be produced in large volumes, but are poor in quality.

Die Casting. Gears are die cast by forcing molten metal under pressure into a form die. As is true of all casting processes, the changes due to shrinkage,

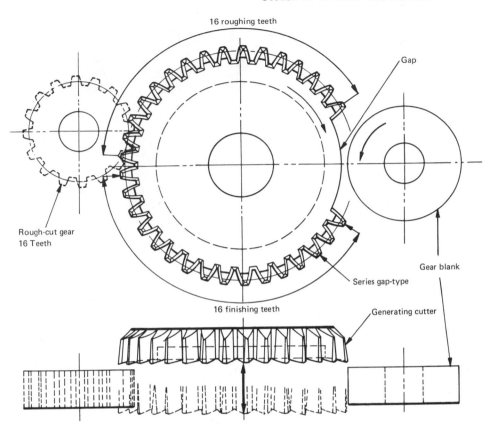

Figure 10-12 The "conjugate" method of generating with a reciprocating gear shaper cutter is illustrated. The cutter shown has a gap separating the roughing and finishing teeth. The advantages of this "interrupted" generation method are greater accuracy, higher production, and lower costs. [Courtesy Fellows Corporation.]

the accuracy with which the mold is constructed, and so on, result in a cast gear that is of rather low quality. In order to improve the precision of the gear, additional finishing operations of the type to be discussed in Section 10-11 are required. However, the added expense of the finishing operation negates the economical advantage gained from casting. As a result, casting is generally used only as a means of producing large numbers of relatively low quality gears.

Drawing. In the cold drawing process, the metal is drawn through several dies and emerges as a long piece of gear from which gears of smaller widths can be sliced. The advantages and disadvantages are similar to those discussed in the casting process.

Extruding. A process in which the metal is pushed through rather than being drawn through the dies. This method is similar to the drawing process, except that the material used is usually hot.

Figure 10-13 The hobbing process, when used to cut gears, is very fast for coarse pitches, better for higher hardnesses, and has the advantages of a generated gear. The hobbing process is usually used to manufacture spur gears which must operate smoothly at higher speeds. [Courtesy Horseburgh-Scott.]

Sintered Powder Gears. The sintering process consists of applying pressure and heat to a metallic powder in order to form the gear. The precision obtained by this process is better than with the others discussed but, because of the high cost of the equipment needed, production must be high in order to make the process feasible.

Stamping. In this process, a press and a die are used to cut out the gear shape. The gear that results is of necessity quite thin because the stamping process is limited to rather thin materials. In order to obtain gears of normal widths, some form of lamination is required. Press fitting, welding, or similar procedures can be used to fasten together the number of stamped gears needed to produce the required width.

Injection Molding. With the advent of plastic materials, it became possible to produce nonmetallic gears by the injection molding process. Large quantities of gears can be produced by this process, but their quality is relatively poor.

SECTION 10-11

Gear Finishing Methods

Grinding. A process whereby the finish on gears is improved and the tolerance of the dimensions to which the gear is to be cut is enhanced. This is accomplished by the use of some form of abrasive grinding wheel, Figure 10-14.

Shaving. A machining operation that removes small amounts of material to accomplish the same result as grinding.

Burnishing. A process whereby the gear to be smoothed is rolled with a specially hardened gear.

Lapping. A method whereby a gear is run with another gear that has some abrasive material embedded in it.

Honing. A process that employs a tool known as a hone to drive the gear to be finished. The hone, which can be abrasive impregnated or coated, drives the gear in both directions.

Of the refining methods discussed, grinding and shaving are used to finish precision gears, while the others are used mostly for low quality gears.

Figure 10-14 Gear grinding is a tooth finishing process that greatly enhances the gear tooth accuracy. The grinding operation results in gear teeth whose tooth profile, tooth spacing, and backlash can be well controlled. [Courtesy Horseburgh-Scott.]

SECTION 10-12

Tooth Loads

In designing gears, the power to be transmitted and the angular speeds involved are usually known. From this information the torque to be transmitted from one gear to another can be calculated from equation (10-11).

$$\text{hp} = \frac{Tn}{63,000} \tag{10-11}$$

where hp = input horsepower, n = revolutions per minute, and T = torque in inch-pounds.

The force that the tooth of one gear exerts on the meshing tooth of the other gear is normal to the tooth surface, and therefore acts along the pressure line. Figure 10-15 shows two gears having their teeth in contact at the pitch point, P. The normal force F_n is the force exerted by the follower gear tooth on the driver gear tooth. Obviously, the driver tooth would exert a force equal to F_n in magnitude, but acting in the opposite direction. The

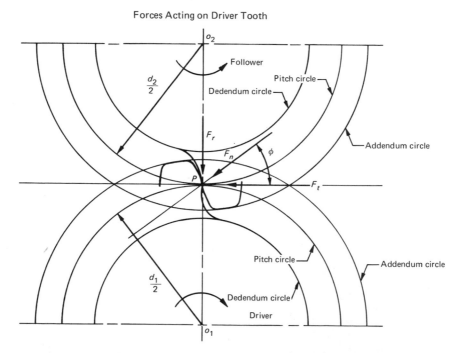

Figure 10-15 Two gear teeth in contact at the pitch point. The normal force and its components, the radial and tangential force, are shown.

normal force can be resolved into two components F_t (tangential force) and F_r (radial force) related by equations (10-12) and (10-13).

$$F_t = F_n \cos \phi \qquad (10\text{-}12)$$

and

$$F_r = F_n \sin \phi = F_t \tan \phi \qquad (10\text{-}13)$$

where ϕ = pressure angle, degrees.

The radial force is sometimes called the separating force because it tends to separate the gears or, in other words, to move them out of contact.

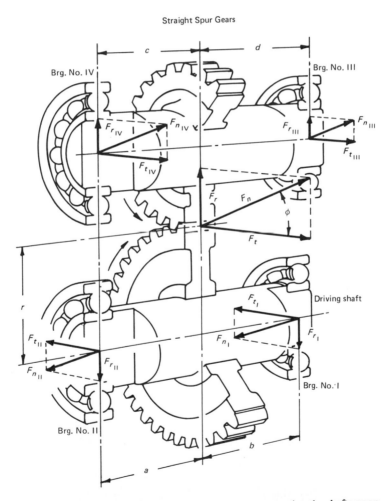

Straight Spur Gears

Figure 10-16 The loads acting on the bearings supporting the shafts upon which two meshing gears are mounted are shown. [Courtesy New Departure—Hyatt Bearings Division, General Motors Corporation.]

In design it is assumed that the tangential force remains constant as the contact between two teeth moves from the top of the tooth to the bottom of the tooth. The torque that the normal force produces with respect to the center of the gears is

$$T = F_n \frac{d_1}{2} \cos \phi = F_t \frac{d_1}{2} \tag{10-14}$$

where d_1 is the pitch circle diameter in inches.

The pitch line velocity is given by

$$V_p = \frac{\pi \, dn}{12} \tag{10-15}$$

where V_p = pitch line velocity in feet per minute.

Substituting these values in equation (10-11) results in

$$\text{hp} = \frac{Tn}{63,000} = \frac{F_t(d/2)[(12V_p)/(\pi d)]}{63,000}$$

Therefore

$$F_t = \frac{(\text{hp})(33,000)}{V_p} \tag{10-16}$$

An important consideration in designing systems that make use of gears to transmit power is the proper design of the bearings supporting the shafts upon which the gears are mounted. This basically means calculating the resultant bearing loads.

Figure 10-16 shows two straight spur gears in mesh, with the tooth loads and bearing loads represented vectorially.

Example 10-5. Determine the reactions on the bearings supporting the shaft upon which gears 2 and 3 are mounted. Gear number 1, the driver, is a 20-tooth 4-pitch 20-deg full depth gear, rotating at 2000 rpm clockwise and transmitting 100 hp. Gear number 2 has 40 teeth, and gear number 3 is a 5-pitch, 25-deg pressure angle with 30 teeth. Gear number 4 has 45 teeth.

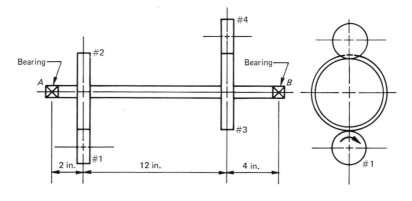

Solution:

For gear number 1:

$$d_1 = \frac{N_{t_1}}{P} = \frac{20}{4} = 5 \text{ in.}$$

$$V_{p_1} = \frac{\pi d_1 n}{12} = \frac{\pi \times 5 \times 2000}{12} = 2620 \text{ ft/min}$$

$$F_{t_1} = \frac{(33,000)(\text{hp})}{V_{p_1}} = \frac{33,000 \times 100}{2620} = 1260 \text{ lb}$$

$$F_{r_1} = F_{t_1} \tan \phi = 1260 \times \tan 20 \deg$$
$$= 1260 \times 0.364 = 458 \text{ lb}$$

For gear number 3:

$$n_2 = n_1 \frac{N_{t_1}}{N_{t_2}} = 2000 \times \frac{20}{40} = 1000 \text{ rpm}$$

$$d_3 = \frac{N_{t_3}}{P} = \frac{30}{5} = 6 \text{ in.}$$

$$V_{p_3} = \frac{\pi d_3 n_3}{12} = \frac{\pi \times 6 \times 1000}{12} = 1573 \text{ ft/min}$$

$$F_{t_3} = \frac{(33,000)(\text{hp})}{V_{p_3}} = \frac{33,000 \times 100}{1573} = 2100 \text{ lb}$$

$$F_{r_3} = F_{t_3} \tan \phi = 2100 \times \tan 25 \deg$$
$$= 2100 \times 0.466 = 980 \text{ lb}$$

The tooth loads on the gears of the shaft in question are shown in the following figure:

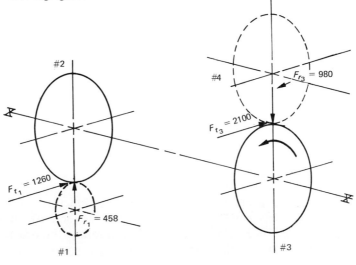

In order to determine the bearing reactions we consider the front view and the top view as shown in the following figure.

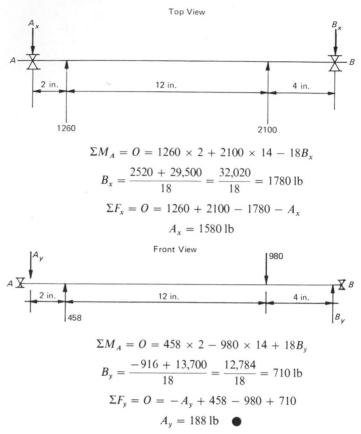

$$\Sigma M_A = 0 = 1260 \times 2 + 2100 \times 14 - 18B_x$$

$$B_x = \frac{2520 + 29{,}500}{18} = \frac{32{,}020}{18} = 1780 \text{ lb}$$

$$\Sigma F_x = 0 = 1260 + 2100 - 1780 - A_x$$

$$A_x = 1580 \text{ lb}$$

$$\Sigma M_A = 0 = 458 \times 2 - 980 \times 14 + 18B_y$$

$$B_y = \frac{-916 + 13{,}700}{18} = \frac{12{,}784}{18} = 710 \text{ lb}$$

$$\Sigma F_y = 0 = -A_y + 458 - 980 + 710$$

$$A_y = 188 \text{ lb} \quad \bullet$$

When a combination of several gears is used in a system, as in a gear train, the problem is a little more complex. Often the shafts supporting the gears lie in different planes. For this situation, the tangential and radial components of force of one gear must be further resolved into components in the same plane as the components of the meshing gear, thus permitting the algebraic addition of forces along two mutually perpendicular directions. Figure 10-17 shows such a system (also see Chapter 7).

SECTION 10-13

Beam Strength of Spur Gear Teeth

Designing gears presents an extremely difficult problem because it is primarily a trial and error procedure. However, there are several methods that can be used to develop a design. We will follow the procedure of getting a first design by the simplest method (Lewis equation) and then analyze and

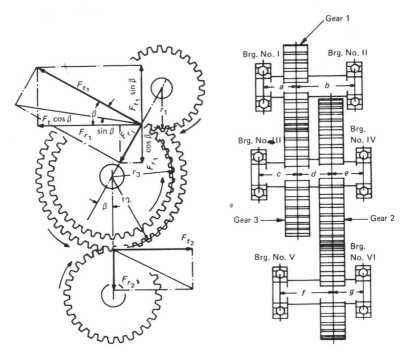

Figure 10-17 The forces acting on various gears making up a gear train. [Courtesy New Departure—Hyatt Bearings Division, General Motors Corporation.]

modify this design by the AGMA method. This approach has the advantage of showing students the fundamental and professional methods that are available. At a later date, when they have gained some experience, they will be in a position to make judgments as to which approach will give better results in a given problem.

Gears generally fail because the actual loads applied to the teeth are greater than the allowable loads based upon either the beam strength of the tooth (tooth fracture) or its wear strength (surface failure). We will first consider how the designer may reasonably determine the beam strength of a gear tooth.

Wilfred Lewis, in a paper published in 1892 [2], derived an equation for determining the stress in a gear tooth by treating the tooth as a cantilever beam. This so-called Lewis equation is still used for preliminary design calculations or in those instances where a high degree of accuracy is not necessary.

Figure 10-18 shows a gear tooth with the force acting at the tip of the tooth. This normal force F_n, is resolved into components F_r and F_t acting at point A, the intersection of the line of action of the normal tooth load and the center of the tooth. The usual assumption made at this point is that the load is uniformly distributed across the width of the tooth, b.

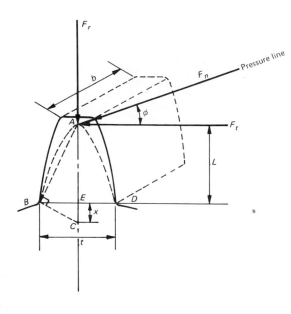

Figure 10-18 The geometric factors that are used to determine the Lewis form factor.

This assumption is wrong because the gear as well as its mountings are elastic, and we would therefore expect a nonuniform load distribution. The basic Lewis equation can be modified to include the effect of nonuniformity of load distribution. However, in deriving the simplified Lewis equation, we will accept the assumption of uniformity. To minimize the difficulties resulting from this assumption, most designers limit the value of gear tooth face width compared to tooth thickness. This is done by limiting the ratio of tooth width to circular pitch to a maximum value of 4 or 5. It should be emphasized that the above limits are merely suggested ones, and many exceptions do occur. However, the designer would do well to investigate the possible effects of nonuniformity of load distribution whenever the recommended limits are exceeded.

The radial component F_r will produce a uniform, direct compressive stress over the tooth cross section, while the tangential load F_t will produce a flexural or bending stress. We will make the usual assumption that the direct compressive stress is small enough compared to the bending stress as to be ignored in determining the strength of the tooth. To further justify the assumption we are making, it is clear that including the direct compressive stress will increase the bending stress on the compression side of the tooth and decrease the resultant stress on the tensile side. For the many gear materials that are stronger in compression than in tension, the assumption made will result in a stronger tooth design. The final and clinching argument for ignoring the direct compressive stress is as follows. Because gear teeth are subjected to fatigue failures and the fatigue failures start on the tension side of the tooth, the direct compressive stress reduces the resultant tensile stress and thus strengthens the tooth.

If we now treat the tooth as a cantilever beam having its fixed end at BD, the stress may be obtained from equation (10-17).

$$\sigma = \frac{Mc}{I} = \frac{F_t L(t/2)}{bt^3/12} = \frac{6F_t L}{bt^2}$$

$$F_t = \frac{\sigma bt^2}{6L} \qquad (10\text{-}17)$$

In a well designed beam, the stress should be uniform in every section of the beam. In other words, in a gear tooth of uniform strength the stress is a constant, and since the gear width and gear load are also constants, equation (10-17) can be rewritten as

$$L = \frac{\sigma b}{6F_t} t^2 = \text{constant} \times t^2$$

Clearly this is the equation of a parabola. Referring to Figure 10-18, the weakest section of the tooth, BED, can be determined by inscribing the parabola through point A, and locating the points at which the parabola is tangent to the tooth profile, B and D. Equation (10-17) was therefore derived for the section having the maximum stress.

Triangle ABE is similar to triangle BCE and thus

$$\frac{x}{t/2} = \frac{t/2}{L} \quad \text{or} \quad L = \frac{t^2}{4x}$$

$$F_t = \frac{\sigma bt^2}{6t^2} 4x = \sigma b \frac{4x}{6} \qquad (10\text{-}18)$$

multiplying and dividing by the circular pitch p, gives

$$F_t = \sigma b \frac{4x}{6} \times \frac{p}{p} \qquad (10\text{-}19)$$

since x and p are geometric properties depending upon the size and shape of the tooth, it is possible to define a factor

$$y = \frac{2x}{3p}$$

y is the so-called Lewis form factor and therefore permits us to write the Lewis equation as

$$F_t = \sigma byp \qquad (10\text{-}20)$$

Because the diametral pitch, rather than circular pitch, is usually used to designate gears, the following substitution may be made: $p = \pi/P$ and $Y = \pi y$

$$F_t = \sigma b \frac{Y\pi}{\pi P} = \sigma b \frac{Y}{P} \qquad (10\text{-}21)$$

Table 10-2 Values for Lewis Form Factor

No. of Teeth	Load at Tips								Load Near Middle			
	14½ deg FD		20 deg FD		20 deg Stub		25 deg		14½ deg FD		20 deg FD	
	Y	y	Y	y	Y	y	Y	y	Y	y	Y	y
10	0.176	0.056	0.201	0.064	0.261	0.083	0.238	0.076				
11	0.192	0.061	0.226	0.072	0.289	0.092	0.259	0.082				
12	0.210	0.067	0.245	0.078	0.311	0.099	0.277	0.088	0.355	0.113	0.415	0.133
13	0.223	0.071	0.264	0.083	0.324	0.103	0.293	0.093	0.377	0.120	0.443	0.141
14	0.236	0.075	0.276	0.088	0.339	0.108	0.307	0.098	0.399	0.127	0.468	0.149
15	0.245	0.078	0.289	0.092	0.349	0.111	0.320	0.102	0.415	0.133	0.490	0.156
16	0.255	0.081	0.295	0.094	0.360	0.115	0.332	0.106	0.430	0.137	0.503	0.160
17	0.264	0.084	0.302	0.096	0.368	0.117	0.342	0.109	0.446	0.142	0.512	0.163
18	0.270	0.086	0.308	0.098	0.377	0.120	0.352	0.112	0.459	0.146	0.522	0.167
19	0.277	0.088	0.314	0.100	0.386	0.123	0.361	0.115	0.471	0.150	0.534	0.170
20	0.283	0.090	0.320	0.102	0.393	0.125	0.369	0.118	0.481	0.153	0.544	0.173
21	0.289	0.092	0.326	0.104	0.399	0.127	0.377	0.120	0.490	0.156	0.553	0.177
22	0.292	0.093	0.330	0.105	0.404	0.129	0.384	0.122	0.496	0.158	0.559	0.178
23	0.296	0.094	0.333	0.106	0.408	0.130			0.502	0.160	0.565	0.180
24	0.302	0.096	0.337	0.107	0.411	1.032	0.396	0.126	0.509	1.062	0.572	0.183

Table 10-2   (continued)

No. of Teeth	Load at Tips								Load Near Middle			
	14½ deg FD		20 deg FD		20 deg Stub		25 deg		14½ deg FD		20 deg FD	
	Y	y	Y	y	Y	y	Y	y	Y	y	Y	y
25	0.305	0.097	0.340	0.108	0.416	0.133	0.402	0.128	0.515	0.164	0.580	0.184
26	0.308	0.098	0.344	0.109	0.421	0.135	0.407	0.130	0.522	0.166	0.584	0.186
27	0.311	0.099	0.348	0.111	0.426	0.136	0.412	0.131	0.528	0.168	0.588	0.187
28	0.314	0.100	0.352	0.112	0.430	0.137	0.417	0.133	0.534	0.170	0.592	0.189
29	0.316	0.101	0.355	0.113	0.434	10.38	0.421	0.134	0.537	0.171	0.599	0.191
30	0.318	0.101	0.358	0.114	0.437	0.139	0.425	0.135	0.540	0.172	0.606	0.193
31	0.320	0.101	0.361	0.115	0.440	0.140	0.429	0.137	0.554	0.173	0.611	0.195
32	0.322	0.101	0.364	0.116	0.443	0.141	0.433	0.139	0.547	0.174	0.617	0.196
33	0.324	0.103	0.367	0.117	0.445	0.142	0.436	0.139	0.550	0.175	0.623	0.198
34	0.326	0.104	0.371	0.118	0.447	0.142	0.440	0.140	0.553	0.177	0.628	0.200
35	0.327	0.104	0.373	0.119	0.449	0.143	0.443	0.141	0.556	0.177	0.633	0.201
36	0.329	0.105	0.377	0.120	0.451	0.144	0.446	0.142	0.559	0.178	0.639	0.203
37	0.330	0.105	0.380	0.121	0.454	0.144	0.449	0.143	0.563	0.179	0.645	0.205
38	0.333	0.106	0.384	0.122	0.455	0.145	0.452	0.144	0.565	0.180	0.650	0.207
39	0.335	0.107	0.386	0.123	0.457	0.146	0.454	0.145	0.568	0.181	0.655	0.209
40	0.336	0.107	0.389	0.124	0.459	0.146	0.457	0.145	0.570	0.182	0.659	0.210
43	0.339	0.108	0.397	0.126	0.467	0.147	0.464	0.148	0.574	0.183	0.668	0.212
45	0.340	0.108	0.399	0.127	0.468	0.149	0.468	0.149	0.579	0.184	0.678	0.214

Table 10-2 (continued)

No. of Teeth	Load at Tips								Load Near Middle			
	14½ deg.		20 deg. FD		20 deg. Stub		25 deg		14½ deg.		20 deg FD	
	Y	y	Y	y	Y	y	Y	y	Y	y	Y	y
50	0.346	0.110	0.408	0.130	0.474	0.151	0.477	0.152	0.588	0.187	0.694	0.221
55	0.352	0.112	0.415	0.132	0.480	0.153	0.484	0.154	0.596	0.190	0.704	0.224
60	0.355	0.113	0.421	0.134	0.484	0.154	0.491	0.156	0.603	0.192	0.713	0.227
65	0.358	0.114	0.425	0.135	0.483	0.155	0.496	0.158	0.607	0.193	0.721	0.229
70	0.360	0.115	0.429	0.136	0.493	0.157	0.501	0.160	0.610	0.194	0.728	0.231
75	0.361	0.115	0.433	0.138	0.496	0.158	0.506	0.161	0.613	0.195	0.735	0.233
80	0.363	0.116	0.436	0.139	0.499	0.159	0.509	0.162	0.615	0.196	0.739	0.235
90	0.366	0.117	0.442	0.141	0.503	0.160	0.516	0.164	0.619	0.197	0.747	0.237
100	0.368	0.117	0.446	0.142	0.506	0.161	0.521	0.166	0.622	0.198	0.755	0.240
150	0.375	0.119	0.458	0.146	0.518	0.165	0.537	0.171	0.635	0.202	0.778	0.247
200	0.378	0.120	0.463	0.147	0.524	0.167	0.545	0.174	0.640	0.204	0.787	0.250
300	0.382	0.122	0.471	0.150	0.534	0.170	0.554	0.176	0.650	0.207	0.801	0.255
Rack	0.390	0.124	0.484	0.154	0.550	0.175	0.566	0.180	0.660	0.210	0.823	0.262

Values for the Lewis form factor have been computed for standard gear systems and are readily available (see Table 10-2).

An examination of equation (10-21) shows that the maximum allowable tangential or transmitted load can now be determined if the allowable stress for the gear material is used. In order to avoid confusion, the usual procedure is to designate the allowable load based on bending as F_b. Therefore, we will write the Lewis equation as

$$F_b = Sbyp = Sb\frac{Y}{P} \tag{10-22}$$

At this point it would be well to consider the effect of another assumption made in deriving the Lewis equation. It was assumed that the full transmitted load F_t acted at the tip of the tooth. Because most gears are designed with a contact ratio between 1.2 and 1.6, it is clear that when the load acts on the tip of one tooth, another tooth is still in contact, and the full load does not act on the number one tooth.

In Figure 10-19, the load has been moved away from the tooth tip to a point near the middle of the tooth (the second tooth has gone out of contact, and the full load does act on the tooth shown). As can be seen from the diagram, the derivation of the Lewis equation would follow exactly as the previous one. The only difference would be in the values for the Lewis form factor. Table 10-2 also lists values for the Lewis form factor when the load acts near the center of the tooth.

This form of the Lewis equation will reduce the size and weight of the gears because a smaller actual stress is being used. However, the equation is only used for those designs where weight and size reduction is of major importance.

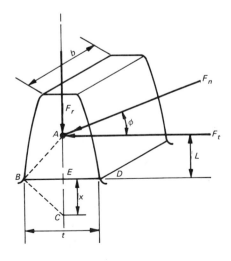

Figure 10-19 The load acts near the center of the tooth, the other pair of teeth, which were originally in contact, have separated, and the total load being transmitted acts on the tooth shown.

At this point in our discussion, it is possible to design a gear, by using equation (10-22), that will have the required strength, providing the proper allowable stress for the gear material is used. The allowable stresses presented in Table 10-3 are based upon investigations of the performance of gears in actual use. Therefore, gears to be used for ordinary applications will give satisfactory service. However, a much better design procedure is to use equation (10-22) and Table 10-3 to come up with a preliminary design and then to check the gear for the items to be discussed in succeeding sections.

Table 10-3   Safe Static Stresses for Use in The Lewis Equation

Material	S_0, psi	BHN
Gray cast iron		
ASTM 25	8,000	174
ASTM 35	12,000	212
ASTM 50	15,000	223
Cast steel (low carbon)		
0.20% C not heat treated	20,000	180
0.20% C WQT	25,000	250
Forged carbon steel		
SAE 1020 case hardened and WQT	18,000	156
SAE 1030 not heat treated	20,000	180
SAE 1035 not heat treated	23,000	190
SAE 1040 not heat treated	25,000	202
SAE 1045 not heat treated	30,000	215
SAE 1045 hardened by WQT	32,000	205
SAE 1050 hardened by OQT	35,000	223
Alloy Steels		
SAE 2320 case hardened and WQT	50,000	225
SAE 2345 hardened by OQT	50,000	475
SAE 3115 case hardened and OQT	37,000	212
SAE 3145 hardened by OQT	53,000	475
SAE 3245 hardened by OQT	65,000	475
SAE 4340 hardened by OQT	65,000	475
SAE 4640 hardened by OQT	55,000	475
SAE 6145 hardened by OQT	67,500	475
Copper base materials		
SAE 43 (ASTM B147–52, 8A) (manganese bronze)	20,000	100
SAE 62 (ASTM B143–52, 1A) (gun metal)	10,000	80
SAE 65 (ASTM B144–52, 3C) (phosphor bronze)	12,000	100
SAE 68 (ASTM B148–52, 98) (aluminum bronze, heat treated)	22,000	180
Nonmetals		
Bakelite, Micarta, Celeron	8,000	

SECTION 10-14

Stress Concentration

Another important factor affecting the stress in a gear tooth, and not included in the simplified Lewis equation, is the stress concentration existing at the root of the tooth. It is extremely difficult to determine the theoretical values of stress concentration for the rather complex shape of a gear tooth. Fortunately, photoelastic investigations have resulted in empirical equations giving reasonable values for stress concentration. Dolan and Broghamer [3] established equations (10-23a–c).

$$K_t = 0.22 + \left(\frac{t}{r}\right)^{0.2} \left(\frac{t}{L}\right)^{0.4} \text{ for } 14\tfrac{1}{2}\text{-deg pressure angle} \qquad (10\text{-}23a)$$

$$K_t = 0.18 + \left(\frac{t}{r}\right)^{0.15} \left(\frac{t}{L}\right)^{0.45} \text{ for } 20\text{-deg pressure angle} \qquad (10\text{-}23b)$$

$$K_t = 0.14 + \left(\frac{t}{r}\right)^{0.11} \left(\frac{t}{L}\right)^{0.5} \text{ for } 25\text{-deg pressure angle} \qquad (10\text{-}23c)$$

where K_t = stress concentration factor; t = thickness of tooth at base of tooth (weakest section); r = radius of fillet at root of tooth; L = height of load above weakest section.

Figure 10-20 shows the stress concentration present in gear teeth.

Since the stress concentration as obtained by the above equation is for static stress and a gear tooth is subjected to fatigue stress, the factors obtained by equations (10-23) should be modified by the notch sensitivity factors, q discussed in Chapter 3. As a reasonable approximation, students may use 1.5 for the stress concentration.

Equation (10-22) can now be modified to include the effect of stress concentration, and can be used for final design.

$$F_b = \frac{SbY}{K_f P} \qquad (10\text{-}24)$$

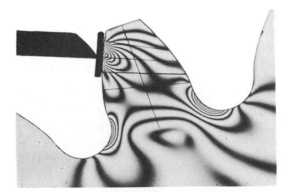

Figure 10-20 Stress concentration in gear tooth. [Courtesy T. J. Dolan, Univ. of Illinois.]

SECTION 10-15

AGMA Equation[1]

The final strength equation to be presented is the AGMA modification of the Lewis equation. This equation is particularly useful to the designer because it applies correction factors to the original Lewis equation that compensate for some of the erroneous assumptions made in the derivation as well as for important factors not originally considered. Furthermore, since most of the factors are obtained empirically, the equation can be kept up to date by merely changing the values of the factors as more information about gear behavior is obtained.

The equation is written as follows:

$$\sigma_t = \frac{F_t K_o P K_s K_m}{K_v b J} \tag{10-25}$$

where

σ_t = calculated stress at root of tooth, psi
F_t = transmitted load, lb
K_o = overload correction factor
P = diametral pitch
K_s = size correction factor
K_m = load distribution correction
K_v = dynamic factor
b = face width, in.
J = geometry factor

As an aid in understanding and using the equation, the following discussion of the correction factors is presented.

The overload correction factor, K_o, accounts for the fact that, while F_t is an average value for the transmitted load, the actual maximum load may be as much as two times as great due to shock loading in either the driven or the driving system. Table 10-4 gives some suggested values for K_o.

The size factor K_s is designed to account for nonuniformity of material properties. It is a function of tooth size; diameter of parts; ratio of tooth size to diameter of parts; face width; area of stress pattern; ratio of case depth to tooth size; quality, hardenability, and heat treatment of materials; magnitude and gradient direction of residual stresses. For spur gear applications the size factor is usually taken as unity.

The load distribution factor K_m depends upon the combined effects of misalignment of axes of rotation due to machining error and bearing clearances; load deviations; elastic deflection of shafts, bearings, and housing

[1] The material in this section is extracted from AGMA information sheet, *Strength of Spur, Helical, Herringbone, and Bevel Gear Teeth* (AGMA 225.01) with the permission of the publisher, the American Gear Manufacturers Association, 1330 Massachusetts Avenue, N.W., Washington, D.C. 20005.

Table 10-4 Overload Factor, K_o (for speed increasing and decreasing drives)*

Power Source	Load on Driven Machine		
	Uniform	Moderate Shock	Heavy Shock
Uniform	1.00	1.25	1.75 or higher
Light shock	1.25	1.50	2.00 or higher
Medium shock	1.50	1.75	2.25 or higher

*For speed increasing drives of spur and bevel gears (but not helical and herringbone gears), add 0.01 $(n_G/n_p)^2$ to the factors in Table 10-4, where N_{tp} = number of teeth in pinion;

N_{tg} = number of teeth in pinion;

SOURCE: AGMA

due to load. The AGMA information sheet presents tables and figures that give values for K_m when misalignment information is available. However, when estimated or actual misalignment is not known, the K_m factor for spur, helical, and herringbone gears as given in Table 10-5 may be used.

The dynamic factor K_v depends on the effect of tooth spacing and profile errors; effect of pitch line speed and revolutions per minute; inertia and stiffness of all rotating elements; transmitted load per inch of face; tooth stiffness. Figure 10-21 shows three of the commonly used dynamic factors.

Table 10-5 Load Distribution Factor, K_m

Condition of Support	Face Width							
	2-in. Face and under		6-in. Face		9-in. Face		16-in. Face and Over	
	Spur	Helical	Spur	Helical	Spur	Helical	Spur	Helical
Accurate mounting, low bearing clearances, minimum elastic deflection, precision gears	1.3	1.2	1.4	1.3	1.5	1.4	1.8	1.7
Less rigid mountings, less accurate gears, contact across full face	1.6	1.5	1.7	1.6	1.8	1.7	2.0	2.0
Accuracy and mounting such that less than full face contact exists	Over 2.0							

SOURCE: AGMA

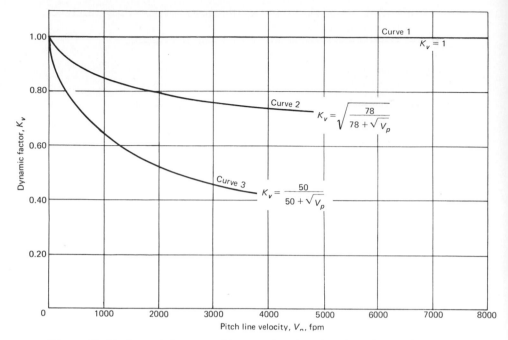

Figure 10-21 Dynamic factor, K_v. [Courtesy American Gear Manufacturers' Association.]

Curve 1 is used for (1) high precision helical and shaved or ground spur gears where the effects previously mentioned do not cause an appreciable dynamic load to be developed and (2) generated bevel gears having the preferred pattern of tooth contact and accurate tooth spacing and concentricity. Curve 2 is used for (1) high precision helical and shaved or ground spur gears where the effects previously mentioned can develop an appreciable dynamic load, (2) commercial helical gears, and (3) large planed spiral bevel gears. Curve 3 is used for (1) spur gears finished by hobbing or shaping and (2) large planed straight bevel gears.

Lower dynamic factors than those shown in the figure must be used when milling cutters are used to cut the teeth or inaccurate teeth are generated.

The geometry factor J accounts for the effect of the shape of the tooth, the position at which the most damaging load is applied, the stress concentration, and the sharing of load between one or more pairs of teeth.

Tooth shape depends upon the geometry of the tooth system. In other words, such factors as pressure angle, number of teeth, whether full depth, stubbed, and so on.

The position at which the most damaging load is applied depends upon how accurately the gears have been cut. For accurately cut teeth, the greatest stress will occur when the load acts at the greatest height for which only one pair of teeth are in contact. In other words, when the load acts at the tip of

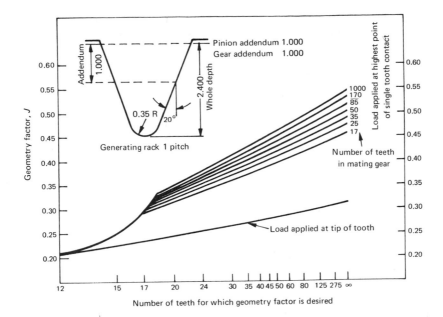

Figure 10-22 Geometry factors, 20 deg spur, standard addendum. [Courtesy American Gear Manufacturers' Association.]

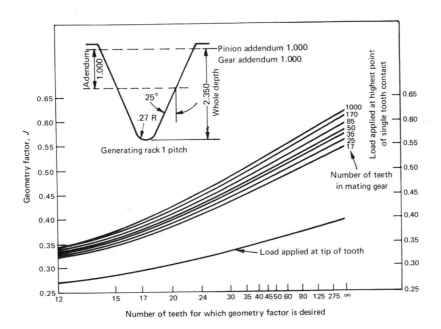

Figure 10-23 Geometry factors, 25 deg spur, standard addendum. [Courtesy American Gear Manufacturers' Association.]

Table 10-6 Guide to Limiting Error in Action for Steel Spur Gear (variation in base pitch)

Number of Pinion Teeth	Allowable Error When Teeth Share Load					Amount of Error When Teeth Fail to Share Load				
	Load per in. of Face, lb					Load per in. of Face, lb				
	500	1000	2000	4000	8000	500	1000	2000	4000	8000
15	0.0004	0.0007	0.0014	0.0024	0.0042	0.0006	0.0011	0.0023	0.0039	0.0064
20	0.0003	0.0006	0.0011	0.0020	0.0036	0.0006	0.0011	0.0023	0.0039	0.0064
25 and higher	0.0002	0.0005	0.0009	0.0017	0.0030	0.0006	0.0011	0.0023	0.0039	0.0064

SOURCE: AGMA

the tooth another pair of teeth are in contact and are sharing the load and thus the greatest stress does not occur at this position. For less accurately cut gears errors may prevent two pair of teeth from sharing the load, and the greatest stress probably will occur when the load acts at the tip of the tooth.

The geometry factor also includes the effect of stress concentration as determined by the Dolan-Broghamer equations discussed in Section 10-14, as well as tangential (bending stress) load and radial (compressive stress) load.

Figure 10-22 may be used to determine the geometry factor for 20-deg spur gears, and Figure 10-23 may be used to determine the geometry factor for 25-deg spur gears. Both of these figures are presented by the AGMA and assume that the theoretical stress concentration factor is not greatly affected by such factors as surface finish, plasticity, residual stresses, or other factors. As can be seen from Figures 10-22 and 10-23, the upper set of curves are used when the load is applied at the highest point of single tooth contact, while the lowest curve in each figure is used when the load acts at the tip of the tooth.

Table 10-6 lists the allowable variations in base pitch between gear and pinion that can be used to determine whether load sharing exists or not. For errors less than those shown in the left hand half of Table 10-6, the upper curves in Figures 10-22 and 10-23 may be used. If the errors are greater than those shown in the right hand half of the table, the lower curve in both Figures 10-22 and 10-23 is to be used. Obviously, there will be cases where the error lies between the two extremes shown in the table. In this situation, the designer must exercise judgment in the geometry factor by considering such things as material hardness, surface finish, wearing-in, and lubrication.

All the information needed to calculate the actual bending stress by the AGMA formula is now available. All that remains is to compare this stress with the maximum allowable design stress. The AGMA equation for maximum allowable design stress is

$$S_{ad} = \frac{S_{at}K_L}{K_T K_R} \tag{10-26}$$

Table 10-7   Strength of Spur, Helical, Herringbone, and Bevel Gear Teeth

Material	Heat Treatment	Min. Material Hardness or Min. Tensile Strength	S_{at}, psi	
			Spur, Helical, and Herringbone	Bevel
Steel	Normalized	140 BHN	19–25,000	11,000
	Quenched and tempered	180 BHN	25–33,000	14,000
	Quenched and tempered	300 BHN	36–47,000	19,000
	Quenched and tempered	450 BHN	44–59,000	25,000
	Case carburized	55 R_c	55–65,000	27,500
	Case carburized	60 R_c	60–70,000	30,000
	Induction or flame Hardened, hardness Pattern A of Footnote 1	54 R	45-55,000*	
	Hardness Pattern of Footnote 1	54 R_c at Hardened surface	22,000	13,500
	Nitrided AISI 4140	53 R_c case † 300 BHN core	37–42,000*	20,000
Cast Iron				
AGMA Grade 20			5,000	2,700
AGMA Grade 30		175 BHN	8,500	4,600
AGMA Grade 40		200 BHN	13,000	7,000
Nodular Iron				
ASTM Grade 60-40-18	Annealed		15,000	8,000
ASTM Grade 80-55-06			20,000	11,000
ASTM Grade 100-70-03	Normalized		26,000	14,000
ASTM Grade 120-90-02	Quenched and tempered		30,000	18,500
Bronze				
AGMA 2c (10%-12% Tin)		40,000 psi	5,700	3,000
Aluminum Bronze				
ASTM B-148-52				
Alloy 9C-H.T.		90,000 psi	23,600	12,000

Footnote (1)

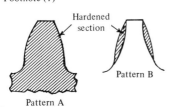

Pattern B

Pattern A

SOURCE: AGMA

* Values for teeth 6 DP and finer

†For heavy gears these hardnesses will be lower, hence, lower values of allowable stress should be used.

where

S_{ad} = maximum allowable design stress, psi
S_{at} = allowable stress for material, psi
K_L = life factor
K_T = temperature factor
K_R = factor of safety (reliability factor)

The allowable stresses for standard gear materials will vary with such factors as material quality, heat treatment, forging or casting practices, and material composition. Table 10-7 gives the values of the allowable fatigue bending stress (S_{at}) as recommended by the AGMA. Note that R_c refers to case carburized Rockwell hardness numbers.

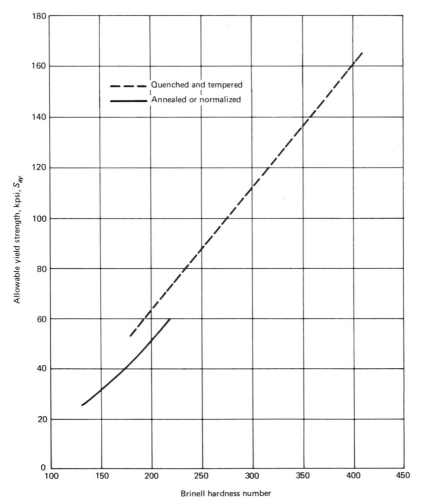

Figure 10-24 Allowable yield strength, S_{ay}. [Courtesy American Gear Manufacturers' Association.]

Table 10-8 Life Factor, K_L

Number of Cycles	Spur, Helical and Herringbone				Bevel Gears
	160 BHN	250 BHN	450 BHN	Case Carburized[†]	Case Carburized[†]
Up to 1,000	1.6	2.4	3.4	2.7	4.6
10,000	1.4	1.9	2.4	2.0	3.1
100,000	1.2	1.4	1.7	1.5	2.1
1 million	1.1	1.1	1.2	1.1	1.4
10 million	1.0	1.0	1.0	1.0	1.0
100 million and over	1.0–0.8[*]	1.0–0.8[*]	1.0–0.8[*]	1.0–0.8[*]	1.0

[*]The life factor for over 100 million cycles is sometimes handled by service factor, the factor of safety, or by reduced allowable stresses. For reference purposees, see Standard AGMA 151.02, Application classification for helical, herringbone and spiral bevel gear speed reducers, and Standard AGMA 411.02, Design procedure for aircraft engine and power take-off spur and helical gears.

[†]Case carburized 55-63R_c.

SOURCE: AGMA

As can be seen from Table 10-7 some of the allowable stresses are given as a range of values. The lower range values should be used for general design, whereas the upper range values are suggested when high quality material is used, heat treatment is sure to be effective, and good quality control is possible. The AGMA also suggests that 70% of the value given in Table 10-7 be used for designing idler gears and other gears subjected to reversed loading.

For gears that are subjected to infrequent momentary high overloads, the AGMA suggests using the allowable yield properties to determine the maximum allowable design stress, rather than the fatigue strength of the material. Figure 10-24 can be used to obtain allowable yield strengths for through-hardened steels.

The life factor K_L corrects the allowable stress for the required number of stress cycles. Table 10-8 lists the recommended values for the life factor.

The temperature factor K_T is an attempt to adjust the allowable stress for the effect of operating temperature. For oil or gear blank temperatures less than 250°F, K_T is usually taken as unity.

An alternative correction factor may be obtained by using equation (10-27)

$$K_T = \frac{460 + T_F}{620} \tag{10-27}$$

where T_F = peak operating oil temperatures in degrees Fahrenheit. This equation is used for case carburized gears at temperatures above 160°F.

Table 10-9 Factors of Safety, K_R
(fatigue strength)

Requirements of Application	K_R
High reliability	1.50 or higher
Fewer than 1 failure in 100	1.00
Fewer than 1 failure in 3	0.70

SOURCE: AGMA

Table 10-10 Factors of Safety, K_R
(yield strength)

Requirements of Application	K_R
High Reliability	3.00 or higher
Normal Design	1.33

SOURCE: AGMA

The factor of safety K_R, sometimes called the reliability factor, is introduced into the equation in order to ensure high reliability or, in some cases, to allow for designing for calculated risks. Table 10-9 lists some typical K_R values that are to be applied to the fatigue strength of the material. It should be pointed out that, although these factors are smaller than one would normally expect in machine design, they are applied to the fatigue strength of the material; thus, a failure simply means that the gear will have a shorter life than the minimum designed for.

Table 10-10 lists safety factors to be used for noncarburized gears. These factors are applied to the yield strength of the material, and the maximum load to which the gears are subjected.

To sum up the AGMA method for designing spur gears for strength, the calculated stress σ_t of equation (10-25) must always be less than or equal to the maximum allowable design stress as determined by equation (10-26).

Example 10-6. A conveyor system is to be driven by an electric motor turning at 1200 rpm. The velocity ratio of the gears connecting the motor and conveyor is to be 1:3. The pinion is a 6-diametral pitch, 18-tooth 20-deg full depth 140-BHN steel gear. Both gears are of the same material and have a face width of 2 in. What is the maximum horsepower than can be transmitted, based upon strength only and using the AGMA method?

Solution: By equation (10-26)

$$S_{ad} = \frac{S_{at}K_L}{K_T K_R}$$

From Table 10-7, the lower value of 19,000 psi will be used because it falls in the category of general design. The life factor, from Table 10-8, will be taken as 1, based upon the assumption that we are designing the system for indefinite life. We may assume that the oil temperature is less than 160°F; therefore, K_T may be taken as unity. K_R will be taken from Table 10-9 as 1.2. For this application this value will give reasonable reliability.

Before proceeding with the solution, it should be emphasized that this type of decision making (choosing reasonable values) is common in all design work. The student will doubtless experience considerable difficulty in making these decisions but, as a designer gains more experience, decisions will be more easily reached.

Substituting the chosen values into equation (10-26), we get

$$S_{ad} = \frac{19,000 \times 1}{1 \times 1.2} = 15,800 \text{ psi}$$

This value is now used for σ_t in equation (10-25), and that equation is solved for the maximum allowable transmitted load. In other words

$$F_t = \frac{15,800 \times K_v bJ}{K_o P K_s K_m} \tag{a}$$

The pitch diameter

$$d_p = \frac{N_{tp}}{P} = \frac{18}{6} = 3 \text{ in.}$$

$$V_p = \frac{\pi d_p n}{12} = \frac{\pi \times 3 \times 1200}{12} = 942 \text{ ft/min}$$

From curve 3 of Figure 10-21 $K_v = 0.62$.

The geometry factor J is obtained from Figure 10-22, with the upper curves used; in other words the load is assumed to act at the highest point of single tooth contact. In practice, the determination as to whether to use upper or lower curves would be made by using Table 10-6 and having some information regarding the error in action for the gear.

$$N_{t_g} = N_{t_p} \times \frac{1}{r_v} = 18 \times 3 = 54 \text{ teeth};$$

therefore from Figure 10-22,

$$J = 0.32.$$

The overload factor can be obtained from Table 10-4.

The power source (electric motor) is considered a uniform source of power, the conveyor is assumed to have moderate shock. Therefore $K_o = 1.25$.

The size factor for spur gears is usually taken as unity, that is, $K_s = 1$.

Because no information concerning misalignment is available, Table 10-5 is used to obtain $K_m = 1.6$.

We are now in a position to calculate the allowable F_t from equation (a)

$$F_t = \frac{15,800 \times 0.62 \times 2 \times 0.32}{1.25 \times 6 \times 1 \times 1.6}$$

$$= 522 \text{ lb}$$

$$\text{hp allowable} = \frac{F_t V_p}{33,000} = \frac{522 \times 942}{33,000}$$

$$= 15 \text{ hp} \quad \bullet$$

SECTION 10-16

Surface Durability of Spur Gears

Having discussed the first of the two general causes of tooth failure, breakage based on the strength of the gear tooth, it is now appropriate to consider in detail the second category, namely, surface destruction. The following types of surface destruction are usually lumped together under the general term wear:

1. Abrasive wear. A failure due to the presence of foreign material in the lubricant that can scratch the tooth surface.
2. Corrosive wear. A failure due to chemical reaction on the tooth surface.
3. Pitting. A fatigue failure due to repeated application of stress cycles.
4. Scoring. A failure due to metal-to-metal contact attributable to lubricant failure.

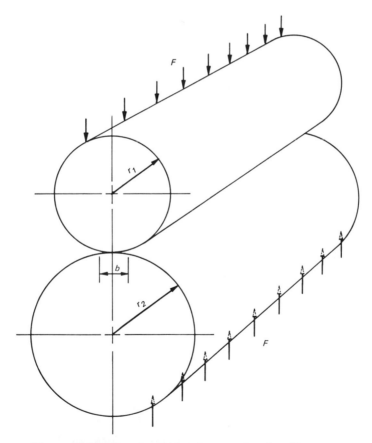

Figure 10-25 The two cylinders shown are kept in rolling contact by the forces *F*.

Abrasion, wear, and scoring are clearly failures that are the results of improper lubrication and gear enclosure. Pitting, on the other hand, is primarily a fatigue stress failure and is the type of failure the designer protects against in determining the so-called allowable wear load, to be discussed shortly. Tests have shown that pitting usually occurs on those portions of a gear tooth that have relatively little sliding motion compared to rolling motion. Clearly then spur gears will have pitting occurring near the pitch line where the motion is almost all of the rolling form.

In designing a gear, the material chosen must have an endurance limit large enough to resist the repeated dynamic load gear teeth are subjected to. As will be seen shortly, the basic tooth proportions also are entailed in the wear load calculation.

In order to obtain a formula for the actual compressive surface stress that exists between two meshing gear teeth, the Hertz equation for the surface stress between two cylinders in rolling contact is used.

Two similar equations are commonly used to determine the surface wear strength of gears. The first of these is the so-called Buckingham equation and the second is the AGMA formula.

Figure 10-25 shows the two cylinders and the dimensions used to obtain the Hertz stress equation

$$\sigma = \sqrt{\frac{F\left(\dfrac{1}{r_1} + \dfrac{1}{r_2}\right)}{\pi L\left[\dfrac{(1 - \mu_1^2)}{E_1} + \dfrac{(1 - \mu_2^2)}{E_2}\right]}} \qquad (10\text{-}28)$$

where

σ = surface stress, psi

r_1 = radius of smaller cylinder, in.

r_2 = radius of larger cylinder, in.

L = length of contact of cylinders

μ = Poisson's ratio

E = modulus of elasticity

In applying the Hertz equation to spur gears, the contact between the teeth is taken at the pitch point, for the reasons mentioned previously. The force F is replaced by the allowable wear load F_w, r_1 and r_2 are replaced by r_{c_p} and r_{c_g} the radii of curvature of the respective gear teeth at the point of contact, and σ is replaced by S_e, the allowable surface endurance strength.

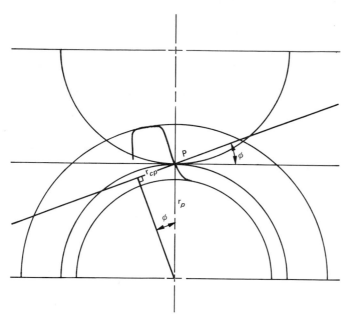

Figure 10-26 The relationship between the radius of curvature of a gear tooth profile and the pitch circle radius.

As can be seen in Figure 10-26, the radii of curvature are related to the pitch circle radii by equation (10-29).

$$r_{c_p} = r_p \sin \phi$$
$$r_{c_g} = r_g \sin \phi \qquad (10\text{-}29)$$

$$S_e = \sqrt{\dfrac{F_w \left(\dfrac{1}{\dfrac{r_p}{\sin \phi}} + \dfrac{1}{\dfrac{r_g}{\sin \phi}} \right)}{\pi b \left[\dfrac{(1 - \mu_p^2)}{E_p} + \dfrac{(1 - \mu_g^2)}{E_g} \right]}} \qquad (10\text{-}30)$$

We can simplify the above equation by considering the term

$$\dfrac{1}{\dfrac{r_p}{\sin \phi}} + \dfrac{1}{\dfrac{r_g}{\sin \phi}} = \dfrac{1}{\sin \phi} \left(\dfrac{1}{r_p} + \dfrac{1}{r_g} \right) = \dfrac{1}{\sin \phi} \dfrac{(r_p + r_g)}{r_p r_g}$$

now since the pitch circle diameter $d = 2r$ we have

$$\dfrac{1}{\sin \phi} \dfrac{\left(\dfrac{d_p}{2} + \dfrac{d_g}{2} \right)}{\dfrac{d_p d_g}{4}} = \dfrac{1}{\sin \phi} \left[\dfrac{2(d_p + d_g)}{d_p d_g} \right] = \dfrac{2(d_p + d_g)}{\sin \phi \, d_p d_g}$$

Assuming that the gears are made of materials having the same value for the Poisson's ratio ($\mu = 0.3$ is a reasonable value for most metallic gears), the denominator of equation (10-30) can be written as

$$\pi b \left[\frac{(1 - \mu_p^2)}{E_p} + \frac{(1 - \mu_g^2)}{E_g} \right] = \pi b [1 - (0.3)^2] \left(\frac{1}{E_p} + \frac{1}{E_g} \right)$$

$$= 2.86b \left(\frac{1}{E_p} + \frac{1}{E_g} \right)$$

If we perform the substitutions just discussed into equation (10-30) we get

$$S_e = \sqrt{\frac{2F_w \dfrac{(d_p + d_g)}{\sin \phi \, d_p d_g}}{2.86b \left(\dfrac{1}{E_p} + \dfrac{1}{E_g} \right)}}$$

This equation is then solved for the allowable wear load F_w

$$F_w = \frac{S_e^2 b \sin \phi \left(\dfrac{1}{E_p} + \dfrac{1}{E_g} \right)}{0.35 \times 2 \dfrac{(d_p + d_g)}{d_p d_g}} \tag{10-31}$$

Table 10-11 Wear Load Factor, K, and Surface Endurance Limit

Materials in Pinion and Gear	Surface Endurance Limit, S_e, psi	K		
		$\phi = 14\frac{1}{2}$ deg.	$\phi = 20$ deg.	$\phi = 25$ deg.
Both gears steel, with average brinell hardness number of pinion and gear				
150	50,000	30	41	51
175	60,000	43	58	72
200	70,000	58	79	98
225	80,000	76	103	127
250	90,000	96	131	162
275	100,000	119	162	200
300	110,000	144	196	242
325	120,000	171	233	288
350	130,000	196	270	333
375	140,000	233	318	384
400	150,000	268	366	453
Steel (BHN 150) and cast iron	50,000	44	60	74
Steel (BHN 200) and cast iron	70,000	87	119	147
Steel (BHN 250) and cast iron	90,000	144	196	242
Steel (BHN 150) and phosphor bronze	59,000	46	62	77
Steel (BHN 200) and phosphor bronze	65,000	73	100	123
Steel (BHN 250) and phosphor bronze	85,000	135	184	228
Cast iron and cast iron	90,000	193	264	327
Cast iron and phosphor bronze	83,000	170	234	288

Values for the allowable surface endurance strength are given in Table 10-11.

For steel gears, the following formula may be used to obtain approximate values for S_e when more exact values are not available:

$$S_e = (400)(BHN) - 10,000 \text{ psi}$$

where BHN is the Brinell hardness number.

The allowable wear load as obtained by the above equation is clearly a normal force (see Figures 10-25 and 10-26). Because Buckingham compared the allowable wear load to the dynamic load (a function of the transmitted load, F_t), some further manipulation of equation (10-31) is necessary. Letting

$$K = \frac{S_e^2 \sin \phi}{1.4} \left(\frac{1}{E_p} + \frac{1}{E_g} \right) \tag{10-31a}$$

and

$$Q = \frac{2d_g}{d_p + d_g} = \frac{2N_{t_g}}{N_{t_p} + N_{t_g}}$$

where N_t = number of teeth. The wear load can be written as

$$F_w = d_p b Q K \tag{10-32}$$

Values of S_e and K are listed in Table 10-11 for various combinations of materials for the pinion and the gear and different pressure angles. Equation (10-32) is the Buckingham Equation.

SECTION 10-17

AGMA Wear Equation

An alternate method of determining gear safety as far as wear is concerned is the AGMA[2] method. The fundamental wear equation is given by

$$\sigma_c = C_p \sqrt{\frac{F_t C_o C_s}{C_v} \frac{C_m C_f}{db} \frac{C_f}{I}} \tag{10-33}$$

where

σ_c = calculated contact stress number
C_p = coefficient depending on elastic properties of materials
F_t = transmitted tangential load, lb
C_o = overload factor
C_v = dynamic factor
d = pinion operating pitch diameter, in.

[2] Extracted from AGMA information sheet, *Surface Durability* (Pitting of spur, helical, herringbone, and bevel gear teeth), (AGMA 215.01) with the permission of the publisher, the American Gear Manufacturers Association, 1330 Massachusetts Ave., N.W., Washington, D.C. 20005.

b = net face width of the narrowest of the mating gears, in.
C_s = size factor
C_m = load distribution factor
I = geometry factor
C_f = surface condition factor

The elastic coefficient, as the name implies, is determined by the elastic properties of the pinion and gear materials. It can be obtained from equation (10-34).

$$C_p = \sqrt{\frac{k}{\pi \left[\frac{(1 - \mu_p^2)}{E_p} + \frac{(1 - \mu_g^2)}{E_g} \right]}} \tag{10-34}$$

where μ_p and μ_g = Poisson's ratio for pinion and gear, respectively, and E_p and E_g = modulus of elasticity for pinion and gear respectively; $k = 1$ (for most spur, helical, and herringbone gears) and $k = \frac{3}{2}$ for most bevel gears.

Table 10-12 lists the values for C_p for spur, helical, and herringbone gears.

The overload factor, C_o, is meant to adjust for overloads due to the operating characteristic of both the driving and driven apparatus, as well as momentary overloads due to momentary conditions of operation such as starting. The designer should usually draw upon his experience in a particular field of application in determining proper numerical value for C_o. If no specific information is available, the factors given in Table 10-4 may be used.

The dynamic factor, C_v, is primarily a function of the interaction of the teeth in mesh. The magnitudes used for the dynamic factor depend upon such factors as tooth spacing accuracy, profile error, pitch line velocity, angular speed, the inertia and stiffness of the rotating masses, the transmitted load,

Table 10-12   Elastic Coefficient, C_p

Non-localized Contact

Pinion Material and Modulus of Elasticity, E		Gear Material and Modulus of Elasticity			
		Steel	Cast Iron	Aluminum Bronze	Tin Bronze
		30×10^6	19×10^6	17.5×10^6	16×10^6
Steel	30×10^6	2300	2000	1950	1900
Cast iron	19×10^6	2000	1800	1800	1750
Aluminum	17.5×10^6	1950	1800	1750	1700
Tin bronze	16×10^6	1900	1750	1700	1650

SOURCE: AGMA.
Poisson's ratio = 0.30
NOTE: When more exact values of E are obtained from roller contact tests, they can be used.

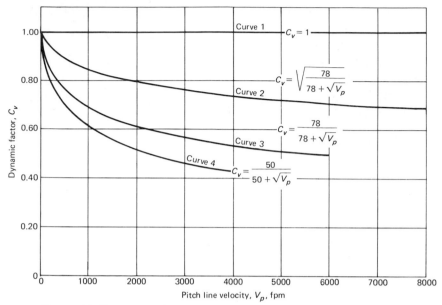

Figure 10-27 Dynamic factor, C_v. [Courtesy American Gear Manufacturers' Association.]

viscosity of the lubricant, and tooth stiffness. If the dynamic loads can be determined, either computed or measured, they can be used instead of the transmitted load; then there would be no need for the dynamic factor.

The curves shown in Figure 10-27 may be used to obtain reasonable values for the dynamic factor. The AGMA recommends that the proper curve to be used, of the four shown in the figure, is to be determined by the following general considerations:

Curve 1 is used for: (1) Shaved or ground spur gears, when a relatively small dynamic load exists. (2) High precision helical gears, also with a relatively small dynamic load. (3) Accurately generated bevel gears.

Curve 2 is used for (1) Shaved or ground spur gears when a light dynamic load can develop. (2) High precision helical gears with a light dynamic load. (3) Large planed spiral bevel gears, again with a light dynamic load.

Curve 3 is used for (1) Commercial helical gears. (2) High precision helical gears with a moderate dynamic load.

Curve 4 is used for (1) Shaved or ground spur gears when a moderate dynamic load is expected. (2) Commercial spur gears.

The size factor C_s takes into account the effect of gear size, gear-tooth size, area of tooth-contact pattern, hardness and efficiency of heat treatment. If gears have been properly proportioned, the proper type of steel chosen, and effective heat treatment used, the size factor is taken as unity. However, since fatigue tests indicate that the allowable stress for a given fatigue life decreases as the size of the gear increases, it may be necessary for the designer to use a value for C_s as high as 1.25.

The AGMA suggests that the effective case depth be used to determine whether a factor greater than unity should be employed. Figure 10-28 is a plot of effective case depth, at pitch line, versus normal diametral pitch. The curves may be used for spur, helical, and herringbone gears. If the effective case depth agrees with the value obtained from Figure 10-28, unity is used for C_s. If the effective depth does not agree with values from Figure 10-28, a value larger than unity should be used. Although there are no established standard values for C_s, a maximum value of 1.25 seems appropriate. In Figure 10-29 the effective depth of the case hardening can be seen as the dark strip around the surface of the tooth.

The load distribution factor, C_m, as the name clearly implies, is an attempt to take into account the nonuniformity of load distribution on the gear tooth. The AGMA lists the following factors upon which the magnitude of C_m depends: cutting errors; error in rotating axis in mounting due to bore tolerances; internal bearing clearance; paralellism of shafts carrying each gear (includes runout); tooth, blank, shaft, and housing stiffness; bearing and Hertz deflection; and thermal expansion and distortion due to operating temperatures.

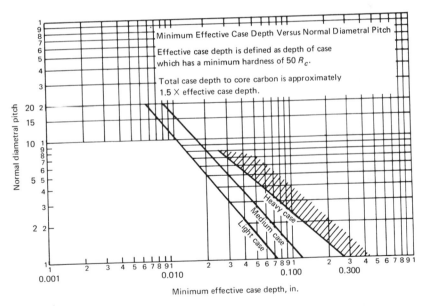

Figure 10-28 Depth of effective case at pitch line for spur, helical, and herringbone gears. The values and ranges shown on the case depth curves are to be used as guides. For gearing in which maximum performance is required, detailed studies must be made of the application, loading, and manufacturing procedures to obtain desirable gradients of both hardness and internal stress. Furthermore, the method of measuring the case as well as the allowable tolerance in case depth should be a matter of agreement between the customer and the manufacturer. [Courtesy American Gear Manufacturers' Association.]

Figure 10-29   The effective depth of the case hardening of the gear tooth shown can be determined by the dark strip around the surface of the tooth. [Courtesy Arrow Gear Company.]

Because of the difficulty of evaluating the stiffness of gear mounting, most manufacturers run deflection tests on prototypes before producing the gear systems. This is especially true in the aircraft and automotive industries. The tests also allow the tooth contact under service loads to be studied.

Figure 10-30 shows curves that illustrate the effect of different rates of misalignment. In the figure, b_m represents the face width having just 100% contact for a given tangential load and alignment error.

For wide-face gears, Table 10-13 gives reasonable values for C_m.

Figure 10-31 shows values for C_m that can be used for spur and helical gears similar in quality to those used in commercial gear units. When the b/d ratio is greater than 2, a more detailed analysis is suggested.

Since the gear hardening process results in distortion, it is suggested that, for gears which have been hardened without having a finishing operation (as for example, grinding), the C_m factor obtained from Figure 10-31 should be multiplied by 1.05 if one element is hardened and by 1.10 if both elements are hardened after cutting.

The geometry factor I, is a function of the following factors: pressure angle, gear ratio, load sharing ratio, length of the line of contact, base pitch, and length of action. Figure 10-32 presents values of the geometry factor for standard spur gear systems. For gears having pressure angles other than those shown in Figure 10-32, the AGMA in Appendix B of the information sheet *Surface Durability* (see footnote 2), presents a procedure that can be used to determine reasonable values of the geometry factor.

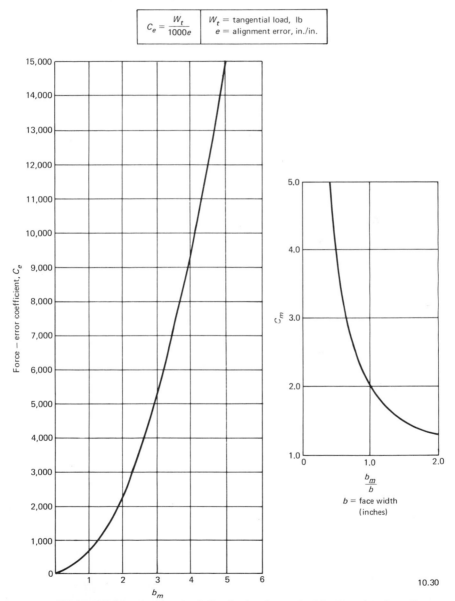

$$C_e = \frac{W_t}{1000e}$$

W_t = tangential load, lb
e = alignment error, in./in.

10.30

Figure 10-30 Spur gear load distribution factor, C_m. [Courtesy American Gear Manufacturers' Association.]

Table 10-13 Load Distribution Factor for Spur, Helical, and Herringbone Gears, C_m

Ratio of $\frac{b}{d}$	Contact	C_m
1.0 or less	95% face width contact obtained at one-third torque 95% face width contact obtained at full torque	1.4 at $\frac{1}{3}$ torque 1.1 at full torque
	75% face width contact obtained at one-third torque 95% face width contact obtained at full torque	1.8 at $\frac{1}{3}$ torque 1.3 at full torque
	35% face width contact obtained at one-third torque 95% face width contact obtained at full torque	2.5 at $\frac{1}{3}$ torque 1.9 at full torque
	20% face width contact obtained at one-third torque 75% face width contact obtained at full torque	4.0 at $\frac{1}{3}$ torque 2.5 at full torque
	Teeth are crowned 35% face width contact obtained at one-third torque 85% face width contact obtained at full torque	2.5 at $\frac{1}{3}$ torque 1.7 at full torque
Over 1 but less than 2	Calculated combined twist and bending of pinion not over 0.001″ over entire face Pinion not over 250 BHN hardness 75% contact obtained at one-third torque 95% contact obtained at full torque	2.0 at $\frac{1}{3}$ torque 1.4 at full torque
	Calculated combined twist and bending of pinion not over 0.0007″ over entire face Pinion not over 350 BHN hardness 75% contact obtained at one-third torque 95% contact obtained at full torque	2.0 at $\frac{1}{3}$ torque 1.4 at full torque
	30% contact obtained at one-third torque 75% contact obtained at full torque	4.0 at $\frac{1}{3}$ torque 3.0 at full torque
	Twist and bending exceeds 0.001″ over entire face	Calculate effects of deflection and either adjust helix angle to compensate for deflection or increase C_m to allow for both alignment errors and deflection

SOURCE: AGMA

The surface condition factor C_f is an attempt to take into account such considerations as surface finish, residual stress, and plasticity effects. C_f is usually taken as unity when the surfaces have a good finish, resulting either from a finishing operation or the running-in process. When rough finishes are present or when the possibility of high residual stresses exists, a value of 1.25 is reasonable. If both rough finish and residual stresses exist, 1.5 is the suggested value.

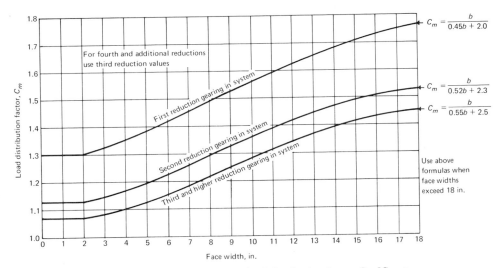

Figure 10-31 Spur and helical gear load distribution factor, C_m. [Courtesy American Gear Manufacturers' Association.]

Thus, when reasonable values of the factors discussed are chosen, based either on the values suggested by the AGMA or upon personal experience or tests run on prototypes, the designer can calculate the contact stress number from equation (10-33). Clearly, this calculated or actual stress number must be compared to an allowable value in order to determine whether or not the gears will be satisfactory as far as wear is concerned.

The AGMA specifies that the calculated stress number must be less than or equal to an allowable contact stress number, which has been modified by several correction factors. In equation form, the relationship that must be satisfied is as follows:

$$\sigma_c \leq S_{ac}\left(\frac{C_L C_H}{C_T C_R}\right) \tag{10-35}$$

where

S_{ac} = allowable contact stress number

C_L = life factor

C_H = hardness ratio factor

C_T = temperature factor

C_R = factor of safety

We will present a brief discussion of the factors indicated above. It should be noted that both the pinion and gear must be checked because of the difference in material properties and number of tooth contact cycles under load.

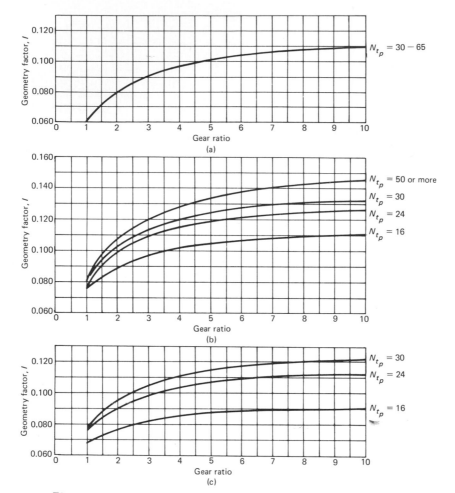

Figure 10-32 External spur pinion geometry factor, I, for standard center distances. All curves are for the lowest point of single tooth contact on the pinion. (a) $14\frac{1}{2}$ deg pressure angle full depth teeth, standard addendum $= 1/P$. (b) 20 deg pressure angle full depth teeth, standard addendum $= 1/P$. (c) 20 deg pressure angle stub teeth, standard addendum $= 0.8/P$. [Courtesy American Gear Manufacturers' Association.]

The allowable contact stress number S_{ac} is a function of such factors as the material of the pinion and gear, the number of cycles of load application, the size of the gears, the temperature, the type of heat treatment or work hardening to which the gears have been subjected, and the presence of residual stress.

The AGMA publishes many standards that give values for the contact stress number. If the particular application the designer is working on does not fall into one of the categories mentioned, Table 10-14 may be used to obtain reasonable values for S_{ac}. As can be seen, ranges of values are given in

Table 10-14 Allowable Contact Stress Number, S_{ac}

Material	Surface Hardness, min	S_{ac}	Material	Surface Hardness, min	S_{ac}
Steel	Through hardened		Cast iron		50–60,000
	180 Bhn	85–95,000	AGMA grade 20	—	65–75,000
	240 Bhn	105–115,000	AGMA grade 30	175 Bhn	75–85,000
	300 Bhn	120–135,000	AGMA grade 40	200 Bhn	
	360 Bhn	145–160,000	Nodular iron		90–100% of
	440 Bhn	170–190,000			the S_{ac}
			Annealed	165 Bhn	value of
					steel with
			Normalized	210 Bhn	the same
	Case carburized		Oil quench and temper	255 Bhn	hardness
	55 R_c	180–200,000		Tensile Strength	
	60 R_c	200–225,000	Bronze	psi (min)	S_{ac}
			Tin bronze		
			AGMA 2C (10-	40,000	30,000
	Flame or induction		12% Tin)		
	hardened		Aluminum bronze		
			ASTM B 148–52	90,000	65,000
	50 R_c	170–190,000	(Alloy 9C-H.T.)		

SOURCE: AGMA.

the table. The upper range values should be used for problems where high quality material is used, there is reason to expect maximum response to heat treatment, and when adequate inspection is available to ensure proper quality control. The lower range values are to be used for general design purposes.

The life factor C_L accounts for the expected life of the gear. In other words, the fewer the number of load cycles during the lifetime of the gear, the greater can be the allowable contact stress number. While, at present, there is insufficient information available to plot accurate fatigue curves, Figure 10-33 can be used to obtain reasonable values for C_L. As can be seen from

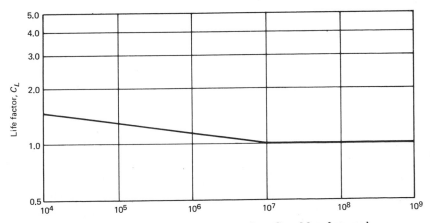

Figure 10-33 Life factor. [Courtesy American Gear Manufacturers' Association.]

Table 10-15 Typical Gear and Pinion
Hardness Combinations

Gear BHN	Pinion BHN
180	210
210	245
225	265
245	285
255	300
270	315
285	335
300	350

SOURCE: AGMA.

the curve, for a required life of 10×10^6 cycles or more, the factor is taken as unity, but a factor as large as 1.5 can be used if the required life is 10,000 cycles.

The hardness ratio factor C_H, although clearly a function of the hardness of the two gears in mesh, is also dependent upon the gear ratio. Table 10-15 shows some typical gear pinion hardness combinations that have worked well in applications. Figure 10-34 can be used to obtain reasonable values for C_H.

Because the allowable stress of steel varies with temperature, a temperature modifying factor C_T is desirable. A value of unity is usually used for C_T when the lubricant or gear blank temperature does not exceed 250°F. Values greater than unity may be required for carburized gears operating at lubricant temperatures above 180°F. Until more data is available, it is suggested that the empirical equation for the strength temperature factor, K_T, be used when values for C_T greater than unity seem to be indicated. In other words, for this situation, equation (10-36) may be used.

$$C_T = \frac{460 + T_F}{620} \tag{10-36}$$

where T_F = the peak operating oil temperature in degrees Fahrenheit.

The factor of safety C_R enables the designer to design for a calculated risk or to design for high safety, which means high reliability. Table 10-16 lists some suggested values for C_R. It should be noted that the values shown are much smaller than those customarily used in machine design. These smaller values are suggested because they are applied to the fatigue strength of the material rather than its tensile strength, and if failure occurs it is not an abrupt failure under the applied load but rather a shortening of the expected minimum life.

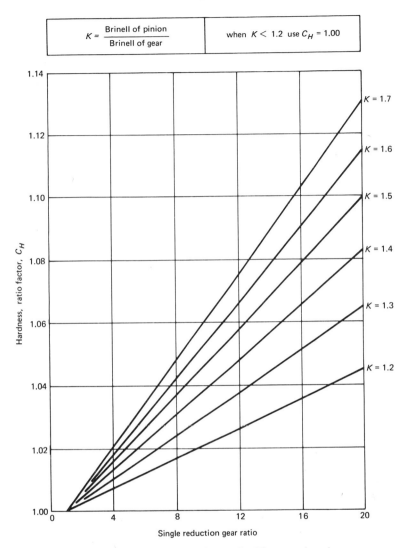

Figure 10-34 Hardness, ratio factor, C_H. [Courtesy American Gear Manufacturers' Association.]

To sum up the discussion of the wear strength of gears, a gear is considered safe in wear if equation (10-35) is satisfied. Namely, if,

$$\sigma_c \leq S_{ac}\left(\frac{C_L C_H}{C_T C_R}\right)$$

where σ_c is determined by equation (10-33)

$$\sigma_c = C_p\sqrt{\frac{F_t C_o}{C_v}\frac{C_s}{db}\frac{C_m C_f}{I}}$$

Table 10-16 Factor of Safety, C_R

Requirements of Application	C_R
High reliability	1.25 or higher
Fewer than one failure in 100	1.00
Fewer then one failure in three	0.80*

SOURCE: AGMA.
*At this value plastic profile deformation might occur before pitting.

A designer very often is interested in calculation of the maximum allowable horsepower a gear set can transmit as based upon the surface durability of the gears. Equation (10-37) may be used to determine this power in one step.

$$P_{ac} = \frac{n_p b}{126,000} \frac{IC_v}{C_s C_m C_f C_o} \left(\frac{S_{ac} d}{C_p} \frac{C_L C_H}{C_T C_R} \right)^2 \tag{10-37}$$

where P_{ac} = allowable power, in horsepower and n_p = pinion speed, in revolutions per minute.

Example 10-7. Check to see if Example 10-6 is safe in wear according to the AGMA method.

Solution: Using equation (10-33)

$$\sigma_c = C_p \sqrt{\frac{F_t C_o}{C_v} \frac{C_s}{db} \frac{C_m C_f}{I}}$$

From Table 10-12: $C_p = 2300$; $F_t = 522$ lb from Example 10-6; $C_o = 1.25$ (same value as K_o in Example 10-6); and $V_p = 942$ ft/min from Example 10-6.
For curve 4 from Figure 10-27: $C_V = 0.62$; $C_s = 1$; $d_p = 3$ in. from Example 10-6; $b = 2$ in. from Example 10-6.

$$\frac{b}{d} = \frac{2}{3} < 1$$

From Figure 10-31: $C_m = 1.3$; $C_f = 1$. And from Figure 10-32b, $I = 0.1$.
Thus

$$\sigma_c = 2300 \sqrt{\frac{522 \times 1.25}{0.62} \times \frac{1}{3 \times 2} \times \frac{1.3 \times 1}{0.1}}$$
$$= 2300\sqrt{2290} = 2300 \times 47.8 = 110,000$$

Then from equation (10-35)

$$S_{ac} \left(\frac{C_L C_H}{C_T C_R} \right)$$

From Table 10-14 use lowest value for 180 BHN to approximate 140 BHN so that $S_{ac} = 85,000$; $C_L = 1$ from Figure 10-33; $C_H = 1$ from Figure 10-34; $C_T = 1$ and $C_R = 1.15$ from Table 10-16. Therefore

$$S_{ac}\left(\frac{C_L C_H}{C_T C_R}\right) = 85,000 \times \frac{1 \times 1}{1 \times 1.15} = 74,000$$

$$\sigma_c > S_{ac}\left(\frac{C_L C_H}{C_T C_R}\right)$$

and therefore, the gears are not safe as far as wear is concerned. ●

SECTION 10-18

Gear Design

The first step in a discussion of spur gear design should be the selection of the type of gear to be used. When the design problem involves nonparallel shafts, one of the gear types to be discussed in Chapter 11 should be used. For parallel shaft applications, either spur or helical gears may be used. Since helical gears are usually more expensive than spur gears, the designer is advised to use spur gears wherever feasible. A reasonable rule to follow is to use spur gears for low speed applications and helical gears for high speed applications. Clearly then, the first design step is to choose the proper type of gear.

A reasonable criterion is to consider the application to be a high speed one if the pitch line velocity exceeds 5000 ft/min or the rotational speed of the pinion exceeds 3600 rpm. It should be pointed out that this criterion is perfectly arbitrary, and spur gears may be used for applications exceeding the limiting speed. This is particularly true if noise limitation is not important, if end thrust load is to be avoided, or if the spur gears can be manufactured with great precision.

At this point, the design procedure becomes one of trial and error because the size, tooth form, and dimensions of the gear must be known before the actual loads and stresses can be determined. Clearly then the simplest type of analysis should be used to determine preliminary values, and then the more accurate procedures used to finalize the design.

There are many possible design procedures that will give a satisfactory result. It should be obvious that the more experienced a designer is, the easier it will be for him to assume values which will work well. The following procedure usually gives good results:

Step 1. The required horsepower, revolutions per minute, velocity ratio, and center distance are used to obtain values for the gear diameters, tangential force, pitch line velocity, and the class of gear. In many problems the center distance and velocity ratio are either not specified or are not critical. In this situation the designer must assume reasonable values for these quantities.

Step 2. The dynamic effect on gear teeth, due to such factors as in-accurately cut teeth, improper tooth spacing, improper mounting, deflections due to elasticity of the gears and shaft, and irregular load requirements must be taken in account in this preliminary design stage. The simplest method by which to accomplish this is to use the appropriate equation of the following three to calculate the so-called dynamic load.

$$F_d = \frac{600 + V_p}{600} F_t \tag{10-38}$$

for $0 < V_p \leqslant 2000$ ft/min

$$F_d = \frac{1200 + V_p}{1200} F_t \tag{10-39}$$

for $2000 < V_p \leqslant 4000$ ft/min

$$F_d = \frac{78 + \sqrt{V_p}}{78} F_t \tag{10-40}$$

for $V_p > 4000$ ft/min where $F_w \geqslant F_d$ and $F_b \geqslant F_d$

Step 3. Choose values for pressure angle, tooth type, and gear material. In choosing the material to be used, it should be kept in mind that softer materials are usually less expensive.

Step 4. Since the wear load does not depend on the diametral pitch, the dynamic load can be substituted into equation (10-32) and the required gear width determined. Generally, the width should be greater than $9/P$ and less than $13/P$. These limits are used because a small width tends to cause alignment problems, whereas too large a width can produce twisting which results in nonuniform load distribution.

Step 5. The diametral pitch is determined by substituting the dynamic load into the simple Lewis equation (10-22). The Lewis form factor Y must be estimated, and after determining P the number of teeth are calculated, which enables Y to be obtained from the table. If there is a difference between the assumed and calculated values of P, the calculation must be done again.

Clearly standard values of diametral pitch should be used. However, most gear manufacturers have their own set of standard pitches, and these are not necessarily all in agreement. Typical standard pitches would be 2, $2\frac{1}{2}$, 3, 4, 5, 6, 8, 10, 12, 16, 20, 24, 32, 48.

The minimum number of teeth for standard gears is usually taken as 18, although for light loads as few as 14 may be permitted. Gears with fewer than 14 teeth can be used, but they must be specially modified.

Step 6. The gear dimensions have now been determined and the usual procedure is to recheck the design using the AGMA method. In other words by using equations (10-25), (10-26), (10-33), and (10-35).

It should be remembered that both the pinion and the gear must be checked.

Many designers have found through experience, that certain modifications in this procedure are desirable. For example, designers often make a gear weaker in wear than in bending because an impending wear failure gives visible evidence in the form of pitting, whereas the first sign of a bending failure is usually a broken tooth.

Finally, it should be stated once again that the procedure outlined above is but one of many that can be and are used by designers.

Example 10-8. A pair of gears is to be designed to transmit 40 hp for a pinion speed of 1000 rpm and a velocity ratio of 1 to 5.

Solution: Since the rotational speed of the pinion is less than 3600 rpm, spur gears will be chosen for this problem.

No condition regarding center distance is given, so it will be assumed that the center distance should be kept as small as possible in order to conserve space. Let the pinion have the minimum number of teeth, $N_{t_p} = 15$. Then the gear will have $N_{t_g} = 75$ teeth. Assume the teeth are to be 20-deg full depth. The Lewis form factors from Table 10-2

$$Y_p = 0.289 \qquad Y_g = 0.433$$

We will next choose the gear materials so that their strengths are roughly the same. Let us try as the pinion material gray cast iron ASTM35, $S_o = 12,000$, BHN = 212 (Table 10-3) and for the gear gray cast iron ASTM25, $S_o = 8000$, BHN = 174.

$$S_o Y \text{ for pinion} = 12,000 \times 0.289 = 3468 \text{ psi}$$

$$S_o Y \text{ for gear} = 8000 \times 0.433 = 3464 \text{ psi}$$

Therefore both gears are of approximately the same strength.

Because

$$\text{hp} = \frac{Tn}{63,000}$$

$$T = \frac{40 \times 63,000}{1000} = 2520 \text{ in.-lb}$$

The diametral pitch should be as large as possible in order to obtain the best economy. Assume $P = 5$. Then

$$d_p = \frac{N_{t_p}}{5} = 3 \text{ in.}$$

$$V_p = \frac{\pi d_p n}{12} = \frac{\pi \times 3 \times 1000}{12} = 785 \text{ ft/min}$$

$$F_t = \frac{T}{d_p/2} = \frac{2520}{\frac{3}{2}} = 1800 \text{ lb}$$

$$F_d = \frac{600 + V_p}{600} F_t = \frac{600 + 785}{600} 1800$$

$$= 4160 \text{ lb}$$

$$F_w = d_p b Q K$$

$$Q = \frac{2 \times 75}{15 + 75} = \frac{150}{90} = 1.67$$

From Table 10-11, $K = 264$

$$b = \frac{F_d}{d_p QK} = \frac{4160}{3 \times 1.67 \times 264}$$

$$= 3.15 \text{ use 3 in.}$$

Now

$$\frac{9}{P} = \frac{9}{5} = 1.8 \qquad \frac{13}{P} = \frac{13}{5} = 2.6$$

Because $3 > 2.6$, $P = 5$ is no good. Try $P = 4$

$$d_p = \frac{N_{tp}}{P} = \frac{15}{4} = 3.75 \text{ in.}$$

$$V_p = \frac{\pi dn}{12} = \frac{\pi \times 3.75 \times 1000}{12} = 982 \text{ ft/min}$$

$$F_t = \frac{2520}{3.75/2} = 1345 \text{ lb}$$

$$F_d = \frac{600 + 982}{600} 1345 = 3550 \text{ lb}$$

$$b = \frac{3550}{3.75 \times 1.67 \times 264} = 2.15 \text{ in. use 2 in.}$$

Now $9/P = 9/4 = 2\frac{1}{4}$; while $2 < 2\frac{1}{4}$, it is close enough to be acceptable.

$$F_b = Sb\frac{Y}{P} = \frac{12{,}000 \times 2 \times 0.289}{4} = 1734 \text{ lb}$$

Therefore strength is unacceptable because $1734 < 3550$. Either the material can be rechosen or face width increased

$$b = \frac{F_d P}{SY} = \frac{3550 \times 4}{12{,}000 \times 0.289}$$

But $13/P = 13/4 = 3.25$ is maximum; therefore, increasing face width is not enough. Therefore, we must also choose new material for the pinion. Assume $b = 3\frac{1}{4}$ in. and ASTM 50 gray cast iron is used, $S_o = 15{,}000$ psi. Now

$$F_b = Sb\frac{Y}{P} = \frac{15{,}000 \times 3\frac{1}{4} \times 0.289}{4}$$

$$= 3522 \approx 3550 \text{ is satisfactory}$$

The BHN of ASTM 50 is greater than that of ASTM35 cast iron and $3\frac{1}{4}$ is greater than 3 in. width. Therefore the pinion is also safe in wear.

Check of gear is also necessary.

$$S_o Y \text{ for pinion now} = 15{,}000 \times 0.289 = 4335$$

$$S_o Y \text{ for gear} = 8000 \times 0.433 = 3464$$

$$F_{b_{gear}} = S_o b\frac{Y}{P} = \frac{8000 \times 3\frac{1}{4} \times 0.433}{4}$$

$$= 2820 < 3550 \text{ is unsatisfactory}$$

Therefore choose gear material ASTM35 $S_o = 12,000$

$$F_{b_{gear}} = \frac{12,000 \times 3\frac{1}{4} \times 0.433}{4} = 4230 > 3550 \text{ is satisfactory}$$

Final check of gear design using AGMA method for pinion.

$$S_{ad} = \frac{S_{at}K_L}{K_T K_R}$$

ASTM 50 from Table 10-7 gives by extrapolation $S_{at} = 17,500$ psi. $K_L = 1$ for indefinite life; $K_T = 1$; $K_R = 1.2$. Then

$$S_{ad} = \frac{17,500 \times 1}{1 \times 1.2} = 14,583 \text{ psi}$$

$$\sigma_t = \frac{F_t K_o P K_s K_m}{K_v b J}$$

$V_p = 982$ ft/min. From Figure 10-21 curve 3, $K_v = 0.62$. From Figure 10-22 $N_{t_p} = 15$, $N_{t_g} = 75$, $J = 0.25$. Table 10-4 gives $K_o = 1.25$, $K_s = 1$, and $K_m = 1.7$ from Table 10-5. Then

$$\sigma_t = \frac{1345 \times 1.25 \times 4 \times 1 \times 1.7}{0.62 \times 3.25 \times 0.25}$$

$$= 22,800 \text{ psi}$$

$$22,800 > 14,583; \text{ is not safe}$$

From Table 10-3, SAE 1040 has BHN 202; from Table 10-7 for BHN 202; interpolation gives $S_{at} = 27,000$ psi.

$$S_{ad} = \frac{27,000 \times 1}{1 \times 1.2} = 22,500$$

22,500 is close enough to 22,800 to be satisfactory.

Check of gear strength

$$S_{ad} = \frac{S_{at}K_L}{K_T K_R}$$

ASTM 35 (same as AGMA 35) has BHN = 212 from Table 10-3. Table 10-7 gives by interpolation $S_{at} = 10,750$ psi. Therefore

$$S_{ad} = \frac{10,750 \times 1}{1 \times 1.2} = 8,958 \text{ psi}$$

$V_p = 982$ ft/min; $K_v = 0.62$; $N_{t_g} = 75$; $N_{t_p} = 15$; $J = 0.42$; $K_o = 1.25$; $K_s = 1$; $K_m = 1.7$.

$$\sigma_t = \frac{1345 \times 1.25 \times 4 \times 1 \times 1.7}{0.62 \times 3\frac{1}{4} \times 0.42}$$

$$= 13,000 \text{ psi}$$

Since $S_{ad} < \sigma_{at}$ gear is unsafe.

Try ASTM 50, $S_{at} = 17,500$ psi, then $S_{ad} = 14,583 > 13,000$, gear OK.

Wear check by AGMA formula. The pinion: SAE 1040 BHN = 202; gear: ASTM 50 BHN = 223.

$$\sigma_c = C_p \sqrt{\frac{F_t C_o}{C_v} \frac{C_s}{db} \frac{C_m C_f}{I}}$$

For the pinion from Table 10-12, $c_p = 2000$; $F_t = 1345$ lb; $C_o = 1.25$ (same as K_o); $V_p = 982$ ft/min. From Figure 10-27 and curve 4, $C_v = 0.62$; $C_s = 1$; $d_p = 3.75$ in.; $b = 3\frac{1}{4}$ in. From Figure 10-31, $C_m = 1.33$; $C_f = 1$. From Figure 10-32b $I = 0.103$.

$$\sigma_c = 2000 \sqrt{\frac{1345 \times 1.25}{0.62} \times \frac{1}{3.75 \times 3.25} \times \frac{1.33 \times 1}{0.103}}$$

$$= 107,000.$$

Evaluate

$$S_{ac}\left(\frac{C_L C_H}{C_T C_R}\right)$$

From Table 10-14, by interpolation $S_{ac} = 98,000$. From Figure 10-33, $C_L = 1$. From Figure 10-34, $K = \text{BHN}_p/\text{BHN}_g = 202/212 < 1.2$. Therefore $C_H = 1$ and $C_T = 1$. From Table 10-16, $C_R = 1.15$.

$$98,000\left(\frac{1 \times 1}{1 \times 1.15}\right) = 85,217$$

Since $85,217 < 107,000$, the pinion is unsafe in wear. Try a BHN of 300, that has an $S_{ac} = 135,000$. Then allowable is equal to

$$135,000\left(\frac{1 \times 1}{1 \times 1.15}\right) = 117,400.$$

The pinion is now safe in wear since

$$117,400 > 107,000.$$

It is clear by inspection that the gear will also be safe in wear. ●

In conclusion, it should be emphasized once again that the above design is by no means the only solution to the problem. In fact, the designer might try several other approaches, giving different gears, and then pick the best of these solutions.

SECTION 10-19

Backlash Control

As was stated in Section 10-2, a certain amount of backlash is necessary when two gears are in mesh. In other words, if the space between teeth were not made larger than the tooth width as measured on the pitch circle, the gears could not mesh without jamming. However, any amount of backlash greater than the minimum amount necessary to ensure satisfactory meshing of gears can result in instability in dynamic situations and position errors in gear trains. In fact, there are many applications such as instrument differential gear trains and servomechanisms that require the complete elimination of backlash in order to function properly. Figure 10-6 is reproduced here to show graphically again the angular and linear backlash present in two meshing gears.

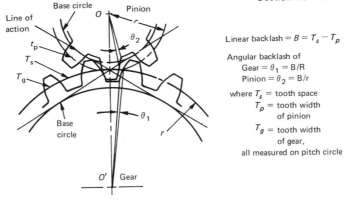

where T_s = tooth space
T_p = tooth width of pinion

Linear backlash $= B = T_s - T_p$

Angular backlash of
Gear $= \theta_1 = B/R$
Pinion $= \theta_2 = B/r$

where T_s = tooth space
T_p = tooth width of pinion
T_g = tooth width of gear,
all measured on pitch circle

(a) Angular backlash

Backlash, along line-of-action $= B_{LA} = B \cos \phi$

(b) Linear backlash

Figure 10-6 Backlash, the amount by which the width of a tooth space exceeds the thickness of the engaging tooth on the pitch circles is shown. Backlash can be designated as (**a**) angular, or (**b**) linear. [Courtesy Designatronics, Mineola, N.Y.]

Many schemes have been propounded to control the amount of backlash. It is the purpose of this section to explore a few of the more commonly used procedures. Backlash is generally considered to result from two general areas: those due to (1) fixed magnitude sources such as gear tooth width compared to mating gear tooth space, errors in actual center-to-center distance compared to ideal distances, and radial clearance in gear shaft bearings, and (2) those associated with gear rotation such as composite error, rolling bearing element eccentricity, and eccentricity resulting from clearance between gear bore and mounting shaft diameter.

One method used to eliminate much of the unnecessary backlash is the use of adjustable center gears. Clearly this procedure cannot eliminate the backlash due to gear rotation because the gears must be free to mesh before rotation occurs. The method does have a number of other disadvantages,

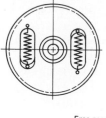

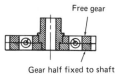

Free gear

Gear half fixed to shaft

Figure 10-35 Typical spring loaded scissor gear. [Courtesy Designatronics, Mineola, N.Y.]

namely, much skill is required to set up the gears, proper adjustment must be maintained while the gears are in motion, and the provision for adjustable centers results in increased costs.

Another procedure commonly used to eliminate backlash is the spring-loaded scissor gear, shown in Figure 10-35. As can be seen in the figure, the gear is made of two halves, one of which is fixed to the shaft and connected to the free half by means of springs. In operation, these gear halves are forced to move relative to each other by the spring force until the tooth space of the mating gear is completely filled. The advantages of this procedure are simplicity, standardization, interchangeability, and reliability. The disadvantage is that the springs must be given a torque larger than the load to be driven, or else the springs will deflect, resulting in lost motion. As a result, spring loaded gears are used for light duty torque applications. Torque values would typically be measured in inch-ounces (in.-oz.).

For high torque applications it is possible to use fixed or locked spring-loaded gears. In this procedure, the split gears are assembled and the halves of each gear are permanently joined by means of rivets or screws. Thus, all of the backlash except that due to rotation is eliminated. Clearly the transmitted torque capacity is limited by the strength of the fastening element. The primary disadvantage of this procedure is the fact that it is no longer possible to interchange gears without removing the permanent connection (rivets or screws).

Many schemes of a similar nature to those we have discussed are available. However, generally speaking, some form of spring-loaded gear is probably the best solution to the problem of backlash control and elimination.

SECTION 10-20

Gear Lubrication

With the advent of high load, high speed gears, the problem of proper lubrication of such gear trains became extremely important. In general, the purpose of the lubricant was to separate the tooth surfaces and remove heat from the gears. As can be demonstrated by a kinematic analysis of two meshing gears, the relative motion between two teeth in contact is a combination of rolling and sliding motion. This combination of motions increases the lubrication problem.

Splash lubrication and pump fed lubrication are the two methods by which oil is usually applied to gear systems. Which of the two systems is used is usually determined by the pitch-line velocity. For low velocities, under 3000 ft/min, the splash system is used, whereas for velocities above 5000 ft/min pump fed lubrication is indicated.

A brief discussion of what type of lubricant should be used in gear applications is presented in the following extract from reference [5].[3]

> For many enclosed gear drives operating under light loads and normal speeds, straight mineral oils provide satisfactory lubrication. Small gears operating at speeds below 1200 rpm and lightly loaded should be lubricated with an oil having a viscosity of 700 to 1000 SUS at 100°F. Large gears operating at speeds up to 2000 rpm and normally loaded should be lubricated with a gear oil having a viscosity of 80 to 105 SUS at 210°F. This gear oil should be the mild extreme pressure type. Gears operating at low speeds and heavily loaded should be lubricated with an E.P. inactive-type multi-purpose gear oil of SAE 90 grade at normal ambient temperatures and SAE 140 grade at high ambient temperatures.
>
> Applications such as aircraft turbine engines, which are required to operate under extreme temperature conditions ($-60°F$ to $+500°F$), are generally lubricated with synthetic oils. It is obvious that petroleum base products could not operate under these extremes of temperature. Synthetic lubricants are either chemical compounds or mixtures of compounds of of the same chemical class produced to meet operating requirements beyond the normal capabilities of petroleum lubricants. Among the most important of these requirements are high viscosity index, high temperature stability, low oil volatility, and foam resistance. Synthetic oils must pass engine qualification tests to insure satisfactory performance. The military is becoming concerned with the synthetic lubricants and their load carrying ability. Currently investigations are under way to provide this type lubricant with increased film strength and to give greater protection of the gears under higher horsepower loadings encountered in high speed aircraft.

An interesting new development in gear lubrication is the so-called self-lubricating gear. It is a laminated gear made up of alternating layers of metal and dry lubricant. After the sandwich has been bonded it is machined to form a standard gear. During rotation, the lubricant moves across the entire surface of the meshing gear.

SECTION 10-21

Gear Materials

Gears are manufactured from a wide variety of materials, both metallic as well as nonmetallic. This section will be devoted to a discussion of metallic materials, and non-metallic materials will be considered in Section 10-22.

[3] Courtesy of Gleason Works, Rochester, N.Y.

As is the case with all materials used in design, the material chosen for a particular gear should be the cheapest available that will ensure satisfactory performance. Before a choice is made, the designer must decide which of several criteria is most important to the problem at hand. If high strength is the prime consideration, a steel should usually be chosen rather than cast iron. If wear resistance is the most important consideration, a nonferrous material is preferable to a ferrous one. As still another example of how a choice can be made, for problems involving noise reduction, nonmetallic materials perform better than metallic ones. However, as is true in most design problems, the final choice of a material is usually a compromise. In other words, the material chosen will conform reasonably well to all the requirements mentioned previously, although it will not necessarily be the best in any one area. To conclude this discussion we will consider the characteristics of various metallic gear materials according to their general classifications.

Cast irons

Cast iron is one of the most commonly used gear materials. Its low cost, ease of casting, good machinability, high wear resistance, and good noise abatement property make it a logical choice. The primary disadvantage of cast iron as a gear material is its low tensile strength, which makes the gear tooth weak in bending and necessitates rather large teeth. ASTM numbered cast irons between 20 and 60 are commonly used for gears. It should be pointed out that the corresponding AGMA numbered cast irons have the same tensile strength as the ASTM ones.

Another type of cast iron is nodular iron, which is made of cast iron to which a material such as magnesium or cerium has been added. The result of this alloying is a material having a much higher tensile strength while retaining the good wear and machining characteristics of ordinary cast iron.

Very often the combination of cast iron gear and a steel pinion will give a well balanced design with regard to cost, strength, and wear.

Steels

Steel gears are usually made of plain carbon steels or alloy steels. They have the advantage, over cast iron, of higher strength without undue increase in cost. However, they usually require heat treatment to produce a surface hard enough to give satisfactory resistance to wear. Unfortunately, the heat treatment process usually produces distortion of the gear, with the result that the gear load is not uniformly distributed across the gear tooth face. Since alloy steels are subject to less distortion due to heat treatment than carbon steels, they are often chosen in preference to the carbon steels.

Although it is not the purpose here to discuss the various heat treatment methods and their effect on the properties of materials so treated, the designer should be aware of possible problems arising from the use of heat treated materials.

Gears are often through-hardened by water or oil quenching in order to increase their resistance to wear. If a low degree of hardness is satisfactory, through-hardening is probably the most desirable heat treatment process to be used because of its inexpensiveness.

Case hardening is used for gears that require a hard surface and for which good accuracy is not necessary. The case hardening process results in gears that have much harder surfaces than cores. The advantage of case hardening is that, while the surface becomes hard and wear resistant, the toughness associated with the core remains. The effect of case hardening a gear tooth was seen in Figure 10-29. The shaded strip along the surface of the tooth is the hardened case, while the major portion of the tooth (lighter area) remains unaffected.

Carburizing, cyaniding, nitriding, flame hardening, and induction hardening are some of the processes commonly used to produce the case hardening effect. If great accuracy is required, the gear must be ground. For problems in which corrosion resistant surfaces are desirable, nitriding is the process most often used. However, nitriding is a relatively expensive process and is used only if other processes do not produce satisfactory results. Flame hardening and induction hardening are the methods usually used to harden larger gears.

To sum up this discussion of specially heat treated steels, the designer should make use of carbon or alloy steels without special heat treatment if the relatively low surface hardening of these untreated materials is satisfactory. As the hardness requirement increases, the heat treated steels should be considered, with the least expensive steel that satisfies the strength and wear requirements being chosen.

Nonferrous metals

Copper, zinc, aluminum, and titanium are materials used to obtain alloys that are useful gear materials. The copper alloys, known as bronzes, are perhaps the most widely used. They are useful in problems where corrosion resistance is important and also where large sliding velocities exist. Because of their ability to reduce friction and wear, they are usually used as the material for making the worm wheel in a worm gear set. Aluminum and zinc alloys are used to manufacture gears by the diecasting process.

SECTION 10-22

Nonmetallic Gears

Gears have been manufactured of nonmetallic materials for many years. Rawhide, nylon, various types of plastics, and so on, have been used. The advantages obtained by using these materials are quiet operation, internal lubrication, dampening of shock and vibration, and manufacturing economy. Their primary disadvantages are lower load carrying capacity and low heat conductivity, which results in heat distortion of the teeth and may result in a serious weakening of the gear teeth.

Recently thermoplastic resins, with glass-fiber reinforcement and a lubricant as additives, have been used as gear materials. The composite material has resulted in greater load carrying capacity, a reduced thermal expansion, greater wear resistance and fatigue endurance. However, a major problem facing the designer is that gears made of these plastic materials exhibit a variation in properties that does not depend only on the testing method used. It is therefore necessary to test each design to determine whether its performance conforms to the values of material properties used.

In reference [6] a table containing the properties of reinforced thermoplastics is presented. The base plastics, such as styrene acrylonitrite, polycarbonate, polysulfane, acetal, polypropylene, nylon, polyurethane, and polyester, had 30% glass and 15% lubricant, both percentages by weight, as additives. The properties listed were obtained by testing gears that were injection molded, 20-pitch, 20-deg pressure angle, full-depth, $2\frac{1}{2}$-in. pitch, diameter, $\frac{1}{2}$-in. face width spur gears.

To sum up this discussion, thermoplastics are desirable engineering materials because of their versatility. However, because of the difficulty in predicting their performance, it is usually necessary to test the performance of the gear on a prototype.

SECTION 10-23

Gear Blank Design

The gear blanks from which gears are manufactured are usually produced by casting or machining from a solid blank. As was mentioned earlier in this chapter, there are other processes used, but these two are the most prevalent. Gears are cut on blanks that are either solid or webbed. Figure 10-36 shows three types of gear construction, single web, double web, and spoked. When gear pitch diameters are relatively large, the gear is made in two halves. Figure 10-37 shows a typical split gear. The decision as to whether to use a solid or webbed blank depends on the tooth size (pitch) and the pitch circle diameter. As a guide, maximum solid diameters are

For $P = 3$, $d = 7$ in.; for $P = 4$, $d = 6$ in.
For $P = 5$, $d = 5$ in.; for $P = 6\text{--}10$, $d = 4$ in.
For $P = 12\text{--}20$, $d = 3$ in.

Larger gears are made with arms, hubs, and rims. In other words, very much the same as flywheels, which are discussed in Chapter 18. The stress analysis of the rim and arms, is done exactly as shown for the flywheel. In general, the diameter of the hub is made twice the shaft diameter. The length of the hub is usually determined by the length of key required. However, the length should not be made less than the width of the gear. On the other hand,

Figure 10-36 Typical construction showing oval arm (spoke). H type (double web) and single web gears. [Courtesy Horseburgh and Scott.]

Figure 10-37 Typical split gears showing tongue and groove and pin to insure accurate and positive reassembly. [Courtesy Horseburgh and Scott.]

the hub length should not be made excessively large. The usual range for hub length is 1.5–2 times the shaft diameter. If the hub length exceeds the upper value, because of the length of key required, two keys should be used.

SECTION 10-24

Gear Trains

Up to this point in our discussion of gears, we have concerned ourselves with no more than a pair of gears in mesh. Clearly, many applications exist where many pairs of gears are in mesh. We generally term such a system, a gear train. The important kinematic relationships that exist for gear trains may be found in reference [1].

The efficiency of gear trains depends upon the power loss at each tooth mesh. The amount of loss varies with the tooth characteristics, such as tooth system, gear material, finish of tooth surface, lubrication, and pitch line velocity. In general, each mesh should have no more than a 2 % loss.

Usually this power loss does not present an overheating problem. However, as a rough guide, gears having a pitch line velocity exceeding 2000 ft/min should be checked to see if enough heat dissipation is possible without external cooling. Worm gearsets usually present the biggest overheating problems. In the section on worm gearsets in Chapter 11, a discussion on heat dissipation is presented. The general procedure shown can be used for spur gear trains as well as others. The AGMA also suggests equations that can be used to determine thermal capacity for gear trains.

Excessive noise is another problem associated with gear trains. Although it is impossible to produce gear trains that are completely free of noise, it is possible to keep the noise level within acceptable bounds. Noise in gear train systems is due to several causes, such as vibrations, both lateral and torsional, bearing noise, inaccurate gear action, and possible noise resulting from lubricant circulation. Clearly the noise due to inaccurate gear action can be reduced by improving the precision of the gear teeth. The noise due to vibrations can be reduced by considering rigidity in the design stage, by proper balancing, and by avoiding critical speeds.

The designer can eliminate some of the problems associated with torsional vibrations by considering the following suggestions. Because lateral vibrations can induce torsional vibrations, all lateral frequencies within 150 % of maximum operating speed should be checked. Clearly the system should not be operating at a lateral resonance speed. For gear systems operating at moderate to high speeds, extremely accurately finished gears are desirable.

All torsional normal mode frequencies within 150 % of the maximum operating speed of the slowest shaft should be calculated. Amplitudes due to these excitations should be determined in order to assure that they are within predetermined maximum acceptable amplitude values. Torsional vibration amplitudes should be measured during the test runs of the gear train to see if they are in agreement with the calculated values.

Calculations should be made to determine whether the shaft is reasonably well balanced. Damping in the system may be increased by using journal or tilting-pad bearings rather than rolling element bearings. The casing used to enclose the gear train system should be designed for maximum possible reasonable rigidity.

To sum up the important question of the vibration problems associated with gear trains, it should be pointed out that, although every rotating system is subjected to torsional vibrations, when a system has a gear in it the failure usually occurs in the gear. However, the gear is rather a scapegoat in this connection because its backlash is usually the only source of rotational clearance that can produce a vibrational failure. It is very often other elements in the system that are causing the problem, but the only place where the effect of the vibration can manifest itself is in the gear. Thus, it is clearly necessary to do a torsional analysis of the entire system and not just of the gear.

PROBLEMS

The problems in this section dealing with the AGMA method of solution are to be done using the following assumptions: gears are to be used for general industrial application, power source is subjected to light shock, driven machine is subject to moderate shock, a life of 1×10^6 cycles and high reliability is required.

1. A pinion having 30 teeth, a circular pitch of 0.2618 in. and rotating at 2000 rpm is to drive a gear rotating at 500 rpm. Determine the diametral pitch, number of teeth of gear, and center distance.

2. A 20-deg full depth spur gear has 30 teeth and a diametral pitch of 4. Determine the working depth, base circle radius, and outside radius.

3. A pair of spur gears in mesh have diametral pitches of 3, and a velocity ratio of $\frac{1}{4}$. How many teeth must the gears have if the center distance is to be approximately 12 in.?

4. What is the approximate center distance for an external 20-deg full depth gear having a circular pitch of 0.7854 in. that drives an internal gear having 80 teeth, if the velocity ratio is to be $\frac{1}{4}$?

5. What is the contact ratio for two meshing, full depth spur gears having $14\frac{1}{2}$-deg pressure angles, having addendums of 0.25 in., and a velocity ratio of $\frac{1}{2}$. The pinion has 30 teeth.

6. Two meshing $14\frac{1}{2}$-deg pressure angle full depth spur gears have a circular pitch of 0.7854 in. The pinion has a pitch diameter of 7 in. and the velocity ratio is to be 0.6. **(a)** How many teeth does each gear have? **(b)** What is the whole depth? **(c)** The clearance? **(d)** Root diameter? **(e)** Outside diameters? **(f)** Addendum circle radius? **(g)** Will interference occur?

7. A gear having 30 teeth and a circular pitch of 1.0472 in. is in mesh with another gear having a pitch diameter of 15 in. The teeth are $14\frac{1}{2}$ deg full depth. Determine **(a)** The pitch diameter of the first gear. **(b)** The number of teeth of the second gear. **(c)** The addendum. **(d)** The maximum addendum for the first gear for which no interference will occur.

8. The pinion of two meshing $14\frac{1}{2}$-deg full depth gears has 15 teeth and a circular pitch of 1.0472 in. The velocity ratio is to be 0.25. Is interference present? If so, what value should the actual pressure angle be made in order to eliminate the interference?

9. A 20-tooth steel pinion is to drive a 30-tooth steel spur gear. Values of diametral pitch and pressure angle are 2 and 20 deg, respectively. Tooth proportions are standard stub involute. **(a)** Will the gear-tooth action in approach and recess be satisfactory from the standpoint of interference? Compute the following: **(b)** Length of contact path. **(c)** Angular speed ratio of follower to driver.

10. For the gear set shown in Problem Figure 10 the pinion, gear 1, delivers 20 hp at 3000 rpm, has a diametral pitch of 3, 30 teeth, and rotates in the counterclockwise direction. Gear 2, an idler, has 60 teeth, and the driven gear, 3, has 40 teeth. All gears are 20-deg full depth. **(a)** What are the pitch diameters for the gears? **(b)** Assuming 100% efficiency for the gears, what is the torque on shaft 3? **(c)** Draw a free body diagram of the forces acting on each gear, and calculate the resultant forces.

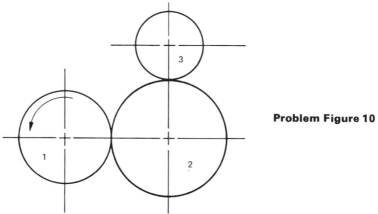

Problem Figure 10

11. Repeat Problem 10 for clockwise rotation of the driver.

12. For the gear train shown in Problem 12, the shafts 1 and 3 are to be 15 in. apart. The driver gear A has 20 teeth, a diametral pitch of 5, and is rotating at 2500 rpm. The velocity ratio between gears A and D is to be $\frac{1}{5}$. Gear D has 70 teeth and a diametral pitch of 7. All gears are 20-deg full depth. **(a)** How many teeth do gears B and C have? **(b)** What is the torque acting on each shaft if the input horsepower is 90? **(c)** what are the resulting shaft reactions if gear A rotates clockwise?

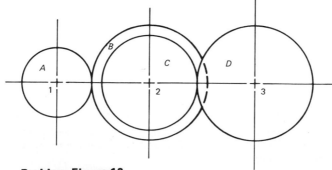

Problem Figure 12

13. Repeat part c of Problem 12 for counterclockwise rotation of gear A.

14. For the planetary gear train shown in Problem Figure 14, the pinion 1 rotates clockwise at 1000 rpm. It has 30 teeth, a diametral pitch of 6, a 20-deg pressure angle, and is to transmit 5 hp. Gear 2 has 60 teeth. What torque can the arm deliver? Draw free body diagrams of all the components and show the forces acting.

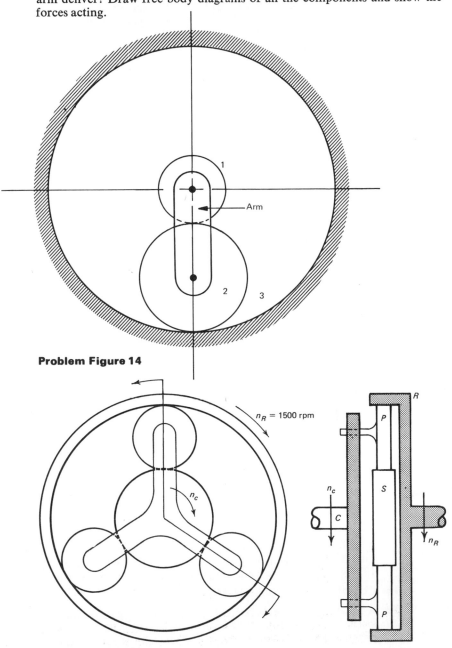

Problem Figure 14

Problem Figure 15

15. A planetary transmission consists of a ring gear R (the input), three planets, a fixed sun gear, and the planet carrier C (the output) (see Problem Figure 15). The diametral pitch is 10 and the pressure angle is 20 deg. 15 hp is transmitted with input speed $n_R = 1500$ rpm clockwise. The pitch diameters are 5 in. for the sun gear, $2\frac{1}{2}$ in. for the planets, and 10 in. for the ring. **(a)** Determine the numbers of teeth and speeds n_p and n_c. **(b)** Find the torque on input and output shafts and sun gear. **(c)** Draw a free body diagram of the top planet. Indicate all forces in pounds.

16. In the planetary gear system shown in Problem Figure 16, gears B and C are keyed to a shaft carried on revolving arm E. Arm E turns about the axis of gears A and D. The tooth numbers are as follows: gear A, 100 teeth; gear B, 20 teeth; and gear C, 50 teeth. **(a)** If all the gears have a diametral pitch of 5, and a 20-deg pressure angle, determine the number of teeth on D. **(b)** If gear D rotates at 1500 rpm clockwise and transmits 8 hp, determine the angular speed (rpm) and direction of rotation of arm E. **(c)** What torque can the arm deliver? **(d)** Draw a free body diagram of all components and show the forces acting.

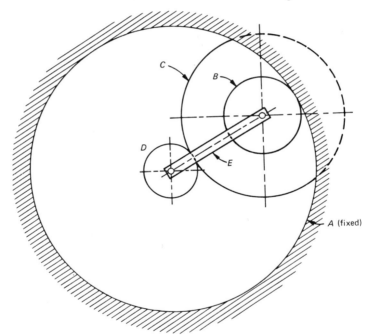

Problem Figure 16

17. Determine a suitable pitch and width for a pair of meshing 20-deg gears, which are to transmit 8 hp. The center distance may be taken as 10 in. and the velocity ratio is to be $\frac{2}{3}$. The pinion is rotating at 150 rpm and is made of mild steel, SAE 1030, while the gear is made of cast iron, grade 50. Consider strength only.

18. Check Problem 17 by the AGMA method.

19. A tentative design of an external spur-gear set specifies the following: Gear tooth system, 20-deg full depth; Pinion material. steel, BHN $= 200$; Gear material. phosphor bronze; diametral pitch. 6; Face width of gears, 0.60 in.; Pitch diameter of pinion, 3.00 in.; Pitch diameter of gear, 5.00 in. Class 2 gears (gears cut with great care) are to be used.

The design requirement is that the pinion transmit $1\frac{1}{2}$ hp to the gear at a pinion speed of 1200 rpm. Design bending stress values are as follows: pinion, 0.70 times the endurance limit in reversed bending; gear, 15,000 psi. (*Note:* These values include the effect of stress concentration.)

Determine the beam strength of the (a) pinion tooth and (b) gear tooth. (c) Are the gears satisfactory from the standpoint of beam strength? (d) On the basis of wear strength, are the gears satisfactory?

Use the Lewis and Buckingham equations.

20. Repeat Problem 19 using the AGMA method. Use $S_{at} = 10,000$ psi; $S_{ac} = 38,000$ psi.

21. Two meshing gears are 20-deg full depth, have a diametral pitch of 5. The gear is made of phosphor bronze, has 20 teeth, rotates at 500 rpm. The pinion is made of SAE 1040 steel and rotates at 125 rpm. Both gears have face widths of 4 in. Based upon strength only, what is the maximum horsepower that can be transmitted? Use Lewis equation method.

22. Repeat Problem 21 using the AGMA method.

23. For the horsepower calculated in Problem 21, will the gearset be safe with regards to wear?

24. Repeat Problem 23 by the AGMA method.

25. A pair of meshing gears have face widths of $2\frac{1}{2}$ in., and diametral pitches of 4. The gears are both made of a steel having a BHN of 400, and are 20-deg full depth. The pinion is rotating at 500 rpm, has 30 teeth, and the velocity ratio is to be $\frac{2}{3}$. Assuming average operating conditions, what is the maximum horsepower that can be transmitted, based on wear only?

26. Repeat Problem 25 by the AGMA method.

27. Design a gearset to transmit 50 hp at a pinion speed of 1200 rpm. Assume average conditions of operation, and a velocity ratio of 0.25.

REFERENCES

[1] C. E. Wilson and W. J. Michels: *Mechanisms-Design Oriented Kinematics.* American Technical Society, Chicago, Ill., 1969.

[2] Wilfred Lewis: *Investigation of the Strength of Gear Teeth.* Engineers' Club of Philadelphia, Phildelphia, Pa., Oct. 1892.

[3] T. J. Dolan and E. L. Broghamer: A photoelastic study of stresses in gear tooth profiles. *Bull. No. 335, Eng. Exp. Sta. University of Illinois*, Urbana, Ill., 1942.

[4] Earle Buckingham: *Analytical Mechanics of Gears.* McGraw-Hill Book Co., New York, 1949.

[5] Harry Palton: *Basic Fundamentals of Gear Lubrication.* Gleason Works, Rochester, N.Y.

[6] John Theberse: A guide to the design of plastic gears and bearings. *Mach. Des.* (Feb. 5, 1970).

[7] D. W. Dudley: *Gear Handbook.* McGraw-Hill Book Co., New York, 1962.

[8] AGMA Publications.

[9] D. W. Dudley: *Practical Gear Design.* McGraw-Hill Book Co., New York, 1954.

[10] *The Internal Gear*. Fellows Gear Co., Springfield, Vt., 1956.

[11] *The Involute Curve and Involute Gearing*. The Fellows Gear Co., Springfield, Vt., 1955.

[12] *The Art of Generating with a Reciprocating Tool*. The Fellows Gear Co., Springfield, Vt., 1958.

[13] P. L. Balise: *Spur Gear Design Manual*. University of Washington, Seattle, Wash., 1957.

11

Helical, Worm, Bevel, and Other Gear Types

SYMBOLS

c = center distance
C_{cr} = combined heat transfer coefficient
F_b = bending load
F_d = dynamic load
F_n = normal force
F_r = radial or separating force
F_t = tangential load
F_w = wear load
n = rpm
N_t = number of teeth
N_t' = virtual number of teeth of bevel gears
N_{t_e} = virtual or formative teeth of helical gears

P = diametral pitch in transverse plane
p = transverse circular pitch
p_a = axial circular pitch
p_n = normal circular pitch
r_v = velocity ratio
V_p = pitch line velocity
Y = Lewis form factor
ψ = helix angle
λ_w = lead angle of worm
ϕ = transverse pressure angle
ϕ_n = normal pressure angle

In this chapter we will discuss the important gear types other than spur gears used in design. The format employed in the previous chapter will again be followed. Namely, a brief review of the kinematics involved will be followed by a detailed discussion of the factors that must be considered in designing systems using these gear types. However, because much of the discussion of the previous chapter applies equally well to the present chapter, it will not be necessary to go into as great detail in these areas.

SECTION 11-1

Helical Gears

Figure 11-1 shows helical gears in mesh. The pair shown is mounted on parallel shafts, the most common situation for which helical gears are used. However, helical gears are sometimes used for nonparallel, nonintersecting shaft applications. When used in this manner, they are known as crossed helical gears. Figure 11-2 illustrates a pair of crossed helical gears in mesh. We will discuss crossed helical gears in detail after considering helical gears on parallel shafts.

Figure 11-1 When a pair of meshing helical gears are mounted on parallel shafts, as shown, they must be of opposite hand. [Courtesy Horseburgh and Scott.]

Figure 11-2 When meshing helical gears are mounted on
nonparallel shafts, they are known as crossed helical gears.
Crossed helical gears may be of the same or opposite hand.
[Courtesy Eaton Corporation, Industrial Drive Division.]

Before continuing with our discussion, it would be well to repeat the
criteria mentioned in Chapter 10 for determining whether spur gears or
helical gears are to be used for a given design. Spur gears are used for low speed
applications and those situations where noise control is not a problem. Use
of helical gears is indicated when the application involves high speeds, large
power transmission, or where noise abatement is important. We consider the
speed to be high when the pitch line velocity exceeds 5000 ft/min or the
rotational speed of the pinion exceeds 3600 rpm.

Whereas spur gears have their teeth cut parallel to the gear axis, helical
gear teeth are cut in the form of helices making a constant angle with respect
to the gear axis. Since it is obvious that the helix can slope either in the upward
or downward direction, the terms right hand and left hand helical gear are
used to distinguish between the two types. The rule for determining whether
a helical gear is right or left handed is the same as that used for determining
right and left handed screws. The helical gear shown in Figure 11-3 is right
handed, whereas the pinion in the figure is left handed.

SECTION 11-2

Helical Gear Tooth Loads

In order for two helical gears on parallel shafts to mesh, they must have the
same helix angle and be of opposite hands, in addition to having the same
pitch and pressure angle.

One prime disadvantage of spur gears is that their initial contact upon
meshing is a line contact. The resulting instantaneous line contact produces
shock effects that tend to limit the magnitude of the load that can be transmitted and result in rough, noisy operation. This problem is alleviated when

Figure 11-3 The gear shown is right handed, the pinion left handed. Because of the large size of the gear, it was manufactured in two halves and then assembled as shown. When gears are made in this manner, they are known as split gears. [Courtesy Illinois Gear Division, Wallace Murray Corporation.]

helical gears are used because the initial contact is a point, which becomes a line of increasing length as contact continues.

A disadvantage associated with the use of helical gears is that the helix angle results in a thrust load in addition to the usual tangential and separating loads. The three components of the normal load acting on a helical gear shown in Figure 11-4 can be written as follows:

$$F_t = F_n \cos \phi_n \cos \psi$$

$$F_r = F_t \tan \phi = F_n \sin \phi_n$$

$$F_{\text{thrust}} = F_t \tan \psi = F_n \cos \phi_n \sin \psi$$

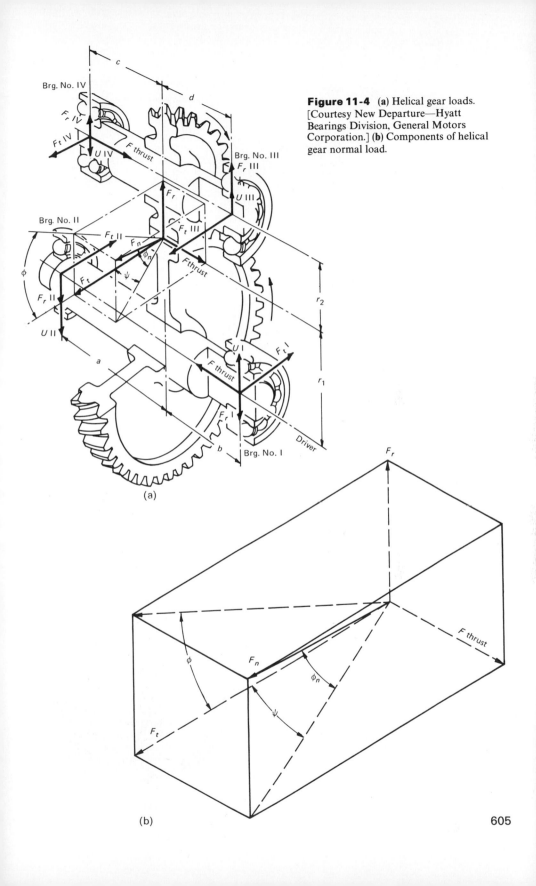

Figure 11-4 (a) Helical gear loads. [Courtesy New Departure—Hyatt Bearings Division, General Motors Corporation.] (b) Components of helical gear normal load.

(a)

(b)

(a)

Figure 11-5 (a) Train of continuous tooth herringbone gears. In the continuous variety of herringbone gears, the tceth are cut up to the center of the gears. (b) Herringbone gears cut with a center space, or clearance, for the cutting tool. [Courtesy Illinois Gear Division, Wallace Murray Corporation.]

(b)

Any Helical on Parallel Shafts

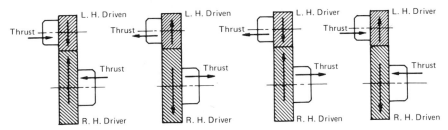

Figure 11-6 The diagram shown can be used to determine the direction of the axial thrust load, which is always present with helical gears. The thrust loads must be considered when choosing thrust washers or bearings. [Courtesy Insco Corporation, Groton, Mass.]

The thrust load requires the use of bearings that can resist thrust loads as well as radial loads. The need for a thrust resistant bearing can be eliminated by using a herringbone gear. This is simply a helical gear with half of its face cut with teeth of one hand while the other half has teeth of the opposite hand. It should be clear that the thrust loads for each set of teeth will cancel each other.

Figure 11-5 shows two typical herringbone gear types. The direction in which the thrust load acts is determined by applying the right or left hand rule to the driver. In other words, for a right hand driver, if the fingers of the right hand are pointed in the direction of rotation of the gear, the thumb points in the direction of the thrust load. The driven gear then has a thrust load acting in the opposite direction to that of the driver. Figure 11-6 may be used to determine the direction of the thrust load for helical gears on parallel shafts.

Example 11-1. A helical gear set consists of a left handed driver, gear 1, having a 25-deg pressure angle, and a 30-deg helix angle, an idler, and a driven gear, the centers of all gears are in line. Assuming that a 1000-lb load is to be transmitted, determine the resultant loads on the shafts.

Solution:

$$F_{thrust} = F_t \tan \psi$$
$$= 1000 \times \tan 30 \deg = 577 \text{ lb}$$
$$F_r = F_t \tan \phi = 1000 \times \tan 25 \deg = 466 \text{ lb}$$

Clearly, the resultant thrust load on an idler gear is zero. ●

SECTION 11-3

Helical Gear Terminology

Figure 11-7 shows a helical gear with some of the more important geometric quantities indicated. The helix angle ψ is the angle between a line drawn through one of the teeth and the center line of the shaft on which the

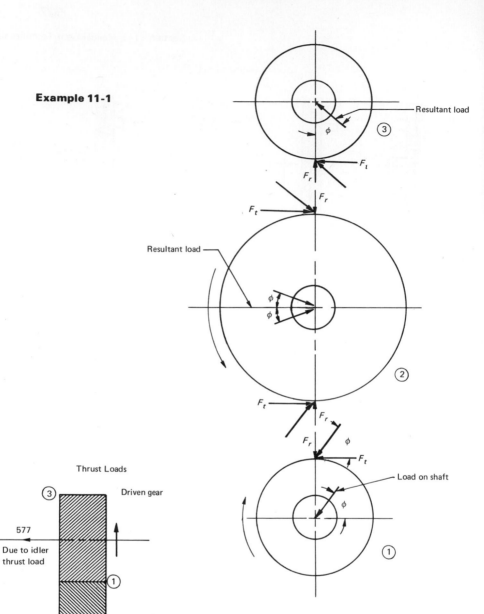

Example 11-1

Resultant load

③

F_t

F_r

F_r

F_t

Resultant load

②

F_t

F_r

F_r

F_t

ϕ

Load on shaft

ϕ

①

Thrust Loads

③ Driven gear

577

Due to idler
thrust load

①

577   577

Due to gear ②   Idler

577

Assume rotation of
driver

①

Driver-LH

gear is mounted. There are no standard values for helix angles because the gears are rarely used interchangeably. The usual range of values used for the helix angle is between 15 and 30 deg. Gears are sometimes made with helix angles falling outside this range. However, since the thrust load varies directly with the magnitude of the tangent of the helix angle, there is an upper limit to the magnitude of the helix angle in order to prevent excessive thrust loads. A lower limit is also necessary to ensure smooth transference of load.

Although spur gears involved only the diametral and circular pitch, helical gear geometry requires additional pitches. The normal circular pitch p_n is the distance between corresponding points of adjacent teeth as measured in a plane perpendicular to the helix (the B-B plane in Figure 11-7). The transverse circular pitch p is measured in a plane perpendicular to the shaft axis (A-A plane). The axial pitch p_a is a similar distance measured in a plane parallel to the shaft axis. All three pitches are shown in Figure 11-7.

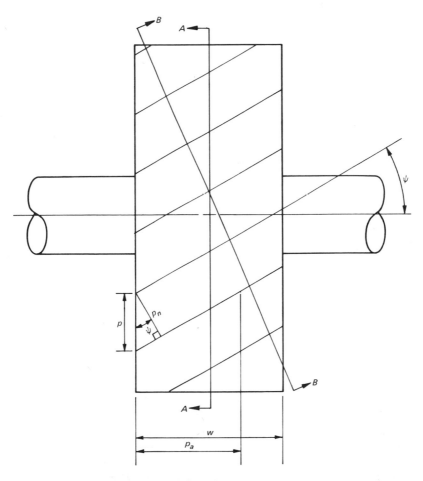

Figure 11-7 Helical gear geometry.

Equations (11-1) through (11-6) represent the geometric relationships between the various pitches.

$$p_n = p \cos \psi \tag{11-1}$$

$$p_a = p \cot \psi \tag{11-2}$$

$$P = \frac{N_t}{d} \tag{11-3}$$

where P = diametral pitch in transverse plane, N_t = number of teeth of the gear, d is the diameter of the pitch circle, and P_n is the normal diametral pitch.

$$Pp = \pi \tag{11-4}$$

$$P_n p_n = \pi \tag{11-5}$$

$$P_n = \frac{P}{\cos \psi} \tag{11-6}$$

In order to ensure a smooth transference of load, the face width of a helical gear is usually made at least 20% greater than the axial pitch. As will be seen later in this section, the face width is determined by the load acting on the gear. The 20% greater than axial pitch is merely a suggested minimum value for face width. In fact, some designers prefer that the face width be at least twice the axial pitch.

Two pressure angles are associated with helical gears, one is measured in the transverse plane (*A-A* plane in Figure 11-7) and the other in the normal plane (*B-B* plane in Figure 11-7). Figure 11-8 shows the tooth profiles in the normal and transverse plane.

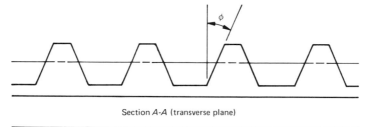

Section *A-A* (transverse plane)

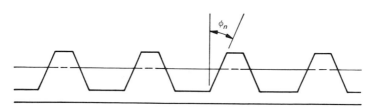

Section *B-B* (normal plane)

Figure 11-8 The transverse and normal pressure angles are illustrated by drawing sections *A–A* and *B–B* in Figure 11-7.

Simple trigonometric relationships can be used to arrive at equation (11-7) which relates the three angles associated with helical gears.

$$\tan \phi_n = \tan \phi \cos \psi \tag{11-7}$$

where ϕ_n is the normal pressure angle, ϕ is the transverse pressure angle, and ψ is the helix angle.

Other geometric quantities are similar to those for spur gears.

$$d = \frac{N_t p}{\pi} = \frac{N_t p_n}{\pi \cos \psi} \tag{11-8}$$

$$c = \frac{d_1 + d_2}{2} = \frac{p}{2\pi}(N_{t_1} + N_{t_2}) = \frac{p_n(N_{t_1} + N_{t_2})}{2\pi \cos \psi}$$

$$= \frac{N_{t_1} + N_{t_2}}{2P_n \cos \psi} \tag{11-9}$$

Example 11-2. Two helical gears are to connect shafts 6 in. apart. The pinion has a diametral pitch of 6, a normal diametral pitch of 7, and a pressure angle of 20 deg. If the velocity ratio is to be $\frac{1}{2}$, determine the number of teeth of each gear and the normal pressure angle.

Solution: The velocity ratio $r_v = N_{t_1}/N_{t_2}$. Then

$$\frac{1}{2} = \frac{N_{t_1}}{N_{t_2}} \quad \text{or} \quad N_{t_2} = 2N_{t_1}$$

$$p = \frac{\pi}{P} = \frac{\pi}{6} = 0.5236 \text{ in.}$$

$$c = \frac{p}{2\pi}(N_{t_1} + N_{t_2})$$

$$N_{t_1} + N_{t_2} = N_{t_1} + 2N_{t_1} = \frac{c2\pi}{p} = \frac{6 \times 2 \times \pi}{0.5236} = 72$$

$$3N_{t_1} = 72$$

So that $N_{t_1} = 24$ teeth and $N_{t_2} = 48$ teeth.

For the normal pressure angle

$$\cos \psi = \frac{P}{P_n} = \frac{6}{7} = 0.857$$

$$\psi = 31 \text{ deg}$$

and

$$\tan \phi_n = \tan \phi \cos \psi = \tan 20 \cos \psi$$

$$= 0.364 \times 0.857$$

$$\phi_n = 17.3 \text{ deg} \quad \bullet$$

SECTION 11-4

Virtual or Formative Number of Teeth

Referring back to Figure 11-7, the plane normal to the gear teeth, *B-B*, intersects the pitch cylinder to form an ellipse. The gear tooth profile generated in this plane, using the radius of curvature of the ellipse, would be a spur gear having the same properties as the actual helical gear. The radius of curvature of an ellipse is given by

$$r_c = \frac{d}{2 \cos^2 \psi} \tag{11-10}$$

where r_c = radius of curvature of ellipse and d = pitch circle diameter.

The number of teeth of the equivalent spur gear in the normal plane is known as either the formative or equivalent number of teeth. The equivalent number of teeth can be found by applying equation (11-11)

$$N_{t_e} = P_n 2 r_c \tag{11-11}$$

where P_n is the normal diametral pitch. Therefore

$$N_{t_e} = P_n \times 2 \times \frac{d}{2 \cos^2 \psi}$$

But since

$$P_n = \frac{P}{\cos \psi} \qquad \text{and} \qquad P = \frac{N_t}{d}$$

we get

$$N_{t_e} = \frac{P}{\cos \psi} \frac{d}{\cos^2 \psi} = \frac{N_t}{\cos^3 \psi}$$

or

$$N_{t_e} = \frac{N_t}{\cos^3 \psi} \tag{11-12}$$

In other words, the equivalent number of teeth, can be obtained by dividing the actual number of teeth of the helical gear by $\cos^3 \psi$. The equivalent number of teeth is used to determine the Lewis factor Y in the bending stress formula for helical gears to be discussed shortly.

SECTION 11-5

Dynamic Load for Helical Gears

The dynamic load acting on helical gears can be approximated by equation (10-40).

$$F_d = \frac{78 + \sqrt{V_p}}{78} F_t$$

SECTION 11-6

Bending Strength of Helical Gears

The bending strength of helical gears can be obtained by using a modified form of the Lewis equation or by using the AGMA formula.

The Lewis equation (slightly modified)

$$F_b = \frac{SbY}{K_f P_n} \tag{11-13}$$

can be used to determine the bending strength of helical gears, provided that the form factor Y is obtained from Table 10-2, using the formative or equivalent number of teeth. The normal diametral pitch is used because the tooth load causing the bending stress is normal to the tooth surface in the normal plane. F_b must then be equal to or greater than the dynamic load F_d as calculated by the equation from Section 11-5.

The same AGMA equations used for spur gears (10-25) and (10-26) apply to helical gears. The correction factors are obtained from the table and figures as indicated below.[1] Equations (10-25) and (10-26) are repeated below for convenience.

$$\sigma_t = \frac{F_t K_o P K_s K_m}{K_v b J} \tag{10-25}$$

$$S_{ad} = \frac{S_{at} K_L}{K_T K_R} \tag{10-26}$$

The overload factor K_o can be obtained from Table 10-4. The size factor K_s is equal to unity for helical and herringbone gears. The dynamic factor K_v can be determined from the appropriate curve in Figure 10-21. The load distribution factor K_m can be obtained from Table 10-5.

The discussion of the geometry factor presented in Chapter 10 on spur gears applies equally well to helical gears. However, the figures used for spur gear geometry factors do not apply. Figures 11-9 through 11-13 can be used for helical gear geometry factors.

The factors to be used in equation (10-26) as applied to helical gears are obtainable from the tables and figures given in Chapter 10, namely, Table 10-7 for S_{at}, Table 10-8 for K_L, and Table 10-9 or Table 10-10 for K_R. K_T is either taken as unity or equation (10-27) may be used if appropriate.

---

[1] Extracted from *AGMA Information Sheet—Strength of Spur, Helical, Herringbone, and Bevel Gear Teeth* (AGMA 225.01) with the permission of the publisher, the American Gear Manufacturers Association, 1330 Massachusetts Ave., N.W. Washington, D.C. 20005.

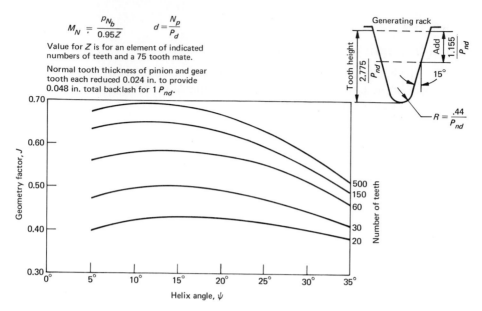

Figure 11-9 Geometry factor (J) 15 deg normal pressure angle—indicated addendum. [Courtesy American Gear Manufacturers Association.]

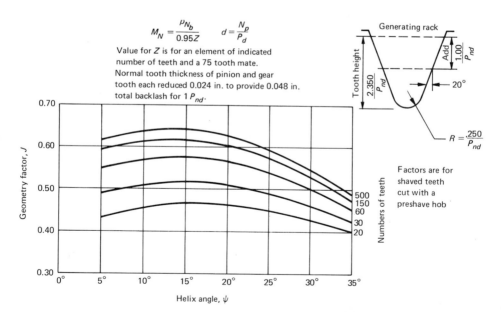

Figure 11-10 Geometry factor (J) 20 deg normal pressure angle, standard addendum preshave hob. [Courtesy American Gear Manufacturers Association.]

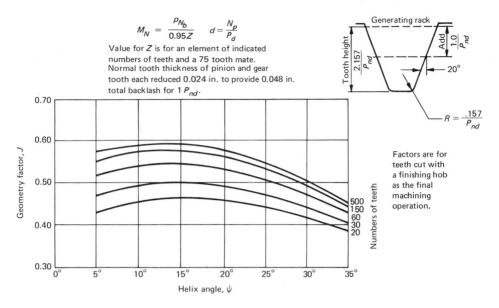

Figure 11-11 Geometry factor (J) 20 deg normal pressure angle, standard addendum finishing hob. [Courtesy American Gear Manufacturers Association.]

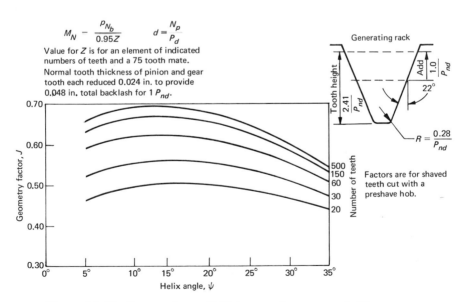

Figure 11-12 Geometry factor (J) 22 deg normal pressure angle. [Courtesy American Gear Manufacturers Association.]

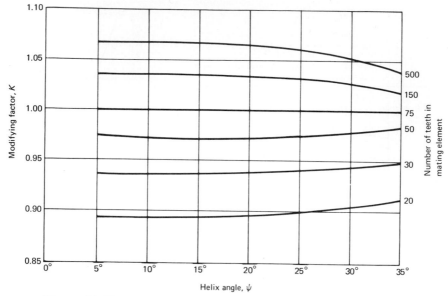

Figure 11-13 J factor multipliers for 15 deg normal pressure angle. The modifying factor can be applied to the J factor when other than 75 teeth are used in the mating element. [Courtesy American Gear Manufacturers Association.]

SECTION 11-7

Surface Durability of Helical Gears

The equations that were discussed in Chapter 10 on spur gears for wear loads can be used to determine the wear load on helical gears.

The Buckingham equation for allowable wear load, equation (10-32), can be used with only slight modification. Namely,

$$F_w = \frac{d_p b Q K}{\cos^2 \psi} \tag{11-14}$$

The symbols in the above equation have the same meaning as defined in equation (10-32), except that K is determined by using the normal pressure angle, ϕ_n.

As was the case with spur gears, the alternate wear load equation for helical gears is taken from the AGMA bulletin cited previously.

Equations (10-33) and (10-35) are repeated here for convenience.

$$\sigma_c = C_p \sqrt{\frac{F_t C_o}{C_v} \frac{C_s}{db} \frac{C_m C_f}{I}} \tag{10-33}$$

$$\sigma_c \leq S_{ac} \left[\frac{C_L C_H}{C_T C_R} \right] \tag{10-35}$$

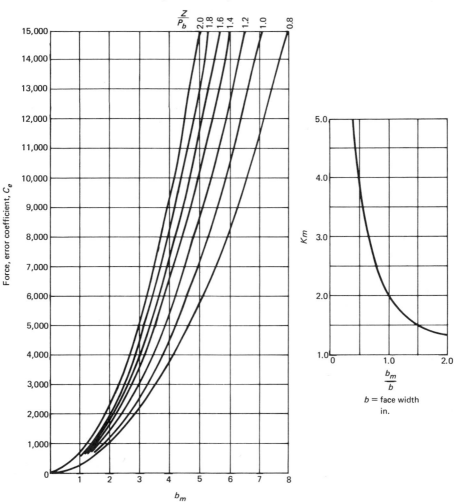

$C_e = \dfrac{W_t}{1000\,e}$	W_t = tangential load, lb e = alignment error under load, in./in.

Z = length of action
p_b = base pitch, normal to involute, transverse plane

Figure 11-14 Helical gear load distribution factor (under load), C_m [Courtesy American Gear Manufacturers Association.]

The curves and table previously presented in Section 10-17 apply equally well except for the following:

1. Instead of Figure 10-30, which illustrates the effect of different rates of misalignment, Figure 11-14 should be used if enough information is available.

2. The geometry factor I is not presented in tabular or graph form by the AGMA, and it is thus necessary to calculate I for helical gears by the use of equation (11-15) as given in the AGMA bulletin

$$I = \frac{C_c}{M_N} \qquad (11\text{-}15)$$

where C_c = curvature factor at pitch line, and M_N = load sharing ratio. C_c is given by

$$C_c = \frac{\cos \phi \sin \phi}{2} \left[\frac{M_g}{M_g + 1} \right] \qquad (11\text{-}16)$$

where: ϕ = operating transverse pressure angle in degrees and M_g = gear ratio = $\frac{1}{r_v}$.

$$M_N = \frac{p_{n_b}}{0.95\, Z} \qquad (11\text{-}17)$$

where p_{n_b} is the normal base pitch in inches, and Z is the length of action in transverse plane in inches. Equation (10-7) may be used to calculate the value for Z, where the addendum is equal to $1/P_n$, and $p_{n_b} = p_n \cos \phi_n$.

Example 11-3. How much horsepower can be safely transmitted by a pair of helical gears, 20-deg full depth, 25-deg helix, having a normal diametral pitch of 5, both made of SAE 1040 steel, and having a face width of 3 in. The pinion is rotating at 2000 rpm has 20 teeth, and the velocity ratio is to be 1 to 5. Determine the maximum horsepower that can be transmitted (a) using the modified Lewis and Buckingham equations, and (b) the AGMA method based on strength only.

Solution:
Part a. We will first use the modified Lewis equation (11-13) to determine the allowable strength in bending. Because both gears are made of the same material and the pinion will have a smaller Lewis form factor, it will be the weaker.

From Table 10-3 $S_o = 25,000$ psi. To obtain the Lewis form factor Y, we must calculate the formative number of teeth. From equation (11-12)

$$N_{t_e} = \frac{N_t}{\cos^3 \psi} = \frac{20}{(\cos 25)^3} = \frac{20}{(0.906)^3} = \frac{20}{0.744} = 27 \text{ teeth}$$

From Table 10-2, $Y = 0.348$.

When it is assumed that the tooth load acts at the tip of the gear, the stress concentration factor may be taken as 1. Therefore, from equation (11-13)

$$F_b = \frac{Sb\,Y}{K_f P_n} = \frac{25,000 \times 3 \times 0.348}{1 \times 5}$$

$$= 5220 \text{ lb}$$

The allowable wear load will now be determined from equation (11-14)

$$F_w = \frac{d_p b Q K}{\cos^2 \psi}$$

From equation (11-7)

$$\tan \phi_n = \tan \phi \cos \psi$$
$$= \tan 20 \cos 25$$
$$= 0.364 \times 0.906 = 0.33$$
$$\phi_n = 18.3 \deg$$

From equation (11-6)

$$P = P_n \cos \psi = 5 \times 0.906 = 4.53$$

$$d_p = \frac{N_t}{P} = \frac{20}{4.53} = 4.4 \text{ in.}$$

$$r_v = \frac{1}{5} = \frac{N_{t_1}}{N_{t_2}}$$

$$N_{t_2} = 5N_{t_1} = 5 \times 20 = 100 \text{ teeth}$$

Since

$$Q = \frac{2N_{t_g}}{N_{t_p} + N_{t_g}} = \frac{2 \times 100}{20 + 100}$$

$$= \frac{200}{120} = 1.67$$

From Table 10-3, BHN $= 202$. From Table 10-11, $K = 79$. Therefore

$$F_w = \frac{d_p b Q K}{\cos^2 \psi}$$

$$= \frac{4.4 \times 3 \times 1.67 \times 79}{(0.906)^2}$$

$$= 2122 \text{ lb}$$

The dynamic load can be determined from equation (10-40)

$$F_d = \frac{78 + \sqrt{V_p}}{78} F_t$$

Because the allowable load in wear is less than the allowable in bending, it is used for F_d.

$$V_p = \frac{\pi dn}{12} = \frac{\pi \times 4.4 \times 2000}{12}$$

$$= 2304 \text{ ft/min}$$

$$F_t = \frac{78 F_d}{78 + \sqrt{V_p}} = \frac{78 \times 2122}{78 + \sqrt{2304}}$$

$$= 1312 \text{ lb.}$$

$$\text{safe horsepower} = \frac{F_t V_p}{33,000}$$

$$= \frac{1312 \times 2304}{33,000} = 91.6 \text{ hp}$$

Part b. AGMA strength equation from equation (10-26)

$$S_{ad} = \frac{S_{at}K_L}{K_TK_R}$$

From Table 10-7 for BHN of 202 interpolation yields $S_{at} = 27,000$ psi. For indefinite life $K_L = 1$; $K_T = 1$ is reasonable and $K_R = 1.5$ from Table 10-9. Therefore

$$S_{ad} = \frac{27,000 \times 1}{1 \times 1.5} = 18,000 \text{ psi}$$

from equation (10-25)

$$F_t = \frac{S_{ad}K_vbJ}{K_oPK_sK_m} \qquad \text{where } \sigma_t \text{ is equal to } S_{ad}.$$

$K_o = 1.5$ assuming moderate shock and a light shock power source. $K_s = 1$ for helical gears. From Figure 10-21 curve 2, $K_v = 0.79$. From Table 10-5, $K_m = 1.2$.

For $\phi_n = 18.3$ deg, we can estimate J by interpolation, using Figure 11-9 for 15 deg and Figure 11-10 for 20 deg. For $\phi_n = 15$ deg, $J = 0.42$; for $\phi_n = 20$ deg, $J = 0.45$. Therefore, for $\phi_n = 18.3$ deg, $J = 0.44$. But because the number of teeth in the mating element is not 75, correction factor K must be applied to J. From Figures 11-13, $K = 1.01$ (approximate). Then

$$J = 1.01 \times 0.44 = 0.444$$

$$F_t = \frac{18,000 \times 0.79 \times 3 \times 0.444}{1.5 \times 4.53 \times 1 \times 1.2}$$

$$= 2320 \text{ lb}$$

Therefore

$$\text{hp} = \frac{F_tV_p}{33,000}$$

$$= \frac{2320 \times 2304}{33,000} = 132 \text{ hp}$$

compared to 91.6 for Part a. ●

SECTION 11-8

Crossed Helical Gears

When helical gears are used to transmit power between nonparallel, non-intersecting shafts, they are known as crossed helical gears. Figure 11-2 depicted a pair of crossed helical gears in mesh. It should be emphasized that crossed helical gears are not a breed in themselves but rather are ordinary helical gears used in a nonparallel shaft application. In order for two helical gears to operate as crossed helical gears, they must have the same normal pitch P_n, and normal pressure angle, ϕ_n. In other words, in the crossed gear application, the gears do not need to have the same helix angle, nor must they be of opposite hand. In fact, in most crossed gear applications, the gears have the same hand. Crossed helical gears have point contact, rather than the line contact of regular helical gears. Although the running-in period tends to extend the point contact into line contact, the contact still remains poor, and crossed gears are usually used only for problems involving small transmissions of load.

The important kinematic relationships associated with crossed helical gears, may be summed up by the discussion of the following equations. The relationship between the helix angles of the gears and the angle between the shafts on which the gears are mounted is given by

$$\Sigma = \psi_1 + \psi_2 \qquad\qquad (11\text{-}18)$$

for gears having the same hand, and

$$\Sigma = \psi_1 - \psi_2 \qquad\qquad (11\text{-}19)$$

for gears having opposite hands, where Σ = shaft angle.

A very common use for crossed gears is the one where the shaft angle is 90 deg. Clearly, for this situation, the helical gears must be of the same hand.

Equation (11-20) can be used to calculate the center distance between crossed helical gears.

$$c = \frac{1}{2P_n}\left(\frac{N_{t_1}}{\cos\psi_1} + \frac{N_{t_2}}{\cos\psi_2}\right) \qquad\qquad (11\text{-}20)$$

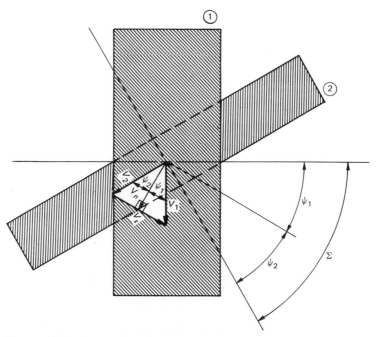

Figure 11-15 The diagram shows a pair of meshing crossed helical gears. The relationship between the helix angles and the shaft angle is shown.

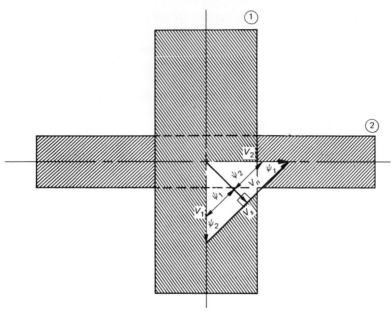

Figure 11-16 The relationship between the pitch line velocities and the sliding velocity of two meshing crossed helical gears mounted on shafts 90 deg apart.

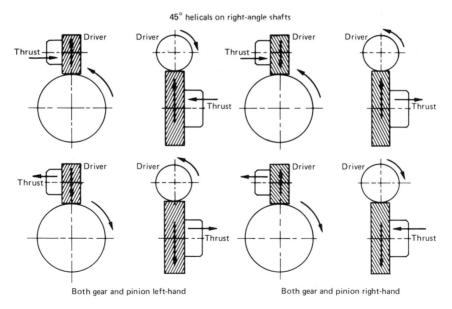

Figure 11-17 The diagram shows the direction of the thrust load for two meshing crossed helical gears mounted on shafts that are oriented 90 deg to each other. [Courtesy Insco Corporation, Groton, Mass.]

where c = center distance; P_n = normal diametral pitch; N_t = number of teeth; ψ = helix angle.

$$r_v = \frac{N_{t_1}}{N_{t_2}} = \frac{d_1 \cos \psi_1}{d_2 \cos \psi_2} \tag{11-21}$$

The sliding velocity, V_s, acts along the tooth surface, in other words, in the tangential direction and can be obtained from equation (11-22).

$$V_s = V_2 \sin \psi_2 + V_1 \sin \psi_1 \tag{11-22}$$

Figure 11-15 illustrates the situation given by the above equation.

As was indicated previously, the most common application for crossed helical gears occurs for shaft angles of 90 deg. For this special case, the velocity situation is as shown in Figure 11-16, and the sliding velocity is given by

$$V_s = \frac{V_1}{\cos \psi_2} = \frac{V_2}{\cos \psi_1} \tag{11-23}$$

Figure 11-17 may be used to determine the direction of the thrust load for crossed helical gears.

Crossed helical gear teeth do not conform to any specific standard as far as tooth proportions are concerned. With regard to contact ratio (number of teeth in contact) the designer is advised to use a value of at least 2, since the teeth have point rather than line contact.

The forces that act on crossed helical gears are the same as those for worm gearsets to be described in Section 11-9.

As for wear and strength, the bending stress does not limit the design if the teeth have a reasonable pitch. Thus, there is no need to analyze the bending strength. An allowable wear load calculation can be found in reference [1].

The efficiency of crossed helical gears is determined by the same procedure used in Section 11-9, dealing with worm gears.

SECTION 11-9

Worm Gears

Although crossed helical gears can be used for applications involving nonparallel, nonintersecting shafts, they are rather limited in their load transmission capacity. In addition, large speed ratios, on the order of say 200 to 1, could not be reasonably achieved in one reduction because of the size of gear required. For example, if the smaller gear had 20 teeth, the larger would have to have 4000 teeth. A much more feasible solution to the problem would be the use of a worm gear set.

A worm gear set such as shown in Figure 11-18 consists of the worm, which is very similar to a screw, and the worm gear, which is a helical gear. The shafts upon which the worm and the gear are mounted are usually 90 deg

Figure 11-18 A single enveloping worm gear set. [Courtesy Illinois Gear Division, Wallace-Murray Corporation.]

apart. One of the advantages associated with the use of worm gears is that the tooth engagement occurs without the shock prevalent in other gear types. In fact the meshing of two teeth occurs with a sliding action which, while resulting in very quiet operation, may produce overheating.

Worm gears may be either single or double enveloping. In a single enveloping set, Figure 11-18, the helical gear has its width cut into a concave surface, thus partially enclosing the worm when in mesh. An example of the double enveloping type is shown in Figure 11-19. In addition to having the helical gear width cut concavely, this type also has the worm length cut concavely. The result is that both the worm and the gear partially enclose each other. A double enveloping set will have more teeth in contact and will have area rather than line contact, thus permitting greater load transmission.

Figure 11-19 A double enveloping worm gear set. [Courtesy Michigan Tool Company.]

All worm gears must be carefully mounted in order to assure proper operation. The double enveloping or cone type is much more difficult to mount than the single enveloping.

The worms are usually made of case hardened alloy steel, and the gear is usually made of one of the bronzes. The worm is usually cut on a lathe, whereas the gear is hobbed.

SECTION 11-10

Worm Gear Terminology

The terminology used to describe the worm is very much like that used in discussing power screws. The axial pitch of the worm is the distance between corresponding points on adjacent teeth, and the lead is the axial distance the worm advances during one revolution of the worm. For shafts that are 90 deg apart, the axial pitch of the worm is equal to the circular pitch of the gear. Most worms have multiple threads so that the lead is obtained by multiplying the number of threads (or number of teeth) by the pitch.

The more important kinematic equations applying to worm gearing are listed below.

$$\tan \lambda_w = \frac{l}{\pi \, d_w} = \frac{V_{P_g}}{V_{P_w}} \qquad (11\text{-}24)$$

where

V_{P_g} = pitch line velocity of gear
V_{P_w} = pitch line velocity of worm
λ_w = lead angle of worm, the angle between a tangent to the pitch helix and the plane of rotation
l = lead = $N_{t_w} \times p_{a_w}$ = number of teeth or threads of worm times the axial pitch of worm.
d_w = pitch diameter of worm

Relations involving the angles of the worm and gear are

$$\lambda_w + \psi_w = 90 \text{ deg} \qquad (11\text{-}25)$$

where ψ_w = helix angle of worm

also

$$\lambda_g + \psi_g = 90 \text{ deg} \qquad (11\text{-}26)$$

and for 90 deg shaft angles

$$\lambda_w = \psi_g \qquad (11\text{-}27)$$

The center distance is given by

$$c = \frac{d_w + d_g}{2} \qquad (11\text{-}28)$$

The AGMA recommends the following equation be used to check the magnitude of d_w

$$d_w \geq \frac{c^{0.875}}{2.2} \approx 3p_g \qquad (11\text{-}29)$$

where p_g = circular pitch of gear in inches.

The velocity ratio is given by

$$r_v = \frac{\omega_g}{\omega_w} = \frac{N_{tw}}{N_{tg}} = \frac{l}{\pi d_g} \qquad (11\text{-}30)$$

Example 11-4. A triple-threaded worm, having a lead of 3 in., meshes with a gear having 45 teeth and a normal circular pitch of 0.9455 in. Find the center distance between the shafts if they are 90-deg. apart.

Solution: Since $l = N_{tw} \times p_{aw}$

$$p_{aw} = \frac{l}{N_{tw}} = \frac{3}{3} = 1 \text{ in.}$$

From equation (11-6), $P_n = P/\cos \psi_g$ `

$$\cos \psi_g^{'} = \frac{P_g}{P_{ng}} = \frac{p_{ng}}{p_g}$$

but $p_{aw} = p_g$. Therefore

$$\cos \psi_g = \frac{p_{ng}}{p_{aw}} = \frac{0.9455}{1} = 0.9455$$

$$\psi_g = 19 \text{ deg}$$

Therefore from equation (11-27), $\lambda_w = \psi_g = 19$ deg, and from equation (11-24)

$$\tan \lambda_w = \frac{l}{\pi d_w}$$

$$d_w = \frac{l}{\pi \tan \lambda_w} = \frac{3}{\pi \times 0.344}$$

$$= 2.8 \text{ in.}$$

$$r_v = \frac{N_{tw}}{N_{tg}} = \frac{3}{45} = \frac{1}{15}$$

But

$$r_v = \frac{l}{\pi d_g}$$

Thus

$$d_g = \frac{l}{\pi r_v} = \frac{3}{\pi \times \frac{1}{15}} = 14.33 \text{ in.}$$

From equation (11-28)

$$c = \frac{d_w + d_g}{2} = \frac{2.8 + 14.33}{2}$$

$$= 8.57 \text{ in.} \quad \bullet$$

SECTION 11-11

Worm Gear Strength

In worm gear sets, the teeth on the worm are always stronger than the worm gear teeth. The simplified Lewis equation is therefore applied to the worm gear in determining strength.

$$F_b = \frac{SYb}{P_n} = Sbyp_n \qquad (11\text{-}31)$$

where the terms in the equation have the usual meaning.

Values for the Lewis form factor can be obtained from the following table. It is suggested that the values be used only if the sum of the worm and worm gear teeth exceeds 40.

SECTION 11-12

Dynamic Load

The dynamic load can be estimated by using the equation (11-32)

$$F_d = \left(\frac{1200 + V_{pg}}{1200}\right) F_t \qquad (11\text{-}32)$$

where V_{pg} = pitch line speed of the gear in feet per minute, and F_t = transmitted load as determined by the horsepower applied to the gear.

It should be pointed out that the horsepower on the gear is the output horsepower, which will depend on the efficiency of the set. However, since the efficiency is not known at the initial design stage, the usual procedure is to use the input horsepower, realizing that the F_d value thus obtained will be higher than is the actual case. But, since we require F_b to be greater than or equal to F_d, this procedure is clearly conservative.

Table 11-1 Normal Pressure Angle

ϕ_n, deg.	Y	y
14 1/2	0.314	0.100
20	0.392	0.125
25	0.470	0.150
30	0.550	0.175

SECTION 11-13

Wear Load Equation

An approximate equation suggested by Buckingham [1] is usually used to determine the allowable wear load.

$$F_w = d_g b K^1 \qquad (11\text{-}33)$$

where d_g = pitch diameter of gear; b = face width of gear; and K^1 = constant which depends on the material and geometry of the gear. Table 11-2 may be used to obtain values of K^1.

The usual requirement is that $F_w \geq F_d$.

SECTION 11-14

Efficiency of Worm Gears

In order to discuss the efficiency of worm gears properly, it is necessary to consider the tooth loads that are acting. The forces acting on worm gears are shown in Figure 11-20. The normal force F_n acts perpendicularly to the tooth surface and is broken up into the following three components:

F_t = transmitted force which is tangential to worm and axial to the gear = $F_n \cos \phi_n \sin \lambda_w$

F_{thrust} = axial thrust load on worm and tangential or transmitted force on worm gear = $F_n \cos \phi_n \cos \lambda_w$

F_r = the radial or separating force = $F_n \sin \phi_n$.

Figure 11-21 may be used to determine the direction of the thrust load on a worm gear set.

Table 11-2 Wear Constant, K^1, for Worm Gears with θ_n 20 deg*

Worm	Gear	K^1
Steel, 500 BHN	Bronze	80
Steel, 250 BHN	Bronze	60
Steel, 500 BHN	Chilled bronze	115
Steel, 500 BHN	Cast iron	50

*The values for K^1 given above are typical values. The wear load should only be estimated from equation (11-33). A more complete set of values may be found in reference [1].

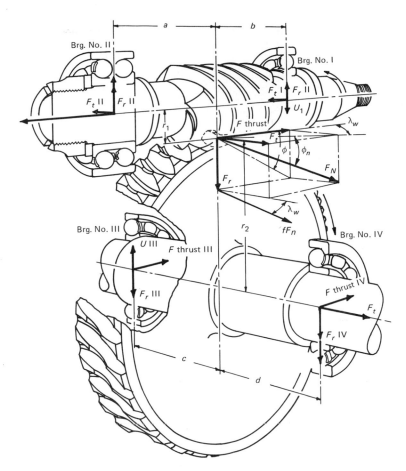

Figure 11-20 Bearing loads due to worm gearing. [Courtesy New Departure—Hyatt Bearings Division, General Motors Corporation.]

The efficiency of a worm gear set is defined as the output horsepower divided by the input horsepower. The frictional force acting between the worm and the gear is equal to fF_n and is resolved into components $fF_n \cos \lambda_w$ along the axis of the worm and $fF_n \sin \lambda_w$ along the axis of the gear.

The resultant force along the axis of the gear (in the tangential direction for the worm), and therefore the input force of the worm, is equal to $F_n \cos \phi_n \sin \lambda_w + fF_n \cos \lambda_w$, while the resultant force in the tangential direction of the gear (in the thrust direction for the worm), and therefore the output force on the gear, is equal to $F_n \cos \phi_n \cos \lambda_w - fF_n \sin \lambda_w$.

The input and output power can thus be determined as follows:

$$\text{power}_i = (F_n \cos \phi_n \sin \lambda_w + fF_n \cos \lambda_w)V_{pw}$$

$$\text{power}_o = (F_n \cos \phi_n \cos \lambda_w - fF_n \sin \lambda_w)V_{pg}$$

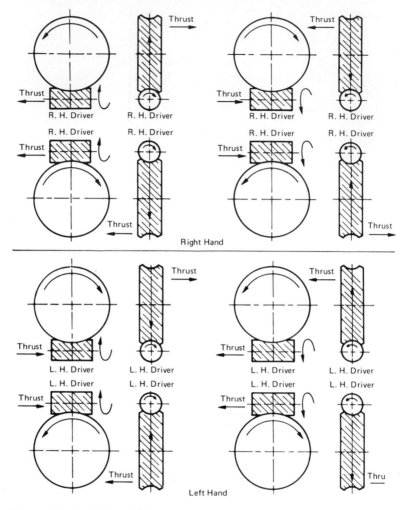

Figure 11-21 Direction of thrust load for a worm gear set. [Courtesy Insco Corporation, Groton, Mass.]

where V_{p_w} = pitch velocity of worm and V_{p_g} = pitch line velocity of gear. Therefore

$$\text{eff} = \frac{\text{power}_o}{\text{power}_i} = \frac{F_n(\cos \phi_n \cos \lambda_w - f \sin \lambda_w)V_{p_g}}{F_n(\cos \phi_n \sin \lambda_w + f \cos \lambda_w)V_{p_w}}$$

$$= \frac{(\cos \phi_n \cos \lambda_w - f \sin \lambda_w) \tan \lambda_w}{(\cos \phi_n \sin \lambda_w + f \cos \lambda_w)}$$

$$= \tan \lambda_w \left(\frac{\cos \phi_n - f \tan \lambda_w}{\cos \phi_n \tan \lambda_w + f} \right) \qquad (11\text{-}34)$$

Another useful form is

$$\text{eff} = \frac{\cos \phi_n - f \tan \lambda_w}{\cos \phi_n + f \cot \lambda_w} \tag{11-35}$$

Comparison of this equation with the power screw efficiency equation, shows that they are the same.

Most references give values for the coefficient of friction as a function of the sliding velocity, V_s.

$$V_s = \frac{V_{pw}}{\cos \lambda_w} \tag{11-36}$$

There seems to be no agreement as to a uniform set of values for the coefficient of friction. The following equations are suggested by Faires [2] as a reasonable compromise for a carburized and ground worm driving a phosphor bronze gear.

$$f = \frac{0.155}{V_s^{0.2}} \qquad \text{where } 3 < V_s < 70 \text{ ft/min} \tag{11-37}$$

or

$$f = \frac{0.32}{V_s^{0.36}} \qquad \text{for } 70 < V_s < 3000 \text{ ft/min} \tag{11-38}$$

Another consideration regarding the frictional force in worm gearsets is the question of whether the gearset is reversible or not. Most sets are speed reduction units; in other words, the worm is the driver. The gearset can be a speed increasing unit if the gear is the driver. Thus a reversible gearset is one in which either the worm or the gear can be the driver. If the frictional force developed is large enough, the gearset will be irreversible or self-locking. In general, when the lead angle of the worm is 10 deg or less, the set will be self-locking. This self-locking effect can be an advantage in applications where a braking action is needed. However, the designer is cautioned to include a secondary braking device in the design, because otherwise a gear failure will result in the complete loss of braking power.

Finally, it should be obvious that the irreversible gearset will have a much lower efficiency than a reversible set because of the large frictional force developed.

SECTION 11-15

Thermal Capacity of Worm Gearsets

One of the major problems associated with worm gearsets is the question of how much heat is developed during operation and whether the gear case is capable of dissipating this heat. In fact, most worm gear units have their horsepower capacity limited by the heat dissipation ability of the casing.

The transfer of heat from the casing is accomplished by both radiation and convection. In arriving at an equation to determine how much heat can be dissipated, such factors as housing area, temperature change between lubricant and the ambient air, and a combined heat transfer coefficient must be considered. The usual heat transfer equation can be written as follows:

$$H = C_{cr}A_c\Delta t \tag{11-39}$$

where

H = the energy dissipated through the housing (lost energy or frictional energy) ft-lb/min

C_{cr} = combined heat transfer coefficient, ft-lb/[(min)(in.^{2})($°F$)] (Figure 11-22)

A_c = area of housing exposed to ambient air, in.^{2}

Δt = temperature difference between oil and ambient air, $°F$

The cooling surface area of the housing can be estimated by equation (11-40) which is recommended by the AGMA.

$$A_c = 43.2c^{1.7} \tag{11-40}$$

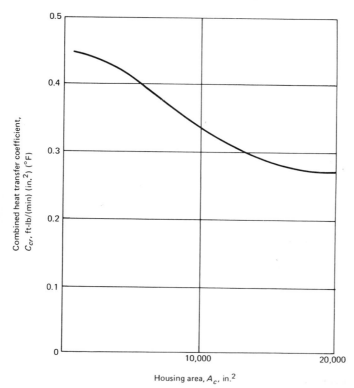

Figure 11-22 Plot of heat transfer coefficient versus gear housing area.

where A_c = housing cooling area in square inches and c = center distance in inches.

The heat that must be dissipated from the casing can be determined by considering the frictional or lost horsepower. Since

$$\text{eff} = \frac{\text{hp}_o}{\text{hp}_i}$$

and

$$\text{hp}_o = \text{hp}_i - \text{hp}_{\text{lost}}$$

$$e\,\text{hp}_i = \text{hp}_i - \text{hp}_{\text{lost}}$$

or

$$\text{hp}_{\text{lost}} = \text{hp}_i - e\,\text{hp}_i = \text{hp}_i(1 - e)$$

Then the energy which must be dissipated is given by

$$H_d = \text{hp}_i(1 - e) \times 33{,}000 \qquad (11\text{-}41)$$

Clearly the heat energy developed H_d as determined by equation (11-41) must be equal to or less than the heat energy dissipation capacity H as determined by equation (11-39).

SECTION 11-16

Worm Gear Standards and Proportions

There are no real standards or proportions that are accepted universally. However, some suggested values, which may be of some use to the designer are now presented.

With regard to the axial pitch of the worm, the AGMA suggests the following values as standards:

$$\tfrac{1}{4}, \tfrac{5}{16}, \tfrac{3}{8}, \tfrac{1}{2}, \tfrac{5}{8}, \tfrac{3}{4}, 1, 1\tfrac{1}{4}, 1\tfrac{1}{2}, 1\tfrac{3}{4}, 2$$

The choice of pressure angle and lead angle must be made, keeping in mind that too large a lead angle for a specific pressure angle will result in excessive undercutting of the gear tooth. Buckingham [3] recommends the following limiting values for lead angles.

Normal Pressure Angle, ϕ_n	Lead Angle, λ_w Should Not Exceed
14 1/2 deg	16 deg
20 deg	25 deg
25 deg	35 deg
30 deg	45 deg

A reasonable value for the lead angle has been suggested as 6 deg of lead angle for each thread of worm. Thus a quadruple threaded worm would have a lead angle of 24 deg.

The face length, or axial length of the worm may be approximated by equation (11-42)

$$L = P_g\left(4.5 + \frac{N_{t_g}}{50}\right) \tag{11-42}$$

As far as the gear face width is concerned, care should be exercised by the designer to prevent the width from becoming too large. Because of the non-uniform distribution of load across the face of the gear, the larger the width the greater will be the difference between the average load and the maximum load. A reasonable proportion would seem to be that the width should be no more than the radius of the outside circle of the worm.

Finally, it should be stressed that the suggested proportions given above are merely that, suggested values. They can help the designer start his solution, but they are relationships that can be deviated from. Rather than going into an extensive discussion of a typical worm gearset design procedure, the following example will be used to demonstrate one possible approach to the problem.

Example 11-5. Design a worm gearset to deliver 15 hp from a shaft rotating at 1500 rpm to another rotating at 75 rpm.

Solution: Assume that the normal pressure angle is to be 20 deg. The lead angle λ_w should therefore not exceed 25 deg (from the table on page 633). Allowing 6 deg per thread of worm, the worm could have 4 or less teeth. Let us try a triple threaded worm.

$$r_v = \frac{n_g}{n_w} = \frac{75}{1500} = \frac{1}{20} = \frac{N_{t_w}}{N_{t_g}}$$

Therefore

$$N_{t_g} = 20 \times N_{t_w} = 20 \times 3 = 60 \text{ teeth}$$

Assume a center distance of 10 in. The magnitude for center distance is based upon actual limitations in design or is based upon designer's judgement.

$$d_w \approx \frac{c^{0.875}}{2.2} = \frac{10^{0.875}}{2.2} = 3.41 \text{ in. Try } d_w = 4 \text{ in.}$$

Since $d_w \approx 3p_g$

$$P_g = \tfrac{1}{3}d_w = 1.33 \text{ in.} = p_{w_a}. \text{ Try } p_{w_a} = 1.$$

$$P_g = \frac{\pi}{P_g} = 3.1416$$

$$d_g = \frac{N_{t_g}}{P_g} = \frac{60}{3.1416} = 19.1 \text{ in.}$$

$$\text{actual } c = \frac{d_w + d_g}{2} = \frac{4 + 19.1}{2}$$

$$= 11.55 \text{ in.}$$

Check $d_w = 11.55^{0.875}/2.2 = 3.87$ in. Therefore d_w of 4 is satisfactory.

$$\text{lead} = N_{t_w} \times p_{w_a} = 3 \times 1 = 3 \text{ in.}$$

$$\tan \lambda_w = \frac{l}{\pi d_w} = \frac{3}{\pi \times 4} = 0.239$$

$$\lambda_w = 13.43 \text{ deg}$$

$$\lambda_w = \psi_g = 13.43 \text{ deg}$$

$$P_{n_g} = \frac{P_g}{\cos \psi_g} = \frac{3.1416}{\cos 13.43} = 3.23$$

$$V_{p_g} = 75 \frac{\text{rev}}{\text{min}} \times \frac{2\pi \text{ rad}}{\text{rev}} \times \frac{d_g}{2} \times \frac{1 \text{ ft}}{12 \text{ in.}}$$

$$= \frac{75 \times 2\pi \times 19.1}{2 \times 12} = 375 \text{ ft/min}$$

$$T = \frac{\text{hp} \times 63,000}{n} = \frac{15 \times 63,000}{75}$$

$$= 12,600 \text{ in.-lb}$$

$$F_t = \frac{T}{d_g/2} = \frac{12,600}{19.1/2} = 1310 \text{ lb} = F_{\text{thrust worm}}$$

$$F_d = \frac{(1200 + V_{p_g})}{1200} F_t$$

$$= \frac{(1200 + 375)}{1200} 1310 = 1730 \text{ lb}$$

Assume $b = \frac{1}{2}d_w = \frac{1}{2} \times 4 = 2$ in. from Table 11-1, $Y = 0.392$. From equation (11-31)

$$F_b = \frac{SYb}{P_n} = F_d$$

Therefore

$$S = \frac{F_d P_n}{Yb} = \frac{1730 \times 3.23}{0.392 \times 2}$$

$$= 7131 \text{ psi}$$

From Table 10-3 it can be seen that a phosphor bronze gear having an S_o of 12,000 psi will be satisfactory, since $12,000 > 7131$.

Check for wear. Assume worm is made of hardened steel. From Table 11-2, $K^1 = 80$. From equation (10-33)

$$F_w = d_g b K^1$$

$$= 19.1 \times 2 \times 80 = 3056 \text{ lb}$$

Since $F_w > F_d$, the gearset is satisfactory for wear.

The AGMA recommendation for axial length of worm is

$$L = P_g \left(4.5 + \frac{N_{t_g}}{50} \right)$$

$$= 1 \left(4.5 + \frac{60}{50} \right) = 5.7 \text{ in.}$$

Cooling check. We will first determine the heat developed by using equation (11.41).

$$V_{p_w} = 1500 \frac{\text{rev}}{\text{min}} \times 2\pi \frac{\text{rad}}{\text{rev}} \times \frac{d_w}{2} \times \frac{1 \text{ ft}}{12 \text{ in.}}$$

$$= \frac{1500 \times 2\pi \times 4}{2 \times 12} = 1571 \text{ ft/min}$$

From equation (11-36)

$$V_s = \frac{V_{p_w}}{\cos \lambda_w} = \frac{1571}{\cos 13.43}$$

$$= 1615 \text{ ft/min}$$

From equation (11-38)

$$f = \frac{0.32}{V_s^{0.36}} = \frac{0.32}{(1615)^{0.36}} = 0.0224$$

$$F_{t_g} = F_n \cos \phi_n \cos \lambda_w$$

$$F_n = \frac{F_t}{\cos \phi_n \cos \lambda_w} = \frac{1310}{\cos 20 \cos 13.43}$$

$$= 1433.3 \text{ lb}$$

$$\text{power}_i = (F_n \cos \phi_n \sin \lambda_w + f F_n \cos \lambda_w) V_{p_w}$$

$$= (1433.3 \times 0.940 \times 0.232 + 0.0241 \times 6041 \times 0.973)1571$$

$$= 540{,}130 \text{ ft-lb/min} = 16.37 \text{ hp}$$

$$\text{eff} = \frac{\cos \phi_n - f \tan \lambda_w}{\cos \phi_n + f \cot \lambda_w}$$

$$= \frac{\cos 20 - 0.0224 \times \tan 13.43}{\cos 20 + 0.0224 \cot 13.43}$$

$$= \frac{0.938 - 0.0224 \times 0.239}{0.938 + 0.0224 \times 4.19}$$

$$= \frac{0.9345}{1.041} = 90.4\%$$

From equation (11-41)

$$H_d = \text{hp}_i(1 - e) = 16.37(1 - 0.904)$$

$$= 1.57 \text{ hp} = 51{,}860 \text{ ft-lb/min}$$

We will next use equation (11-39) to determine the heat that can be dissipated. We will further specify that the gearset is to be enclosed in a case and oil be supplied to the case. Then from equation (11-40)

$$A_c = 43.2c^{1.7} = 43.2(11.55)^{1.7}$$

$$= 2766 \text{ in.}^2$$

From Figure 11-22

$$C_{cr} = 0.43 \text{ ft-lb/(min)(in.}^2)(°F)$$

A reasonable temperature difference would be 100°F (ambient air ≈ 80°F, oil film ≈ 180°F). Then from equation (11-39)

$$H = C_{cr}A_c\,dt$$

$$= 0.43 \times 2766 \times 100 = 119{,}000 \text{ ft-lb/min}$$

Therefore 51,860 ft-lb/min are developed while 119,000 ft-lb/min can be dissipated.

Overheating will not be a problem. ●

SECTION 11-17

Bevel Gears

The last important type of gear used to transmit power between non-parallel, intersecting shafts is the bevel gear. Bevel gears can perhaps be best described as being conical gears. In other words, whereas the gears discussed to this point were cut on cylindrical blanks, bevel gears are cut on conical blanks.

There are four primary types of bevel gears, shown in Figures 11-23 through 11-26.

Figure 11-23 Straight bevel gears. [Courtesy Eaton Corporation, Industrial Drives Division.]

Figure 11-24 ZEROL bevel gears. [Courtesy Gleason Works, Rochester, N. Y.]

Figure 11-25 Spiral bevel gears. [Courtesy Gleason Works, Rochester, N.Y.]

Figure 11-26 Hypoid bevel gears. [Courtesy Gleason Works, Rochester, N.Y.]

SECTION 11-18

Straight Bevel Gears

The simplest of the four types of bevel gears mentioned above is the so-called straight bevel gear. The name is derived from the fact that the teeth are cut straight, have a taper, and if extended inward, would intersect each other at the axis. Straight bevel gears are used primarily for relatively low speed applications with pitch line velocities up to 1000 ft/min and where smoothness and quietness are not an important consideration. However, with the use of a finishing operation, such as grinding, speeds up to 15,000 ft/min have been successfully handled by straight bevel gears.

The terminology and important physical characteristics associated with bevel gears are shown in Figure 11-27.

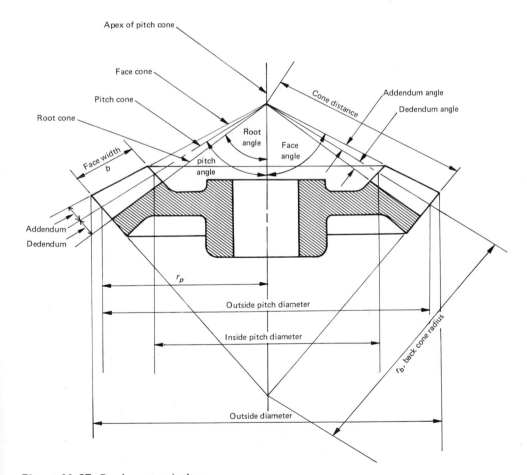

Figure 11-27 Bevel gear terminology.

Bevel gears are also classified according to the pitch angle of the gear. Figure 11-28 shows a pair of regular bevel gears with a shaft angle of 90 deg. Most bevel gear applications involve shaft angles of 90 deg, but there are applications for which the angle is something other than 90 deg. When the shaft angle is 90 deg and the gears are of the same size (the velocity ratio is equal to 1), the gearset is known as a miter gearset, and each gear has a pitch angle of 45 deg.

When the pitch angle of a bevel gear is less than 90 deg, as is the case with the gears shown in Figure 11-28, it is known as an external bevel gear. Gears having a pitch angle of 90 deg, Figure 11-29, are known as crown gears, and those having pitch angles greater than 90 deg are called internal gears.

Straight bevel gears may be cut with a wide range of pressure angles, such as $14\frac{1}{2}$ deg, and so on, but the basic standard pressure angle is 20 deg. The working depth is $2/P$ in., the clearance is $(0.188/P) + 0.002$ in., the pinion is cut with a long addendum whereas the gear has a short addendum, and the teeth are not stubbed.

The wearing characteristics improve as the number of teeth is increased. It is suggested, therefore, that the minimum number of teeth for most bevel gears be 13, whereas for miter gears the limiting value should be taken as 16 teeth.

Straight bevel gears are the most economical of the various types of bevel gears to be discussed.

Finally, a modified type of straight bevel gear called a coniflex gear has been developed, Figure 11-30. It has generated and ground teeth and is formed to have localized lengthwise tooth contact. The result is that the concentration of load on the ends of the teeth, due to assembling or deflection under load, is prevented.

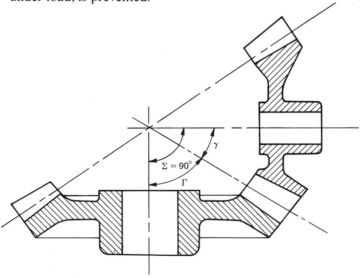

Figure 11-28 Regular bevel gears with 90 deg shaft-angle.

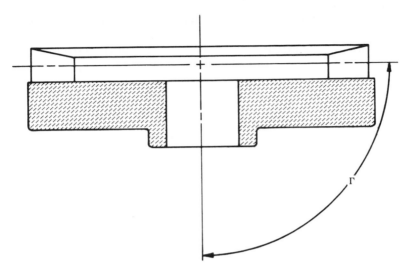

Figure 11-29 Bevel gears having a pitch angle of 90 deg are known as crown gears.

The velocity ratio for bevel gears is given by

$$r_v = \frac{n_{\text{driven}}}{n_{\text{driver}}} \tag{11-42}$$

As can be seen in Figure 11-28, the shaft angle is equal to the sum of the pitch angle of the pinion and gear.

$$\Sigma = \Gamma + \gamma \tag{11-43}$$

Figure 11-30 Coniflex bevel gear. [Courtesy Arrow Gear Company.]

where Σ = shaft angle; Γ = pitch angle of gear; and γ = pitch angle of pinion.

The pitch angles can be determined by equations (11-44) and (11-45).

$$\tan \Gamma = \frac{\sin \Sigma}{(N_{t_p}/N_{t_g}) + \cos \Sigma} \qquad (11\text{-}44)$$

$$\tan \gamma = \frac{\sin \Sigma}{(N_{t_g}/N_{t_p}) + \cos \Sigma} \qquad (11\text{-}45)$$

Clearly if the shaft angle is equal to 90 deg, the equations become

$$\tan \Gamma = \frac{N_{t_g}}{N_{t_p}} \qquad (11\text{-}46)$$

$$\tan \gamma = \frac{N_{t_p}}{N_{t_g}} \qquad (11\text{-}47)$$

SECTION 11-19

Formative or Equivalent Number of Teeth

In the discussion of helical gears, it was pointed out that the tooth profile in the normal plane would be a spur gear having an ellipse as its radius of curvature. The result was that the form factors for spur gears applied, providing that the formative number of teeth were used in determining the tabular values.

A somewhat similar situation exists with regard to bevel gears. The tooth profile in the plane perpendicular to an element of the pitch cone will have a radius equal to the back cone radius, shown in Figure 11-27. It is then a relatively simple matter to derive equation (11-48) for determining the formative number of teeth.

$$N'_{tg} = \frac{N_{tg}}{\cos \Gamma} \quad \text{and} \quad N'_{tp} = \frac{N_{tp}}{\cos \gamma} \qquad (11\text{-}48)$$

where N'_t = formative number of teeth; N_t = actual number of teeth; Γ = pitch cone angle of gear, and γ = pitch cone angle of pinion.

SECTION 11-20

Strength of Bevel Gears by Modified Lewis Equation

The geometric shape of bevel gear teeth results in several problems when attempting to derive an equation for the beam strength. As can be seen in Figure 11-31, the load acting on a bevel gear tooth varies linearly along the face of the tooth. It should also be clear from the sketch that the tooth

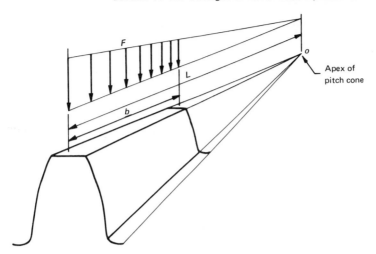

Figure 11-31 The linear variation in tooth load and tooth thickness for bevel gears.

thickness also varies linearly along the face of the gear. This variation, in turn, results in linear variations of circular and diametral pitch. Because of these variations, it is necessary when applying the Lewis equation to bevel gear teeth to consider an element dx along the face of the tooth, for which these variables can be considered constant. Figure 11-32 shows the element dx, as well as the other terms we will use in deriving the strength equation. In the figure, L is the cone distance, b is the face width, and r is the pitch radius. The Lewis equation is now applied to the element, dx.

$$dF_x = \frac{SYdx}{P_x} \qquad (11\text{-}49)$$

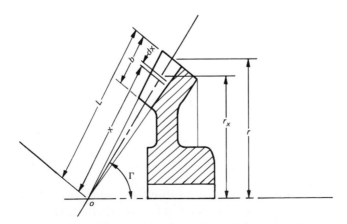

Figure 11-32 The linear variation of the pitch and pitch radius.

where dF_x = incremental allowable bending force acting on dx; Y = Lewis form factor; and P_x = diametral pitch of tooth at distance x from apex of pitch cone.

Multiplying both sides by r_x and integrating we get

$$\int r_x \, dF_x = \int \frac{S Y r_x \, dx}{P_x} \tag{11-50}$$

But the $\int r_x \, dF_x$ is equal to the total torque T transmitted by the gear.

Consideration of Figure 11-32 indicates that the circular pitch decreases linearly as x decreases. Since the diametral pitch varies inversely as the circular pitch, it follows that the diametral pitch varies inversely with x. Therefore, because the largest value of circular pitch occurs at $x = L$, the largest value of P_x will occur at $x = L - b$.

This fact can be written as follows:

$$\frac{P_x}{P} = \frac{L}{x}$$

where P = diametral pitch at $x = L$.

It will also be clear from an inspection of Figure 11-32 that the following relationship holds because of the similar triangles involved.

$$\frac{r_x}{r} = \frac{x}{L}$$

Substituting these relationships into equation (11-50) gives us

$$T = \int \frac{S Y (r/L) x \, dx}{PL/x}$$

and since dx varies from $x = (L - b)$ to $x = L$ we get

$$T = \frac{S Y r}{PL^2} \int_{L-b}^{L} x^2 \, dx$$

$$= \frac{S Y r}{PL^2} \left(\frac{x^3}{3} \right)_{L-b}^{L}$$

$$= \frac{S Y r}{PL^2} \left[\frac{L^3 - (L - b)^3}{3} \right]$$

$$= \frac{S Y r}{PL^2} \left[\frac{L^3 - L^3 + 3L^2 b - 3Lb^2 + b^3}{3} \right]$$

$$T = \frac{S Y r b}{P} \left(1 - \frac{b}{L} + \frac{b^2}{3L^2} \right) \tag{11-51}$$

Before continuing with our derivation, it would be well to consider limitations upon the values of maximum face width. If the face width is made too large, the inevitable deflections that occur in a bevel gear installation will cause a greater concentration of load at the small end of the tooth. Because this is the weakest part of the tooth, it is obvious that failure will occur much more readily than if the face width had been kept smaller.

Most designers limit the maximum value of the face width to one third the cone distance. In other words,

$$b \leqslant \frac{L}{3}$$

It is clear, therefore, that the maximum value of $b^2/3L^2 = 1/27$. A consideration of the terms in the parenthesis of equation (11-51) indicates that $b^2/3L^2$ is small enough compared to the other terms so that it may be neglected. If we also divide both sides by r, we get the equation for the allowable bending load,

$$F_b = \frac{SYb}{P}\left(1 - \frac{b}{L}\right) \tag{11-52}$$

where Y is the Lewis form factor as determined by using the formative number of teeth.

SECTION 11-21

Dynamic Load for Bevel Gears

The dynamic load equations given for spur gears, equations (10-38) through (10-40), may be used to obtain reasonable values for the dynamic loads on bevel gears. The pitch line velocity V_p to be used in these equations is obtained by using the mean pitch diameter.

This approach then requires that $F_b \geqslant F_d$.

SECTION 11-22

Allowable Wear Load for Bevel Gears

The allowable wear equation is based upon the Hertz contact stress equation and the Buckingham application of it to gears. Equation (11-53) may be used to estimate the allowable wear load.

$$F_w = \frac{d_p K Q'}{\cos \gamma} \tag{11-53}$$

where d_p = pitch diameter measured at back of tooth.

$$Q' = \frac{2N'_{t_g}}{N'_{t_p} + N'_{t_g}}$$

(N'_{t_p} and N'_{t_g} refer to formative number of teeth.) The other terms in the equation are the same as previously discussed. Again it is required that

$$F_w \geqslant F_d$$

It is suggested that the designer use this method involving F_b, F_w, and F_d only in the preliminary design stage and then finalize the design by the AGMA method to be discussed in the next section.

SECTION 11-23

AGMA Method for Designing Bevel Gears

The recommended procedure for analyzing bevel gears is that presented by the AGMA.[2] The equations are similar to those presented in the discussion of spur gears, with some of the values of the correction factors applicable to bevel gears only.

Equation (10-25) is repeated here for convenience

$$\sigma_t = \frac{F_t K_o P K_s K_m}{K_v b J} \tag{10-25}$$

where

σ_t = calculated stress at root of tooth, psi
F_t = transmitted load, lb, based upon the large end pitch diameter
K_o = overload correction factor; Table 10-4 should be used
P = diametral pitch at large end of tooth
K_s = size correction factor, Figure 11-33 gives the values of the size factor for bevel gears
K_m = load distribution correction. When the deflections or displacements of gear and pinion are known Figure 11-34 can be used; when this information is not available, Table 11-3 should be used. The smaller values are for those cases where the mountings are extremely rigid, whereas the larger values are to be used if the rigidity is questionable
K_v = dynamic factor, Figure 10-21 is to be used
b = face width, in.
J = geometry factor, Figure 11-35 gives the values for the geometry factor for a 25-deg straight bevel gear. Charts giving values for many other combinations of pressure and shaft angle can be obtained from the Gleason Works, Rochester, N.Y.

It is now possible to calculate the allowable bending stress by the AGMA formula. The AGMA maximum allowable design stress discussed in Chapter 10 is here repeated.

$$S_{ad} = \frac{S_{at} K_L}{K_T K_R} \tag{10-26}$$

---

[2] Reference and acknowledgement cited in Section 11-6.

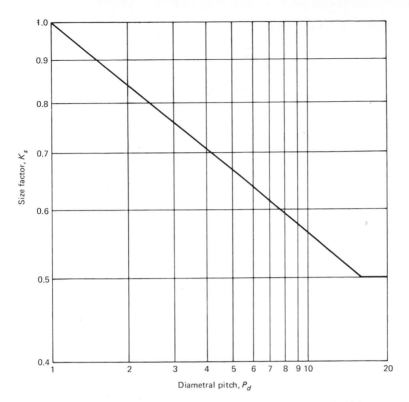

Figure 11-33 Size factor for bevel gears, K_s. [Courtesy AGMA.]

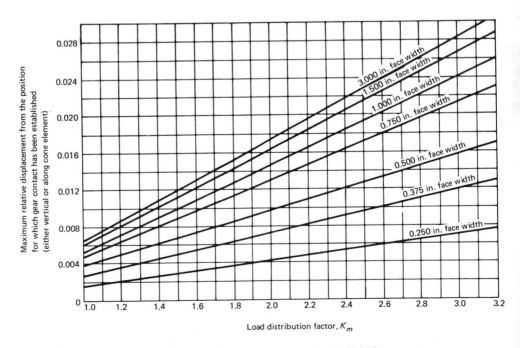

Figure 11-34 Load distribution factor for bevel gears. [Courtesy AGMA.]

Table 11-3 Bevel Gear Load Distribution Factors, K_m

Application	Both Members Straddle Mounted	One Member Straddle Mounted	Neither Member Straddle Mounted
General industrial	1.00–1.10	1.10–1.25	1.25–1.40
Automotive	1.00–1.10	1.10–1.25	
Aircraft	1.00–1.25	1.10–1.40	1.25–1.50

SOURCE: AGMA.

NOTE: Because of the smaller bearing loads for straddle mountings, the overall designs are sometimes smaller and lighter for equal rigidity. Frequently, space limitations dictate the type of mounting for a particular installation. Usually one member of the pair can be straddle mounted, but it is not always feasible to use a straddle mounting for both members. An overhung mounting may be just as good as, or better than, a straddle mounting arrangement. However, rigid supports as well as adequate capacity are required for both types of mountings.

where

S_{ad} = maximum allowable design stress, psi

S_{at} = allowable stress for the material, psi; Table 10-7 or Figure 10-24 can be used

K_L = life factor, Table 10-8 may be used; see paragraph 2, p. 561.

K_T = temperature factor, same values suggested in Chapter 10 are to be used

K_R = factor of safety (reliability factor), Tables 10-9 and 10-10 are to be used.

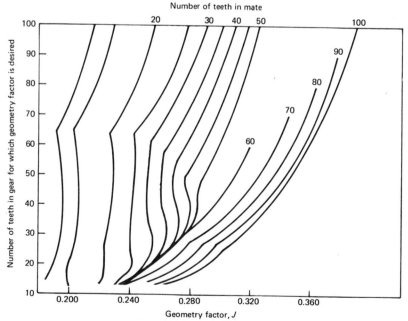

Figure 11-35 Geometry factor for coniflex straight bevel gears with 25 deg pressure angle and 90 deg shaft angle. [Courtesy Gleason Works, Rochester, N.Y.]

Table 11-4   Elastic Coefficient, C_p—Localized Contact (for most bevel gears)

Pinion Material and Modulus of Elasticity, E		Gear Material and Modulus of Elasticity			
		Steel	Cast Iron	Aluminum Bronze	Tin Bronze
		30×10^6	19×10^6	17.5×10^6	16×10^6
Steel	30×10^6	2800	2450	2400	2350
Cast iron	19×10^6	2450	2250	2200	2150
Aluminum bronze	17.5×10^6	2400	2200	2150	2100
Tin bronze	16×10^6	2350	2150	2100	2050

SOURCE: AGMA
Poisson's ratio = 0.30
NOTE: When more exact values of E are obtained from roller contact test, they can be used.

As was noted in our discussion of spur gears, the calculated stress σ_t, equation (10-25), must always be less than or equal to the maximum allowable design stress as determined by equation (10-26).

The AGMA fundamental wear equation is repeated here.

$$\sigma_c = C_p \sqrt{\frac{F_t C_o}{C_v} \frac{C_s}{db} \frac{C_m C_f}{I}} \qquad (10\text{-}33)$$

where

σ_c = calculated contact stress number

C_p = coefficient depending on elastic properties of materials, equation (10-34) may be used to obtain values for C_p or Table 11-4 may be used

F_t = transmitted tangential load, lb, based upon the large end pitch diameter

C_o = overload factor, Table 10-4 may be used

C_v = dynamic factor, Figure 10-27 may be used

d = pinion pitch diameter at large end, in.

b = net face width of the narrowest of the mating gears, in.

C_s = size factor, discussion given for spur gears applies, except that Figure 11-33 should be used

C_m = load distribution factor, Figure 11-36 is used when deflections are known, and Table 11-3 is used when they are not known (K_m)

I = geometry factor, Figure 11-37 gives values for the geometry factor for a bevel gear having $\phi = 25$ deg, and $\Sigma = 90$ deg. More complete charts are available from the Gleason Works, Rochester, N.Y.

C_f = surface condition factor, same discussion and values given for spur gears apply.

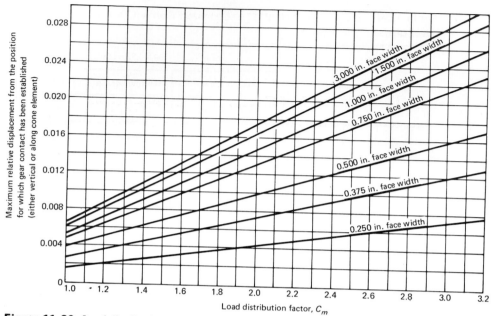

Figure 11-36 Load distribution factor for bevel gears. [Courtesy AGMA.]

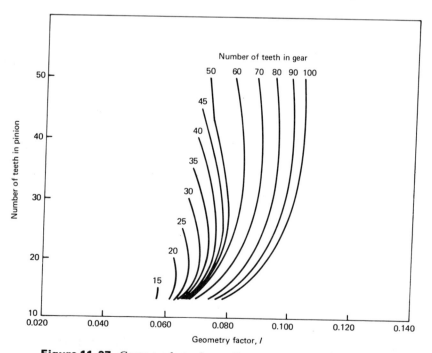

Figure 11-37 Geometry factor for coniflex straight bevel gears with 25 deg pressure angle and 90 deg shaft angle. [Courtesy Gleason Works, Rochester, N.Y.]

The calculated stress number σ_c can now be evaluated and must satisfy the equation

$$\sigma_c \leqslant S_{ac}\left[\frac{C_L C_H}{C_T C_R}\right] \tag{10-35}$$

where

S_{ac} = allowable contact stress number, the values in Table 10-14 may be used

C_L = life factor, Figure 10-33 can be used

C_H = hardness ratio factor, Table 10-15 or Figure 10-34 may be used

C_T = temperature factor, same values suggested for spur gears should be used

C_R = factor of safety, Table 10-16 may be used.

Therefore, if equation (10-35) is satisfied, the bevel gears will be safe in wear.

The maximum allowable transmitted horsepower (based on wear) is given by equation (10-37)

$$P_{ac} = \frac{n_p bI C_v}{126,000 C_s C_m C_f C_o}\left(\frac{S_{ac}d}{C_p}\frac{C_L C_H}{C_T C_R}\right)^2 \tag{10-37}$$

SECTION 11-24

Tooth Loads on Straight Bevel Gears

The usual assumption made in determining the loads acting on bevel gears is that the resultant tooth load acts at the midpoint of the tooth face. The inherent error in this assumption is so slight that it may safely be made. Figure 11-38 shows the normal tooth load and the three components into which it is usually resolved. It is clear from the diagram that a thrust load is developed in bevel gears.

Example 11-6. A pair of bevel gears is to be used to transmit 12 hp from a pinion rotating at 360 rpm to a gear mounted on a shaft which intersects the pinion shaft at an angle of 70 deg. Assume the pinion is to have an outside pitch diameter of 8 in., a pressure angle of 20 deg, a face width of $1\frac{1}{2}$ in., and the gear shaft is to rotate at 120 rpm. Determine (a) the pitch angles for the gears, (b) the forces on the gear, and (c) the torque produced about the shaft axis.

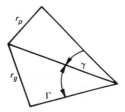

Solution: *Part a.*

$$r_v = \frac{n_g}{n_p} = \frac{120}{360} = \frac{1}{3} = \frac{d_p}{d_g}$$

$$d_g = 3d_p = 3 \times 8 = 24 \text{ in.}$$

Therefore

$$r_p = 8/2 = 4 \text{ in.} \qquad r_g = 24/2 = 12 \text{ in.}$$

$$\Sigma = 70 \text{ deg}$$

$$\tan \Gamma = \frac{\sin \Sigma}{\left(\dfrac{N_{t_p}}{N_{t_g}}\right) + \cos \Sigma} = \frac{\sin 70}{\frac{1}{3} + \cos 70} = 1.39$$

$$\Gamma = 54.3 \text{ deg}$$

$$\gamma = \Sigma - \Gamma = 70 - 54.3 = 15.7 \text{ deg}$$

$$r_{g_{aver}} = r_g - \frac{b}{2} \sin \Gamma = 12 - \frac{1\frac{1}{2}}{2} \sin 54.3 = 11.4 \text{ in.}$$

$$r_{p_{aver}} = r_p - \frac{b}{2} \sin \gamma = 4 - \frac{1\frac{1}{2}}{2} \sin 15.7 = 3.8 \text{ in.}$$

Part b.

$$F_t = \frac{\text{hp} \times 33,000}{\dfrac{\pi dn}{12}} = \frac{12 \times 33,000 \times 12}{\pi \times 7.6 \times 360} = 553 \text{ lb}$$

$$F_n = \frac{F_t}{\cos \phi} = \frac{553}{\cos 20} = \frac{553}{0.94} = 588 \text{ lb}$$

$$F_{\text{thrust}} = F_n \sin \phi \sin \Gamma = F_t \tan \phi \sin \Gamma$$
$$= 553 \times \tan 20 \times \sin 54.3$$
$$= 553 \times 0.364 \times 0.812 = 163 \text{ lb}$$

$$F_r = F_n \sin \phi \cos \Gamma = F_t \tan \phi \cos \Gamma$$
$$= 553 \times \tan 20 \cos 54.3$$
$$= 553 \times 0.364 \times 0.584 = 117.6 \text{ lb}$$

Part c.

$$\text{torque} = F_t \times \frac{d_g}{2} = 553 \times \frac{22.8}{2} = 6304 \text{ in.-lb} \quad \bullet$$

SECTION 11-25

ZEROL Bevel Gears

A ZEROL bevel gear is somewhat like a straight bevel gear, except that the teeth are curved. They can also be thought of as being spiral bevel gears whose spiral angle is zero. The big advantage ZEROL gears have, compared

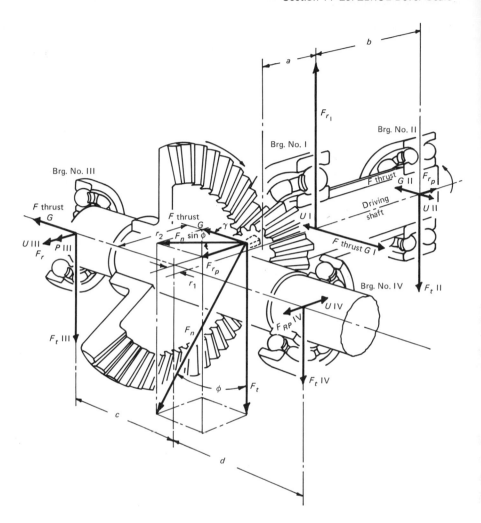

Figure 11-38 Straight bevel gear tooth loads. [Courtesy New Departure—Hyatt Bearings Division, General Motors Corporation.]

to straight bevel gears, is that they have localized tooth contact. The advantages associated with coniflex gears thus apply also to ZEROL bevel gears. In addition since the thrust loads are the same as for straight bevel gears, they may be used in the same mountings.

The applications to which ZEROL gears are applied are very much the same as those for straight bevel gears. The minimum suggested number of teeth is 14, one or more teeth should always be in contact, and the basic pressure angle is 20 deg, although angles of $22\frac{1}{2}$ or 25 deg are sometimes used to eliminate undercutting.

SECTION 11-26

Spiral Bevel Gears

Spiral bevel gears have curved oblique teeth, which allow contact to develop gradually and smoothly. They are, therefore, extremely useful for high speed applications and for problems where noise and vibration reduction are important. An analogy for the relationship that exists between straight and spiral bevel gears is that existing between spur and helical gears. Localized tooth contact is also achieved, which means that some mounting and load deflections can occur without a resultant load concentration at the ends of the teeth.

The standard pressure angle is 20 deg, although $14\frac{1}{2}$-deg and 16-deg angles are used. The usual spiral angle is 35 deg. Because spiral gears are much stronger than similar sized straight or ZEROL gears, they can be used for large speed reduction ratio applications at a reduced overall installation size.

Figure 11-39 shows the normal tooth load, and the components it is usually resolved into.

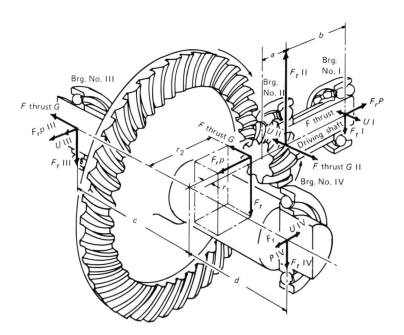

Figure 11-39 Spiral bevel gear tooth loads. [Courtesy New Departure—Hyatt Bearing Division, General Motors Corporation.]

SECTION 11-27

Hypoid Gears

Hypoid gears are very similar to spiral bevel gears. The main difference is that their pitch surfaces are hyperboloids rather than cones. As a result, their pitch axes do not intersect, the pinion axis being above or below the gear axis.

In general hypoid gears are most desirable for those applications involving large speed reduction ratios, those having nonintersecting shafts, and those requiring great smoothness and quietness of operation. Hypoid gears are almost universally used for automotive applications.

The pressure angles usually range between 19 and $22\frac{1}{2}$ deg. The minimum number of teeth suggested is eight for speed ratios greater than 6 to 1, and six for smaller ratios.

Figure 11-40 shows the tooth load situation for hypoid gears.

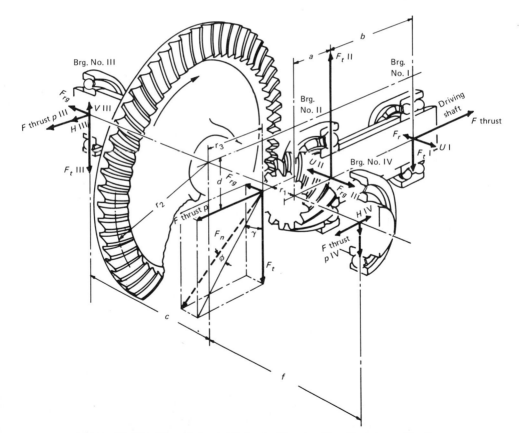

Figure 11-40 Hypoid gear tooth loads. [Courtesy New Departure—Hyatt Bearing Division, General Motors Corporation.]

PROBLEMS

1. A left handed helical gear is to transmit 30 hp at 900 rpm. The gear has 42 teeth, a 30-deg helix angle, a 20-deg transverse pressure angle, and is rotating in the clockwise direction. Draw a sketch of the gear, showing all the forces acting. Let P be 7.

2. A left handed helical gear having 20 teeth is driven by a motor at 2000 rpm in the clockwise direction. The gear has a normal pressure angle of 20 deg, a helix angle of 30 deg, a normal diametral pitch of 10, and a normal force of 80 lb. The gear meshes with another helical gear having 50 teeth. Draw a sketch of the second gear showing all the forces acting, and calculate the torque acting.

3. In the Figure Problem 3, gear 1 has 25 teeth, is left handed, has a normal diametral pitch of 5, is to transmit 15 hp at 1400 rpm clockwise, has a ϕ of 20 deg, and a ψ of 30 deg. Gear 2 has 40 teeth, and the velocity ratio for gears 1 and 3 is to be 0.5. What are the forces acting on each gear? What is the torque on each shaft?

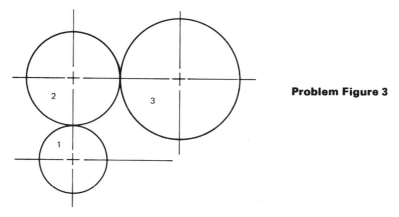

Problem Figure 3

4. For the reverted gear train shown in Problem Figure 4 the input and output shafts have the same center line and 225 hp is to be transmitted. ϕ_n for all gears is to be 20 deg.

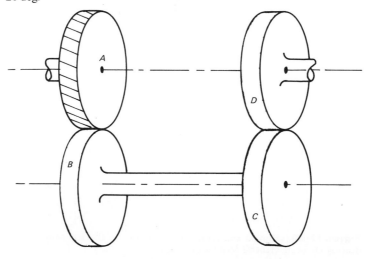

Problem Figure 4

Complete the following table, specifying the helix angles so that there is no net thrust on shaft 2.

Gear	rpm	No. of Teeth	Helix Angle and Hand	d, in.	Tangential Force*	Radial Force*	Thrust Force*
A	2250	30	30 R.H.	5			
B							
C							
D	1000	30					

*Specify load applied to gear and direction up, down, right, left, in, out.

5. A pair of meshing helical gears are mounted on parallel shafts 10 in. apart. Their normal diametral pitch is 6. If the pinion has 30 teeth and the speed ratio is 0.5, what is the required helix angle?

6. Two meshing helical gears of the same hand are mounted on shafts that are 90 deg apart. What is the center distance if the pinion has 30 teeth, a helix angle of 30 deg, and a normal diametral pitch of 4? The velocity ratio is to be 0.4.

7. Two meshing helical gears are both made of SAE 1020 case hardened and WQT steel, and are mounted on parallel shafts 10 in. apart. The gears are to have a velocity ratio of 0.33, are 20 deg full depth with 35 deg helix angles. The diametral pitch is 20 and the face width of the gears may be taken as $1\frac{1}{2}$ in. What is the maximum horsepower that can safely be transmitted? Use the modified Lewis equation for strength and the Buckingham equation for wear. The pinion speed is equal to 2000 rpm.

8. Repeat Problem 7 using the AGMA method and the assumptions given in the preface to the problems of Chapter 10.

9. The pinion of a pair of helical gears mounted on parallel shafts is to transmit 5 hp at 8000 rpm. Both gears have 30 deg helix angles, transverse pressure angles of 20 deg, are full depth, are made of SAE 1030 steel and have a face width of $\frac{1}{2}$ in. If the pinion is to have 25 teeth and the gear 100 teeth, what are the minimum diameters, and what is the required BHN?

10. Check the gears of Problem 9 by the AGMA method and use the same assumptions as in Problem 8.

11. A 24-tooth pinion, 6 diametral pitch, is attached to a drive shaft that is rotating at 2400 rpm. This pinion meshes with a spur gear mounted on a shaft that is 6 in. from the drive shaft and parallel to it. Also, on this shaft is a triple threaded, right hand worm that drives a 75-tooth worm wheel. On the same shaft with the worm wheel is an 8-in. hoisting cylinder. The cylinder is to lift a weight by means of a cable. How long will it take for the weight to be lifted through a distance of 30 ft?

12. Two shafts at right angles, with center distance of 7 in., have to be connected by worm gearing. They have a velocity ratio of 0.025, lead angle of worm of 42 deg and a normal pitch of 0.4 in. for the worm wheel. (a) Determine the pitch diameter, lead, and number of teeth of the worm. (b) Determine the number of teeth and pitch diameter of the worm wheel.

13. A triple threaded worm having a $2\frac{1}{2}$ in. diameter receives 30 hp at 1500 rpm. The worm wheel has 100 teeth and is 12 in. in diameter. What is the tangential force on the wheel teeth if the efficiency is 80%?

14. A 2-tooth worm that has an input of 630 hp at 1800 rpm drives a 50-tooth wheel. What is the output torque for 80% efficiency?

15. A hoisting system has a drum 30 in. diameter with a 1-in. diameter wire, mounted on the same shaft with a worm wheel having 90 teeth. A triple threaded worm is to drive the wheel and raise a 5000 lb load at 80 ft/min. If the system has an efficiency of 70%, how much horsepower must be supplied to the worm gear shaft?

16. For the gears of Problem 12, if the worm is transmitting 15 hp at 1500 rpm and the worm gear has a 25 deg normal pressure angle, determine the forces acting on the worm and on the worm wheel.

17. If the worm in Problem 14 has a pitch diameter of 3 in. and the worm gear has a circular pitch of 0.8 in. and 25-deg full depth teeth, determine the forces acting on the worm and the worm wheel.

18. A worm gearset is to transmit power between two shafts that are to be approximately 8 in. apart. If the velocity ratio is to be 0.05 determine the number of teeth ·in the gears and the required pitch diameters. Assume AGMA recommendations have been followed.

19. A triple threaded worm having a $2\frac{1}{2}$ in. pitch diameter meshes with a worm wheel having a diametral pitch of 5 and 60 teeth. Determine (**a**) lead, (**b**) lead angle, and (**c**) center distance.

20. What should be the numbers of teeth for a worm gearset having a velocity ratio of 0.05, and a center distance of approximately 5 in.? The worm lead angle is 15 deg and the normal diametral pitch is 6.

21. Design a worm gearset to transmit 20 hp at a worm rpm of 1500 and a velocity ratio of 0.04.

22. A quadruple threaded cast steel worm (0.2% C WQT) is to be used with a bronze worm wheel to give a velocity ratio of 0.04: 20 hp is to be transmitted at 1000 rpm worm speed. Determine the pitch and face width based on strength and wear if the normal pressure angle is 20 deg. Will special cooling be needed?

23. Design a speed reducer to transmit 2 hp at 1800 rpm of worm. The bronze worm gear is to be 20-deg normal pressure angle and a speed ratio of 0.025 is desired. The worm is to be cast steel.

24. Design a speed reducer to transmit 20 hp at 1250 rpm of the worm and to have a velocity ratio of 0.06.

25. A gear train consists of a triple threaded worm that drives a worm wheel having 75 teeth. A bevel gear is mounted on the same shaft as the worm wheel. The meshing driven bevel gear has 75 teeth and the velocity ratio for the gears is to be 0.4. How many revolutions will the worm make for two revolutions of the larger bevel gear? If the worm has an input of 3 hp at 1500 rpm and the efficiency of the gear train is 90%, what will be the output torque of the gear train?

26. A pair of bevel gears are mounted on shafts that are 90 deg apart. The set is to transmit 10 hp at 300 rpm. The pinion has a 6-in. outside pitch diameter, 2-in. face width, a diametral pitch of 6, and is 20 deg full depth. For a velocity ratio of 0.4, draw a free body diagram of the gears showing all forces acting. What is the torque produced about the gear axis?

27. Repeat Problem 26 for a 60-deg shaft angle.

28. If the gears of Problem 26 are made of cast steel, WQT, will they be satisfactory from the strength and wear viewpoint? Use the Lewis and Buckingham equations.

29. Repeat Problem 28 using the AGMA method. Assume one gear is straddle mounted, the gears are to be used for a general industrial application, power source has light shock, driver machine is subject to moderate shock, a life of 1×10^6 cycles, and high reliability is required.

30. Repeat Problem 28 for the gears of Problem 27.

31. A pair of meshing steel bevel gears are mounted on shafts 90 deg apart. Both are 20 deg full depth, have a diametral pitch of 5, a strength of 20,000 psi, BHN of 300, and a face width of $2\frac{1}{2}$ in. If the pinion has 30 teeth and is turning at 1500 rpm, what horsepower can the gears transmit if the velocity ratio is to be 0.5? Draw a free body diagram for the pinion and its shaft, showing all forces and moments acting. It may be assumed that the apex of the pitch cone is at the center of a 20-in. long, simply supported shaft. The left hand bearing only is able to resist a thrust load. Use the Lewis and Buckingham equations.

32. Repeat Problem 31 using the AGMA method. Assume the conditions of Problem 29.

REFERENCES

[1] E. Buckingham and Ryffel: *Design of Worm and Spiral Gears.* The Industrial Press.

[2] V. M. Faires: *Design of Machine Elements.* The Macmillan Company, New York, 1965.

[3] E. Buckingham: *Analytical Mechanics of Gears.* McGraw-Hill Book Co., New York, 1949.

[4] *Spiroid Gearing.* Illinois Tool Works, Chicago, Ill., 1966.

[5] D. L. Seager: Dynamic behavior of helical gears. *ASME 69-VIBR-16.*

[6] *How to Test Bevel Gears.* Gleason Works, Rochester, N.Y., 1955.

[7] *Bevel and Hypoid Gear Design.* Gleason Works, Rochester, N.Y., 1956.

12

Belt and Chain Drives

SYMBOLS

c = center distance, in.
e = base of naperian logarithms
f = coefficient of friction
F_1 = maximum belt tension, lb
F_2 = minimum belt tension, lb
F_c = inertia force on belt, lb
g = acceleration of gravity, in./sec^2
H = transmitted horsepower, hp
L = pitch length of belt, in.

ln = naperian logarithm
n = speed, rpm
N_t = number of sprocket teeth
p = pitch, in.
T = torque, in.-lb
w' = belt weight, lb/in.
β = half of included angle of V-belt
θ_1 = angle of contact, rad
ω = angular velocity, rad/sec

Belt and chain drives offer a maximum of versatility as power transmission elements. They allow the designer considerable flexibility in location of driver and driven machinery, and tolerances are not critical as is the case with gear drives. Another advantage of chain drives, and particularly of belt drives, is that they reduce vibration and shock transmission. Furthermore, belt drives are relatively quiet.

Large flat leather belts were in general use many years ago, when the usual practice was to use one large engine to drive several different pieces of machinery. Some leather belts are in use at this time as well as flat steel, rubber, plastic, and fabric belts. Light, thin flat belts are practical on high speed machinery where vibration may be a problem.

A smooth surfaced flat belt must operate with higher tensions to transmit the same torque as a V belt. Positive-drive type flat belts, commonly known as timing belts (Figure 12-1), have evenly spaced teeth on the inner surface and operate on toothed pulleys. The speed ratio is inversely proportional to the number of pulley teeth. Required belt tensions are low and, consequently, bearing loads are reduced.

V belts are probably the most common means of transmitting power between fractional horsepower electric motors and driven machinery. V belts are also used in other household, automotive and industrial applications. Multiple-belt drives with capacities up to a few hundred horsepower

660

Figure 12-1 Timing® belt drive (Licensed TM). Drives of this type are designed to transmit fractional horsepower up to 600 hp or more. Belt speeds range up to 16,000 ft/min. [Courtesy Dodge Manufacturing Division, Reliance Electric Co.]

Figure 12-2 Adjustable speed belt drive. If the center distance between shafts is increased, the sides of the drive pulley separate, decreasing its effective radius. Drives of this type are designed to transmit from $\frac{1}{2}$ to 20 hp at 1750 rpm. [Courtesy Dodge Manufacturing Division, Reliance Electric Co.]

Figure 12-3 Variable speed chain drive. [Courtesy Link-Belt Enclosed Drive Division, FMC Corporation.]

are available for industrial use. Conventional V belts are made of rubber covered with rubber impregnated fabric and reinforced with nylon, dacron, rayon, glass fiber, or steel tensile cords. Automotive and agricultural belt drives are generally designed for 750–1000 hr average life, whereas industrial belt drive design is based on longer service. Most often, both driver and driven pulleys lie in the same vertical plane, and the speed ratio is constant. Quarter-turn drives are used to transmit power between horizontal and vertical shafts, using deep groove pulleys and relatively long center distances.

Smooth flat belts and V belts depend on friction for traction on the pulleys, and some slippage is inherent in their operation. Therefore, speed ratios are not precise. Variable-pitch pulleys are used to change the input to output speed ratio of a V belt drive (see Figure 12-2). Some variable-pitch drives will change speed ratios when the belt is transmitting power. Most heavy duty pulleys (sheaves) are made of cast iron or formed steel.

Chain drives generally have far greater life expectancies than belt drives, up to 20,000 hr with lubrication and regular maintainance. For heavy loads, roller chain and inverted tooth chain are used on toothed sprockets. Roller chain, available in single and multiple strand form, is used at speeds up to 2500 ft/min. Inverted tooth chain is used at speeds up to 4000 ft/min. Both are available with capacities over 1000 hp. Figure 12-3 shows a variable speed chain drive.

SECTION 12-1

Belt Drives

Flat belt drives

Consider a flat belt drive operating at its maximum capacity. Taking an element of the belt as shown in Figure 12-4, the friction force is limited by the normal force dN (the pulley reaction) and the coefficient of friction f. The local belt tension is F. In the direction of a tangent through the center of the element, equilibrium of forces yields

$$(F + dF) \cos (d\theta/2) - f dN - F \cos (d\theta/2) = 0 \qquad (12\text{-}1)$$

Simplifying, and noting that for small angles the cosine approaches unity, we obtain

$$dF = f dN \qquad (12\text{-}2)$$

when the belt is on the verge of slipping on the pulley.

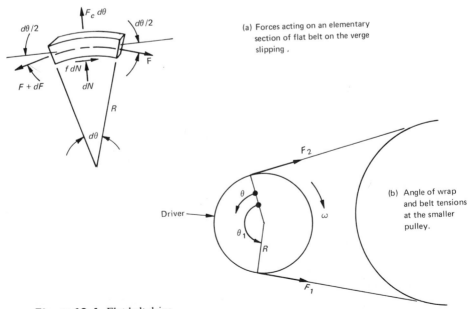

(a) Forces acting on an elementary section of flat belt on the verge slipping .

(b) Angle of wrap and belt tensions at the smaller pulley.

Figure 12-4 Flat belt drive.

For radius R measured to the belt center and belt weight w' lb/in. of length, the length of the elementary section of belt is $R\, d\theta$ and its mass is

$$\frac{w'}{g} R\, d\theta$$

For angular velocity ω, the normal acceleration is $\omega^2 R$ and the inertia force $F_c\, d\theta$ where we define

$$F_c = \frac{w'\omega^2 R^2}{g} \tag{12-3}$$

Equilibrium of forces in the radial direction yields

$$dN + F_c\, d\theta - (F + dF + F)\sin(d\theta/2) = 0 \tag{12-4}$$

We first observe that for small angles the sine of the angle approaches the angle itself. Next, the higher order term $dF\, d\theta$ may be neglected. Finally, using equation (12-2) to eliminate dN from equation (12-4) and separating the variables, we obtain

$$\frac{dF}{F - F_c} = f\, d\theta \tag{12-5}$$

Referring to Figure 12-4b, the solution of equation (12-5) is obtained by integrating from minimum tension F_2 to maximum tension F_1 through the angle of contact of the belt, $\theta = 0$ to θ_1 rad. Thus, we have

$$\ln\left(\frac{F_1 - F_c}{F_2 - F_c}\right) = f\theta_1 \tag{12-6}$$

or

$$\frac{F_1 - F_c}{F_2 - F_c} = e^{f\theta_1} \tag{12-7}$$

for the belt operating at maximum capacity. Note that the smaller angle of contact (usually corresponding to the smaller pulley) is critical and design of the belt drive is based on that value.

V-belt drives

For V belts, the inertia effect F_c is given by equation (12-3) where R is the pitch radius of the pulley, somewhat less than the outside radius. The weight density of a typical V belt is approximately 0.05 lb/in.[3] The normal force is applied to the sides of the belt since the belt rides against the pulley sides (Figure 12-5). Let the normal force on each side be $dN'/2$ producing a total friction force $f\, dN'$ on an element of V belt. The radial force dN in equation (12-4) is replaced by $dN'\sin\beta$ for pulley included angle 2β. Making the indicated substitutions, we see that the coefficient of friction f in equations

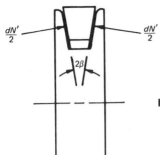

Figure 12-5 V belt.

(12-6) and (12-7) may be replaced by $f/\sin \beta$. The V-belt tension relationships are then given by

$$\ln \left(\frac{F_1 - F_c}{F_2 - F_c} \right) = \frac{f\theta_1}{\sin \beta} \tag{12-8}$$

or

$$\frac{F_1 - F_c}{F_2 - F_c} = e^{f\theta_1/\sin \beta} \tag{12-9}$$

Transmitted power

For belt drives, the torque on a pulley is given by

$$T = (F_1 - F_2)R \tag{12-10}$$

where pitch radius R is measured from the center of a pulley to the neutral axis of the belt. The transmitted horsepower is

$$H = \frac{nT}{63,025} \tag{12-11}$$

where n is the speed of a given pulley in revolutions per minute and T is the torque on the same pulley in inch-pounds. Most belt drives are designed to produce a speed reduction. Pulley rotation speeds are inversely proportional to pulley radii. Belt strength limits maximum tension F_1 and the minimum tension F_2 depends on the angle of contact, the coefficient of friction, and whether we are using a flat belt or a V belt.

Belt drive design

Since V belts vary considerably in cross section and amount of reinforcement, the design of V-belt drives is usually based on tables given by the manufacturers. However, the following alternate method may be used. Let the input and output speeds and horsepower of a belt drive be given. Suppose we are to design the drive. Using equation (12-11), we may find torque at the smaller pulley as a function of its revolutions per minute, n_1

$$T_1 = \frac{63,025H}{n_1} \text{ in.-lb} \tag{12-12}$$

Radius R_1 of the smaller pulley may be tentatively selected. The radius of the larger pulley, R_2 is found on the basis of the ratio of pulley speeds. We use

$$\frac{R_2}{R_1} = \frac{n_1}{n_2} \tag{12-13}$$

where n_1 and n_2 are, respectively, speeds of the smaller and larger pulleys. If we estimate belt weight, the inertia effect F_c is given by equation (12-3). In order to reduce the problem to finding one unknown tension, we rewrite equation (12-10) in the form

$$F_2 = F_1 - \frac{T_1}{R_1} \tag{12-14}$$

When equation (12-14) is used to eliminate F_2 from equation (12-9), the results may be rearranged to give maximum tension

$$F_1 = F_c + \left(\frac{\gamma}{\gamma - 1}\right) \frac{T_1}{R_1} \tag{12-15}$$

where

$$\gamma = e^{f\theta_1/\sin \beta} \tag{12-16}$$

When it is necessary to estimate V-belt tensions, a ratio between 3 to 1 and 5 to 1 is reasonable. For example, we may estimate

$$\frac{F_1}{F_2} = 5$$

from which

$$F_1 = 1.25\frac{T}{R} \quad \text{and} \quad F_2 = 0.25\frac{T}{R}$$

If a flat belt is used, $\sin \beta = 1$. For standard V belts, β ranges from 17 to 19 deg, producing a greater friction effect. Thus, V belts are usually preferred over flat belts because, for a given maximum tension F_1, a V belt can transmit more power. We may obtain the approximate value of the smaller angle of contact θ_1 by sketching the drive as in Figure 12-4b. Unless an idler pulley is used, θ_1 will generally be equal or less than π rad. When convenient, the rotation direction is selected so that the lower section of belt has the maximum tension, producing a slightly greater angle of contact. This would be the case for clockwise rotation if the smaller pulley is the driver in Figure 12-4b.

Table 12-1   Service Factors for V-Belt Drives

Driven Machine	Driver					
The types listed below are representative samples only. Select the group listed below whose load characteristics most closely approximate those of the machine being considered. If idlers are used, add the following to the service factor. Idler on slack side (inside the belts) . . None Idler on slack side (outside the belts) . . 0.1 Idler on tight side (inside the belts) . . . 0.1 Idler on tight side (outside the belts) . . 0.2	AC Motors: Normal Torque, Squirrel Cage, Synchronous, Split Phase. DC Motors: Shunt Wound. Engines*: Multiple Cylinder Internal Combustion.			AC Motors: High Torque, High Slip, Repulsion-Induction, Single Phase, Series Wound, Slip Ring. DC Motors: Series Wound, Compound Wound. Engines*: Single Cylinder Internal Combustion. Line Shafts Clutches		
	Intermittent Service, 3–5 hr Daily or Seasonal	Normal Service 8–10 hr Daily	Continuous Service, 16–24 hr Daily	Intermittent Service, 3–5 hr Daily or Seasonal	Normal Service, 8–10 hr Daily	Continuous Service, 16–24 hr Daily
Agitators for liquids Blowers and exhausters Centrifugal pumps and compressors Fans up to 10 hp Light duty conveyors	1.0	1.1	1.2	1.1	1.2	1.3
Belt conveyors for sand, grain, etc. Dough mixers Fans over 10 hp Generators Line shafts Laundry machinery Machine tools Punches-presses-shears Printing machinery Positive displacement rotary pumps Revolving and vibrating screens	1.1	1.2	1.3	1.2	1.3	1.4
Brick machinery Bucket elevators Exciters Piston compressors Conveyors (drag-pan-screw) Hammer mills Paper mill beaters Piston pumps Positive displacement blowers Pulverizers Saw mill and woodworking machinery Textile machinery	1.2	1.3	1.4	1.4	1.5	1.6
Crushers (gyratory-jaw-roll) Mills (ball-rod-tube) Hoists Rubber calenders-extruders-mills	1.3	1.4	1.5	1.5	1.6	1.8
Chokable equipment† Fire hazard conditions†	2.0	2.0	2.0	2.0	2.0	2.0

SOURCE: Dodge Manufacturing Division, Reliance Electric Co.

*Apply indicated service factor to continuous service engine rating. Deduct 0.2 (with a minimum service factor of 1.0) when applying to maximum engine rating.

†Where fire hazards are prevalent and fire prevention laws apply, it is recommended that drives be designed using a service factor of 2.0 on the HP rating of the motor.

V belts are generally made from reinforced rubber and the required belt strength is governed by maximum tension F_1. Maximum tension should be multiplied by a service factor based on the number of hours per day of operation and the type of machinery. Typical service factors are given in Table 12-1.

The coefficient of friction f between rubber and dry steel is about 0.3, but a much lower value occurs in the presence of oil or grease. If the belt is not permitted to slip, the static coefficient of friction applies. If the belt is allowed to slip, that is, if it is used as a clutch, then the coefficient of sliding friction applies. The latter value is somewhat lower.

In order to solve equation (12-15), we originally estimated belt cross-section size to compute the inertial effect F_c. If we must select a belt much larger than our approximation, the above steps may be repeated to find new values of F_c and F_1 and a new belt selection. Minimum tension F_2 is given by equation (12-14). Mean shaft load at the pulley is made up of torque T and the force vector sum $\mathbf{F_1} \leftrightarrow \mathbf{F_2}$ (approximately equal to the scalar sum $F_1 + F_2$ in most cases).

When a single V belt is inadequate, a multiple V belt drive may be specified. Standard pulleys are available with 1, 2, 3, 4, 5, 6, 8, and 10 grooves in a wide range of pitch diameters. Figure 12-6 shows a multiple V belt drive.

Figure 12-6 Multiple V belt drive. [Courtesy Dodge Manufacturing Division, Reliance Electric Co.]

Belt length, center distance, and contact angle

For a belt drive employing two pulleys of the same radius R_1 with center distance c, the theoretical length of the belt is $L = 2(c + \pi R_1)$ and the contact angle is $\theta_1 = \pi$ rad. If pulley pitch radius is used, the result will be the pitch length of the belt, measured along its neutral axis. Note, however, that belt length and pulley radius must be adjusted when ordering because belts are identified by outside circumference and V-belt pulley sizes are based on outside diameter.

For unequal pulley pitch radii R_1 and R_2, referring to Figure 12-7, we see that the angle α is given by

$$\sin \alpha = \frac{R_2 - R_1}{c} \qquad (12\text{-}17)$$

and that the angle of contact

$$\theta_1 = \pi - 2\alpha \text{ rad} \qquad (12\text{-}18)$$

on the small pulley.

The length of a straight section of belt

$$a = [c^2 - (R_2 - R_1)^2]^{1/2} \text{ in.} \qquad (12\text{-}19)$$

and the total pitch length of the belt is

$$L = 2a + R_1(\pi - 2\alpha) + R_2(\pi + 2\alpha) \text{ in.} \qquad (12\text{-}20)$$

Approximating the dimension a by two terms of a binomial expansion and substituting $\sin \alpha$ for α, we obtain

$$L \approx 2c + \pi(R_1 + R_2) + \frac{(R_2 - R_1)^2}{c} \qquad (12\text{-}21)$$

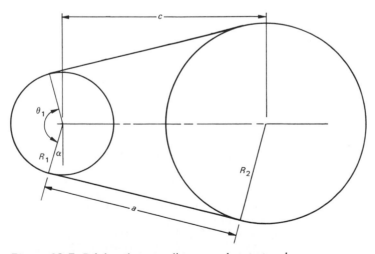

Figure 12-7 Belt length, center distance, and contact angle.

from which center distance

$$c \approx \frac{b + \sqrt{b^2 - 8(R_2 - R_1)^2}}{4} \tag{12-22}$$

where $b = L - \pi(R_1 + R_2)$.

Sometimes the center distance c between pulleys is governed by the size of the machinery involved or restricted in other ways. If not, a reasonable value of center distance is given *by the larger of*

$$c = 3R_1 + R_2 \quad \text{or} \quad c = 2R_2 \tag{12-23}$$

where R_2 is the pitch radius of the larger pulley.

This value of c is used in equation (12-21) to find L. If a standard belt is selected, the actual pitch length is substituted into equation (12-22) to find center distance. The manufacturer's specifications should be consulted to relate pitch length and pitch diameter to nominal sizes of belts and pulleys. Wherever possible, belt drives should be designed with provision for center distance adjustment, unless an idler pulley is employed, because belts tend to stretch in use. When adjustment is provided, the accuracy of length and center distance calculations is not critical.

Example 12-1: Design of a Belt Drive. *Required.* A belt drive to transmit 30 hp when input speed is $n_1 = 1750$ rpm and the driven pulley is to rotate at approximately 1040 rpm. The load is steady, service is continuous, and a high degree of reliability is required.

Design decisions. One or more V belts will be used for this drive. We note that the pulley pitch radii $R_1 = 3.7$ and $R_2 = 6.2$ in. will produce an output speed $n_2 = 1042$ rpm, which is satisfactory. These pitch radii correspond to standard size pulleys with outside diameters of 7.5 and 12.5 in. Suppose we tentatively select a V-belt cross section that is nominally $\frac{5}{8}$ in. wide by $\frac{17}{32}$ in. deep weighing 0.012 lb/in. of length. We will specify the drive components based on our calculations rather than using the belt manufacturer's recommendations.

Solution: In the absence of other criteria, equations (12-23) will be used to obtain a reasonable center distance. For this problem, the first equation governs and the distance between pulley centers will be approximately $c = 17.3$ in. The pitch length of the belt given by equation (12-21) is about 66 in. for this value of c. Using the nearest standard size listed in manufacturers' catalogs, we might specify a belt of 67 in. nominal length, which corresponds to a pitch length of 66.6 in. Using equation (12-22), we recalculate center distance $c = 17.6$ in. Of course, provision should be made for adjustment for installation of belts and for belt stretching.

Using equations (12-17) and (12-18) we obtain $\alpha = 8.16$ deg and the angle of contact $\theta_1 = 163.7$ deg $= 2.86$ rad for the small pulley.

Using equation (12-12), we find driven torque $T_1 = 1080$ in.-lb. Angular velocity of the drive pulley is $2\pi n_1/60 = 183$ rad/sec. Then, based on our tentative belt section, $F_c = 14.3$ lb from equation (12-3). It will be assumed that the coefficient of friction f will not be less than 0.2 and that the pulley angle β will be 18 deg. From equations (12-15) and (12-16), we obtain $\gamma = 6.36$ and maximum tension $F_1 = 361$ lb. Using equation (12-14), we find minimum tension $F_2 = 69$ lb.

The nature of the loading is complicated because the belt is subject to varying tension as well as bending as it goes around the pulleys. Furthermore, a typical V belt is not uniform in section but made of rubber reinforced by synthetic fiber cords. We do know, however, based on tests, that a $\frac{5}{8}$ by $\frac{17}{32}$ in. V belt can operate satisfactorily over long periods with maximum tensile loads of 200 lb. If we apply a safety factor of 1.5, because a high degree of reliability is required, we would have a working maximum tensile load of 133 lb per belt. Applying a service factor of 1.3 to F_1 (for continuous service) we obtain a maximum tensile force of 471 lb applied to the belts. Four belts carried on multiple pulleys would therefore be satisfactory. If a single large belt is chosen instead, larger pulleys and a greater center distance would be required, changing the solution entirely.

Based on our selection of four V belts, the input and output shafts would be subject to a bending load equal to the vector sum $F_1 \leftrightarrow F_2 = 430$ lb (almost the same as the scalar sum) applied, roughly, at the center of each multiple pulley. The input shaft torque $T_1 = 1080$ in.-lb and the output shaft torque $T_2 = 63{,}025H/n_2 = 1813$ in.-lb. ●

SECTION 12-2

Chain Drives

Chains are used for power transmission and as conveyors. They can be used for high loads and where precise speed ratios must be maintained. Although location and alignment tolerances need not be as precise as with gear drives, the best service can be expected when both input and output sprockets lie in the same vertical plane.

The ratio of output speed n_2 to input speed n_1 is given by

$$\frac{n_2}{n_1} = \frac{N_{t_1}}{N_{t_2}} \tag{12-24}$$

where N_{t_1} and N_{t_2} represent the number of teeth on the input and output sprockets respectively.

For a tentative center distance c between shafts, chain length L may be approximated by equation (12-21) of the preceding section where R_1 and R_2 refer to pitch radii of the input and output sprockets respectively. We then select an exact chain length for a whole number of chain links (preferably an even number) and recompute center distance from equation (12-22) of the preceding section. The length of an individual link from pin center to pin center is the pitch p. The pitch radius of a sprocket with N_t teeth may be defined by

$$R = \frac{N_t p}{2\pi} \tag{12-25}$$

Angle of contact for the chain is given by equation (12-18) of the preceding section. For the small pulley, it is desirable to have an angle of contact not less than 120 deg. For speed ratios $n_1/n_2 \geqslant 3$ this restriction is met if

$c = 2(R_2 - R_1)$. For smaller n_1/n_2 ratios, a practical center distance will fall between a value that just permits the sprockets to clear and $c = 2(R_1 + R_2)$. When longer chains are used, it is advisable to investigate the need for idlers on the slack section of chain.

Inverted tooth (silent) chain

Figure 12-8 shows inverted tooth or silent chain. Chain pitch is defined as in Figure 12-9. Smaller pitch chain ($p = \frac{3}{8}$ in. and $\frac{1}{2}$ in.) is commonly available in widths from $\frac{1}{2}$ to 4 in., whereas $1\frac{1}{2}$-in. pitch chain is available in widths from 3 to 16 in. The chain usually has guide links on the sides or in the center to keep it on the sprocket. Inverted-tooth chain is made of steel, and sprockets are made of steel in the smaller sizes and cast iron in the larger sizes. Inverted tooth chain is typically quieter than roller chain and may be operated at higher speeds because there is less impact force when chain links engage the sprocket. Lubrication is generally provided and, at full load, drive efficiency may be as high as 99 %.

Figure 12-8 Inverted tooth (silent) chain. (**a**) A silent chain drive. Drives of this type are possible with speed ratios as high as 10:1. The guide link engages grooves cut in the sprocket teeth. Most silent chain drives are of this type. [Courtesy Link-Belt Chain Division, FMC Corporation.] (**b**) Side-guide silent chain. The alternate guide links at the outer edges of the chain straddle the sprocket face. [Courtesy Ramsey Products Corporation, Charlotte, N.C.]

(a)

(b)

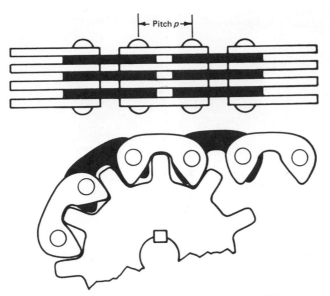

Figure 12-9 Chain pitch (inverted tooth or silent chain).

Roller chain

Roller chain is available in single and multiple strands, as shown in Figure 12-10. The chain is made up of side plates, pins, bushings, and rollers. Pitch p is measured from pin center to pin center. Single strand roller chain for industrial drives is generally available in pitches from $\frac{1}{4}$ to 3 in. and multiple strand chain in pitches from $\frac{3}{8}$ to 3 in. Conveyor chain is available in larger sizes. Roller chain is usually made of hardened steel and sprockets of steel or cast iron, but stainless steel and bronze chains are available where corrosion resistance is required. Lubrication is generally provided. However, if lubrication is undesirable, as in food processing, oil impregnated sintered metal bushings may be used in place of rollers.

Chordal action

Roller chain and inverted tooth chain are made up of links of finite length and, as these links engage the sprocket teeth, the chain velocity varies. Figure 12-11a shows the pitch line of a chain in its highest position, a distance r_a from the sprocket center. Part (b) of the figure shows the pitch line of the chain in its lowest position, a distance r_b from the sprocket center. If a constant driving speed ω rad/sec is maintained, the pitch line velocities of the chain in its highest and lowest positions are

$$v_a = \omega r_a \qquad (12\text{-}26)$$

and

$$v_b = \omega r_b$$

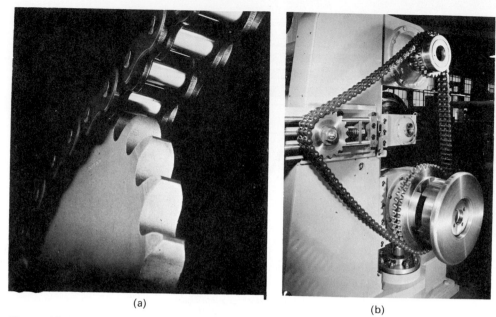

(a)

(b)

Figure 12-10 Roller chain. **(a)** A single-strand roller chain drive. [Courtesy Link-Belt Chain Division, FMC Corporation.] **(b)** A double-strand roller chain drive. [Courtesy Acme Chain Division, North American Rockwell.]

respectively, and the velocity changes cyclically N_t times per sprocket rotation for N_t sprocket teeth. Referring to Figure 12-11a, we see that

$$r_b = r_a \cos \frac{180 \text{ deg}}{N_t}$$ (12-27)

and that the pitch line changes in height by

$$\delta = r_a - r_b = r_a \left(1 - \cos \frac{180 \text{ deg}}{N_t} \right)$$ (12-28)

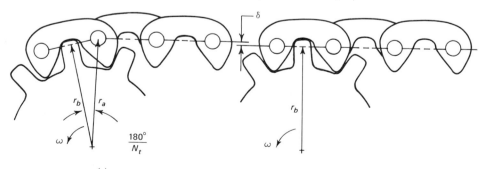

(a)

(b)

Figure 12-11 Chordal action. **(a)** Chain in highest position. **(b)** Chain in lowest position.

Expanding the cosine term, the change in height becomes approximately

$$\delta = \frac{r_a \pi^2}{2N_t^2} \tag{12-29}$$

Inverted tooth chain sprockets generally have no less than 17 teeth. The radius change is then, approximately $\delta/r_a = 1.7\%$ for the worst case. Roller chain sprockets are commonly available with as few as eight teeth, and the corresponding radius change is $\delta/r_a = 7.7\%$ for the worst case, corresponding to a velocity change of almost $\pm 4\%$ from the mean. The corresponding accelerations result in severe fatigue loads on chain components. The effects of chordal action can be alleviated by sprocket and link design. One design uses an involute form of sprocket tooth for inverted tooth chain. Another inverted tooth chain design uses two-part link pins that roll upon one another and effectively change chain pitch by a small amount as the chain engages the sprocket.

Failure of chain drives

Most industrial roller chains and inverted tooth chains are designed for service of many thousands of hours if adequate lubrication is maintained. Engagement and disengagement of the chain with sprocket teeth, however, results in fatigue loading, particularly when one of the sprockets is small, and chordal action contributes to the problem. The link plates are subject to varying tension and, thus, must be designed to prevent tensile fatigue failure. At low speeds, failure is more probable in the link plates than elsewhere, particularly in the case of roller chain. Roller chain roller bushings are subject to impact against sprocket teeth and are more susceptible to failure at high and moderate speeds. At very high speeds and loads, lubrication breakdown may cause instantaneous seizing or galling at the chain joints. Current standards, however, allow operation at very high speeds and loads (the range where galling is possible) if the design calls for an adequate lubrication system.

PROBLEMS

1. Find maximum torque at the small pulley of a V-belt drive if maximum belt tension cannot exceed 300 lb. The included angle of the pulley groove is 35 deg, the coefficient of friction is 0.2, the small pulley has an angle of wrap of 170 deg, a pitch diameter of 8 in., and a speed of 4000 rpm. The belt weighs 0.01 lb/in.

2. Find the maximum torque at the small pulley in Problem 1 if maximum belt tension cannot exceed 1500 lb and the belt weighs 0.05 lb/in.

3. A single V-belt drive with included angle 36 deg is to have a capacity of 16.55 hp based on a coefficient of friction of 0.2 and estimated belt weight of 0.012 lb/in. Speed is to be reduced from 1750 rpm to 1170 rpm using a drive pulley pitch radius of 3.5 in. Shafts are 16 in. apart. (**a**) Find belt tensions at full load. (**b**) Find shaft torques and bending loads. (**c**) Find initial tension when the drive is not operating.

4. The capacity of a V-belt drive is to be 10 hp based on a coefficient of friction of 0.2, a drive pulley pitch radius of 4 in., a driven pulley pitch radius of 8 in. and an input speed of 1725 rpm. The shafts are 18 in. apart. Estimated belt weight is 0.012 lb/in., included angle of pulleys is 36 deg. (a) Find required belt tensions. (b) Find shaft torques and bending loads. (c) Find belt tensions when the above drive is transmitting only 2 hp. Assume no adjustments have been made.

5. A single V belt with a pitch length of 79.6 in. is to transmit 10 hp. Input speed is 1720 rpm and output speed is 860 rpm. The drive pulley has a pitch radius of 4 in. and the included angle of the pulleys is 36 deg. Assume the belt tension on the tight side is 5 times the tension on the slack side. (a) Find the center distance of the shafts. (b) Find belt tensions at full load. (c) Find torque and bending load on the shafts. (d) Find the centrifugal effect based on a 5 V section belt weighing 0.012 lb/in. (e) Find the minimum coefficient of friction required.

6. Analyze the belt drive of Problem 5 if 5 hp is to be transmitted and output speed is to be 1720 rpm. Assume belt tension on the tight side is 2.5 times the tension on the slack side.

7. A thin plastic flat belt is to be designed to transmit 12 hp. Input pulley radius is 5 in., input speed is 3000 rpm and output speed is 1670 rpm. Use a center distance of 24 in., and a 0.02-in. thick by 2-in. wide belt with a density of 0.1 lb/in.³ Assume the coefficient of friction is not less than 0.3. (a) Find torque at the small pulley. (b) Find large pulley radius and contact angle for both pulleys. (c) Find inertia effect and belt tensions. Find maximum belt stress without including bending stress.

8. Find stress in the belt in Problem 7 if the drive is designed for a capacity of 5 hp. Find bending and torsion loads on the pulley shafts.

9. The output shaft of a speed reducer rotates at 100 rpm and transmits a steady 10 hp to a 5-in. diameter pulley overhung by 1.75 in. Assume minimum belt tension equals one third maximum tension. Using a corrected endurance limit of 45,000 psi and a yield point of 105,000 psi, find the required shaft diameter based on the maximum shear theory. Use a safety factor of 3.6.

10. The countershaft in Problem Figure 10 has two 6-in. diameter flat belt pulleys. It rotates at 1000 rpm and transmits a steady 50 hp. Assume minimum belt tension

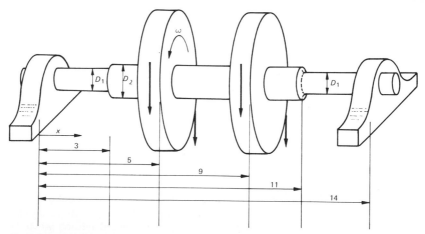

Problem Figure 10

equals one half maximum tension. Both belts are approximately vertical. Use a corrected endurance limit of 40,000 psi and a yield point of 100,000 psi with a factor of safety of 3 for the shaft. Use a stress concentration factor $K_f = 1.4$ at the step. Find the required shaft diameters.

11. The countershaft in Problem Figure 10 has two 7-in. diameter V-belt pulleys. It rotates at 1160 rpm and transmits a steady 7.0 hp. Assume minimum belt tension equals one third maximum tension. Both V-belts are approximately vertical. Use a corrected endurance limit of 40,000 psi and a yield point of 100,000 psi with a factor of safety of 3 for the shaft. Use a stress concentration factor $K_f = 1.4$ at the step. **(a)** Show moment and torque loading on the shaft due to the V-belt drive. **(b)** Determine diameters D_1 and D_2 based on the Maximum Shear Theory—Soderberg Criterion. **(c)** Find the required minimum coefficient of friction if the included angle of the pulleys is 38°, the angle of belt contact 180° and the belt weight 0.017 lb/in.

12. If pulleys are to turn in opposite directions, a belt may be crossed in the form of a "figure eight." Find approximate belt length in terms of pulley radii and center distance.

13. Find the horsepower capacity of a V-belt drive with a 5-in. pitch diameter driver pulley having a 155-deg angle of contact, 35-deg included angle, a coefficient of friction of 0.12, 1800 rpm driver speed, 900 rpm driven speed, belt weight of 0.05 lb/in. and a maximum allowable tension of 500 lb.

14. Find the capacity of the drive in Problem 13 if belt tension is limited to 350 lb.

15. A $\frac{1}{2}$-in. pitch inverted tooth chain operates on a 20-tooth drive sprocket rotating at 5000 rpm. The driven sprocket rotates at 1250 rpm. Find the recommended minimum center distance.

16. Find the minimum center distance for a $\frac{3}{4}$-in. pitch roller chain operating on a 16-tooth drive sprocket rotating at 4800 rpm and a driven sprocket rotating at 2400 rpm.

17. A 12-tooth $\frac{3}{4}$-in. pitch roller chain sprocket rotates at 1800 rpm. Find the approximate amplitude and frequency of chain motion due to chordal action.

REFERENCES

[1] *Engineering Steel Chains*. American Steel Chain Association, St. Petersburg, Fla., 1971.

[2] *Roller Chain Engineering*. Rex Chainbelt, Inc., Milwaukee, Wis., 1962.

[3] C. E. Wilson and W. Michels: *Mechanism—Design Oriented Kinematics*. American Technical Society, Chicago, Ill., 1969.

[4] *Design Manual for Roller and Silent Chain Drives*. American Sprocket Chain Manufacturers Association, Park Ridge, Ill., 1955.

[5] *Belt Conveyors for Bulk Materials*. Conveyor Equipment Manufacturers Association, Cahners Publishing Co., Boston, Mass., 1966.

13

Brakes and Clutches

SYMBOLS

C = specific heat
E_f = frictional energy
f = coefficient of friction
F = force
F_a = actuating force
F_n = normal force
g = acceleration of gravity
J = mass moment of inertia
KE = kinetic energy
n = speed, rpm
p = pressure

PE = potential energy
r = radius
T = torque
v = volume
V = velocity
w = width
W = wear
α = angle of contact
θ = subtended angle
σ = actual stress
τ = shearing stress

In this chapter we will discuss two very similar machine elements: the brake, a frictional device that absorbs the kinetic energy of moving bodies and thus controls their motion, and the clutch, a friction device whose primary function is to transmit power on an intermittent basis.

We will first turn our attention to clutches, which are generally classified as mechanical (Figure 13-1), electrical (Figure 13-2), and hydraulic (Figure 13-3). There are numerous subtypes of these three classifications that will also be discussed.

SECTION 13-1

Positive Contact Clutches

The type of clutch that we designate as mechanical falls into two categories: friction and positive contact. We will first consider the positive contact type, an example of which is shown in Figure 13-4. As is evident from the example shown, this type of clutch transmits power from the driving shaft to the driven shaft by means of jaws or teeth.

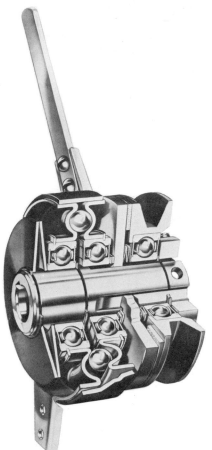

Figure 13-1 A mechanical clutch that has rotary cam actuation. [Courtesy Formsprag Company.]

Figure 13-2 The clutch shown is of the electromagnetic stationary coil tooth type. The direct tooth-to-tooth engagement prevents slippage. Typical applications include packaging and printing machinery, machine tool spindle drives, speed change mechanisms, elevators, heavy duty conveyors, and rolling mill drives. [Courtesy Formsprag Company.]

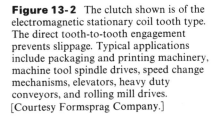

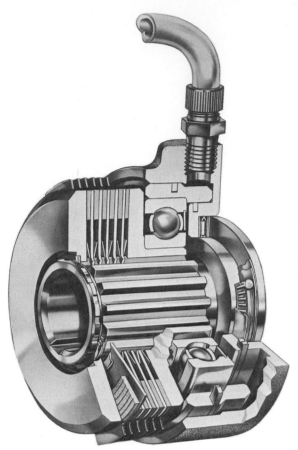

Figure 13-3 The clutch shown is a heavy duty oil-through-the-shaft-type, multiple disc hydraulic clutch. It operates to pressures of 500 psi. [Courtesy Formsprag Company.]

Figure 13-4 Serrated tooth positive contact clutch. [Courtesy Dodge Manufacturing.]

The advantages of these positive contact clutches are that they will not slip, they develop very little heat because they do not depend upon friction, and they are generally lighter and less costly than a friction clutch of similar torque capacity. The disadvantages are that positive contact clutches cannot be engaged at high speeds, shock accompanies engagement at any speed, and they require some relative motion in order to engage when both driving and driven shafts are at rest. Positive clutches, although not as widely used as friction clutches, do find important use in such applications as automotive transmissions, business machines, presses, and household appliances.

In order to demonstrate the procedure to be used in analyzing positive clutches, we will use the square jaw clutch as an example. Figure 13-5 shows half of a square jawed positive clutch. In operation, the half shown slides along the shaft upon which it is mounted until it engages with the similarly shaped other half. Clearly, some device, such as a spring or a hydraulic or pneumatic device, is needed to keep the two halves of the jaw in axial contact. As far as stress analysis is concerned, the jaws are subjected to bearing and shearing stresses.

The force acting on the jaw that produces these stresses depends upon the horsepower and speed that the clutch is to transmit. Equation (13-1) can be used to determine the torque acting on the clutch.

$$T = \frac{\text{hp} \times 63,000}{n} \tag{13-1}$$

where T = torque in inch-pounds; hp = horsepower to be transmitted; and n = revolutions per minute.

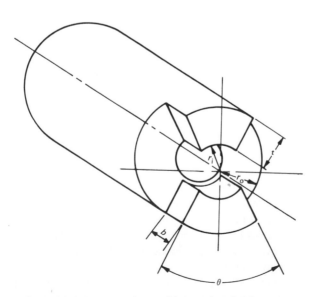

Figure 13-5 Square-jaw positive-contact clutch.

At this point the average force, assumed to be acting at the center of each jaw, can be determined from equation (13-2).

$$F = \frac{T}{k(r_o + r_i)/2} \qquad (13\text{-}2)$$

where F = average force in pounds; k = number of jaws on one member; r_o = outside jaw radius in inches; and r_i = inside jaw radius in inches.

The shearing stress, in pounds per square inch, acting on one jaw is then given by

$$\tau = \frac{F}{\dfrac{2\pi(r_o + r_i)}{2} \times \dfrac{\theta \times t}{360}} \qquad (13\text{-}3)$$

where t = thickness of jaw, in inches and θ = angle subtended by one jaw in degrees.

Clearly, $2\pi(r_o + r_i)/2$ represents the average circumference of the jaws.

The bearing stress can be found from equation (13-4).

$$\sigma_b = \frac{F}{bt} \qquad (13\text{-}4)$$

where b = length of jaw.

As was pointed out earlier in this discussion, positive clutch engagement is accompanied by shock, which can be rather severe. As a result, the stresses calculated by the previous equations must be multiplied by appropriate shock factors. Some designers make the assumption that only one of the jaws takes the entire load, thus making the design even more conservative.

SECTION 13-2

Disc Clutches

The first of the friction type clutches to be discussed is the disc clutch, also known as an axial or plate clutch. This type of clutch is able to transmit torque from the input to the output shaft because of the frictional force developed between the two plates or discs. Figure 13-6 is a simplified sketch showing the basic components of this type of clutch.

The input disc is free to move axially along the shaft but is pinned, splined, or keyed to the shaft so that it must rotate with the shaft. Clearly, the torque that can be transmitted will depend upon the frictional force developed, which in turn depends, among other factors, upon the axial force developed between the discs. The axial force can be applied in several ways, such as by mechanical means (levers, springs, linkages), hydraulic or pneumatic pressure, or electromagnetic means.

The primary advantages of friction clutches are that, because they can slip relative to each other, there is very little shock during engagement and

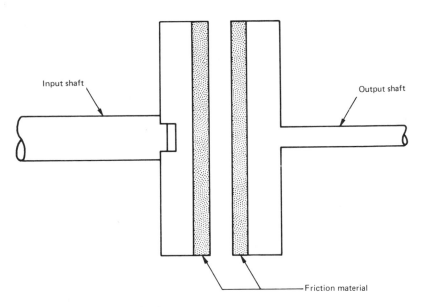

Figure 13-6 Disc type clutch.

they can be used for high speed engagement applications. The disadvantages are that they do slip (not suitable for applications that require positive transmission), they do wear out (requiring replacement of friction material), and heat is developed (might require external cooling).

Before proceeding with the analysis of disc clutches it is necessary to consider the physical situation that occurs when the discs are in contact and transmitting power. If the discs or plates used in the clutch are relatively flexible, it is possible to obtain relatively uniform pressure on the friction surfaces. On the other hand, if the plates are relatively rigid, the wearing of the friction surface is approximately uniform after an initial wearing-in has taken place. In analyzing the clutch, either the assumption of uniform wear or uniform pressure must be made. Neither assumption is correct, so the designer must decide which assumption more closely approximates the particular clutch he is analyzing. An alternative favored by some designers is to use only the uniform wear assumption, because it turns out to be the more conservative one. It is more conservative because clutch capacities obtained from the equations based upon this assumption are lower than those obtained from the uniform pressure approach. We will present both and allow the designer to use his own judgment as to which is more appropriate for a specific problem.

Uniform wear

One disc of the clutch to be analyzed is shown in Figure 13-7. The wear may reasonably be assumed to be directly proportional to pressure intensity and velocity at a particular point on the clutch. This velocity is directly

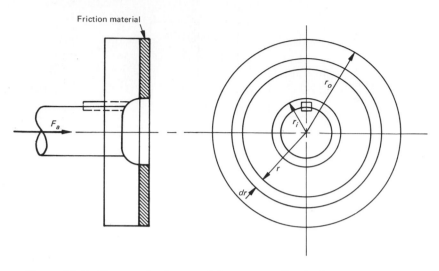

Figure 13-7 The actuating force needed to engage a disc clutch.

proportional to the radius. Letting W be the wear, we have

$$W \propto pV \propto pr$$

where p = pressure intensity in pounds per square inch at some radius r in inches. Therefore

$$W = kpr$$

where k is a constant. Thus

$$\frac{W}{k} = pr = K$$

where K is a constant, since both W and k are constants.

Because pr is a constant, it is obvious that the maximum pressure must occur at the minimum radius, r_i. Thus

$$K = pr = p_{max}r_i \quad \text{or} \quad p = p_{max}r_i/r$$

The numerical value for the maximum permissible pressure depends upon the type of friction material used. Table 13-1 lists some values for maximum pressure as well as values for coefficient of friction for some typical clutch and brake materials.

The actuating force, F_a, is the force pressing the two discs together and is normal to the friction surface. It can be obtained by multiplying the pressure between the friction surfaces by the area of the surfaces. However, since the pressure is not constant with respect to r, we must write the force for the elemental ring shown in Figure 13-7 and integrate between appropriate limits.

Table 13-1 Brake and Clutch Material Properties

Material	Maximum Drum Temperature, °F	Coefficients of friction, f	Maximum Allowable Pressure, psi
Metal on metal	500–600	0.25	200–250
Wood on metal	200	0.2–0.3	50–90
Leather on metal	150–200	0.3–0.4	15–40
Molded blocks	500–600	0.25–0.5	100–150
Asbestos on metal in oil	500	0.35–0.45	50–150
Sintered metal on cast iron in oil	450	0.2	400

Thus, the equation for actuating force required is

$$F_a = \int_{r_i}^{r_o} p2\pi r \, dr$$

$$= \int_{r_i}^{r_o} p_{max}\frac{r_i}{r}2\pi r \, dr$$

$$= 2\pi r_i p_{max}(r_o - r_i) \tag{13-5}$$

In order to arrive at an equation for the torque capacity of the clutch (the frictional torque developed), the frictional torque for the elemental annular area must be integrated over proper limits. Thus,

$$T = \int_{r_i}^{r_o} rfp2\pi r \, dr$$

or

$$T = \pi f r_i p_{max}(r_o^2 - r_i^2) \tag{13-6}$$

where f = coefficient of friction.

The designer often finds it convenient to have an equation available relating torque capacity and actuating force. Since $F_a = 2\pi r_i p_{max}(r_o - r_i)$, from equation (13-5), and equation (13-6) can be written

$$T = \pi f r_i p_{max}(r_o - r_i)(r_o + r_i)$$

equation (13-7) is valid.

$$T = \frac{f F_a(r_o + r_i)}{2} \tag{13-7}$$

Uniform pressure

Under the assumption of uniform pressure, every part on the clutch face can be subjected to the maximum permissible pressure. Clearly, under this assumption the wear will not be constant. Proceeding in the same manner as was used previously, the actuating force equation is

$$F_a = \int_{r_i}^{r_o} p_{max} 2\pi r \, dr$$

$$= \pi p_{max}(r_o^2 - r_i^2) \qquad (13\text{-}8)$$

The torque capacity of the clutch is then

$$T = \int_{r_i}^{r_o} rf p_{max} 2\pi r \, dr$$

$$= \tfrac{2}{3}\pi f p_{max}(r_o^3 - r_i^3) \qquad (13\text{-}9)$$

And the torque capacity expressed in terms of the actuating force becomes

$$T = \frac{2}{3} f F_a \left(\frac{r_o^3 - r_i^3}{r_o^2 - r_i^2} \right) \qquad (13\text{-}10)$$

Friction clutches are also made in the form of rims or drums. As can be seen in Figure 13-8, the friction material is placed around the outer surface of the drum. Since the analysis of this type of clutch is similar to that for drum brakes, to be discussed in Section 13.6 of this chapter, we will not discuss that type of clutch at this time. An advantage that the disc clutch enjoys over the drum clutch is that multiple discs can be used with a resultant increase in torque capacity and with the same actuating force as is required for a single disc. Other advantages are the absence of centrifugal effects and efficient heat dissipation surfaces.

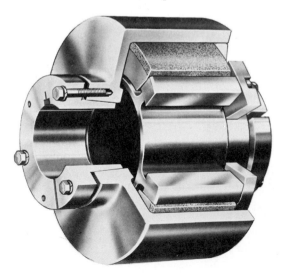

Figure 13-8 A friction clutch of the rim or drum type. [Courtesy Formsprag Company.]

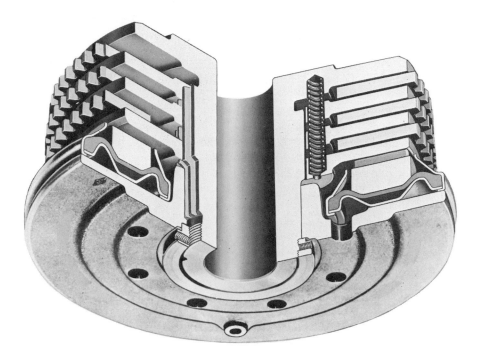

Figure 13-9 A typical multiple-disc dry clutch. This type of clutch is air or mechanically actuated. [Courtesy Twin Discs Incorporated.]

The multiple disc plate clutch of the type shown in Figure 13-9 can have as many as 50 or 60 discs, with the discs being alternately driving and driven discs. Although the torque capacity equations we developed were for a single pair of friction surfaces, they can be used for multiple discs by merely multiplying the values obtained by the number of active surfaces.

Example 13-1. A single plate disc clutch, with both sides of the plate effective, is to be used in an automobile. The friction material that the clutch is made of has a coefficient of friction of 0.3 and a maximum allowable pressure of 15 psi. If the outside radius of the clutch is 10 in. and the inside radius is 8 in., determine the torque that can be transmitted and the actuating force required of the springs.

Solution: We will solve this problem using both the uniform wear and the uniform pressure assumptions in order to verify the earlier statement that the uniform wear assumption results in a more conservative estimate.

Uniform wear. From equation (13-6)

$$T = \pi f r_i p_{max}(r_o^2 - r_i^2)$$
$$= \pi \times 0.3 \times 8 \times 15(10^2 - 8^2)$$
$$= 4070 \text{ in.-lb for one side effective}$$

Therefore for two sides effective

$$T = 2 \times 4070 \text{ in.-lb} = 8140 \text{ in.-lb}$$

Now from equation (13-5)

$$F_a = 2\pi r_i p_{max}(r_o - r_i)$$
$$= 2\pi \times 8 \times 15(10 - 8)$$
$$= 1507 \text{ lb}$$

or by equation (13-7) for one side

$$T = \frac{f F_a (r_o + r_i)}{2}$$

For two sides then

$$\frac{T}{2} = \frac{f F_a (r_o + r_i)}{2}$$

and

$$F_a = \frac{T}{f(r_o + r_i)} = \frac{8140}{0.3(10 + 8)} = 1507 \text{ lb}$$

Uniform pressure. From equation (13-9)

$$T = \tfrac{2}{3}\pi f p_{max}(r_o^3 - r_i^3)$$
$$= \tfrac{2}{3}\pi \times 0.3 \times 15(10^3 - 8^3)$$
$$= 4437 \text{ in.-lb for one side effective}$$

For two sides effective

$$T = 2 \times 4437 = 8874 \text{ in.-lb}$$

By equation (13-8)

$$F_a = \pi p_{max}(r_o^2 - r_i^2)$$
$$= \pi \times 15 \times (10^2 - 8^2)$$
$$= 1696 \text{ lb}$$

Thus, it is obvious that the uniform wear assumption gave a smaller torque capacity and actuating force; therefore, it is the more conservative of the two assumptions. ●

SECTION 13-3

Cone Clutch

Another type of axial clutch is the cone clutch, shown in Figure 13-10. Cone clutches have the advantage of being able to transmit a larger torque than disc clutches with the same outside diameter and actuating force. The reason for this capability is the increased frictional area and the wedging action that takes place. Cone clutches find their widest use in relatively low peripheral speed applications.

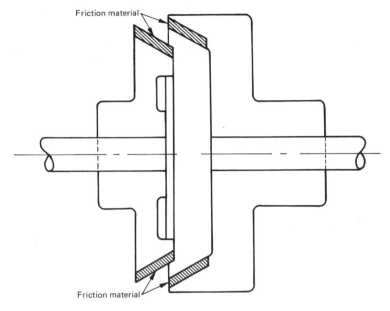

Figure 13-10 Cone clutch.

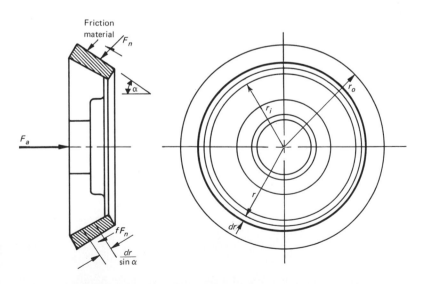

Figure 13-11 Free body diagram of one half of a cone clutch showing the normal and actuating force.

In Figure 13-11 a free body diagram of one half of a cone clutch is drawn. The activating force F_a, which is usually produced by means of a spring, must be large enough to produce the normal force required as well as to overcome the frictional force $f F_n$ present during engagement.

Summing the horizontal forces will result in the actuating force equation (13-11)

$$F_a = F_n \sin \alpha + f F_n \cos \alpha \quad \text{or} \quad F_a = F_n(\sin \alpha + f \cos \alpha) \quad (13\text{-}11)$$

If we assume that the resultant frictional force $f F_n$ acts at the mean diameter of the clutch cone, we can obtain the following equation for the frictional torque, or torque capacity of the clutch.

$$T = f F_n \frac{d_{av}}{2}$$

but

$$d_{av} = r_o + r_i$$

thus

$$T = \frac{f F_n(r_o + r_i)}{2} \qquad (13\text{-}12)$$

The torque can also be expressed in terms of the actuating force by combining equations (13-11) and (13-12).

$$T = \frac{f F_a}{\sin \alpha + f \cos \alpha} \frac{(r_o + r_i)}{2}$$

$$= \frac{f(r_o + r_i)F_a}{2(\sin \alpha + f \cos \alpha)} \qquad (13\text{-}13)$$

An analysis similar to the uniform wear assumption made for disc clutches in Section 13.2 results in the following equations (13-14) through (13-16).

$$F_n = \frac{2\pi r_i p_{max}}{\sin \alpha}(r_o - r_i) \qquad (13\text{-}14)$$

$$F_a = 2\pi r_i p_{max}(r_o - r_i) \qquad (13\text{-}15)$$

$$T = \frac{\pi f r_i p_{max}}{\sin \alpha}(r_o^2 - r_i^2) = \frac{F_a f (r_o + r_i)}{2 \sin \alpha} \qquad (13\text{-}16)$$

The angle α has a minimum value of 8 deg and, although there is no upper limit, a typical value would be about 12 deg.

SECTION 13-4

Other Types of Clutches

The functions performed by the mechanical clutches, discussed in the previous sections, can be performed equally well by electric clutches, which utilize magnetic fields to produce torque transmission. The basic operational procedure involved in electro-magnetic clutches can be illustrated by Figure 13-12.

Electric clutches are usually classified into the following categories: friction disc, serrated tooth, hysteresis, magnetic particle, and eddy current. Another general type of clutch is the hydraulic or pneumatic clutch, which has the advantage of minimizing shock and vibration. Figure 13-13 is an example of a pneumatic air clutch.

There are many applications such as washing machines, textile machinery, pumps, appliances, helicopter rotors, and so on, for which it is desirable to have automatic, smooth engagement between driven and driving member whenever some minimum speed is exceeded. The ideal clutch for this type of problem is the centrifugal clutch, such as the one shown in Figure 13-14.

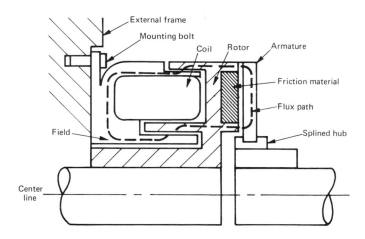

Clutch and Clutch Coupling Flux Path

Figure 13-12 Clutch and clutch coupling. The clutch-coupling and the clutch consist of three basic elements: the field, the rotor and the armature. The field and its coil are held stationary. The rotor is normally driven by a prime mover such as an electric motor and the armature is attached to the load. When the field coil is energized, a flux path is set up and the armature is magnetically attracted to the rotor. Through friction, the armature and the load to which it is connected will lock in at the same speed as the rotor, as long as the field coil is energized. When the field coil is de-energized, the armature disengages, no torque is transmitted, and the armature and load come to rest. [Courtesy General Time Corp., Thomaston, Conn.]

Figure 13-13 Pneumatic air type clutch. [Courtesy Horton Manufacturing Company, Inc., Minneapolis, Minn.]

Figure 13-14 The centrifugal type clutch illustrated engages when some minimum speed has been exceeded. [Courtesy Mercury Clutch.]

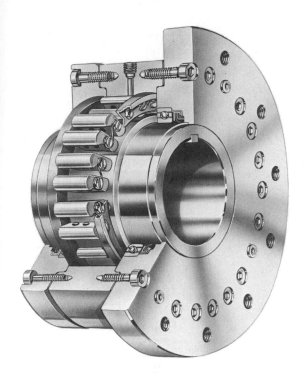

Figure 13-15 The clutch shown is designed for low speed overrunning and indexing applications. [Courtesy Formsprag Company.]

The last type of clutch we will discuss is the overrunning or freewheeling clutch. They are generally classified into three categories, roller, sprag, and wrapped spring. This clutch permits torque transmission in one direction only and thus is useful in such applications as feed mechanisms, bicycle coaster brakes, automotive clutch freewheeling, and so on.

As a typical example of an overrunning clutch, the Formsprag clutch is shown in Figure 13-15. The description on p. 694 is by courtesy of the Formsprag Company, Warren, Mich.

To conclude this discussion of clutches, it should be emphasized that the designer will very often find it more economical to choose a standard clutch from a manufacturer's catalog rather than going through an analysis and design himself. In other words, if the designer needs a clutch capable of transmitting 5000 in.-lb of torque, there are any number of standard clutch types from which he can choose one whose operating characteristics most nearly solve the particular problem. However, there are many instances where the designer will have to check the claims made by a manufacturer or where he will have unique problems that do not lend themselves to solution by standard items. It is hoped that when these situations arise, the designer will be able to use the analysis procedures presented to solve them.

Stripped of such items as gears, splines, bearings, oil seals and other attachments, a Formsprag over-running clutch consists basically of a cylindrical inner race and a cylindrical outer race surrounding it, with an annular space left between the two races. A full complement of accurately formed sprags fills this annular space.

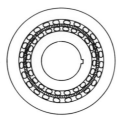

Each sprag is essentially a strut placed between the races in such a way that it transmits power from one race to the other by a wedging action when either race is rotated in the driving direction. Rotation in the other direction frees the sprags and the clutch is disengaged, or overruns. Either race may be the driven member.

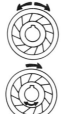

If one race of the over-running clutch is securely fixed to a grounded member, so that it cannot rotate, and the other race is free to turn, the free race will turn freely in one direction of rotation, but will be locked to the ground in the opposite direction. If the grounded race is connected instead to a moving mechanism rather than to ground, then the over-running clutch will transmit torque to the moving mechanism in one direction, but will free-wheel, and transmit no torque when turned in the opposite direction.

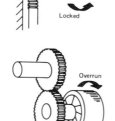

In a Formsprag clutch, each "strut" in the previous examples is actually a fully formed sprag. The cross sectional shapes of these sprags have been developed by Formsprag engineers to meet most conceivable types of clutch applications. Since different types of over-running applications will involve different loading characteristics, clutch technology is varied to provide the greatest possible life, torque capacity and functional characteristics for the three basic types of over-running clutch applications.

Simple over-running

This class of application is typified by standby and compound drives. For example, a steam turbine and a standby electric motor may be connected to a single driven shaft through over-running clutches. The shaft can then be driven by either the turbine or the motor or *both*, with no further modification of the installation. The turbine drive clutch automatically engages when the turbine starts to drive, but automatically over-runs when the load is transferred to electric motor.

Indexing

In this type of application, reciprocating motion applied to the driving race is transformed into intermittent motion in only one direction at the driven race. For example, if a pinion is connected to the driving race, a rack meshing with the pinion can give reciprocating motion to the driving race. The clutch will then advance or "index" the work (driven race) on each forward stroke of the rack, but will not return or back-up on the return stroke of the rack.

Holdbacks/Backstops

In backstopping or holdback applications, one race is always fixed to a stationary member. The function of the clutch is to permit rotation of the mechanism, connected to the other race, in one direction only, and to prevent any rotation in the reverse direction at any time. Although the clutch normally overruns most of the time, it is referred to as a holdback or backstop in conveyors, gear reducers and similar equipment because its function is to prevent run-back.

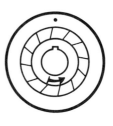

694

SECTION 13-5

Brakes

A brake may be simply defined as a machine element that is used to control the motion of a moving body by absorbing kinetic energy. This is the case in the usual applications where a rotating body is being slowed down or stopped, although there are instances, such as bodies being lowered by hoists, cranes, and so on, where the energy to be absorbed is potential energy. A last general class of problem involves the use of brakes to keep bodies at rest.

Although one important requirement in selecting a brake is its torque capacity, which was also the case with clutches, another vital consideration is the ability of the brake to absorb and dissipate heat. This additional consideration is necessary because clutches usually connect two moving bodies, whereas brakes connect a moving and a stationary body. In general, however, the types of brakes to be discussed could also be used as clutches with some slight modifications.

SECTION 13-6

Energy and Power Considerations

As has already been mentioned, the function of a brake is absorbing energy and dissipating the resultant heat. The question of the time it takes for a brake to dissipate heat compared to the time during which it is absorbing energy is quite important. Another way of saying this is that, although a brake may act satisfactorily when used at largely spaced intervals, it could overheat when applied steadily. Most of us at one time or another have experienced the unpleasant burning smell of overheated brakes when applying the brake too often in trying to control the speed of a car going down a long hill. Carried to an extreme, the temperature of the brake lining could become high enough to cause the brakes to fail completely. The point being made here is that the *rate* at which energy must be absorbed and heat dissipated by a brake is extremely important.

As the temperature of the brake increases, its coefficient of friction will decrease. The result is fading, which simply means that the effectiveness of the brake may be sharply curtailed. Clearly, the designer must avoid fading by designing the brake for a more efficient dissipation of heat.

In considering the energy to be absorbed, it is obvious that the energy equation will depend upon the type of motion the body is undergoing. To illustrate, let us consider the following examples.

1. A crane is to lower a body of weight W, from a height h_1 to a height h_2. The change in potential energy, which is also the energy that must be absorbed by the brake is given by

$$\Delta PE = W(h_1 - h_2) \qquad (13\text{-}17)$$

2. A body, of weight W, is translating at a speed V_i and is to be slowed down to a speed V_f. The change in kinetic energy is

$$\Delta KE = \frac{1}{2}\frac{W}{g}(V_i^2 - V_f^2)$$ (13-18)

where g = acceleration of gravity.

3. A body of weight W, rotating at a speed of ω_i rad/sec, is to be braked down to a speed of ω_f rad/sec. The change in kinetic energy is then

$$\Delta KE = \tfrac{1}{2}J(\omega_i^2 - \omega_f^2)$$ (13-19)

where J is the mass moment of inertia of the body about its axis of rotation.

The three cases cited above are the most common types encountered. However, it should be obvious that more complicated problems can be broken up into combinations of these three types.

At this point, we may assume that the frictional energy developed must be absorbed by the material adjacent to the brake lining (usually a metal drum). It is then possible to calculate the temperature increase for the brake by means of equation (13-20)

$$E_f = \rho v C \Delta t$$ (13-20)

where

E_f = frictional energy the brake must absorb, ft-lb
ρ = weight density of the drum material, lb/in.^{3}
v = volume of drum material absorbing the frictional energy, in.^{3}
C = specific heat of the brake drum material,

$$\frac{\text{ft-lb}}{(\text{lb})(^\circ \text{F})}$$

Δt = increase in temperature of the brake drum, $^\circ$F.

Faires [1] suggests the following as suitable values for specific heat: cast iron = 101, steel = 93, aluminum = 195.

To recapitulate, the energy a brake must absorb is calculated by the appropriate equations (13-17) through (13-19), and equation (13-20) is then used to determine the temperature of the drum material. If enough time is allowed for the brake drum to radiate and conduct the heat that was developed before the next braking operation, then there will be no buildup of heat. However, if cooling does not take place rapidly enough, there will be a higher initial temperature at the start of every braking operation. The result will still be an equilibrium temperature, but a much higher one. An exact determination of this equilibrium temperature is not possible because of the uncertainty about the brake's environment. Approximate methods are available, such as the one shown in reference [2].

Table 13-1 listed some of the maximum drum temperatures for some commonly used brake and clutch materials. These temperatures are the maximum values for steady operation

As will be shown in Section 13.11, the torque capacity of brakes depends, among other factors, upon the maximum permissible pressure that can be developed between the braking surfaces. Table 13-1 listed some suggested values for maximum pressure. The designer must exercise his judgment with regard to what pressure to use by evaluating the effects of such operational characteristics as length and frequency of braking.

Most brake lining manufacturers include the effect of the rate of energy dissipation by giving limiting values of pV for given materials. The units for pV, energy dissipation rate, are expressed as foot pounds per square inch per minute (ft-lb)/(in.^{2})/(min) or horsepower per square inch (hp/in.^{2}). To give the designer a feel for the numbers involved, the following pV values are typical [1].

1. Less than 28,000 in applications involving continuous operation, and inadequate heat dissipation.
2. Less than 55,000 for intermittent operation and poor heat dissipation but with long periods of rest.
3. Less than 83,000 for continuous application with good heat dissipation.

The values given above are merely guidelines, and the manufacturers' catalogs should be consulted for values to be used for specific materials and applications.

SECTION 13-7

Band Brakes

The band brake, Figure 13-16, is perhaps the simplest of the many braking devices. The braking action is obtained by tightening the band wrapped around the drum that is to be slowed down or halted. The difference in the tensions at each end of the band determines the torque capacity.

The relationship between the tensions, F_1 and F_2, is derived in exactly the same manner as that used for flexible belts, with the exception that the centrifugal force acting on belts does not act. Rather than go through the analysis again, we will simply repeat the relationship here.

$$\frac{F_1}{F_2} = e^{f\theta} \qquad (13\text{-}21)$$

where

$$F_1 = \text{larger tensile force, lb}$$

$$F_2 = \text{smaller tensile force, lb}$$

$$f = \text{coefficient of friction}$$

$$\theta = \text{angle of contact between band and drum, rad}$$

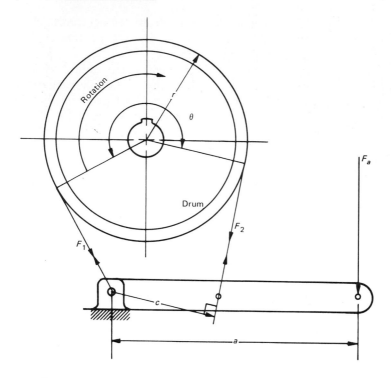

Figure 13-16 The simple band brake shown is operated by tightening the band wrapped around the drum that must be slowed down.

The relationship between the actuating force F_a and the slack side tension F_2 is obtained by summing moments about point O.

$$F_a = F_2 \frac{c}{a} \tag{13-22}$$

where a and c are the distances shown in Figure 13-16.

The torque capacity is obtained by summing moments about the center of rotation of the drum.

$$T = (F_1 - F_2)r \tag{13-23}$$

where r = radius of drum.

Referring again to the analysis of belts, a similar equation for maximum tension exists

$$F_1 = p_{max}wr \tag{13-24}$$

where w is width of band.

SECTION 13-8

Differential Band Brakes

The differential band brake, shown in Figure 13-17, is similar to the simple band brake just discussed, except that the tight side tension helps the actuating force. A brake of this type is called self-energizing and, as will be shown shortly, may even be self-locking. The equations discussed in the previous section apply, except that the actuating force equation, obtained by summing moments about the pivot point O, becomes

$$F_a = \frac{eF_2 - cF_1}{a} \qquad (13\text{-}25)$$

It is obvious from an inspection of the equation that the actuating force required is less than if F_1 had been attached at point O. In fact if cF_1 is greater than eF_2, the brake will be self-acting or self-locking. Obviously, if a brake is designed to be self-locking for one direction of rotation, it can be free to rotate in the opposite direction. Therefore, a self-locking brake can be used in those applications where rotation in one direction only is to be permitted.

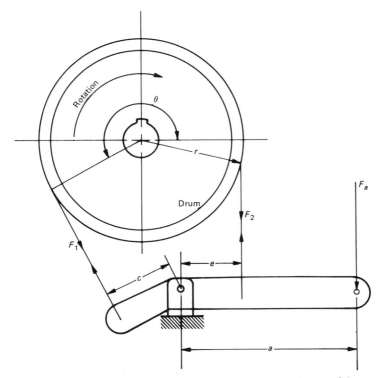

Figure 13-17 Because the differential band brake makes use of the tight side tension to help the actuating force, it is called self-energizing.

SECTION 13-9

Disc Brakes

Disc brakes, Figure 13-18, are very much like the disc clutches discussed in article 13-2. In fact, since the analysis follows exactly that presented previously, there is no need to spend time discussing them in detail.

Disc brakes are used in heavy duty industrial applications because they can be designed to dissipate heat quickly and thus have relatively little problem due to fading. They have also been used to a limited extent in automotive applications, one reason being that they provide equal braking torque for either direction of rotation.

Figure 13-18 Disc brakes of the type shown are used in heavy duty industrial applications because of their ability to dissipate heat quickly. [Courtesy Goodyear Tire and Rubber Company, Industrial Brake Department.]

SECTION 13-10

Short Shoe Block Brake

A block brake, Figure 13-19a, is considered to be a short shoe brake if the pressure distribution is constant along the shoe; in other words, if the angle of contact θ is small enough to assume uniform pressure distribution.

With uniform pressure distribution, the resultant normal force will act at the center of the shoe. Figure 13-19b is a free body diagram of the forces acting on the shoe.

The normal force can be determined from equation (13-26)

$$F_n = p_{max}r\theta w \qquad (13\text{-}26)$$

The torque capacity of the brake is then given by

$$T = fF_n r \qquad (13\text{-}27)$$

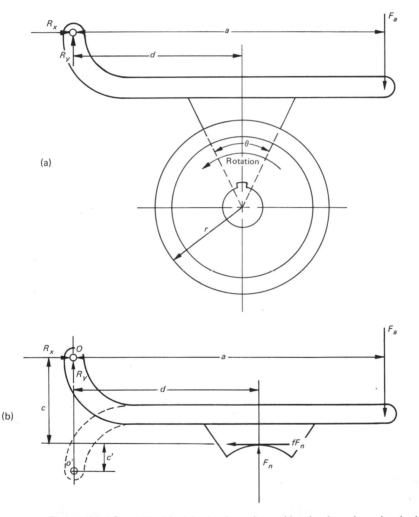

Figure 13-19 (a) The block brake shown is considered to be a short shoe brake if the angle of contact is small enough to permit the assumption of uniform pressure distribution along the shoe. (b) The free body figure shows the forces acting on the shoe and the actuating arm. When the arm pivot is located at O, the brake is self-energizing; if it is located at O', it is not self-energizing.

Summing moments about the pivot point O, will give the equation for determining the actuating force.

$$\Sigma M_o = F_a a - F_n d + f F_n c$$

or

$$F_a = \frac{F_n}{a}(d - fc) \tag{13-28}$$

where F_a is the actuating force in pounds, and d is the distance shown in Figure 13-19.

The horizontal and vertical components of the pin reaction at O can be found by summing the horizontal and vertical forces.

$$R_x = f F_n \tag{13-29}$$

$$R_y = F_n - F_a \tag{13-30}$$

The brake as drawn is self-energizing because the frictional force helps the actuating force (reduces the actuating force required for a given braking torque). It should also be obvious that if $d = fc$, no actuating force is required, and if $d < fc$, the actuating force F_a is negative, which means the brake is self-locking and a force is required to disengage the brake once it has been engaged. The self-energizing effect is useful, but the self-locking effect is generally undesirable. The usual procedure is to design the brake so that d is at least 25–50% greater than fc. This will ensure proper utilization of the self-energizing effect while preventing self-locking.

Two other points are germane to this discussion. If the pivot point O had been located below the line of action of the frictional force, say at O' in Figure 13-19b, the moment due to frictional force would oppose that of the actuating force, and the brake would not be self-energizing. Finally, both of the situations discussed, pivot at O or at O', will be reversed if the direction of rotation is reversed.

SECTION 13-11

Long Shoe External Block Brake

When the angle of contact θ is greater than say 50 or 60 deg, the assumption of uniform pressure distribution and normal and frictional forces acting at the center of the shoe can lead to appreciable errors. Since most shoe brakes have contact angles of 90 deg or more, it is clear that a more exact analysis is required. The obvious problem concerns the determination of the pressure distribution. Because the shoe is not rigid, it will deflect, and this effect in addition to the load applied will probably cause the pressure distribution to be different than that assumed. However, we will make the usual assumption, namely, that the pressure varies directly as the distance from the pivot point, O. This assumption is equivalent to assuming that the wear is proportional to pV, (pressure times velocity).

Figure 13-20, depicts a long shoe external contacting brake. The pressure at some arbitrary angle θ is proportional to $c \sin \theta$, but since c is a constant, the pressure varies directly as $\sin \theta$. In equation form

$$p \propto c \sin \theta \propto \sin \theta$$

or $p = k \sin \theta$ where k is a proportionality constant, and p is the pressure at some arbitrary angle θ. If p_{max} is the maximum allowable pressure, as determined by the properties of the brake lining material, then

$$k = \frac{p}{\sin \theta} = \frac{p_{max}}{\sin \theta_{max}}$$

and

$$p = \frac{p_{max}}{\sin \theta_{max}} \sin \theta \tag{13-31}$$

This equation gives the pressure distribution at a particular angle θ. Obviously for small values of θ, very little pressure is developed, and therefore the brake is usually designed for $\theta_1 \geqslant 10$ deg. The maximum pressure occurs at $\theta = 90$ deg, and if θ_2 is made larger, the magnitude of the pressure developed decreases. As a result, there is very little braking capacity to be gained by letting θ_2 exceed 120 deg.

Finally, the term $\sin \theta_{max}$ is evaluated as follows:

if $\qquad\qquad \theta_2 \leqslant 90$ deg, $\sin \theta_{max} = \sin \theta_2$

if $\qquad\qquad \theta_2 > 90$ deg, $\sin \theta_{max} = \sin 90$ deg

Since the pressure is not constant around the shoe, it will be necessary to analyze an element $r\,d\theta$ as shown in Figure 13-20. Our immediate objective will be to obtain an equation for calculating the actuating force F_a. Obviously, summing moments about pivot point O will be the procedure used. Although it is a relatively simple matter to obtain equations for determining the magnitudes of the total normal and frictional forces acting on the shoe, determining their point of application and lines of action is not simple. Because we are primarily interested in the moments they produce about O, we will go right to the determination of the total moments.

The moment due to the normal force is

$$M_{F_n} = \int_{\theta_1}^{\theta_2} pwr\,d\theta\,c \sin \theta$$

$$= \int_{\theta_1}^{\theta_2} \frac{p_{max}}{\sin \theta_{max}} \sin \theta wr\,d\theta\,c \sin \theta$$

$$= \frac{p_{max}}{\sin \theta_{max}} wrc[\tfrac{1}{2}(\theta_2 - \theta_1) - \tfrac{1}{4}(\sin 2\theta_2 - \sin 2\theta_1)] \tag{13-32}$$

The moment due to the frictional force is

$$M_{F_f} = \int_{\theta_1}^{\theta_2} fpwr \, d\theta(r - c\cos\theta)$$

$$= \int_{\theta_1}^{\theta_2} f\frac{p_{max}}{\sin\theta_{max}} \sin\theta wr \, d\theta(r - c\cos\theta)$$

$$= f\frac{p_{max}w}{\sin\theta_{max}}r\left[-r(\cos\theta_2 - \cos\theta_1) - \frac{c}{2}(\sin^2\theta_2 - \sin^2\theta_1)\right] \quad (13\text{-}33)$$

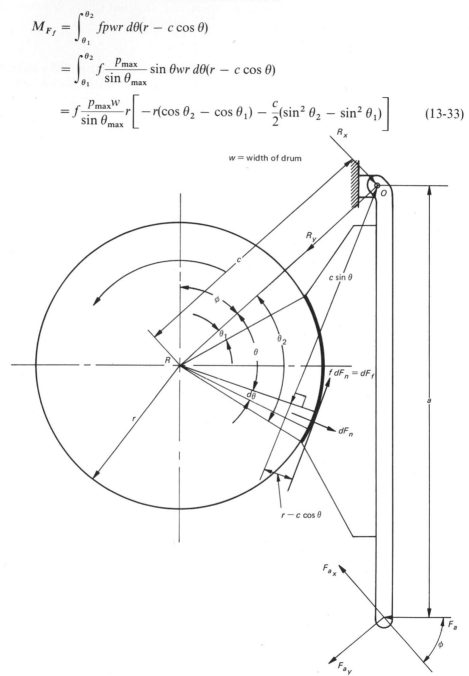

Figure 13-20 The long-shoe external brake shown cannot be analyzed by assuming a uniform pressure distribution across the shoe.

If we now sum moments about the pivot point O, we get

$$F_a = \frac{M_{F_n} + M_{F_f}}{a} \tag{13-34}$$

The signs of the moments in the above equation depend upon the location of the pivot point. When using the equation to determine the actuating force, the algebraic sign obtained for the moment should be used. It is also obvious that if both M_{F_n} and M_{F_f} have the same sign, self-locking cannot occur.

Reversing the direction of rotation of the drum will reverse the sign of the moment due to the frictional force, and the actuating force equation becomes

$$F_a = \frac{M_{F_n} - M_{F_f}}{a} \tag{13-35}$$

Clearly, for this situation, self-locking will occur if $M_{F_f} > M_{F_n}$.

The torque capacity equation for the brake can be obtained by integrating the product of the frictional force and the drum radius.

$$T_f = \int_{\theta_1}^{\theta_2} fpwr \, d\theta \, r$$

$$= \int_{\theta_1}^{\theta_2} f \frac{p_{max}}{\sin \theta_{max}} \sin \theta wr^2 \, d\theta$$

$$= f \frac{p_{max}}{\sin \theta_{max}} wr^2 (\cos \theta_1 - \cos \theta_2) \tag{13-36}$$

Finally, the designer will find it useful to have equations for determining the pin reaction at the pivot point O. Summing forces in the y direction we get

$$R_y = -F_a \sin \phi + \int_{\theta_1}^{\theta_2} pwr \, d\theta \cos \theta + \int_{\theta_1}^{\theta_2} fpwr \, d\theta \sin \theta$$

$$= -F_a \sin \phi + \frac{p_{max}}{\sin \theta_{max}} wr \int_{\theta_1}^{\theta_2} \sin \theta \cos \theta \, d\theta$$

$$+ \frac{p_{max}}{\sin \theta_{max}} fwr \int_{\theta_1}^{\theta_2} \sin^2 \theta \, d\theta$$

$$= -F_a \sin \phi + \frac{p_{max}}{\sin \theta_{max}} wr \left\{ \left(\frac{\sin^2 \theta_2}{2} - \frac{\sin^2 \theta_1}{2} \right) \right.$$

$$\left. + f \left[\frac{1}{2}(\theta_2 - \theta_1) - \frac{1}{4}(\sin 2\theta_2 - \sin 2\theta_1) \right] \right\} \tag{13-37}$$

Similarly

$$R_x = F_a \cos \phi - \int_{\theta_1}^{\theta_2} pwr \, d\theta \sin \theta + \int_{\theta_1}^{\theta_2} fpwr \, d\theta \cos \theta$$

$$= F_a \cos \phi + \frac{p_{max}}{\sin \theta_{max}} wr \left[-\frac{1}{2}(\theta_2 - \theta_1) + \frac{1}{4}(\sin 2\theta_2 - \sin 2\theta_1) \right.$$

$$\left. + f\left(\frac{\sin^2 \theta_2}{2} - \frac{\sin^2 \theta_1}{2} \right) \right]$$

(13-38)

Reversing the direction of rotation will change the sign of the terms containing the coefficient of friction.

SECTION 13-12

Long Shoe Internal Brake

A type of brake that is widely used in automotive applications is the internal contacting shoe brake shown in Figure 13-21. The method of analysis and resulting equations are identical with those discussed in the previous section [equations (13-32), (13-33), and (13-36)].

The actuating force for a counterclockwise rotating drum, Figure 13-21 is given by

$$F_a = \frac{M_{F_n} - M_{F_f}}{a}$$

(13-39)

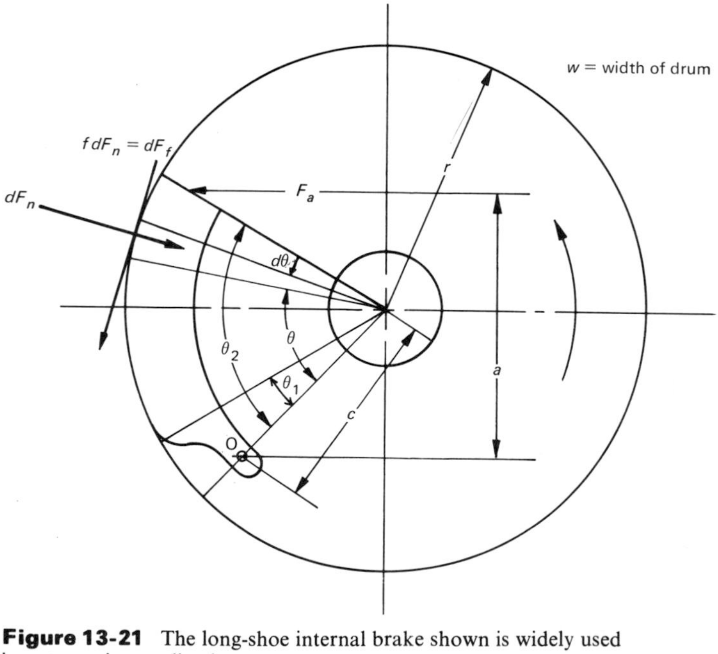

Figure 13-21 The long-shoe internal brake shown is widely used in automotive applications.

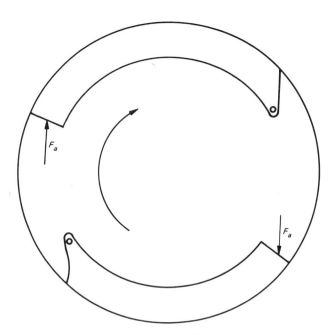

Figure 13-22 When the shoes are pivoted as shown and the rotation is clockwise, both are self-energizing. However, for counter clockwise rotation, neither is.

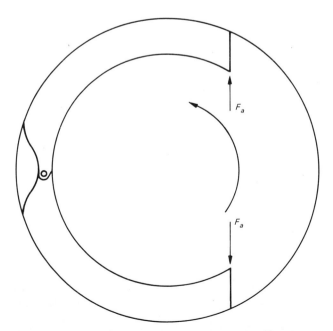

Figure 13-23 When the shoes are pivoted as shown, only the upper shoe is self-energizing. However, reversing the direction of rotation will make the lower shoe self-energizing.

If the direction of rotation is reversed, the equation becomes

$$F_a = \frac{M_{F_n} + M_{F_f}}{a} \tag{13-40}$$

As was mentioned previously, drum brake shoes usually do not exceed angles of contact of 120 deg. The result is that most internal brakes are of the double shoe type. The shoes are usually pivoted either as shown in Figure 13-22 or Figure 13-23. When the pivots are located as shown in Figure 13-22, both shoes are self-energizing; but when the direction of rotation is reversed, neither is. For the brake shown in Figure 13-23, the upper shoe is self-energizing and the lower shoe is not. However, if the direction of rotation is reversed, the lower shoe is self-energizing and the upper shoe is not. For a given actuating force, the braking capacity with both shoes self-energizing is clearly greater than if only one were. Automotive brakes are usually made with both shoes self-energizing, with the result that braking ability in reverse is much less than for forward motion.

SECTION 13-13

Materials for Brakes

The materials used to manufacture brakes fall into two general classifications, those used for the drums and those used for the linings. Drums are usually made of cast iron with some alloying materials added. More expensive materials such as stainless steel, aluminum, monel, and so on, are used when good heat conduction is important.

Brake linings on the other hand are usually made of some form of asbestos and binders. Most asbestos based linings are molded, although there are some special applications for woven linings. Linings of this type are normally not used if the operating temperature is expected to exceed 400°F. For brakes, in which the temperature is expected to be in the 400–750°F range, sintered metal linings are usually used. If the temperature range falls into the 750–1000° F category ceramic particles are added to the sintered metal linings. In fact, if the ceramic content is high, operating temperatures as high as 1800°F can be tolerated.

The sintered linings have the advantage of high thermal conductivity, a long life span, and very stable friction characteristics. The disadvantages are that they are relatively expensive, they have a lower coefficient of friction, and they must be manufactured to shape because of their rigidity.

Most linings are attached to the drums by either riveting or bonding. Although riveting has the advantage of low cost and relative ease and simplicity of installation, it does have the disadvantage of having the usable lining thickness dependent upon the depth to which the rivet head can be countersunk.

Bonded linings afford more friction area and greater effective thickness but are more expensive and require more elaborate equipment and careful control when they need to be replaced.

SECTION 13-14

Electrical Brakes

Figure 13-24 illustrates a typical electromagnetic brake. Brakes of this type have two basic components, the armature and a friction forced magnet that attracts the armature when power is applied. By making or breaking an electric contact, the two moving parts are either engaged or disengaged. Although the electromagnetic brake is the most commonly used electrical brake, three other types—hysteresis, eddy-current, and magnetic particle brakes—have some use in certain applications.

SECTION 13-15

Brake Actuation

One of the important problems with which a brake designer must concern himself is the method by which the brake is to be activated. Mechanical brakes are activated mechanically, pneumatically, hydraulically, or electrically.

Mechanical activation is used for low torque, low speed applications such as scooters, conveyors, golf carts, garden tractors, minibikes, and so on. Clearly, a limiting value on the braking torque that can be developed by

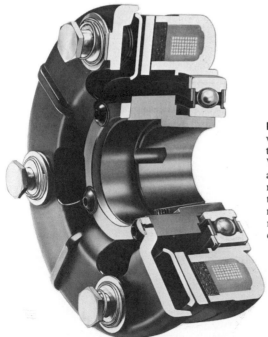

Figure 13-24 The electric brake shown is very much like an electromagnet in that it has two basic parts, the magnet and the armature. When power is applied, the magnet attracts the armature. The magnet is faced with friction material, thus eliminating slippage between the two parts when they are engaged. The two moving parts can thus be engaged or disengaged merely by making or breaking an electrical contact. [Courtesy Warner Electric Corporation]

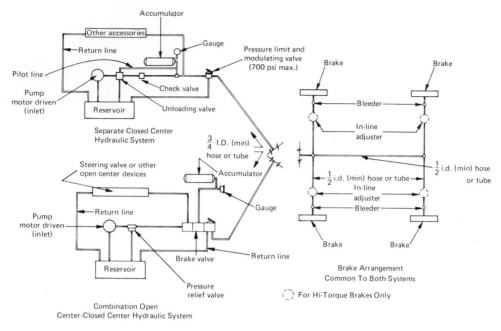

Figure 13-25 Typical straight hydraulic system, open center–closed center. [Courtesy B. F. Goodrich.]

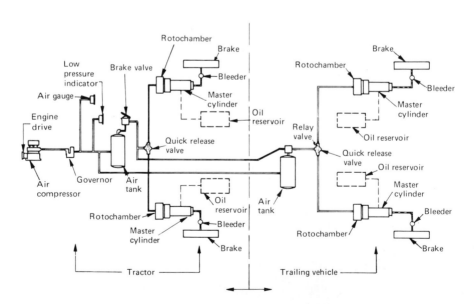

Figure 13-26 Typical air-over-hydraulic system. [Courtesy B. F. Goodrich.]

this type of activation is the magnitude and length of time the operator can exert the required pressure. Another disadvantage is that mechanical linkages usually require lubrication.

Most brakes, however, are activated either pneumatically, hydraulically, or by a combination of the two. A typical hydraulic brake system is shown in Figure 13-25. Combination brakes, also called air-over-hydraulic brakes, of the type shown in Figure 13-26, are used for heavy rolling equipment.

Electrically activated brakes are of two main types. The first, which was discussed in the previous section, depended upon a friction-faced magnet attracting a rotating armature. In the other type the brake is spring-set and is released by magnetic means. The advantage of the second type is that it is independent of the power. In other words, in the event of a power failure, the brake will be in operation until the power is restored to release it. The first type will not hold if there is a loss of power.

SECTION 13-16

Design Considerations

Brakes and clutches are available in commercial units. As is true of the other machine elements discussed previously, the designer must decide whether the particular brake or clutch is to be designed and manufactured or a commercially available unit is to be used. In general, unless large numbers are required, it is more economical to use commercial units. Even if the problem requires a nonstandard unit, most companies will be willing to have their engineering staffs solve the problem.

In the event, however, that large quantities or unusual conditions of operation necessitate the manufacture of a system, the following general steps can be used as a guide. The analysis will usually be based upon the torque capacity required and the energy that must be absorbed and dissipated. Factors such as required lining area, method of activation, available space, the characteristics of the friction material, effect of the activating force on the structure supporting the element, characteristics of the machine of which the element is to be a part, and the environment in which the machine is operating must all be considered. The usual result is a compromise of all these factors so as to ensure an economically competitive product.

PROBLEMS

1. For the square-jaw clutch shown in the Problem Figure 1, $r_o = 2$ in., $r_i = 1\frac{3}{8}$ in., $b = \frac{1}{2}$ in.; 75 hp is to be transmitted at 650 rpm. Each of the jaws subtends an arc of 90 deg. In other words, only 180 deg of the clutch surface has jaws on it. Calculate the shear and bearing stresses if $t = \frac{5}{8}$ in.

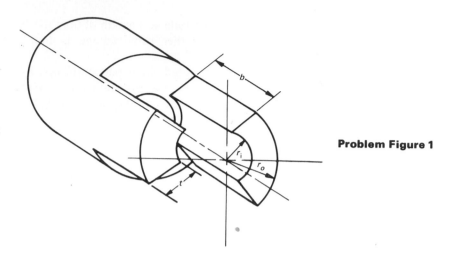

Problem Figure 1

2. Part of the transmission system of an automobile consists of a single disc clutch, both sides of which are effective; 25 hp is to be developed at 200 rpm. Experience has indicated that an outside diameter that is 3 times the inside diameter gives good results. If the friction material of the clutch has a coefficient of friction of 0.3 and can develop a maximum pressure of 15 psi, calculate the inside and outside diameters as well as the actuating force required. Assume uniform wear.

3. Repeat Problem 2, but assume uniform pressure.

4. A single disc clutch having both faces effective is to be used in an application where 60 hp are to be developed at 600 rpm. If the outside diameter is 9 in. and the inner radius 4 in., what will be the actuating force required and the average pressure for a clutch material having a coefficient of friction of 0.3? Assume uniform wear.

5. Repeat Problem 4 for uniform pressure.

6. A multiple disc clutch has four active faces, it is rated at 40 hp at 250 rpm. The coefficient of friction is 0.3, outside diameter = 16 in., inside diameter = 8 in. Determine the actuating force required and the average pressure between the discs.

7. A multiple disc clutch has an outside diameter of 6 in. and an inside diameter of 3 in. The clutch material permits a maximum pressure of 40 psi and has a coefficient of friction of 0.2. Determine the actuating force required, the number of discs needed, the average pressure, and the actual maximum pressure. Uniform wear may be assumed and a torque of 2800 in.-lb is to be transmitted.

8. A multiple disc clutch having four pairs of mating friction surfaces operates at a speed of 945 rpm. The maximum permissible magnitude of the axial actuating force is 800 lb. Coefficient of friction equals 0.15. The inside and outside radii of contact of the friction surfaces are 1 in. and 2 in., respectively. If conditions are such that uniform wear prevails, determine: **(a)** The torque capacity per pair of friction surfaces. **(b)** The total horsepower capacity. **(c)** The maximum pressure. **(d)** The minimum pressure.

9. Derive the torque capacity equation and the actuating force equation for a cone clutch similar to that shown in Figures 13-10 and 13-11 for the assumption of uniform pressure.

10. A cone clutch, which is made with an average diameter of 12 in., has friction material whose coefficient is 0.3, and whose maximum allowable average pressure is 50 psi, is used to transmit 20 hp at 500 rpm. If $\alpha = 8$ deg and uniform wear is assumed, calculate the actuating force and face width.

11. Repeat Problem 10 assuming uniform pressure.

12. Repeat Problem 10 for an α of 12 deg.

13. A cone clutch has an average diameter of 10 in., an α of 10 deg, and a coefficient of friction of 0.3. If an actuating force of 700 lb is applied, what is the torque that the clutch can transmit. Assume uniform wear.

14. Repeat Problem 13 for a uniform pressure of 50 psi.

15. A drum having a diameter of 5 ft is used to support a wire that is attached to a weight of 8000 lb. The drum is rotating at 60 rpm, has a radius of gyration of 2 ft, and weighs 10,000 lb. A brake is to bring the drum to rest in 15 ft. What is the average braking torque?

16. Repeat Problem 15 but for a drum rotation of 90 rpm.

17. If the brake rim in Problem 15 is made of steel, has a 10-in. diameter, $\frac{1}{2}$-in. thickness, and a 4-in. face width, what will be the temperature rise assuming all the energy is absorbed by the rim?

18. Repeat Problem 17 for the data of Problem 16.

19. For the drum brake shown in the Problem Figure 19, determine the actuating force F_a required to decelerate the drum at a rate of 120 rad/sec^2. The coefficient of friction of the drum may be taken as 0.25 and the moment of inertia of the rotating system as 2 ft-lb-sec^2.

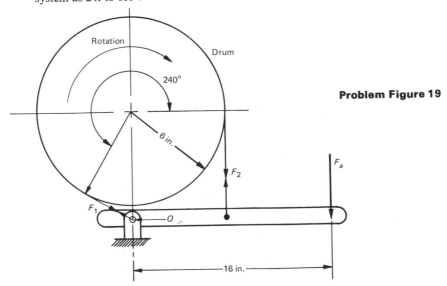

Problem Figure 19

20. Repeat Problem 19, but assume counterclockwise rotation of the drum.

21. For the band brake shown in Problem Figure 19, the angle of wrap is 270 deg, coefficient of friction is 0.3, and the drum radius is 8 in. What are the tight and loose side tensions required to have a friction horsepower of 30 hp at 900 rpm.

22. A simple band brake similar to that in Problem Figure 19 has an angle of wrap of 270 deg, a coefficient of friction of 0.3, a 12-in. drum diameter, and a maximum allowable pressure of 100 psi. If the band width is 3 in., determine the tight and loose side tensions and the torque capacity. What is the limiting actuating force?

23. The band brake shown in the Problem Figure 23 is to rotate in both directions. If a frictional horsepower of 100 is to be developed at 500 rpm, determine the actuating force required for a coefficient of friction of 0.1.

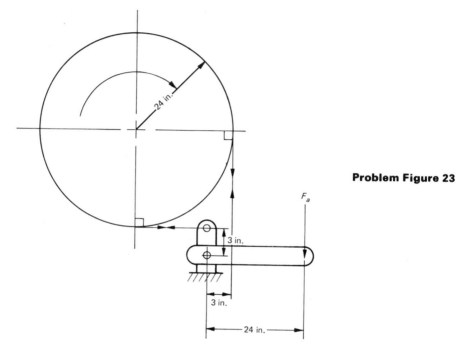

Problem Figure 23

24. For the brake in Problem Figure 24 a frictional horsepower of 10 is to be developed at 600 rpm. Will the brake be self-locking? The coefficient of friction may be taken as 0.4. What actuating force is required if $a = 10$ in.?

25. A brake similar to the one in Problem Figure 24 has a diameter of 20 in., an angle of wrap of 200 deg, the distance from the pivot point to where T_1 attaches is 1 in., and the distance from the pivot point to where T_2 attaches is 5 in. If the actuating force is 40 lb, $a = 25$ in., and $f = 0.3$, will the brake be self locking? What is the maximum braking torque?

26. Repeat Problem 25 for counterclockwise rotation of the drum.

27. If the brake in Problem Figure 19 is to absorb 30 hp at 700 rpm and the maximum pressure that can be developed is 70 psi, the drum width is 2 in., and the coefficient of friction is 0.2, what angle of wrap will be required? What actuating force will be required?

28. For the short shoe block brake shown in Problem Figure 28 $r = 15$ in., $a = 40$ in., $c = 2$ in., $d = 15$ in. For a coefficient of friction of 0.3, a frictional horsepower of 20 at 650 rpm is to be absorbed. What actuating force is required? Can the brake be self-locking? Calculate the pin reaction at O.

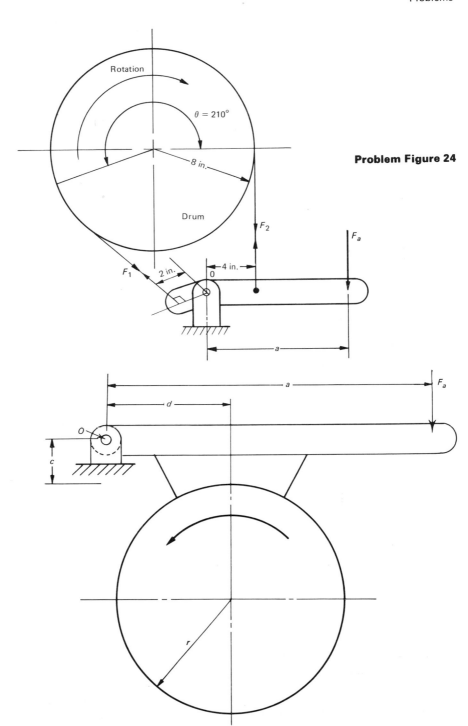

Problem Figure 24

Problem Figure 28

29. Repeat Problem 28 for clockwise rotation. What must c be to have self-locking? Calculate the pin reaction at O.

30. An external long shoe brake similar to the one shown in Figure 13-20 has the following dimensions: $a = 25$ in., $c = 12$ in., $\theta_1 = 10$ deg, $\theta_2 = 100$ deg, $w = 3$ in., $\phi = 20$ deg, $r = 8$ in., rpm $= 600$. If the maximum permissible pressure is 100 psi and the coefficient of friction 0.3, determine the actuating force required, the horsepower the brake will absorb, and the pin reaction at O.

31. Repeat Problem 30 for counterclockwise rotation.

32. The brake shown in Problem Figure 32 has a coefficient of friction of 0.25, an allowable maximum pressure of 100 psi, and a face width of 2 in. Determine the actuating force required, the horsepower that can be absorbed at 200 rpm, and the reactions at the pin.

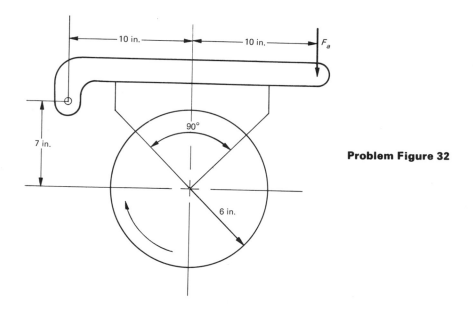

Problem Figure 32

33. Repeat Problem 32 for counterclockwise rotation.

34. The block type hand brake shown in Problem Figure 34 has a face width of $1\frac{3}{4}$ in. The frictional material permits a maximum pressure of 80 psi and a coefficient of friction of 0.24. **(a)** Determine the force F_a. **(b)** What is the maximum torque capacity? **(c)** If the speed is 100 rpm and the brake is applied for 5 sec at full capacity to bring the shaft to a stop, how much heat is generated?

35. Repeat Problem 34 for counterclockwise rotation.

36. An internal long shoe brake similar to the one shown in Figure 13-21 has the following dimensions: radius of drum $= 6$ in., $a = 9$ in., $c = 5$ in., $\theta_1 = 10$ deg, $\theta_2 = 120$ deg, coefficient of friction $= 0.3$, lining width $= 3$ in., maximum allowable pressure $= 90$ psi. What actuating force is required, and how much horsepower can be absorbed at 400 rpm.

37. Repeat Problem 36 for clockwise rotation.

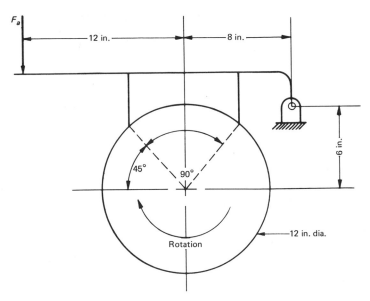

Problem Figure 34

38. The automotive type brake shown in Problem Figure 38 has a drum of radius 7 in., a coefficient of friction of 0.4, and an actuating force of 600 lb. What is the torque capacity of the brake?

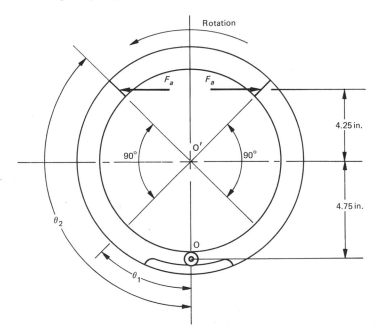

Problem Figure 38

39. Repeat Problem 38 for clockwise rotation of the drum.

40. In Problem Figure 38 assume the right hand shoe is pivoted at the top and the actuating force is applied at the bottom. The left hand shoe remains the same. What is the torque capacity?

41. Repeat Problem 40 for clockwise rotation.

REFERENCES

[1] V. M. Faires: *Design of Machine Elements*. The Macmillan Company, New York, 1965.

[2] Gagne: Torque capacity and design of cone and disc clutches. *Mach. Des.*, **24**(12): 182–187 (Dec. 1953).

[3] *Mechanical Drives Issue, Machine Design*. The Penton Publishing Co., Cleveland, Ohio, 1969.

[4] Peter Black: *Mechanics of Machines*. Pergamon Press, Elmsford, N.Y., 1967.

[5] H. S. Rothbart: *Mechanical Design and Systems Handbook*. McGraw-Hill Book Co., New York, 1964.

[6] A. W. Frehse: Fundamentals of brake design. *SAE J.*, **27**.

[7] A. C. Rasmussen: Internal friction, blocks and shoes. *Prod. Eng.*, **18**(3): 133 (1947).

[8] L. D. Hagenbook: Design of brakes and clutches of the wrapping band type. *Prod. Eng.*, **16**: 321 (1945).

[9] Z. J. Jania: Friction clutch transmission. *Mach. Des.*, **30** (1958).

[10] C. L. Eksergian: High speed braking. *ASME Trans.*, **73**: 935 (1951).

[11] H. A. Borchardt: Designing external shoe brakes. *Mach. Des.*, **32**(13): 163 (1960).

[12] R. L. Kotnik: Electromagnetic disc clutches. *Mach. Des.*, **32**(16): 113 (1960).

[13] A. J. Bette: Friction materials. *Mach. Des.*, **32**(20): 141 (1960).

14

Springs

SYMBOLS

C = spring index
D = diameter of wire, in.
g = acceleration of gravity
    (386 in./sec²)
h_f = free height, in.
h_s = solid height, in.
K = spring rate, lb/in.
N = factor of safety
N_a = number of active coils
R = mean coil radius or moment arm of load.

S'_{se} = endurance limit in shear, psi
S_{syp} = shear yield strength, psi
δ_s = solid deflection, in.
δ_w = working deflection, in.
τ = shear stress, psi
τ_m = mean shear stress, psi
τ_r = range shear stress, psi
v = Poisson's ratio
ω_n = natural frequency, rad/sec

Many machine members are designed on the basis of strength. In most cases, deflection is of secondary importance. Usually deflection is checked to see whether it is reasonable. In the design of springs, however, deflection is as important as strength. A significant deflection is necessary to most spring applications. These include the storage of energy, isolation of vibration, application of a steady force or torque, force measurement, and so on.

SECTION 14-1

Torsion Bars

A hollow or solid bar (Figure 14-1) may serve as a spring where significant angular deflection results from a torsional load. For torque PR, the relative rotation of the ends is given by

$$\phi = \frac{LPR}{GJ} \text{ rad} \tag{14-1}$$

where G is the shear modulus of the bar, and the relative displacement

$$\delta = \phi R = \frac{LPR^2}{GJ} \tag{14-2}$$

719

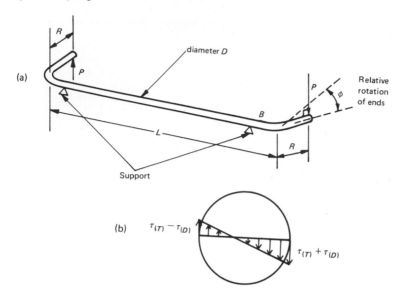

(a)

(b)

Figure 14-1 (a) Torsion bar subject to load P at moment arm R. (b) Cross section at B showing approximate shear stress distribution on a horizontal diameter.

Bending is neglected in both cases. For a solid circular cross section, the polar moment of inertia

$$J = \frac{\pi D^4}{32} \tag{14-3}$$

and for a hollow circular section of inside diameter D_i,

$$J = \frac{\pi(D^4 - D_i^4)}{32} \tag{14-4}$$

Shear stress due to torsion alone is proportional to distance from the center of the bar. The maximum value that occurs on the surface is

$$\tau_{(T)} = \frac{TD}{2J} = \frac{16PR}{\pi D^3} \tag{14-5}$$

for the solid bar.

For the part of the bar that does not lie between supports, there is a direct shear load P and an average direct shear stress P/A for cross section area A. For vertical load P, the torsional shear stress and direct shear stress combine to give the maximum shear stress at the end of a horizontal diameter nearest to the point of load application (Figure 14-1b). At that point, the direct shear is somewhat greater than its average value. Based on the theory of elasticity, it is

$$\tau_{(D)} = \frac{(1 + 2v)PD^2}{16(1 + v)I} \tag{14-6}$$

where $I = \pi D^4/64$ for a solid section. Adding equations (14-5) and (14-6), and using $v = 0.3$, we obtain the maximum shear stress

$$\tau = \frac{16PR}{\pi D^3}\left(1 + \frac{0.3075D}{R}\right) \tag{14-7}$$

where the effects of the end curvature and the effects of bending are neglected.

SECTION 14-2

Helical Springs under Static and Dynamic Loads

Helical springs of various proportions are shown in Figure 14-2. The load stress and load deflection relationships for helical springs under axial load closely resemble those relationships for torsion bars. Consider, for example, the compression spring sketched in Figure 14-3. If the resultant load and reaction P lie on the axis of the spring coil, then an element of the spring is subject to a torque PR where R is the mean coil radius (the average of inside radius and outside radius). There is no bending moment resulting from the load P, and deflection is due almost entirely to torsion in the wire. Using equation (14-2), we have

$$\delta = \frac{LPR^2}{GJ} \tag{14-8}$$

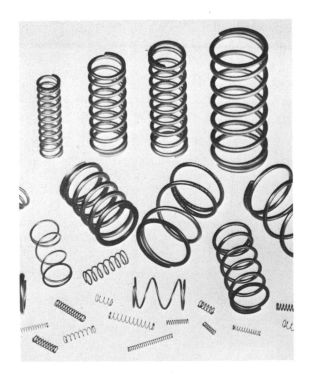

Figure 14-2 Helical compression springs. Most of the larger springs have squared and ground ends. [Courtesy Associated Spring Corporation, Bristol, Conn.]

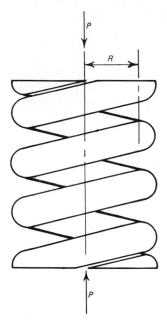

Figure 14-3 Helical compression spring with squared and ground ends.

Effective wire length L is a function of the mean coil radius R and the number of active coils N_a:

$$L = 2\pi R N_a \qquad (14\text{-}9)$$

Substituting equation (14-9) and the value of polar moment of inertia for a solid wire of diameter D into equation (14-8), we obtain the **deflection of a helical compression spring**

$$\delta = \frac{64 N_a P R^3}{G D^4} \qquad (14\text{-}10)$$

and a **spring rate**

$$K = \frac{P}{\delta} = \frac{G D^4}{64 N_a R^3} \qquad (14\text{-}11)$$

The number of active coils, N_a, may be one or two coils less than the total number of spring coils N_t. The spring of Figure 14-3 has squared and ground ends, and it is apparent that the end coils do not participate in the spring deflection. For springs with squared and ground ends, there are about two inactive coils and we have

$$N_a = N_t - 2$$

For squared ends, Figure 14-4, the approximate number of active coils is given by

$$N_a = N_t - 1.5$$

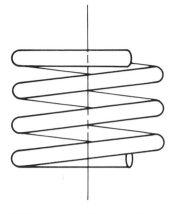

Figure 14-4 Helical compression spring with squared ends.

With squared ends, also called closed ends, the end turns lie in a plane approximately perpendicular to the spring axis.

Working deflection

Let us define the **working load** P_w on a compression spring as the greatest expected load and the working deflection δ_w as the deflection corresponding to the working load P_w. Furthermore, referring to Figures 14-5 and 14-6, we will define the **solid deflection** as the difference between the free (no load) height and the solid height

$$\delta_s = h_f - h_s \qquad (14\text{-}12)$$

The **clash allowance** is defined by

$$r_c = \frac{\delta_s - \delta_w}{\delta_w} \qquad (14\text{-}13)$$

which is a margin of extra deflection divided by the working deflection. A clash allowance of 0.20 (20%) is satisfactory for most applications. Using this value, an overload of 20% will deflect the spring to its maximum deflection δ_s and greater overload will have no effect on deflection or stress. Thus, with a sufficient safety factor, a compression spring is protected against failure after it reaches its solid deflection. Of course, the spring may fail to perform its primary function. For example, when compressed to its solid height, a spring mount can no longer protect a piece of equipment from shock or vibration damage.

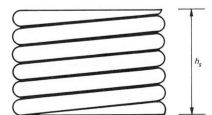

h_s

Figure 14-5 The solid height of a spring.

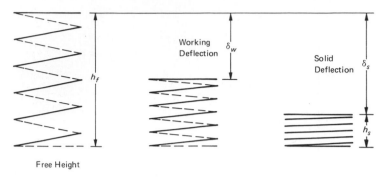

Free Height

Figure 14-6 Working and solid deflection of a helical spring.

Shear stress

While shear stress due to torsion in the straight bar (Figure 14-1) is given by

$$\tau_{(T)} = \frac{16PR}{\pi D^3} \tag{14-14}$$

the effect of curvature increases the above value by the factor

$$\frac{4C - 1}{4C - 4}$$

for a helical spring where the ratio of mean coil diameter to wire diameter

$$C = \frac{2R}{D} \tag{14-15}$$

is called the **spring index.** Using the above correction factor (called the Wahl curvature correction) we revise equation (14-7) to read

or

$$\left. \begin{aligned} \tau &= \frac{16PR}{\pi D^3}\left(\frac{4C - 1}{4C - 4} + \frac{0.615}{C}\right) \\[2ex] \tau &= \frac{8CP}{\pi D^2}\left(\frac{4C - 1}{4C - 4} + \frac{0.615}{C}\right) \end{aligned} \right\} \tag{14-16}$$

Some designers treat the Wahl curvature correction as a stress concentration factor and neglect it for static loading. This practice is equivalent to simply using equation (14-7). However, considering the nature of typical spring materials and the stress distributions encountered we will use equation (14-16) for static loading and for the mean and range stress components for fatigue loading.

Design for static load

Let the working strength S_{syp}/N and working load P_w be given. If we are required to design a spring with only these restrictions, we must make some assumptions. Suppose we decide that the spring index C will be no less than 5. Then, from equation (14-16), shear stress

$$\tau \leqslant \frac{21P_w R}{\pi D^3} \qquad (14\text{-}17)$$

Selecting a reasonable mean coil radius R and setting $\tau = S_{syp}/N$, the working strength in shear, we obtain the required wire diameter D for the spring. If the result is reasonable and if the spring index C is no less than the minimum selected above, we go to the next step in the design.

Let us assume that the spring rate K is specified (as it might be if the spring is to be used for vibration isolation). Selecting a material, we may then rewrite equation (14-11) to obtain the number of active coils

$$N_a = \frac{GD^4}{64KR^3} \qquad (14\text{-}18)$$

If squared and ground ends are selected, the total number of coils is

$$N_t = N_a + 2$$

The solid height is given by

$$h_s = N_t D \qquad (14\text{-}19)$$

If we select a 20% clash allowance, we will reach the solid height with a 20% overload. Thus, solid deflection

$$\delta_s = 1.20 \frac{P_w}{K}$$

and the free (unloaded) height is given by

$$h_f = h_s + \delta_s$$

The spring should be wound so that the center-to-center spacing between active coils (the pitch) is

$$p = D + \frac{\delta_s}{N_a}$$

when there is no load.

Example 14-1: Design for Static Loading. *Required:* Design a set of helical compression springs to support a load $P = 700$ lb/spring. The natural frequency of the system is not to exceed 100 cpm. *Design decisions:* Let us select steel with a shear yield point $S_{syp} = 70{,}000$ psi and a shear modulus

$G = 11.5 \times 10^6$ psi. If we use a clash allowance of 20%, the spring will be protected in case of overloads in excess of 20%, and a low safety factor, say $N = 1.5$, will be reasonable. A spring index $C = 6$ will be used and the coil ends will be squared and ground.

Solution: Rearranging the second of equations (14-16) and setting $\tau = S_{syp}/N$, we obtain

$$D^2 = \frac{8PCN}{\pi S_{syp}}\left(\frac{4C - 1}{4C - 4} + \frac{0.615}{C}\right)$$

Then for the given values, the result is a wire diameter $D = 0.536$ in., or we might use $D = \frac{9}{16}$ in. At this point, we must check the availability of this diameter steel with the assumed yield point. Mean coil radius is

$$R = \tfrac{1}{2}CD = \tfrac{27}{16} \text{ in.}$$

The spring rate K is related to the natural frequency f_n(cpm) and supported mass by

$$\omega_n = \frac{2\pi}{60}f_n = \sqrt{\frac{gK}{w}} \tag{14-20}$$

Using the maximum allowed frequency $f_n = 100$ cpm, a supported weight $w = 700$ lb, and $g = 386$ in./sec^2, we obtain

$$K = \frac{w}{g}\left[\frac{2\pi f_n}{60}\right]^2 = 199 \text{ lb/in.} \tag{14-21}$$

Then substituting this value of K in equation (14-18) we obtain $N_a = 18.8$ active coils, from which $N_t = N_a + 2 = 20.8$ total coils. The solid height h_s is $N_t D = 11.7$ in. and, with 20% clash allowance, the solid deflection is 120% of the working deflection or

$$\delta_s = 1.2\frac{P}{K} = 4.23 \text{ in.}$$

Thus, the free height is given by $h_f = h_s + \delta_s = 15.93$ in. ●

The design is not complete, however, until we consider surging and buckling which are treated in the Sections 14.3 and 14.4, respectively.

Design for fatigue loading

If we know the endurance limit in reversed shear stress and the shear yield point, the Soderberg criterion may be used directly on the basis of shear stress. If the endurance limit of the spring wire is given for one-way shear, a **modified Soderberg procedure** is used. The one-way shear test is based on a shear stress varying continually from zero to a maximum value S'_{se} (Figure 14-7a). It is assumed that S'_{se} is the value of shear stress for which a part is on the verge of failure after an "infinite" number of cycles. In many cases, S'_{se} may be based on 1×10^6 or 1×10^7 cycles of shear loading. Referring to Figure 14-7a, we see that the range and mean components of the shear loading are both $\tfrac{1}{2}S'_{se}$. Thus, we will designate points $(\tfrac{1}{2}S'_{se}, \tfrac{1}{2}S'_{se})$ and $(S_{syp}, 0)$ as failure points on a modified Soderberg plot, Figure 14-7b. The line between the failure points will be used to predict failure due to

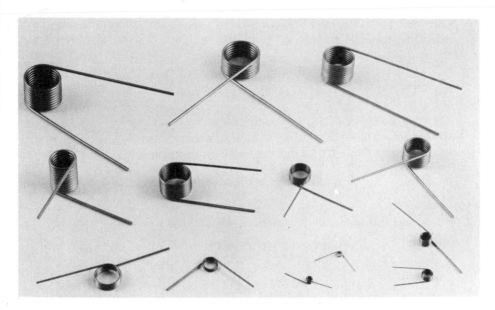

Figure 14-17 Helical torsion springs. Torsion springs are wound both left hand and right hand. The straight ends are normally as shown in Figure 14–18a when the spring is loaded. [Courtesy Associated Spring Corporation, Bristol, Conn.]

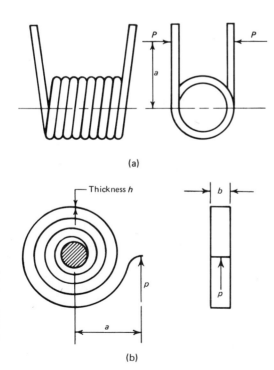

(a)

(b)

Figure 14-18 Torsion springs. **(a)** Helical torsion spring. **(b)** Spiral torsion spring.

Helical torsion spring deflection is principally due to bending moment which corresponds to torque about the coil central axis. Thus, we have angular deflection

$$\theta = \frac{ML}{EI} \text{ rad} \tag{14-57}$$

Referring to Figure 14-18, the bending moment about any section is $M = aP$ and the length $L = 2\pi R N_a$ for N_a coils of mean radius R. For circular wire of diameter D, $I = \pi D^4/64$ and the angular deflection is

$$\theta = \frac{128 a N_a PR}{ED^4} \text{ rad} \tag{14-58}$$

A **torsional spring rate** may be defined as

$$K_{\text{torsional}} = \frac{M}{\theta} = \frac{ED^4}{128 N_a R} \text{ lb-in./rad} \tag{14-59}$$

If we ignore residual stress, the bending stress is

$$\sigma = \frac{K_f Mc}{I} \tag{14-60}$$

where c is the distance from the neutral axis in bending to the extreme fiber. For circular wire the bending stress is

$$\sigma = \frac{32 K_f aP}{\pi D^3}$$

The stress concentration factor K_f, which depends on wire diameter and curvature, may be obtained by analyzing the spring as a curved beam, following the methods given in Chapter 18. Maximum stress occurs at the inner surface. For spring index $C = 4$, the stress concentration factor $K_f = 1.23$ and for $C = 6$, $K_f = 1.14$. For curved or hooked ends, K_f may be greater.

Spiral torsion springs

Analysis of a spiral-wound torsion spring (Figure 14-18b) is similar because moment on any section is given by the torque aP. For total length L, and moment of inertia $I = bh^3/12$, we have angular deflection

$$\theta = \frac{12 a L P}{b h^3 E} \text{ rad} \tag{14-61}$$

and a torsional spring rate

$$K_{\text{torsional}} = \frac{b h^3 E}{12 L} \text{ lb-in./rad} \tag{14-62}$$

Bending stress

$$\sigma = \frac{K_f Mc}{I} \tag{14-63}$$

where $I/c = bh^2/6$ and K_f is based on analysis of curved beams. If the minimum value of $R/h = 2$, stress concentration factor $K_f = 1.2$; for $R/h = 3$, $K_f = 1.12$.

SECTION 14-8

Rubber Mounts

Natural and synthetic rubber shock and vibration mounts are frequently selected because of their inherent damping qualities and low elastic moduli. These characteristics tend to dissipate energy and prevent sound transmission.

Compression mounts

The rubber compression mount, Figure 14-19a, having dimensions $a \times b \times h$ will be subject to a nominal compressive stress

$$\sigma = \frac{P}{ab} \text{ psi} \tag{14-64}$$

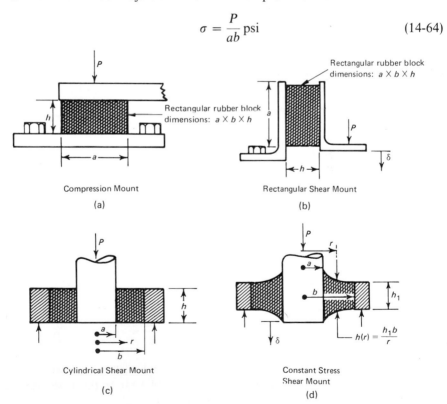

Compression Mount
(a)

Rectangular Shear Mount
(b)

Cylindrical Shear Mount
(c)

Constant Stress
Shear Mount
(d)

Figure 14-19 Rubber shock and vibration mounts.

and will deflect an amount

$$\delta = \frac{Ph}{abE} \text{ in.} \tag{14-65}$$

for a load P lb/mount. Poisson's ratio $v = 0.5$ (approximately) for rubber and, considering the low elastic modulus E, the mount will tend to expand laterally. The rubber, however, may be bonded to metal supports that limit lateral expansion and effectively increase the modulus as a function of displacement. Equations (14-64) and (14-65) are only approximate, and E depends on the hardness of durometer of the rubber selected for the mount.

Shear mounts

The rectangular shear mount, Figure 14-19b, will be subject to a nominal shear stress

$$\tau = \frac{P}{ab} \text{ psi} \tag{14-66}$$

and will deflect an amount

$$\delta = \frac{Ph}{abG} \text{ in.} \tag{14-67}$$

in the direction of the load P lb/mount. Shear modulus G, like E, is dependent on deflection and on rubber hardness.

If the mount is cylindrical in form (Figure 14-19c), shear stress

$$\tau = \frac{P}{2\pi hr} \text{ psi} \tag{14-68}$$

with a maximum value

$$\tau_{max} = \frac{P}{2\pi ah} \text{ psi} \tag{14-69}$$

Shear strain

$$\gamma = \frac{\tau}{G} \tag{14-70}$$

and the total deflection of the load is

$$\delta = \int_a^b \gamma \, dr = \frac{P}{2\pi hG} \int_a^b \frac{dr}{r} = \frac{P \ln (b/a)}{2\pi hG} \tag{14-71}$$

For more efficient material use, we might let h vary with r to obtain constant shear stress throughout (Figure 14-19d). In this case, shear stress

$$\tau = \frac{P}{2\pi hr} = \frac{P}{2\pi bh_1} \text{ psi} \tag{14-72}$$

shear strain

$$\gamma = \frac{\tau}{G}$$

and deflection

$$\delta = \gamma(b - a) = \frac{(b - a)P}{2\pi bh_1 G} \tag{14-73}$$

SECTION 14-9

Air Springs

Air springs are particularly effective for isolation of low frequency vibrations. The natural frequency for a single degree of freedom spring-mass system is given by

$$f_n = \frac{1}{2\pi} \sqrt{\frac{K}{m}} \ \text{cps} \tag{14-74}$$

for mass m and spring rate K. The spring rate was independent of the supported mass for the springs treated above and, thus, natural frequency was mass dependent. Most air springs have the peculiar characteristic that natural frequency is practically independent of mass.

Consider the air spring system illustrated schematically in Figure 14-20. Let the total volume of air or other medium in the reservoir and bellows be V_0 and the absolute pressure p_0 at static equilibrium conditions. Let us utilize the gas law

$$pV^n = \text{constant} \tag{14-75}$$

where $n = 1$ for a constant temperature process and $n = 1.4$ for air in an adiabatic process. The value $n = 1$ would hold for very low frequencies. Near the natural frequency (say 1 to 5 cps) much of the heat of compression would be retained in the system, in which case a value of n between unity and the adiabatic value would be appropriate.

Using the gas law, equation (14-75), we may write

$$p_0 V_0^n = p(V_0 - A\delta)^n \tag{14-76}$$

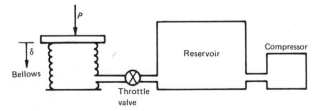

Figure 14-20 Air spring.

for pressure p, deflection δ, and volume change $A\delta$ where A is the effective bellows area. The spring rate is given by the force change per unit displacement change or

$$K = \frac{A\,dp}{d\delta}\ \text{lb/in.} \tag{14-77}$$

Rewriting equation (14-76) to obtain p, differentiating, and assuming a large reservoir (that is, volume change $A\delta \ll V_0$) we obtain

$$K = \frac{A^2 n p_0}{V_0}\ \text{lb/in.} \tag{14-78}$$

For supported weight $P = Ap_0'$, the natural frequency, from equations (14-74) and 14-78) is given by

$$f_n = \frac{1}{2\pi}\sqrt{\frac{Agn(p_0' + p_a)}{V_0 p_0'}}\ \text{cps} \tag{14-79}$$

where p_0' is the gage pressure at static equilibrium conditions and p_a is atmospheric pressure. For relatively high pressures $(p_0' \gg p_a)$ natural frequency is nearly independent of p_0' and the supported weight P.

PROBLEMS

1. Design a steel torsion bar for a static load of 400 lb with a moment arm $R = 6$ in. Use steel with a shear yield point of 50,500 psi and a safety factor of 2. **(a)** Find wire diameter. **(b)** Find length for a static deflection of 1.5 in.

2. Design a torsion bar for the same application as Problem 1 except that the static load is 800 lb and $R = 4$ in.

3. Design a set of helical steel compression springs to support a static load of 350 lb/spring. In order to provide isolation, the natural frequency of the system must not exceed 100 cpm based on each spring supporting a 350-lb weight. Use a shear yield point of 70,000 psi, a safety factor of 3, and a spring index of 6. Design for squared and ground ends and a 20% clash allowance.

4. Design a set of springs as in Problem 3 except that the load varies from 300 to 400 lb/spring. Use an endurance limit of 30,000 psi in one-way shear.

5. Design a helical compression spring for 1200-lb maximum load and a spring rate of 350 lb/in. Use an outside diameter of approximately 5 in., 25% clash allowance and squared and ground ends. Use alloy steel with a yield point of 120,000 psi, $G = 11.5 \times 10^6$, and a safety factor of 1.5.

6. Design a spring for the same requirements as in Problem 5 except that the spring rate is to be 150 lb/in.

7. Design a helical compression spring for a load that varies continuously from 0 to 900 lb. Use squared and ground ends, a spring index of 5 and 20% clash allowance. Design for steel with a shear yield point of 70,000 psi and an endurance limit of 40,000 psi in one-way shear. The safety factor is to be 1.4 and the spring rate 480 lb/in.

8. Design a spring as in Problem 7 except that the load varies from 450 to 900 lb.

9. A small steel helical compression spring must exert a force of 3 lb when its height is 2.5 in. and a maximum force of 10 lb when compressed to a height of 2.2 in. Base design on fatigue loading using a shear yield point of 80,000 psi and one-way shear endurance limit of 45,000 psi. Use a spring index of 6 (if possible) and a safety factor of 1.75. Use squared ends.

10. Design a spring as in Problem 9 except the force is 1 lb at 4 in. height and a maximum of 5 lb at 3.5 in. height.

11. Design a helical compression spring for a working load of 60 lb and a spring rate of 120 lb/in. *Decisions:* Use steel with squared and ground ends. Let the spring index be 6 and the clash allowance 20%. Allow a shear stress of 30,000 psi. **(a)** Find required wire diameter. **(b)** Find mean coil diameter. **(c)** Find the number of active coils. **(d)** Find the solid height and the free height.

12. Design a spring as in Problem 11 except that the spring rate is to be 60 lb/in.

13. A helical coil spring is adequate for static load F_1. It has N_{a1} active coils. A second spring is required to support a static load of $2F_1$. How many coils must it have if mean coil diameter, spring rate, and working stress are to be the same as for the first spring? Assume a spring index $C = 6$ for the first spring.

14. Design a helical steel compression spring for a maximum static load of 25 lb, a spring index of 8, a spring rate of 40 lb/in. and a safety factor of 3. Assume a tensile yield point of 120,000 psi; use squared and ground ends and a 20% clash allowance.

15. A helical tension spring has a mean coil diameter of 1 in. and a wire diameter of 0.1 in. It has 10 active coils. If a second spring were made with a mean coil diameter of 8 in., what wire diameter would be required to yield the same spring rate as the first spring?

16. Design a helical steel compression spring mount to support 1000 lb/spring. Use wire with a shear yield point of 60,000 psi and a safety factor of 3. Use a spring index of 6. **(a)** Find wire diameter. **(b)** Find the number of active coils to produce a natural frequency of 2 cps with the 1000 lb/spring load. **(c)** Find solid height and free height based on $1\frac{1}{2}$ inactive coils and a 20% clash allowance.

17. A helical compression spring has a spring rate of 28.5 lb/in., 14 active coils, and a wire diameter of 0.092 in. Find the pitch so that the allowable load (39.6 lb) will just be reached when the spring is compressed solid. Use zero clash allowance.

18. Find the wire diameter of a helical spring required to carry a 500 lb maximum load if the spring index is 6 and maximum shear stress cannot exceed 50,000 psi.

19. The shear yield point of a certain spring material is 60,000 psi and the endurance limit in one-way shear is 40,000 psi. Use a safety factor of 2. A spring mounting is to be designed for a varying load of 200–400 lb/spring. Find the required wire diameter for a mean coil diameter of 6 in.

20. A helical extension spring has 88 turns of 0.020-in. diameter wire and an outside diameter of 0.120 in. The initial tension is 0.30 lb. Write an expression for load versus deflection.

21. A helical extension spring has an outside diameter of 6.10 mm and 49 turns of 0.79 mm wire. Write an expression for extension in millimeters in terms of load in kilograms if the spring is made of steel and the initial tension is 0.227 Kg.

22. Find the first three surging frequencies of a helical extension spring having 63 turns of 0.020-in. steel wire and an outside diameter of 0.120 in.

23. A 0.057-in. outside diameter steel compression spring is made of 0.008-in. wire and has a free length of 0.56 in. and a solid height of 0.217 in. (a) Find the equivalent moment of inertia. (b) Find the buckling load if the spring has squared ends (not ground). Assume pinned-pinned end conditions.

24. A steel leaf spring similar to Figure 14-16 has $\frac{1}{8}$-in. thick by 3-in. wide leaves. The spring is 26 in. long between supports and there are four leaves at the center. (a) Find spring rate. (b) Find stress and deflection due to a 600-lb load.

25. A helical torsion spring is made of 0.30-mm stainless steel wire and has a 4.42-mm outside diameter. (a) Find the number of turns required for a 360-deg deflection due to a torque of 0.54 kg-mm. (b) Find stress.

26. Find the shear stress in a rubber mount similar to Figure 14-19d where $a = 1$, $b = 2$, and $h_1 = 1.5$ in. for a load of 30 lb/mount.

27. An air spring with an effective area of 12 in.^{2} is to be designed for a natural frequency of 2 cps at a gage pressure of 60 psi. Find the required air volume.

28. (a) Derive an expression for surging in a helical spring with both ends fixed. (b) Find the first three surging frequencies of a helical extension spring having 63 turns of 0.020-in. steel wire and an outside diameter of 0.120 in. if both ends are fixed.

REFERENCES

[1] G. E. Mather: *Mechanical Spring Design Guide*. North American Rockwell, Clawson, Mich., 1972.

[2] M. F. Spotts: *Mechanical Design Analysis*. Prentice-Hall, Inc., Englewood Cliffs, N.J., 1964.

[3] N. P. Chironis (ed.): *Spring Design and Application*. McGraw-Hill Book Co., New York, 1961.

15

Power Screws

SYMBOLS

A = cross-sectional area of the column (or screw), in.^{2}

b = thickness of the tooth at its root diameter, in.

c = distance from the centroid of the column to the outside fiber, in.

d_m = mean screw thread diameter, in.

d_o = major screw diameter, in.

d_r = root diameter of the screw, in.

E = modulus of elasticity in tension, psi

e = eccentric distance of the column load, in.

e = efficiency of the screw

F_f = friction force, lb

F_n = normal thread load, lb

f_c = coefficient of sliding friction between screw collar and support

f_s = coefficient of sliding friction between thread and nut

h = depth of thread, in.

K = factor depending on column supports

k = least radius of gyration, in.

L = length between column supports, in.

l = lead of thread, in.

n = number of threads

P = column load, lb

P_{cr} = critical buckling load, in.

p = thread pitch, in.

r_m = mean screw thread radius, in.

S_{yp} = yield point, psi

T_L = lowering torque, lb-in.

T_o = overhauling torque, lb-in.

T_R = raising torque, lb-in.

W = load being lowered or raised, in.

α = thread helix angle, deg

θ = thread angle, deg

θ_n = angle between F_n and OB, deg (see Figure 15-10)

σ_B = bearing pressure on threads, psi

σ_b = bending stress of screw threads, psi

σ_c = compressive stress of the screw, psi

σ_c = stress induced at the concave side of the screw, psi

σ_t = tensile stress, psi

τ = torsional stress, psi

τ = transverse shearing stress, psi

$\tau_{\max}$ = maximum combined shearing stress, psi

Power screws are used for transmitting motion in a smooth and uniform manner. They also may be thought of as linear actuators that transform rotary motion into linear motion. The kinematics of power screws is the same as that for nuts and screws, the only difference being the geometry of the threads (see Chapter 16). Whereas power screws find application as motion devices, ordinary screws find application in holding parts together (that is, as fastening devices).

Typical applications for power screws are (1) automobile jacks, (2) lead screw for lathes, (3) screw type presses, (4) C clamps, (5) valve stems, (6) hospital beds, (7) nuclear reactor control rod drives, and so on.

Power screws generally have an efficiency of the order of 30–75%, depending upon the thread helix angle and the coefficient of sliding friction between the nut and the screw. However, if higher efficiencies (for example, 90% and higher) are required, the designer may use a "ball screw." Ball screws were developed by the Saginaw Steering Division, General Motors Corp., to be used, originally, in the steering mechanism of automobiles. But, due to an ever widening field of application, they are now available as stock items from a variety of manufacturers.

SECTION 15-1

Power Screw Thread Forms

The thread forms used for power screws are (1) Acme screw threads, (2) stub Acme screw threads, (3) 60-deg stub Acme threads, (4) modified square threads, and (5) buttress threads. The specifications for these threads are covered by the ANSI Standards for translating screws [1].

Acme threads are the earliest type of power screw threads. They were developed for use with machine tools. Acme threads are cut as either general purpose or centralizing threads. The general purpose threads are classified into three class fits, namely, 2G for general purposes, 3G and 4G for minimal backlash. Centralizing threads have associated tolerances that limit the clearance between the screw's major diameter and the nut. As a result, the

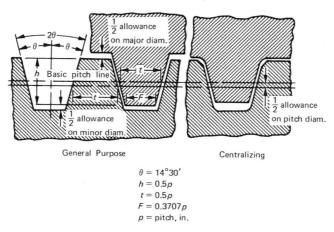

General Purpose   Centralizing

$\theta = 14°30'$
$h = 0.5p$
$t = 0.5p$
$F = 0.3707p$
$p = \text{pitch, in.}$

Figure 15-1 Acme thread forms.

concentricity between the screw and the nut is controlled. Centralizing Acme threads are classed as 2C, 3C, 4C, 5C, and 6C, depending on the fillet at the minor thread diameter, with class 2C priviling the greatest amount of end play (that is, backlash) between the screw and the nut. The basic dimensional proportions and nomenclature for the Acme thread are shown in Figure 15-1.

Stub Acme screws are intended for applications where a coarse pitch and a shallow depth are needed due to heat treating. This thread type has only one class, class 2G for general purposes. Figure 15-2 illustrates the thread form for stub Acme threads. Basic dimensions for the Acme and the stub Acme thread series are given in Table 15-1.

The 60-deg stub Acme thread form is illustrated in Figure 15-3, and thread specifications are listed in Table 15-2.

Figure 15-2 Stub Acme thread forms.

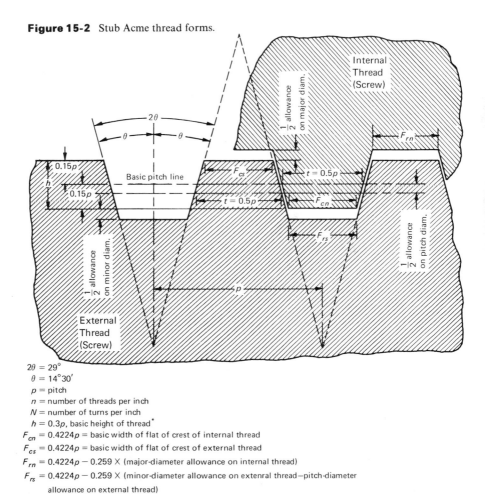

$2\theta = 29°$

$\theta = 14°30'$

$p = $ pitch

$n = $ number of threads per inch

$N = $ number of turns per inch

$h = 0.3p$, basic height of thread[*]

$F_{cn} = 0.4224p = $ basic width of flat of crest of internal thread

$F_{cs} = 0.4224p = $ basic width of flat of crest of external thread

$F_{rn} = 0.4224p - 0.259 \times$ (major-diameter allowance on internal thread)

$F_{rs} = 0.4224p - 0.259 \times$ (minor-diameter allowance on extenral thread−pitch-diameter

allowance on external thread)

[*]Modified stub Acme forms exist having $h = 0.375p$ and $h = 0.250p$.

Table 15-1 Basic Dimensions of Acme and Stub Acme Thread Series (all dimensions in inches)

Nominal Size	Threads per in. $1/p$	Acme Threads					Stub Acme Threads	
		Basic Height of Thread, h	General-purpose (All Classes) and Centralizing Classes 2C, 3C, and 4C		Centralizing Classes 5C and 6C		Basic Height of Thread, h'	Helix Angle at Basic Pitch Diameter
			Basic Major Diameter, D	Helix Angle at Basic Pitch Diameter, α	Basic Major Diameter, B	Helix Angle at Basic Pitch Diameter α		
$1/4$	16	0.03125	0.2500	5° 12'	——	——	0.01875	4° 54'
$5/16$	14	0.03571	0.3125	4° 42'	——	——	0.02143	4° 28'
$3/8$	12	0.04167	0.3750	4° 33'	——	——	0.02500	4° 20'
$7/16$	12	0.04167	0.4375	3° 50°	——	——	0.02500	3° 41'
$1/2$	10	0.05000	0.5000	4° 3'	0.4823	4° 13'	0.03000	3° 52'
$5/8$	8	0.06250	0.6250	4° 3'	0.6052	4° 12'	0.03750	3° 52'
$3/4$	6	0.08333	0.7500	4° 33'	0.7284	4° 42'	0.05000	4° 20'
$7/8$	6	0.08333	0.8750	3° 50'	0.8516	3° 57'	0.05000	3° 41'
1	5	0.10000	1.0000	4° 3'	0.9750	4° 10'	0.06000	3° 52'
$1 1/8$	5	0.10000	1.1250	3° 33'	1.0985	3° 39'	0.06000	3° 25'
$1 1/4$	5	0.10000	1.2500	3°10'	1.2220	3° 15'	0.06000	3° 4'
$1 3/8$	4	0.12500	1.3750	3° 39'	1.3457	3° 44'	0.07500	3° 30'
$1 1/2$	4	0.12500	1.5000	3° 19'	1.4694	3° 23'	0.07500	3° 12'
$1 3/4$	4	0.12500	1.7500	2° 48'	1.7169	2° 52'	0.07500	2° 43'
2	4	0.12500	2.0000	2° 26'	1.9646	2° 29'	0.07500	2° 22'
$2 1/4$	3	0.16667	2.2500	2° 55'	2.2125	2° 58'	0.10000	2° 50'
$2 1/2$	3	0.16667	2.5000	2° 36'	2.4605	2° 39'	0.10000	2° 32'
$2 3/4$	3	0.16667	2.7500	2° 21'	2.7085	2° 23'	0.10000	2° 18'
3	2	0.25000	3.0000	3° 19'	2.9567	3° 22'	0.15000	3° 12'
$3 1/2$	2	0.25000	3.5000	2° 48'	3.4532	2° 51'	0.15000	2° 43'
4	2	0.25000	4.0000	2° 26'	3.9500	2° 28'	0.15000	2° 22'
$4 1/2$	2	0.25000	4.5000	2° 8'	4.4470	2° 10'	0.15000	2° 6'
5	2	0.25000	5.0000	1° 55'	4.9441	1° 56'	0.15000	1° 53'

SOURCE: Colin Carmichael (ed.): *Kent's Mechanical Engineer's Handbook,*
12th ed. John Wiley & Sons, Inc., New York, 1960.
   For general-purpose and centralizing classes 2C, 3C, and 4C, basic pitch diameter $E = D - h$; basic minor diameter $K = D - 2h$.
   For centralizing classes 5C and 6C, basic pitch diameter $E = B - h$; basic minor diameter $K = B - 2h$.
   For stub Acme, basic pitch diameter $E = D - h'$; basic minor diameter $K = D - 2h'$.

Table 15-2 Basic Dimensions of 60 deg Stub Acme Thread Series

Threads per in.	Pitch p, in.	Depth of Thread (Basic) $h = 0.433p$, in.	Total Depth of Thread $(h + 0.02p)$, in.*	Thread Thickness (Basic) $t = 0.5p$, in.	Width of flat, in.	
					Crest of Screw (Basic) $F = 0.250p$	Root of Screw $F_c = 0.227p$
16	0.06250	0.0271	0.0283	0.0313	0.0156	0.0142
14	0.07143	0.0309	0.0324	0.0357	0.0179	0.0162
12	0.08333	0.0361	0.0378	0.0417	0.0208	0.0189
10	0.10000	0.0433	0.0453	0.0500	0.0250	0.0227
9	0.11111	0.0481	0.0503	0.0556	0.0278	0.0252
8	0.12500	0.0541	0.0566	0.0625	0.0313	0.0284
7	0.14286	0.0619	0.0647	0.0714	0.0357	0.0324
6	0.16667	0.0722	0.0755	0.0833	0.0417	0.0378
5	0.20000	0.0866	0.0906	0.1000	0.0500	0.0454
4	0.25000	0.1083	0.1133	0.1250	0.0625	0.0567

SOURCE: Acme threads, ANSI Standard B1.5-1972;
stub Acme threads, ANSI Standard B1.8-1972; buttress
threads, ANSI Standard B1.9-1972.

*A clearance of at least $0.02p$ is added to h to produce extra depth, thus avoiding inter-
ference with threads of mating part at minor or major diameters.

A **square threaded screw** (also known as the Sellers' thread) is the most efficient type of sliding friction screw as verified from equation (15-14), but it has a comparatively poor mechanical advantage. In addition, the square thread (Figure 15-4) is difficult and expensive to machine. Furthermore, it is not as compatible as the Acme thread for use with a split nut. As a result, a modified square thread has been established which is shown in Figure 15-5.

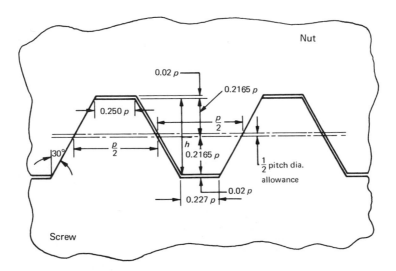

Figure 15-3 60 deg Acme stub thread form.

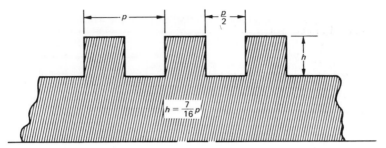

Figure 15-4 Square thread form.

This thread is as efficient as the square thread but is much more economical to manufacture. Table 15-3 gives some nominal basic dimensions for square and modified square threads.

The **Buttress thread** (Figure 15-6) is a type of thread that is intended to resist loads in only one direction. Also, it is stronger than the other forms because the tooth thickness at the root is bigger for corresponding sizes. As may be seen from Figure 15-6, the side of the thread that carries the load has a slope of 7 deg. This small angle produces a minimal radial force component, making this thread form approach the efficiency of the square thread. The buttress thread is easy to cut, making the cost reasonable.

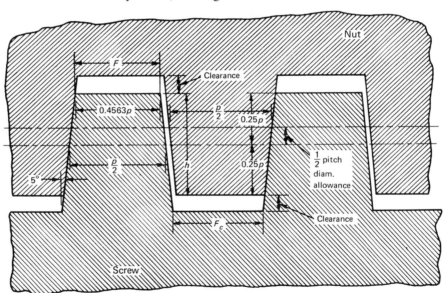

p = pitch
h (basic depth of thread) = $0.5p$
H (total depth of thread) = $0.5p$ + clearance)
t (thickness of thread) = $0.5p$
F_c (flat at root of thread) = $0.4563p - (0.17 \times$ clearance)
F (basic width of flat at crest of thread) = $0.4563p$

Figure 15-5 Modified square thread form. [From U.S. Department of Commerce: *National Bureau of Standards Handbook, H28*, Part III. Washington, D.C., 1957.]

Table 15-3 Some Nominal Dimensions for
Square and Modified Square Threads

Square Threads			Modified Square Threads
Nominal dia., in.	Threads per inch	Minor Dia., in.	Thickness of the Thread at the Root,* in.
$\frac{1}{4}$	10	0.163	0.0544
$\frac{3}{8}$	8	0.266	0.0680
$\frac{1}{2}$	$6\frac{1}{2}$	0.366	0.0837
$\frac{3}{4}$	5	0.575	0.1087
1	4	0.781	0.1357
$1\frac{1}{2}$	3	1.208	0.1812
2	$2\frac{1}{4}$	1.612	0.2416
$2\frac{1}{2}$	2	2.063	0.2718
3	$1\frac{3}{4}$	2.500	0.3160
4	$1\frac{1}{2}$	3.418	0.3624

*Neglecting the effect of major diameter and minor diameter allowances, the thickness at the root of the thread is 0.5436p

Although this thread form has particularly been applied to screwing tubular members together, it has also found application in the breech mechanisms of large guns, cannons, and airplane propeller hubs.

Since buttress threads are employed mainly for special applications, there is no standard size series in common use. However, nominal major diameters should be selected from the following geometric series:

Inches				
1/2	1 1/8	2 1/2	5 1/2	12
9/16	1 1/4	2 3/4	6	14
5/8	1 3/8	3	7	16
11/16	1 1/2	3 1/2	8	18
3/4	1 3/4	4	9	20
7/8	2	4 1/2	10	22
1	2 1/4	5	11	24

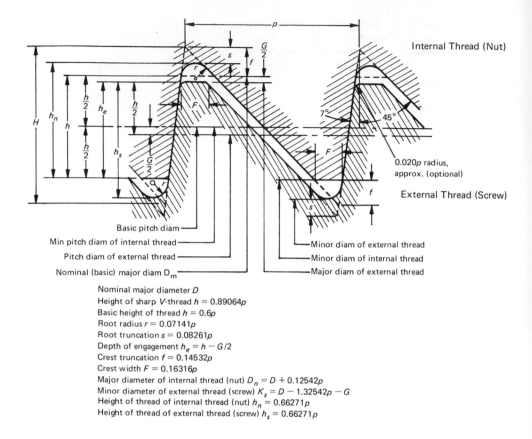

Nominal major diameter D
Height of sharp V-thread $h = 0.89064p$
Basic height of thread $h = 0.6p$
Root radius $r = 0.07141p$
Root truncation $s = 0.08261p$
Depth of engagement $h_e = h - G/2$
Crest truncation $f = 0.14532p$
Crest width $F = 0.16316p$
Major diameter of internal thread (nut) $D_n = D + 0.12542p$
Minor diameter of external thread (screw) $K_s = D - 1.32542p - G$
Height of thread of internal thread (nut) $h_n = 0.66271p$
Height of thread of external thread (screw) $h_s = 0.66271p$

Figure 15-6 Buttress thread form. [From ANSI Standard BI.9–1972.]

Similarly it is suggested that the pitches for buttress threads be selected from the following geometric series:

		Threads Per Inch		
20	10	5	2 1/2	1 1/4
16	8	4	2	1
12	6	3	1 1/2	

To assist the designer in selecting a compatible diameter-pitch combination, he may make his choice from the following:

Diameter Range, in.	Associated Pitches, threads/in.
From 1/2 to 11/16 incl.	20, 16, 12
Over 11/16 to 1 incl.	16, 12, 10
Over 1 to 1 1/2 incl.	16, 12, 10, 8, 6
Over 1 1/2 to 2 1/2 incl.	16, 12, 10, 8, 6, 5, 4
Over 2 1/2 to 4 incl.	16, 12, 10, 8, 6, 5, 4
Over 4 to 6 incl.	12, 10, 8, 6, 5, 4, 3
Over 6 to 10 incl.	10, 8, 6, 5, 4, 3, 2 1/2, 2
Over 10 to 16 incl.	10, 8, 6, 5, 4, 3, 2 1/2, 2 1 1/2, 1 1/4
Over 16 to 24 incl.	8, 6, 5, 4, 3, 2 1/2, 2 1 1/2, 1 1/4, 1

SECTION 15-2

Some Definitions

Before deriving the applicable design relations for power screws, we shall redefine some important terms from kinematics relating to screw threads.

Pitch (*p*). Defined as the axial distance along an element of the pitch cylinder, measured from one thread to an adjacent thread (see Figure 15-2).

Lead (*l*). The axial distance a nut will advance for one revolution of the screw. Lead is measured along an element of the pitch cylinder. For a screw with a single thread, the lead is equal to the pitch. For a multiple threaded screw, the lead is equal to the product of the number of threads (*n*) and the pitch (*p*). We therefore have

$$l = np \qquad (15\text{-}1)$$

From equation (15-1), we can readily see that a multiple threaded screw will advance a nut more rapidly than a single threaded screw of the same pitch.

Helix angle[1] (*α*). That angle of a thread formed by a plane drawn tangent to the pitch helix and a plane drawn normal to the axis of the screw.

To understand how the lead, helix angle, and the pitch are related, the reader should refer to Figure 15-7. If one visualizes a single turn of a square thread as being equivalent to having wrapped an inclined plane around the

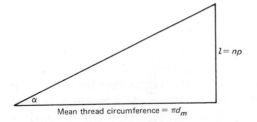

$l = np$

Mean thread circumference $= \pi d_m$

Figure 15-7 A developed screw thread.

[1] This is also, at times, referred to as the lead angle.

root diameter of a cylinder, it will appear as shown in Figure 15-7 when unwrapped from the cylinder. In Figure 15-7, the unwrapped inclined plane is that which has a thickness equal to the difference between the screw thread mean radius and the root radius. Thus, the unwrapped inclined plane has a circumference equal to πd_m, where d_m is the mean screw diameter.

From Figure 15-7, we have

$$\tan \alpha = \frac{l}{\pi d_m} = \frac{np}{\pi d_m} \tag{15-2}$$

Figure 15-8 identifies the aforementioned terms on a single, double, and triple threaded screw.

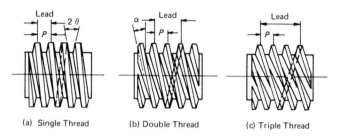

(a) Single Thread   (b) Double Thread   (c) Triple Thread

Figure 15-8 Multiple threaded power screws.

SECTION 15-3

Torque Equation for Power Screws

To assist us in deriving the torque equation, we shall use the model of the screw jack shown in Figure 15-9. The platform that supports the load W is an integral part of the screw and is prevented from rotating by being contained between fixed walls as shown. The rollers between the platform and the walls imply that the platform (and therefore the screw) cannot rotate but can move freely up or down without any frictional resistance from the wall. The platform and screw are raised or lowered by rotating the nut which is supported by a thrust collar as shown in Figure 15-9.

Assuming that an outside force F applied at a mean radius r_m causes W to be raised, let us consider the forces acting on a portion of the thread as shown in Figure 15-10. Our model shows all of the reactive forces acting at point O on the surface of the thread that have a helix angle (that is, lead angle) α and a thread angle θ. The resultant force F_n is normal to the thread surface, and has vector components of interest: $\overrightarrow{OD}$, $\overrightarrow{OB}$, and $\overrightarrow{OA}$. Vector $\overrightarrow{OD}$ is the frictional force F_f lying in the plane of the thread and is drawn in the direction shown because the weight is being raised. If the weight were being lowered, its direction would oppose the motion of the screw and it would have been drawn opposite to that shown in Figure 15-10. Vector $\overrightarrow{OA}$ is equal in magnitude, but opposite in direction to the load W. Vector $\overrightarrow{OB}$ is the resultant

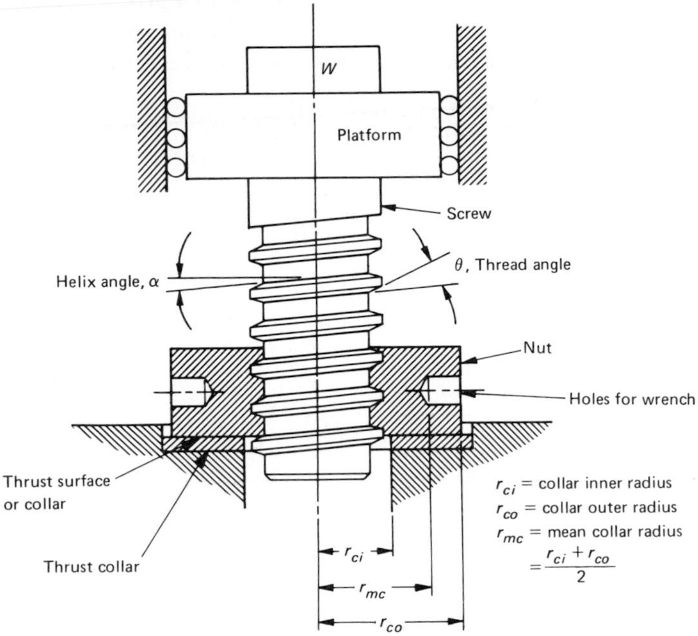
W
Platform
Screw
Helix angle, α
θ, Thread angle
Nut
Holes for wrench
Thrust surface
or collar
Thrust collar
r_{ci} = collar inner radius
r_{co} = collar outer radius
r_{mc} = mean collar radius
$= \frac{r_{ci} + r_{co}}{2}$
r_{ci}
r_{mc}
r_{co}

Figure 15-9 Model of a power screw used as a screw jack.

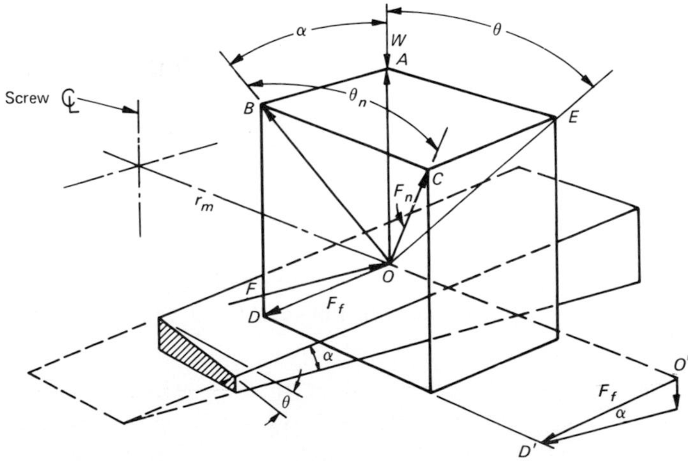
α
θ
W
A
Screw ℄
B
θ_n
E
C
F_n
r_m
O
F
D
F_f
α
θ
O'
F_f
α
D'

Figure 15-10 Reactive force diagram on a thread due to raising a load W.

of $\overrightarrow{OA}$ and $\overrightarrow{OD}$, and forms an angle θ_n with vector $\mathbf{F_n}$ (that is, angle θ_n lies in the plane OCB). If the coefficient of sliding friction between the nut and screw is f_s and we sum the forces in the vertical direction, we have

$$F_n \cos\theta_n \cos\alpha = W + F_f \sin\alpha$$

Replacing the friction force F_f by its equivalent value $f_s F_n$ and then solving the above relation for F_n, we obtain

$$F_n = \frac{W}{\cos\theta_n \cos\alpha - f_s \sin\alpha} \tag{15-3}$$

Next, we sum the moment of the forces about the centerline of the screw. Thus, the torque T_R required to raise the load W (that is, move W up the inclined plane) is

$$T_R = Fr_m = r_m(F_f \cos\alpha + F_n \cos\theta_n \sin\alpha)$$

Replacing F_f by $f_s F_n$ results in

$$T_R = r_m(f_s F_n \cos\alpha + F_n \cos\theta_n \sin\alpha) \tag{15-4}$$

However, the normal reactive force acting on the thrust surface due to W results in an additional frictional force $f_c W$—where f_c is the sliding coefficient of friction between the thrust surface (or thrust collar) and the surface that supports the screw. It is assumed that this frictional force acts at the mean collar radius r_{mc} (see Figure 15-9). The total torque required to raise W is then equal to equation (15-4) plus $r_{mc} f_c W$ or

$$T_R = r_m(f_s F_n \cos\alpha + F_n \cos\theta_n \sin\alpha) + r_{mc} f_c W$$

Replacing F_n by equation (15-3) and noting that $r_m = d_m/2$, we get

$$T_R = \frac{d_m W}{2}\left[\frac{f_s \cos\alpha + \cos\theta_n \sin\alpha}{\cos\theta_n \cos\alpha - f_s \sin\alpha}\right] + \frac{d_{mc} f_c W}{2}$$

Dividing the numerator and denominator of the first term by $\cos\alpha$ results in

$$T_R = \frac{d_m W}{2}\left[\frac{f_s + \cos\theta_n \tan\alpha}{\cos\theta_n - f_s \tan\alpha}\right] + \frac{d_{mc} f_c W}{2} \tag{15-5}$$

where T_r = the torque in inch-pounds needed to raise (that is, lift) the load W, and d_m is in inches.

In applying equation (15-5), it is necessary to know θ_n. It can be obtained from the trigonometric relationship between θ_n, θ, and α as follows: From Figure 15-10

$$\tan\theta_n = \frac{BC}{OB}$$

But, $BC = AE = OA \tan\theta = (OB \cos\alpha)\tan\theta$ and therefore by substitution we obtain

$$\tan \theta_n = \cos \alpha \tan \theta \qquad (15\text{-}6)$$

In most applications, the helix angle α is relatively small, and so $\cos \alpha \approx 1$. Therefore, we can let $\theta_n = \theta$ and equation (15-5) can be written as

$$T_R = \frac{d_m W}{2} \left[\frac{f_s + \cos \theta \tan \alpha}{\cos \theta - f_s \tan \alpha} \right] + \frac{d_{mc} f_c W}{2} \qquad (15\text{-}7)$$

The torque T_L required to lower load W is obtained in the same manner as T_R. However, in this instance, both the applied force F and the friction force F_f act in a direction opposite to that shown in Figure 15-10. The reader should also note that the frictional torque of the thrust surface is positive because it always opposes the effort of the applied torque. The result of this procedure leads to the equation for T_L, the torque required to lower the load, namely

$$T_L = \frac{d_m W}{2} \left[\frac{f_s - \cos \theta_n \tan \alpha}{\cos \theta_n + f_s \tan \alpha} \right] + \frac{d_{mc} f_c W}{2} \qquad (15\text{-}8)$$

Equations (15-7) and (15-8) can also be expressed in terms of the lead l by replacing $\tan \alpha$ by equation (15-2). The respective torque equations for raising or lowering a load are

$$T_R = \frac{d_m W}{2} \left[\frac{\pi f_s d_m + l \cos \theta_n}{\pi d_m \cos \theta_n - f_s l} \right] + \frac{d_{mc} f_c W}{2} \qquad (15\text{-}9)$$

$$T_L = \frac{d_m W}{2} \left[\frac{\pi f_s d_m - l \cos \theta_n}{\pi d_m \cos \theta_n + f_s l} \right] + \frac{d_{mc} f_c W}{2} \qquad (15\text{-}10)$$

Equations (15-9) and (15-10) can also be written in terms of the number of threads n, and the screw pitch p, by noting that $l = np$.

For applications where a ball or roller thrust bearing is used in place of a thrust collar, f_c can be considered as zero. The term $d_{mc} f_c W/2$ can therefore be eliminated from any of the above torque equations.

SECTION 15-4

Overhauling

In Figure 15-10, if the force F were removed and the helix angle α gradually increased to a value such that the load W would slide down the inclined plane, the screw would be performing an action called overhauling. In other words, the raised load W would lower itself causing the screw to rotate. In such a situation, an outside torque would be required not only to raise a load, but also to maintain the load in its raised position. It can be shown that the torque

T_O of a screw which *is* overhauling is

$$T_O = \frac{d_m W}{2} \left[\frac{-f_s + \cos \theta_n \tan \alpha}{\cos \theta_n + f_s \tan \alpha} \right] - \frac{d_{mc} f_c W}{2} \quad \text{(that is, } T_O < 0)$$

(15-11)

In equation (15-11), if we neglect the collar friction (that is, because of a thrust roller bearing) and make $T_O = 0$, we can solve for a helix angle α. This helix angle would then be the one that would permit the screw to overhaul. Thus, from equation (15-11), since $d_m W/2$ and $\cos \theta_n + f_s \tan \alpha$ cannot be zero, we have

$$\tan \alpha = \frac{f_s}{\cos \theta_n}$$

(15-12)

If the parameters in equation (15-12) are such that $f_s/\cos \theta_n > \tan \alpha$, then the screw will not overhaul. A screw and nut (also a worm and wheel—see Chapter 11) having this property are said to be self-locking. This is a desirable characteristic in many applications (for example, a nonreversible drive).

SECTION 15-5

Screw Efficiency

The efficiency of a screw may be defined as the ratio of the torque required to raise a load W without friction to the torque required to raise the load W with friction. Applying this definition to equation (15-5), we have for no friction

$$T_R = \frac{d_m W}{2} \tan \alpha$$

Dividing this equation by equation (15-5) and cancelling $W/2$ from the numerator and denominator, the efficiency of a screw is expressed as

$$e = \frac{d_m \tan \alpha}{d_m \left[\dfrac{f_s + \cos \theta_n \tan \alpha}{\cos \theta_n - f_s \tan \alpha} \right] + d_{mc} f_c}$$

(15-13)

If the collar friction is negligible, the efficiency is

$$e = \frac{\cos \theta_n - f_s \tan \alpha}{\cos \theta_n + f_s \cot \alpha}$$

(15-14)

Representative curves showing how the efficiency varies with the helix angle for an Acme screw are shown in Figure 15-11. The curves in this figure are based on a screw without collar friction.

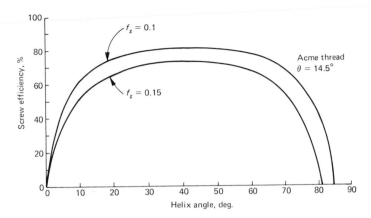

Figure 15-11 Typical efficiency curves for Acme thread screws.

At best, the values for the coefficients of friction for various screw materials are somewhat wide in range due to such factors as lubrication, surface finish, tolerance, alignment, and load distribution. Table 15-4 contains values for the coefficients of friction f_s and f_c and is based on the assumption that the screw assembly has been "well run-in." Starting friction can be taken as 1.33 times the values listed in Table 15-4. In selecting friction values from Table 15-4, the lower number should be used for good workmanship, the higher number for poor workmanship, and some in between number for other gradations of work quality.

In some applications, particularly when a power screw is used as a linear actuator (for example, instruments, motion control, mechanical computing devices), it is desirable to eliminate or minimize backlash between the nut and screw. A common procedure used to achieve this condition is to split the nut in a plane normal to its rotational axis and then bolt the two halves together. Tightening the bolts brings the two halves closer together axially and thereby eliminates the clearance between the nut and the screw. This technique is also used to eliminate increased backlash caused by normal wear over an extended time period.

Table 15-4   Coefficients of Friction f_s and f_c

Screw Material	Steel	Brass	Bronze	Cast Iron
Steel (dry)	0.15–0.25	0.15–0.23	0.15–0.19	0.15–0.25
Steel (lubricated)	0.11–0.17	0.10–0.16	0.10–0.15	0.11–0.17
Bronze	0.08–0.12	0.04–0.60	—	0.06–0.09

Example 15-1. An Acme thread automobile screw jack is made of cold rolled 1045 steel having a diameter of $1\frac{1}{8}$ in. The thread is cut for general purpose application, but the workmanship is of poor quality. When used to raise an automobile, the base of the screw is supported by a steel collar having a mean diameter of $1\frac{1}{2}$ in. The nut that does the lifting is made of the same material as the screw. To raise a 5000-lb car to change a tire, what would be the required torque and the screw efficiency?

Solution: For a $1\frac{1}{8}$-in. diameter screw, we obtain from Table 15-1 the helix angle $\alpha = 3° 33'$, and basic thread height, $h = 0.100000$ in. From Table 15.1, the coefficient of friction for a dry screw and nut made of steel and having poor workmanship is $f_s = f_c = 0.25$. The coefficient of friction for starting is $1.33(0.25) = 0.33$. For an Acme thread $\theta = 14° 30'$ (see Figure 15-1).

Using equation (15-6), we determine $\tan \theta_n$. Thus

$$\tan \theta_n = \cos \alpha \tan \theta = \cos 3° 33' \tan 14° 30' = (0.9981)(0.2586) = 0.2581$$

Therefore $\theta_n = 14° 24.43'$. Knowing the basic thread height and the basic major diameter, we calculate the mean screw diameter

$$d_m = 1.1250 - 0.1000 = 1.0250 \text{ in.}$$

Applying equation (15-5) to initially calculate the starting torque, we have

$$T_R = \frac{(1.0250)(5000/4)}{2}\left[\frac{0.33 + \cos 14° 24.43' \tan 3° 33'}{\cos 14° 24.43' - 0.33 \tan 3° 33'}\right] + \frac{1.5(0.33)(5000/4)}{2}$$

$$= 573.5 \text{ lb-in.}$$

The running torque required to raise the car is based upon the coefficient of friction $f_s = 0.25$. Therefore, using the above calculation with the only change being the friction coefficient, we find that

$$T_R = 443.25 \text{ in.-lb}$$

We see from these calculations that it requires a 29.3% higher torque to start the screw in motion than it does to keep the screw in motion. We also see that, if we assume a reasonable crank arm length, say 18 in., the operator is required to exert a starting force of 31.9 lb (that is, 573.5/18). Not too many people can continuously exert this force. Consequently, the screw jack will have to be lubricated or have an improved quality of manufacture or a longer crank arm.

The screw efficiency is determined from equation (15-13) as follows:

$$e = \frac{(1.0250)(0.0620)}{1.0250\left[\dfrac{0.25 + 0.9685(0.0620)}{0.9685 - 0.25(0.0620)}\right] + 1.5(0.25)} = 0.0897$$

$$= 8.97\%$$

This screw efficiency, which is relatively poor, can be markedly improved by reducing the friction coefficient, increasing the helix angle, or by making both changes. ●

Example 15-2. In Example 15-1, will the screw overhaul after the load W has been raised?

Solution: For overhauling to occur, it is necessary for the lowering torque, equation (15-8), to be negative. Substituting the appropriate numerical values of Example 15-1 into equation (15-8), we have

$$T_L = \frac{1.025(5000)}{2}\left[\frac{0.25 - 0.9685(0.0620)}{0.9685 + 0.25(0.0625)}\right] + \frac{1.5(0.25)(5000)}{2}$$

$$= 1433 \text{ lb-in.}$$

Since T_L is positive, the screw will not overhaul. ●

Example 15-3. What helix angle would be required in order that the screw of Example 15-1 would just begin to overhaul? What would be the efficiency of a screw with this helix angle?

Solution: For incipient overhauling to occur, T_L in equation (15-8) must zero. Therefore, we have

$$0 = d_m\left[\frac{f_s - \cos\theta_n \tan\alpha}{\cos\theta_n + f_s \tan\alpha}\right] + d_{mc}f_c$$

Solving for tan α

$$\tan\alpha = \frac{f_s + f_c \cos\theta_n(d_{mc}/d_m)}{\cos\theta_n - f_c f_s(d_{mc}/d_m)}$$

Substituting the numerical values results in

$$\tan\alpha = \frac{0.25 + 0.25(\cos 14° \ 24.43')(1.5/1.025)}{\cos 14° \ 24.43' - 0.25(0.25)(1.5/1.025)} = 0.689$$

$$\alpha = 34.6°$$

Thus, for overhauling to occur, the helix angle must be at least slightly larger than 34.6°.

Using equation (15-13) to determine screw efficiency, we have

$$e = \frac{1.025 \tan 34.6°}{1.025\left[\dfrac{0.25 + \cos 14° \ 24.43' \tan 34.6°}{\cos 14° \ 24.33' - 0.25 \tan 34.6°}\right] + 1.5(0.25)} = 0.455 \quad ●$$

$$= 45.5\%$$

SECTION 15-6

Stress Considerations for Power Screws

In analyzing the strength of a power screw and nut, or any screw or nut, the designer should be aware of the limitations of his calculations. We do not mean to imply by this statement that the analytical expression used to define a particular stress is no longer applicable to a screw. We do wish, instead, to emphasize that the stress "picture" of the thread engagement between the screw and nut is not completely understood. As an illustration, it is commonly accepted that the load carried by a screw and nut is uniformly distributed throughout the thread engagement. This is not, in fact, the case. Goodier [5] showed that, due to deflection, only the first one or two threads in engagement carry the major portion of the load. The remaining threads carry lesser or greater portions of the load depending upon the elastic-plastic deformation of the first couple of threads.

Goodier's analysis also obviates the assumption that the bearing stress is uniformly distributed throughout the thread engagement. However proper lubrication can be a factor in support of this hypothesis.

Again citing Goodier's analysis, the tensile stress of the screw across the root area is greater at that point where the load "flows" from the screw to the nut than it is at any other root area.

Lastly, we note that additional factors such as fillet radii, surface finish, class fit, and so on, also have significant affects on the actual stress values.

Thus, the analytical relations that follow, although not exact, provide the designer with some simple tools to help him achieve a reasonable design—particularly when conservative design stresses are used.

The main stress considerations in designing a power screw are (1) bearing pressure, (2) bending stress, (3) shearing stress, (4) tensile or compressive stress, (5) combined stress, and (6) buckling stress.

Bearing pressure

The bearing pressure is the crushing stress between the surface of the screw thread and the contacting surface of the nut. The relationship for this stress is

$$\sigma_B = \frac{W}{\pi d_m h n} \tag{15-15}$$

where

σ_B = bearing pressure (that is, crushing stress of projected thread area), psi
W = load, lb
d_m = mean screw thread diameter, in.
h = depth of thread, in.
n = number of threads in engagement

Table 15-5 lists the design bearing pressures for some representative applications, materials, and speeds.

Table 15-5   Design Bearing Pressures for Screws

Type of Service	Material		Design Bearing Pressure, psi	Rubbing Speed at the Mean Diameter of the Thread
	Screw	Nut		
Hand press	Steel	Bronze	2500–3500	Low speed, well lubricated
Jackscrew	Steel	Cast iron	1800–2500	Low speed, not over 8 fpm
Jackscrew	Steel	Bronze	1600–2500	Low speed, not over 10 fpm
Hoisting screw	Steel	Cast iron	600–1000	Medium speed, 20–40 fpm
Hoisting screw	Steel	Bronze	800–1400	Medium speed, 20–40 fpm
Lead screw	Steel	Bronze	150–240	High speed, 50 fpm and over

Bending stress

The bending stress in the thread is determined by treating it as a short cantilever beam with a built-in end at the root diameter (see Figure 15-12). The load W is assumed to be uniformly distributed over the mean screw diameter (that is, the load W acts at a point which is one half the distance of the thread depth, h).

The cross-section of the developed thread at the root is a rectangle with a beam depth of b and a beam width of $\pi d_m n$. We thus have a section modulus for the thread of

$$\frac{I}{C} = \frac{(\pi d_m n)b^2}{6} \tag{15-16}$$

The maximum bending moment for this cantilever beam is

$$M = \frac{Wh}{2} \tag{15-17}$$

The bending stress equation is

$$\sigma_b = \frac{MC}{I} \tag{15-18}$$

Substituting equations (15-16) and (15-17) into (15-18), we arrive at

$$\sigma_b = \frac{3Wh}{\pi d_m nb^2} \tag{15-19}$$

where σ_b = the maximum bending stress in pounds per square inch, and all other terms are as earlier defined.

Shearing stress

Both the threads on the screw and the threads on the nut experience a transverse shearing stress due to bending. For a rectangular cross section, the transverse shearing stress according to Section 5.6 in Chapter 5 (for $z = 0$) is

$$\tau = \frac{3}{2}\frac{W}{A}$$

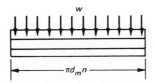

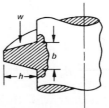

Figure 15-12 Screw thread loaded as a cantilever beam.

where A is the cross-sectional area at the built-in end of the beam. This area for the screw is $\pi d_r n b$, and for the nut, the area is $\pi d_o n b$. Thus, the transverse shearing stress for the screw is

$$\tau = \frac{3W}{2\pi d_r n b} \qquad (15\text{-}20)$$

The transverse shearing stress for the nut is

$$\tau = \frac{3W}{2\pi d_o n b} \qquad (15\text{-}21)$$

where τ is the transverse shearing stress in pounds per square inch, d_r is the root diameter of the screw, d_o is the major diameter of the screw, and the remaining terms are as earlier defined.

Tensile or compressive stress

Depending upon the particular design, a power screw may be subjected to a tensile or compressive stress by the load W. The area used to calculate the tensile or compressive stress is called the "tensile stress area" in the various screw thread tables (see references [1] and [4]). This stress area is slightly larger than the area that would be calculated by using the root diameter. This larger area is determined by a circle having a diameter equal to the average of the root and pitch diameters. The basis for using the tensile stress area is found in the experimental results which have demonstrated that a threaded tensile test specimen is stronger than a plain specimen (that is, no threads) whose diameter is the same as the root diameter of the threaded specimen.

We can now write the expression for direct tensile or compressive stress as

$$\sigma_{t \text{ or } c} = \frac{W}{A} \qquad (15\text{-}22)$$

where

$\sigma_{t \text{ or } c}$ = the tensile or compressive stress, psi

$A = \dfrac{\pi}{4}\left(\dfrac{d_r + d_p}{2}\right)^2$, in.^{2}

d_r = root diameter, in.

d_p = pitch diameter, in.

Should the designer wish to be more conservative in his calculations, he would be justified, then, in using d_r only in calculating A.

Combined stress

When the unsupported length of the screw is so short that column action can be ignored, the screw is then treated purely as a compression member. In such an instance, the area of the screw which is at the root diameter is subjected to a biaxial stress. Specifically, we have the combined stress effects of equation (15-22) and the shearing stress caused by the applied torque. Recall from Chapter 5 that the combined biaxial stress equation employing the maximum shear theory of failure is

$$\tau_{max} = \sqrt{(\sigma/2)^2 + (\tau)^2} \qquad (15\text{-}23)$$

The shearing stress τ, caused by the applied torque is

$$\tau = \frac{T(d_r/2)}{J} = \frac{T(d_r/2)}{\pi(d_r^4/32)} = \frac{16T}{\pi d_r^3} \qquad (15\text{-}24)$$

where T = the applied torque in pounds-inches. Substituting equations (15-22) and (15-24) into equation (15-23), we get

$$\tau_{max} = \sqrt{\left(\frac{W}{2A}\right)^2 + \left(\frac{16T}{\pi d_r^3}\right)^2} \qquad (15\text{-}25)$$

Because column action plays no role when the screw is subjected to a tensile stress, equation (15-25) always applies when the screw is under combined tension and torsion, regardless of the screw length.

Buckling stress

When the unsupported screw length is equal to or greater than 8 times the root diameter, the screw must be treated as a column. As the reader may recall, analysis of column stability leads to the Euler column formula, which is restricted to long columns only. For ductile materials, short columns are defined as those having a slenderness ratio[2] up to and including 100, whereas columns having a slenderness ratio greater than 100 are considered as long columns.[3] Short columns are assumed to fail due to compression and bending on the concave side. Long columns fail due to buckling (that is, instability).

There are a number of different short column formulas that extend the Euler equation into the short column region. Many of these are intended for structural applications, and are included as part of the requirements of different codes (for example, building codes, and so on). In machine design, a convenient short column formula, known as the Ritter equation, is often

[2] Slenderness ratio is defined as L/k, where L is the column length between supports, and k is the least radius of gyration.

[3] Some specifications use a slenderness ratio greater than 120 to define long columns. This limit is particularly used for structural members.

used. This equation is a modification of the more widely known Gordon–Rankine formula. The Ritter equation is

$$\sigma_c = \frac{P}{A}\left[1 + \left(\frac{L}{k}\right)^2 \frac{S_{yp}}{\pi^2 KE}\right] \qquad (15\text{-}26)$$

where

σ_c = the stress induced on the concave side of the column, psi. The stress value should not exceed the design compressive stress of the material.

S_{yp} = the yield point of the material, psi.

A = cross-sectional area of the column, in.^{2}

L = column length between supports, in.

k = least radius of gyration = $\sqrt{I/A}$, in.

P = column load, lb.

E = modulus of elasticity, psi

K = factor depending on the end supports of the column; 0.25 for one end fixed, and the other end free; 1 for both ends pin-connected; 2 for one end fixed, and the other end pin-connected; and 4 for both ends fixed

Equation (15-26) is applicable only when the load is purely axial. If, however, the load P is eccentric by a distance e from the column centroid, the additional stress caused by the bending moment P_e must be added to equation (15-26). The resulting combined maximum stress equation becomes

$$\sigma_c = \frac{P}{A}\left[1 + \left(\frac{L}{k}\right)^2 \frac{S_{yp}}{\pi^2 KE} + \frac{ce}{k^2}\right] \qquad (15\text{-}27)$$

where c is the distance from the centroid to the outermost fiber of the column in inches.

Although the use of long, slender screws should be avoided, it is sometimes not possible to do so. In such cases, Euler's column formula should be used. As previously derived in Section 5.10, Euler's column formula is

$$P_{cr} = \frac{K\pi^2 AE}{(L/k)^2}$$

where P_{cr} is the critical buckling load in pounds, and all the other terms are as defined above.

SECTION 15-7

Ball Screws

A ball screw is a linear actuator that transmits a force or motion with minimum friction. A basic ball screw assembly is shown in Figure 15-13. As can be observed from this figure, there is a circular groove cut to proper conformity with the balls. The groove has a helix angle that matches the

Figure 15-13 Ball screw assembly showing the component parts. [Courtesy Saginaw Steering Gear Division, General Motors Corporation.]

helix angle of the ball nut. When the screw and nut rotate relative to each other, the balls are diverted from one end of the ball nut and are carried by ball guides to the opposite end of the ball nut. Such recirculation permits unrestricted travel of the nut relative to the screw.

Because the balls roll, as in a ball bearing, the frictional losses are minimal. This characteristic is one of the important advantages that ball screws have over threaded screws. Efficiencies of 90% or higher are possible with ball screws over a wide range of helix angles when converting rotary to axial motion because of minimum friction (see Figure 15-14). When a ball screw is used to convert axial to rotary motion, efficiencies as high as 80% can be expected, even when the helix angle is so small as to cause threaded power screws to be self-locking.

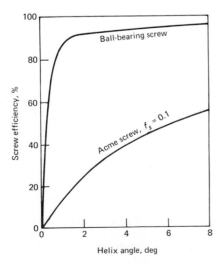

Figure 15-14 Comparative efficiencies of an Acme screw and a Ball screw. [Courtesy Saginaw Steering Gear Division, General Motors Corporation.]

Comparing ball screws with threaded power screws we can cite the following advantages and disadvantages:

Advantages

1. High efficiency—approximately 90 % or higher.
2. Predictable life expectancy.
3. Precise positioning and position repeatability permitted.
4. No tendency to "stick-slip" as with screws.
5. Negligible heat expansion due to friction.
6. Easily preloaded to eliminate backlash at virtually no frictional increase.
7. Because starting torque is low, smaller motors can be used.
8. Smooth movement and control over its entire stroke.
9. The overall silhouette of the ball nut is much smaller because the balls can withstand higher loads than screw threads.

Disadvantages

1. Requires lubrication to realize its maximum useful life.
2. Ball screws, because of their high efficiency, tend to overhaul. Thus, if self-locking is required, an outside brake must be added.
3. The inclusion of dirt or foreign matter in ball screws can reduce or even end their life.
4. Because the load carrying capacity of a ball screw is greater than an equivalently sized power screw, it is not as stiff as a power screw. Consequently, the deflection and critical speed of a ball screw can become significant factors for certain applications.

The uses of ball screws are as varied as threaded power screws. Typical of such uses are

1. Machine tools—numerical control positioning, feed control, table drives, and slides.
2. Airplanes—flap and slat drives, landing gear actuation, canopy actuation, air inlet controls, and thrust reverses.
3. Weapon systems—elevation actuation on cannons, missile and rocket launches, and leveling jacks.
4. Materials handling—balance hoists, conveyor drop sections, die tables, and crane boom actuators.
5. Miscellaneous—jacks, antenna leg actuators, hospital bed articulation, valve operators, instrument drives, and antenna drives.

PROBLEMS

1. A $1\frac{1}{2}$-in. diameter square thread screw 3 ft long is used as an automobile bumper jack. When in use, the base of the screw is supported by a $2\frac{1}{2}$-in. diameter collar that rests on a recessed metal plate. The screw, nut, collar, and metal plate are all made of steel and operate without lubrication. If the workmanship is considered poor, calculate (**a**) the torque required to lift 1500 lb, (**b**) the length of crank required if 20 lb is considered a reasonable force that can be exerted by an operator, (**c**) the torque required to lower 1500 lb, (**d**) the efficiency of the screw when lifting the load, (**e**) the efficiency of the screw when lowering the load, (**f**) the torque required to lift the load if a thrust ball bearing were used in place of the plain collar, and (**g**) the efficiency of the screw when lifting the load if a thrust ball bearing is used.

2. Solve Problem 1 for an Acme thread having the same outer diameter.

3. (**a**) For a power screw with a ball bearing thrust collar (that is, little or no collar friction) determine the expression for the maximum efficiency when raising a load. (**b**) Assuming a coefficient of moving friction of 0.15, what is the maximum efficiency for a square threaded screw? (**c**) For the same friction coefficient, what is the maximum efficiency for an Acme thread? As a check, your results should coincide with the value from Figure 15-11 for the same helix angle.

4. For the screw of Problem 1, determine (**a**) the minimum length of nut engagement required if the permissible bearing pressure is 1800 psi,[4] (**b**) the factor of safety of the threads in bending if all of the components are made of AISI 1030 cold drawn steel, (**c**) the factor of safety of the nut and screw in shear, and (**d**) the factor of safety of the screw in buckling. Assume that the bumper is supported by the nut extension at a distance of 4 in. from the centroidal axis of the screw.

5. A sluice gate of a dam is raised and lowered by two 3-in. diameter modified square threads, that are run by a gear reducer, motor, and brake combination. The nuts, which are attached to the gate, are made of bronze and the screws are made of steel. Because each screw is supported by a thrust ball bearing, collar friction can be neglected. The workmanship of the assembly is considered to be very good and requires only a moderate amount of grease for lubrication. If the gate, which weighs 50 tons, is to be raised or lowered at $2\frac{1}{2}$ ft/min, determine (**a**) the revolutions per minute of the screws, (**b**) the motor horsepower required to lift the gate assuming that the overall mechanical efficiency of the motor and reducer is 87%.

6. A toggle device for a baling machine is driven by a gear reduction motor as shown in the Problem Figure 6. The two cast iron non-rotating nuts move axially in opposite directions against two 6000 lb forces. The opposite directional motion of the nuts is due to a left and right hand thread cut in the screw (see figure). The screw, which is made of steel, is cut to a standard $2\frac{1}{2}$ in. nominal outside diameter square thread and rotates at 80 rpm. The workmanship is considered excellent and the assembly will be lubricated. Calculate the motor horsepower required if the mechanical efficiency of the gear reduction motor is 85 per cent. Because ball bearings are used at the three bearing supports, the frictional torque at these points may be neglected.

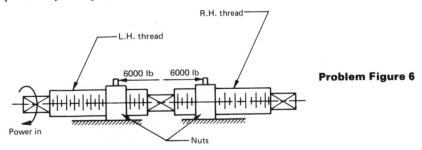

R.H. thread

L.H. thread

6000 lb   6000 lb

Power in

Nuts

Problem Figure 6

---

[4] See Table 15-5. Although a steel screw and steel nut combination is not listed, it is assumed that a steel screw and cast iron nut combination permit comparable pressures.

7. Show that a screw just on the verge of overhauling when lifting a load has an efficiency of about 50%.

8. A vertically mounted linear power actuator has a single threaded Acme screw with a nominal outside diameter of 2 in. A split nut (2 in. long) which is kept from rotating moves along the axis of the screw at a rate of 5 ft/min while raising a 6-ton load. The screw is supported on the bottom end by a thrust ball bearing with an I.D. of 1.3780 in. and an O.D. of 1.457 in. and on the other by a deep groove ball bearing. The screw is made of steel and the nut of cast iron. The workmanship is considered to be of the highest quality. If the screw and nut are lubricated, determine the following: (*Note:* The coefficients of friction for roller bearings are listed in Table 9-4). (**a**) The starting torque. (**b**) The running horsepower. (**c**) The running efficiency. (**d**) The thread bearing pressure. The length of the nut is 2 in.

9. Repeat Problem 8 for a double threaded stub Acme thread.

10. A 2-in. outer diameter modified square thread screw is suggested for use in a power press which is to exert a maximum force of 6 tons. The screw is to be made of AISI 1118 carburized steel and the nut, which is to be locked into the upper press platen, is to be made of ASTM class 50 cast iron. The workmanship is expected to be of the highest quality. To minimize torque requirements, a thrust ball bearing is to act as a collar in supporting the screw. Both the screw and nut will be lubricated. Determine (**a**) the running torque required to act against the maximum load, (**b**) the efficiency of the screw system, (**c**) the height of the nut required for a thread bearing pressure of 1000 psi, (**d**) the number of threads on the nut, (**e**) the bending stress of the thread and the factor of safety, (**f**) the shear stress of the thread, and nut and their factors of safety, and (**g**) the combined stress of the screw and the factor of safety based on the maximum distortion failure theory, and the maximum shear failure theory.

11. A vertical actuator is used to raise and lower a platform of a paper feeder. A 1-in. diameter modified square thread is cut in the screw which is supported on the lower end by a thrust ball bearing. Both the screw and the nut are made of steel and are lubricated. The workmanship is considered to be of average quality. When the platform rises with a full paper load, the total weight is 5000 lb. When the empty platform is lowered, it weighs 1500 lb. Determine the following mean and varying stresses: (**a**) the thread bearing pressure for a $1\frac{1}{2}$-in. long nut, (**b**) the bending stress of the thread, (**c**) the shearing stress of the thread, and (**d**) the combined stress of the screw. No column action is considered in this problem since the screw is assumed to be short.

If the platform rises at the rate of 2 ft/min, what size gear motor drive (that is, horsepower) would be required if the mechanical efficiency of the drive is 85%?

12. Problem Figure 12 shows a schematic drawing of a screw jack which is widely used in construction, in rigging machinery, and in equipment for many applications requiring the movement of heavy equipment. Design a screw jack similar to that which is shown, capable of lifting 15,000 lb to a maximum height of 20 in. The screw is to have a square thread and is to be made of AISI 1040 cold-drawn steel. The base is to be made of ASTM class 40 cast iron. The threads, which are cut in the base, will run lubricated with the screw threads. The quality of manufacture and workmanship is to be assumed as being average. Because infrequent use will be made of the jack, the bearing pressures listed in Table 15-5 can be doubled (for example, in this case use 3600 psi to determine the nut height *h*).

If 50 lb is considered a reasonable force that a man can exert, what should the length of the turning lever be? What is its diameter if it is made of AISI 1040 cold drawn steel?

In determining the length of the turning lever, keep in mind that the starting friction is one third greater than the running friction (see Section 15.5).

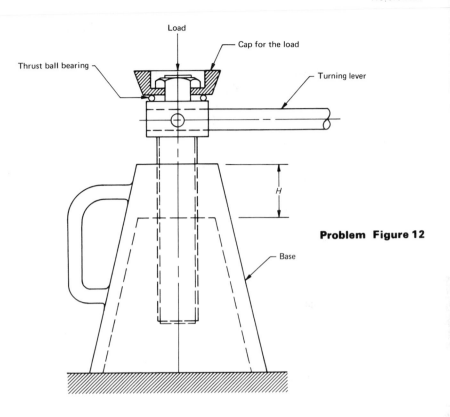

Problem Figure 12

[1] Acme Threads—ANSI Standard B 1.5—1972. Stub Acme Threads—ANSI Standard B 1.8—1972. Buttress Threads—ANSI Standard B 1.9—1972.

[2] Harold A. Rothbart (ed.): *Mechanical Design and Systems Handbook.* McGraw-Hill Book Co., New York, 1964.

[3] Colin Carmechael (ed.): *Kent's Mechanical Engineers' Handbook, Design and Production Volume,* 12th ed. John Wiley & Sons, Inc., New York, 1961.

[4] *National Bureau of Standards Handbook H28,* Part III. U.S. Department of Commerce, Washington, D.C., 1957.

[5] J. N. Goodier: The distribution of load on the thread of screws. *J. Appl. Mech., Trans. ASME,* **62**, 1940.

16

Fasteners

SYMBOLS

A = cross-sectional area
C = stiffness coefficient
d = diameter
d_{eff} = effective hole diameter
E = modulus of elasticity
F = applied force
F_i = initial load
K = stress concentration factor
k = stiffness constant

P = allowable load
p = pressure
t = thickness
w = width
S = allowable stress
δ = deflection
σ = actual stress
τ = actual shear stress

In discussing fasteners or connectors, we will make a distinction between permanent fasteners, such as rivets and weldments, and detachable fasteners, such as screws, cotter pins, keys, and snap rings. The permanent fasteners will be discussed first, and because weldments are discussed in Chapter 17, we will start with a consideration of riveted connections.

SECTION 16-1

Axially Loaded Rivets

Although there are many ways of classifying rivets, the first distinction we will make is between axially loaded and eccentrically loaded rivets. In an axially loaded riveted connection, the line of action of the applied force passes through the center of gravity of the rivet group, whereas for the eccentrically loaded connection it does not. At the moment we will concern ourselves only with the axial loaded problem. Further, although we will consider rivets as the connector to be analyzed, it should be pointed out that the analysis applies equally well to bolts. Finally, although it is true that a bolt is a form of screw, we are considering the bolt, as used in these applications, to be a permanent rather than a detachable fastener.

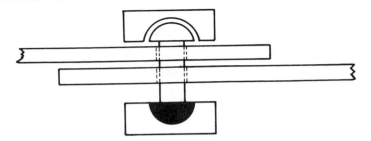

Figure 16-1   Steps followed in forming a rivet.

Rivets are used in many applications, such as for boilers, buildings, bridges, ships, and so on. Because of the danger to human life that could result from a failure of such applications, the design of riveted connections are rigorously governed by construction codes such as *American Institute of Steel Construction (AISC) Code, American Railway Engineering Association Code*, and *Boiler Construction Code of the American Society of Mechanical Engineers*. Clearly, the code applicable to the particular problem on hand should be followed. When rivets are used in a machine design, there is no code, which means the designer is left to his own resources with regard to method of analysis, materials, and so on. It is not feasible to discuss each of the codes with regard to rivet analysis; therefore, to illustrate one approach to the problem, we will in general, follow the AISC structural code.

Before proceeding further, it would be desirable to define a rivet. It may be described as a cylindrical body, known as the shank, with a rounded end called the head. When used to join two plates together, the rivet is heated to a red glow, and the shank is placed in the hole that has been made in the plates. If the rivet is heated before being placed in the hole, it

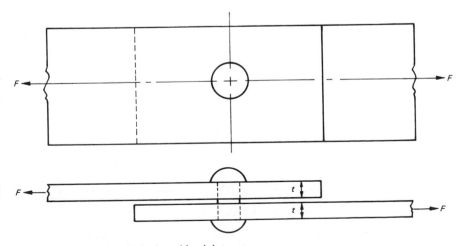

Figure 16-2   Single riveted lap joint.

is known as a hot-driven rivet, whereas if it is not heated, it is known as a cold driven rivet. The preformed head is then supported, as shown in Figure 16-1, while a hammer or some other means of applying pressure is used to form the shank into another head. Upon completion of this operation, the rivet will have two heads and look something like the one shown in Figure 16-2. Thus, the purpose of the rivet is to join two plates together while ensuring proper strength and tightness. The holes in the plates are either punched or drilled.

SECTION 16-2

Methods of Rivet Failure

In analyzing the various methods by which a riveted connection may fail, we will first consider the stress situations that exist for a single rivet. Let us assume that the two plates to be joined overlap each other and are held by a single rivet as shown in Figure 16-2.

If we assume that the forces act along the center of each plate, it is clear that the loading is eccentric and an unbalanced moment Ft exists. Figure 16-3 is an exaggerated drawing of the effects of this unbalanced moment. The effect of the moment is to put a crushing or bearing load on the corners of the plate, subject the rivet shank to a tensile stress, and cause a shear stress in the rivet heads. It should also be clear that, since a moment exists, there will be a flexural or bending stress Mc/I present. However, because of a lack of information concerning how the load is applied, and therefore doubt about what the magnitude of the moment is, the usual procedure is to ignore the bending stress and to compensate for its presence by a larger factor of safety.

The rivet itself may fail because of the shear stress that is developed in it. The rivet in Figure 16-4 is subjected to single shear (one cross-sectional shearing area), whereas the one shown in Figure 16-5 is subjected to double shear (two cross-sectional shearing areas). The way failure will occur for each of these methods is also illustrated in each figure.

The shearing stress present in the rivet is given by equation (16-1).

$$\tau = \frac{F}{\pi d^2/4} \tag{16-1}$$

where d = diameter of rivet, and F = force applied. If the rivet is in double shear, the area $\pi d^2/4$ is simply multiplied by 2. If a connection has more

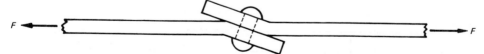

Figure 16-3 An exaggerated drawing of the effect of the unbalanced moment acting on a single riveted lap joint.

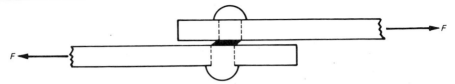

Figure 16-4 Rivet in single shear.

than one rivet, the usual assumption made is that each rivet takes an equal share of the load. The actual shear stress is now compared to the allowable shear stress. Clearly, the allowable must be equal to or greater than the actual.

Another possible method of failure is a tensile rupture of either plate. Figure 16-6 shows this situation. The tensile stress can be calculated from equation (16-2).

$$\sigma_t = \frac{F}{(w - d_{\text{eff}})t} \tag{16-2}$$

where w is the width of plate, d_{eff} is the effective diameter of the hole, and t is the thickness of the plate.

An explanation of effective diameter is now in order. Rivet holes are usually either drilled or punched. When the holes are drilled, they are usually made $\frac{1}{16}$ in. larger than the rivet diameter to ensure that the hot rivet will easily fit into the hole. On the other hand, when the holes are punched, some damage occurs to the material around the edges of the hole, and this

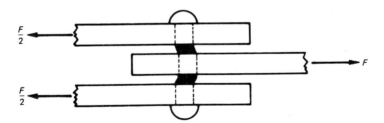

Figure 16-5 Shearing failure in double shear.

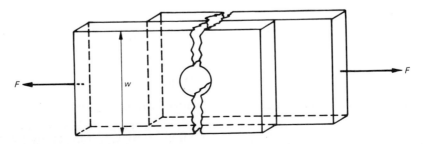

Figure 16-6 Tensile failure of plate.

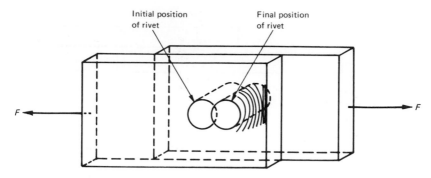

Figure 16-7 Compressive or crushing failure of plate commonly known as a bearing failure.

damaged material is unable to resist the load. As a result, an additional $\frac{1}{16}$ in. is added to the rivet diameter in order to obtain the effective diameter. To sum up, the effective diameter for a drilled hole is $\frac{1}{16}$ in. larger than the rivet diameter, and the effective diameter of a punched hole is $\frac{1}{8}$ in. larger than the rivet diameter.

The third method by which failure may occur is by a crushing of the plate or the rivet. This compressive failure is commonly referred to as a bearing failure. Figure 16-7 depicts this type of failure. The usual assumption made in calculating the bearing stress is that the load is distributed over the projected area of the rivet. The bearing stress is thus given by

$$\sigma_b = \frac{F}{dt} \tag{16-3}$$

where d = diameter of rivet and t = thickness of plate.

Once again, for those problems involving connections containing more than one rivet, the usual assumption made is that each rivet takes an equal share of the load when bearing and shear failure are considered. The assumption is reasonable because yielding of rivets which are slightly overloaded will tend to distribute the load equally.

Another mode of failure is the shearing of the edge of the plate, as shown in Figure 16-8. This failure is usually designated as a shear tearout. As can be seen from the figure, shear tearout is dependent on how far a rivet is located from the edge of the plate. The shear tearout stress is given by

$$\tau_t = \frac{F}{2at} \tag{16-4}$$

where a = closest distance from rivet to the edge of plate and t = thickness of plate.

The structural code specifies minimum edge distances, so that shear tearout and tearing of the edge (Figure 16-9) do not have to be checked.

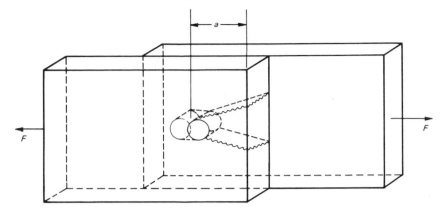

Figure 16-8 Shearing tearout or shearing failure of edge of plate.

For example, the code would specify that the distance from the center of a rivet to a plate edge parallel to the line of action of the force be at least 1.5 times the rivet diameter, whereas the distance from the center of the rivet to the plate edge normal to the line of action of the force must be at least 2 times the rivet diameter. The 1.5 and 2 mentioned above are simply average examples because the actual values as specified by the code depend upon the magnitude of the rivet diameter.

To sum up, there are basically three modes of failure that must be considered, shearing of the rivets, bearing failure of the plate or the rivet, and tensile failure of the plate.

SECTION 16-3

Lap and Butt Joints

Axially loaded riveted joints are of two types, lap joints (Figure 16-10) and butt joints (Figure 16-11).

A comparison of Figures 16-10 and 16-11 makes clear why the joints are called lap and butt joints. In a lap joint, the two plates to be joined

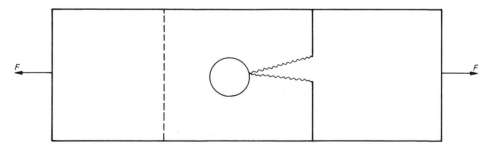

Figure 16-9 Failure due to edge of plate tearing out.

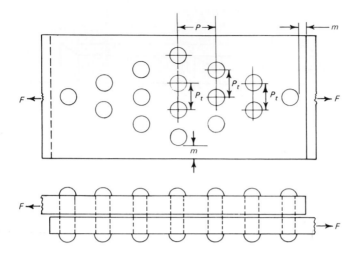

Figure 16-10 Riveted lap joint.

overlap each other, whereas in a butt joint the two plates to be joined (the main plates) butt against each other. The minimum edge distances m mentioned earlier are shown in Figure 16-10.

Another important geometric property is the pitch, which is defined as the distance between adjacent rivet centers. We usually speak of the pitch for rivets along a line parallel to the edge of the plate, whereas the corresponding distance along a line perpendicular to the edge of the plate is known as the transverse pitch, p_t. Both types of pitch are shown in Figure 16-10.

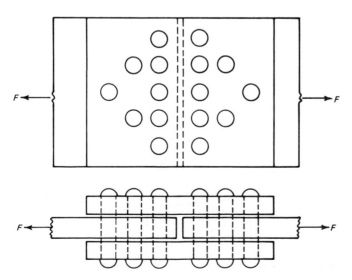

Figure 16-11 Riveted butt joint.

It is useful, in comparing different joints, to have some idea about how efficiently they connect the plates in question. The usual comparison used is the efficiency of the joints as obtained from equation (16-5).

$$\text{eff} = \frac{P_{\text{allowable max}}}{\text{strength of plate with no hole}} \tag{16-5}$$

where $P_{\text{allowable max}}$ = the smallest of the allowable loads in shear, bearing, and tension, and strength of plate with no hole = the tensile strength of the plates to be joined if there were no holes in them.

Clearly, the most efficient joint possible would be one which will be as strong in tension, shear, and bearing as the original plate to be joined is in tension. This can never be achieved, because there must be at least one rivet hole in the plate, and the joints' allowable load in tension will thus always be less than the strength of the plate with no holes.

It should be obvious at this point that most joints will have many rivets in a variety of patterns. The analysis required for such joints is much more complicated than that for a single rivet presented previously. We will demonstrate the procedures that are followed in order to solve these more complicated problems by means of the following examples. It is strongly suggested that they be read over very carefully.

Example 16-1. Two 15-in. by $\frac{1}{2}$-in. plates are to be connected by means of a lap joint. The rivets to be used are $\frac{7}{8}$-in. diameter, and the working stresses are as follows: shear, 13,500 psi; bearing, 27,000 psi; tension, 18,000 psi. Design the connection.

Solution: The connection should be designed for maximum efficiency, and, since it is usually assumed that the row of rivets immediately adjacent to the load carries the full load, the maximum tensile load carried by such a row occurs when only one rivet is in that row. The portion of the load carried by an interior row can be determined from equation (16-6).

$$P_{t(\text{actual})} = \frac{n - n'}{n} P \tag{16-6}$$

where $P_{t(\text{actual})}$ = portion of externally applied load P acting on a particular row; n = total number of rivets in the connection; and n' = total number of rivets in the rows between the row being checked in tension and the external load. The use of this equation will be illustrated later on in this example.

The strength of the plate with one rivet is

$$F_{t_1} = S_{t(\text{allow})}(w - d_{\text{eff}})t$$

Since the rivets are $\frac{7}{8}$-in. diameter and the holes must be assumed to have been punched, $d_{\text{eff}} = \frac{7}{8} + \frac{1}{8} = 1$ in.

$$F_{t_1} = 18{,}000(15 - 1)(\tfrac{1}{2}) = 126{,}000 \text{ lb}$$

The strength of the joint in bearing and shear depends on the number of rivets.

Strength of one rivet. In shear

$$F_s = S_s \frac{\pi}{4}(d^2)$$

$$= 13,500 \times \frac{\pi}{4} \times (\tfrac{7}{8})^2 = 8110 \text{ lb}$$

In bearing

$$F_b = S_b td = 27,000 \times \tfrac{1}{2} \times \tfrac{7}{8}$$

$$= 11,800 \text{ lb}$$

Therefore rivets are weaker in shear and the number of rivets necessary is

$$\frac{126,000}{8110} = 15.55$$

Thus 16 rivets are necessary in order to permit 126,000 lb to be applied. Clearly, with 16 rivets, the allowable load in bearing will be greater than 126,000 lb.

The remaining problem now is to determine how the 16 rivets are to be distributed. In doing this, it should be made clear that, for lap joints having equal plate thicknesses, the last row of rivets (farthest from the load) in the upper plate is the first row (row closest to the load) of the lower plate. Therefore, the first and last row will have one rivet. The situation is as shown in the figure below.

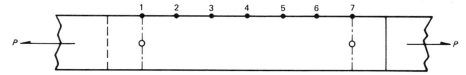

Let us next check the situation in row 2 if there are two rivets in that row.
Load on row 2. By equation (16-6)

$$P_{t2(\text{actual})} = \frac{n - n'}{n}P = \frac{(16 - 1)}{16}126,000$$

$$= 118,000 \text{ lb}$$

Strength of plate row 2

$$P_{t2(\text{allow})} = 18,000(15 - 2)\tfrac{1}{2} = 117,000 \text{ lb}$$

The actual load is slightly higher than the allowable, but the difference is small enough to be acceptable. Therefore, rows 2 and 6 will have 2 rivets.
Let us next check row 3 if three rivets are in it.
Load on row 3. By equation (16-6)

$$P_{t3(\text{actual})} = \frac{16 - 3}{16}126,000$$

$$= 102,500 \text{ lb}$$

Strength of plate in row 3

$$P_{t3(\text{allow})} = 18,000(16 - 3)\tfrac{1}{2} = 108,000 \text{ lb}$$

Since $108,000 > 102,500$ row 3 is satisfactory. Therefore, rows 3 and 5 have three rivets.

We have so far accounted for 12 rivets, let us therefore check row 4 with four rivets in it.

$$P_{t4(actual)} = \frac{16 - 6}{16} 126{,}000 = 78{,}000 \text{ lb}$$

$$P_{t4(allow)} = 18{,}000(15 - 4)\tfrac{1}{2} = 99{,}000 \text{ lb}$$

Row 4 satisfactory.

We should also check the spacing requirements for row 4. Assume that the minimum center-to-center distance between rivets is $3d$ (AISC code); as mentioned previously the minimum edge distance is $2d$. Therefore

$$\text{required width} = 3(3 \times \tfrac{7}{8}) + 2(2 \times \tfrac{7}{8})$$

$$= \tfrac{63}{8} + \tfrac{28}{8} = \tfrac{91}{8} = 11\tfrac{3}{8} \text{ in.}$$

Since this is less than 15 in., the spacing requirement is met. The final rivet pattern is thus satisfactory.

All that remains is to calculate the efficiency of the connection.

$$\text{eff} = \frac{P_{allow\,max}}{\text{tensile strength of plate}}$$

$$= \frac{126{,}000}{18{,}000 \times 15 \times \tfrac{1}{2}} = \frac{126{,}000}{135{,}000} = 93\% \quad \bullet$$

Example 16-2. A butt joint, whose rivet pattern is shown in Figure 16-12, is to be used to form a circular steel boiler. The boiler is to have a 5-ft diameter and be able to withstand an internal pressure p of 500 psi. Determine the required main plate thickness as well as the efficiency of the joint. The rivets are to be $\tfrac{7}{8}$-in. diameter, and the rivet holes are drilled to $\tfrac{15}{16}$ in. in diameter. The working stresses are as follows: tension, 20,000 psi; shear, 16,000 psi; bearing, 20,000 psi in single shear and 28,000 psi in double shear.

Solution: The rivet pattern shown is but a small section of a much longer pattern. Clearly it would not be feasible to attempt to analyze the joint by considering the whole length of rivets. The usual procedure is to determine the minimum repeating section, which is the smallest length for which each row of rivets repeats itself exactly. The rivets in row A and B repeat themselves for a length equal to the distance between two adjacent rivets, but the rows C and D do not. If the distance between adjacent rivets in row C were used as the repeating length, rows A, B, and C would repeat their pattern, but D would not. However, if the distance between adjacent rivets in row D, L, were used, all four rows would repeat their pattern over this length. Thus, L is the minimum repeating section for the rivet pattern shown. There are eleven rivets in the repeating section, as can be clearly seen if section L to the right of row A is considered.

Because the shear strength is independent of plate thickness, the maximum allowable load the joint can resist is determined by the shearing of the rivets. The rivets are in double shear so that $2 \times 16{,}000$ psi will be used as the allowable stress.

$$P_{S(allow)} = nS_{S(allow)} \frac{\pi}{4} d^2$$

$$= 11(2 \times 16{,}000) \frac{\pi}{4} \left(\frac{7}{8}\right)^2$$

$$= 212{,}000 \text{ lb}$$

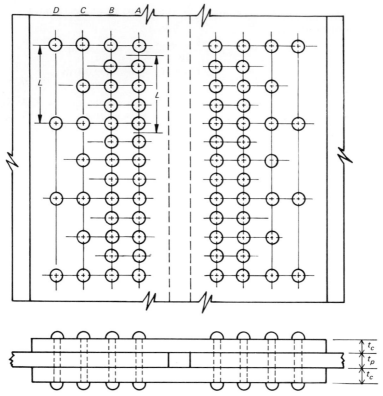

Figure 16-12

The next step in our solution will be to determine how long the repeating section will be. In Figure 16-13, a free body diagram of a length of the boiler L and with the resulting cylinder slit in half lengthwise is shown. The force T represents the tensile load acting in the boiler plates.

Summation of forces in the vertical direction yields

$$2T = p2RL$$

or

$$L = \frac{T}{pR}$$

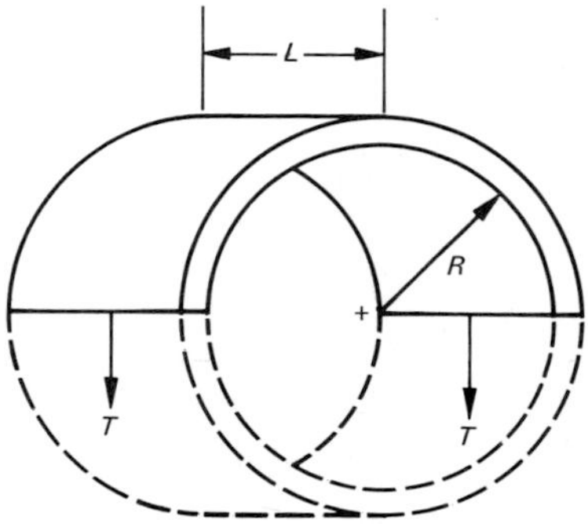

Figure 16-13

Because the load cannot exceed 212,000 lb in shear, we will let T, the tensile load, be 212,000 lb. Then

$$L = \frac{212,000}{500 \times \frac{5}{2} \times 12} = 14.1 \text{ in.}$$

In order to determine the thickness of the main plate, the larger of the thicknesses as determined by bearing and tension is used.

$$P_{b(\text{allow})} = nS_{b(\text{allow})} \, dt_p$$
$$212,000 = 11 \times 28,000 \times \tfrac{7}{8} \times t_p$$
$$t_p = 0.79 \text{ in.}$$

Tension row D

$$P_t = S_{t(\text{allow})}(w - d_{\text{eff}})t_p$$
$$212,000 = 20,000(14.1 - \tfrac{15}{16})t_p$$
$$t_p = 0.81 \text{ in. or } \tfrac{13}{16} \text{ in.}$$

Actual load acting on row C is

$$P_{t(\text{actual})} = \frac{n - n'}{n}P = \frac{11 - 1}{11}212,000$$
$$= 193,000 \text{ lb}$$

Strength across row C is

$$P_t = S_{t(\text{allow})}(w - d_{\text{eff}})t_p$$
$$= 20,000(14.1 - 2 \times \tfrac{15}{16})\tfrac{13}{16}$$
$$= 200,000 \text{ lb}$$

Since 200,000 lb > 193,000 lb, the plate is safe in tension across row C. Actual load on row B

$$P_{t(\text{actual})} = \frac{11 - 3}{1} \times 212,000 = 154,000 \text{ lb}$$

Strength across row B

$$P_t = S_{t(\text{allow})}(w - d_{\text{eff}})t_p$$
$$= 20,000(14.1 - 4 \times \tfrac{15}{16}) \times \tfrac{13}{16}$$
$$= 168,000 \text{ lb}$$

Since 168,000 lb > 154,000 lb, the plate is safe in tension across row B.

Row A will clearly be safe since the strength is the same as for row B, and the actual load acting is less than the actual load on row B. Therefore, the required main plate thickness is $\tfrac{13}{16}$ in. The efficiency of the connection remains to be calculated.

$$\text{eff} = \frac{P_{\text{allow max}}}{\text{tensile strength of plate}}$$
$$= \frac{212,000}{20,000 \times 14.1 \times \tfrac{13}{16}} = 92.6\% \quad \bullet$$

SECTION 16-4

Eccentrically Loaded Rivets

Up to this point in our discussion of riveted connections, we have considered only those problems in which the rivets were axially loaded (the load passed through the center of gravity of the rivet group). However, many examples exist for which the load does not pass through the center of gravity of the rivet group. A typical problem encountered in structural work is the situation that occurs when a horizontal beam is supported by a vertical column by means of a gusset plate, see Figure 16-14. As is shown in the figure, the left hand reaction on the beam is F, this force is transmitted to the gusset plate, which in turn transmits the force to the column. It is obvious from an inspection of Figure 16-15 that the rivets will be subjected to a twisting moment as well as a direct shearing force.

Making use of the law of statics, which says that a force may be moved to a parallel coplanar position by replacing it by an equivalent force and couple, we replace the actual force F (solid line) by the equivalent force F (dotted), acting through the center of gravity of the rivet group, and equivalent couple Fe.

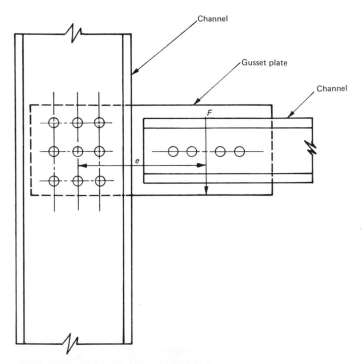

Figure 16-14 Sketch of horizontal beam attached to a vertical channel by means of a gusset plate.

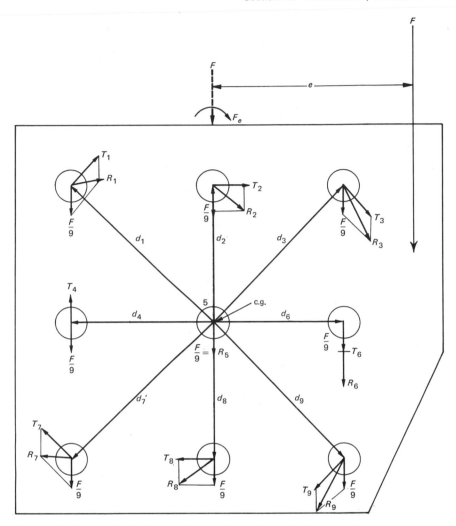

Figure 16-15 Free body diagram showing the twisting, direct, and resultant forces acting on the rivets and due to the gusset plate.

If we assume that each rivet takes an equal share of the load (a reasonable assumption, since the force now acts through the center of gravity of the rivet group) we can draw a force vector through the center of each rivet, acting in the same direction as F, and having a magnitude of F/n, where n is equal to the number of rivets in the group. (For the group shown in Figure 16-15, $n = 9$.)

The couple, Fe, which tries to rotate the plate about the center of gravity of the rivet group, is prevented from doing so by the resistance of the rivets. As a result, there are forces, T, acting through the center of each rivet, and perpendicular to the distance d, drawn from the center of gravity to the center of each rivet.

Let us turn our attention for a moment to the determination of the magnitude of these turning forces. Assuming for the moment that the plate can be rotated about the center of gravity through a small angle θ, it is clear that the displacement a rivet would go through would be directly proportional to its distance d. It follows that the unit strain resulting from such a displacement would be directly proportional to d. Because we may assume stress proportional to strain, the stress is also directly proportional to d. Finally since the force T varies directly as the stress, it follows that the force T varies linearly and directly as the distance d.

Clearly, the external moment Fe must be resisted by the sum of the internal moments Td. In other words,

$$Fe = T_1 d_1 + T_2 d_2 + \cdots + T_n d_n \tag{16-7}$$

But since T is directly proportional to d it follows that

$$\frac{T_1}{d_1} = \frac{T_2}{d_2} = \frac{T_3}{d_3} = \cdots = \frac{T_n}{d_n}$$

Therefore

$$T_2 = T_1 \frac{d_2}{d_1} \qquad T_3 = T_1 \frac{d_3}{d_1} \qquad \cdots \qquad T_n = T_1 \frac{d_n}{d_1}$$

Then substituting in equation (16-7), we obtain

$$Fe = T_1 d_1 \frac{d_1}{d_1} + T_1 \frac{d_2}{d_1} d_2 + T_1 \frac{d_3}{d_1} d_3 + \cdots + T_1 \frac{d_n}{d_1} d_n$$

$$= \frac{T_1}{d_1}(d_1^2 + d_2^2 + d_3^2 + \cdots + d_n^2)$$

or

$$T_1 = \frac{Fed_1}{d_1^2 + d_2^2 + d_3^2 + \cdots + d_n^2}$$

Similarly

$$T_2 = \frac{Fed_2}{\sum_{k=1}^{n} d_k^2}$$

and, in general

$$T_j = \frac{Fed_j}{\sum_{k=1}^{n} d_k^2} \tag{16-8}$$

The final step is to find the resultant force on the rivets, in other words, to combine algebraically or graphically the force vectors F/n and T. Fortunately, it is not necessary to find the resultant on each of the rivets, because the usual procedure is to make the rivet diameters the same. It is therefore only necessary to calculate the maximum resultant load. An inspection of the vector force diagrams is usually sufficient to eliminate all but two or three rivets as candidates for worst loaded rivet.

As an example, consider the rivet group shown in Figure 16-15. Obviously, rivets 4 and 5 have smaller resultants than rivet 6; rivets 1 and 7, 2 and 8, and 3 and 9 have equal respective resultants. Also, it is clear from the vector diagrams that 3 and 9 have a larger resultant than the other pairs mentioned. Therefore, all that is necessary is to calculate R_3 and R_6, in order to determine the maximum resultant load.

Although a shearing failure of the rivets is usually the only type of failure that must be checked, in some problems the gusset plate thickness should also be checked. In other words, the resistance to a bearing failure must be determined.

Before ending this discussion of rivets with an example, it would be well to reiterate a statement made earlier: If bolts or other removable fasteners had been used instead of rivets, the analysis presented would be equally valid.

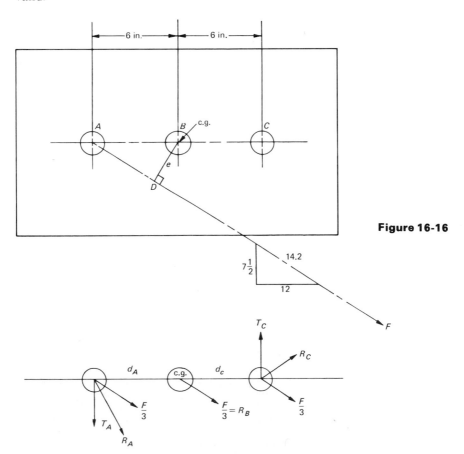

Figure 16-16

Example 16-3. Determine the maximum allowable load F that can be applied to the rivet group shown in Figure 16-16 considering shear failure of the rivets only. Diameter of rivets is $\frac{7}{8}$ in. and allowable shear stress is 16,000 psi.

Solution: It is clear from an inspection of the force diagrams, that rivet A has the greatest resultant load acting on it. It should be obvious that rivet B, the rivet at the center of gravity, has no twisting force acting on it.

$$T_A = T_c = \frac{Fed_A}{d_A^2 + d_C^2}$$

The eccentricity e can be found by considering triangle ABD since

$$\frac{e}{6} = \frac{7\frac{1}{2}}{14.2}, e = 3.18 \text{ in.}$$

Therefore

$$T_A = \frac{F \times 3.18 \times 6}{6^2 + 6^2} = 0.265F$$

The vector sum of T_A and $F/3$ can be obtained either graphically or algebraically.

$$\Sigma F_A(\text{vertical}) = 0.265F + 0.333F \times \frac{7\frac{1}{2}}{14.2}$$

$$= 0.265F + 0.176F$$

$$= 0.441F$$

$$\Sigma F_A(\text{horizontal}) = 0.333F \times \frac{12}{14.2}$$

$$= 0.281F$$

$$R_A = \sqrt{(0.441F)^2 + (0.281F)^2}$$

$$= 0.523F$$

$$F_{(\text{allowable in shear})} = S_{S(\text{allow})} \times \frac{\pi}{4} \times (\tfrac{7}{8})^2 = 9630 \text{ lb}$$

Therefore

$$0.523F = 9630$$

or

$$F = 18,400 \text{ lb maximum allowable load} \quad \bullet$$

Example 16-4. A problem somewhat similar to eccentrically loaded rivets occurs with eccentrically loaded bolted connections. The resulting stress in the bolts is due to both shear and tension. To demonstrate an approach to the solution of this type of problem, consider the following example.

Figure 16-17 shows a machine part that is to be bolted to a support by means of two rows of bolts. Each row also has two bolts. If the bolts are $\frac{3}{4}$-in.–10 ($\frac{3}{4}$-in. outside diameter, 10 threads/in.), having a stress area of 0.334 in.^{2}, an allowable tensile stress S_t of 20,000 psi, and an allowable shear stress, S_s of 11,000 psi, determine the maximum load F that can safely be applied.

Solution: The force F produces a simple shear stress in the bolts, and a reasonable assumption would be that each bolt takes an equal share of the load. The load on each bolt is therefore $F/4$. The part of the bolt being subjected to shear is unthreaded, therefore the shear area is $(\pi/4)(\frac{3}{4})^2 = 0.442$ in.^{2} for direct shear,

$$\tau = \frac{P}{A} = \frac{F/4}{0.442} = 0.565F$$

The effect of the moment $F \times 15$ is to cause the machine part to pivot about point A. Therefore the force produced in the bolts due to this moment will be proportional to the distance from the center line of the bolts to A. The resulting equation is

$$T_n = \frac{Md_n}{\Sigma d_k^2}$$

Clearly the bolts in row 2 will have a greater load than those in row 1.

$$T_2 = \frac{Md_2}{(d_1^2 + d_2^2)} = \frac{F \times 15 \times (8+4)}{[2 \text{ bolts} \times (4)^2 + 2 \text{ bolts} \times (12)^2]}$$
$$= 0.562F$$

Therefore the tension force due to the moment on each bolt in row 2 is $0.562F$. The maximum tensile stress occurs in the threaded portion of the bolt, thus

$$\sigma_t = \frac{0.562F}{0.334} = 1.69F$$

The combined stress equations can now be used to determine the maximum tensile and shear stresses

$$\sigma_{t(\max)} = \frac{\sigma_t}{2} + \sqrt{\left(\frac{\sigma_t}{2}\right)^2 + \tau^2}$$

$$= \frac{1.69F}{2} + \sqrt{\left(\frac{1.69F}{2}\right)^2 + (0.565F)^2}$$

$$= 1.87F = S_{t(\text{allow})}$$

$$20,000 = 1.87F$$

$$F = 10,700 \text{ lb}$$

$$\tau_{(\max)} = \sqrt{(\sigma_t/2)^2 + \tau^2} = \sqrt{(1.69F/2)^2 + (0.565F)^2}$$
$$= 1.02F = S_{s(\text{allow})}$$

$$11,000 = 1.02F$$

$$F = 10,000 \text{ lb}$$

Therefore maximum allowable load $= 10,000$ lb. ●

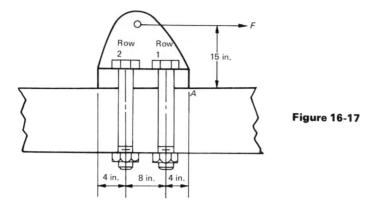

Figure 16-17

Screw Fasteners

The discussion presented in the earlier part of this chapter dealt with permanent fasteners, rivets and bolts. Since most machine parts that require connection must usually be made in such a way that they can easily be disassembled as well as assembled, nonpermanent fasteners are required. These so-called detachable fasteners come in a variety of types, and the one chosen by the designer for a particular application depends primarily upon the major requirements of the problem. For example, a machine part that is subjected to vibrations must be fastened by a screw and nut arrangement that will not shake loose under vibration. The first, and perhaps the most often used, fastener we will discuss is the screw.

Standardized Screw Threads

The various types of threads used on screws have been standardized, and it is important that the designer be aware of the various types available and what their important characteristics are. Power screw threads are of an entirely different type, and will not be discussed in this section.

One of the earliest types of screw threads was the V thread, Figure 16-18. However, the sharpness of the crest made the thread very susceptible to

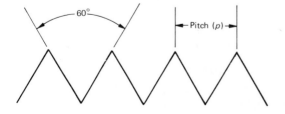

Figure 16-18 V thread type of screw thread.

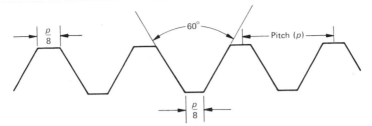

Figure 16-19 Sellers thread, in which the sharp crests and roots of the the V thread are replaced by flat surfaces.

damage. In addition, the sharp root resulted in large stress concentrations. It became obvious that the V thread would have to be modified in order to relieve the conditions mentioned.

The Sellers thread, Figure 16-19, alleviated the problem by replacing the sharp crests and roots with flat surfaces. Another solution was the Whitworth thread, Figure 16-20, in which the crest and root were rounded. The Sellers thread was formerly the United States standard, whereas the Whitworth thread was the former British standard. Both countries now have as their standard the unified thread, Figure 16-21.

The major or outside diameter is measured at the crests of the threads for external threads and at the roots for internal threads. This is the diameter used to designate a thread. As an example, a $\frac{3}{4}$-10 screw has an outside diameter of $\frac{3}{4}$ in., and 10 threads/in. The pitch of a screw is defined as the distance between corresponding points of adjacent threads. It is equal to the reciprocal of the number of threads per inch. The $\frac{3}{4}$-10 screw has a pitch of 0.1 in.

The lead is the distance a screw moves axially during 1 revolution of the screw. As was mentioned previously, in the section on worm gearing, the lead of a single threaded screw is equal to its pitch, a double threaded screw has a lead equal to twice its pitch, a triple threaded screw has a lead 3 times its pitch, and so on.

The following threads are the most commonly used ones, and are thus designated as "standard" threads.

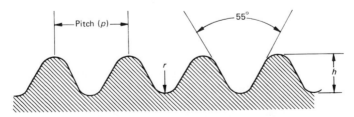

Figure 16-20 Whitworth thread, which further modified the V thread by rounding the crests and roots.

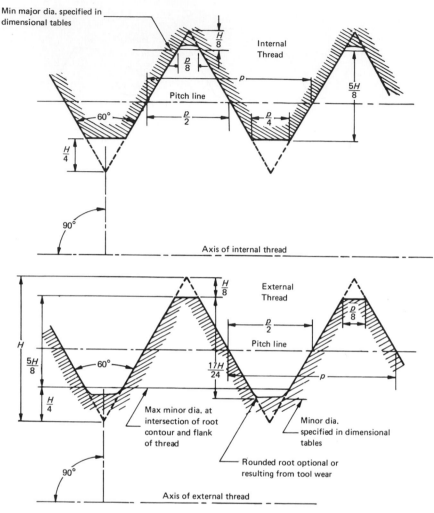

Figure 16-21 Unified internal and external screw thread (maximum material condition) design forms. [From *American Standard Unified Screw Threads* (ASA B1.1–1960), with the permission of the publisher, The American Society of Mechanical Engineers, New York.]

1. Coarse (designated as UNC). Used for general assembly work, especially where frequent assembly and disassembly is necessary. Should not be used for designs in which vibration problems may be encountered. They are also recommended for use in nonsteel metals. A good rule of thumb for the designer to follow is "always specify coarse threads unless a specific factor of design indicates otherwise."

2. Fine (designated as UNF). This series is widely used in automotive, aircraft, and other applications where vibrations are likely to occur. They are also recommended for use in designs involving holes tapped in steel.

3. Extra-Fine (designated as UNEF). Used in instrument applications, particularly in aircraft work, and also for problems involving large vibrations and shock. The screws in this series are usually made of a high-grade alloy steel.

4. There are several standard constant pitch threads available. As the name implies, these are threads that have the same pitch for all diameters. As can be seen by looking at Table 16-1, the pitch for the threads discussed previously increases as the diameter increases. As a result, it may be impossible to tighten large bolts enough to induce the required initial tension.

Table 16-1   Tables of Basic Dimensions, Standard Series Threads

(a)—COARSE THREAD SERIES, UNC AND NC—BASIC DIMENSIONS

Sizes	Basic Major Diameter, D, in.	Threads per inch, n	Basic Pitch Diameter, E, in.	Minor Diameter External Threads, K_s, in.	Minor Diameter Internal, Threads, K_n, in.	Lead Angle at Basic Pitch Diameter, λ deg	min	Section at Minor Diameter at D-$2h$, in.^{2}	Tensile Stress Area, in.^{2}
1(0.073)	0.0730	64	0.0629	0.0538	0.0561	4	31	0.00218	0.00263
2(0.086)	0.0860	56	0.0744	0.0641	0.0667	4	22	0.00310	0.00370
3(0.099)	0.0990	48	0.0855	0.0734	0.0764	4	26	0.00406	0.00487
4(0.112)	0.1120	40	0.0958	0.0813	0.0849	4	45	0.00496	0.00604
5(0.125)	0.1250	40	0.1088	0.0943	0.0979	4	11	0.00672	0.00796
6(0.138)	0.1380	32	0.1177	0.0997	0.1042	4	50	0.00745	0.00909
8(0.164)	0.1640	32	0.1437	0.1257	0.1302	3	58	0.01196	0.0140
10(0.190)	0.1900	24	0.1629	0.1389	0.1449	4	39	0.01450	0.0175
12(0.216)	0.2160	24	0.1889	0.1649	0.1709	4	1	0.0206	0.0242
1/4	0.2500	20	0.2175	0.1887	0.1959	4	11	0.0269	0.0318
5/16	0.3125	18	0.2764	0.2443	0.2524	3	40	0.0454	0.0524
3/8	0.3750	16	0.3344	0.2983	0.3073	3	24	0.0678	0.0775
7/16	0.4375	14	0.3911	0.3499	0.3602	3	20	0.0933	0.1063
1/2	0.5000	13	0.4500	0.4056	0.4167	3	7	0.1257	0.1419
9/16	0.5625	12	0.5084	0.4603	0.4723	2	59	0.162	0.182
5/8	0.6250	11	0.5660	0.5135	0.5266	2	56	0.202	0.226
3/4	0.7500	10	0.6850	0.6273	0.6417	2	40	0.302	0.334
7/8	0.8750	9	0.8028	0.7387	0.7547	2	31	0.419	0.462
1	1.0000	8	0.9188	0.8466	0.8647	2	29	0.551	0.606
1-1/8	1.1250	7	1.0322	0.9497	0.9704	2	31	0.693	0.763
1-1/4	1.2500	7	1.1572	1.0747	1.0954	2	15	0.890	0.969
1-3/8	1.3750	6	1.2667	1.1705	1.1946	2	24	1.054	1.155
1-1/2	1.5000	6	1.3917	1.2955	1.3196	2	11	1.294	1.405
1-3/4	1.7500	5	1.6201	1.5046	1.5335	2	15	1.74	1.90
2	2.0000	4-1/2	1.8557	1.7274	1.7594	2	11	2.30	2.50
2-1/4	2.2500	4-1/2	2.1057	1.9774	2.0094	1	55	3.02	3.25
2-1/2	2.5000	4	2.3376	2.1933	2.2294	1	57	3.72	4.00
2-3/4	2.7500	4	2.5876	2.4433	2.4794	1	46	4.62	4.93
3	3.0000	4	2.8376	2.6933	2.7294	1	36	5.62	5.97
3-1/4	3.2500	4	3.0876	2.9433	2.9794	1	29	6.72	7.10
3-1/2	3.5000	4	3.3376	3.1933	3.2294	1	22	7.92	8.33
3-3/4	3.7500	4	3.5876	3.4433	3.4794	1	16	9.21	9.66
4	4.0000	4	3.8376	3.6933	3.7294	1	11	10.61	11.08

SOURCE: Extracted from American Standard Unified Screw Threads (ASA B1.1–1960) with permission of the publisher The American Society of Mechanical Engineers, New York.

Obviously this problem can be alleviated by holding the pitch constant, as the diameter is increased. Some of the standard constant pitch threads available are 8 pitch (8 UN), 12 pitch (12 UN), 16 pitch (16 UN), and 20 pitch (20 UN). Some of the applications for which constant pitch threads are useful are high pressure pipe flanges, cylinder-head studs, heavy machinery, and so on.

In designating threads, the letter A is used for external threads, and B is used for internal threads. Threads are further classified according to fit. Class 1 fits have the widest tolerances and thus are the loosest fits, they are used when rapid assembly and disassembly is required. Class 2 fits are the most widely used and are recommended for most applications, except when contraindicated for some specific reason. Class 3, the final standard fit, is the one having the tightest fit and is used for precision applications. A variation of these fits can be obtained by using a different class of fit for the external and internal threads.

Table 16-1   Tables of Basic Dimensions, Standard Series Threads

(b)—FINE THREAD SERIES, UNF AND NF—BASIC DIMENSIONS

Sizes	Basic Major Diameter, D, in.	Threads per inch, n	Basic Pitch Diameter, E, in.	Minor Diameter External Threads, K_s, in.	Minor Diameter Internal Threads, K_n, in.	Lead Angle at Basic Pitch Diameter, λ deg	min	Section at Minor Diameter at $D\text{-}2h$, in.^{2}	Tensile Stress Area, in.^{2}
0(0.060)	0.0600	80	0.0519	0.0447	0.0465	4	23	0.00151	0.00180
1(0.073)	0.0730	72	0.0640	0.0560	0.0580	3	57	0.00237	0.00278
2(0.086)	0.0860	64	0.0759	0.0668	0.0691	3	45	0.00339	0.00394
3(0.099)	0.0990	56	0.0874	0.0771	0.0797	3	43	0.00451	0.00523
4(0.112)	0.1120	48	0.0985	0.0864	0.0894	3	51	0.00566	0.00661
5(0.125)	0.1250	44	0.1102	0.0971	0.1004	3	45	0.00716	0.00830
6(0.138)	0.1380	40	0.1218	0.1073	0.1109	3	44	0.00874	0.01015
8(0.164)	0.1640	36	0.1460	0.1299	0.1339	3	28	0.01285	0.01474
10(0.190)	0.1900	32	0.1697	0.1517	0.1562	3	21	0.0175	0.0200
12(0.216)	0.2160	28	0.1928	0.1722	0.1733	3	22	0.0226	0.0258
1/4	0.2500	28	0.2268	0.2062	0.2113	2	52	0.0326	0.0364
5/16	0.3125	24	0.2854	0.2614	0.2674	2	40	0.0524	0.0580
3/8	0.3750	24	0.3479	0.3239	0.3299	2	11	0.0809	0.0878
7/16	0.4375	20	0.4050	0.3762	0.3834	2	15	0.1090	0.1187
1/2	0.5000	20	0.4675	0.4387	0.4459	1	57	0.1486	0.1599
9/16	0.5625	18	0.5264	0.4943	0.5024	1	55	0.189	0.203
5/8	0.6250	18	0.5889	0.5568	0.5649	1	43	0.240	0.256
3/4	0.7500	16	0.7094	0.6733	0.6823	1	36	0.351	0.373
7/8	0.8750	14	0.8286	0.7874	0.7977	1	34	0.480	0.509
1	1.0000	12	0.9459	0.8978	0.9098	1	36	0.625	0.663
1-1/8	1.1250	12	1.0709	1.0228	1.0348	1	25	0.812	0.856
1-1/4	1.2500	12	1.1959	1.1478	1.1598	1	16	1.024	1.073
1-3/8	1.3750	12	1.3209	1.2728	1.2848	1	9	1.260	1.315
1-1/2	1.5000	12	1.4459	1.3978	1.4098	1	3	1.521	1.581

SOURCE: Extracted from American Standard Unified Screw Threads (ASA B1.1–1960) with permission of the publisher The American Society of Mechanical Engineers, New York.

Table 16-1 Tables of Basic Dimensions, Standard Series Threads

(c)—EXTRA-FINE THREAD SERIES, UNEF AND NEF—BASIC DIMENSIONS

Sizes	Basic Major Diameter, D, in.	Threads per inch, n	Basic Pitch Diameter, E, in.	Minor Diameter External Threads, K_s, in.	Minor Diameter Internal Threads, K_r, in.	Lead Angle at Basic Pitch Diameter, λ deg	min	Section at Minor Diameter at $D - 2h$, in.	Tensile Stress Area in.^{2}
12(0.216)	0.2160	32	0.1957	0.1777	0.1822	2	55	0.0242	0.0270
1/4	0.2500	32	0.2297	0.2117	0.2162	2	29	0.0344	0.0379
5/16	0.3125	32	0.2922	0.2742	0.2787	1	57	0.0581	0.0625
3/8	0.3750	32	0.3547	0.3367	0.3412	1	36	0.0878	0.0932
7/16	0.4375	28	0.4143	0.3937	0.3988	1	34	0.1201	0.1274
1/2	0.5000	28	0.4768	0.4562	0.4613	1	22	0.162	0.170
9/16	0.5625	24	0.5354	0.5114	0.5174	1	25	0.203	0.214
5/8	0.6250	24	0.5979	0.5739	0.5799	1	16	0.256	0.268
11/16	0.6875	24	0.6604	0.6364	0.6424	1	9	0.315	0.329
3/4	0.7500	20	0.7175	0.6887	0.6959	1	16	0.369	0.386
13/16	0.8125	20	0.7800	0.7512	0.7584	1	10	0.439	0.458
7/8	0.8750	20	0.8425	0.8137	0.8209	1	5	0.515	0.536
15/16	0.9375	20	0.9050	0.8762	0.8834	1	0	0.598	0.620
1	1.0000	20	0.9675	0.9387	0.9459	0	57	0.687	0.711
1-1/16	1.0625	18	1.0264	0.9943	1.0024	0	59	0.770	0.799
1-1/8	1.1250	18	1.0889	1.0568	1.0649	0	56	0.871	0.901
1-3/16	1.1875	18	1.1514	1.1193	1.1274	0	53	0.977	1.009
1-1/4	1.2500	18	1.2139	1.1818	1.1899	0	50	1.090	1.123
1-5/16	1.3125	18	1.2764	1.2443	1.2524	0	58	1.208	1.244
1-3/8	1.3750	18	1.3389	1.3068	1.3149	0	45	1.333	1.370
1-7/16	1.4375	18	1.4014	1.3693	1.3774	0	43	1.464	1.503
1-1/2	1.5000	18	1.4639	1.4318	1.4399	0	42	1.60	1.64
1-9/16	1.5625	18	1.5264	1.4943	1.5024	0	40	1.74	1.79
1-5/8	1.6250	18	1.5889	1.5568	1.5649	0	38	1.89	1.94
1-11/16	1.6875	18	1.6514	1.6193	1.6274	0	37	2.05	2.10

SOURCE: Extracted from American Standard Unified Screw Threads (ASA B1.1–1960) with permission of the publisher The American Society of Mechanical Engineers, New York.

Example 16-5. What type of screw does the following designation represent, $\frac{3}{4}$ in.-10 UNC-3B-LH?

Solution: $\frac{3}{4}$ in. outside diameter, 10 threads/in., unified coarse thread, class 3 fit, internal thread, left hand thread. ●

SECTION 16-7

Various Types of Screws, Bolts, and Other Fasteners

The only difference between a screw and a bolt is that the bolt needs a nut in order to be used as a fastener, whereas a screw fits into a threaded hole. Some of the more common types of fasteners as well as some special application types are shown in Figures 16-22 and 16-23.

Figure 16-22 Shock absorber bolt. A rubber cap is molded over and under the ribbed head of this steel bolt. The ribs on the top or under side of the head prevent the molded rubber from turning or loosening. [Courtesy Elco Corporation, Rockford, Ill.]

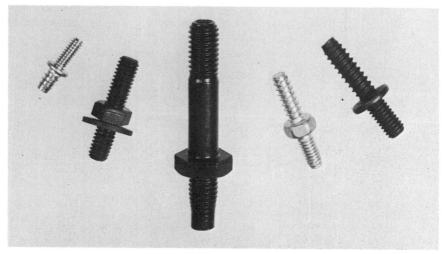

Figure 16-23 Some typical examples of stud bolts. A stud bolt has threads on both ends and is particularly useful in applications where a plate is to be bolted to a larger part and a through bolt cannot be used. A prime example for which a stud is useful is the head on an automotive engine. [Courtesy Camcar Screw and Mfg. Division.]

Nuts

Many varieties of nuts exist, both the common variety as well as ones for special applications. It would be impossible to discuss all the types that have been developed, much less to consider the many new types that are constantly being developed. Some typical examples are shown in Figures 16-24 through 16-26.

Screws

Sems are preassembled fasteners that eliminate the need for hand assembling of screws and washers. Some common types of sems are shown in Figure 16-27.

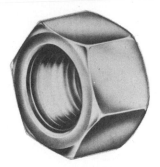

Figure 16-24 The self-locking fastener pictured is a locknut that makes use of a nylon locking patch (the lighter portion of the threads). This type of nut is useful for those applications involving severe shock and vibratory loads. [Courtesy Amerace Esna Corporation, Union, N.J.]

Figure 16-25 A standard lock washer of the type shown has maximum resistance to loosening since the teeth are formed and twisted to bite deeply into both nut and work surfaces. [Courtesy Shakeproof, Division Illinois Tool Works, Inc.]

Figure 16-26 (a) The speed nut fastener shown is a self-locking device that provides both an inward thread lock and an arched spring lock. (b) The principle upon which speed nut fasteners operate. [Courtesy Eaton, Yale, and Towne.]

(a)

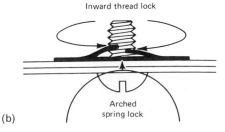

Prelocked position

Arched prongs

Arched base

Double-locked position

Inward thread lock

Arched spring lock

(b)

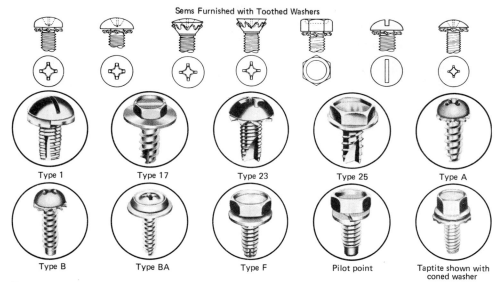

Figure 16-27 Various types of preassembled fasteners known as Sems are shown. [Courtesy Camcar Screw and Mfg. Division.]

Set screws are a type of semipermanent fastener used to prevent relative motion between sliding surfaces. In general, they are useful in low torque applications involving rotary motion. Set screws are made in a variety of heads and points. Some of the common types of set screws are shown in Figure 16-28.

It is extremely important for the designer to choose the proper type of point. We will now briefly discuss some of the types and applications for which they are used.

1. Cone Point. Used for designs where the parts to be joined will have the same relative position with respect to each other. Standard cone angles are 90 and 118 deg. The usual procedure is to make the cone angle 118 deg when the set screw length is less than or equal to its nominal diameter, whereas the angle is 90 deg when the length is greater than the nominal diameter.

The following rules of thumb are suggested for all types of set screws. The size of the set screw is usually taken as $\frac{1}{4}-\frac{1}{2}$ times the shaft diameter it is to fasten. The minimum length of engagement for a set screw is about $1-1\frac{1}{2}$ times the diameter if the set screw is threaded in brass and $\frac{3}{4}-1$ times for use in steel.

The torque capacity can be increased by using two set screws. If they are used side by side, the torque capacity is almost doubled, whereas if they are placed 180 deg apart the capacity is increased by about one third.

2. Cup Point. Perhaps the most commonly used type of point because of the ease and rapidity of assembly. It is rarely used in applications involving hardened shafts.

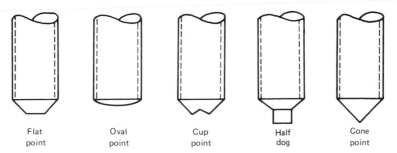

| Flat point | Oval point | Cup point | Half dog | Cone point |

Figure 16-28 Common types of set screws. [Courtesy Amerace Esna Corporation, Union, N.J.]

3. Flat Point. Useful for applications involving hardened shafts and where frequent adjustment is needed.

4. Full Dog. Used for those designs that involve permanent relative location of parts. It is necessary to drill a hole in the part that is to receive the set screw.

5. Half Dog. Same as full dog except for length of insert.

6. Oval Point. Similar to cup point, except that a groove for spotting the set screw is usually needed on the receiving part.

The tensilock screw, shown in Figure 16-29, has a rolled nylon washer preassembled to a standard screw.

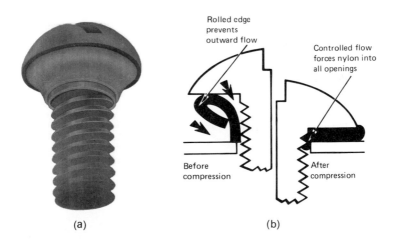

(a)　　　　(b)

Figure 16-29 (a) This fastener consists of a rolled nylon washer, preassembled to a standard screw. Because the outside rolled edge of the washer is stronger than the inside edge, it resists outward flow during compression and the inside edge is forced inward into the screw threads and into any space between screw shank and hole. As a result the fastener seals, locks, isolates vibrations, is corrosion resistant, and provides electrical insulation. (b) Sketch showing how fastener operates. [Courtesy Nyltite Corporation, South Plainfield, N.J.]

(a)

(b)

Figure 16-30 Self-drilling fasteners, known as TEKS® are shown. They drill their own hole, tap a mating thread, and then fasten, all in a single operation. [Courtesy Shakeproof, Division Illinois Tool Works, Inc.]

Figure 16-31 A standard helicoil insert used to prevent thread failures caused by high tensile and torsional stresses, eliminate corrosion and seizure, and prevent stripping. [Courtesy Heli-Coil Products, Division Mite Corporation.]

Thread-cutting screws, as the name implies, cut their own threads, thus eliminating the need for tapping. Basically, they cut threads because they are slotted off center, presenting a sharp acute cutting edge to the area being threaded. The screws shown in Figure 16-30 are typical and are used to cut threads in (a) metal, (b) castings, (c) plastics, (d) sheet metal, (e) wood.

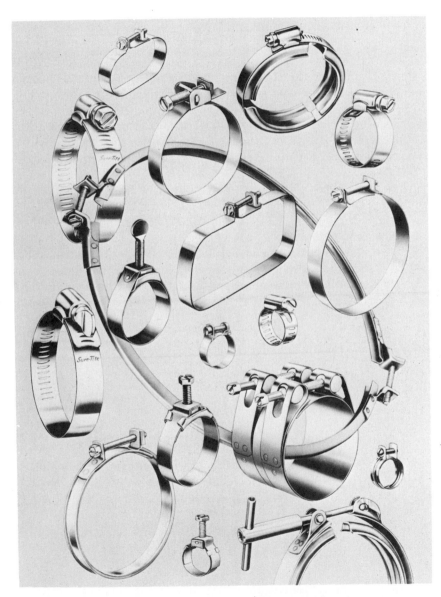

Figure 16-32 Various types of clamps. [Courtesy Wittek Manufacturing Company.]

Helicoil inserts are screw thread coils that are inserted into tapped holes to salvage threads which have been damaged or stripped. They may also be used to protect and strengthen tapped threads. A typical insert is shown in Figure 16-31. When helical inserts are used to replace a damaged thread, the following steps are generally followed.

1. A larger hole must be drilled.
2. This hole is then threaded by tapping.
3. The helicoil is inserted.

Other fasteners

Clamps are used to attach hoses, flexible plastic pipes, and ducts. Some examples of the wide variety of clamps available are shown in Figure 16-32.

Spring clips are relatively light duty fasteners that can perform multiple functions and are one piece devices that eliminate the need for handling several smaller parts. There are no standard clips because most are designed to meet specific requirements. Some typical spring clips are shown in Figure 16-33.

Pins are fastening devices, usually used in applications where the loading is primarily shear. They are useful in such applications as a hinge, shear pin, retaining shoulder, and so on. Some common examples of pins are shown in Figure 16-34.

Retaining rings, sometimes called snap rings provide a removable shoulder for accurately locating, retaining, or locking components on shafts and in bores and housings. Some applications for which retaining rings are used are shown in Figure 16-35.

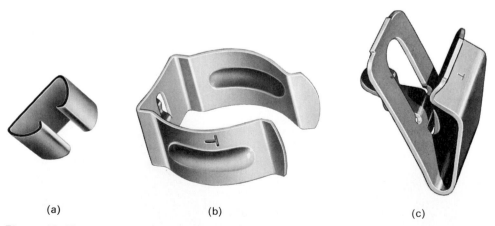

(a)   (b)   (c)

Figure 16-33   (a) The "C" clip is used for attaching plastic or die cast knobs. (b) A capacitor clip used as a fastener on electronic equipment. (c) A cable clip. [Courtesy Eaton, Yale, and Towne.]

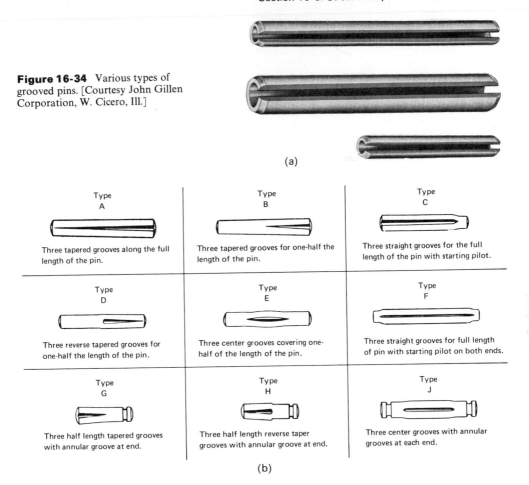

Figure 16-34 Various types of grooved pins. [Courtesy John Gillen Corporation, W. Cicero, Ill.]

(a)

Type
A

Three tapered grooves along the full length of the pin.

Type
B

Three tapered grooves for one-half the length of the pin.

Type
C

Three straight grooves for the full length of the pin with starting pilot.

Type
D

Three reverse tapered grooves for one-half the length of the pin.

Type
E

Three center grooves covering one-half of the length of the pin.

Type
F

Three straight grooves for full length of pin with starting pilot on both ends.

Type
G

Three half length tapered grooves with annular groove at end.

Type
H

Three half length reverse taper grooves with annular groove at end.

Type
J

Three center grooves with annular grooves at each end.

(b)

SECTION 16-8

Stress Analysis of Screws and Bolts

In doing a stress analysis of a bolt or screw, the first step is to calculate the required diameter by using the direct tension or compression formula,

$$\sigma = \frac{F}{A}$$

where F is the load to be supported and A is the cross-sectional area based upon the root diameter. If bending or column failure is possible, the diameter should be checked for these conditions.

Another possible method of failure would be the threads stripping. Figure 16-36 is an illustration of a nut and bolt being used to clamp two plates together. It is clear from an inspection of the figure that the length of engagement of the nut will affect the strength of threads in shear and bearing.

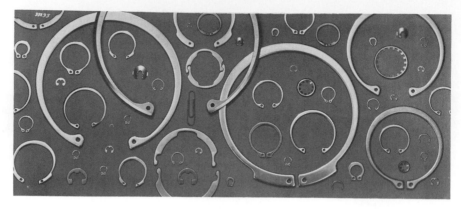

(a)

(b)

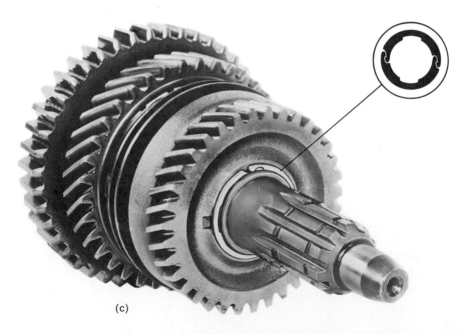

(c)

Figure 16-35 Opposite: (a) Representative ring types. "Internal" rings are used in bores and housings; "external" rings on shafts, studs, bosses, and similar parts.

(b) Automotive rocker arm. Two different types of retaining rings solved a critical problem for the manufacturer of this aluminum roller-tip needle bearing rocker arm for racing cars. The rings reduce the size and weight of the rocker arms and prevent costly field failures. The rocker arms oscillate through a 0.560-in. range at a frequency of up to 5000 times per minute. Because of the oscillation, the roller-tip must be secured in the housing with positive-locking fasteners that will resist inertia and vibration forces.

(c) Truck transmission. Two-part interlocking retaining ring secures third-speed gear on main shaft of truck transmission. Balanced to withstand high revolutions per minute the ring is installed radially in a deep groove on the shaft and must withstand heavy thrust loads created when the gear is engaged. The fastener also must remain secure against relative rotation which occurs when gear is disengaged and rotates at different speed from shaft. Ability to withstand wear and abrasion is another quality standard for the application.
[Courtesy Waldes Kohinoor, Inc., Long Island City, N.Y.]

If we assume that the threads take an equal share of the stress, equations (16-9), (16-10), and (16-11) can be used to calculate the shear stress on the screw and nut threads and the bearing stress between the threads.

$$\tau_{(\text{nut})} = \frac{F}{\pi d(h/2)} \tag{16-9}$$

$$\tau_{(\text{screw})} = \frac{F}{\pi d_r(h/2)} \tag{16-10}$$

$$\sigma_b = \frac{F}{(\pi/4)(d^2 - d_r^2)(h/p)} \tag{16-11}$$

where τ = shear stress, σ_b = bearing stress, d = outside diameter of screw, h = height of nut, d_r = root diameter of screw, and p = pitch of screw.

Unfortunately, the threads do not take an equal share of the load. In fact, a conservative estimate would be that one thread takes all the load. However, yielding of the threads will allow some of the load to be transferred to other threads. It would, therefore, be desirable to choose a soft nut material so that the yielding and consequent spreading of the load can take place.

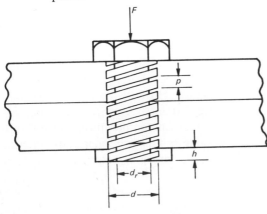

Figure 16-36 An illustration of a nut and bolt being used to clamp two plates together.

To sum up, because it is not clear how many of the threads are in engagement and can share the load, the designer can either assume all threads share the load equally (with this assumption, a large factor of safety should be used) or all of the load is taken by one thread (a very conservative assumption). In any event, a reasonable length of thread engagement can be approximated by the following rules of thumb.

1. For steel, the length should be at least equal to the outside diameter of the thread.
2. For cast iron, brass, or bronze the thread engagement should be at least $1\frac{1}{2}$ times the outside diameter of the thread.
3. For aluminum, zinc, or plastics it should be at least 2 times.

SECTION 16-9

Materials for Screws and Bolts

A designer has an almost endless choice when it comes to selecting the material of which a fastener is to be made. It is therefore imperative for the designer to choose the material to suit the particular application.

Some of the factors that must be evaluated are the following: What will be the environment in which the fastener is to be used? Should the material have special electrical or heat conductivity properties? Is the fastener to be opened and closed often? Will it be subjected to vibrations? Is weight going to be a factor? What is the life expectancy to be? And other similar questions.

The designer should also bear in mind that coatings may very often be applied to more economical materials so that they may be used in special applications, in place of a more expensive material. Table 16-2 lists the properties of some commonly used steel fasteners, as well as nonferrous fasteners. As an aid to the designer, the materials suggested in *Machine Design Fasteners* issue, which are typically used for certain kinds of fasteners, are presented in Table 16-3.

Steel is the material of which most fasteners are made. Table 16-4 lists some of the grades of SAE steel with the marking system used to identify the various grades. Aluminum is often used in fasteners because of its relative low weight, high electrical and heat conductivity, resistance to corrosion, and good appearance. Brass is a relatively inexpensive material, is quite malleable, can be given a very high finish, is nonmagnetic and is resistant to corrosion. Copper is extremely malleable, has very high electrical conductivity, and is very corrosion resistant. Nickel is corrosion resistant, does not discolor, and has good strength at high temperatures. Stainless steels are useful in applications where corrosion, temperature, and strength may be a problem. Finally, there are some nonmetallic materials, such as plastics, which are very corrosion resistant, are good electrical and heat insulators, and are relatively light weight.

Table 16-2   Properties of Commonly Used Metal Fasteners

C1015-C1018 Steel—Used for machine screws and wood screws, and specials where material is specified as low carbon and is not heat treated. The guaranteed minimum tensile strength is 55,000 psi. Low carbon steel is also used for sheet metal and thread-cutting screws where no mechanical properties are specified by the customer, but a case hardened surface is required.

C1019-C1021 Steel (Same as C1022 Steel)—Most parts made from these grades are sems and thread-cutting screws requiring high torque and toughness. These are killed steels in the medium low carbon group and have closely controlled mechanical properties such as tensile strength, hardenability, and torque.

C1029 Steel—Used in applications similar to C1038 when better cold working properties are needed.

C1038 Steel—This grade is considered a medium carbon steel and is used on Grade 5 bolts and special parts requiring a minimum tensile strength of 120,000 psi.

C1062 Steel—A high carbon grade with limited cold workability. It is used in applications where extremely high strength and high hardness (50 Rc and above) are required.

4037-H Alloy Steel—This grade is in the medium carbon, low alloy group. Parts made of 4037-H have a high yield to tensile strength ratio and very consistent properties. Used for Grade 7 and Grade 8 bolts and special applications requiring 133,000 psi minimum tensile strength.

Brass—An alloy of copper and zinc, brass is a tough, rustless, non-magnetic material possessing mechanical properties similar to low carbon steel. It can be easily formed into intricate shapes and is relatively inexpensive compared to other copper base alloys.

Copper—Copper in various grades such as Electrolytic Tough Pitch, Oxygen Free and Tellurium bearing is used extensively in architectural, automotive, electrical, and hardware applications. It can be easily formed by many methods and has relatively high corrosion resistance.

Silicon Bronze—High tensile strength superior to mild steel. It has corrosion resistance to salt and fresh water, atmospheric conditions and a variety of industrial gases and chemicals. It can be readily cold worked and is non-magnetic and non-sparking.

T305 Stainless Steel (18-8)—Has excellent corrosion resistance, heat resistance and high mechanical properties but has a fairly high rate of work hardening. This enables parts only with rather modest upsets to be made. This type has slightly better corrosion resistance than 16-18 and is lower in cost.

16-18 Stainless Steel—Type 16-18 stainless is a modified austenitic chrome-nickel steel that is particularly useful for cold-headed and upset parts because it work hardens much slower than any of the conventional T305 (18-8) analyses. Type 16-18 resists a wide variety of organic and inorganic chemicals and food-stuffs. Its corrosion resistance compares to the 300 series.

T410 Stainless Steel—The most widely used of all hardenable types of corrosion resisting steels. It is capable of attaining high mechanical properties when heat treated. For maximum corrosion resistance, T410 should be used in the hardened condition. Since it is also ductile and workable, it is particularly suited to cold heading. Not recommended for applications in which severe corrosion is encountered.

T430 Stainless Steel—A ductile, non-hardening stainless steel exhibiting mechanical properties higher than mild steel with good resistance to general corrosion and oxidation at temperatures up to 1400°F. All forms are magnetic.

Aluminum—While there are many grades of aluminum used, the most common for us is 2024. It actually meets the tensile strength of mild steel at only $\frac{1}{3}$ the weight, 2024 is fabricated in the H-13 temper but heat treated to T-4 temper in finished stage.

Nickel #400 (Monel)—Monel is approximately $\frac{2}{3}$ Nickel and $\frac{1}{3}$ copper with a small amount of iron. Monel makes an excellent fastener material because of its high strength, resistance to heat and corrosion and good cold workability. Monel has wide use in chemical, electrical, marine and construction applications.

Grade ▶	1100	2024-T4	6061-T6
Aluminum Alloys Composition ▶	Al, 99.0 min	Cu, 3.8-4.9 Mn, 0.3-0.9 Mg, 1.2-1.8 Al, Balance	Mg, 0.8-1.2 Si, 0.4-0.8 Cu, 0.15-0.40 Cr, 0.15-0.35 Al, Balance
Physical properties Density lb/in.^{3}	0.098	0.100	0.098
Melting temperature range, °F	1190-1215	935-1180	1080-1200
Ther cond. (77°F, ann) Btu/hr/ft/°F/ft	128	111	99
Coef of therm. exp (68-212°F) per °F	13.1×10^{-6}	12.6×10^{-6}	13.0×10^{-6}
Spec heat (212°F) Btu/lb/°F	0.22	0.22	0.23
Elec res (68°F) microhm—cm annealed	2.92	3.45 (0), 5.75 (T4)	3.8 (0)
Mechanical properties Tensile strength	13,000	55,000 (T4)	45,000 (T6)
Yield strength (0.2% elong)	5,000	50,000 (T4)	40,000 (T6)
Hardness (Rockwell)	F20-25	B53-64	B60

Grade ▶	Monel	Inconel
Nickel Alloys Composition ▶	Ni, 66 Fe, 1.35 Cu, 31.5	Ni, 77.0 Cr, 15.0 Fe, 7.0
Physical properties Density lb/in.^{3}	0.319	0.304
Melting temp. Range, °F	2370-2460	2540-2600
Ther cond (80-212) BTU/hr/ft^2/°F/ft	15	8.7
Coef of ther exp (77-212), per °F	7.8×10^{-6}	6.4×10^{-6}
Spec ht (70-750°F) Btu/lb/°F	0.127	0.109
Elec res (68°F) microhm-cm	482	98.1
Magnetic	Slightly magnetic	Nonmagnetic
Mechanical properties Tensile strength	80,000 min.	80,000 min.
Yield strength (0.2% offset)	60,000 min.	45,000 min.
Hardness	B90	B72 min.

Table 16-2 (continued)

Grade		0	1	2	3	5	8
Steel	Material ▶	1010 1012 1015 1018	1010 1015 1018	1015 1018 1020	1030 1035 1038	1035 1038 1040 1045	8635 8640 4140 4037
Physical properties							
Density lb/in.³		0.283	0.283	0.283	0.283	0.283	0.283
Melting temp range, °F		2750–2775	2750–2775	2750–2775	2700–2750	2700–2750	–
Coef of ther exp (70–1200°F), per °F		8.4 × 10⁻⁶	8.4 × 10⁻⁶	8.4 × 10⁻⁶	8.3 × 10⁻⁶	8.3 × 10⁻⁶	8.3 × 10⁻⁶
Spec ht, Btu/lb/°F		0.10–0.11	0.10–0.11	0.10–0.11	0.10–0.11	0.10–0.11	0.10–0.11
Elec res (68 F), microhm-cm		14.3	14.3	14.3	19	19	19
Magnetic		Yes	Yes	Yes	Yes	Yes	Yes
Mechanical properties							
Tensile strength		No req.	55,000	69,000	110,000	120,000	150,000
Yield strength		–	–	55,000	85,000	85,000	120,000
Brinell hardness		–	207 max	241 max	207–269	241–302	302–352
Rockwell hardness		–	B95 max	B100 max	B95–104	C23–32	C32–38
Other requirements		–	–	–	Stress Relieved	Min. tempering temp. 800°F	Min. tempering temp. 800°F

Copper Alloys	Grade ▶	Copper (Electrolytic Tough Pitch)	Yellow Brass	Cartridge Brass	Commercial Bronze
Physical properties	Composition ▶	Cu, 99.9 min. O₂, 0.04	Cu, 63–68.5 Zn, Bal	Cu, 68.5–71.5 Zn, Bal	Cu, 89–91 Zn, Bal
Density lb/in.³		0.321–0.323	0.306	0.308	0.318
Melting temp range °F		1949–1981	1660–1710	1680–1750	1870–1910
Ther cond (77°F, ann) Btu/hr/ft² /°F/ft		226	67	70	109
Coef of ther exp (68–572°F) per °F		9.8 × 10⁻⁶	11.3 × 10⁻⁶	11.1 × 10⁻⁶	10.2 × 10⁻⁶
Spec heat (68°F) Btu/lb/°F		0.092	0.09	0.09	0.09
Elec res (68°F)microhm-cm		1.71	6.4	6.2	3.9
Mechanical Properties					
Tensile strength		35,000–45,000	60,000 min	60,000 min	45,000 min
Yield strength (0.5% elong)		10,000–35,000	40,000 min	40,000 min	40,000 min
Rockwell hardness		F40–80	B55–65	B55–65	B40–50

Copper Alloys	Grade ▶	Naval Bronze	Low Silicon Bronze B	High Silicon Bronze A	Phosphor Bronze A
Physical properties	Composition ▶	Cu, 62–65 Sn, 0.5–1.0 Zn, Balance	Cu, 96 Min Si, 0.8–2.0 Zn, 1.5 Max	Cu, 94.8 Min Si, 2.7–3.75	Cu, 95 Sn, 3.5–5.8 P, 0.03–0.35
Density lb/in.³		0.304	0.316	0.308	0.320
Melting temp range °F		1630–1650	1890–1940	1780–1880	1750–1920
Ther cond (77°F, ann) Btu/hr/ft³ /°F/ft		67	33	–	47
Coef of ther exp (68–572°F) per °F		11.8 × 10⁻⁶	9.9 × 10⁻⁶	10 × 10⁻⁶	9.9 × 10⁻⁶
Spec heat (68°F) Btu/lb/°F		0.09	0.09	0.09	0.09
Elec res (68°F) microhm cm		6.6	14.4	24.6	9.6
Mechanical Properties					
Tensile strength		50,000 min	70,000 min	70,000 min	70,000 min
Yield strength (0.5% elong)		30,000 min	35,000 min	38,000 min	40,000 min
Rockwell hardness		B45–55	B65–75	B74–80	B70–80

Table 16-2 (continued)

Grade			305	16-18	12-15	410	430
Stainless Steel	Approximate Chemical ▶ Composition		C 0.12 max Mn 2.00 max Si 1.00 max Cr 17.00–19.00 Ni 10.00–13.00	C 0.08 max Mn 0.50 max Si 0.50 max Cr 16.00–18.00 Ni 14.50–18.50	C 0.08 max Mn 2.00 max Si 1.00 max Cr 11.50–13.00 Ni 14.00–16.00	C 0.15 max Mn 1.00 max Si 1.00 max Cr 11.50–13.50	C 0.12 max Mn 1.00 max Si 1.00 max Cr 14.00–18.00
Physical properties							
Density lb/in.^{3}			0.29	0.29	0.29	0.28	0.28
Mean coefficient of thermal expansion per °F × 10^{-6} 32–212°F			9.6	–	–	5.5	5.8
32–600°F			9.9	–	–	5.6	6.1
32–1000°F			10.2	–	–	6.4	6.3
32–1200°F			10.4	10.4	10.45	6.5	6.6
Melting point range			2550–2650°F	–	–	2700–2790°F	2600–2750°F
Magnetism (*in fully annealed condition)			*Nonmagnetic	*Nonmagnetic	*Nonmagnetic	Magnetic	Magnetic
Mechanical properties							
Brinell, Hardness Annealed			130–150	130–150	100–130	135–165	140–160
Ultimate, Tensile strength, psi							
Annealed			80,000–95,000	70,000–90,000	70,000–90,000	65,000–85,000	70,000–90,000
Cold worked			100,000–180,000	85,000–160,000	80,000–160,000	100,000	90,000–130,000
Yield, point, psi							
Annealed			35,000–45,000	30,000–40,000	25,000–35,000	35,000–45,000	40,000–55,000
Cold worked			50,000–150,000	45,000–120,000	45,000–120,000	85,000	65,000–130,000
Elongation in 2 in.							
Annealed			60–55%	60–50%	60–50%	30–20%	30–20%
Heat resistance							
Scaling temperature							
Continuous service			1600°F	1600°F	–	1250°F	1500°F
Intermittent service			1450°F	1450°F	–	1400°F	1600°F
Cold-heading properties			Fair to good	Good	Good	Good	Good
Corrosion resistance			Very good resistance to atmosphere. Good resistance to many organic and inorganic chemicals.	Similar to 305	Excellent resistance to atmosphere and weathering. Resistance to organic and inorganic chemicals. Superior to type 430 but is not equal to that of type 304, 305 or 16-18.	In both the hardened and unhardened condition it has very good resistance to atmosphere, water, carbonic acid, crude oil, gasoline, blood, perspiration, alcohol, amonia, mercury, soap, sugar solutions and many other reagents	Excellent resistance to weather, water, good resistance to most chemicals and food products.

SOURCE: Elco Industries, Rockford, Ill.

Table 16-3 Materials for Typical Applications

Material	Application
Steel	
SAE 1010	Useful for low strength requirements, such as carriage bolts and machine screws
SAE 1018, 1020, 1021	Cap screws
SAE 1038	High strength cap screws and bolts
Aluminum	
2024-T4	Machine screw nuts, cold formed bolts, rivets
2011-T3	Screws and bolts
1100	Cold formed rivets
Brass	
Yellow brass	Cold-headed bolts, screws, rivets
Bronze	
Commercial bronze	Cold-headed bolts, screws, rivets
Naval bronze	Hot-forged bolts, cold formed bolts, nuts
Copper	
High-silicon bronze	Hot-forged bolts, nuts, set screws
Low-silicon bronze	Cold-formed bolts, nuts, rivets, screws
Nickel	
Monel	Bolts, nuts, screws, rivets
Nickel	For applications involving contamination, high and subzero temperature operation
Inconel	For applications requiring resistance to oxidation at high temperatures
Stainless steel	
Martensite	Used in magnetic applications, and those requiring hardenability
Ferritic	Used for economic reasons and for those applications where extreme corrosion resistance is not necessary
Austenitic	Best corrosion resistance
Non metallic	
Nylon	Used for applications requiring good insulation and resistance to heat, shock, and vibration, and chemical solvents
Polyvinyl chloride	Used for applications exposed to outdoor weathering
Teflon	Used when resistance to corrosion and high temperature is important

Table 16-4 Grade and Material Identification Markings Required by SAE and GM Specifications

Identification Mark	Grade Designation	Fastener Description	Material	Is Mfr's Identification Symbol Required?	Nominal Size Range, in.	Mechanical Properties			Hardness		Remarks
						Proof Load, psi	Yield Strength, min. psi	Tensile Strength, min. psi	Brinell	Rockwell	
No Mark	SAE grade 0	Bolts and screws	Steel	Yes	$\frac{1}{4}$ to $1\frac{1}{2}$	—	—	—	—		
No Mark	SAE grade 1	Bolts and screws	Carbon steel	Yes	$\frac{1}{4}$ to $1\frac{1}{2}$	—	—	55,000	207 max.	B95 max.	Equivalent to ASTM A307, grade A
	GM 255-M	Bolts and screws	Carbon steel	Optional							
No Mark	SAE grade 2	Bolts and screws	Carbon steel	Yes	$\frac{1}{4}$ to $\frac{1}{2}$ / over $\frac{1}{2}$ to $\frac{3}{4}$	55,000 / 52,000	—	69,000 / 64,000	241 max. / 241 max.	B100 max. / B100 max.	
	GM 260-M	Bolts and Screws	Carbon steel	Optional	over $\frac{3}{4}$ to $1\frac{1}{2}$	28,000	—	55,000	207 max.	B95 max.	
(one line mark)	SAE Grade 3	Bolts and Screws	Medium carbon steel	Yes	$\frac{1}{4}$ to $\frac{1}{2}$ / over $\frac{1}{2}$ to $\frac{5}{8}$	85,000 / 80,000	—	110,000 / 100,000	207/269 / 207/269	B95/104 / B95/104	
(Y mark)	SAE Grade 5	Bolts and Screws	Medium carbon steel, heat treated	Yes	$\frac{1}{4}$ to $\frac{3}{4}$ / over $\frac{3}{4}$ to 1	85,000 / 78,000	81,000	120,000 / 115,000	241/302 / 235/302	C23/32 / C22/32	Equivalent to ASTM A449
	GM 280-M	Bolts and screws		Optional	over 1 to $1\frac{1}{2}$	74,000	77,000	105,000	223/285	C19/30	
(three line mark)	SAE grade 5.1	Sems	Carbon steel, heat treated	Yes	$\frac{3}{8}$ and smaller	85,000	—	120,000	241/375	C23/40	
	GM 275-M	Sems		Optional							
(cross mark)	SAE grade 6	Bolts and screws	Medium carbon steel, heat treated	Yes	$\frac{1}{4}$ to $\frac{5}{8}$ / over $\frac{5}{8}$ to $\frac{3}{4}$	110,000 / 105,000	—	140,000 / 133,000	285/331 / 269/331	C30/36 / C28/36	
(X mark)	SAE grade 7	Bolts and screws	Low alloy steel, heat treated	Yes	$\frac{1}{4}$ to $1\frac{1}{2}$	105,000	110,000	133,000	269/321	C28/34	Threads rolled after heat treatment
	GM 290-M	Bolts and screws		Optional							
(asterisk mark)	SAE grade 8	Bolts and screws	Low alloy steel, heat treated	Yes	$\frac{1}{4}$ to $1\frac{1}{2}$	120,000	125,000	150,000	302/352	C32/38	Equivalent to ASTM A354, grade BD
	GM 300-M	Bolts and screws		Optional							
(one line mark)	GM 455-M	Bolts and screws	Corrosion resistant steel	Optional	$\frac{1}{4}$ to $1\frac{1}{2}$	40,000	—	55,000	143 min.	B79 min.	

SOURCE: Camcar

SECTION 16-10

Preload and Tightening Torque on Bolts

In general, when bolts are used to connect two parts, the strength of the joint depends, among other factors, on the preload applied. The benefits of a preload are especially pronounced in applications involving fatigue loading. The parts to be connected may or may not be separated by a gasket. In this section we will consider the situation when no gasket is used.

Consider the bolt and nut shown in Figure 16-37. The parts are subjected to an external tensile load F_e and external shear load F_s. F_i is the initial

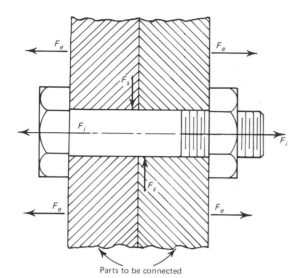

Figure 16-37 The sketch shows two plates being clamped together by a nut and bolt. Shown are the preload, F_i, external tensile load, F_e, and shear load F_s.

Parts to be connected

tensile load placed in the bolt by tightening the nut before the external forces act. Clearly, the preload produces compression between the parts and thus creates sufficient friction between the parts to resist the shear load. Obviously, without this frictional resistance the bolt would be subjected to shear and bearing loads in addition to the tensile loads.

The most important factor that determines the preload induced in a bolt is the torque applied to tighten the bolt. There are several methods commonly used to apply a predetermined torque. The torque may be applied manually by means of a wrench which has a dial attachment that indicates the magnitude of torque being applied. Pneumatic air wrenches are also widely used. In this method the air pressure is cut off automatically when the desired torque is obtained. Another method is to tighten the nut by hand and then to use a wrench to give the nut a predetermined number of turns. Unfortunately, a wide range of torques can result from the use of the techniques described above.

Empirical equation (16-12) can be used to give reasonably accurate results for the relationship between induced preload and applied torque.

$$T = cdF_i \qquad (16\text{-}12)$$

where

T = applied torque, in.-lb
c = torque coefficient
d = nominal bolt diameter, in.
F_i = initial preload, lb

The value for the torque coefficient for dry surfaces and unlubricated bolts is taken as 0.2, and for lubricated bolts a value of 0.15 is suggested.

If a more exact value is required, equation (16-13) can be used to calculate the torque coefficient.

$$c = \frac{d_m}{2d}\left(\frac{\mu_t \sec \phi + \tan \psi}{1 - \mu_t \sec \phi \tan \psi}\right) + \mu_c\frac{d_c}{2d} \tag{16-13}$$

where

d_m = mean bolt diameter, in.
d = nominal bolt diameter, in.
d_c = mean bearing face or collar diameter, in.
μ_t = bolt thread coefficient of friction
μ_c = coefficient of friction at bearing face of bolt or nut
ϕ = thread half angle, deg
ψ = thread helix angle, deg

A comparison of this equation with the power screw equation, (15-5), will immediately make obvious that they are essentially the same.

The determination of the exact tightening torque required in a particular problem can probably best be determined experimentally. In other words, a prototype can be built and accurate torque testing equipment used on it.

SECTION 16-11

Elastic Analysis and Fatigue Loading

Before considering the effect of preloading with regard to fatigue loads, it is necessary to consider what portion of the externally applied load is taken up by the bolt and what portion by the connected parts.

We will now define a spring or stiffness constant. The stiffness constant is defined in the same way as the spring constant is for springs. Namely, it is the ratio of the force applied to the deflection caused by the applied force. In equation form

$$k = \frac{F}{\delta} = \frac{F}{Fl/AE} = \frac{AE}{l} \tag{16-14}$$

where

k = stiffness constant, lb/in.
A = cross-sectional area, in.^{2}
E = modulus of elasticity, lb/in.^{2}
l = length, in.

Referring to the situation shown in Figure 16-37, let us assume that the preload, or initial tensile load F_i, has been applied. Both the bolt and the parts will undergo a deformation due to this load, the bolt increasing in length while the parts contract (see Figure 16-38). At this point the external load F_e is applied, as shown. The result is an increase in the length of the

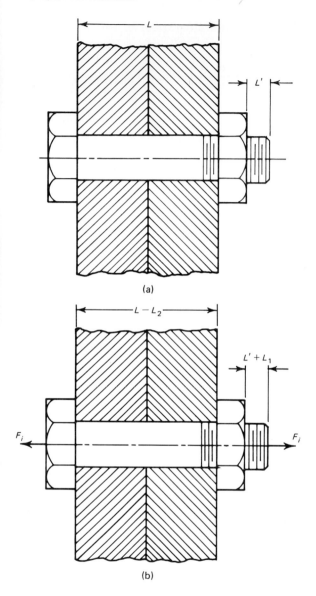

(a)

(b)

Figure 16-38 (a) The plates to be clamped by the nut and bolt are shown. There is no preload, no stress in plates or bolt. The length of the plates is L and the length of the bolt extending beyond the nut is L'. (b) After the preload is applied (by turning the nut against the plate), the length of the plates has been reduced by L_2 and the portion of the bolt extending beyond the nut has been increased by L_1. L_1 is greater than L_2. Clearly, the plates are subjected to a compressive stress while the bolt is subjected to a tensile stress.

bolt equal to F_{e_b}/k_b and a decrease in deformation of the parts equal to F_{e_p}/k_p. These two changes in deformation must be equal, unless the parts have separated. Clearly, if the external force is large enough to separate the parts, all of the load will be taken by the bolt. Assuming separation has not occurred,

$$\frac{F_{e_b}}{k_b} = \frac{F_{e_p}}{k_p}$$

also

$$F_e = F_{e_b} + F_{e_p}$$

$$F_{e_b} = F_{e_p}\frac{k_b}{k_p} = \frac{k_b}{k_p}(F_e - F_{e_b})$$

$$= \frac{k_b}{k_b + k_p}F_e$$

and similarly

$$F_{e_p} = \frac{k_p}{k_b + k_p}F_e$$

The total force on the bolt is then

$$F_b = F_{e_b} + F_i$$

or

$$F_b = \frac{k_bF_e}{k_b + k_p} + F_i \tag{16-15}$$

and the total compressive load on the parts is

$$F_p = F_{e_p} - F_i$$

$$= \frac{k_p}{k_b + k_p}F_e - F_i \tag{16-16}$$

The use of an initial or preload is extremely helpful in problems for which the bolt is subjected to fluctuating loads, and also to maintain a seal in pressure vessels, especially when a gasket cannot be used. Although the maximum load on the bolt is greater because of the preload, the minimum load is also greater. As a result, the average load is greater, but the range component is reduced. Because the stress concentration factor is applied to the range component, the reduced range stress results in a much better stress situation. The average and range components of the bolt force are obtained by substituting $F_{e(av)}$ and $F_{e(range)}$ in place of F_e in equation (16-15).

$$F_{b(max)} = \frac{k_bF_{e(max)}}{k_b + k_p} + F_i$$

$$F_{b(min)} = \frac{k_bF_{e(min)}}{k_b + k_p} + F_i$$

$$F_{b(av)} = \frac{F_{b(max)} + F_{b(min)}}{2} = \frac{k_bF_{e(av)}}{k_b + k_p} + F_i$$

$$F_{b(r)} = \frac{F_{b(max)} - F_{b(min)}}{2} = \frac{k_bF_{e(r)}}{k_b + k_p}$$

$F_{b(av)}$ and $F_{b(r)}$ are now used to calculate σ_r and σ_{av}. The fluctuating load analysis previously discussed is then used to complete the problem.

A final word of caution: if the preload is allowed to become too large, a detrimental stress situation may result.

Example 16-6. In order to demonstrate the importance of the preload in fatigue loaded bolts, let us consider the following problem.

The bolt shown in Figure 16-39 is a $\frac{5}{8}$-in. coarse threaded bolt. The parts it connects are subjected to a load F_e that fluctuates from 1000 to 8000 lb. The bolt and the parts being connected are made of the same material. Assume the bolt material has a yield strength of 70,000 psi and an endurance limit of 30,000 psi. Assume that the stress concentration factor for the threads is 3.8 (from Figure B-1 in Appendix B).

(a) Is the bolt safe for continuous action? (b) If the preload is 10,000 lb is it safe for continuous action? (c) If the preload is 16,000 lb is the bolt safe for continuous action?

Solution: *Part a.*

$$F_{e(av)} = \frac{1000 + 8000}{2} = 4500 \text{ lb}$$

$$F_{e_r} = \frac{8000 - 1000}{2} = 3500 \text{ lb}$$

$$\text{stress area} = 0.226 \text{ in.}^2$$

$$\sigma_{av} = \frac{4500}{0.226} = 19,000 \text{ psi}$$

$$K\sigma_r = \frac{3.8 \times 3500}{0.226} = 58,800 \text{ psi}$$

A plot of the stresses shown in Figure 16-40 indicates that failure will occur.

Part b. Because the bolt is only threaded just enough to permit the nut to engage, the gross area should be used to determine the stiffness constant.

$$A_b = \frac{\pi}{4}(\tfrac{5}{8})^2 = 0.31 \text{ in.}^2$$

$$k_b = \frac{A_b E_b}{l_b} = \frac{0.31 E}{l}$$

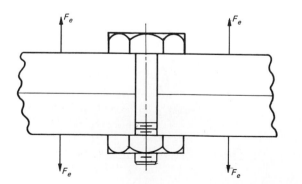

Figure 16-39

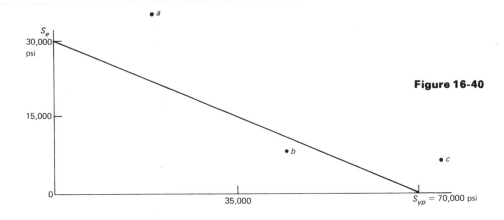

Figure 16-40

The area of the parts to be used to obtain their stiffness constant, is rather difficult to determine. A reasonable approximation might be to assume it to be annular in cross sectional area having an outside diameter three times the bolt diameter and an inside diameter equal to the bolt diameter

$$A_p = \frac{\pi}{4}[(3 \times \tfrac{5}{8})^2 - (\tfrac{5}{8})^2] = 2.47 \text{ in.}^2$$

$$k_p = \frac{A_p E_p}{l} = \frac{2.47E}{l}$$

$$F_{b(av)} = \frac{k_b F_{e(av)}}{k_b + k_p} + F_i$$

$$= \frac{\dfrac{0.31E}{l} 4500}{\dfrac{0.31E}{l} + \dfrac{2.47E}{l}} + 10{,}000 = 10{,}502 \text{ lb}$$

$$\sigma_{b(av)} = \frac{10{,}502}{0.226} = 46{,}500 \text{ psi}$$

$$F_{b(r)} = \frac{k_b F_{e(r)}}{k_b + k_p} = \frac{0.31 \times 3500}{0.31 + 2.47} = 390 \text{ lb}$$

$$K\sigma_r = \frac{3.8 \times 390}{0.226} = 6550 \text{ psi}$$

A plot on the stress diagram shows the bolt is now safe. In other words, with nothing changed in the problem except the addition of a preload, the bolt went from an unsafe to a safe condition.

Part c.

$$F_{b(av)} = \frac{k_b F_{e(av)}}{k_b + k_p} + F_i = \frac{0.31 \times 4500}{0.31 + 2.47} + 16{,}000$$

$$= 16{,}502 \text{ lb}$$

$$\sigma_{b(av)} = \frac{16{,}502}{0.226} = 73{,}000 \text{ psi}$$

$$F_{b(r)} = \frac{k_b F_{e(r)}}{k_b + k_p} = \frac{0.31 \times 3500}{0.31 + 2.47} = 390$$

$$K\sigma_r = \frac{3.8 \times 390}{0.226} = 6550 \text{ psi}$$

A plot on the stress diagram now shows failure will occur. This demonstrates that if the preload is made too large, failure will also occur. ●

SECTION 16-12

Analysis When Gaskets Are Used With the Connected Parts

There are applications for which a sealing or gasketing material must be placed between the parts to be connected. Figure 16-41 shows a bolted connection with a gasket placed between the parts. If the gasket is made of a soft material, a greater proportion of the externally applied load acts on the bolt. Clearly, the stiffer and thinner the gasket, the better.

The total load on the bolt can be calculated from equation (16-17).

$$F_b = CF_e + F_i \qquad (16\text{-}17)$$

where C is a stiffness coefficient and can be determined by using equation (16-18).

$$C = \frac{k_b}{k_b + k_c} \qquad (16\text{-}18)$$

where k_c is a combined elastic constant depending on the different types of material being clamped. The combined constant can be obtained from equation (16-19).

$$\frac{1}{k_c} = \frac{1}{k_1} + \frac{1}{k_2} + \cdots \qquad (16\text{-}19)$$

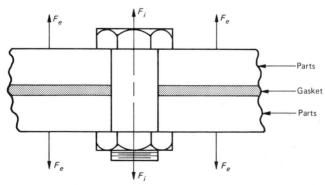

Figure 16-41 An example of two parts to be connected by a nut and bolt and separated by a gasket.

where k_1, k_2, and so on, are the elastic constants for the different materials For example, in the connection shown in Figure 16-41, k_c is found from

$$\frac{1}{k_c} = \frac{1}{k_g} + \frac{1}{k_p}$$

where k_g is the elastic constant of the gasket and k_p is the elastic constant of the connected parts.

In many applications, the stiffness of the connected parts is so great compared to the stiffness of the gasket, that the k_p can be ignored.

PROBLEMS

1. Two rectangular plates are to be joined by a lap joint. The plates are 15 in. wide and $\frac{3}{8}$ in. thick. The rivets are $\frac{7}{8}$ in. diameter, and the working stresses are as follows: tension, 18,000 psi; bearing, 27,000 psi; and shear 13,500 psi. Design a joint for maximum possible efficiency.

2. Design a butt joint, having maximum efficiency, for two tension members, each 12 in. wide and $\frac{5}{8}$ in. thick. The rivet diameters and working stresses are the same as in Problem 1.

3. A longitudinal lap joint is to be used to manufacture a boiler having $\frac{1}{4}$-in. thick plates. Two rows of rivets are to be used. The rivet diameters are $\frac{1}{2}$ in., and the rivets in each row are spaced $1\frac{1}{2}$ in. apart. Determine the efficiency of the joint if the working stresses are as follows: tension, 18,000 psi; bearing, 24,000 psi; shear, 13,500 psi. What change would you make to improve the efficiency of the joint?

4. A boiler with $\frac{5}{16}$-in. thick plates is to be spliced by means of a lap joint. The $\frac{3}{4}$-in. rivets are arranged in three rows with the rivets in the two outer rows spaced 4 in. apart and those in the middle row 2 in. apart. Determine the efficiency of the joint if the working stresses are as follows: tension, 16,000 psi; bearing, 24,000 psi; and shear, 12,000 psi.

5. A boiler having $\frac{3}{8}$-in. thick plates is to be spliced longitudinally by a double riveted lap joint. The rivets, which are $\frac{7}{8}$ in. diameter, are spaced $2\frac{1}{2}$ in. apart in each row. If the boiler is to contain steam at a pressure of 80 psi and have a diameter of 6 ft, determine the tensile, bearing, and shearing stresses.

6. A double riveted, longitudinal lap joint is to be used to splice a boiler having $\frac{5}{16}$-in. thick plates. The $\frac{5}{8}$-in. diameter rivets are spaced 2 in. apart in each row. Determine the efficiency of the joint if the working stresses are as follows: tension, 18,000 psi; bearing, 24,000; and shear, 13,500 psi. The rivet holes have been drilled.

7. A gas tank is to be made of $\frac{3}{8}$-in. thick plates, formed into a cylinder 8 ft in diameter. The rivet holes are drilled to accommodate $\frac{5}{8}$-in. diameter rivets. The longitudinal lap joint is to have three rows of rivets, arranged so that the rivets in the outer rows are spaced 4 in. apart and those in the inner row are 2 in. apart. Determine the efficiency if the working stresses are as follows: tension, 18,000 psi; bearing, 27,000 psi; and shear, 13,500 psi. What will be the magnitude of the maximum allowable pressure?

8. Determine the maximum rivet load for the eccentrically loaded connection shown in Problem Figure 8.

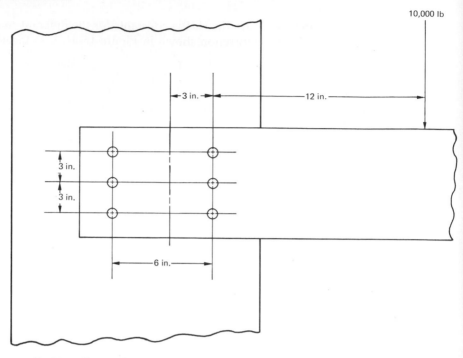

Problem Figure 8

9. A column supports an eccentric load by means of two plates attached to opposite ends of flanges as shown in Problem Figure 9. For an allowable shear stress of 16,000 psi, what size rivet is required?

10. A 1-in. thick steel plate is attached to a column by the unsymmetrical riveted joint as shown in Problem Figure 10. The rivets are 1 in. in diameter. Determine the total stress in the worst stressed rivet under the eccentric loading.

11. In Problem Figure 11, a gusset plate is attached to a vertical column by four rivets. Determine the required rivet diameter if the allowable shear stress is 15,000 psi.

12. In Problem Figure 12 the fitting is to be bolted to a plate by means of three equal size bolts spaced as shown. All parts are made of medium carbon steel, quenched and tempered, having a tensile strength of 125,000 psi and a yield strength of 90,000 psi. A minimum factor of safety of 1.75 is required. Determine bolt diameter required.

13. In Problem Figure 13, three bolts ($\frac{3}{4}$-10) are used to connect the seat shown to a vertical column. If the working stresses for the bolt are 20,000 psi for tension and 12,000 psi for shear, will the bolts be satisfactory?

14. A torque wrench reads 240 in.-lb when it is used to tighten a $\frac{5}{8}$-11 nut on a flange. Assuming 20% of the input torque is needed to overcome the friction under the head of the nut, what is the tensile stress in the bolt if the threads have a coefficient of friction of 0.1.

15. A pipe flange is connected by the turned down bolt shown in Problem Figure 15. The $\frac{3}{4}$-10 bolt is turned down to its root diameter and, after tightening, its length is increased by 0.005 in. What is the preload in the bolt?

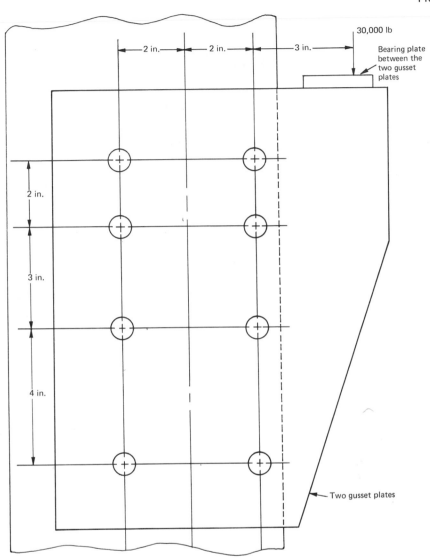

Problem Figure 9

16. For the bolted connection shown in Problem Figure 16, the bolt is $\frac{3}{4}$-10. For a preload of 1500 lb and an external load of 3000 lb, what is the total force on the bolt? The bolt and part are made of the same material, and the part has an area of 1.3 in.^{2}

17. For the bolt of Problem 16, assume the external load fluctuates between 4000 and 10,000 lb. The bolt and the parts are made of the same material, and the part has an area of 1.3 in.^{2} Use a factor of safety of 2, $S_e = 60,000$ psi, and $S_{yp} = 100,000$ psi. (a) Is the bolt safe for continuous operation? (b) If a preload of 8000 lb is applied, is the bolt safe? (c) Is the bolt safe with a preload of 12,000 lb? (d) What is the value for the minimum force in the part for the preload of part (b)?

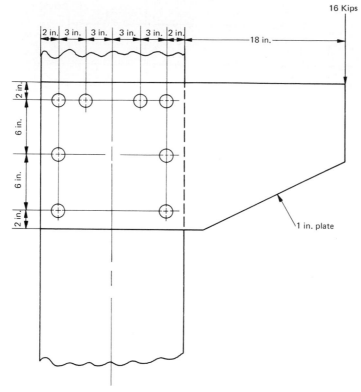

Problem Figure 10

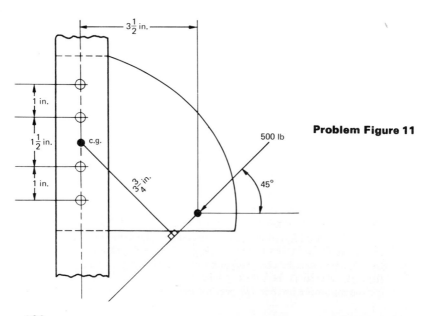

Problem Figure 11

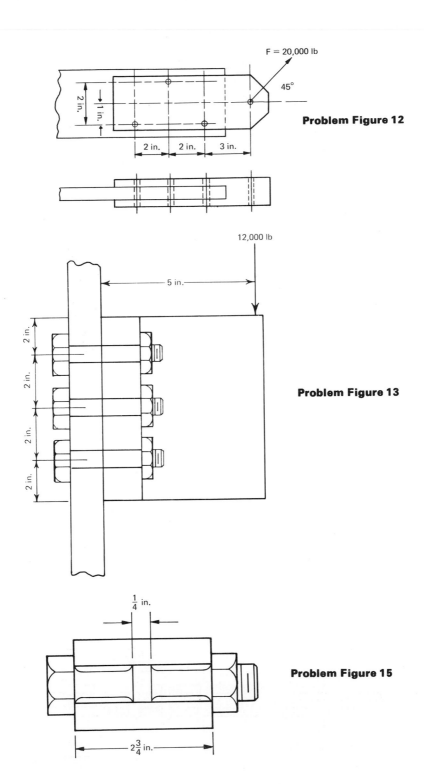

F = 20,000 lb

45°

2 in.

1 in.

2 in. | 2 in. | 3 in.

Problem Figure 12

12,000 lb

5 in.

2 in.

2 in.

2 in.

2 in.

Problem Figure 13

$\frac{1}{4}$ in.

$2\frac{3}{4}$ in.

Problem Figure 15

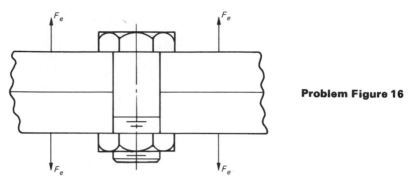

Problem Figure 16

18. For a connection similar to that in Problem 16, the external force varies from 2000 to 3000 lb. The bolt is $\frac{1}{2}$-13 UNC, bolt and part are made of the same material, $S_{yp} = 100,000$ psi, $S_e = 60,000$ psi. Assuming an initial load of 3600 lb is applied to the bolt and parts, determine the factor of safety for the bolt. The cross-sectional area of the parts may be taken as 0.6 in.^{2}

19. In Problem 18 determine the maximum permissible value of the preload, if the factor of safety is to be 1.5.

20. In Problem 17, determine the maximum and minimum values for the external load, if the preload is 5000 lb and the range stress, $\sigma_r = 5000$ psi.

21. The bolt shown in the Problem Figure 16 is used to connect two plates of the same thickness but made of different materials. The bolt is $\frac{1}{2}$-13, one plate is made of a material having a modulus of elasticity of 15,000,000 psi, and the material of the other plate has a modulus of 30,000,000 psi. A preload of 6000 lb is applied to the bolt. If the external force varies from 0 to 3000 lb, and $S_{yp} = 100,000$ psi, $S_e = 60,000$ psi for the bolt, what will be the factor of safety?

22. A boiler drum has a diameter of 90 in. and has the longitudinal butt connection shown in Problem Figure 22. The rivet diameters are $\frac{7}{8}$ in., and the holes are drilled. The design stresses are as follows: tension, 20,000 psi; shear, 12,000 psi; bearing, 24,000 psi. Determine the maximum internal pressure and the joint efficiency.

23. The connecting rod and bolt shown in Problem Figure 23 each have a yield point stress of 90,000 psi and an endurance limit of 58,000 psi. The bolt is $\frac{3}{8}$-24 UNF and is drawn up with an initial tension of 3500 lb. Stress concentration factor for the threads is 3.8 and the bolt load varies continuously from 0 to 2000 lb. What is the factor of safety for the bolt?

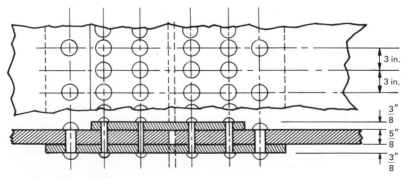

Problem Figure 22

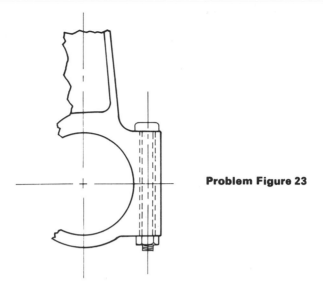

Problem Figure 23

24. Calculate the size of bolts (all bolts of the same size) required to safely support a bracket to which is applied an eccentric load of one ton as shown in Problem Figure 24. $S_{t(allow)} = 20,000$ psi; $S_{s(allow)} = 12,000$ psi.

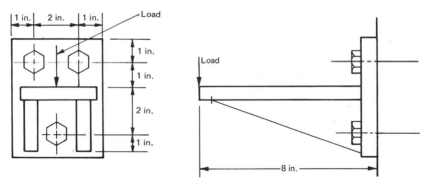

Problem Figure 24

REFERENCES

[1] *Manual of Steel Construction Handbook.* American Institute of Steel Construction, Inc., New York, 1970.

[2] E. C. Harris: *Elements of Structural Engineering.* The Ronald Press, New York, 1954.

[3] L. E. Grinter: *Elementary Structural Analysis and Design.* Macmillan Publishing Co., New York, 1965.

[4] American Standard Unified Screw Threads (ASA B1.1—1960) ASME, New York.

[5] J. E. Lothers: *Design in Structural Steel.* Prentice-Hall, Englewood Cliffs, N.J., 1972.

17

Welds and Adhesive Joints

SYMBOLS

e = load eccentricity, in.

h = nominal size of weld, in.

I = moment of inertia of weld group

I' = moment of inertia based on 1-in. throat

J = polar moment of inertia of weld group

J' = polar moment of inerta based on 1-in. throat

N = factor of safety

S_s = shear strength of adhesive, psi

S_{syp} = shear yield strength, psi

S_{yp} = yield strength, psi

S_{sw} = working strength in shear, psi

t_w = throat dimension, in.

$\bar{x}$ = horizontal distance to center of gravity, in.

$\bar{y}$ = vertical distance to center of gravity, in.

τ = shear stress, psi

Most weldments are produced by fusion processes. These involve establishment of a metallurgical bond between two parts by melting together the base metals or by melting the base metals with a filler metal. Important factors in successful welding are the elimination of surface barriers to joining and minimizing of damage (distortion and unfavorable heat treatment) to areas adjacent to the weld.

The necessary welding temperature may be produced by a gas flame or by an electric arc. Coated metal electrodes are used most commonly for manual arc welding. Gas shielded metal arc welding is also common. Electroslag welding, electron beam welding, and laser and plasma-arc methods are used on a small scale for very special applications.

Thin metal parts may be joined by resistance welding, particularly spot and seam welding. A spot weld is produced by a pair of electrodes that apply pressure to either side of a lap joint and form a complete circuit (Figure 17-1a). Resistance is a maximum between the parts, and heat generation at that point causes local fusion. Figure 17-1b shows a portable spot welder.

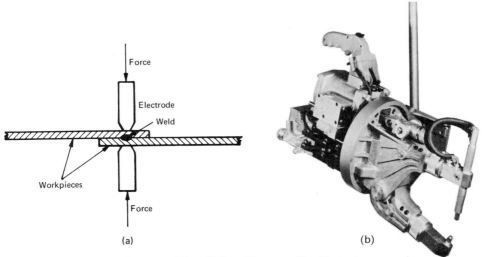

Figure 17-1 (a) Spot welding. (b) Portable spot welder. Electrode pressure is provided by air cylinders. [Courtesy Falstrom Company, Passaic, N.J.]

High strength adhesives are also utilized to join machine elements and in structural applications, particularly when the area to be bonded is relatively large. Plastics may be joined by various welding processes including induction welding, heated tool welding, friction welding, and hot air welding. Figure 17-2 shows a hot air type plastics welder.

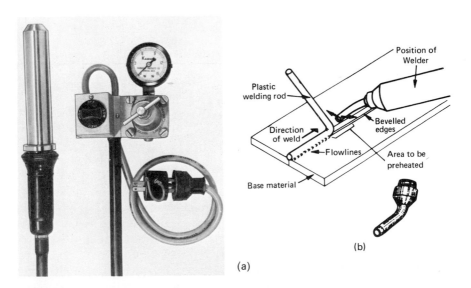

Figure 17-2 Plastics welder. (a) A hot-air welder shown without welding tip. Units of this type heat compressed air or inert gas to 400–900°F to weld thermoplastics. (b) Joining plastic sheets using a hot-air welder with a round tip. [Courtesy Kamweld Products Company, Inc., Norwood, Mass.]

SECTION 17-1

Arc Welding

Among the many manufacturing processes described in Chapter 4, arc welding is one of the most important. Common methods of arc welding include manual arc welding using coated metal electrodes, metal–inert gas arc welding and tungsten–inert gas welding.

Coated metal electrodes may be used in the field for manual arc welding (Figure 17-3a). The coating is vaporized to provide a shielding gas which prevents oxidation at the weld. The coating also acts as a flux and directs the arc. The electrode itself becomes the filler metal in the joint. If postweld heat treatment is used, the electrode composition should ordinarily be similar to that of the base metal. Because the electrodes are consumed rapidly in welding and must be replaced, a process using coated metal electrodes is not easy to automate.

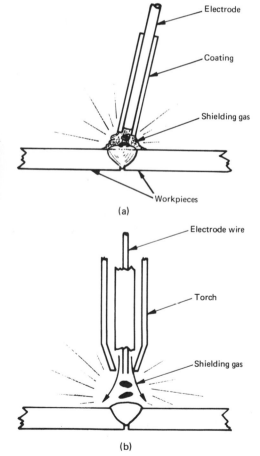

(a)

(b)

Figure 17-3 (a) Arc welding. (b) Metal–inert gas (MIG) arc welding.

The use of inert shielding gases reduces the operator skill required and makes automation possible. In **metal–inert gas arc welding** (MIG) a bare or plated wire is continuously fed into the weld from a large spool (Figure 17-3b). The wire acts as electrode and becomes the filler in the joint. (It would be impractical to feed a coated electrode in this way.) An inert gas is also fed into the torch. Cooling water may also be supplied through the power cable jacket and into the torch so that a lighter cable can be used. High production rates and uniform quality welds are possible with MIG welding.

Tungsten–inert gas welding (TIG) utilizes a "nonconsumable" tungsten electrode and usually argon or helium as the shielding gas. This process is particularly useful for welding aluminum. A separate filler rod is melted into the joint when required, but the electrode is not used as a filler.

The fundamental types of welded joints and the standard welding symbols are given in Table D-1 of the appendix.

SECTION 17-2
Design of Symmetrically Loaded Weldments

Coated metal welding electrodes are designated according to tensile strength of the completed weld and according to the intended welding method. The last two digits represent the type of weld application and the position of the weld. The two or three digits immediately following the prefix E give approximate minimum tensile strength in thousands of pounds per square inch. Most machinery welding is done with electrodes in the E60XX group. These give minimum ultimate tensile strengths $S_u = 60{,}000$ psi or higher in the as-welded condition and minimum yield strengths $S_{yp} = 50{,}000$ psi. Electrodes in the E70XX group are also commonly available. They provide 70,000 psi or higher minimum ultimate strengths and 60,000 psi minimum yield strengths. High strength welds are made by electrodes in the E100XX group, which form welds that self-temper on cooling, providing ultimate strengths in excess of 100,000 psi.

Butt welds in tension

When designing welds, we should specify an electrode with properties comparable to the base metal when possible. In the case of butt welds (Figure 17-4) the joint strength should then approximate the strength of the base metal, giving us an efficiency near 100 % for static loads. Thus for **full strength butt welds,** the joint strength is

$$P = \frac{S_{yp}Lt}{N} \tag{17-1}$$

for plate thickness t, weld length L, and safety factor N for *static tensile loads* in the plane of the plates perpendicular to the weld. There are, of course, certain side effects, principally due to the intense welding heat. These problems

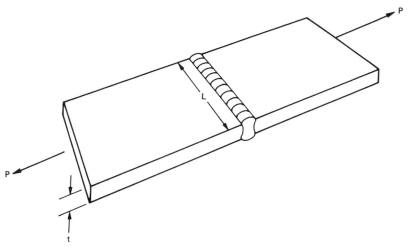

Figure 17-4 Butt weld in tension.

include residual stresses, distortion of the part, and cracking. Stress corrosion and a lowered endurance limit may also appear after the part has been in use. In addition, slag, voids, and other imperfections may occur in the weld.

For *fluctuating loads*, a butt weld made with an electrode having properties similar to the base metal will have a fatigue strength about 15% below the fatigue strength of the base metal. Weld metal that extends above or below the surface of the base metal of a butt joint is called "reinforcement." This is thought by some to increase the joint strength and compensate for weld imperfections. Reinforcement is probably of little consequence for welds subject to static loads but may be detrimental as a source of stress concentration (as noted in Chapter 3) if loads fluctuate. Thus reinforcement should be kept to a minimum or ground down for weldments subject to fatigue loads.

Example 17-1. An E60XX group electrode is used to butt weld two $\frac{1}{4}$-in. steel plates. The yield point of the base metal is 50,000 psi. Find the strength of the joint for a safety factor of $N = 2$. The plates are subject to a static tensile load perpendicular to the joint.

Solution: A butt weld in $\frac{1}{4}$-in. plate can be made with or without edge preparation. In either case, full strength should be developed and the weld will not materially reduce the strength of the plates. Thus, we have

$$P = \frac{S_{yp}t}{N} = \frac{50,000(\frac{1}{4})}{2}$$

$$= 6250 \text{ lb/in. of weld.} \quad \bullet$$

Welds in shear

When a butt weld joining two plates is loaded in the plane of the plates parallel to the weld, shear failure is likely to occur. For total weld length L, plate thickness t and safety factor N, the allowable load will be

$$P = \frac{S_{syp}Lt}{N} \tag{17-2}$$

for **full strength butt welds in shear** on a static basis. If the shear yield point is not known, we may generally assume

$$S_{syp} = \tfrac{2}{3}S_{yp}$$

Thus, for E60XX group electrodes with a yield point of 50,000 psi S_{syp} is approximately 33,000 psi. In every case, $S_{syp} \geq \tfrac{1}{2}S_{yp}$.

Figure 17-5a shows a fillet weld in shear. If the weld cross section has the form of an equilateral triangle, Figure 17-5b, the probable line of shear failure will be the weld throat as shown. For nominal size (leg dimension) h, the throat dimension is given by $t_w = 0.707h$. In most welds, the minimum failure dimension will exceed 0.707 times the nominal size, but we will still base our calculations on the throat dimension $t_w = 0.707h$ (see Figure 17-5c).

For the total weld length L counting all welds, the joint strength for **fillet welds loaded symmetrically in shear** as in Figure 17-5 is given by

$$P = \frac{0.707hLS_{syp}}{N} \tag{17-3}$$

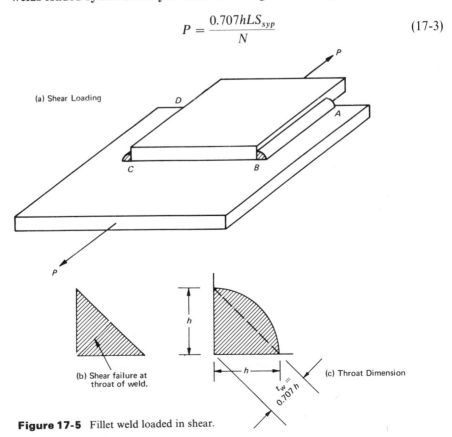

(a) Shear Loading

(b) Shear failure at throat of weld.

(c) Throat Dimension

Figure 17-5 Fillet weld loaded in shear.

Actual stress distribution in a weld of this type is quite complicated and depends on the stiffness of the base metal, slight bending of the plates, and other factors that we will neglect. The result is valid for design, however, because weld strengths are based on tests on joints of this type.

If fillet welds are also placed perpendicular to the direction of loading (say, along edges BC and AD of the plates in Figure 17-5a), both tension and shear stresses will occur on the throat section of those welds. Equation (17-3) will still give reasonable results for design purposes, however, if L is taken as the total length of all welds.

SECTION 17-3

Eccentrically Loaded Joints

When practical, welds should be symmetric about the line of action of the resultant load. If the load vector does not go through the center of the weld group, we must consider twisting and/or bending as well as direct shear.

Loading in the plane of the weld group

Figure 17-6 illustrates an eccentrically loaded joint. The exact stress distribution is complicated and depends on the rigidity of the parts being joined as well as the weld geometry, but the following method will give reasonable engineering results.

Assume the parts are relatively rigid. Then, stress due to load eccentricity is proportional to distance from the center of the weld group. As with symmetrically loaded fillet welds, we approximate the stress area in shear by the throat area. Shear stress in the weld at radius r is given by the vector sum

$$\tau = \frac{\mathbf{P}}{A} \leftrightarrow \frac{\mathbf{T}r}{J} \tag{17-4}$$

where

$\mathbf{P}$ = applied load
A = total throat area
$\mathbf{T}$ = torque, the product of applied load and its distance from the center of gravity of the weld group
$\mathbf{r}$ = distance from the center of gravity of the weld group
J = polar moment of inertia of the weld group about its center of gravity (based on throat area)

The design of weldments calls for an even simpler procedure. Because weld throat area will not, in general, be known at the start of the design process, we temporarily specify a unit throat dimension. Equation (17-4) then becomes

$$\tau' = \frac{\mathbf{P}}{L} \leftrightarrow \frac{\mathbf{T}r}{J'} \tag{17-5}$$

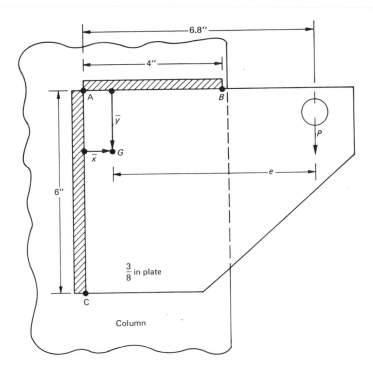

Figure 17-6 Eccentric loading. G is the center of gravity of the weld group.

where L is the total length of the fillet weld and J' is the polar moment of inertia based on a 1-in. throat. Furthermore, when locating the center of gravity and determining $\mathbf{r}$ and J' the weld will be treated simply as one or more lines. We will measure only to the near edge of the weld, ignoring the weld thickness and ignoring the contribution of moment of inertia about the weld's own central axis. Once τ' is thus computed, we compare it with allowable shear stress to specify true weld size. For working strength $S_{sw} = S_{syp}/N$, the nominal weld size (leg dimension) is given by

$$h = \frac{\tau'}{0.707S_{sw}} \tag{17-6}$$

Ordinarily the nominal size h that we specify would be the nearest "round number" size ($\frac{1}{8}$, $\frac{3}{16}$, $\frac{1}{4}$ in., and so on) equal to or greater than the computed value. Using this method, all welds on the joint will have the same nominal size.

If the weld group is symmetric, the location of the center of gravity will be obvious. Otherwise we will select a convenient origin and compute horizontal and vertical distances $\bar{x}$ and $\bar{y}$ to the center of gravity. We treat the weld as a series of lines of length L_1, L_2, and so on at the plate edges with their own centers at horizontal distances x_1, x_2, and so on, from the origin. Horizontal distance to the *center of gravity* is given by

$$\bar{x} = \frac{\Sigma L_i x_i}{\Sigma L_i} \tag{17-7}$$

Similarly, vertical distance is

$$\bar{y} = \frac{\Sigma L_i y_i}{\Sigma L_i} \tag{17-8}$$

where the subscript $i = 1, 2, \ldots, n$ for n welds. Once the center of gravity is found, the polar moment of inertia may be calculated, treating each weld as a line. The contribution of a single weld parallel to the x axis is

$$I'_{x(i)} = L_i \bar{y}_i^2$$

$$I'_{y(i)} = \frac{L_i^3}{12} + L_i \bar{x}_i^2$$

where $\bar{x}_i$ and $\bar{y}_i$ are the distances from the center of gravity to the center of that particular weld. We add the contributions of all welds to obtain I'_x and I'_y and then obtain $J' = I'_x + I'_y$.

In most cases, it is easiest to compute horizontal and vertical components of shear stress and then combine them. We replace equation (17-5) by equations (17-9), (17-10), and (17-11).

$$\tau'_V = \frac{P_V}{L} \pm \frac{ePr_H}{J'} \tag{17-9}$$

$$\tau'_H = \frac{P_H}{L} \pm \frac{ePr_V}{J'} \tag{17-10}$$

$$\tau' = \sqrt{(\tau'_V)^2 + (\tau'_H)^2} \tag{17-11}$$

where P_V and P_H are the vertical and horizontal components of the load and r_V and r_H are the vertical and horizontal distances from the center of gravity of the weld group to the point where we wish to determine stress. The plus sign in equations (17-9) and 17-10) applies if the direct load component (the first term) results in shear in the same sense as the torsion component. For a point nearest to the line of action of the load, the plus sign applies. Shear stress is ordinarily greatest at a point in the weld group nearest to the line of action of the load. If the weld group is not symmetric, we may have to check two or more of the points in the weld that are farthest from the center of gravity.

Example 17-2. A bracket is to be joined to a column by fillet welds. The dimensions of this weldment are shown in Figure 17-6. Find the required weld size (leg dimension).

Given. $P = 2000$ lb. Allowable shear stress in welds $S_{sw} = 7000$ psi.

Solution: The center of gravity is given by

$$\bar{x} = \frac{\Sigma L_i x_i}{\Sigma L_i} = \frac{4 \times 2 + 0}{4 + 6} = 0.8 \text{ in.}$$

$$\bar{y} = \frac{\Sigma L_i y_i}{\Sigma L_i} = \frac{0 + 6 \times 3}{4 + 6} = 1.8 \text{ in.}$$

from which the load eccentricity is

$$e = 6.8 - \bar{x} = 6 \text{ in.}$$

Based on a 1-in. throat, the moments of inertia are

$$I_x' = 4(1.8)^2 + \frac{6^3}{12} + 6(3 - 1.8)^2 = 39.65$$

$$I_y' = 6(0.8)^2 + \frac{4^3}{12} + 4(2 - 0.8)^2 = 14.93$$

and

$$J' = 54.58$$

By inspection, either point B or point C is subject to the greatest stress. At those points, shear stresses based on a 1-in. throat are:

at B $\begin{cases} \tau_V' = \dfrac{P}{L} + \dfrac{Per_H}{J'} = \dfrac{2000}{4 + 6} + \dfrac{2000(6)(3.2)}{54.58} = 904 \quad \text{(vertical component)} \\[3mm] \tau_H' = \dfrac{Per_V}{J'} = \dfrac{2000(6)(1.8)}{54.58} = 396 \quad \text{(horizontal component)} \\[3mm] \tau' = [(\tau_V')^2 + (\tau_H')^2]^{1/2} = 987 \quad \text{(total shear stress based on 1-in. throat)} \end{cases}$

at C $\begin{cases} \tau_V' = \dfrac{P}{L} - \dfrac{Per_H}{J'} = \dfrac{2000}{4 + 6} - \dfrac{2000(6)(0.8)}{54.58} = 24 \\[3mm] \tau_H' = \dfrac{Per_V}{J'} = \dfrac{2000(6)(4.2)}{54.58} = 925 \\[3mm] \tau' = 925 \end{cases}$

Point B governs.

$$h = \frac{\tau'}{0.707 S_{sw}} = \frac{987}{0.707(7000)} = 0.199 \text{ in.} \quad \text{(leg dimension)}$$

For convenience, we might specify $\frac{1}{4}$ in. (leg dimension) fillet welds throughout. ●

Loads that do not lie in the plane of the weld group

A somewhat different treatment is indicated when the loading lies outside the plane of the weld group. Consider the angle section of Figure 17-7 which is welded to a column. Load P is applied at a distance e from the plane of the welds. The actual stress distribution in the weld group is very complicated. However, for design purposes, we may assume a linear distribution of shear stress due to moment $M = Pe$ and a uniform distribution of direct shear stress.

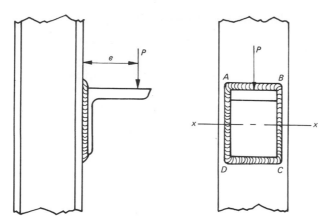

Figure 17-7 Loading that does not lie in the plane of the welding group.

We begin by locating the center of gravity of the weld group. As in the previous example, the weld may be treated as a line in these calculations. Consider the case in which the plane of the weld group is perpendicular to the plane determined by the line of action of the force and the weld group center of gravity. In this case there is no tendency toward twisting in the weld group plane. The weld is subject to direct shear stress P/A and a moment-induced stress Mc/I_x. Moment of inertia I_x is computed with respect to an axis perpendicular to the load line of action and through the center of gravity. Distance c is measured from that axis to the farthest point on the weld. In spite of the resemblance to bending of the moment-induced stress, we will design on the basis of shear in the weld. Shear stress in the weld is approximated by the vector sum

$$\tau = \frac{\mathbf{P}}{A} \leftrightarrow \frac{\mathbf{M}c}{I_x} \tag{17-12}$$

If the above equation is to be used for design purposes, we may treat the weld as a line, but base the area and moment of inertia on a 1-in. throat dimension. Analogous to equation (17-5), we obtain

$$\tau' = \frac{\mathbf{P}}{L} \leftrightarrow \frac{\mathbf{M}c}{I_x'} \tag{17-13}$$

Based on the geometry and loading of Figure 17-7, we see that the direct shear effect is downward and that the moment-induced stress along edge AB is outward. The vector sum is simply

$$\tau' = \left[\left(\frac{P}{L} \right)^2 + \left(\frac{Mc}{I_x'} \right)^2 \right]^{1/2} \tag{17-14}$$

For a shear working stress S_{sw}, the required minimum leg dimension is given by

$$h = \frac{\tau'}{0.707 S_{sw}}$$

Example 17-3. Referring to Figure 17-7, let us find the required weld size if dimension $AB = 3$ in., dimension $BC = 4$ in., eccentricity $e = 2.5$ in., and load $P = 2000$ lb. Allow a working stress in shear of $S_{sw} = 5000$ psi.

Solution: Moment $M = 2000(2.5) = 5000$. The center of gravity is located by inspection and the moment of inertia I'_x is calculated with respect to an axis 2 in. below AB. Based on a 1-in. throat dimension,

$$I'_x = 2(3)(2)^2 + 2(4)^3/12 = 34.67$$

$$L = 2(3 + 4) = 14$$

$$\tau' = \left[\left(\frac{2000}{14} \right)^2 + \left(\frac{5000(2)}{34.67} \right)^2 \right]^{1/2} = 321.9$$

from which the required leg dimension is

$$h = \frac{321.9}{0.707(5000)} = 0.091 \text{ in.}$$

(For convenience, we would specify $\frac{1}{8}$-in. leg dimension throughout.) ●

SECTION 17-4

Adhesive Joints

It is beyond the scope of this paragraph even to list the adhesives currently available. A large number of engineering adhesives fall into the categories of thermosetting and thermoplastic. The latter, of course, are limited by their tendency to soften at elevated temperatures and may even tend to creep at room temperature when subject to heavy loading. There are many other adhesive cure mechanisms. Anaerobic curing materials, for example, remain liquid in the presence of oxygen but harden in confined spaces such as on bolt threads or in the space between a shaft and a hub.

Types of joints

Joint geometry is most important when we join relatively high strength materials. Large bond areas are suggested, particularly in the joining of metals. The lap joint (Figure 17-8a) is inexpensive because no preparation is required except possibly surface cleaning. For an in-plane load P, we may specify the bond area so that the total adhesive strength in shear is equal to the plate strength in tension. Shear strengths of 2000–2800 psi were recorded in laboratory tests of one commercial cyanoacrylate type adhesive bonding steel to steel and aluminum to aluminum. Higher values were reported for some epoxies. Recommended working strengths are much lower.

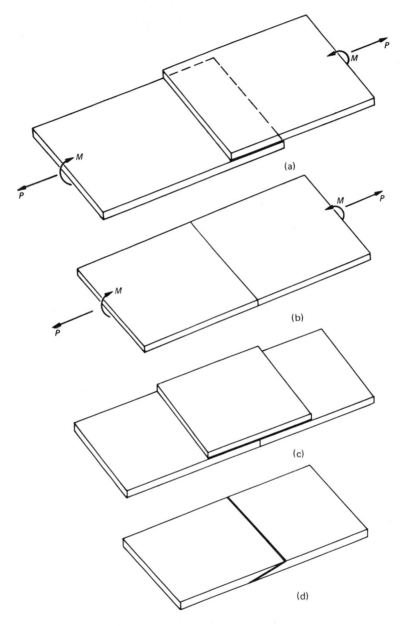

Figure 17.8 Adhesive joints. (**a**) Lap joint. (**b**) Butt joint (generally unsatisfactory). (**c**) Single reinforced butt joint. (**d**) Scarf joint.

The butt joint, Figure 17-8b, is generally avoided since adhesive bond area is inadequate. In cases where the lap joint is not desirable, however, a reinforced butt joint, Figure 17-8c, may be used. A double reinforced joint utilizes a similar reinforcement plate on both sides of the joint. Another alternative, the scarf joint, Figure 17-8d, provides the desired bond area. The cost of machining for a scarf joint, however, is seldom justified, and with thin materials, the machining of a scarf joint is highly impractical.

Stress distribution

Shear stress in the adhesive in a lap joint is not evenly distributed. The actual stresses depend on the thickness and elasticity of the joined members and the adhesive. We will investigate a metal-to-metal lap joint, Figure 17-9a, in an attempt to approximate maximum adhesive stress. It will be assumed that the adhesive remains elastic under load.

Let us assume that the adhesive is subject to shear strain γ and the metal subject to tensile strain ε_1 and ε_2 (for plates 1 and 2). Based on the geometry of an element of the adhesive layer of thickness t_a, Figure 17-9b, we have

$$(1 + \varepsilon_2)\,dx + t_a\left(\gamma + \frac{d\gamma}{dx}\,dx\right) = t_a\gamma + (1 + \varepsilon_1)\,dx$$

for small γ, from which

$$\frac{d\gamma}{dx} - \frac{(\varepsilon_1 - \varepsilon_2)}{t_a} = 0 \qquad (17\text{-}15)$$

Differentiating with respect to x, we obtain

$$\frac{d^2\gamma}{dx^2} - \frac{1}{t_a}\frac{d}{dx}(\varepsilon_1 - \varepsilon_2) = 0 \qquad (17\text{-}16)$$

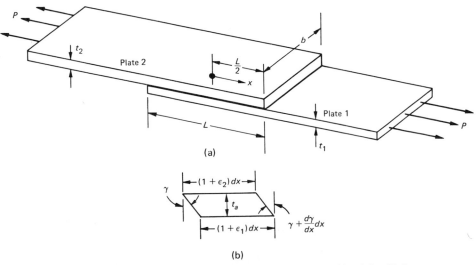

(a)

(b)

Figure 17-9 Analysis of an adhesive joint. **(a)** Metal-to-metal lap joint. **(b)** An element of adhesive with thickness t_a and unstrained length dx.

If we equate the change in tensile force in the plate for a distance dx to the shear force applied by the adhesive over the same distance, we obtain

$$E_1 bt_1 \frac{d\varepsilon_1}{dx} dx = G\gamma b \, dx$$

or

$$\frac{d\varepsilon_1}{dx} = \frac{G\gamma}{E_1 t_1} \tag{17-17}$$

Similarly,

$$\frac{d\varepsilon_2}{dx} = \frac{-G\gamma}{E_2 t_2} \tag{17-18}$$

for adhesive shear modulus G and tensile modulus E_1 and E_2 for the plates.
Using equations (17-17) and (17-18) in equation (17-16), we obtain

$$\frac{d^2\gamma}{dx^2} - C^2\gamma = 0 \tag{17-19}$$

where

$$C^2 = \frac{G}{t_a}\left(\frac{1}{E_1 t_1} + \frac{1}{E_2 t_2}\right)$$

The solution to equation (17-19) is given by

$$\gamma = A \cosh Cx + B \sinh Cx \tag{17-20}$$

where arbitrary constants A and B are found by substituting the appropriate boundary values of ε_1 and ε_2 in equation (17-15).

An adhesive lap joint with both plates of the same metal and thickness

Consider the joint of Figure 17-9 with plate thickness t and total force P at each end. Let the coordinate x be measured from the midpoint of the joint. By symmetry, constant $B = 0$ in equation (17-20). At $x = L/2$ we have $\varepsilon_1 = P/(btE)$ and $\varepsilon_2 = 0$. Using these values and equation (17-20) in equation (17-15) we obtain

$$AC \sinh\left(\frac{CL}{2}\right) - \frac{P}{btt_a E} = 0$$

from which

$$A = \frac{P}{btt_a CE \sinh(CL/2)}$$

and shear stress in the adhesive

$$\tau = G\gamma = \frac{GP \cosh Cx}{btt_a CE \sinh(CL/2)} = \frac{CP \cosh Cx}{2b \sinh(CL/2)} \tag{17-21}$$

where

$$C = \left(\frac{2G}{tt_a E}\right)^{1/2} \tag{17-22}$$

It is important to note that G is the shear modulus of the *adhesive* and E is the elastic modulus of the *plates*.

It might be necessary for the designer to obtain thickness t_a and adhesive properties experimentally if these values are not provided by the manufacturer. Maximum adhesive shear stress occurs at $x = \pm L/2$. It is

$$\tau_{(max)} = \frac{CP}{2b \tanh(CL/2)} \tag{17-23}$$

Equation (17-23) may be written in the form

$$\tau_{(max)} = \frac{K_s P}{bL} \tag{17-24}$$

where K_s is the stress-distribution factor. This number is analogous to a stress concentration factor, except that stress gradients are not as sharp as in typical cases of stress concentration.

Figure 17-10 shows relative shear stress distribution for the case where $C = 4/L$. In that case, maximum shear stress is

$$\tau_{(max)} = 2.08\frac{P}{bL}$$

Since average shear stress is $P/(bL)$, we have a *stress-distribution factor* of 2.08.

Let us define a working strength for an adhesive as $S_{sw} = S_s/N$ where S_s is the shear strength and N the factor of safety. Rewriting equation (17-23), we see that joint strength is given by

$$P = \frac{2bS_{sw} \tanh CL/2}{C} \tag{17-25}$$

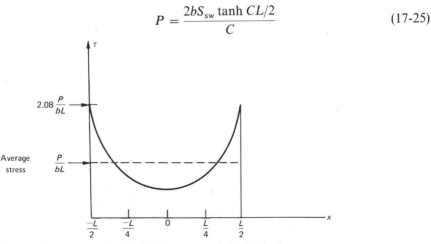

Figure 17-10   An example of shear stress distribution in the adhesive joint shown in Figure 17-9 (where $C = 4/L$).

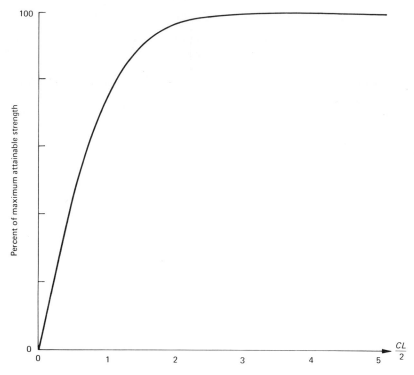

Figure 17-11 Theoretical effect of overlap L in a lap joint with both plates of the same metal and thickness.

If only the overlap L is varied, strength is proportional to the hyperbolic tangent, Figure 17-11. For small values of $CL/2$ (up to 0.3 or so) $\tanh CL/2$ is approximately equal to $CL/2$ and joint strength approaches

$$P = bLS_{sw} \tag{17-26}$$

For large values of $CL/2$ (say, 2 or greater), $\tanh CL/2$ approaches unity. Thus, based on the stated assumptions, an increase in overlap is beneficial up to a point. An overlap $L = 1.1/C$ theoretically yields about 90% of maximum attainable strength. Further increases in overlap are theoretically of little value unless adhesive yielding tends to redistribute the stress.

Example 17-4. Find the required overlap L if we are required to join two aluminum plates in a lap joint as in Figure 17-9.

Given: Plate thickness $t = 0.020$ in; yield strength $S_{yp} = 15,000$ psi for the plates; shear strength of the adhesive $S_s = 1500$ psi.

Solution: Because the adhesive shear modulus and thickness are not given, we will estimate a stress distribution factor $K_s = 2$. Setting $\tau_{(max)} = S_s$ in equation (17-24), we have joint strength $P = bLS_s/K_s$ at failure. The strength of the aluminum plate in tension is $P = S_{yp}bt$ at failure. Equating joint strength and plate strength, we obtain a required overlap of

$$L = K_s t S_{yp}/S_s = 0.4 \text{ in.} \quad \bullet$$

PROBLEMS

1. Two $\frac{3}{16}$-in. thick steel plates are butt welded and loaded as in Figure 17-4. An E60XX group electrode is used and the yield strength of the base metal is 50,000 psi. Find the strength of the joint based on a safety factor of 3.

2. Two $\frac{3}{8}$-in. thick steel plates are butt welded and loaded as in Figure 17-4. An E60XX group electrode is used and the yield strength of the base metal is 50,000 psi. Find joint strength using a safety factor of 2.5.

3. A fillet weld is loaded in shear as in Figure 17-5. Find the load which may be safely carried by $\frac{1}{4}$-in. nominal size welds with a total length of 8 in. if E60XX group electrodes are used and the safety factor is 3.

4. (a) Find the safe load if $\frac{3}{8}$-in. welds are used in Problem 3. (b) What is the percent increase in strength of the $\frac{3}{8}$-in. weld over the $\frac{1}{4}$ in. weld? (c) Find the percent increase in weight of the weld.

5. A $\frac{1}{4}$-in. nominal size fillet weld is loaded in shear as in Figure 17-5. Find the required weld length for a load of 11,000 lb. Allow 15,000 psi in shear.

6. A 4000-lb load is applied as in Figure 17-5. Dimensions AB and CD total 7.5 in. Find the required weld size. Use a shear yield point of 33,000 psi and a safety factor of 2.5.

7. Locate the center of gravity and calculate the polar moment of inertia of the weld group in Problem Figure 7. Find the nominal weld size required based on an allowable shear stress of 10,000 psi.

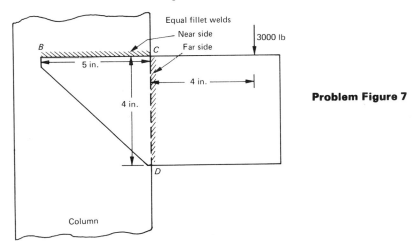

Problem Figure 7

8. Design a welded joint similar to the one in Problem Figure 7 if the 3000-lb load is applied at a distance of 8 in. from the column. Allow 10,000 psi in shear. Let dimension $AB = 4$ in., dimension $BC = 4$ in. and eccentricity $e = 6$ in.

9. Find the required weld size for the bracket in Figure 17-7 if a 5000-lb load is applied. Assume E60XX type welding rod is used and apply a safety factor of 2.5. Let $AB = BC = 4$ in. and $e = 6$ in.

10. Find the required weld size for the bracket in Figure 17-7 if a 2000-lb load is applied with eccentricity $e = 9.8$ in. Allow 8000 psi in shear and let dimension $AB = 3$ in. and dimension $BC = 4$ in.

11. An angle bracket is loaded as in Figure 17-7. Using $AB = 3$ in. and $BC = 4$ in. find the required weld size for a 3000-lb load applied with 3.5-in. eccentricity. Allow 7000 psi in shear.

12. Find the load that would cause weld failure in the angle bracket of Figure 17-7 where $AB = 3$ in., $BC = 4$ in., and eccentricity is 4.5 in. Use a $\frac{1}{4}$-in. weld with a shear yield point of 33,000 psi.

13. In Figure 17-7, let $AB = 3$ in., $BC = 4$ in., and $e = 2.5$ in. Load P varies continuously from 2000 lb upward to 2000 lb downward. Find the required weld size based on an allowable stress of 4000 psi in reversed shear.

14. The two brackets in Problem Figure 14 support a static load of 3000 lb/bracket. Find the required weld size based on an allowable shear stress of 15,800 psi.

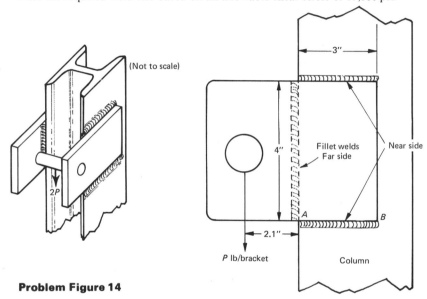

Problem Figure 14

15. Each weld in Problem Figure 15 supports a load of 2000 lb. Find the required weld size based on an allowable shear stress of 13,600 psi.

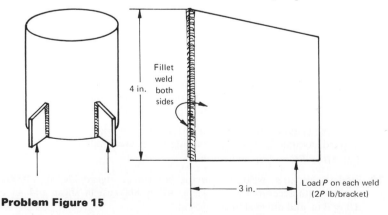

Problem Figure 15

16. Load P in Problem Figure 15 varies continuously from 500 to 2500 lb/weld. Let $S_{syp}/N = 13,600$ psi and $S_{se}/N = 6000$ psi. Find the required weld size.

17. Two 0.010-in. thick steel plates are to be joined as in Figure 17-9. Find the required overlap if the plates have a yield strength of 40,000 psi and the shear strength of the adhesive is 1200 psi. Assume the stress distribution factor for the adhesive is 2.0.

18. Find the joint strength of an adhesive joint with $\frac{1}{2}$-in. overlap. Let the adhesive shear strength be 1550 psi and use a safety factor of 1.5. Assume a stress distribution factor of 2.0.

19. Find the strength of an adhesive joint with $\frac{3}{8}$-in. overlap where adhesive strength is 1200 psi in shear. Use a safety factor of 2.5 and a stress distribution factor of 3.0.

20. Find the required overlap if two $\frac{1}{16}$-in. thick aluminum plates are joined as in Figure 17-9. Use a yield strength of 18,000 psi for the aluminum and a shear strength of 1600 psi for the adhesive where $K_s = 2$.

REFERENCES

[1] J. M. Alexander and R. C. Brewer: *Manufacturing Properties of Materials*. Van Nostrand-Reinhold Books, New York, 1963.

[2] E. P. DeGarmo: *Materials and Processes in Manufacturing*, 2nd ed. The Macmillan Company, New York, 1962.

[3] R. A. Lindberg: *Processes and Materials of Manufacture*. Allyn and Bacon, Inc., Rockleigh, N.J., 1964.

[4] O. W. Blodgett: *Design of Weldments*. Lincoln Arc Welding Foundation, Cleveland, Ohio, 1963.

[5] E. J. Bruno (ed.): *Adhesives in Modern Manufacturing*. Society of Manufacturing Engineers, Dearborn, Mich., 1970.

[6] C. V. Cagle: *Adhesive Bonding*. McGraw-Hill Book Company, New York, 1968.

[7] A. R. Pfluger and R. E. Lewis (eds.): *Symposium on Weld Imperfections*. Addison-Wesley Publishing Company, Reading Mass., 1966.

[8] J. A. Newman and F. J. Bockhoff: *Welding of Plastics*. Reinhold Publishing Company, New York, 1959.

[9] A. L. Phillips (ed.): *Welding Handbook* (5 Sections). American Welding Society, New York, 1968.

[10] *Welding Technology, NASA SP-5918(01)*. National Aeronautical and Space Administration, 1970.

[11] N. M. Bikales (ed.): *Adhesion and Bonding*. John Wiley & Sons, New York, 1971.

[12] F. Koenigsberger and J. R. Adair: *Welding Technology*. Hart Publishing Company, New York, 1968.

18

Axisymmetric Problems in the Design of Machines

SYMBOLS

a = inner radius, in.

b = outer radius, in.

E_k = kinetic energy, in.-lb

J = mass moment of inertia, lb-sec²-in.

p = internal pressure, psi

q = external pressure, psi

u = radial displacement, in.

U = radial interference, in.

ε_r = radial strain, in./in.

ρ = mass density, lb-sec²/in.⁴

σ_θ = tangential stress, psi

σ_r = radial stress, psi

τ_{max} = maximum shear stress, psi

v = Poisson's ratio

ω = angular velocity, rad/sec

In the class of machine elements with axisymmetric geometry and axisymmetric loading, the basic problem may be defined in terms of a single coordinate—the radial coordinate. A number of important applications fall into this category, including thick wall cylinders, interference fits, rotating disks, and curved beams subjected to pure bending.

SECTION 18-1

The Thick Wall Cylinder

Radial stresses are necessarily very small in a thin wall pressure vessel. However when wall thickness is of the same order of magnitude as the vessel radii, we must consider both radial stress σ_r and tangential stress σ_θ. When uniform internal and external pressure act on a circular cylindrical vessel we have axisymmetry. Then, there is no variation in stress with the coordinate θ. In order to find stress and displacement everywhere, we proceed as follows.

Consider an element of a thick wall cylinder, Figure 18-1 having unit thickness in the axial direction. Equilibrium of forces in the radial direction yields

$$\frac{d(r\sigma_r)}{dr} d\theta\, dr - 2\sigma_\theta\, dr \sin\frac{d\theta}{2} = 0$$

Recalling $\lim_{x\to 0} \sin x = x$, applying it to the infinitesimal angle, and simplifying the result, we obtain

$$\sigma_\theta = \frac{d(r\sigma_r)}{dr} \tag{18-1}$$

For outward radial displacement u, the **strain-displacement** relationships in polar coordinates are

$$\varepsilon_r = \frac{du}{dr} \quad \text{and} \quad \varepsilon_\theta = \frac{u}{r} \tag{18-2}$$

and the **stress-strain laws** for a perfectly elastic material are

$$\varepsilon_r = \frac{1}{E}(\sigma_r - v\sigma_\theta)$$

$$\tag{18-3}$$

$$\varepsilon_\theta = \frac{1}{E}(\sigma_\theta - v\sigma_r)$$

where axial stress is neglected.

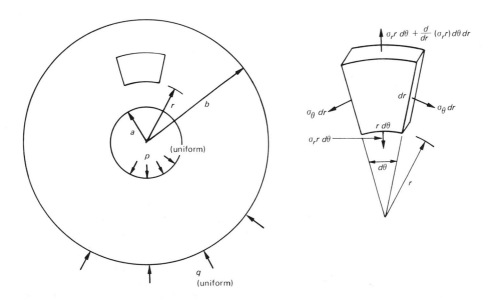

Figure 18-1 Thick wall cylinder.

With five equations and five unknowns, a solution will be attempted. Because the boundary conditions (the internal and external pressure) correspond to radial stresses, equations (18-1) through (18-3) will be combined to form a single equation in σ_r. We begin by combining equations (18-2) and (18-3) to obtain

$$\frac{du}{dr} = \frac{1}{E}(\sigma_r - v\sigma_\theta)$$

and

(18-4)

$$u = \frac{r}{E}(\sigma_\theta - v\sigma_r)$$

These two equations are combined to eliminate u by differentiating the second. The result is an equation in stress only

$$r\frac{d\sigma_\theta}{dr} - vr\frac{d\sigma_r}{dr} + (1 + v)(\sigma_\theta - \sigma_r) = 0$$

Finally, eliminating tangential stress through equation (18-1), the result is

$$\frac{d^2\sigma_r}{dr^2} + \frac{3}{r}\frac{d\sigma_r}{dr} = 0 \qquad (18-5)$$

which is satisfied by

$$\sigma_r = C_1 + \frac{C_2}{r^2} \qquad (18-6)$$

Arbitrary constants C_1 and C_2 are found by setting $-\sigma_r(a) = p$ (the internal pressure) and $-\sigma_r(b) = q$ (the external pressure). Tangential stress σ_θ is given by equation (18-1) and displacement u by the second of equations (18-4). The resulting equations for stress and displacement are

$$\sigma_r = \frac{-a^2 p\left(\dfrac{b^2}{r^2} - 1\right) - b^2 q\left(1 - \dfrac{a^2}{r^2}\right)}{b^2 - a^2} \qquad (18-7)$$

$$\sigma_\theta = \frac{a^2 p\left(\dfrac{b^2}{r^2} + 1\right) - b^2 q\left(1 + \dfrac{a^2}{r^2}\right)}{b^2 - a^2} \qquad (18-8)$$

$$u = \frac{r(1 - v)(a^2 p - b^2 q) + (1 + v)(p - q)\dfrac{a^2 b^2}{r}}{E(b^2 - a^2)} \qquad (18-9)$$

Hollow cylinders subject to internal pressure

For internal pressure p and zero external pressure, equations (18-7) and (18-8) reduce to

$$\sigma_r = \frac{-a^2 p \left(\dfrac{b^2}{r^2} - 1 \right)}{b^2 - a^2} \tag{18-10}$$

and

$$\sigma_\theta = \frac{a^2 p \left(\dfrac{b^2}{r^2} + 1 \right)}{b^2 - a^2} \tag{18-11}$$

By inspection, the normal stress of greatest magnitude is the tangential stress at the inner surface.

$$\sigma_\theta(a) = p \frac{b^2 + a^2}{b^2 - a^2} \tag{18-12}$$

If the cylinder wall thickness is t, where $t \ll a$, the second of equations (18-11) may be approximated by the familiar $\sigma_\theta = pa/t$.

As a result of the symmetry, shear stress $\tau_{r\theta} = 0$, and the principal stresses are σ_r (radial), σ_θ (tangential), and σ_z (axial), which is equal to zero. Maximum shear stress is given by

$$\tau_{max} = \text{the largest of} \begin{cases} \dfrac{|\sigma_\theta - \sigma_r|}{2} \\[2ex] \dfrac{|\sigma_\theta - \sigma_z|}{2} \\[2ex] \dfrac{|\sigma_r - \sigma_z|}{2} \end{cases} \tag{18-13}$$

Noting the sign of σ_r and σ_θ in equations (18-10) and (18-11), we see that τ_{max} will be equal to

$$\tau_{max} = \frac{\sigma_\theta - \sigma_r}{2}$$

for the case of internal pressure. Using equations (18-10) and (18-11), we have

$$\tau_{max} = \frac{a^2 b^2 p}{r^2 (b^2 - a^2)} \tag{18-14}$$

By inspection, **maximax** shear stress (maximum for any location and orientation) occurs at the inner surface and is given by

$$\tau_{max}(a) = \frac{b^2 p}{b^2 - a^2} \quad \text{or} \quad \tau_{max}(a) = \frac{\sigma_\theta(a) + p}{2} \tag{18-15}$$

Example 18-1. *Given:* A pressure of 4000 psi in a pipe with 3-in. inside diameter and 0.5-in. wall. Neglect axial force. (a) Find maximum stress. (b) Find maximum shear stress.

Solution: *Part a.* Using equation (18-12), we have maximum normal stress given by

$$\sigma_\theta(a) = p\frac{b^2 + a^2}{b^2 - a^2} = 14{,}300 \text{ psi}$$

The approximation for thin wall cylinders gives a result about 16% low for σ_θ in this example of a thick wall cylinder.

Part b. Maximum shear stress occurs at the inner surface ($r = a$) where $\sigma_r = -p$. It is

$$\tau_{max} = \frac{\sigma_\theta(a) + p}{2} = 9150 \text{ psi} \quad \bullet$$

SECTION 18-2

Interference Fits

Loose, free, medium, and snug fits (classes 1 through 4 respectively) provide for positive clearance between a shaft and hub. For a 1-in. diameter shaft, diametral clearances range from 0 to 0.001 in. for a snug fit and from 0.003 to 0.009 in. for a loose fit. Force and shrink fits have negative clearance (interference); a heavy force fit or shrink fit of a hub on a 1-in. diameter shaft has about 0.001-in. diametral interference. Although the equations of the preceding section are based on circular cylindrical bodies, they should give reasonable results for bodies with irregular external surfaces, such as gears and pulleys, where an effective outside diameter can be approximated.

Let us consider an interference fit between a solid shaft and a hub of outside radius b and inside radius a. Subscripts h and s will refer to the hub and shaft respectively. The resulting pressure p will subject the shaft to a uniform stress $\sigma_r = \sigma_\theta = -p$ throughout, and a radial displacement at its surface.

$$u_s = \frac{-(1 - v_s)ap}{E_s} \tag{18-16}$$

The shaft length and the axial length of the hub will, of course, be different but nevertheless we will assume an axisymmetric stress field. Then, for the hub, the internal displacement is

$$u_h = \frac{ap}{E_h}\left(\frac{b^2 + a^2}{b^2 - a^2} + v_h\right) \tag{18-17}$$

Total radial interference U is made up of the two radius changes (Figure 18-2)

$$U = u_h - u_s = ap\left(\frac{\dfrac{b^2 + a^2}{b^2 - a^2} + v_h}{E_h} + \frac{1 - v_s}{E_s}\right) \tag{18-18}$$

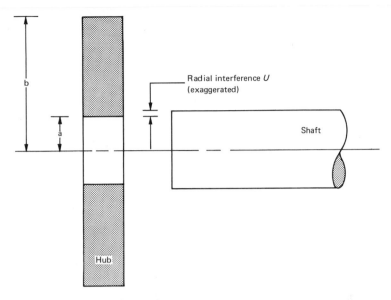

Radial interference U (exaggerated)

Shaft

Hub

Figure 18-2 Interference fit.

An approximation of torque capacity and force required to assemble the shaft and hub may be made on the basis of a coefficient of friction around $f = 0.1$.

Example 18-2. A 4-in. diameter, 2-in. face width, 20-tooth cast iron pinion is to transmit a maximum torque of 1200 in.-lb at low speed. Find the required radial interference on a 1-in. diameter steel shaft and the stress in the gear due to a press fit.

Solution: The shaft radius $a = 0.5$. Based on stub teeth, let us use the dedendum radius

$$b = \frac{D}{2} - \frac{1}{P_d} = 1.8$$

Poisson's ratio will be taken as $v = 0.3$ for both metals and Young's modulus $E_s = 30 \times 10^6$ for steel and $E_h = 15 \times 10^6$ for cast iron. For torque $T = 1200$ in.-ib, required tangential force at the shaft is $F = T/a = 2400$ lb. Based on a coefficient of friction $f = 0.1$ and hub length $L = 2$, the same as the face width, the tangential force due to friction (at incipient slipping)

$$F = 2\pi a L f p = 2400 \text{ lb}$$

from which the minimum contact pressure is 3820 psi. If we include a 50% margin of safety to insure transmission of power, then the contact pressure will be specified as $p = 5740$ psi.

Using equation (18-18), the required radial interference is $U = 0.00035$ in.; a nominal hub inside diameter 0.0007 less than the shaft diameter. Since tolerances must be applied to both dimensions, selective assembly would probably be necessary, that is, a large shaft would be assembled with a gear having a large hole, and so on. Assuming a radial interference that did not exceed 0.0005 in., maximum possible contact pressure would be $p = 8200$ psi.

Using equation (18-11), the maximum tensile stress in the gear due to the force fit occurs at the inner surface. At that point,

$$\sigma_\theta(a) = p\frac{b^2 + a^2}{b^2 - a^2} = 9570 \text{ psi}$$

based on 0.0005-in. radial interference.

The maximum interference assumed above falls into the heavy force fit category and is not generally recommended for cast iron. Based on the value of σ_θ, however, we might find the design conditions acceptable for high strength cast iron. ●

SECTION 18-3

Stresses and Displacements in Rotating Disks

Considerable stress may be induced in bodies rotating at high speed. Analysis of this effect is important because failure of rotating machine members is particularly hazardous.

Consider a rotating disk with inside radius a and outside radius b (Figure 18-3). The force equilibrium equations of Section 18-1 did not include body forces. If we include rotational effects, there is an additional force term $\rho\omega^2 r^2 \, dr \, d\theta$, where mass density is given by $\rho(\text{lb-sec}^2/\text{in.}^4)$ and angular velocity is given by ω (rad/sec). For a rotating disk with no external loading but with an internal pressure p (due to a force fit or shrink fit), equations (18-9), (18-10), and (18-11) become

$$\sigma_r = \frac{-a^2 p\left(\frac{b^2}{r^2} - 1\right)}{b^2 - a^2} + \rho\omega^2\left(\frac{3 + v}{8}\right)\left(a^2 + b^2 - \frac{a^2 b^2}{r^2} - r^2\right) \tag{18-19}$$

$$\sigma_\theta = \frac{a^2 p\left(\frac{b^2}{r^2} + 1\right)}{b^2 - a^2} + \rho\omega^2\left(\frac{3 + v}{8}\right)\left[a^2 + b^2 + \frac{a^2 b^2}{r^2} - \left(\frac{1 + 3v}{3 + v}\right)r^2\right] \tag{18-20}$$

$$u = \frac{a^2 p}{E(b^2 - a^2)}\left[r(1 - v) + \frac{b^2(1 + v)}{r}\right] + \frac{\rho\omega^2 r}{E}\left(\frac{3 + v}{8}\right)$$
$$\times \left[(a^2 + b^2)(1 - v) + \frac{a^2 b^2}{r^2}(1 + v) - \left(\frac{1 - v^2}{3 + v}\right)r^2\right] \tag{18-21}$$

Ordinarily, inertial stress and displacement of a shaft would be neglected. Thus, for a shaft, we have approximately

$$\sigma_r = \sigma_\theta = -p$$
$$u = \frac{-(1 - v)pr}{E} \tag{18-22}$$

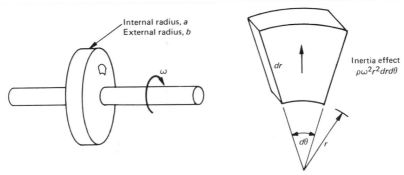

Figure 18-3 Inertia loading of a rotating disk.

We note, however, that the contact pressure p depends on rotation speed ω. For any value of ω, the initial radial interference U equals the sum of the expansion of the hub and the contraction of the shaft at radius a. Using equations (18-21) and (18-22) for u, and distinguishing between the physical properties of hub and shaft, we have **initial radial interference**

$$U = ap \left[\frac{\dfrac{b^2 + a^2}{b^2 - a^2} + v}{E_h} + \frac{1 - v}{E_s} \right] + ap\omega^2 \left[\frac{(1 - v)a^2 + (3 + v)b^2}{4E_h} \right] \quad (18\text{-}23)$$

which is required for a given contact pressure p at rotation speed ω rad/sec. This equation is valid as long as a positive contact pressure is maintained.

Example 18-3. A 16-in. diameter steel flywheel is to be force fit on a 2-in. diameter steel shaft. At maximum speed of 4000 rpm, a contact pressure of 1000 psi is to be maintained. (a) Find required interference and maximum normal stress at assembly. (b) Find speed at which the contact pressure becomes zero.

Solution: *Part a.* Substituting $a = 1$ in., $b = 8$ in., $v = 0.3$, $E = 30 \times 10^6$ psi and $\rho = (0.280 \text{ lb/in.}^3)/(386 \text{ in./sec}^2)$ in equation (18-23), we obtain

$$U = 67.7 \times 10^{-9} p + 1.28 \times 10^{-9} \omega^2$$

For $p = 1000$ psi and $\omega = (2\pi/60)(4000) = 418$ rad/sec, the required initial interference is $U = 0.000292$ in.

Part b. Substituting this value of U and setting p equal to zero in the equation relating U, p, and ω^2, we obtain

$$\omega^2 = \frac{0.000292}{1.28 \times 10^{-9}}$$

corresponding to 4560 rpm. At this speed, the force fit becomes completely ineffective. ●

Figure 18-4 shows a miniature turbine designed for high rotation speeds. Due to the variation in rotor thickness, however, the procedure outlined above would be modified if we were to find stresses in the rotor. Some problems of this type are treated by Den Hartog [1].

Figure 18-4 Cutaway view of a miniature high speed turbojet engine. [Courtesy Lab Sciences, Inc., Boca Raton, Fla.]

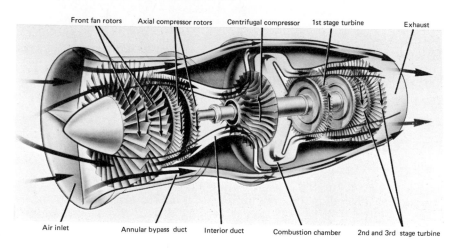

SECTION 18-4

Energy Storage in Flywheels

Heavy disks often serve as flywheels designed to store energy for the purpose of maintaining reasonably constant speed in a machine in spite of variations in input and output power. In a similar application the stored energy is used in a short burst as in a punch press or shear.

Stored energy in a flywheel is in the form of kinetic energy

$$E_k = \tfrac{1}{2}J\omega^2$$

where J is the mass moment of inertia and ω is the speed in radians per second. For a solid circular disk of radius b in. and weight W lb, $J = b^2W/2g$ lb-sec²-in. where $g = 386$ in./sec². In the case of a heavy rim of inside radius a, outside radius b, and a light hub

$$J = \frac{(b^2 - a^2)W}{2g}$$

For a conservative (loss free) system, this energy is available as work output

$$\text{work} = E_k \quad \text{or} \quad \int T d\theta = \tfrac{1}{2}J\omega^2$$

Example 18-4. A 10-in. diameter solid disk weighing 40 lb rotates at 3000 rpm. Its energy is to be used to punch metal during one third revolution of the disk. What is the average torque available?

Solution: We set

$$T\theta = \tfrac{1}{2}J\omega^2$$

where $\theta = 2\pi/3$ and $J = b^2W/(2g)$.

Using $\omega = (2\pi/60)(3000)$, we obtain $T = 30,400$ in.-lb if the disk goes from 3000 to 0 rpm in one third revolution. The braking torque required to stop a similar disk in one third revolution would have the same value. ●

SECTION 18-5

Design Based on Plastic Analysis

Due to the fluctuating nature of the loading of most machine members, plastic analysis is seldom appropriate to machine design. In certain cases, however, a saving of material can be effected by designing on the basis of yielding throughout a part, rather than basing the design on loads at which yielding first occurs. The thick wall cylinder furnishes one such example.

We will base our analysis on the *maximum shear theory*. Suppose we assume an idealized shear stress–shear strain relationship as in Figure 18-5.

The elastic region

In the elastic region, the equations of the first section of this chapter apply. In particular we will utilize the equilibrium equation

$$\sigma_\theta = \frac{d(r\sigma_r)}{dr} \tag{18-25}$$

from which

$$\frac{d\sigma_r}{dr} = \frac{\sigma_\theta - \sigma_r}{r} \tag{18-26}$$

and the equations for radial and tangential stress due to internal pressure p:

$$\sigma_r = \frac{-a^2p\left(\dfrac{b^2}{r^2} - 1\right)}{b^2 - a^2} \tag{18-27}$$

$$\sigma_\theta = \frac{a^2p\left(\dfrac{b^2}{r^2} + 1\right)}{b^2 - a^2} \tag{18-28}$$

For the case of internal pressure, maximum shear stress at radius r is given by

$$\tau_{max} = \frac{\sigma_\theta - \sigma_r}{2} \tag{18-29}$$

In the elastic region, we may use equations (18-27) and (18-28) in equation (18-29) to obtain

$$\tau_{max} = \frac{a^2b^2p}{r^2(b^2 - a^2)} \tag{18-30}$$

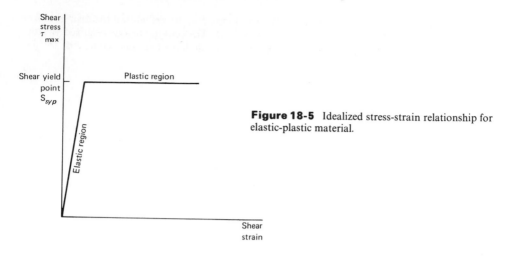

Figure 18-5 Idealized stress-strain relationship for elastic-plastic material.

The maximax shear stress occurs at the inner radius. It is

$$\tau_{max}(a) = \frac{b^2 p}{b^2 - a^2} \tag{18-31}$$

When $\tau_{max}(a)$ reaches the shear yield point S_{syp}, we are at the transition between the perfectly elastic case and the elastic-plastic case. That is, yielding begins at this instant. The pressure corresponding to the beginning of yielding is, from equation (18-31)

$$p_1 = S_{syp} \frac{b^2 - a^2}{b^2} \tag{18-32}$$

The elastic-plastic region

At internal pressure p_1 obtained from equation (18-32), yielding has just begun at the inner surface. If we continue to increase the internal pressure, yielding will progress through the thickness of the cylinder until finally the maximum shear stress at the outer surface reaches the shear yield point. During the period of yielding, the equilibrium relationships still hold, but the stress–strain laws are not the same as for the completely elastic region. The equilibrium equation (18-26) for axisymmetric loading still applies

$$\frac{d\sigma_r}{dr} = \frac{\sigma_\theta - \sigma_r}{r}$$

but the maximum shear stress must not exceed the shear yield point

$$\tau_{max} = \frac{\sigma_\theta - \sigma_r}{2} \leqslant S_{syp} \tag{18-33}$$

Let internal pressure be slowly increased until yielding progresses just to the outer surface. Then, at that time, the maximum shear stress will be a constant throughout. From equation (18-33),

$$\frac{\sigma_\theta - \sigma_r}{2} = S_{syp} \tag{18-34}$$

Using equation (18-33) in equation (18-26), we obtain the differential equation governing the state of total yielding. This will be considered the **failure criterion for plastic design**

$$\frac{d\sigma_r}{dr} = \frac{2S_{syp}}{r} \tag{18-35}$$

The general solution of equation (18-35) is

$$\sigma_r = 2S_{syp}(\ln r + C)$$

The arbitrary constant C is found by equating the external pressure to zero.

$$\sigma_r(b) = 0 = 2S_{syp}(\ln b + C)$$

from which $C = -\ln b$ and we may write

$$\sigma_r = -2S_{syp} \ln \frac{b}{r} \tag{18-36}$$

for the completely plastic cylinder.

The pressure corresponding to plasticity throughout the cylinder is given by the negative radial stress at the inner surface. For plastic design, the **failure pressure** is

$$p_2 = -\sigma_r(a) = 2S_{syp} \ln \frac{b}{a} \tag{18-37}$$

Since we have used the maximum shear theory, the shear yield point should be taken as half the tensile yield point. The allowable shear stress is

$$S_{s(allow)} = \frac{S_{syp}}{N} = \frac{S_{yp}}{2N} \tag{18-38}$$

for safety factor N. Using equation (18-37), the allowable internal pressure for plastic design will then be

$$p_{(allow)} = \frac{S_{yp}}{N} \ln \frac{b}{a} \tag{18-39}$$

This result is reasonably valid if we use a ductile material and a generous factor of safety so that expected pressures do not exceed p_1, the limit for complete elasticity. Then, in the event of a single overpressure up to p_2, failure will not occur. This criterion is unsatisfactory for repeated loading in the vicinity of pressure p_2. In the case of a brittle material, plastic analysis is inappropriate. When the ultimate strength of a brittle material is reached at any point, we expect a crack to form and propagate through the part, possibly resulting in a catastrophic failure.

Example 18-5: Plastic Analysis. Consider a thick wall pipe where $a = 1.5$ and $b = 2$. Find maximum allowable internal pressure, before yielding begins, and on the basis of plastic analysis. The yield point of the material $S_{yp} = 60,000$ psi and we will use a factor of safety $N = 4$.

Solution: Based on yielding, maximum allowable pressure is given by equating $\sigma_\theta(a)$ to the working strength

$$\sigma_\theta(a) = p\frac{b^2 + a^2}{b^2 - a^2} = 3.57p = \frac{S_{yp}}{N}$$

from which the maximum allowable pressure based on the *maximum stress theory* (in terms of the onset of yielding) is

$$P_{(allow)} = 4200 \text{ psi}$$

We will now base our results on the *maximum shear theory* and the onset of yielding. Maximum shear stress occurs at the inner surface where

$$\tau_{max} = \frac{\sigma_\theta(a) + p}{2} = 2.29p$$

Maximum internal pressure is given by equating τ_{max} to the working strength based on shear yielding

$$S_{sw} = \frac{S_{yp}}{2N}$$

from which

$$2.29p = \frac{S_{yp}}{2N}$$

or

$$P_{(allow)} = 3280 \text{ psi}$$

Now, suppose we assume an idealized stress-strain relationship, as in Figure 18-5, and design on a plastic basis. Using equation (18-39) we have

$$P_{(allow)} = \frac{S_{yp}}{N} \ln\frac{b}{a} = 4314 \text{ psi} \quad \bullet$$

SECTION 18-6

Initially Curved Members

When a machine member with considerable initial curvature is subjected to pure bending (Figure 18-6), the form of the stress distribution resembles that of the thick wall cylinder except that there is a logarithmic term. The results for a curved rectangular bar (see Timoshenko and Goodier [2]) are

$$\sigma_r = C_1 + \frac{C_2}{r^2} + C_3 \ln r$$

$$\sigma_\theta = C_1 - \frac{C_2}{r^2} + C_3(1 + \ln r)$$

(18-40)

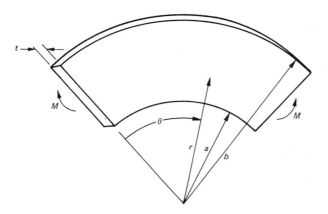

Figure 18-6 Bending of an initially curved member.

This stress distribution is independent of the tangential coordinate θ, but, unlike the above axisymmetric problems, there is a θ-dependent tangential displacement.

For boundaries at $r = a$ and $r = b$, as in Figure 18-6, we have

$$\sigma_r(a) = \sigma_r(b) = 0 \tag{18-41}$$

Moment M at the ends yields the condition

$$M = -t \int_a^b \sigma_\theta r \, dr \tag{18-42}$$

Applying the boundary conditions, we obtain the arbitrary constants from which tangential stress

$$\sigma_\theta = \frac{-4M\left(-\dfrac{a^2 b^2}{r^2}\ln\dfrac{b}{a} + b^2 \ln\dfrac{r}{b} + a^2 \ln\dfrac{a}{r} + b^2 - a^2\right)}{t\left[(b^2 - a^2)^2 - 4a^2 b^2\left(\ln\dfrac{b}{a}\right)^2\right]}$$

The condition of zero net load on the ends is identically satisfied. Maximum tangential stress occurs at the inner surface and radial stress is nowhere as great as this value. Substituting $r = a$, we have

$$\sigma_\theta(a) = \frac{-4M\left(b^2 - a^2 - 2b^2 \ln\dfrac{b}{a}\right)}{t\left[(b^2 - a^2)^2 - 4a^2 b^2\left(\ln\dfrac{b}{a}\right)^2\right]} \tag{18-43}$$

A detailed treatment of curved flexural members is given by Seely and Smith [3]. They examine I and T sections as well as circular and rectangular sections.

PROBLEMS

1. A steel cylinder with 1-in. internal radius and 3-in. external radius is subject to 10,000 psi internal pressure. Axial stress is zero. (a) Compute and plot tangential stress at $r = 1$, 2, and 3. (b) Compute and plot radial stress at $r = 1$, 2, and 3. (c) Compute and plot maximum shear stress at $r = 1$, 2, and 3. (d) Find factor of safety N based on yielding due to normal stress where $S_{yp} = 60,000$ psi. (e) Find N based on shear yielding where $S_{syp} = S_{yp}/2$.

2. Repeat Problem 1 for a cylinder with 1-in. internal radius and 2-in. external radius. Plot values at $r = 1$, 1.5 and 2.

3. A long steel cylinder with an inside diameter of 4 in. is to hold liquid at a static pressure of 8000 psi. (a) Find the required thickness based on thin wall theory, using a yield point of 68,000 psi and a safety factor of 4. (b) Find the maximum tangential stress and the factor of safety based on the maximum normal stress theory, using the thickness found above. (c) Find the maximum shear stress and the factor of safety based on the maximum shear theory.

4. Repeat Problem 3 for an internal pressure of 4000 psi.

5. A 2-in. inside diameter cylinder is to be made of steel with a yield point of 75,000 psi. Find wall thickness based on the maximum normal stress theory and a safety factor of 3 for 5000 psi internal pressure.

6. Repeat Problem 5 using the maximum shear theory.

7. A long thick wall pressure vessel is subjected to internal and external pressure. It is free to expand axially. Show that axial strain is constant, that is, independent of the radial coordinate. (This condition justifies our neglecting axial stress except that caused by pressure on the ends of the vessel.)

8. A thick wall cylinder is subjected to internal pressure p. Plot σ_θ/p, σ_r/p, and τ_{max}/p versus r for the elastic case; $b/a = 2$.

9. (a) Find allowable internal pressure p for a 6-in. O.D. 4-in. I.D. steel vessel based on the maximum normal stress theory (that is, σ_θ shall not exceed S_{yp}/N) where $S_{yp} = 60,000$ psi and $N = 3$. (b) Repeat using the maximum shear theory.

10. Find (a) interface pressure and (b) maximum stress due to an interference fit between a 1.5-in. diameter solid steel shaft and a 6-in. O.D. steel disk where *radial* interference $= 0.0005$ in.

11. A $2\frac{1}{4}$-in. long by 3-in. outside diameter hub is pressed on a $1\frac{1}{2}$-in. diameter steel shaft. (a) Find tangential stress in the hub if interface pressure is 25,000 psi. (b) Find the radial interference.

12. A 5-in. O.D. aluminum disk with 1.5-in. axial length is press fit on a 2-in. diameter steel shaft. Radial interference is 0.0012 in. Find low speed torque capacity for this fit based on a coefficient of friction of 0.1. Plot radial, tangential, and shear stress versus radius for the disk (when torsion free).

13. A 10-in. diameter hub is shrunk on a 2-in. diameter shaft producing a pressure of 10,000 psi where the surfaces contact. (a) Find maximum normal stress in the hub. Where does it occur? (b) Find maximum shear stress in the hub. Where does it occur?

14. An 8-in. diameter steel disk is force fit on a 1.5-in. diameter steel shaft. (a) Find the initial contact pressure required if contact pressure is to be 500 psi at 3000 rpm. (b) Find maximum stress at zero speed.

15. Solve Problem 14 if contact pressure is to be 200 psi at 2500 rpm.

16. A 6-in. diameter steel disk with 2-in. axial thickness is force fit on a 1-in. diameter steel shaft. The radial interference is 0.0005 in. At what speed in revolutions per minute will the fit become completely ineffective?

17. Repeat Problem 16 for a 4.5-in. diameter disk.

18. The speed of disks A and B in Problem Figure 18 must be reduced from 2000 rpm to 1000 rpm in 3 rev. Find the average braking torque required. The disks are made of steel with a density of 0.28 lb/in.^{3} and rotate as a unit.

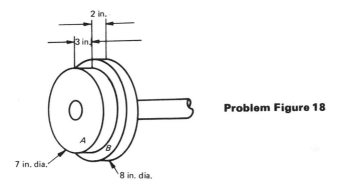

Problem Figure 18

19. Find the average braking torque required to stop disks A and B in Problem Figure 18 in 10 rev if their initial velocity is 6000 rpm and they are made of aluminum of density 0.10 lb/in.^{3}

20. A thick wall cylinder is subjected to an internal pressure p. Plot σ_θ/p, σ_r/p, and τ_{max}/p versus r for the fully plastic case; $b/a = 2$; p is the failure pressure.

21. Design a pressure vessel using (**a**) thin wall theory, (**b**) maximum normal stress theory for the elastic case, (**c**) maximum shear theory for the elastic case, and (**d**) maximum shear theory for the plastic case. The yield point in tension is 120,000 psi; the shear yield point is 60,000 psi; internal pressure p is 20,000 psi; the inside diameter of the vessel is 6 in.; and a factor of safety of 3 is used.

22. A curved beam is subject to a bending moment M. Show the effect of initial curvature by plotting

$$\frac{\sigma_\theta(a)}{\sigma_o} \quad \text{for } 1.2 \leqslant b/a \leqslant 5$$

where

$$\sigma_o = \frac{6M}{t(b-a)^2}$$

represents maximum bending stress in a straight beam.

REFERENCES

[1] J. P. Den Hartog: *Advanced Strength of Materials*. McGraw-Hill Book Company, New York, 1952.

[2] S. Timoshenko and J. N. Goodier: *Theory of Elasticity*, 2nd ed. McGraw-Hill Book Company, New York, 1951.

[3] F. B. Seely and J. O. Smith: *Advanced Mechanics of Materials*, 2nd ed. McGraw-Hill Book Company, New York, 1952.

[4] J. H. Potter (ed.): *Handbook of the Engineering Sciences*, Vol. 2, Sect. 13. Van Nostrand-Reinhold Books, New York, 1967.

[5] C.-T. Wang: *Applied Elasticity*. McGraw-Hill Book Company, New York, 1953.

[6] *1st International Conference on Pressure Vessel Technology Proceedings*, (3 parts). American Society of Mechanical Engineers, New York, 1969.

[7] R. W. Nichols (ed.): *Pressure Vessel Engineering Technology*, American Elsevier Publishing Co., New York, 1971.

Appendix A

Material Properties

Table A-1 Mechanical Properties of Some Cast Ferrous Materials

Identification Number or Specification	Modulus of Elast. in Tension, psi	Tensile Strength, ksi	Yield Strength, ksi	Elongation in 2 in., %	Hardness BHN	Endurance Limit ksi	Modulus of Elast. in Compression, psi	Compressive Strength ksi	Shear Strength, ksi	Impact Strength, (Charpy), ft-lb
Gray Cast Irons										
ASTM, Class 20	12×10^6	20	—	—	160	10	—	95	32	55
ASTM, Class 25	13×10^6	25	—	—	165	12.5	—	100	37	55
ASTM, Class 30	15×10^6	30	—	—	195	14.5	—	115	44	60
ASTM, Class 40	17×10^6	40	—	—	220	19	—	143	57	70
ASTM, Class 50	19×10^6	50	—	—	238	22	—	150	65	80
ASTM, Class 60	20×10^6	60	—	—	260	24	—	170	72	115
Malleable Cast Irons										
32510 (ASTM A47)	25×10^6	50	32.5	10	133	28	25×10^6	208	47	16.5
35018 (ASTM A47)	25×10^6	53	35	18	133	31	25×10^6	220	51	16.5
45010 (ASTM A220)	26×10^6	65	45	10	185	32	23.2×10^6	242	49	14
50007 (ASTM A220)	26.5×10^6	75	50	7	204	37	23.2×10^6	242	75	14
60003 (ASTM A220)	27×10^6	80	60	3	226	39	23.2×10^6	242	80	14
80002 (ASTM A220)	27×10^6	100	80	2	255	40	23.2×10^6	242	100	14
Nodular or Ductile Cast Irons										
60-40-18 (ASTM) or 60-45-12 (A536)	23.5×10^6	70	52.5	10-25	178	35	—	140	—	—
80-55-06 (")	23.5×10^6	100	67.5	3-10	217	50	—	200	—	—
100-70-03a (")	23.5×10^6	110	72.5	6-10	257	55	—	220	—	—
120-90-02a (")	23.5×10^6	135	108	2-7	283	63	—	270	—	—
Heat Resistant	18.5×10^6	73	40	7-40	170	37	—	146	—	—

SOURCE: Compiled from *1973 Materials Selector*, Reinhold Publishing Co., New York; *Tool Engineers' Handbook*, 2nd. ed., McGraw-Hill Book Co., New York, and *ASME Handbook-Metal Properties,* McGraw-Hill Book Co., New York.

[a] Obtained by heat treatment involving normalizing or quenching and tempering.
[b] Below 8% total all content.
[c] Normalized and tempered.
[d] Quenched and tempered.
[e] Annealed.
[f] Normalized.
[g] Wear resistant.
[h] Corrosion resistant.
[i] Heat and corrosion resistant.
[j] 2000F, Water quenched.

Identification Number or Specification	Modulus of Elast. in Tension, psi	Tensile Strength, ksi	Yield Strength, ksi	Elongation in 2 in., %	Hardness BHN	Endurance Limit, ksi	Modulus of Elast. in Compression, ksi	Compressive Strength, ksi	Shear Strength, ksi	Impact Strength, (Charpy), ft-lb
Cast Alloy Steels[b]										
Class 65,000	30×10^6	68[c]	38	32	137	32	—	—	—	60
Class 80,000	30×10^6	86[c]	54	24	170	39	—	—	—	48
Class 105,000	30×10^6	110[c]	91	21	217	53	—	—	—	58
Class 150,000	30×10^6	158[d]	142	13	311	74	—	—	—	30
Class 200,000	30×10^6	205[d]	170	8	401	88	—	—	—	14
Cast Carbon Steels										
Class 60,000[e]	30×10^6	63	35	30	131	30	—	—	—	12
Class 70,000[f]	30×10^6	75	42	27	143	35	—	—	—	30
Class 85,000[c]	30×10^6	90	55	20	179	39	—	—	—	26
Class 100,000[d]	30×10^6	105	75	19	212	45	—	—	—	40
Alloy Cast Irons										
Ni-Hard Type 2[g]	25×10^6	60	—	—	575	—	—	—	—	38
Duriron[h]	23×10^6	16	—	—	520	—	—	—	—	3
Ni-Resist Type 1[i]	16×10^6	27	—	—	150	—	—	—	—	60
Cast Stainless Steels										
CB-30[e]	29×10^6	95	60	15	195	—	—	—	—	
CF-8M[j]	28×10^6	80	42	50	163	—	—	—	—	70
CF-20[j]	28×10^6	77	36	50	163	—	—	—	—	75
CN-7M[j]	24×10^6	69	32	48	130	—	—	—	—	70

Table A-2 Mechanical Properties of Plain Carbon and Alloy Steels (based on a 1 in. diameter specimen)

AISI Type	Condition	Tensile Strength, ksi	Yield Strength, ksi	Elongat. in 2 in., %	Reduction in Area, %	Hardness, BHN	Machin-ability (Based on 1112 = 100)
1010	HR	64	42	28	67	107	45
	CD	78	68	16	63	129	55
	CDA	64	48	28	65	131	55
1020	HR	65	43	36	59	143	50
	CD	78	66	20	55	156	65
	A	57	52	37	66	111	90
	N	64	50	36	68	131	75
1030	HR & turned	72	44	31	63	140	—
	CD	84	76	16	57	177	65
	A	67	50	31	58	126	—
	N	76	51	32	61	149	—
1040	HR	91	58	27	50	201	63
	CD	100	88	17	42	207	65
	A	75	51	30	57	149	—
	N	85	50	28	55	170	60
1045	HR	98	59	24	45	212	56
	CD	103	90	14	40	217	60
	A	90	55	27	54	174	60
	N	99	61	25	49	207	—
1050	HR	105	67	15	—	—	—
	CD	114	104	9	—	—	54
	A	92	43	24	40	187	—
	N	109	62	20	39	217	—
1095	HR	142	83	18	38	295	—
	A	95	38	13	21	192	—
	N	147	73	10	14	293	—
1118	HR	75	50	35	55	140	—
	CD	85	75	25	55	170	80
	A	65	41	35	67	131	80
	N	69	46	34	66	143	80
2330	CD	105	90	20	50	212	50
	A	86	61	28	58	179	50
	N	100	68	26	56	207	—
3140	CD	107	92	17	50	212	55
	A	100	61	25	51	197	55
	N	129	87	20	58	262	—
4130	HRA	86	56	29	57	183	65
	CDA	98	87	21	52	201	70
	N	97	63	26	60	197	50

SOURCE: *ASME Handbook-Material Properties*, McGraw-Hill Book Co., 1954; *Ryerson Data Book*, Joseph T. Ryerson and Sons, Inc., 1965.

NOTE: HR = hot rolled, HRA = hot rolled annealed, CD = cold drawn, CDA = cold drawn annealed, HRN = hot rolled normalized, A = annealed, N = normalized.

Table A-2 (continued)

AISI Type	Condition	Tensile Strength, ksi	Yield Strength, ksi	Elongat. in 2 in., %	Reduction in Area, %	Hardness, BHN	Machin-ability (Based on 1112 = 100)
4140	HRA	90	63	27	58	187	57
	CDA	102	90	18	50	223	66
	N	148	95	18	47	302	—
4340	HRA	101	69	21	45	207	45
	CDA	110	99	16	42	223	50
	N	185	126	11	41	363	—
4620	HR	85	63	28	64	183	58
	CD	101	85	22	60	207	64
	A	74	54	31	60	149	55
	N	83	53	29	67	174	—
4640	CDA	117	95	15	43	235	55
	A	98	63	24	51	179	55
	N	123	87	19	51	248	—
5120	CD	92	77	20	55	187	65
	CDA	87	70	23	60	179	65
5140	CDA	105	88	18	52	212	60
52100	HRA	100	81	25	57	192	45
	HRN	185	139	13	20	363	—
6150	CDA	111	95	14	44	223	45
	N	136	89	22	61	269	—
8620	HR	89	65	25	63	192	60
	CD	102	85	22	58	212	63
	A	78	56	31	62	149	—
	N	92	52	26	60	183	—
8640	CD	140	120	11	38	277	—
	CDA	107	90	14	45	217	60
8740	HRA	95	64	25	55	190	56
	CDA	107	96	17	48	223	66
	N	135	88	16	48	269	—
9255	HRA	113	71	22	41	229	45
	N	135	84	20	43	269	—
E9310	HR	115	75	22	58	241	45
	A	119	64	17	42	241	—
	N	132	83	19	58	269	—
9440	HR	123	80	18	47	241	—
	HRA	93	59	26	53	183	—
	N	110	72	25	58	223	—

Table A-3 Mechanical Properties of Carburizing and Hardening Grade Steels[a]

Plain Carbon, Carburized Steels[c] / Plain Carbon, Hardened Steels[c]

AISI Type	Tensile Strength, ksi	Yield Point, ksi	Elongation in 2 in., %	Reduction of Area, %	Impact Strength (Izod), ft-lb	Hardness Case (Brinell)	Hardness Case (Rockwell)	Machining
C1015	73	46	32	71	91	149[b]	C62 (.048")	Poor
C1020	75	48	31	71	93	156[b]	C62 (.046")	Poor
C1022	83	47	27	66	81	163[b]	C62 (.046")	Good
C1117	97	59	23	53	33	192[b]	C65 (.045")	Ver. g'd. to excel.
C1118	113	77	17	45	16	229[b]	C61 (.065")	Ver. g'd. to excel.
C1030	122-75	93-58	18-33	48-71	8-100		495-179[d]	Fair to good
C1040	113-89	86-62	19-33	48-68	36-72		262-183[d]	Fair to good
C1050	143-96	108-61	10-30	42-63	16-53		321-192[d]	Fair to good
C1060	160-103	112-68	12-28	40-60	14-23		321-212[d]	Must be Annl'd.
C1080	190-117	142-70	12-24	35-51	10-22		388-223[d]	Must be Annl'd.
C1095	188-190	120-74	10-26	30-53	5-6		401-229[d]	Must be Annl'd.
C1137	158-87	138-60	6-28	22-70	10-90		352-174[d]	Good to very good
C1141	237-94	188-68[e]	7-28	58-63	9-81		461-192[d]	Good to very good
C1144	128-97	91-68	17-24	35-59	7-62		277-201[d]	Good to very good

Alloy Steels, Hardening Grades[h]

AISI Type	Tensile Strength, ksi	Yield Point, ksi	Elongation in 2 in., %	Reduction of Area, %	Impact Strength (Izod), ft-lb	Hardness Core (Brinell)	Hardness Case (Rockwell)	Machining
4130[i]	234-98	197-89	12-28	44-71	32-108	461-202[d]		—
8630[j]	250-115	230-93	10-26	47-70	33-114	495-217[d]		—
1340	282-100	235-76	9-25	24-61	9-97	578-235[d]		—
3140	280-112	249-92	11-23	49-69	9-97	555-223[d]		—
4140[k]	290-117	251-100	11-23	42-65	11-108	578-235[d]		—
4340[l]	284-142	228-130	11-21	48-64	18-77	555-293[d]		—
5140[k]	278-114	228-84	8-28	28-68	9-93	534-207[d]		—
8740	290-119	240-100	10-25	42-64	21-88	578-241[d]		—
4150	308-128	248-117	10-20	34-60	10-77	578-262[d]		—
5150	312-116	250-102	9-22	31-62	7-78	601-241[d]		—
6150[k]	315-118	270-108	7-22	17-61	14-87	601-241[d]		—
8650[l]	282-123	250-114	11-22	41-62	9-78	555-255[d]		—
9255[n]	305-130	288-102	2-22	4-49	3-25	601-262[d]		—
5160[o]	322-115	260-106	4-24	9-60	2-63	627-229[d]		—
4063[m]	345-114	257-103	4-24	8-60	3-67	557-229[d]		—

Table A-3 (continued)

	Alloy Steels, Carburizing Grades[e, f, g]							
E3310	180, 180	146, 180	14, 15	57, 58	55, 57	363, 363	61, 58 (.047″)	—
4320	218, 211	178, 173	14, 13	48, 51	28, 29	429, 415	63, 59 (.075″)	—
4520	103, 102	65, 62	24, 25	60, 64	61, 90	217, 212	65, 61 (.062″)	—
4620	119, 115	83, 80	20, 21	59, 64	52, 69	277, 248	63, 59 (.075″)	—
4820	207, 205	167, 184	14, 13	52, 53	44, 47	415, 415	61, 58 (.047″)	—
8620	188, 167	149, 120	12, 14	52, 53	26, 30	388, 341	64, 61 (.075″)	—
E9310	173, 168	135, 137	16, 16	60, 60	61, 39	363, 341	62, 60 (.047″)	—

SOURCE: Compiled from *1973 Materials Selector*, Reinhold Publishing Co., New York. (For more details refer to *Modern Steel and Their Properties*, 7th ed., Bethlehem Steel Corp.)

a Average properties for 1-in. rounds, except where noted.
b Carburized at 1675°F for 8 hr, pot cooled, reheated to 1425°F, water quenched and tempered at 350°F; C1117 and C1118 are carburized at 1700°F, reheated to 1450°F, water quenched and tempered at 350°F.
c Except for C1141, ranges correspond to range of values obtainable at tempering temperatures from 400°F to 1300°F. Materials are heat treated as follows: C1050, C1060 and C1080 are normalized at 1650°F, reheated to 1550°F, quenched in oil and then tempered at 400-1300°F. C1040 is normalized at 400-1300°F. C1030 is normalized at 1700°F, reheated to 1600°F, quenched in water and then tempered at 400-1300°F, reheated to 1575°F, quenched in water and then tempered at 400-1300°F. C1095 is normalized at 1650°F, reheated to 1475°F, quenched in oil and then tempered at 400-1300°F. C1137 is normalized at 400-1300°F. C1141 (1/2 inch round) is normalized at 1575°F, reheated to 1500°F, quenched in oil and tempered at 400-1300°F. C1144 is normalized at 1650°F, reheated to 1550°F, quenched in oil and then tempered at 400-1300°F.
d Through hardened.
e Yield strength at 0.2% offset.
f Single heat results.
g Core properties for 0.5-in. rounds. Two figures represent values obtained at tempering temperatures of 300°F and 400°F respectively, for materials in the following condition: carburized at 1700°F for 8 hr, pot cooled, reheated to 1455-1550°F, quenched in agitated oil and then tempered.
h Properties for 0.5-in. rounds. Range of values corresponds to range of tempering temperatures from 400 to 1300°F. Materials (arranged in order of increasing carbon content) are heat treated as follows (unless otherwise indicated): normalized at 1600°F, reheated to 1525°F, quenched in oil and then tempered.
i Reheated to 1575°F, quenched in water.
j Reheated to 1550°F, quenched in water.
k Reheated to 1550°F.
l Reheated to 1475°F.
m Normalized at 1650°F, reheated to 1625°F.
n Normalized to 1575°F.
o Normalized at 1550°F.

Table A-4 Mechanical Properties of Some Heat-Treated Steels at Various Tempering Temperatures

Column headers for each group: Tempering Temp., °F | Tensile Strength, ksi | Yield Point, ksi | Reduction of Area, % | Elongation in 2 in., % | Brinell Hardness

C1040 quenched in oil at 1575°F						C3140 quenched in oil at 1525°F						C5150 quenched in oil at 1525°F					
400	113	86	48	19	262	400	281	248	48	12	555	400	306	250	31	8	601
600	113	86	53	20	255	600	242	218	50	13	477	600	267	238	37	9	514
800	110	81	53	21	241	800	192	178	57	14	388	800	210	195	44	11	415
1000	104	72	58	25	212	1000	152	133	62	18	311	1000	160	149	52	15	321
1200	92	62	65	28	192	1200	125	104	68	21	262	1200	128	117	60	21	269
1300	88	61	68	33	183	1300	112	92	69	23	223	1300	115	102	62	22	241

C1060 quenched in oil at 1550°F						C4027 quenched in water at 1585°F						C6150 quenched in oil at 1550°F					
400	160	112	40	12	321	400	238	189	35	12	415	400	315	270	15	6	601
600	160	112	40	12	321	600	214	188	46	12	415	600	270	240	34	9	534
800	155	111	41	13	311	800	175	160	54	13	363	800	222	208	40	10	444
1000	140	97	45	17	277	1000	145	130	62	16	302	1000	183	173	46	12	375
1200	116	78	53	23	229	1200	116	98	67	21	229	1200	142	131	55	18	293
1300	103	68	60	28	212	1300	97	81	70	26	192	1300	117	107	62	22	241

C1095 quenched in water at 1450°F						C4063 quenched in oil at 1500°F						C8630 quenched in water at 1550°F					
400	216	152	31	10	601	400	314	255	8	5	555	400	251	230	46	10	495
600	212	150	32	10	534	600	285	255	33	8	514	600	221	204	53	11	444
800	199	138	35	12	388	800	228	210	41	10	444	800	186	174	60	14	375
1000	165	110	40	15	293	1000	180	165	45	13	363	1000	152	142	65	18	311
1200	122	84	47	20	235	1200	130	119	54	20	269	1200	121	109	68	22	248
1300	113	73	51	22	201	1300	113	103	60	24	229	1300	105	93	69	25	217

C1137 quenched in water at 1550°F						C4130 quenched in water at 1575°F						C8650 quenched in oil at 1475°F					
400	217	168	18	5	415	400	233	197	44	12	461	400	290	250	41	11	555
600	198	162	23	8	375	600	220	190	50	12	429	600	258	237	41	11	514
800	161	143	40	12	311	800	189	168	54	13	401	800	220	200	42	12	429
1000	120	105	60	19	262	1000	145	132	60	16	302	1000	175	155	48	14	363
1200	94	77	69	25	187	1200	110	97	68	22	241	1200	136	123	57	18	302
1300	86	65	71	28	179	1300	98	88	71	28	202	1300	122	112	62	22	255

C1144 quenched in water at 1550°F						C4140 quenched in oil at 1550°F						C8740 quenched in oil at 1525°F					
400	128	92	35	16	277	400	290	252	42	11	578	400	290	240	41	10	578
600	127	91	40	17	262	600	251	228	46	12	495	600	249	225	45	11	495
800	123	88	42	18	248	800	210	194	50	14	429	800	208	196	50	13	415
1000	117	82	47	20	235	1000	167	152	54	17	341	1000	175	165	54	15	363
1200	105	73	54	22	217	1200	130	113	61	21	277	1200	143	132	60	20	302
1300	96	68	59	24	201	1300	118	101	65	23	235	1300	118	100	63	25	241

C1340 quenched in oil at 1525°F						C4340 quenched in oil at 1475°F						C9255 quenched in oil at 1625°F					
400	285	235	24	8	578	400	284	228	47	12	555	400	305	288	4	1	601
600	245	212	39	10	495	600	248	218	48	13	477	600	272	260	10	3	578
800	193	178	49	12	415	800	210	192	52	14	415	800	233	216	21	8	477
1000	145	132	57	17	363	1000	171	158	57	17	363	1000	182	160	32	15	352
1200	113	92	62	22	293	1200	142	130	64	21	293	1200	144	118	42	20	285
1300	101	75	63	25	235	1300	138	109	65	24	247	1300	130	102	48	22	262

SOURCE: Data compiled from *Modern Steel and Their Properties*, 7th ed., Bethlehem Steel Corp.

NOTES: (a) All the data in this table are based on single heat results.

(b) 1-in. rounds, were treated for 1040, 1060, 1095, 1137, 1144 and 9255 steels. 0.565 in. rounds were treated for 1340, 4027, 6150 and 8750 steels. 0.530-in. rounds were treated for 3140, 4063, 4130, 4140, 4340, 5150, 8630 and 8650 steels. However, for testing, all specimens were turned down to 0.505 in. dia.

(c) Since every grade of steel ranges in composition and the results may vary from heat to heat and so can cause significant differences in the properties attainable by thermal treatment. Hence the properties listed in this table should not be considered as maximum, minimum or average values for a particular application of the grades involved.

Table A-5   Influence of Mass on the Mechanical Properties of Heat Treated Steels

Bar Dia., in.	Tensile Strength, psi.	Yield Point, psi.	Elongation in 2 in., %	Reduction in Area, %	Brinell Hardness	Bar Dia., in.	Tensile Strength, psi.	Yield Point, psi.	Elongation in 2 in., %	Reduction in Area, %	Brinell Hardness
C1040 oil quenched and tempered at 1000°F						C5140 oil quenched and tempered at 1000°F					
1/2	104,750	72,500	27.0	62.0	217	1/2	146,750	131,500	17.8	57.1	302
1	96,250	68,000	26.5	61.1	197	1	141,000	121,500	18.5	58.9	293
2	92,250	59,750	27.0	59.9	187	2	128,000	100,500	19.7	59.1	255
4	90,000	57,500	27.0	60.3	179	4	125,000	81,500	20.2	55.4	248
C1095 oil quenched and tempered at 1100°F						C6150 oil quenched and tempered at 1200°F					
1/2	142,000	87,000	17.4	42.8	293	1/2	147,000	141,500	17.8	53.9	293
1	139,750	79,000	17.2	38.8	277	1	141,250	129,500	18.7	56.3	293
2	134,500	77,250	18.7	43.4	269	2	133,750	116,500	19,5	57.4	269
4	130,000	65,750	17.2	34.4	262	4	121,500	94,500	21.0	59.7	241
C1141 oil quenched and tempered at 1200°F						C8650 oil quenched and tempered at 1000°F					
1/2	105,200	87,400	23.5	63.8	217	1/2	177,500	168,750	14.6	48.2	363
1	96,300	69,600	24.8	64.1	197	1	172,500	159,750	14.5	49.1	352
2	95,800	65,300	25.2	65.1	192	2	165,250	148,500	17.0	55.6	331
4	95,200	60,300	25.2	63.0	183	4	143,250	113,000	18.7	54.9	285
C2340 oil quenched and tempered at 1200°F						C3140 oil quenched and tempered at 800°F					
1/2	118,000	95,000	22.0	68.0	250	1/2	194,000	163,000	14.0	52.5	400
1	112,000	90,000	24.0	65.0	240	1	188,000	156,000	14.5	50.0	375
2	107,000	82,000	27.0	61.0	222	2	145,000	114,000	15.0	46.0	295
4	105,000	77,000	28.0	58.0	210	4	136,000	105,000	15.3	45.0	279
C4130 water quenched and tempered at 1100°F						C9255 oil quenched and tempered at 1000°F					
1/2	133,000	122,500	20.7	69.0	269	1/2	170,000	146,500	14.9	40.0	331
1	128,000	113,250	21.2	67.5	262	1	164,250	133,750	16.7	38.3	321
2	114,500	91,500	21.7	67.7	229	2	154,750	102,500	18.0	45.6	302
4	101,500	77,500	24.5	69.2	197	4	149,000	94,000	19.2	43.7	293
C4340 oil quenched and tempered at 1200°F						C9840 oil quenched and tempered at 800°F					
1/2	145,000	135,500	20.0	59.3	285	1/2	218,000	198,000	12.0	45.1	430
1	139,000	128,000	20.0	59.7	277	1	216,000	197,000	13.0	45.3	425
2	134,750	121,000	20.5	62.5	269	2	211,000	192,000	13.5	45.4	421
4	124,000	105,750	21.7	63.0	255	4	200,000	149,000	13.5	45.0	398

SOURCE: Data compiled from *Modern Steels and Their Properties*, 7th ed.
Bethlehem Steel Corp. except for C2340, C3140 and C9840 which is from
the International Nickel Co., Inc.

Table A-6 Mechanical Properties of Some Wrought Stainless Steels

AISI Type	Tensile Strength, ksi			Yield Strength, ksi			Elong. in 2 in., %			Red. of Area, %		Brinell Hardness BHN			Impact Strength (Izod), ft-lb			Endurance Limit, kpsi		Machinability (Based on BHN) = 100	Weldability
	Annealed	Cold Worked	Hardened & Tempered	Annealed	Cold Worked	Hardened & Tempered	Annealed	Cold Worked	Hardened & Tempered	Annealed	Cold Worked	Annealed	Cold Worked	Hardened & Tempered	Annealed	Cold Worked	Hardened & Tempered	Annealed	Cold Worked		
Austenitic																					
302	85	110	–	35	75	–	60	35	–	70	60	150	240	–	110	–	–	34	–	55	Excellent
304	85	110	–	35	75	–	60	60	–	70	–	149	240	–	110	90	–	34	–	55	Excellent
310, 310S	95	–	–	45	–	–	50	–	–	65	–	179	–	–	90	–	–	–	–	50	Good
316	80	90d	–	30	60d	–	60	45d	–	70	65d	149	190d	–	110	–	–	38	40d	50	Excellent
321	85	100d	–	35	65d	–	55	40d	–	65	60d	150	212d	–	110	–	–	38	–	50	Excellent
347, 348	90	100d	–	35	65d	–	50	40d	–	–	60d	160	212d	–	110	–	–	39	–	–	Excellent
Martensitic																					
403	73a	–	110	43a	–	85	30a	–	23	70	–	155	–	225	90	–	75	40	–	Fair	Fair
410	70	100b	110b	40a	85	85	40a	17	23	70	60	155	205	225	90	80a	75	40	–	55c	Fair—needs precautions
414	117a	130d	160a	98a	115d	127a	17a	15d	17a	60	58d	235	270e	–	50	–	48a	45	–	Fair	Fair with preheat & postheat
416, 416Sc	75	100e	110	40	85e	85	30	13e	18	60	55	155	205e	230	70	20e	25	40	53e	80	Not recom.
420	95	105d	230	50	85d	195	25	17d	8	55	50d	195	215d	500	–	–	10	40	–	45c	Fair with preheat & postheat
431	125	130d	165a	95	110d	125a	20	15d	17a	55	35d	260	270d	338a	50	–	40a	45	–	45c	Weldable with great care
440 A,B,C	105	115b,d	260	60	90b,d	240	20	7b,d	5	25b,d	20	215	240b,d	510	2	2b,d	4	40	–	40	–
Ferritic																					
405	68a	85	–	40	70	–	27a	20	–	60	60	150	185	–	25b	–	–	–	–	60	Excellent for fusion welding
430, 430F	75	83a	–	43a	63a	–	27a	20a	–	62a	60a	155	212	–	–	–	–	40b	46b	Fair	Fair, post annealed recom.
446	83a	85	–	53a	70	–	23a	20	–	45	45	163	183	–	2	–	–	47	–	Fair	Fair but care must be taken

SOURCE: Data was compiled from *1973 Materials Selector*, Reinhold Publishing Co., New York. New York, *ASME Handbook: Metals Properties*, McGraw-Hill Book Co., Inc., New York, 1954.

a Average values.
b Minimum values.
c Hardened to 200-220 BHN.
d Annealed and cold drawn.
e Tempered and cold drawn.

Table A-7   Mechanical Properties of Some Wrought Aluminum Alloys

Alloy and Temper	Tensile Str. ksi	Yield Str. ksi	Elong. in 2 in. % 1/16 in. Thk. Sheet	Elong. in 2 in. % 1/2 in. Dia. Rod	Brinell Hard. BHN 500 Kg: 10 mm ball	Shearing Str. ksi	Endur. Limit ksi Based on 5 × 10⁸ cyc.	Corrosion Resist. General	Corrosion Resist. Stress Cracking	Cold Working	Machinability	Brazing	Gas Welding	Arc Welding	Resistance Welding	Some Applications
1100- 0	13	5	35	45	23	9	5	A	A	A	E	A	A	A	B	Heat exchangers, pressure and storage tanks, chemical equipment, reflectors, sheetmetal work; cooking utensils.
-H14	18	17	9	20	32	11	7	A	A	C	D	A	A	A	A	
-H18	24	22	5	15	44	13	9	A	A	C	D	A	A	A	A	
2011-T3	55	43	—	15	95	32	18	D	C	C	A	D	D	D	D	Screw machine products
-T8	59	45	—	12	100	35	18	D	A	D	A	D	D	D	D	
2014- 0	27	14	22	18	45	18	13	—	—	—	—	—	—	—	—	Heavy duty forgings, power shovel bails, aircraft fittings, structural members, aircraft structures, truck frames.
-T4	63	40	18	20	105	38	20	D	C	C	B	D	B	B	B	
-T6	70	63	10	13	135	42	18	D	—	D	B	D	B	B	B	
2017- 0	26	10	—	22	45	18	13	—	—	—	—	—	—	—	—	Screw machine products
-T4	62	40	—	22	105	38	18	D	—	C	B	D	D	B	B	
2018-T6	55	43	—	15	100	39	17	—	C	—	A	—	—	B	—	Cylinder heads, pistons
2024- 0	27	11	20	22	47	18	13	—	—	—	—	—	—	—	—	Screw machine products, truck wheels, aircraft structural parts
-T4	68	47	20	19	120	41	20	D	C	C	B	D	D	B	B	
-T86	75	71	6	7	135	—	—	D	A	D	B	D	D	B	B	
3003- 0	16	6	30	40	28	11	7	A	A	A	E	A	A	A	B	Ductwork, truck panels, builders hardware, chemical eg'l., pressure vessels, storage tanks; piping, architectural appl.
-H18	29	27	4	10	55	16	10	A	A	C	C	A	A	A	A	
5005- 0	18	6	30	—	30	11	—	A	A	A	D	B	A	A	B	Appliances, cooking utensils, architectural applications, builders' hardware; coiled tubes.
-H14	23	22	6	—	41	14	—	A	A	A	C	B	A	A	A	
-H18	29	27	5	—	51	16	—	A	A	C	C	B	A	A	A	
6061- 0	18	8	25	30	30	12	9	B	A	A	D	A	A	A	B	Transportation eg'l., heavy duty structures, marine uses, pipe, flanges, bridge rails, R.R. cars; trailers.
-T6	45	40	12	17	95	30	14	B	A	C	C	A	A	A	A	
6063- 0	13	7	—	—	25	10	8	A	A	A	D	A	A	A	B	Pipe, railings, hardware, architectural uses
-T6	36	32	13	18	74	22	10	A	A	C	C	A	A	A	A	
6066- 0	22	12	—	18	43	14.5	—	—	—	—	B-D	—	—	—	—	Forgings and extrusions for welded structures
-T6	57	52	—	12	120	34	16	A	A	A-B	B	—	A	A	A	
7039- 0	32	—	—	—	—	—	—	—	—	—	B	—	—	—	—	Welded cryogenic and missile applications
-T61	60	50	14	—	123	—	—	A	A	C	B	—	A	A	A	
7075- 0	33	15	17	16	60	22	—	—	—	—	—	—	—	—	—	Structural parts for aircraft.
-T6	83	73	11	11	150	48	23	C	C	D	B	D	D	D	C	

SOURCE: Data was compiled from *1970 Metals Reference Issue-Machine Design*, The Penton Publishing Co., Cleveland, Ohio; *1973 Materials Selector Issue*, Reinhold Publishing Co., New York; *The Aluminum Data Book*, The Reynolds Metal Co.; *Alcoa Structural Handbook*, Aluminum Co. of America.

NOTE: A, B, C, D and E are relative merit ratings.

Table A-8 Mechanical Properties of Some Cast Aluminum Alloys

Type	Tensile Strength, ksi			Yield Str. (0-2% offset), ksi			Elongation[a] in 2 in., %			Brinell Hardness			End. Limit[b] ksi		Comp. Yield Str., ksi			Shear Strength ksi			Machinability	Weldability		
	As Cast	Solution Heat Treat	Solution Treated & Aged	As Cast	Solution Heat Treat	Solution Treated & Aged	As Cast	Solution Treated & Aged	Solution Treated & Aged	As Cast	Solution Heat Treat	Solution Treated & Aged	Solution Heat Treat	Solution Treated & Aged	As Cast	Solution Heat Treat	Solution Treated & Aged	As Cast	Solution Heat Treat	Solution Treated & Aged		Gas	Arc	Resistance
Gen'l Purpose Castings																								
195	–	32	36	–	16	24	–	8.5	5.0	–	60	75	7	8	–	17	25	–	26	30	AB	C	B	B
B195	–	37	40	–	19	26	–	9.0	5.0	–	75	90	9.5	10	–	20	26	–	30	32	AB	C	B	B
Corrosion Resist. Castings																								
43	19	–	–	8	–	–	8	–	–	40	–	–	–	–	9	–	–	14	–	–	C	A	A	A
214	25	–	–	12	–	–	9	–	–	50	–	–	–	–	12	–	–	20	–	–	A	B	A	B
220	–	48	–	–	26	–	–	16	–	–	75	–	8	8	–	27	–	–	34	–	A	D	C	B
356	–	–	25, 38c	–	–	20, 27c	–	–	2.5c	–	–	60, 80c	–	8, 13c	–	–	21, 27c	–	20, 30c	–	AB	AB, AB^d	AB, AB^d	AB, AB^d
High Temp. Resist. Castings																								
40-E	35e	–	–	25e	–	–	3e	–	–	70c	–	–	10f	–	17c	–	–	28e	–	–	A	C	C	C
355	28, 30d,e	–	35, 42d	23, 24d,e	–	25, 27d	1.5, 2d,e	–	3, 4d	65, 75d,e	–	80, 90d	8, 7d,f	9, 10d	24, 24d,e	–	26, 27d	22, 24d,e	–	28, 34d	B	A, A^d	A, A^d	A, A^d

SOURCE: Data was compiled from the *1973 Materials Selector*, Reinhold Publishing Co., New York.

A = excellent, AB = very good, B = good, C = fair, D = poor

[a] 1/2 inch dia. test specimen.

[b] Rotating beam test of 50 × 10[7] cycles.

[c] First value obtained by artificial aging; second value by solution treatement and aging.

[d] Where two values are given they refer to sand and permanent mold castings respectively.

[e] Artificially aged.

[f] Not solution heat treated but artificially aged.

Table A-9 Mechanical Properties of Some Wrought Copper Alloys

CDA[a] Number and Type	Tensile Strength, ksi				Yield Strength, ksi				Elongation in 2 in., %				Rockwell Hardness				Shear Str., ksi		Machinability[b]	Joining					Mod. of Elasticity in tension, psi
	Annealed	Half Hard	Hard	Spring Hard	Annealed	Half Hard	Hard	Spring Hard	Annealed	Half Hard	Hard	Spring Hard	Annealed	Half Hard	Hard	Spring Hard	Annealed	Hard		Soft Soldering	Silver Alloy Brazing	Oxyacetylene Welding	Carbon Arc Welding	Butt Resistance Welding	
172[c] (Beryllium copper)	70	—	175	—	30	—	150	—	43	—	7	—	R_B 58	—	R_C 39	—	55	95	20	A	B	D	A	A	19×10⁶
260 (Cartridge brass, 70%)	44	—	76	—	11	—	63	—	66	—	8	—	R_F 54	—	R_B 82	—	—	44	30	A	A	B	B	—	16×10⁶
280 (Muntz metal)	54	—	—	—	21	—	—	—	45	—	—	—	R_F 80	—	—	—	40	—	40	A	A	B	B	—	15×10⁶
340 (Medium-leaded brass)	51	—	74	—	19	—	60	—	53	—	7	—	R_F 72	—	R_B 80	—	—	43	70	A	B	Not Rec.	C	—	15×10⁶
360 (Free-cutting brass)	49	—	68	—	18	—	52	—	53	—	18	—	R_F 68	—	R_B 80	—	30	38	100	A	B	Not Rec.	C	—	14×10⁶
377 (Forging brass)	52	—	—	—	20	—	—	—	45	—	—	—	R_F 78	—	—	—	—	—	80	A	B	Not Rec.	C	—	15×10⁶
442, 443, 444, 445 (Admirality brass)	53	—	—	—	22	—	—	—	65	—	—	—	R_F 75	—	R_B 87	—	—	—	30	A	A	B	—	B	16×10⁶
464, 465, 466, 467 (Naval brass)	57	75	—	—	25	53	—	—	47	20	—	—	R_B 55	R_B 82	—	—	—	—	30	A	A	B	—	B	15×10⁶
510 (Phosphor bronze A)	47,50[d]	68,85[d]	81,110[d]	100,140[d]	19,20[d]	55,80[d]	75	—	64,58[d]	28,8[d]	10	4	R_B 26	R_B 78	R_B 87	R_B 95	—	—	20	A	A	B	—	A	16×10⁶
639 (Al-Si bronze)	85-90[e]	—	90[f]	—	44-60[e]	—	50[f]	—	20-30[e]	—	4[f]	—	R_B 74-90[e]	—	R_B 92[f]	—	—	—	60	Not Rec.	C	D	—	C	16×10⁶
647 (Precip. hard, Si bronze)	65	—	100	—	60	—	88	—	20	—	22	—	—	—	R_B 90	—	—	—	40	A	A	A	A	A	18×10⁶
655 (High silicon bronze)	56-63[e]	—	92[f]	—	20-30[e]	—	55[f]	—	55-63[e]	—	22[f]	—	R_B 40-66[e]	—	R_B 90	—	—	—	30	B	A	C	—	A	15×10⁶
675 (Manganese bronze A)	65	84	—	—	30	60	—	—	33	19	—	—	R_B 65	R_B 90	—	—	—	—	30	A	A	B	B	B	15×10⁶
715 (Cupro-nickel, 30%)	52	73	75	—	21	68	—	—	43	12	45	—	R_B 43	R_B 80	R_B 85	—	—	—	20	A	A	—	—	B	22×10⁶
770 (Nickel-silver, 55-18)	60	—	100	108	27	—	85	—	40	—	3	2.5	R_B 55	—	R_B 91	R_B 96	—	—	30	A	A	B	B	B	18×10⁶

SOURCE: Data was compiled from the 1973 Materials Selector, Reinhold Publishing Co., New York. [a]Copper Development Association, [b]Based on Free Machining Brass = 100, [c]Average values, [d]Where two values appear, second is for wire, [e]Strip and rod respectively, [f]Rod only.

Table A-10 Mechanical Properties of Some Cast Copper Base Alloys

BBI[b] Grade and Composition, %	Modulus of Elast. in Tension, psi	Tensile Strength, ksi	Yield Strength, (0.5% ext.), ksi	Elongation in 2 in., %	Reduction of Area, %	Brinell Hardness (500 kg)	Impact Strength (Izod), ft-lb	Compressive Strength 0.001-in. set, ksi	0.010-in. set, ksi	0.100-in. set, ksi	Fatigue Strength, 10⁸ cycle, ksi	Machinability (based on free cutting brass = 100)	Typical Uses
Tin bronze, 1B	13×10^6	40	18	25	20	60	14	12	—	—	—	40	Bearings, bushings, piston rings, pump bodies, valves, impellers, steam fittings, gears.
Leaded tin bronze, 2C	11×10^6	36	18	20	15	65	7	12	—	40	—	50	Bolts, nuts, gears, valves, pump pistons, pressure pipe fittings, expansion joints.
High leaded tin bronze, 3C	11×10^6	28	15	25	20	55	8	13	—	—	—	70	Machine tool bearings, general bearing uses.
Leaded red brass, 4A	12×10^6	33	15	22	17	62	11	14	17	37	11	84	Low pressure valve bodies, pipe fittings, plumbing parts.
High strength yellow brass, 8C	14×10^6	112	65	12	10	210	14	71	97	—	25	8	Spur gears, bridge parts, screw down nuts, bearings.
Aluminum bronze, 9A	16×10^6	70	25	22	20	110[a]	35	27	—	65	25	20	Machine parts, pump impellers and castings, gears, rolling mill bearings, washers, chemical plant equipment, marine propellers, pump casings, fittings, chains and hooks.
Aluminum bronze, 9D	18×10^6	90	40	7	10	175[a]	9	—	—	—	—	20	
Leaded nickel brass and bronze, 11A	19×10^6	40	17	15	11	76	11	24	31	57	16	71	Marine fittings, furniture and building trim, various hardware parts.
Silicon brass and bronze, 13B	15×10^6	60	25	17	20	134[a]	32	27	43	84	22	50	Bearings, gears, rocker arms, impellers, valve stems, propellers.

SOURCE: Data was compiled from the *1973 Materials Selector*, Reinhold Publishing Co., New York, and the *ASME Handbook-Metal Properties*, McGraw-Hill Book Co., New York, 1954.

[a] 3000 kg.
[b] Brass and Bronze Ingot Institute

Table A-11   Mechanical Properties of Some Wrought and Cast Magnesium Alloys

ASTM Type	Tensile Strength, ksi	Yield Strength in Tension, ksi	Elongation in 2 in., %	Shear Strength, ksi	Brinell Hardness	Endurance Strength, ksi	Yield Strength in Compression, ksi	Machinability (Based on Mild Steel = 100)	Weldability Inert-Gas Arc	Weldability Resistance Welding	Corrosion Resistance[b]	Available Forms	Typical Applications
AZ31B-H24	42	32	15	23	49	20[a]	24	500	A	A	A	S, P	Aircraft, missiles, office machines, jigs & fixtures, foundry pattern plate.
HK31A-H24	37	29	8	27	—	18[c]	23	500	A	A	A	S, P	Same as AZ31B-H24
AZ31B-F	37	26	14	19	41	18[d]	13	500	B	A	A	R, Ba, E, T	Aircraft, missiles, office machines, jigs & fixtures, foundry pattern plate, electronic eq't., machine parts, oil well tools, mat'ls, handling, wheels.
AZ61A-F	43	28	15	20	55	20[d]	19	500	B	A	A	R, Ba, E, T	Same as AZ31B-F
AZ80A-T5	53	39	7	24	82	22[d]	32	500	B	A	A	R, Ba, E, T	Same as AZ31B-F
ZK60A-T5	52	42	13	25	82	20[d]	33	500	D	A	A	R, Ba, E, T	Same as AZ31B-F
AZ63A	40[e]	13[e]	12[e]	17[e]	55[e]	15[d,e]	14[e]	500	D	—	A	C, c	Aircraft, missile parts, wheels, ordnance eq't., auto & truck parts, reciprocating mach. parts, hand tools, mat'ls, handling eq't., cameras,
AZ81A	40[e]	12[e]	15[e]	17[e]	55[e]	13[d,e]	14[e]	500	B	—	A	C, c	Same as AZ63A
AZ91C	40[e]	13[e]	14[e]	17[e]	53[e]	14[d,e]	14[e]	500	C	—	A	c	Same as AZ63A
AM100A	40[e]	13[e]	10[e]	—	—	—	—	500	A	—	A	C, c	Aircraft and missile components
HK31A-T6	31	16	6	21	55	11[d]	15	500	A	—	A	C, c	Same as AZ63A
HZ-32A-T5	29	15	6	20	57	10[d]	14	500	B	—	A	C, c	Same as AZ63A

SOURCE: Data was compiled from the *1973 Materials Selector*, Reinhold Publishing Co., New York.

NOTES: A = most favorable, B = less favorable, C = least favorable.
S = sheets, P = plates, C = sand castings, R = rods, c = permanent mold castings, E = extrusions, Ba = bars, T = tubes.
[a] Axial reversed load, 10[7] cycles.
[b] Attacked by salt water unless finished.
[c] Axial load, 10[7] cycles, R = 1/4
[d] Rotating beam test, 10[8] cycles.
[e] Solution heat treated.

Table A-12 Mechanical Properties of Some Die Casting Materials

Material	Modulus of Elast. in Tension, psi	Tensile Strength, ksi	Yield Strength, ksi	Elongation in 2 in, %	Brinell Hardness	Shear Strength, ksi	Endurance Strength, ksi	Machinability (Based on mild steel = 100)	Weldability	Impact Strength (Charpy), ft-lb	Compressive Strength, ksi	Corrosion Resistance	Typical Uses
Magnesium alloy (ASTM AZ91); and (ASTM AZ91B)	6.5×10^6	34	23	3	60	20	12[a]	500	—	—	—	b	Automotive parts, missile and aircraft parts, electronic housings, appliances, cameras, handtools.
Zinc alloy AG40A (ASTM XXII)	—	41	—	10	82	31	6.9	Good	Fair	43	60	c	Automotive parts, office eq't., toys.
Zinc alloy AC41A (ASTM XXV)	—	48	—	7	91	38	8.2	Good	Fair	48	87	c	Same as AC41A and also drop hammer dies.
Tin alloy 1 (ASTM B23-61); (ASTM B105-52)	—	—	4.4	—	17	—	3.8	—	—	—	12.9	d	Bearings, die castings for dairy machinery, dental appliances, surgical instruments.
Tin-Lead-Antimony Alloy 8 (ASTM B23-61); (ASTM B105-52)	—	—	3.4	—	20	—	3.9	—	—	—	15.6	e	Bearings for light loads and moderate speeds, mining and transmission machinery, car journals.

SOURCE: Data was compiled from the *1973 Materials Selector*, Reinhold Publishing Co., New York.

[a]10^8 cycles by rotating beam teat

[b]Good resistance to atmosphere; attacked by salt water unless finished.

[c]Excellent resistance to rural and city atmospheres, hot soapy water, printing inks, trichloroethylene, carbon tetrachloride, dry illuminating gas and dry and acid free hydrocarbons. Fair resistance to pure ethyl and methyl alcohols, glycerin, water and petroleum products. Poor resistance to steam, animal oils, strong acids and bases and mixtures of glycerine or alcohol and water.

[d]Resists oxidation products of lubricants; food products; beer and carbonated beverages.

[e]Resists oxidation by normal lubricants.

Table A-13 Mechanical Properties of Some Nickel Alloys and Nickel Base Alloys[b,c]

Material	Modulus of Elast. in Tension, psi	Tensile Strength, ksi	Yield Strength, ksi	Elongation in 2 in., %	Brinell Hardness	Endurance Strength, psi	Impact Strength (Izod), ft-lb	Machinability	Weldability	Available Forms	Typical Applications
Duranickel 301	30 × 10⁶	175[a]	28[a,d]	18[a]	35[e]	47[f]	—	175-300[g]	TA	S, R, B, Sh	Corrosion resistant parts with high strength and hardness, spring properties to 600°F
Monel K-500	26 × 10⁶	150[a]	105[a]	20[a]	24[e]	43[f]	—	150-425[g]	TA, O, B	S, R, B, T, Sh	Corrosion resistant parts with ductility to 420°F and dimensional stability.
Monel 505	24 × 10⁶	127[a,h]	87[a,h]	2.5[a,h]	340[a,h]	—	4[i]	—	Not Rec.	Casting	Valve seats, liners, pump rods, bushings, nozzles, turbine blading, laundry machines, paper mill and oil ref. eq't, food handling, boilers. Excellent resistanct to galling and erosion
Inconel X-750[l]	31 × 10⁶	162	97	24	286	—	37-33[j]	15[k]	Satis.	S, R, B, Sh, T	Jet engines, missiles, furnaces, etc. where high temp. strength and corrosion resist. are vital
Hastelloy B[l]	27 × 10⁶	121	57	63	205	66	60-53[j]	12[k]	Good	S, P, B, T, F, Inv.	Same as Inconel X-750
Udimet 500[l]	32 × 10⁶	197	110	18	37[e]	48[m]	—	Satis.	Satis.	B, P, S	Jet engines, turbine, missiles, etc. where high temp. strength and corrosion resist. are vital.
Waspaloy[l]	32 × 10⁶	188	120	29	37[e]	40[m]	—	Satis.	Satis.	B, W, P, S	Same as Udimet 500

SOURCE: Data was compiled from the *1973 Materials Selector*, Reinhold Publishing Co,, New York.

NOTES: Sh = shapes, F = forgings, Inv. = investment castings, W = wire, B = bars, S = strip, R = rods, T = tubing, P = plate
TA = inert gas, tungsten-arc welding with a filler metal, O = oxyacetylene, B = silver and copper brazing

[a] Average values,
[b] Values are for materials that have been annealed and age hardened.
[c] Values are for 1600°F.
[d] Annealed.
[e] Rockwell C.
[f] 10⁸ cycles.
[g] Surface speed in fpm with a single point cemented carbide tool.
[h] Annealed and aged.
[i] Charpy test at room temp.
[j] First figure is for room temp, and the second is at minus 320°F.
[k] Based on AISI B1112 = 100.
[l] These values are at room temp. For higher temp. values, refer to ASM Handbook, Vol I.
[m] 10⁷ cycles at 1500°F.

Table A-14 Low-Temperature Properties of Nickel and Nickel Alloys

Alloy and Form	Temp (F)	Yield Strength at 0.2% Offset (ksi)	Tensile Strength (ksi)	Elongation in 2 in., %	Reduction of Area, %	Charpy V-Notch Impact Strength, (ft-lb)
Wrought nickel						
Annealed bar	Room	23.0	72.7	48.0	75.0	—
	−100	25.3	81.4	58.0	76.0	—
Cold-drawn bar	Room	97.4	103.4	16.3	66.9	—
	−110	101.8	112.3	21.5	60.9	—
Berylco nickel 440						
Annealed and	Room	160.0	225.0	15.0	—	10 to 25
age hardened at	−100	—	—	—	—	10 to 23
950°F for	−200	—	—	—	—	10 to 22
1½ hr	−300	195.0	282.0	16.0	—	10 to 21
	−425	204.2	303.0	16.0	—	—
Monel 400						
Annealed bar	Room	31.3	78.7	51.5	75.0	189 to 216
	−297	49.5	115.3	49.5	73.9	184 to 212
Cold-drawn bar	Room	93.7	103.8	19.0	71.0	181
	−110	100.9	117.5	21.8	70.2	178
Monel K-500						
Annealed bar, aged	Room	100.0	140.0	25.0	40.0	—
	−300	112.4	177.2	39.0	52.1	—
Cold-drawn bar, aged	Room	120.0	160.0	20.0	35.0	—
	−300	160.2	202.0	27.0	47.3	—
Hastelloy B						
Bar, heat treated	Room	55.0	127.0	52.0	—	—
at 2125°F	−148	61.0	144.0	62.0	53.0	53
	−321	84.0	173.0	58.0	46.0	53
Hastelloy C						
Bar, heat treated	Room	51.0	121.0	50.0	—	—
at 2225°F	−148	79.0	143.0	25.0	26.0	—
	−321	97.0	160.0	24.0	22.0	—
Hastelloy X						
Plate, heat treated	Room	47.0	104.5	46.2	—	54.1
at 2150°F	−108	—	118.8	51.0	—	50.6
	−321	—	150.2	45.5	—	36.8
Waspaloy						
Bar	Room	122.0	195.0	28.0	28.0	14
	−104	132.0	203.0	24.0	26.0	—
	−320	157.0	235.0	17.0	18.0	—
	−423	163.0	243.0	18.0	14.0	—
René 41						
Bar, solution	Room	140.0	192.0	26.0	33.0	—
treated at 1975°F	−100	142.0	200.0	29.5	34.0	—
	−200	150.0	216.0	29.0	30.0	—
	−300	160.0	235.0	28.5	27.0	—
	−400	172.0	252.0	27.0	26.0	—
Sheet, 0.062-in. thick	Room	159.0	204.0	16.0	—	—
	−100	174.0	227.0	16.0	—	—
	−200	180.0	238.0	16.0	—	—
	−300	189.0	252.0	16.0	—	—
	−400	197.0	265.0	16.0	—	—
Inconel 600						
Annealed bar	Room	36.8	93.8	37.3	64.1	236
	−110	42.4	106.5	39.8	64.0	206
	−310	—	—	—	—	187
Cold-drawn bar	Room	147.7	152.1	7.0	49.3	69
	−110	154.9	163.9	9.8	51.2	—
	−315	—	182.0	10.0	49.5	—
Inconel X-750						
Hot-rolled bar, aged	Room	135.0	191.0	26.0	46.0	40
at 1300°F for 2 hr	−110	140.0	202.0	30.5	48.0	38
	−200	145.0	212.0	32.0	48.0	37
	−300	149.0	225.0	33.0	47.0	35
	−400	152.0	240.0	34.0	43.0	—
Annealed and	Room	110.0	170.0	25.0	28.0	33
age hardened	−110	115.0	184.0	22.0	25.0	36
	−200	118.0	192.0	20.5	23.0	37
	−300	119.0	200.0	18.0	20.0	37
	−400	130.0	210.0	16.0	16.0	—

SOURCE: Reproduced from the *1970 Metals Reference Issue, Machine Design* by permission of the Penton Publishing Co., Cleveland, Ohio.

Table A-15 Properties of Some Typical Plastics

Generic Name	Typical Tensile strength, ksi	Typical Impact Strength, ft-lb/in of notch	Typical Flexural Modulus, 10⁵ psi	PV Rating, dry, continuous × 1000	Deflection Temperature °F, 66 psi	Deflection Temperature °F, 264 psi	Abrasion Resist., mg. loss/1000 cycles	Endurance Limit ksi	Thermal Expansion, per °F × 10⁵	Heat Resistance, Continuous, °F	Thermal Conductivity Btu/in/hr/ft²/°F	Water Absorption in 24 hr, %	Flammability	Formability	Machinability	Coeff. of Friction Slip-Stick	Coeff. of Friction Dry	Coeff. of Friction Lubricant-ed	Resistance to Acids	Resistance to Alkalies	Resistance to Solvents	Resistance to Oils	Brittle Point, °F
Materials for Housings, Shrouds, Containers, Ducts																							
ABS	5	6	2.4	—	—	—	—	—	3.2-5.8	140-250	—	0.1-0.3	Slow	G	—	—	—	—	G	E	F	G	—
Styrenes, high-impact	4.3	1	2.3	—	—	—	—	—	2.2-5.6	126-165	—	0.03-0.2	Slow	G	—	—	—	—	G	E	P	F	—
Polypropylenes	5.5	1	1.75	—	—	—	—	—	3.4-6.2	230-320	—	0.01-0.03	Slow	G	—	—	—	—	E	E	G	E	—
Polyprohylenes high-density	4.2	12	2	—	—	—	—	—	6.5-16.7	170-260	—	<0.01	Very Slow	E	—	—	—	—	E	E	G	G	—
Cellulose Acetate Butyrates	5.5	2.1	1.3	—	—	—	—	—	6-10	140-220	—	0.9-2.8	Slow	E	—	—	—	—	P	P	P	F	—
Acrylics, modified	5.5	2	2.8	—	—	—	—	—	3-6	140-195	—	0.2-0.4	Slow	E	—	—	—	—	G	E	F	E	—
Acrylics-PVC alloy	6.5	15	4	—	—	—	—	—	3.5	165	—	0.06	Non-burn.	E	—	—	—	—	E	E	E	E	—
Polyester-Glass	16.5	15	15	—	—	—	—	—	1-1.4	200-550	—	0.1-2	Slow to nil	G	—	—	—	—	G	F	G	E	—
Epoxy-Glass	36	12.4	25	—	—	—	—	—	0.3-0.6	250-400	—	0.02-0.08	Slow to nil	G	—	—	—	—	G	E	E	E	—
Materials for Low Friction Applications (e.g. Bearings, Slides, Guides, Valve Liners, Wear Surfaces, etc.)																							
TFE	—	—	—	1-2.5	—	250	7	—	5.5	—	1.7	None	—	—	—	No	0.04	0.04	—	—	—	—	—
FEP	—	—	0.95	.6-.9	—	<250	13.2	—	4.6	—	1.4	<0.01	—	—	—	No	0.08	0.08	—	—	—	—	—
TFE fabric	—	—	—	5-50	—	—	—	—	8	—	1.7	None	—	—	—	No	0.02-0.25	0.02-0.25	—	—	—	—	—
Filled TFE	—	—	1.2-2	5-35	—	>250	8-26	—	3-9.7	—	1.7-20	None	—	—	—	No	0.16-0.28	0.06	—	—	—	—	—

Table A-15 (Continued)

Generic Name	Typical Tensile strength, ksi	Typical Impact Strength, ft-lb/in of notch	Typical Flexural Modulus, 10^5 psi	PV Rating, dry, continuous × 1000	Deflection Temp. °F, 66 psi	Deflection Temp. °F, 264 psi	Abrasion Resist., mg. loss/1000 cycles	Endurance Limit ksi	Thermal Expansion, per °F × 10^5	Heat Resistance, Continuous, °F	Thermal Conductivity Btu/hr/in./ft²/°F	Water Absorption in 24 hr., %	Flammability	Formability	Machinability	Coeff. of Friction Slip-Stick	Coeff. of Friction Dry	Coeff. of Friction Lubricated	Acids	Alkalies	Solvents	Oils	Brittle Point, °F
Materials for Housings, Shrouds, Containers, Ducts																							
Nylons	—	—	1.5-4	2-3	340-360	—	6-8	—	4.5-7.1	—	1.4-2	0.4-3.3	—	—	—	Yes	0.15-0.40	0.06	—	—	—	—	—
Acetals	—	—	3.1-4.1	2-3	316-338	—	6-20	—	4.5-6	—	1.6-1.9	0.12-0.41	—	—	—	No	0.15-0.35	0.1	—	—	—	—	—
Acetal, self-lubricating	—	—	—	18	302	—	5-12	—	—	—	—	—	—	—	—	No	0.10	0.05	—	—	—	—	—
Acetal, TFE-fiber filled.	—	—	4.14	7.5	329	—	—	—	4.6	—	1.7	0.6	—	—	—	No	0.12	0.07	—	—	—	—	—
Polyethylenes, high-density	—	—	1.3-2.2	—	140-180	—	6	—	6.5-16.7	—	3.4	<0.01	—	—	—	Yes	0.21	0.1	—	—	—	—	—
Materials for Heavily Stressed Mechanical Components (e.g. Gears, Cams, Racks, Couplings, Rollers, etc.)																							
Nylons	7.1-12.6	0.6-4	1.5-4	—	340-360	140-165	6-8	3	—	—	—	—	—	—	E	—	—	—	F	E	E	E	—
Acetals	8.8-10	1.2-1.4	3.7-4.1	—	316-338	230-255	6-20	5	—	—	—	—	—	—	E	—	—	—	P	E	E	E	—
Acetal, TFE-fiber filled	6.9	0.86	4.14	—	329	212	—	—	—	—	—	—	—	—	E	—	—	—	P	P	E	E	—
Polycarbonates	9-10.5	12-16	3.2-3.8	—	283-293	270-280	7-24	2	—	—	—	—	—	—	E	—	—	—	E	G	G	F	—
Phenolics, fabric filled	9-16	1-2.5	8-14	—	320	>320	—	—	—	—	—	—	—	—	F to E	—	—	—	F	F	E	E	—
Materials for Chemical and Thermal Equipment																							
TFE & FEP	1.5-4.5	2.5->16	—	—	250	—	—	—	—	—	—	—	None	—	—	—	—	—	E	E	E	—	-420
CTFE	4.6-5.6	3.1-7.3	—	—	265	—	—	—	—	400	—	—	None	—	—	—	—	—	E	E	G	—	-400
Polypropylenes	3.3-5.7	0.3-3	—	—	210	—	—	—	—	275	—	—	Slow	—	—	—	—	—	G	G	F	—	0
Polyphenylene Oxide	11.6	1.3	—	—	355	—	—	—	—	250	—	—	Self ext.	—	—	—	—	—	G	G	E	—	—
Epoxy-Glass	34-100	10-25	—	—	350-375	—	—	—	—	250-300	—	—	None	—	—	—	—	—	F	F	E	—	—

Table A-16 Miscellaneous Mechanical and Physical Properties of Various Materials[h]

Material	Modulus of Elasticity in Tension, psi	Shear Modulus of Elasticity, psi	Poisson's Ratio	Density lb/in.^{3}	Coefficient of Thermal Expansion, in./in./°F	Thermal Conductivity Btu/hr/ ft^2/°F/ft.	Specific Heat Btu/lb/°F	Melting Point[a] °F
Gray cast iron	See Table A-1	5.5 × 10^6 C1.20 8.0 × 10^6 C1.50	0.27	0.260	6.7 × 10^{-6}	29.0	——	2150
Malleable cast iron	See Table A-1	12.5 × 10^6	0.27	0.264	5.9 × 10^{-6} - 7.5 × 10^{-6}[b]	29.5	0.122	2250
Nodular or ductile iron	See Table A-1	9.3 × 10^6	0.29	0.251	6.6 × 10^{-6} - 10.4 × 10^{-6}[b]	19.0	——	2150
Cast alloy steels	See Table A-1	11.3 × 10^6	0.33	0.283	8.1 × 10^{-6}	27.0	0.105	2740
Cast carbon steels	See Table A-1	11.3 × 10^6 [c]	0.33[c]	0.283	8.3 × 10^{-6}	27.0	——	2250
Alloy cast irons	See Table A-1	11.3 × 10^6 [c]	0.33[c]	0.266	4.5 × 10^{-6} - 10.7 × 10^{-6}[b]	——	——	2500[c]
Cast stainless steels	See Table A-1	11.5 × 10^6 [c]	0.26[c]	0.280	6.4 × 10^{-6} - 10.4 × 10^{-6}[b]	8.2 - 14.5[b]	0.125	2750
Plain carbon steels	30 × 10^6	11.5 × 10^6	0.27-0.30	0.283	6.7 × 10^{-6} - 8.1 × 10^{-6}	27.0	0.105	2775
Alloy steels	30 × 10^6	11.5 × 10^6	0.27-0.30	0.280	6.3 × 10^{-6} - 8.6 × 10^{-6}[b]	21.7 - 38.5[b]	0.110	2760
Wrought stainless steels	28.5 × 10^6	11.5 × 10^6	0.26	0.290	e	f, b	0.120	g
Wrought aluminum alloys	10.3 × 10^6	3.8 × 10^6	0.36	0.097	13 × 10^{-6}	67.4-135[b]	0.230	1215
Cast aluminum alloys	10.3 × 10^6	3.8 × 10^6	0.36	0.097	12.6 × 10^{-6}	66.6	0.230	1195
Wrought copper alloys	15.5 × 10^6	5.8 × 10^6	0.33	0.305	11.0 × 10^{-6}	d	0.090	d
Cast copper base alloys	See Table A-10	5.4 × 10^6	0.33	0.303	10.1 × 10^{-6}	d	0.090	d
Nickel base alloys	See Table A-13	——	0.34	0.304	7.6 × 10^{-6}	d	0.100	d
Wrought and cast magnesium alloys	6.5 × 10^6	2.4 × 10^6	0.35	0.065	14.4 × 10^{-6}	d	0.250	1200

SOURCE: Data was compiled from the *1973 Materials Selector*, Reinhold Publishing Co., New York, and *Properties of Some Metals and Alloys*, International Nickel Co., Inc.

NOTE: The values listed are average values except as indicated.

[a]These are max, values
[b]Where two values are given, they are respectively the low and high values and are too wide for a meaningful average. The reader should refer to the ASM Handbook, Vol 1 for detailed and specific data.
[c]These are approximate values.
[d]Refer to ASM Handbook, Vol. 1 for values of particular materials.

	e	f	g
Ferritic Stainless Steel	5.6 × 10^{-6}	12.1 – 15.1	2790
Martensitic Stainless Steel	6.0 × 10^{-6}	11.7 – 21.2	2800
Austenitic Stainless Steel	9.4 × 10^{-6}	8.0 – 9.4	2650

[k]At room temperature

Table A-17 Standard Gauge Decimals (gauge and equivalent in decimals of an inch)

Ga. No.	Aluminum & Brass Brown & Sharp	Steel Sheets Mfrs. Std.*	Strip & Tubing Birmingham or Stubs	Steel Wire Wire Ga.†	Steel Wire Music Wire	Ga. No.	Aluminum & Brass Brown & Sharp	Steel Sheets Mfrs. Std.*	Strip & Tubing Birmingham or Stubs	Steel Wire Wire Ga.†	Steel Wire Music Wire
6-0's	.5800	—	—	.4615	.004	19	.0359	.0418	.042	.0410	.043
5-0's	.5165	—	.500	.4305	.005	20	.0320	.0359	.035	.0348	.045
4-0's	.4600	—	.454	.3938	.006	21	.0285	.0329	.032	.0317	.047
3-0's	.4096	—	.425	.3625	.007	22	.0253	.0299	.028	.0286	.049
2-0's	.3648	—	.380	.3310	.008	23	.0226	.0269	.025	.0258	.051
0	.3249	—	.340	.3065	.009	24	.0201	.0239	.022	.0230	.055
1	.2893	—	.300	.2830	.010	25	.0179	.0209	.020	.0204	.059
2	.2576	—	.284	.2625	.011	26	.0159	.0179	.018	.0181	.063
3	.2294	.2391	.259	.2437	.012	27	.0142	.0164	.016	.0173	.067
4	.2043	.2242	.238	.2253	.013	28	.0126	.0149	.014	.0162	.071
5	.1819	.2092	.220	.2070	.014	29	.0113	.0135	.013	.0150	.075
6	.1620	.1943	.203	.1920	.016	30	.0100	.0120	.012	.0140	.080
7	.1443	.1793	.180	.1770	.018	31	.0089	.0105	.010	.0132	.085
8	.1285	.1644	.165	.1620	.020	32	.0080	.0097	.009	.0128	.090
9	.1144	.1495	.148	.1483	.022	33	.0071	.0090	.008	.0118	.095
10	.1019	.1345	.134	.1350	.024	34	.0063	.0082	.007	.0104	.100
11	.0907	.1196	.120	.1205	.026	35	.0056	.0075	.005	.0095	.106
12	.0808	.1046	.109	.1055	.029	36	.0050	.0067	.004	.0090	.112
13	.0720	.0897	.095	.0915	.031	37	.0045	.0064	—	.0085	.118
14	.0641	.0747	.083	.0800	.033	38	.0040	.0060	—	.0080	.124
15	.0571	.0673	.072	.0720	.035						
16	.0508	.0598	.065	.0625	.037						
17	.0453	.0538	.058	.0540	.039						
18	.0403	.0478	.049	.0475	.041						

SOURCE: Joseph T. Ryerson & Son, Inc.
*Replaces U.S. Standard (Revised) Gauge.
†Replaces Washburn and Moen Gauge.

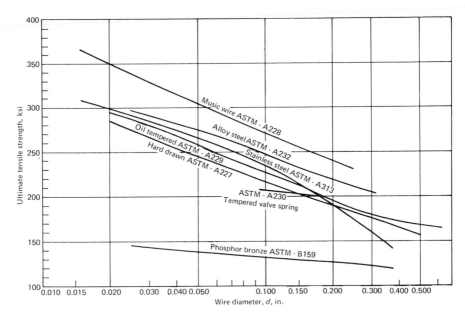

Figure A-1 Minimum tensile strength of spring wires. (Courtesy of Associated Spring Corp.)

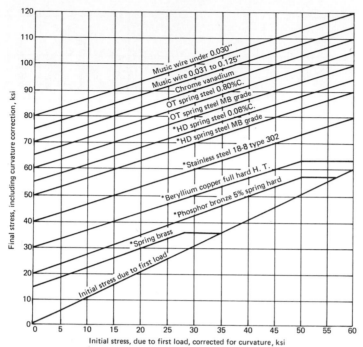

For commercial spring materials with wire dias. up to 1/4 in. except as noted
Stress ranges may be increased approximately 30% for properly heated,
preset, shotpeened springs.
Materials preceded by an * are not ordinarily recommended for long
continued service under severe operating conditions

Figure A-2 Endurance-limit curves for compression springs. These curves cover compression springs that must withstand unlimited fatigue life or at least 10,000,000 deflections. These are based on range of stress caused by the first or initial load and the stress caused by the final load. (Courtesy of The American Society of Tool Engineers.)

Appendix B

Stress Concentration Factors

UNIFIED AND AMERICAN THREAD DESIGN

		BENDING OR TENSION	
		ROLLED	CUT
K_f	ANNEALED	2.2	2.3
	QUENCHED & DRAWN	3.0	3.8

KEYWAYS

PROFILE

SLED-RUNNER

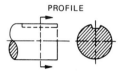 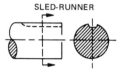

		PROFILE		SLED-RUNNER	
		BENDING	TORSION	BENDING	TORSION
K_f	ANNEALED	1.6	1.3	1.3	1.3
	QUENCHED & DRAWN	2.0	1.6	1.6	1.6

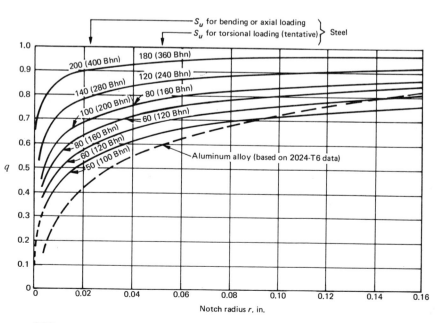

Figure B-1 *Opposite, top and middle*: Fatigue stress concentration factors: threads and keyways. Note that these values are for K_f and not K_t. (By permission of Charles Lipson and Robert C. Juvinall, *Handbook of Stress and Strength*, The Macmillan Co., New York, 1963.)

Figure B-2 *Opposite, bottom*: Notch-sensitivity curves for use with theoretical factors K_t. (Figures B-2 to B-10 inclusive are reprinted by permission of Robert C. Juvinall; *Engineering Considerations of Stress, Strain and Strength*, McGraw-Hill Book Co., 1967. These reprinted charts (with the exception of B-2 and B-3) are based on those found in *Stress Concentration Design Factors* by R. E. Peterson, John Wiley and Sons, Inc., 1953. Fig. B-2 is based on material found on p. 298 of *Metal Fatigue* by George Sines and J. L. Waisman (editors), McGraw-Hill Book Co., 1959. The source material for Fig. B-3 can be found on p. 111 of the same reference as that cited for Fig. B-1.)

Figure B-3 *Below*: Reduction of endurance strength due to surface finish—steel parts.

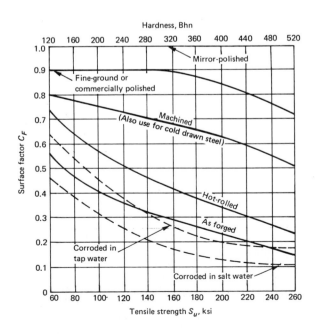

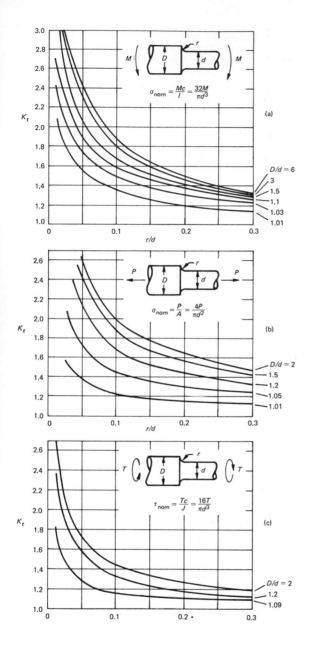

Figure B-4 Shaft with fillet (a) bending; (b) axial load; (c) torsion.

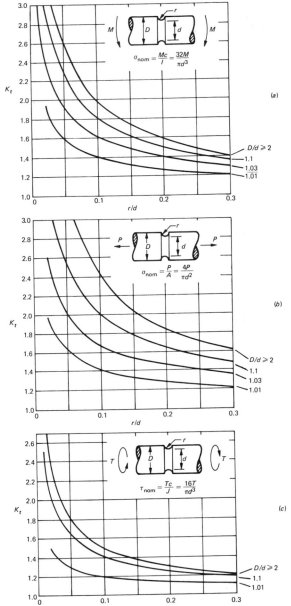

Figure B-5 Grooved shaft (a) bending; (b) axial load; (c) torsion.

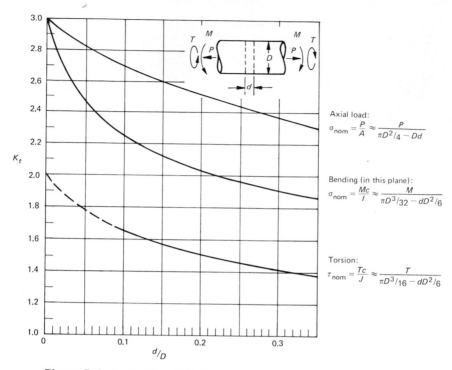

Figure B-6 Shaft with radial hole.

Axial load:
$$\sigma_{nom} = \frac{P}{A} \approx \frac{P}{\pi D^2/4 - Dd}$$

Bending (in this plane):
$$\sigma_{nom} = \frac{Mc}{I} \approx \frac{M}{\pi D^3/32 - dD^2/6}$$

Torsion:
$$\tau_{nom} = \frac{Tc}{J} \approx \frac{T}{\pi D^3/16 - dD^2/6}$$

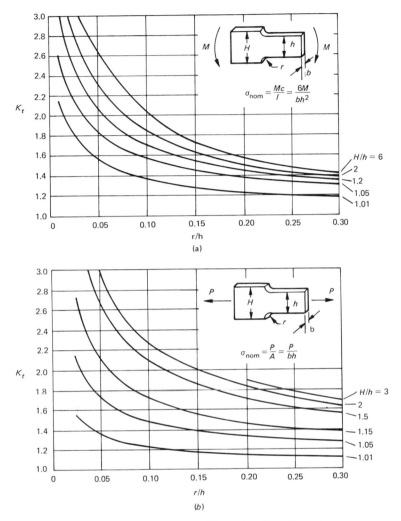

Figure B-7 Bar with shoulder fillet (a) bending; (b) axial load.

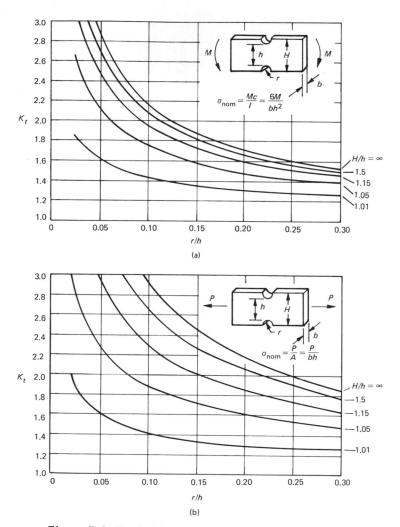

Figure B-8 Notched flat bar (a) bending; (b) tension.

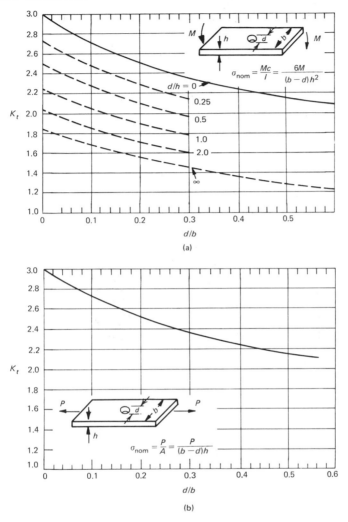

Figure B-9 Plate with central hole (a) bending; (b) axial load.

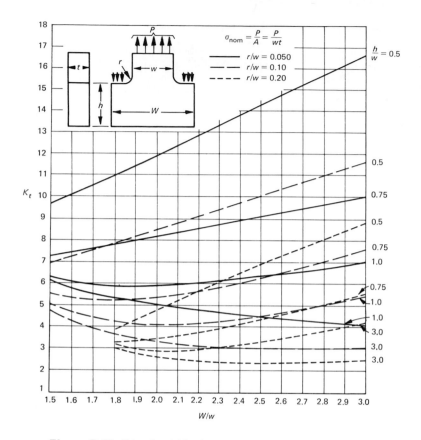

Figure B-10 T-head, axial load.

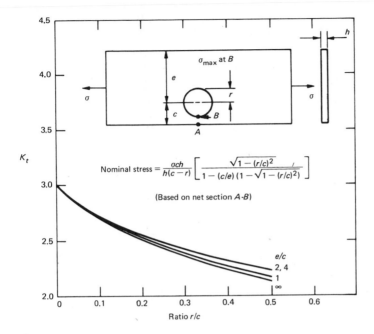

Nominal stress $= \dfrac{\sigma c h}{h(c-r)} \left[\dfrac{\sqrt{1-(r/c)^2}}{1-(c/e)(1-\sqrt{1-(r/c)^2})} \right]$

(Based on net section A-B)

Figure B-11 Tensioning of a plate with an eccentric hole.

Appendix C

Tables of
Fits and Tolerances

Table C-1 Running and Sliding Fits

Nominal Size Range, in. Over–To	Class RC 1			Class RC 2			Class RC 3			Class RC 4		
	Limits of Clearance	Hole H5	Shaft g4	Limits of Clearance	Hole H6	Shaft g5	Limits of Clearance	Hole H7	Shaft f6	Limits of Clearance	Hole H8	Shaft f7
0 – 0.12	0.1 / 0.45	+0.2 / 0	−0.1 / −0.25	0.1 / 0.55	+0.25 / 0	−0.1 / −0.3	0.3 / 0.95	+0.4 / 0	−0.3 / −0.55	0.3 / 1.3	+0.6 / 0	−0.3 / −0.7
0.12– 0.24	0.15 / 0.5	+0.2 / 0	−0.15 / −0.3	0.15 / 0.65	+0.3 / 0	−0.15 / −0.35	0.4 / 1.12	+0.5 / 0	−0.4 / −0.7	0.4 / 1.6	+0.7 / 0	−0.4 / −0.9
0.24– 0.40	0.2 / 0.6	+0.25 / 0	−0.2 / −0.35	0.2 / 0.85	+0.4 / 0	−0.2 / −0.45	0.5 / 1.5	+0.6 / 0	−0.5 / −0.9	0.5 / 2.0	+0.9 / 0	−0.5 / −1.1
0.40– 0.71	0.25 / 0.75	+0.3 / 0	−0.25 / −0.45	0.25 / 0.95	+0.4 / 0	−0.25 / −0.55	0.6 / 1.7	+0.7 / 0	−0.6 / −1.0	0.6 / 2.3	+1.0 / 0	−0.6 / −1.3
0.71– 1.19	0.3 / 0.95	+0.4 / 0	−0.3 / −0.55	0.3 / 1.2	+0.5 / 0	−0.3 / −0.7	0.8 / 2.1	+0.8 / 0	−0.8 / −1.3	0.8 / 2.8	+1.2 / 0	−0.8 / −1.6
1.19– 1.97	0.4 / 1.1	+0.4 / 0	−0.4 / −0.7	0.4 / 1.4	+0.6 / 0	−0.4 / −0.8	1.0 / 2.6	+1.0 / 0	−1.0 / −1.6	1.0 / 3.6	+1.6 / 0	−1.0 / −2.0
1.97– 3.15	0.4 / 1.2	+0.5 / 0	−0.4 / −0.7	0.4 / 1.6	+0.7 / 0	−0.4 / −0.9	1.2 / 3.1	+1.2 / 0	−1.2 / −1.9	1.2 / 4.2	+1.8 / 0	−1.2 / −2.4
3.15– 4.73	0.5 / 1.5	+0.6 / 0	−0.5 / −0.9	0.5 / 2.0	+0.9 / 0	−0.5 / −1.1	1.4 / 3.7	+1.4 / 0	−1.4 / −2.3	1.4 / 5.0	+2.2 / 0	−1.4 / −2.8
4.73– 7.09	0.6 / 1.8	+0.7 / 0	−0.6 / −1.1	0.6 / 2.3	+1.0 / 0	−0.6 / −1.3	1.6 / 4.2	+1.6 / 0	−1.6 / −2.6	1.6 / 5.7	+2.5 / 0	−1.6 / −3.2
7.09– 9.85	0.6 / 2.0	+0.8 / 0	−0.6 / −1.2	0.6 / 2.6	+1.2 / 0	−0.6 / −1.4	2.0 / 5.0	+1.8 / 0	−2.0 / −3.2	2.0 / 6.6	+2.8 / 0	−2.0 / −3.8
9.85–12.41	0.8 / 2.3	+0.9 / 0	−0.8 / −1.4	0.8 / 2.9	+1.2 / 0	−0.8 / −1.7	2.5 / 5.7	+2.0 / 0	−2.5 / −3.7	2.5 / 7.5	+3.0 / 0	−2.5 / −4.5

Table C-1 (continued)

Nominal Size Range, in. Over – To	Class RC 5 Limits of Clearance	Class RC 5 Hole H8	Class RC 5 Shaft e7	Class RC 6 Limits of Clearance	Class RC 6 Hole H9	Class RC 6 Shaft e8	Class RC 7 Limits of Clearance	Class RC 7 Hole H9	Class RC 7 Shaft d8	Class RC 8 Limits of Clearance	Class RC 8 Hole H10	Class RC 8 Shaft c9	Class RC 9 Limits of Clearance	Class RC 9 Hole H11	Class RC 9 Shaft
0 – 0.12	0.6 / 1.6	+0.6 / –0	–0.6 / –1.0	0.6 / 2.2	+1.0 / –0	–0.6 / –1.2	1.0 / 2.6	+1.0 / 0	–1.0 / –1.6	2.5 / 5.1	+1.6 / 0	–2.5 / –3.5	4.0 / 8.1	+2.5 / 0	–4.0 / –5.6
0.12– 0.24	0.8 / 2.0	+0.7 / –0	–0.8 / –1.3	0.8 / 2.7	+1.2 / –0	–0.8 / –1.5	1.2 / 3.1	+1.2 / 0	–1.2 / –1.9	2.8 / 5.8	+1.8 / 0	–2.8 / –4.0	4.5 / 9.0	+3.0 / 0	–4.5 / –6.0
0.24– 0.40	1.0 / 2.5	+0.9 / –0	–1.0 / –1.6	1.0 / 3.3	+1.4 / –0	–1.0 / –1.9	1.6 / 3.9	+1.4 / 0	–1.6 / –2.5	3.0 / 6.6	+2.2 / 0	–3.0 / –4.4	5.0 / 10.7	+3.5 / 0	–5.0 / –7.2
0.40– 0.71	1.2 / 2.9	+1.0 / –0	–1.2 / –1.9	1.2 / 3.8	+1.6 / –0	–1.2 / –2.2	2.0 / 4.6	+1.6 / 0	–2.0 / –3.0	3.5 / 7.9	+2.8 / 0	–3.5 / –5.1	6.0 / 12.8	+4.0 / –0	–6.0 / –8.8
0.71– 1.19	1.6 / 3.6	+1.2 / –0	–1.6 / –2.4	1.6 / 4.8	+2.0 / –0	–1.6 / –2.8	2.5 / 5.7	+2.0 / 0	–2.5 / –3.7	4.5 / 10.0	+3.5 / 0	–4.5 / –6.5	7.0 / 15.5	+5.0 / 0	–7.0 / –10.5
1.19– 1.97	2.0 / 4.6	+1.6 / –0	–2.0 / –3.0	2.0 / 6.1	+2.5 / –0	–2.0 / –3.6	3.0 / 7.1	+2.5 / 0	–3.0 / –4.6	5.0 / 11.5	+4.0 / 0	–5.0 / –7.5	8.0 / 18.0	+6.0 / 0	–8.0 / –12.0
1.97– 3.15	2.5 / 5.5	+1.8 / –0	–2.5 / –3.7	2.5 / 7.3	+3.0 / –0	–2.5 / –4.3	4.0 / 8.8	+3.0 / 0	–4.0 / –5.8	6.0 / 13.5	+4.5 / 0	–6.0 / –9.0	9.0 / 20.5	+7.0 / 0	–9.0 / –13.5
3.15– 4.73	3.0 / 6.6	+2.2 / –0	–3.0 / –4.4	3.0 / 8.7	+3.5 / –0	–3.0 / –5.2	5.0 / 10.7	+3.5 / 0	–5.0 / –7.2	7.0 / 15.5	+5.0 / 0	–7.0 / –10.5	10.0 / 24.0	+9.0 / 0	–10.0 / –15.0
4.73– 7.09	3.5 / 7.6	+2.5 / –0	–2.5 / –5.1	3.5 / 10.0	+4.0 / –0	–3.5 / –6.0	6.0 / 12.5	+4.0 / 0	–6.0 / –8.5	8.0 / 18.0	+6.0 / 0	–8.0 / –12.0	12.0 / 28.0	+10.0 / 0	–12.0 / –18.0
7.09– 9.85	4.0 / 8.6	+2.8 / –0	–4.0 / –5.8	4.0 / 11.3	+4.5 / 0	–4.0 / –6.8	7.0 / 14.3	+4.5 / 0	–7.0 / –9.8	10.0 / 21.5	+7.0 / 0	–10.0 / –14.5	15.0 / 34.0	+12.0 / 0	–15.0 / –22.0
9.85–12.41	5.0 / 10.0	+3.0 / –0	–5.0 / –7.0	5.0 / 13.0	+5.0 / 0	–5.0 / –8.0	8.0 / 16.0	+5.0 / 0	–8.0 / –11.0	12.0 / 25.0	+8.0 / 0	–12.0 / –17.0	18.0 / 38.0	+12.0 / 0	–18.0 / –26.0

*Limits are in thousandths of an inch. Limits for hole and shaft are applied algebraically to the basic size to obtain the limits of the size for the parts. Data in bold face is in accordance with ABC agreements. This data is not completely shown here. The complete table goes to a nominal size range of 200 in. Symbols H5, g5, etc. are Hole and Shaft designations used in ABC system.

Table C-2 Clearance Locational Fits*

Nominal Size Range, in. Over	To	Class LC 1 Limits of Clearance	Class LC 1 Hole H6	Class LC 1 Shaft h5	Class LC 2 Limits of Clearance	Class LC 2 Hole H7	Class LC 2 Shaft h6	Class LC 3 Limits of Clearance	Class LC 3 Hole H8	Class LC 3 Shaft h7	Class LC 4 Limits of Clearance	Class LC 4 Hole H10	Class LC 4 Shaft h9	Class LC 5 Limits of Clearance	Class LC 5 Hole H7	Class LC 5 Shaft g6
0	0.12	0 / 0.45	+0.25 / -0	+0 / -0.2	0 / 0.65	+0.4 / -0	+0 / -0.25	0 / 1	+0.6 / -0	+0 / -0.4	0 / 2.6	+1.6 / -0	+0 / -1.0	0.1 / 0.75	+0.4 / -0	-0.1 / -0.35
0.12	0.24	0 / 0.5	+0.3 / -0	+0 / -0.2	0 / 0.8	+0.5 / -0	+0 / -0.3	0 / 1.2	+0.7 / -0	+0 / -0.5	0 / 3.0	+1.8 / -0	+0 / -1.2	0.15 / 0.95	+0.5 / -0	-0.15 / -0.45
0.24	0.40	0 / 0.65	+0.4 / -0	+0 / -0.25	0 / 1.0	+0.6 / -0	+0 / -0.4	0 / 1.5	+0.9 / -0	+0 / -0.6	0 / 3.6	+2.2 / -0	+0 / -1.4	0.2 / 1.2	+0.6 / -0	-0.2 / -0.6
0.40	0.71	0 / 0.7	+0.4 / -0	+0 / -0.3	0 / 1.1	+0.7 / -0	+0 / -0.4	0 / 1.7	+1.0 / -0	+0 / -0.7	0 / 4.4	+2.8 / -0	+0 / -1.6	0.25 / 1.35	+0.7 / -0	-0.25 / -0.65
0.71	1.19	0 / 0.9	+0.5 / -0	+0 / -0.4	0 / 1.3	+0.8 / -0	+0 / -0.5	0 / 2	+1.2 / -0	+0 / -0.8	0 / 5.5	+3.5 / -0	+0 / -2.0	0.3 / 1.6	+0.8 / -0	-0.3 / -0.8
1.19	1.97	0 / 1.0	+0.6 / -0	+0 / -0.4	0 / 1.6	+1.0 / -0	+0 / -0.6	0 / 2.6	+1.6 / -0	+0 / -1	0 / 6.5	+4.0 / -0	+0 / -2.5	0.4 / 2.0	+1.0 / -0	-0.4 / -1.0
1.97	3.15	0 / 1.2	+0.7 / -0	+0 / -0.5	0 / 1.9	+1.2 / -0	+0 / -0.7	0 / 3	+1.8 / -0	+0 / -1.2	0 / 7.5	+4.5 / -0	+0 / -3	0.4 / 2.3	+1.2 / -0	-0.4 / -1.1
3.15	4.73	0 / 1.5	+0.9 / -0	+0 / -0.6	0 / 2.3	+1.4 / -0	+0 / -0.9	0 / 3.6	+2.2 / -0	+0 / -1.4	0 / 8.5	+5.0 / -0	+0 / -3.5	0.5 / 2.8	+1.4 / -0	-0.5 / -1.4
4.73	7.09	0 / 1.7	+1.0 / -0	+0 / -0.7	0 / 2.6	+1.6 / -0	+0 / -1.0	0 / 4.1	+2.5 / -0	+0 / -1.6	0 / 10	+6.0 / -0	+0 / -4	0.6 / 3.2	+1.6 / -0	-0.6 / -1.6
7.09	9.85	0 / 2.0	+1.2 / -0	+0 / -0.8	0 / 3.0	+1.8 / -0	+0 / -1.2	0 / 4.6	+2.8 / -0	+0 / -1.8	0 / 11.5	+7.0 / -0	+0 / -4.5	0.6 / 3.6	+1.8 / -0	-0.6 / -1.8
9.85	12.41	0 / 2.1	+1.2 / -0	+0 / -0.9	0 / 3.2	+2.0 / -0	+0 / -1.2	0 / 5	+3.0 / -0	+0 / -2.0	0 / 13	+8.0 / -0	+0 / -5	0.7 / 3.9	+2.0 / -0	-0.7 / -1.9

Table C-2 (continued)

Nominal Size Range, in. Over – To	LC 6 Clearance	LC 6 Hole H9	LC 6 Shaft f8	LC 7 Clearance	LC 7 Hole H10	LC 7 Shaft e9	LC 8 Clearance	LC 8 Hole H10	LC 8 Shaft d9	LC 9 Clearance	LC 9 Hole H11	LC 9 Shaft c10	LC 10 Clearance	LC 10 Hole H12	LC 10 Shaft	LC 11 Clearance	LC 11 Hole H13	LC 11 Shaft
0 – 0.12	0.3 / 1.9	+1.0 / 0	−0.3 / −0.9	0.6 / 3.2	+1.6 / 0	−0.6 / −1.6	1.0 / 3.6	+1.6 / 0	−1.0 / −2.0	2.5 / 6.6	+2.5 / 0	−2.5 / −4.1	4 / 12	+4 / 0	−4 / −8	5 / 17	+6 / 0	−5 / −11
0.12– 0.24	0.4 / 2.3	+1.2 / 0	−0.4 / −1.1	0.8 / 3.8	+1.8 / 0	−0.8 / −2.0	1.2 / 4.2	+1.8 / 0	−1.2 / −2.4	2.8 / 7.6	+3.0 / 0	−2.8 / −4.6	4.5 / 14.5	+5 / 0	−4.5 / −9.5	6 / 20	+7 / 0	−6 / −13
0.24– 0.40	0.5 / 2.8	+1.4 / 0	−0.5 / −1.4	1.0 / 4.6	+2.2 / 0	−1.0 / −2.4	1.6 / 5.2	+2.2 / 0	−1.6 / −3.0	3.0 / 8.7	+3.5 / 0	−3.0 / −5.2	5 / 17	+6 / 0	−5 / −11	7 / 25	+9 / 0	−7 / −16
0.40– 0.71	0.6 / 3.2	+1.6 / 0	−0.6 / −1.6	1.2 / 5.6	+2.8 / 0	−1.2 / −2.8	2.0 / 6.4	+2.8 / 0	−2.0 / −3.6	3.5 / 10.3	+4.0 / 0	−3.5 / −6.3	6 / 20	+7 / 0	−6 / −13	8 / 28	+10 / 0	−8 / −18
0.71– 1.19	0.8 / 4.0	+2.0 / 0	−0.8 / −2.0	1.6 / 7.1	+3.5 / 0	−1.6 / −3.6	2.5 / 8.0	+3.5 / 0	−2.5 / −4.5	4.5 / 13.0	+5.0 / 0	−4.5 / −8.0	7 / 23	+8 / 0	−7 / −15	10 / 34	+12 / 0	−10 / −22
1.19– 1.97	1.0 / 5.1	+2.5 / 0	−1.0 / −2.6	2.0 / 8.5	+4.0 / 0	−2.0 / −4.5	3.0 / 9.5	+4.0 / 0	−3.0 / −5.5	5 / 15	+6 / 0	−5 / −9	8 / 28	+10 / 0	−8 / −18	12 / 44	+16 / 0	−12 / −28
1.97– 3.15	1.2 / 6.0	+3.0 / 0	−1.2 / −3.0	2.5 / 10.0	+4.5 / 0	−2.5 / −5.5	4.0 / 11.5	+4.5 / 0	−4.0 / −7.0	6 / 17.5	+7 / 0	−6 / −10.5	10 / 34	+12 / 0	−10 / −22	14 / 50	+18 / 0	−14 / −32
3.15– 4.73	1.4 / 7.1	+3.5 / 0	−1.4 / −3.6	3.0 / 11.5	+5.0 / 0	−3.0 / −6.5	5.0 / 13.5	+5.0 / 0	−5.0 / −8.5	7 / 21	+9 / 0	−7 / −12	11 / 39	+14 / 0	−11 / −25	16 / 60	+22 / 0	−16 / −38
4.73– 7.09	1.6 / 8.1	+4.0 / 0	−1.6 / −4.1	3.5 / 13.5	+6.0 / 0	−3.5 / −7.5	6 / 16	+6 / 0	−6 / −10	8 / 24	+10 / 0	−8 / −14	12 / 44	+16 / 0	−12 / −28	18 / 68	+25 / 0	−18 / −43
7.09– 9.85	2.0 / 9.3	+4.5 / 0	−2.0 / −4.8	4.0 / 15.5	+7.0 / 0	−4.0 / −8.5	7 / 18.5	+7 / 0	−7 / −11.5	10 / 29	+12 / 0	−10 / −17	16 / 52	+18 / 0	−16 / −34	22 / 78	+28 / 0	−22 / −50
9.85–12.41	2.2 / 10.2	+5.0 / 0	−2.2 / −5.2	4.5 / 17.5	+8.0 / 0	−4.5 / −9.5	7 / 20	+8 / 0	−7 / −12	12 / 32	+12 / 0	−12 / −20	20 / 60	+20 / 0	−20 / −40	28 / 88	+30 / 0	−28 / −58

*Limits are in thousandths of an inch. Limits for hole and shaft are applied algebraically to the basic size to obtain the limits of the size for the parts, Data in bold face in accordance with ABC agreements, This data is not completely shown here. The complete table goes to a nominal size range of 200 in, Symbols H6, h5, etc, are Hole and Shaft designations used in ABC system.

Table C-3　Transition Locational Fits*

Nominal Size Range, in. Over	To	Class LT 1 Fit	LT 1 Hole H7	LT 1 Shaft js6	Class LT 2 Fit	LT 2 Hole H8	LT 2 Shaft js7	Class LT 3 Fit	LT 3 Hole H7	LT 3 Shaft k6	Class LT 4 Fit	LT 4 Hole H8	LT 4 Shaft k7	Class LT 5 Fit	LT 5 Hole H7	LT 5 Shaft n6	Class LT 6 Fit	LT 6 Hole H7	LT 6 Shaft n7
0	0.12	−0.10 / +0.50	+0.4 / −0	+0.10 / −0.10	−0.2 / +0.8	+0.6 / −0	+0.2 / −0.2							−0.5 / +0.15	+0.4 / −0	+0.5 / +0.25	−0.65 / +0.15	+0.4 / −0	−0.65 / +0.25
0.12	0.24	−0.15 / +0.65	+0.5 / −0	+0.15 / −0.15	−0.25 / +0.95	+0.7 / −0	+0.25 / −0.25							−0.6 / +0.2	+0.5 / −0	+0.6 / +0.3	−0.8 / +0.2	+0.5 / −0	+0.8 / +0.3
0.24	0.40	−0.2 / +0.8	+0.6 / −0	+0.2 / −0.2	−0.3 / +1.2	+0.9 / −0	+0.3 / −0.3	−0.5 / +0.5	+0.6 / −0	+0.5 / +0.1	−0.7 / +0.8	+0.9 / −0	+0.7 / +0.1	−0.8 / +0.2	+0.6 / −0	+0.8 / +0.4	−1.0 / +0.2	+0.6 / −0	+1.0 / +0.4
0.40	0.71	−0.2 / +0.9	+0.7 / −0	+0.2 / −0.2	−0.35 / +1.35	+1.0 / −0	+0.35 / −0.35	−0.5 / +0.6	+0.7 / −0	+0.5 / +0.1	−0.8 / +0.9	+1.0 / −0	+0.8 / +0.1	−0.9 / +0.2	+0.7 / −0	+0.9 / +0.5	−1.2 / +0.2	+0.7 / −0	+1.2 / +0.5
0.71	1.19	−0.25 / +1.05	+0.8 / −0	+0.25 / −0.25	−0.4 / +1.6	+1.2 / −0	+0.4 / −0.4	−0.6 / +0.7	+0.8 / −0	+0.6 / +0.1	−0.9 / +1.1	+1.2 / −0	+0.9 / +0.1	−1.1 / +0.2	+0.8 / −0	+1.1 / +0.6	−1.4 / +0.2	+0.8 / −0	+1.4 / +0.6
1.19	1.97	−0.3 / +1.3	+1.0 / −0	+0.3 / −0.3	−0.5 / +2.1	+1.6 / −0	+0.5 / −0.5	−0.7 / +0.9	+1.0 / −0	+0.7 / +0.1	−1.1 / +1.5	+1.6 / −0	+1.1 / +0.1	−1.3 / +0.3	+1.0 / −0	+1.3 / +0.7	−1.7 / +0.3	+1.0 / −0	+1.7 / +0.7
1.97	3.15	−0.3 / +1.5	+1.2 / −0	+0.3 / −0.3	−0.6 / +2.4	+1.8 / −0	+0.6 / −0.6	−0.8 / +1.1	+1.2 / −0	+0.8 / +0.1	−1.3 / +1.7	+1.8 / −0	+1.3 / +0.1	−1.5 / +0.4	+1.2 / −0	+1.5 / +0.8	−2.0 / +0.4	+1.2 / −0	+2.0 / +0.8
3.15	4.73	−0.4 / +1.8	+1.4 / −0	+0.4 / −0.4	−0.7 / +2.9	+2.2 / −0	+0.7 / −0.7	−1.0 / +1.3	+1.4 / −0	+1.0 / +0.1	−1.5 / +2.1	+2.2 / −0	+1.5 / +0.1	−1.9 / +0.4	+1.4 / −0	+1.9 / +1.0	−2.4 / +0.4	+1.4 / −0	+2.4 / +1.0
4.73	7.09	−0.5 / +2.1	+1.6 / −0	+0.5 / −0.5	−0.8 / +3.3	+2.5 / −0	+0.8 / −0.8	−1.1 / +1.5	+1.6 / −0	+1.1 / +0.1	−1.7 / +2.4	+2.5 / −0	+1.7 / +0.1	−2.2 / +0.4	+1.6 / −0	+2.2 / +1.2	−2.8 / +0.4	+1.6 / −0	+2.8 / +1.2
7.09	9.85	−0.6 / +2.4	+1.8 / −0	+0.6 / −0.6	−0.9 / +3.7	+2.8 / −0	+0.9 / −0.9	−1.4 / +1.6	+1.8 / −0	+1.4 / +0.2	−2.0 / +2.6	+2.8 / −0	+2.0 / +0.2	−2.6 / +0.4	+1.8 / −0	+2.6 / +1.4	−3.2 / +0.4	+1.8 / −0	+3.2 / +1.4
9.85	12.41	−0.6 / +2.6	+2.0 / −0	+0.6 / −0.6	−1.0 / +4.0	+3.0 / −0	+1.0 / −1.0	−1.4 / +1.8	+2.0 / −0	+1.4 / +0.2	−2.2 / +2.8	+3.0 / −0	+2.2 / +0.2	−2.6 / +0.6	+2.0 / −0	+2.6 / +1.4	−3.4 / +0.6	+2.0 / −0	+3.4 / +1.4
12.41	15.75	−0.7 / +2.9	+2.2 / −0	+0.7 / −0.7	−1.0 / +4.5	+3.5 / −0	+1.0 / −1.0	−1.6 / +2.0	+2.2 / −0	+1.6 / +0.2	−2.4 / +3.3	+3.5 / −0	+2.4 / +0.2	−3.0 / +0.6	+2.2 / −0	+3.0 / +1.6	−3.8 / +0.6	+2.2 / −0	+3.8 / +1.6
15.75	19.69	−0.8 / +3.3	+2.5 / −0	+0.8 / −0.8	−1.2 / +5.2	+4.0 / −0	+1.2 / −1.2	−1.8 / +2.3	+2.5 / −0	+1.8 / +0.2	−2.7 / +3.8	+4.0 / −0	+2.7 / +0.2	−3.4 / +0.7	+2.5 / −0	+3.4 / +1.8	−4.3 / +0.7	+2.5 / −0	+4.3 / +1.8

*Limits are in thousandths of an inch. Limits for hole and shaft are applied algebraically to the basic size to obtain the limits of the size for the parts. Data in bold face is in accordance with ABC agreements. This data is not completely shown here. The complete table goes to a nominal size range of 200 in. "Fit" represents the maximum interference (minus values), and the maximum clearance (plus values). Symbols H7, js, etc, are Hole and Shaft designations used in ABC system.

Table C-4 Interference Locational Fits*

Nominal Size Range in. Over — To	Class LN 1 Limits of Interference	Class LN 1 Standard Limits Hole H6	Class LN 1 Standard Limits Shaft n5	Class LN 2 Limits of Interference	Class LN 2 Standard Limits Hole H7	Class LN 2 Standard Limits Shaft p6	Class LN 3 Limits of Interference	Class LN 3 Standard Limits Hole H7	Class LN 3 Standard Limits Shaft r6
0 – 0.12	0 0.45	+0.25 – 0	+0.45 +0.25	0 0.65	+0.4 – 0	+0.65 +0.4	0.1 0.75	+0.4 – 0	+0.75 +0.5
0.12– 0.24	0 0.5	+0.3 – 0	+0.5 +0.3	0 0.8	+0.5 – 0	+0.8 +0.5	0.1 0.9	+0.5 0	+0.9 +0.6
0.24– 0.40	0 0.65	+0.4 – 0	+0.65 +0.4	0 1.0	+0.6 – 0	+1.0 +0.6	0.2 1.2	+0.6 – 0	+1.2 +0.8
0.40– 0.71	0 0.8	+0.4 – 0	+0.8 +0.4	0 1.1	+0.7 – 0	+1.1 +0.7	0.3 1.4	+0.7 – 0	+1.4 +1.0
0.71– 1.19	0 1.0	+0.5 – 0	+1.0 +0.5	0 1.3	+0.8 – 0	+1.3 +0.8	0.4 1.7	+0.8 – 0	+1.7 +1.2
1.19– 1.97	0 1.1	+0.6 – 0	+1.1 +0.6	0 1.6	+1.0 – 0	+1.6 +1.0	0.4 2.0	+1.0 – 0	+2.0 +1.4
1.97– 3.15	0.1 1.3	+0.7 – 0	+1.3 +0.7	0.2 2.1	+1.2 – 0	+2.1 +1.4	0.4 2.3	+1.2 – 0	+2.3 +1.6
3.15– 4.73	0.1 1.6	+0.9 – 0	+1.6 +1.0	0.2 2.5	+1.4 – 0	+2.4 +1.6	0.6 2.9	+1.4 – 0	+2.9 +2.0
4.73– 7.09	0.2 1.9	+1.0 – 0	+1.9 +1.2	0.2 2.8	+1.6 – 0	+2.8 +1.8	0.9 3.5	+1.6 – 0	+3.5 +2.5
7.09– 9.85	0.2 2.2	+1.2 – 0	+2.2 +1.4	0.2 3.2	+1.8 – 0	+3.2 +2.0	1.2 4.2	+1.8 – 0	+4.2 +3.0
9.85–12.41	0.2 2.3	+1.2 – 0	+2.3 +1.4	0.2 3.4	+2.0 – 0	+3.4 +2.2	1.5 4.7	+2.0 – 0	+4.7 +3.5

*Limits are in thousandths of an inch. Limits for hole and shaft are applied algebraically to the basic size to obtain the limits of the size for the parts. Data in bold face in accordance with ABC agreements. This data is not completely shown here. The complete table goes to a nominal size range of 200 in. Symbols H7, p6, etc. are Hole and Shaft designations used in ABC system.

Table C-5 Force and Shrink Fits*

Values in each cell are given as upper limit / lower limit.

Nominal Size Range, in. Over	To	Class FN 1 Limits of Interference	Class FN 1 Standard Limits Hole H6	Class FN 1 Standard Limits Shaft	Class FN 2 Limits of Interference	Class FN 2 Standard Limits Hole I17	Class FN 2 Standard Limits Shaft s6	Class FN 3 Limits of Interference	Class FN 3 Standard Limits Hole H7	Class FN 3 Standard Limits Shaft t6	Class FN 4 Limits of Interference	Class FN 4 Standard Limits Hole H7	Class FN 4 Standard Limits Shaft u6	Class FN 5 Limits of Interference	Class FN 5 Standard Limits Hole H8	Class FN 5 Standard Limits Shaft x7
0	0.12	0.05 / 0.5	+0.25 / -0	+0.5 / +0.3	0.2 / 0.85	+0.4 / -0	+0.85 / +0.6				0.3 / 0.95	+0.4 / -0	+0.95 / +0.7	0.3 / 1.3	+0.6 / -0	+1.3 / +0.9
0.12	0.24	0.1 / 0.6	+0.3 / -0	+0.6 / +0.4	0.2 / 1.0	+0.5 / -0	+1.0 / +0.7				0.4 / 1.2	+0.5 / -0	+1.2 / +0.9	0.5 / 1.7	+0.7 / -0	+1.7 / +1.2
0.24	0.40	0.1 / 0.75	+0.4 / -0	+0.75 / +0.5	0.4 / 1.4	+0.6 / -0	+1.4 / +1.0				0.6 / 1.6	+0.6 / -0	+1.6 / +1.2	0.5 / 2.0	+0.9 / -0	+2.0 / +1.4
0.40	0.56	0.1 / 0.8	+0.4 / -0	+0.8 / +0.5	0.5 / 1.6	+0.7 / -0	+1.6 / +1.2				0.7 / 1.8	+0.7 / -0	+1.8 / +1.4	0.6 / 2.3	+1.0 / -0	+2.3 / +1.6
0.56	0.71	0.2 / 0.9	+0.4 / -0	+0.9 / +0.6	0.5 / 1.6	+0.7 / -0	+1.6 / +1.2				0.7 / 1.8	+0.7 / -0	+1.8 / +1.4	0.8 / 2.5	+1.0 / -0	+2.5 / +1.8
0.71	0.95	0.2 / 1.1	+0.5 / -0	+1.1 / +0.7	0.6 / 1.9	+0.8 / -0	+1.9 / +1.4				0.8 / 2.1	+0.8 / -0	+2.1 / +1.6	1.0 / 3.0	+1.2 / -0	+3.0 / +2.2
0.95	1.19	0.3 / 1.2	+0.5 / -0	+1.2 / +0.8	0.6 / 1.9	+0.8 / -0	+1.9 / +1.4	0.8 / 2.1	+0.8 / -0	+2.1 / +1.6	1.0 / 2.3	+0.8 / -0	+2.3 / +1.8	1.3 / 3.3	+1.2 / +0	+3.3 / +2.5
1.19	1.58	0.3 / 1.3	+0.6 / -0	+1.3 / +0.9	0.8 / 2.4	+1.0 / -0	+2.4 / +1.8	1.0 / 2.6	+1.0 / -0	+2.6 / +2.0	1.5 / 3.1	+1.0 / -0	+3.1 / +2.5	1.4 / 4.0	+1.6 / -0	+4.0 / +3.0
1.58	1.97	0.4 / 1.4	+0.6 / -0	+1.4 / +1.0	0.8 / 2.4	+1.0 / -0	+2.4 / +1.8	1.2 / 2.8	+1.0 / -0	+2.8 / +2.2	1.8 / 3.4	+1.0 / -0	+3.4 / +2.8	2.4 / 5.0	+1.6 / -0	+5.0 / +4.0
1.97	2.56	0.6 / 1.8	+0.7 / -0	+1.8 / +1.3	0.8 / 2.7	+1.2 / -0	+2.7 / +2.0	1.3 / 3.2	+1.2 / -0	+3.2 / +2.5	2.3 / 4.2	+1.2 / -0	+4.2 / +3.5	3.2 / 6.2	+1.8 / -0	+6.2 / +5.0

2.56 – 3.15	0.7 / 1.9	+0.7 / –0	+1.9 / +1.4	1.0 / 2.9	+1.2 / –0	+2.9 / +2.2	1.8 / 3.7	+1.2 / –0	+3.7 / +3.8	2.8 / 4.7	+1.2 / –0	+4.7 / +4.0	4.2 / 7.2	+1.8 / –0	+7.2 / +6.0
3.15 – 3.94	0.9 / 2.4	+0.9 / –0	+2.4 / +1.8	1.4 / 3.7	+1.4 / –0	+3.7 / +2.8	2.1 / 4.4	+1.4 / –0	+4.4 / +3.5	3.6 / 5.9	+1.4 / –0	+5.9 / +5.0	4.8 / 8.4	+2.2 / –0	+8.4 / +7.0
3.94 – 4.73	1.1 / 2.6	+0.9 / –0	+2.6 / +2.0	1.6 / 3.9	+1.4 / –0	+3.9 / +3.0	2.6 / 4.9	+1.4 / –0	+*4.9 / +4.0	4.6 / 6.9	+1.4 / –0	+6.9 / +6.0	5.8 / 9.4	+2.2 / –0	+9.4 / +8.0
4.73 – 5.52	1.2 / 2.9	+1.0 / –0	+2.9 / +2.2	1.9 / 4.5	+1.6 / –0	+4.5 / +3.5	3.4 / 6.0	+1.6 / –0	+6.0 / +5.0	5.4 / 8.0	+1.6 / –0	+8.0 / +7.0	7.5 / 11.6	+2.5 / –0	+11.6 / +10.0
5.52 – 6.30	1.5 / 3.2	+1.0 / –0	+3.2 / +2.5	2.4 / 5.0	+1.6 / –0	+5.0 / +4.0	3.4 / 6.0	+1.6 / –0	+6.0 / +5.0	5.4 / 8.0	+1.6 / –0	+8.0 / +7.0	9.5 / 13.6	+2.5 / –0	+13.6 / +12.0
6.30 – 7.09	1.8 / 3.5	+1.0 / –0	+3.5 / +2.8	2.9 / 5.5	+1.6 / –0	+5.5 / +4.5	4.4 / 7.0	+1.6 / –0	+7.0 / +6.0	6.4 / 9.0	+1.6 / –0	+9.0 / +8.0	9.5 / 13.6	+2.5 / –0	+13.6 / +12.0
7.09 – 7.88	1.8 / 3.8	+1.2 / –0	+3.8 / +3.0	3.2 / 6.2	+1.8 / –0	+6.2 / +5.0	5.2 / 8.2	+1.8 / –0	+8.2 / +7.0	7.2 / 10.2	+1.8 / –0	+10.2 / +9.0	11.2 / 15.8	+2.8 / –0	+15.8 / +14.0
7.88 – 8.86	2.3 / 4.3	+1.2 / –0	+4.3 / +3.5	3.2 / 6.2	+1.8 / –0	+6.2 / +5.0	5.2 / 8.2	+1.8 / –0	+8.2 / +7.0	8.2 / 11.2	+1.8 / –0	+11.2 / +10.0	13.2 / 17.8	+2.8 / –0	+17.8 / +16.0
8.86 – 9.85	2.3 / 4.3	+1.2 / –0	+4.3 / +3.5	4.2 / 7.2	+1.8 / –0	+7.2 / +6.0	6.2 / 9.2	+1.8 / –0	+9.2 / +8.0	10.2 / 13.2	+1.8 / –0	+13.2 / +12.0	13.2 / 17.8	+2.8 / –0	+17.8 / +16.0
9.85 – 11.03	2.8 / 4.9	+1.2 / –0	+4.9 / +4.0	4.0 / 7.2	+2.0 / –0	+7.2 / +6.0	7.0 / 10.2	+2.0 / –0	+10.2 / +9.0	10.0 / 13.2	+2.0 / –0	+13.2 / +12.0	15.0 / 20.0	+3.0 / –0	+20.0 / +18.0
11.03 – 12.41	2.8 / 4.9	+1.2 / –0	+4.9 / +4.0	5.0 / 8.2	+2.0 / –0	+8.2 / +7.0	7.0 / 10.2	+2.0 / –0	+10.2 / +9.0	12.0 / 15.2	+2.0 / –0	+15.2 / +14.0	17.0 / 22.0	+3.0 / –0	+22.0 / +20.0

*Limits are in thousandths of an inch. Limits for hole and shaft are applied algebraically to the basic size to obtain the limits of the size for the parts. Data in bold face in accordance with ABC agreements. This data is not completely shown here. The complete table goes to a nominal size range of 200 in. Symbols H7, s6, etc; are Hole and Shaft designations used in ABC system.

Appendix D

Standard Welding Symbols and International Conversion Units

Table D-1 Standard welding symbols. (Courtesy of the American Welding Society.

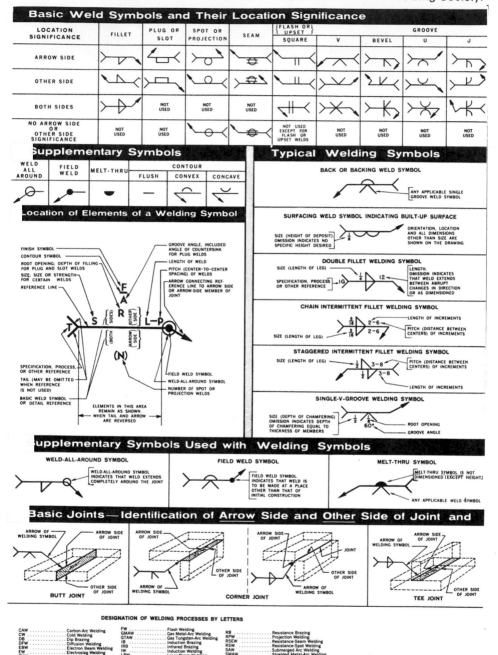

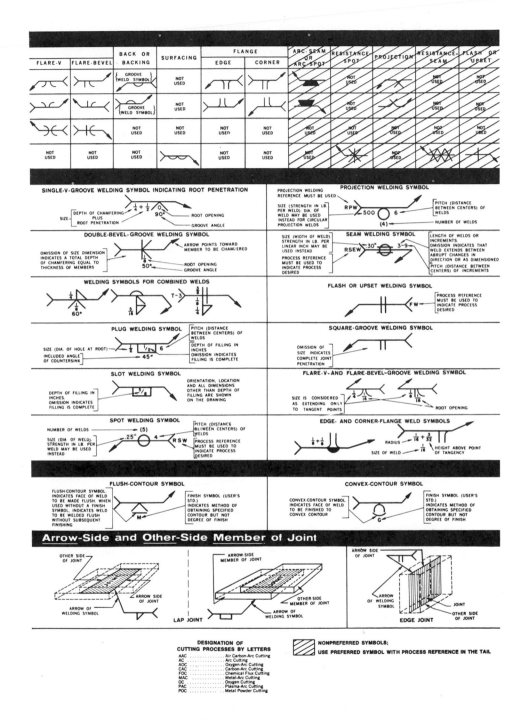

Table D-2 International System of Units (abbreviated SI) and Symbols

Quantity	Unit	SI Symbol	Formula
length	meter	m	—
mass	kilogram	kg	—
time	second	s	—
thermodynamic temperature	kelvin	K	—
plane angle	radian	rad	—
acceleration	meter per second squared	—	m/s²
angular acceleration	radians per second squared	—	rad/s²
angular velocity	radians per second	—	rad/s²
area	square meter	—	m²
density	kilogram per cubic meter	—	kg/m³
energy	joule	J	N·m
force	newton	N	kg·m/s²
frequency	hertz	Hz	(cycle)/s
power	watt	W	J/s
pressure	newton per square meter	—	N/m²
quantity of heat	joule	J	N·m
specific heat	joule per kilogram-kelvin	—	J/kg·K
stress	newton per square meter	—	N/m²
thermal conductivity	watt per meter-kelvin	—	W/m-K
velocity	meter per second	—	m/s
viscosity, dynamic	newton-second per square meter	—	N·s/m²
viscosity, kinematic	meter squared per second	—	m²/s
volume	cubic meter	—	m³
work	joule	J	N·m

Table D-3 Conversion Factors for SI Units (symbols of SI units given in parenthesis)

To convert from	To	Multiply by
atmosphere (normal)	newton/meter² (N/m²)	1.013250×10^5
British thermal unit (Btu)	joule (J)	1.055056×10^3
Btu/hour	watt (W)	2.930711×10^{-1}
Btu/ft²-minute	watt/meters² (W/m²)	1.891489×10^2
centipoise	newton-second/meter² (N·s/m²)	1.000000×10^{-3}
centistoke	meter²/second (m²/s)	1.000000×10^{-6}
cubic foot	meters³ (m³)	2.831685×10^{-2}
cubic inches	meters³ (m³)	1.638706×10^{-5}
cubic foot/minute	meters³/second (m³/s)	4.719474×10^{-4}
cubic foot/second	meters³/second (m³/s)	2.831685×10^{-2}
cubic inches/minute	meters³/second (m³/s)	2.731177×10^{-7}
degree (angle)	radian (rad)	1.745329×10^{-2}
degree Celsius (i.e. centigrade)	kelvin (K)	$t_K = t_C + 273.15$
degree Farenheit	degree Celsius (i.e. centigrade)	$t_C = (t_F - 32)/1.8$
degree Farenheit	kelvin (K)	$t_K = (t_F + 459.67)/1.8$
degree Rankine	kelvin (K)	$t_K = t_R/1.8$
fluid ounce (U.S.)	meter³ (m³)	2.957353×10^{-5}
foot	meter (m)	3.048000×10^{-1}
foot/second	meter/second (m/s)	3.048000×10^{-1}
foot/second²	meter/second² (m/s²)	3.048000×10^{-1}
foot-pound-force	joule (J)	1.355818
foot-poundal	joule (J)	4.214011×10^{-2}
foot-pound-force/hour	watt (W)	3.766161×10^{-4}
foot-pound-force/minute	watt (W)	2.259697×10^{-2}
foot-pound-force/second	watt (W)	1.355818
gallon (U.S. liquid)	meter³ (m³)	3.785412×10^{-3}
gallon (U.S. liquid)/minute	meter³/second (m³/s)	6.309020×10^{-5}
horsepower (550 ft-lb-f/s)	watt (W)	7.456999×10^2
hour (mean solar)	second (s)	3.600000×10^3
inch	meter (m)	2.540000×10^{-2}
inch of mercury (32° F)	newton/meter² (N/m²)	3.386389×10^3
inch of mercury (60° F)	newton/meter² (N/m²)	3.376850×10^3
inch/second	meter/second (m/s)	2.540000×10^{-2}
inch/second²	meter/second² (m/s²)	2.540000×10^{-2}
kelvin	degree Celsius (i.e. centigrade)	$t_C = t_K - 273.15$
kip	newton (N)	4.448222×10^3
kip/inch²	newton/meter² (N/m²)	6.894757×10^6
kilowatt-hour	joule (J)	3.600000×10^6
mile (U.S. statute)	meter (m)	1.609344×10^3
mile/hour (U.S. statute)	meters/second (m/s)	4.470400×10^{-1}
mile/hour (U.S. statute)	kilometer/hour	1.609344
minute (angle)	radian (rad)	2.908882×10^{-4}
moment of inertia (lbm-ft²)	kilogram-meter² (kg·m²)	4.214012×10^{-2}
moment of inertia (lbm-in.²)	kilogram-meter² (kg·m²)	2.926397×10^{-5}
moment of section (second moment of inertia) (in.⁴)	meter⁴ (m⁴)	4.162314×10^{-7}
poise (absolute viscosity)	newton-second/meter² (N·s/m²)	1.000000×10^{-1}
pound-force (lbf avoirdupois)	kilogram-force	4.535924×10^{-1}
pound-mass (lbm avoirdupois)	kilogram (kg)	4.535924×10^{-1}
pound-force/inch	newton/meter (N/m)	1.751268×10^{-2}
pound-force/foot	newton/meter (N/m)	1.459390×10^1
pound-force-inch	newton-meter (N·m)	1.129848×10^{-1}
pound-force-foot	newton-meter (N·m)	1.355818
pound-force-inch/inch	newton-meter/meter (N·m/m)	4.448222
pound-force/foot²	newton/meter² (N/m²)	4.788026×10^1
pound-force/inch² (psi)	newton/meter² (N/m²)	6.894757×10^3
pound-force/inch² (psi)	kilogram-force/mm²	7.030696×10^{-4}
pound-mass/foot²	kilogram/meter² (kg/m²)	4.882428
pound-mass/foot³	kilogram/meter³ (kg/m³)	1.601846×10^1
pound-mass/inch³	kilogram/meter³ (kg/m³)	2.767990×10^4
pound-mass/minute	kilogram/second (kg/s)	7.559873×10^{-3}
pound-mass/second	kilogram/second (kg/s)	4.535924×10^{-1}
second (angle)	radian (rad)	4.848137×10^{-4}
section modulus (ft³)	meter³ (m³)	2.831685×10^{-2}
section modulus (in³)	meter³ (m³)	1.638706×10^{-5}
stoke (kinematic viscosity)	meter²/second (m²/s)	1.000000×10^{-4}
statute mile (U.S.)	meter (m)	1.609344×10^3
sqaure foot	meter² (m²)	9.290304×10^{-2}
square inch	meter² (m²)	6.451600×10^{-4}
square foot/second	meter²/second (m²/s)	9.290304×10^{-2}
ton (short, 2000 lbm)	kilogram (kg.)	9.071847×10^2
watt-hour	joule (J)	3.600000×10^3
watt-second	joule (J)	1.000000
year (calendar)	second (s)	3.153600×10^7

Table D-4 Other Useful Conversions

To convert from	To	Multiply by
British Thermal units (Btu)	foot pounds (ft lb)	7.780000×10^2
cubic inch	centimeter^3 (cm^3)	1.638706×10^1
dyne-centimeter	newton-meter (N·m)	1.000000×10^{-7}
dyne/centimeter^2	newton/meter^2 (N/m^2)	1.000000×10^{-1}
gram-force/centimeter^2	newton/meter^2 (N/m^2)	9.806650×10^1
gravity (standard)	meter/second^2 (m/s^2)	9.806650
kilogram-force/centimeter^2	newton/meter^2 /N/m^2)	9.806650×10^4
kilogram-force-meter	newton-meter (N·m)	9.806650
kilogram-force-meter^2	newton/meter^2 (N/m^2)	9.806650
square inch	centimeter^2 (cm^2)	6.451600

Index

Geometry factor for gears
  bevel gears, 646, 648–50
  helical gears, 613–615, 618
  spur gears, 554, 557, 558, 569, 572, 573, 576
Goodier, J. N., 765
Goodman criterion, 324
Grain size, 18
Graphitizing (temper carbon), 52
Grease lubricated bearing, 438
Grinding of gears, 539
Grooves in bearings, 435

H

Hagan-Poiseuille law, 411
Hand of helical gears, 603
Hand oiling of bearings, 437
Hardenability, 39–45
  Jominy test, 41
Hardening, strain, 18–19
Hardness, 94–100
Hardness ratio factors
  bevel, 651
  helical, 613
  spur, 575, 578–79
Heat balance of bearings, 430
Heat dissipation
  bearings, 432
  brakes, 696–97
  gear cases, 632
Heat transfer coefficient
  bearings, 433
  worm gear casings, 632
Heat treatment of steels, 19, 31–33
  critical cooling rate, 31
  definitions, 45–53
  effect on fatigue, 121–25
  martensite, 31–33, 33n.
  quenching, 32, 52–53
  spheroidite, 33
  spheroidizing, 25n., 53
  tempering, 33, 53
Heating
  of bearings, 430
  of brakes, 695–97
  of worm gear sets, 631–33
Helical gears, 601–623
Helical springs, 721–36
Helical torsion spring, 740–42
Helicoil screw inserts, 804, 806
Helix angle, (lead angle), 757
  helical gears, 607
  worm gears, 625
Herringbone gears, 606–607
Hertz equation, 565
Hertz, H., 446
High strength, low alloy steel, 58
High temperature service steel, 64–65
Hobbing of gears, 536

Homogeneity, 54, 81
Homogenizing, 52
Honing of gears, 539
Hooke's law, 88
Horsepower load for gears, 544
Hot compression molding, 167
Hydraulic clutch, 691–92
Hydrodynamic lubrication, 406, 421
Hydrogen embrittlement, 54
Hydrostatic lifts, 419, 441
Hydrostatic lubrication, 419–20
Hypereutectoid steel, 22
Hypoeutectoid steel, 22
Hypoid bevel gears, 638, 655

I

I section, 247
Identification symbols for screws, 815
Included angle, belt, 664
Induction hardening, 591
Inertia force, 664
Inertia loading, 856, 857
Initial tension in bolts, 815–17
Initial tension of spring, 735
Initially curved members, 862, 863
Injection molding, 167–68
  gears, 539
Inlet hole bearing, 437
Instability, 282
Interference, 854–56
  gear teeth, 531
Interference fits, 854–56
Intermetallic compound, 19
Internal gears
  bevel, 640
  spur, 520, 523
Internal pressure, 853
International Nickel Company, 29
Interstitial solution, 18
Investment casting, 152
Involute gears, 525
Iron-carbon diagram, 19–22
Iron-carbon phases
  alpha iron, 20
  austenite, 21
  cast iron, 22
  cementite, 20
  delta iron, 21
  eutectic point, 21
  eutectoid, 21
  ferrite, 21
  hypereutectoid, 22
  hypoeutectoid, 21
  ledeburite, 21
  pearlite, 21
  steels, 22
Isothermal transformation diagrams (TTT or S diagrams), 34–38
  austempering, 38, 46

Manufacturing processes, classification of, 148
Marin, J., 108
Martempering, 38, 52
Martensite, 33
Materials
  bearings, 438
  brakes and clutches, 685, 708
  gears, 589–92
  screws and bolts, 810–15
Materials, properties of,
  carbon and alloy steels, 870–71
  carburizing and hardening grade steels, 872–75
  cast copper base alloys, 880
  cast ferrous metals, 868–69
  die casting metals, 882
  nickel alloys and nickel base alloys, 883–84
  plastics, 885–86
  wrought aluminum alloys, 877–78
  wrought and cast magnesium alloys, 881
  wrought copper alloys, 879
  wrought stainless steels, 876
Materials for rolling bearings, 479–82
Maximum normal stress theory, 303
Maximum shear, 853–63
Maximum shear theory, 309ff.
  fatigue loading, 321
Mechanical mixture, 19
Mechanical properties of materials, 81–109
  table of, 887
Meehanite, 29
Metal–inert gas arc welding, 833
Metallurgical terms, supplementary, 53–54
Miles, L. D., 13
Milling of gears, 534
Miner's rule, 325
Minimum edge distance, 781
Minimum film thickness, 407, 427
Minimum number of teeth
  bevel gears, 640
  spur gears, 582
Miscellaneous primary processes
  for metals, 161–67
  for plastics, 171
Miter gear, 640
Modulus
  of elasticity, 87–88
  of resilience, 92
  of toughness, 92–94
Mohr circle, 303
Molding
  hot compression, 167
  injection, 167–68
  transfer, 168–69
Moment of inertia, 246

of weld, 836
Mooney, R. N., 13
Moore, R. R., 103
Multiple disc clutch, 687
Multiple V belt drive, 668

N

National Lubrication Grease Institute (NGLI), 501
Natural frequency of springs, 729
Needle roller bearings, 462–63
Neutral surface, 244
Newton-Raphson method, 290–92
Newton's law of viscous flow, 409
Newton's method, 290
Ni-Resist, 29
Nickel alloys, tables of properties, 883–84
Nickel and nickel alloys, 73–74
  table of properties, 883–84
Nitralloy Corporation, 131n.
Nitriding, 48, 52
  effect on fatigue, 130–32
  gears, 591
Nodular iron, 590
Nominal size of weld, 835
Noncircular sections in torsion, 267
Nonmetallic gears, 591–92
Normal force, belt, 663
Normal load on gears
  bevel, 651–55
  helical, 604–605
  spur, 540, 545
  worm, 628–29
Normal pitch
  helical gears, 610
  worm gears, 627
Normal pressure angle
  helical gears, 610
  worm gears, 627, 633
Normalizing, 37, 52
Non-ferrous metals, tables of properties, 877–81
Notch sensitivity, 114
Notch-sensitivity curves, chart of, 892
Number of teeth in contact, 529
Numerical methods, 290–94
Nuts, 800
  locknut, 801
  lockwasher, 801
  speednut, 801

O

Oil bath bearings, 433
Oil grooves in bearings, 435
Oil ring bearing, 433
Open die forging, 158
Overhauling of power screws, 761–62
Overheated, metal, 52

Raimondi, A. A., 425
Ratchet wrench, 248
Rating life of rolling bearings, 483–84
Red shortness, 54
Redundant support, 258
Reliability, 11–13
  factor in fatigue, 109
Reliability factor for gears
  bevel, 648
  helical, 613
  spur, 560, 562
Resilience, modulus of, 92
Resistance welding, 175–78, 830–31
Restrained member, 275
Retaining rings, 806–807
Reversed stress, 325
Reyn, 411
Reynolds, O., 411, 421
Reynolds' equation
  one-dimensional flow, 421
  two-dimensional flow, 425
Rimmed steel, 54
Ring-oiled bearings, 437
Riveted connection, 778–93
  butt joint, 781–87
  lap joint, 781–87
Rockwell hardness, 41, 44, 94–100
Roller bearings
  cylindrical, 460–61
  needle, 462–63
  spherical, 468
  tapered, 463–67
Rolling bearings
  assemblies of, 512–15
  ball bearings, 446–60
  basic load rating of, 485
  basic static load rating of, 483–84
  basis for failure of, 483
  equivalent load for, 485–93
  friction of, 482
  life of, 483–84
  life adjustment for, 495–96
  lubrication of, 500–507
  materials for, 479–82
  nomenclature and types of ball bearings, 446–60
  rating life of, 483–84
  roller bearings, 460
  seals for, 509–12
  speed limitations of, 507–509
  standard dimensions for, 472–78
  survival probabilities of, 493–95
  thrust bearings, 459, 460
  tolerances for, 478–79
  variable loads in, 497–500
Rolling bearings subjected to variable loads, 497–500
Root diameter for gears, 522–23
Root of equation, 290
Rotating disks, 856–59

Rubber bearings, 439
Rubber compression mounts, 743, 744
Rubber mounts, 743–45
Rubber shear mounts, 744, 745

S

Safe stress line, 318
Safety, 14–15
Safety factor, 306, 319
St. Venant, 271
St. Venant's principle, 248
Sand casting, 148–50
Saybolt universal seconds, 414
Saybolt viscosity, 414
Schram, J. 353n.
Schulte, W. C., 108
Scissor gears, 588
Scoring of gears, 564
Screws, 794–801
Seals for rolling bearings, 509–512
Secant formula, 286
Secant method, 292
Secondary production processes, 181–89
  chemical milling, 185–86
  electrochemical machining, 185
  electrodischarge machining, 186
  electrolytic grinding, 186
  external cylindrical surface machining, 184
  flat surface machining, 182
  internal cylindrical surface machining, 183
  photoforming, 187
  ultrasonic machining, 187–89
Self-contained bearings, 432
Self-drilling screw, 804–805
Self-energizing brakes
  differential band, 699
  long shoe external block, 705
  long shoe internal block, 707–708
Self-locking
  differential band brake, 699
  long shoe external block brake, 705
  long shoe internal block brake, 707–708
  worm gears, 631
Sellers thread, 795
Semikilled steel, 54
Sems, 802
Set screws, 802–803
Shaft angle
  bevel gears, 640–41
  crossed helical gears, 621
Shaft deflection
  computer method for, 353–56
  numerical method for, 347–52
Shaft design by computer, 353–56
Shaft design when subject to fluctuating loads
  distortion energy theory, 340